READINGS IN MAN, THE ENVIRONMENT,
AND HUMAN ECOLOGY

Readings in MAN, THE

Arthur S. Boughey
UNIVERSITY OF CALIFORNIA IRVINE

ENVIRONMENT, AND HUMAN ECOLOGY

Macmillan Publishing Co., Inc.
New York

Collier Macmillan Publishers
London

Macmillan Publishing Co., Inc.
866 Third Avenue, New York, New York 10022

Collier-Macmillan Canada, Ltd., Toronto, Ontario

Library of Congress catalog card number: 72-81658

Printing: 1 2 3 4 5 6 7 8   Year: 3 4 5 6 7 8 9

Preface

This is a collection of recent papers relating to current environmental problems and their origins and causes. Its primary purpose is to provide source material for use with the text *Man and the Environment: An Introduction to Human Ecology and Evolution.* The selections reprinted here furnish a comprehensive survey of the areas covered by this text. They supply suitable material for any introductory survey course in human ecology, whether this course stresses the evolutionary or the environmental aspects.

Although "human ecology" is a term that has been used with increasing frequency over three decades, it is still interpreted in many different ways. There remains some tendency to confuse it with "applied ecology," an economic activity encompassing the practical aspects of environmental management. The real meaning of human ecology is given in a selection in the first section of this collection. Briefly, it may be defined as *"the autecological study of man."*

The growing realization that our species now faces unprecedented environmental challenges has prompted the production of numerous collections of readings that document this latest and most serious crisis in human affairs. The disciplinary affiliations of the authors and editors of these various works run the gamut from English through philosophy, geography, sociology, and biology to ecology. Not unexpectedly, these collections show a parallel diversity of form, content, and pedagogical appeal.

This compilation intends to avoid any disciplinary bias by including a wide, sectionalized coverage of source material and by incorporating with each section an extensive and representative list of additional readings. These are essentially contemporary, original papers; older works are listed in the bibliographies of the selections. Few books are so cited, for these are generally not original source material. Moreover, books on the subject are usually available to students in their libraries, where an instructor for a particular course has placed them on reserve. This collection gives students a personal library of source material in an immediately accessible form. Its selections describe for them the origins of and the evidence for many of the current ideas in human ecology.

Among the 73 selections presented, no fewer than 39 have been taken from *Science, Bioscience,* and the *New Scientist.* Together with *Environment* and the *Scientific American,* these publications are the principal current vehicles for the presentation of much introductory information on human ecology. There are, however, many other journals that specialize in or at least include such material. By drawing the remaining articles from them, it has been possible to provide the reader with a wide range of excellent papers from a representative collection of authors and periodicals.

The editor is very appreciative of the generosity of the publishers, journals, and authors who have granted the necessary permission for their work to be reprinted. Full acknowledgment of the origin of the material is provided at the beginning of each article.

A. S. B.

Contents

PART SIX **Conservation and the Future** **489**

READINGS IN MAN, THE ENVIRONMENT,
AND HUMAN ECOLOGY

Introduction

Human ecology is now emerging as a holistic segment of ecology. It remains, nevertheless, deeply rooted in the parent discipline. No specialist aspect represented by a selection in this anthology can be properly understood without reference to basic ecological concepts, nor can its full implications be realized without reference to the other topics included in human ecology. Even pragmatic solutions to environmental problems may prove inadequate if they fail to relate the applied problem to its fundamental ecological origins. Thus no editorial comment is needed to stress that the study of human ecology—demonstrated in these selections to be an investigation of the relationship between man and the environment—has now become the most critical need of our time.

The exploration of human ecology provides the necessary basis for the development of new techniques in environmental management. In this respect human ecology bears much the same relationship to environmental management that ecology bears to the applied sciences of agriculture, forestry, and horticulture. The environmental selections included here, however, are not intended to prescribe the technical procedures of environmental management, but rather to show the likely consequences of failure to institute them and to state the fundamental precepts for their successful operation.

Literature dealing with one aspect or another of human ecology is presently widely dispersed, as is evidenced by the diverse origins of the selections in the various anthologies that have already appeared. Some of these collections of readings are directed toward particular specialist areas of the discipline. They may, for example, be especially concerned with the pragmatic technological problems that are identifiable to our present environmental crises. They may deal with demographic features and with the critical issue of population control. They may be concerned with urban matters, health hazards, and economic or philosophical questions. Few have the declared intent to provide a balanced sampling of the total output of relevant articles written by engineers, humanists, anthropologists, sociologists, biologists, physical scientists, and members of the medical profession about their particular interests in human ecology and evolution. This may be because human ecology has not yet been fully recognized as a discipline in its own right. When it is defined (as it is in *Man and the*

Environment) as the study of the development and interactions of human societies with one another and with their environment, its scope becomes apparent and its purpose more clear.

This collection of readings covers the whole field of human ecology, as so defined, and provides reprints of much source material cited in *Man and the Environment*. The papers are arranged in six sections and follow the same order used in the text. Part One covers the general features of natural ecosystems and the universal disruptive effects that are brought about by human occupation. Part Two deals with the biology of human evolution and the Pleistocene environments in which its latest phase occurred, leading up to the Holocene emergence of *Homo sapiens*. Part Three is concerned with the origin of our present urban ecosystems over the last twelve or thirteen thousand years. Many papers in this third part relate to the *cultural* evolution that is proceeding apace, which has now vastly outstripped and out-distanced our *biological* evolution.

Part Four is concerned with human demography—the structure, density, reproductive rates, and regulation of human populations. Critical and sensitive issues are involved here. The perceptive reader will observe that many of the predictions that are in the selections and in the Additional Readings of this part are already coming to pass. The remarkable equanimity with which we view these disasters as they occur is a sorry commentary on the limits of our humanity.

Part Five describes the various types of pollution that result directly or indirectly from our burgeoning industrial development. Included are the problems that are caused by air and water pollution. Technological problems have technological solutions; these particular modern afflictions are the price of industrial development. To alleviate them, it may well be necessary to impose a quantitative limit to an otherwise continuous process of industrial expansion.

Other environmental limits are considered in Part Six, which is concerned with such matters of universal concern as the quality of life and the limits of conservation. Human life is not limitless; it is bound by the extent of our resources. The rate at which we exploit, reuse, and regenerate them is determined in the end, as these selections illustrate, by the kind of life that we decide we can and should enjoy.

Some of the selections in this volume, as already noted, are cited as bibliographical references in the main text. As two years have elapsed since its publication, the opportunity has been taken in some instances to substitute a more recent paper. Citations in the Additional Readings have also been similarly updated. These lists, it must be emphasized, while not full and comprehensive bibliographies, are intended to provide the most recent references to the literature on each topic. For lower division survey courses on human ecology, sufficient source material is available within this collection. For more advanced work, and for term papers on specific issues, the Additional Readings and the bibliographical references in each selection should be consulted.

PART ONE

The Ecosphere

Cultural evolution has now enabled members of our species to escape from the narrow confines of a single ecological niche and even to travel across space far from our own planet, cocooned in a small portion of our environment. Despite this unique achievement, neither we nor any other living system has yet colonized the whole of the earth's potential habitats. That portion of the planet in which life in some form is presently encountered is known as the *biosphere*. It extends to a height of approximately five miles above and to a depth of several miles below the earth's surface. The complex of living systems within the biosphere, and the environmental and other ecological factors with which this complex interacts, have collectively been called the *ecosphere*. In the opening paper of this section (1) LaMont C. Cole summarizes our current understanding of the basic features of the life-support systems of this planet within this vital but restricted zone.

The next paper (2), by Eugene P. Odum, describes the strategy of ecosystem development. With his early emphasis of the central importance of the ecosystem, Odum made a unique contribution to the establishment of ecology as a concise pedagogic discipline.

An essential concomitant of the ecosystem concept, but one too long neglected, is the recycling of resources. Among the major attempts to measure and record in the form of nutrient budgets this recycling process is the Hubbard Brook experiment. Hubbard Brook is a small natural forest area in New Hampshire that is covered with deciduous woodland. Some conclusions from the initial years of observations on the nutrient intake and outflow of a watershed in this experimental area are described in a paper (3) by two principal investigators in this project, F. H. Bormann and G. E. Likens.

Having in these first three papers surveyed the fundamental ecological principles that provide the basic ecological rules within which any living system must operate, there remains the question of the relationship between natural ecosystems and our own societies. This is indeed the main theme of this collection of readings. This crucial issue is examined first in a paper (4) by Paul Shepard which surveys the discipline of human ecology as it has developed over the last few decades to meet this precise need. Then a man who is capable of presenting a broad and fair assessment of environmental problems, the recently retired Secretary General of the

United Nations, U Thant, discusses some of the applied problems (5). Both the philosophy and the tasks of human ecology should be apparent from these two papers. The basic procedure in both instances is to apply the technique of systems analysis, as variously described in *Man and the Environment* and in many of the selections and citations given in this book.

The selections presented in the remaining parts of this book describe the nature of the disturbance created by the presence in the ecosphere of our own populations at varying levels of density. The interaction between any living system in the biosphere and its environment is always a two-way process; not one but both are modified as a consequence. The five papers in Part One set the scene in basic ecological terms for human ecology and evolution. It is within such general systems as are described in this part that man evolved to his present situation. It is as a result of the confrontations in the ecosphere, between the demands of human societies and the functional operations of natural ecosystems, that our present environmental crises have arisen.

Additional Readings

Arthur, D. R. *Man and His Environment*, New York: American Elsevier, 1969.

Bates, M. "The human ecosystem," in *Resources and Man*, Committee on Resources and Man, San Francisco: Freeman, 1969, pp. 21-30.

Boughey, A. S. *The Ecology of Populations*, 2nd ed., New York: Macmillan, 1973.

Cole, LaMont C. "Playing Russian roulette with biogeochemical cycles," in *The Environmental Crisis*, H. W. Helfrich, ed., New Haven and London: Yale University Press, 1970, pp 1-14.

Holling, C. S. "Stability in ecological and social systems," in *Diversity and Stability in Ecological Systems*, G. M. Woodwell and H. H. Smith, eds., *Brookhaven Symp. Biol.*, Nov. 2, 1969, pp. 128-41.

Hutchinson, G. E. "The biosphere," *Scientific American* 223(3): 44-53, 1970.

McCaull, J. "Conference on the ecological aspects of international development," editorial in *Nature and Resources* (UNESCO) 2:5-12, 1969.

Margalef, R. *Perspectives in Ecological Theory*, Chicago and London: University of Chicago Press, 1968.

Mead, M. "The generation gap," editorial in *Science* 164, April 11, 1969.

Nicholson, M. *The Environmental Revolution: A Guide for the New Masters of the World*, New York: McGraw-Hill, 1970.

Robertson, J. C. "Man's place in the ecological pattern," *Geograph. Mag.* 42(4): 254-65, 1970.

Turner, F. B., ed. "Energy flow and ecological systems," *American Zoologist 8:* 10-69, 1968.

Van Dyne, G. M. "Ecosystems, systems ecology, and systems ecologists," *Oak Ridge Nat. Lab. Rep.* 3957:1-31, 1966.

Watt, K. E. F. *Ecology and Resource Management*, New York: McGraw-Hill, 1968.

Whittaker, R. H. *Communities and Ecosystems*, New York: Macmillan, 1970.

Woodwell, G. M. "The energy cycle of the biosphere," *Scientific American* 223(3): 64-74, 1970.

1

MAN'S ECOSYSTEM

LaMont C. Cole

Introduction

My survey here will be superficial by scientific standards, will almost entirely neglect the very important sociological environments in which modern man lives, and will touch on areas in which I am dependent, at best, on second-hand sources of information. I make the effort less for ecologists than in the hope that the message will eventually reach an audience that has forgotten, or has never learned, that man is a part of nature.

The earth's atmosphere, hydrosphere, biosphere, and the superficial layers of its lithosphere all together constitute a vast ecosphere within which a change in any one component evokes changes in all others. Man's survival will ultimately depend upon an understanding of the functioning of the ecosphere, and I here present my conception of how all these things reached their present state and of where they may go in the future.

Early History of the Earth

We must start by referring to some astronomical accidents. First, the earth originated in, or settled into, an orbit at a distance from the sun such that, after it evolved its definitive atmosphere, temperatures permitted water to be present in the liquid state over most of the surface, most of the time. This must be a cosmic rarity but was vitally important to the origin of life as we know it. Second, the earth's axis of rotation turned out to be tipped away from normal to the plane of its revolution about the sun. This accident, of course, is responsible for the existence of seasons and thus greatly accentuated the diversity between

Reprinted from *Bioscience* 16: 243-48, 1966, with the permission of the publishers.

regions in different latitudes. Another astronomical accident of some sort provided the earth with a moon which, after the oceans developed, was responsible for the existence of an intertidal zone where, eventually, organisms adapted to life in the sea could become tolerant of life out of water and so be prepared to colonize the land.

However, the earth may have originated, some 4.5 billion (4.5×10^9) years ago by present estimates, all theories with which I am familiar agree that at one time it was at too high a temperature to retain an atmosphere composed of the gases that are now present. Oxygen was probably bound in hydrated silicates and metallic oxides, and nitrogen, carbon, and phosphorus may have been bound as nitrides, carbides, and phosphides which occur today in meteorites but which are unstable in an atmosphere containing oxygen and water vapor.

The oldest known rocks show evidence of volcanic activity, and I accept the conclusion of Rubey (1951) that the atmosphere and hydrosphere originated from the degassing of rocks in the earth's interior after the surface had cooled sufficiently for its gravitational field to retain water vapor and other light gasses. I also see no reason to doubt that the primeval atmosphere was a reducing atmosphere lacking free oxygen, because we know that today there are enough reduced compounds of iron and magnesium alone in superficial layers of the lithosphere to extract all of the oxygen from the atmosphere in a geologically very short time, were it not for photosynthesis.

Whether the primeval atmosphere was a strongly reducing one consisting of ammonia, hydrogen, methane, and water, as postulated by Oparin (1936), and supported by observations on the atmospheres of the outer planets (Kniper, 1951), and by the experiments of Miller (1953), or whether it was only weakly reducing as postulated by Rubey (1955) need not concern us here. Abelson (1957) has shown experimentally that electrical discharges can induce the synthesis of amino acids in weakly reducing gaseous mixtures containing oxidized carbon compounds so long as free hydrogen is present. In the more strongly reducing atmosphere, Miller obtained a complex mixture of amino acids, aldehydes, organic acids, and urea.

Electrical discharges doubtless occurred in the primeval atmosphere and, more important, ultraviolet radiation of high energy content per quantum would reach the earth's surface in the absence of atmospheric oxygen and drive unfamiliar chemical reactions. Whether or not carbides, nitrides, and phosphides existed in the primitive solid material of the earth, they must have arrived in meteorites and reacted with water to produce hydrocarbons and other compounds of biological interest.

So the primeval sea gradually became a dilute soup of organic compounds which Urey (1952) postulates may have reached a concentration of 1%. Amino acids polymerize readily and, given as much time as we care to postulate, it is not difficult to conceive of polypeptides or even primitive proteins arising under these conditions. A number of authors (Oparin, 1936) have discussed the possible origin of larger organic complexes through such mechanisms as adsorption on clay particles and there is no need to repeat these speculations here. In this complex primeval soup there may have arisen transient forms exhibiting some of the properties we associate with life; for example, scavenging molecules building large aggregates by ingesting other molecules and perhaps metabolizing them in some simple manner. It is even possible that some primitive photosynthetic process may have arisen because, at wavelengths shorter than 200 nanometers, photons have enough energy to reduce CO_2 and H_2O to carbohydrate as a one-step action. Such a process, however, would be self-defeating because some of the evolved oxygen would be ionized by sunlight to ozone which is responsible in our present atmosphere for limiting the short wavelength end of the solar spectrum to 300 nm where photons lack sufficient energy to drive photosynthesis in a single step. In any case, a single-step photosynthetic process would have had to be a transient phenomenon because the photochemical lysis of water vapor in the thin upper atmosphere would result in the loss of hydrogen to space and the addition of some oxygen to the atmosphere.

Whatever protoliving processes may have occurred in the primitive seas, nothing that we would today be willing to call "life" could exist until some organic system acquired the means of producing replicates of itself—the process of reproduction. It is clear that the formation of a nucleic acid was the key step. Once this step was taken, life in the primitive soup could expand rapidly. This, however, was an exploitive form of life, using up the nonrenewable resources of organic matter that had been accumulating for millions of years. Natural selection and speciation doubtless began to operate with different living forms competing for the energy in the organic compounds and with some forms adopting new modes of life as predators and parasites of other forms. Physico-chemical conditions, then as now, varied with differences of latitude and depth and some of these early living forms doubtless became specialists adapted to particular environmental conditions where they were competitively superior in acquiring the stored energy.

This primitive biosphere would have been destined to eat its way to extinction by virtue of its exploitive economy had there not been another large energy source in the form of solar radiation that could be tapped. As Lotka (1925) describes the situation: "... so long as there is an abundant surplus of available energy running 'to waste' over the sides of the mill wheel, so to speak, so long will a marked advantage be gained by any species that may develop talents to utilize this 'lost portion of the steam.' Such a species will therefore, other things equal, tend to grow in extent (numbers)...."

Pyrrole rings may have appeared as metabolic by-products and complete porphyrins may have been present. It was therefore not too tremendous a step to develop the talent of photosynthesis (Granick, 1957) and, with this process established, the atmosphere necessarily became oxidizing, if it was not so already as a result of the photolysis of water. At this point life acquired the potential for a balanced nonexploitive economy—one not based on the destruction of nonrenewable resources.

All this took place in early pre-Cambrian time, for which, to speak generously, the geological and paleontological record is miserably poor. Possible fossils of photosynthetic organisms from rocks 2.7 billion years old have recently been reported (Cloud et al., 1965) and there is considerable evidence for crude oils and other hydrocarbons of biological origin in rocks 1-2 billion years old (Banghoorn et al., 1965). The deposition of such "fossil fuels," which are potential sources of energy for organisms living in an oxidizing environment, indicates that the biosphere did not at this time achieve the potentially permanent state represented by the legendary "balanced aquarium," but the advent of photosynthesis, employing visible light, certainly made life much less exploitive and gave it a much greater expected duration than had previously been the case.

Despite the poor fossil record we know that a major part of all organic evolution must have occurred in the pre-Cambrian because, immediately after a geological revolution of vulcanism and diastrophism ushered in the Cambrian some 600 million years ago, many modern phyla and even some modern classes of animals were already distinct.

Thus the earth entered the Paleozoic era with a great variety of genetically diverse organisms ready to compete for occupancy of its diverse habitats. At first, no doubt, great quantities of mineral nutrients were washed into the seas by runoff of water from land areas of rough topography that had been elevated in the geological revolution. As erosion of the bare surface proceeded to level mountains and hills, the transport of minerals to the seas decreased and the earth gradually settled down into what Brooks (1949) calls "the normal state of affairs on this our earth." This is a state of low relief of the land with great arms of the sea extending far into the interiors of the continents, with warm ocean currents able to reach high latitudes, and with greatly reduced climatic contrasts between different latitudes. It is a state of arid conditions on land and with freezing temperatures unusual or nonexistent.

By Silurian times plants colonized the land and they evolved greatly during the Devonian, at which time animals began to follow them out of the water. It is tempting to suggest that the great deposits of fossil fuels laid down in Carboniferous times were a result of the fact that biotic communities on land were incomplete—that animals and other heterotrophs had not perfected the talent of land life to the point where they could radiate into all available ecological niches (roles in the economy of nature) and use up the organic matter from plants as rapidly as it was produced. In any case, production of these great unoxidized organic deposits probably brought the oxygen in the atmosphere close to its present concentration of 23.2% by weight. It is a sobering thought that if all of the fossil fuels on earth could be extracted and burned, the process would virtually exhaust the oxygen of the atmosphere.

The Paleozoic ended with another great geological revolution of mountain-building, vulcanism, and glaciation some 200 million years ago and with the wholesale extermination of plants and animals which, under the pressure of competition and natural selection, had become highly efficient by becoming highly specialized for exploiting environments that were wiped out in the geological revolution. Every plant species that became extinct probably took with it specialized herbivores and other dependents of these herbivores.

The same pattern repeated in the Mesozoic with gradual leveling of the land and assumption of the normal geological state of affairs, but this time the predominant organisms were different. Of particular interest to us is the fact that the amniote vertebrates and the flowering plants now came into their own. After some 130 million years of base-leveling of the land and specialization of the biota to outcontend competitors for the various ecological niches, the Mesozoic also ended with a geological revolution and the massive extinction of prominent plants and animals. At this point the geological record is clearer (Newell, 1962), and we know that the wave of extinction involved not just such conspicuous forms as the "ruling reptiles" and the ammonites but also even the marine plankton—a phenomenon which Bramlette (1965) has recently suggested may have been associated with the reduced supply of nutrients reaching the seas from land.

The Cenozoic era again repeated the geological story and, with the start of the Pleistocene, the earth may have entered a new geological revolution. Certainly, mountain-building, vulcanism, and glaciation today are far in excess of the geological norm. But in this particular highly abnormal instant of geological time, a new species, *Homo sapiens,* has risen to prominence.

Ecosystems

It is the nature of ecosystems that they tend toward a steady state in which the organic matter produced by autotrophs is all broken down by heterotrophs and other oxidative processes. We have indicated that there are exceptions and that the 1.2×10^{21} gm of oxygen in the atmosphere plus 1% of this amount dissolved in the oceans all represents organic matter that has not been used up and which is what we refer to as "fossil fuels." This is really a small quantity. Green plant photosynthesis releases one gram of oxygen in storing 3.5 kcal of energy, so that oxygen in the atmosphere represents 4.2×10^{21} *kcal* stored. I have estimated elsewhere (Cole, 1958) the net annual production of organic matter by plants at 5×10^{17} kcal, so the unused potential energy from all of geological time corresponds to about 8400 years of plant production which has gone unutilized in at least two billion years of photosynthesis. This figure is too small if, as Dr. John Cantlon has tried to persuade me, a major part of the earth's oxygen was originally bound as water. In that case, much of the oxygen now bound in oxides of iron and aluminum and in limestones also represents fossil fuel. Putnam (1953), employing such assumptions, has given a maximum estimate 18 times my figure, but even this corresponds to well under 1/100 of 1% of the total organic carbon fixation which has gone unutilized. The approximation to a steady state is evidently very close.

Implicit in the tendency of ecosystems to attain a steady state is the fact that an environ-

mental situation to which it is difficult to adapt will have relatively few species present but that those that do adapt successfully will maintain the largest possible numbers and tend to maximize the energy flux through the system. We recognize this situation, for example, in the large populations of relatively few species living in arctic regions or in difficult habitats, such as salt lakes. On the other hand, an equitable environment where many forms can tolerate the physical and chemical features acquires a great variety of species, most of which become specialists at utilizing some very limited ecological niche within which they are superior to potential competitors. We meet the extreme of this situation in the tropical rain forest or on coral reefs where the energy flux is divided among many species and the mean number of individuals per species is accordingly relatively small. We have learned empirically that complex ecosystems tend towards stability in time while simpler systems are subject to numerical fluctuations often of violent proportions.

Whether simple or complex, just about all of the conceivable niches in any ecosystem tend to be filled because, so long as there remains a way to seize a share of the available energy, natural selection will favor any form that may develop the talent for doing so. Thus, selection pressure tends to produce similar ecosystems in separated regions of similar environment. The tropical rain forests of Africa, South America, and the Pacific area have similar organizations but different origins, and therefore different species (Richards, 1952), and many of the marsupial mammals of Australia are startlingly close ecological counterparts of placental mammals on other continents.

A mature ecosystem has autotrophic organisms producing organic matter, usually a variety of primary consumers, including grazers and decomposers, parasites and predators of these, and a complement of "opportunistic" species with a special talent for finding and colonizing the temporary habitats that appear following events such as fires, landslides, or geological revolutions, and then moving on when exposed to the pressure of competition from more efficient but more specialized forms. There is a balance between energy income and energy output, and a new species can only invade or rise to prominence by displacing forms that are already present.

Primitive man subsisted by hunting, fishing, and gathering wild foods. Of course, we shall never know for certain what forms may have had to suffer reduction of numbers or been brought to extinction to make room for man; or perhaps he appeared at a time when biotic communities were incomplete as a result of wholesale extinctions brought on by glacial periods and merely had to establish himself in a niche from which no competitor could displace him.

Human History

Primitive food gatherers had to learn something about ecology; they had to learn what forms were edible and when and where and how to find these. Early hunters probably used fire to drive game, and perhaps they noticed that this had a subsequent effect on the vegetation as, for example, by increasing berry crops and later by concentrating grazing ungulates. Something like this may have been man's first accomplishment in controlling the other species in his ecosystem for his own advantage.

By more than 10,000 years ago man had domesticated both plants and animals, and some of his accomplishments still merit admiration; for example, he did such a job with the corn (maize) plant that authorities are still not in complete agreement as to what wild species he started with. On the other hand, some species probably practically domesticated themselves. I would expect this of wild canids, and Helback (1959) interprets barley as originally a weed of wheat fields which, when man tried growing wheat with an admixture of barley seed in new environments, may have proved hardier than the wheat and have replaced it in some regions. Rye and oats may have had a similar history.

Food-gathering man probably had to make annual migrations to obtain food at all seasons, but early agricultural man could settle by the river flood plains that were easiest to farm and build permanent settlements that would grow into villages and cities. At this stage, if not before, man must have differentiated his activities into distinct professions comparable to ecological niches. Farming, production of meat and milk products, mining, and trading all seem to be about equally ancient ways of life. By selection of seed and breeding stock man "improved" his domestic forms and continued to bring other species under domestication. With the advent of trade, and probably growing populations, he expanded his agricultural activities and discovered that water shortage often limits plant growth and that he could circumvent this by irrigation.

In places, this type of agriculture was a spectacular success. The annual flood of the Nile was dependable both in time of occurrence and depth attained, and it brought to the flood plain not only water but also an alluvium rich in plant nutrients. Irrigation in Egypt goes back to at least 2000 B.C. and, after continuous use of the land, that country was still the principal granary of the Roman Empire.

Results were less happy in some other regions. At this stage man could hardly have been expected to anticipate that irrigation without adequate drainage would cause the water table to rise and produce waterlogged soils inimical to agriculture, or that evaporation of water moving upward would deposit a crust of salts on the surface, or that insidious erosion by wind and water, so slow as to be barely perceptible, could eliminate the fertile topsoil, ruin the plant cover, and end in violent erosion and gullying. These things had to be learned empirically and at great cost, for they were probably the principal factors causing the collapse of the great Babylonian Empire and other civilizations of the Middle East and Mediterranean regions.

By Plato's time (347 B.C.) a reflective scholar could write of deforestation and grazing as causing the drying up of springs and the destruction of the most fertile soils by causing water to "run from naked earth into the sea" so that lands "resemble the bones of a diseased body; such of the earth as was soft and fat being washed away, and a thin body of the country alone remaining." Virgil (30 B.C.)

recommended crop rotation with wheat following a legume (or vetch or lupine), leaving land fallow on alternate years, dressing exhausted soils with manure or ashes, weeding, repelling birds, and selecting by hand the best quality seed for planting. A century later Pliny (77 A.D.) told of man altering climates by changing river courses and draining a lake with the result that olives and grapes in the region were killed by frost. So, by the beginning of the Christian era, man had acquired a good deal of practical ecological knowledge. But, despite the eminence of these authors, this knowledge failed to enter the mainstream of Western thought.

Meanwhile, agriculture along somewhat different lines had developed under other types of climates. In forested regions the "slash and burn" technique, then as now, was the method of choice. After killing the trees, the land was burned over and crops grown for as long as profitable—then the process was repeated in a new location, giving the exhausted area a chance to recover. Land can often be cultivated less than 10% of the time in tropical regions where humus decomposes rapidly and accumulates little, so a large ratio of land to population is necessary.

Thus man achieved his dominance over the face of the earth, and there is no accurate way of estimating the number of extinctions and displacements that he may have caused by altering and eliminating distinctive habitats and increasing his numbers in an already saturated ecosphere. At the same time he created some new problems for himself. As he crowded into villages and later cities he created ideal conditions for the spread of pathogens and other parasites, and he thus became subject to devastation by frightful epidemics. As populations exhausted or outgrew the resources of their own territories, they came to covet the resources of their neighbors and developed the almost uniquely human institution of war. Man's agricultural technique of simplifying ecosystems to favor a crop plant of his choice also favored the opportunistic species that are present in all ecosystems but usually as a minor element capable of inhabiting temporary habitats by virtue of their hardiness, adapt-

ability, great reproductive potential, and powers of dispersal. The tendency towards monoculture agriculture, often employing annual plants, was as if designed to favor these forms which do not compete successfully in a mature, diverse ecosystem, and they remain today as our important "pest" species.

Just as the crowding of man predisposed him to epidemics, so fields crowded with a single variety of plant provided ideal conditions for the spread of pathogenic fungi and the multiplication of larger consumers, such as insects and rodents. So man at this stage was also subject to mass destruction by famine caused sometimes by pests and sometimes by unfortunate long runs of unfavorable weather.

Despite these occasional setbacks, human numbers gradually increased, and this growth was eventually assisted by the exploitation of new lands, especially in the new world. Then, 300 years ago, the industrial revolution started and initiated a new cycle of population growth that has not yet ended.

Mankind Today

The most significant feature of the industrial world is its dependence on the fossil fuels. In the early stages wood, charcoal, water, wind, and animal power could supply much of the necessary energy, but we are far past that point now; and it is doubtless true that half of all the fuel ever burned by man has been burned in the past 50 years. But the fossil fuels are nonrenewable resources so, for the second time in the history of life, it is running on an exploitive economy that will destroy itself if continued long enough.

As soon as the rate at which fuel is burned comes to exceed the rate of photosynthesis, the oxygen content of the atmosphere must start to decrease. I wish I could estimate how near we are to that frightening compensation point but I have found no reasonably satisfying way of doing so. For the United States, Putnam estimated in 1953 that: "If all the carbon fixed in one year . . . was burned and the energy recovered, it would amount to about one and one-half times the present requirements of the national energy system."

If he was approximately correct, this country and some other industrial nations may by now have passed the compensation point. Fortunately, there remain vast areas, such as the Amazonian rain forest, that have not even started on this hazardous path, but we hear every year of exploitive interests bent on promoting "progress" that are casting covetous eyes on these "undeveloped" areas.

Even modern agriculture is industrialized. We boast of our efficiency in raising more food on less land with the labor of fewer people, but we are deceiving ourselves. If we were to deduct from the food calories that a farmer produces the calories consumed by his machinery, the calories used to build and transport that machinery, to mine raw materials, to process, transport, and apply fertilizers and pesticides, and to process and distribute the food, we would see that modern agriculture is largely a device for exchanging the calories in fossil fuels for calories in food.

The modern world is divided up into a series of nations, each operating under the curious unecological assumption that it is beneficial to export each year more of its resources (including food which represents a portion of its soil fertility) than it receives in return. It is also considered desirable to maximize the rate at which resources such as minerals leave the ground, enter into products, and pass to the scrap heap. The creation of accelerated obsolescence, which some of us took to be a joke when we first heard of it, appears now to be a serious economic policy without concern for the renewability of resources.

I cannot remember at what age or in what young people's magazine I first encountered an arithmetic problem concerning a bowl containing an amoeba which every hour divided into two amoebae the size of the original, and where each descendant continued the process. The computations, of course, led to the ludicrous conclusion that the mass or volume of amoebae would soon exceed that of the earth. The actual human population today, like the hypothetical amoeba, is reproducing in a manner that, if continued, would cause it to double in every generation. The hypothetical consequences in this case are ludicrous also, but

this is no hypothetical problem. Man has some other very serious problems to face but, unless he achieves a rational solution of the problem of his own population growth instead of leaving its control to wars, epidemics, and famine, I see little hope that he will be able to solve the technologically more difficult problems.

Man is damaging the earth in various ways, not the least of which is through environmental pollution. Products of erosion, sewage, and industrial wastes have been polluting environments for a long time, but the problem has become more acute as the population pressure increases. Agriculture has recently embraced the theory that the way to avoid damage from pest organisms is to make the environment poisonous. Naturally poisonous environments often teem with tremendous populations of the few opportunistic species that can adapt to them, and I think it is an ecologically sound prediction that long continued use of toxins with residual action will produce similar effects on agricultural land. After all, bacteria have recently evolved strains that require antibiotics for growth, and we can expect fungi and insects to be only a little slower in evolving. Some pesticides, notably DDT, have become virtually a normal constituent of the world environment and have turned up even in the fat of penguins from Antarctica, where, of course, agricultural chemicals are ridiculous. The frightening thing is that man brought this about in just a few years with an irresponsible disregard for possible effects on ecosystems. He did damage wildlife, but apparently he was lucky this time and did not upset any vital process, such as the activities of the various bacteria involved in the nitrogen cycle, without which man could not survive.

Contamination with radioisotopes is another modern problem that is not being approached with the intelligence or candor it merits. A committee of prominent scientists (Commoner, 1965) has recently called attention to the fact that millions of curies of radioactive fallout have dropped on the earth over the last 20 years, while, as late as 1962, the scientists responsible were "apparently unaware that iodine-131 constitutes the most severe immediate hazard." The findings (Weiss and

Shipman, 1957) of high concentrations of the radioisotope cobalt-60 in clams 2 years after contamination of the water by fallout is instructive for two reasons. First, cobalt-60 is not a product of nuclear fission, so this shows the necessity for considering all of the possible interactions of radioactive materials with other components of the environment. Second, this illustrates the ability of an organism to take an unnatural chemical from an almost infinitely dilute medium and concentrate it to hazardous levels. This biological concentration of novel materials has also often been a factor in the killing of wildlife by pesticides (Cottam, 1965) and it shows the necessity for a full understanding of the food chains in ecosystems before subjecting them to contamination.

Mankind must outgrow its ancient illusion that the atmosphere and hydrosphere represent waste receptacles of infinite capacity. In this country we are beginning to be disillusioned about this for rivers and lakes, and a few local areas are even beginning to try to do something about the pollution of the atmosphere and of harbors. However, the predominating attitude was illustrated less than 2 years ago by a leading news magazine *(Time)* which, in reporting a proposal to dig a new Panama canal with nuclear explosives, explained that the amount of radioactivity that would get into the water cannot be estimated, "but the strong current that will run through the canal should carry most of it away." And so it should, at the risk of making seafood from the Atlantic Ocean unsafe to eat!

I have been given to understand that solid-fuel rocket engines release beryllium into the atmosphere but, despite some inquiries, I know absolutely nothing about the quantities involved. I do know that there have been a number of reports of beryllium toxicity to vertebrate animals and that the 1938 *USDA Yearbook of Agriculture* reports that very low concentrations of beryllium are toxic to citrus cuttings in solution culture (McMurtrey and Robinson, 1938). I should like to feel confident that due consideration was given to this, and appropriate experiments performed, prior to the decision to test such rocket engines at ground level in southern California, but I do

not expect such reassurance to be forthcoming. I offer this as a fairly typical example of the things that make ecologists distrustful of many of the decisions being made by society.[1]

I could go on listing things that, from an ecological viewpoint, man is clearly doing wrong, such as depleting the supply of fresh water and developing increased reliance on monoculture and animal husbandry, and I could draw up a long list of man-made changes I deplore. I regret that I can never expect to see a wild wolverine in the eastern United States, but I recognize that the wolverine's requirements and habits are incompatible with man's. I regret that the same processes that have made it possible for me to live in a house built of cypress have brought America's largest woodpecker, the ivory-bill, to the verge of extinction, but I recognize that some such displacements are inevitable when any species greatly expands its sphere of activity. However, I can see no excuse for the extinction, through reckless overexploitation, of species man values. One would think that the most primitive savage could understand that a species once gone cannot be restored, and that his greatest harvest in the long run depends upon always preserving a breeding stock. Yet today, whaling ships from scientifically and technologically advanced nations are threatening the existence of the largest animal that has ever lived on the earth.

Conclusion

If the picture I have painted of man and his ecosystem appears to be a gloomy one, let me state that the situation is not hopeless. Man has the necessary technology to regulate his population size; what is needed is a consensus as to how many people should be allowed to inhabit the earth at one time. Because our present economy is exploitive, we are in need of a breakthrough comparable in significance to the discovery of photosynthesis. Atomic energy does not quite represent such a breakthrough

[1] Since this was written the toxicity of beryllium has been explicitly acknowledged (Glassman, 1965) and it is noted that ". . . currently, Be is under active investigation."

because it depends on a nonrenewable resource, but I think it can take us quite a way into the future if man will use it responsibly. Also, a large amount of deuterium is found in the oceans, and future technology may include a way to use that source of potential energy. And, finally, there is solar radiation, which must ultimately become man's energy source if the species persists long enough.

With an adequate energy supply assured, man can solve many of his other problems by methods that are shunned today as too expensive. He can distill sea water and transport the distillate to regions of shortage; the scrap heaps and junk yards of today can become the mines tomorrow, and it will almost certainly become necessary to mine the ocean bottoms, at least for phosphorus fertilizer.

The problems I have dealt with here are all essentially ecological. I have not ventured to suggest what the world we are developing may do to man's mental health, nor have I discussed the factors that have given man the capacity to render the earth uninhabitable almost instantaneously, nor the social factors that make it a real possibility that man will use that destructive capacity. The ecological problems are serious enough and, unfortunately, the most prestigious bodies of scientists, the ones that administrators listen to most intently, are woefully ignorant of ecology. I am encouraged that a prominent committee of scientists (Commoner, 1965), including no ecologists, has surveyed the current status of "the integrity of science" and has caught a glimpse of the fundamental role of ecology. I hope that this news will spread quickly.

References

Abelson, P. H. 1957. Some aspects of paleobiochemistry. *Ann. N.Y. Acad. Sci.*, **69:** 176-285.

Banghoorn, E. S., W. G. Meinschein, and J. W. Schopf. 1965. Paleobiology of a Pre-Cambrian shale. *Science*, **148:** 461-472.

Banghoorn, E. S. 1957. Origin of life. *Mem. Geol. Soc. Am.*, **67:** 75-86.

Bramlette, M. N. 1965. Massive extinctions in biota at the end of Mesozoic time. *Science*, **148:** 1696-1699.

Brooks, C. E. P. 1949. *Climate through the Ages*. Rev. ed. McGraw-Hill Book Co., New York.

Cloud, P. E., J. W. Gruner, and H. Hagen, 1965. Carbonaceous rocks of the Soudan iron formation (early pre-Cambrian). *Science*, **148:** 1713-1716.

Cole, L. C. 1958. The ecosphere. *Sci. Am.*, **198:** 83-92.

Commoner, B. (Chairman). 1965. The integrity of science. A report by the AAAS Committee on Science in the Promotion of Human Welfare. *Am. Scientist*, **53:** 174-198.

Cf. Cottam, C. 1965. The ecologists' role in problems of pesticide pollution. *BioScience*, **15:** 457-463.

Glassman, I, 1965. The chemistry of propellants. *Am. Scientist*, **53:** 508-524.

Cf. Granick, S. 1957. Speculations on the origins and evolutions of photosynthesis. *Ann. N.Y. Acad. Sci.*, **69:** 292-308.

Helbaek, H. 1959. Domestication of food plants in the old world. *Science*, **130:** 365-372.

Kuiper, G. P. (ed.) 1951. *The Atmospheres of the Earth and Planets*. University of Chicago Press, Chicago.

Lotka, A. J. 1925. *Elements of Physical Biology*. Williams & Wilkins Co., Baltimore, p. 190.

McMurtrey, J. E., Jr., and W. O. Robinson. 1938. Neglected soil constituents that affect plant and animal development, in: Soils and man. *USDA Yearbook of Agriculture*. Govt. Printing Office, Washington, D.C., pp. 807-829.

Miller, S. L. 1953. A production of amino acids under possible primitive earth conditions. *Science*, **117:** 528-529.

Miller, S. L. 1955. Production of some organic compounds under possible primitive earth conditions. *J. Am. Chem. Soc.*, **77:** 2351-2361.

Newell, N. D., 1962. Paleontological gaps and geochronology *J. Paleontol.*, **36:** 592-610.

Oparin, A. I. 1936. *The Origin of Life*. (English translation, 1938). Macmillan Co., New York.

Oro, J., D. W. Nooner, A. Zlatkis, S. A. Wikstrom, and E. S. Banghoorn. 1965. Hydrocarbons of biological origin in sediments about two billion years old. *Science*, **148:** 77-79.

Plato. ca 347 B.C. Critias. in: *The Timaeus and The Critias or Atlanticus*. The Thomas Taylor translation. Pantheon Books, New York, 1944.

Pliny the Elder. ca. 77 A.D. *Natural History*.

Putnam, P. C. 1953. *Energy in the Future*. D. Van Nostrand Co., Inc., New York, p. 117.

Richards, P. W. 1952. *The Tropical Rain Forest*. Cambridge University Press, New York.

Rubey, W. W. 1951. Geological history of sea water. *Bull. Geol. Soc. Am.*, **62:** 1111-1148

Rubey, W. W. 1955. Development of the hydrosphere and atmosphere with special reference to the probable composition of the early atmosphere. *Spec. Papers, Geol. Soc. Am.*, **62:**631-650.

Time Magazine, January 21, 1964, p. 36.

Urey, H. C. 1952. On the early chemical history of the earth and the origin of life. *Proc. Natl. Acad. Sci. U.S.*, **38:** 351-363.

Virgil, ca. 30 B.C. *First Georgics.*

Wald, G. 1954. The origin of life. *Sci. Am.,* **191:** 44-53.

Weiss, H. V., and W. H. Shipman. 1957. Biological concentration by killer clams of cobalt-60 from radioactive fallout. *Science,* **125:** 695.

2

THE STRATEGY OF ECOSYSTEM DEVELOPMENT

Eugene P. Odum

The principles of ecological succession bear importantly on the relationships between man and nature. The framework of successional theory needs to be examined as a basis for resolving man's present environmental crisis. Most ideas pertaining to the development of ecological systems are based on descriptive data obtained by observing changes in biotic communities over long periods, or on highly theoretical assumptions; very few of the generally accepted hypotheses have been tested experimentally. Some of the confusion, vagueness, and lack of experimental work in this area stems from the tendency of ecologists to regard "succession" as a single straight-forward idea; in actual fact, it entails an interacting complex of processes, some of which counteract one another.

As viewed here, ecological succession involves the development of ecosystems; it has many parallels in the developmental biology of organisms, and also in the development of human society. The ecosystem, or ecological system, is considered to be a unit of biological organization made up of all of the organisms in a given area (that is, "community") interacting with the physical environment so that a flow of energy leads to characteristic trophic structure and material cycles within the system. It is the

Reprinted from *Science* **164**: 262-70, 1969, with the permission of the publishers. Copyright 1969 by the American Association for the Advancement of Science.

purpose of this article to summarize, in the form of a tabular model, components and stages of development at the ecosystem level as a means of emphasizing those aspects of ecological succession that can be accepted on the basis of present knowledge, those that require more study, and those that have special relevance to human ecology.

Definition of Succession

Ecological succession may be defined in terms of the following three parameters (1). (i) It is an orderly process of community development that is reasonably directional and, therefore, predictable. (ii) It results from modification of the physical environment by the community; that is, succession is community-controlled even though the physical environment determines the pattern, the rate of change, and often sets limits as to how far development can go. (iii) It culminates in a stabilized ecosystem in which maximum biomass (or high information content) and symbiotic function between organisms are maintained per unit of energy flow. In a word, the "strategy" of succession as a short-term process is basically the same as the "strategy" of long-term evolutionary development of the biosphere—namely, increased control of, or homeostasis with, the physical environment in the sense of achieving maximum protection from its perturbations. As I illustrate below, the strategy of "maximum protection" (that is, trying to achieve maximum support of complex biomass structure) often conflicts with man's goal of "maximum production" (trying to obtain the highest possible yield). Recognition of the ecological basis for this conflict is, I believe, a first step to establishing rational land-use policies.

The earlier descriptive studies of succession on sand dunes, grasslands, forests, marine shores, or other sites, and more recent functional considerations, have led to the basic theory contained in the definition given above. H. T. Odum and Pinkerton (2), building on Lotka's (3), "law of maximum energy in biological systems," were the first to point out that succession involves a fundamental shift in energy flows as increasing energy is relegated to maintenance. Margalef (4) has recently documented this bioenergetic basis for succession and has extended the concept.

Changes that occur in major structural and functional characteristics of a developing ecosystem are listed in Table 1. Twenty-four attributes of ecological systems are grouped, for convenience of discussion, under six headings. Trends are emphasized by contrasting the situation in early and late development. The degree of absolute change, the rate of change, and the time required to reach a steady state may vary not only with different climatic and physiographic situations but also with different ecosystem attributes in the same physical environment. Where good data are available, rate-of-change curves are usually convex, with changes occurring most rapidly at the beginning, but bimodal or cyclic patterns may also occur.

Bioenergetics of Ecosystem Development

Attributes 1 through 5 in Table 1 represent the bioenergetics of the ecosystem. In the early stages of ecological succession, or in "young nature," so to speak, the rate of primary production or total (gross) photosynthesis (P) exceeds the rate of community respiration (R) so that the P/R ratio is greater than 1. In the special case of organic pollution, the P/R ratio is typically less than 1. In both cases, however, the theory is that P/R approaches 1 as succession occurs. In other words, energy fixed tends to be balanced by the energy cost of maintenance (that is, total community respiration) in the mature or "climax" ecosystem. The P/R ratio, therefore, should be an excellent functional index of the relative maturity of the system.

So long as P exceeds R, organic matter and biomass (B) will accumulate in the system (Table 1, item 6), with the result that ratio P/B will tend to decrease or, conversely, the B/P, B/R, or B/E ratios (where $E = P + R$) will increase (Table 1, items 2 and 3). Theoretically, then, the amount of standing-crop biomass

supported by the available energy flow (E) increases to a maximum in the mature or climax stages (Table 1, item 3). As a consequence, the net community production, or yield, in an annual cycle is large in young nature and small or zero in mature nature (Table 1, item 4).

Comparison of Succession in a Laboratory Microcosm and a Forest

One can readily observe bioenergetic changes by initiating succession in experimental laboratory microecosystems. Aquatic microecosystems, derived from various types of outdoor systems, such as ponds, have been cultured by Beyers (5), and certain of these mixed cultures are easily replicated and maintain themselves in the climax state indefinitely on defined media in a flask with only light input (6). If samples from the climax system are inoculated into fresh media, succession occurs, the mature system developing in less than 100 days. In Fig. 2-1 the general pattern of a 100-day autotropic succession in a microcosm based on data of Cooke (7) is compared with a hypothetical model of a 100-year forest succession as presented by Kira and Shidei (8).

During the first 40 to 60 days in a typical microcosm experiment, daytime net production

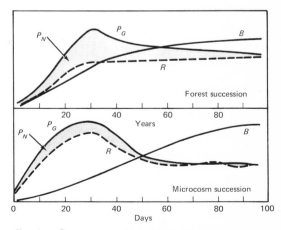

Fig. 2-1. Comparison of the energetics of succession in a forest and a laboratory microcosm. P_G, gross production; P_N, net production; R, total community respiration; B, total biomass.

(P) exceeds nighttime respiration *(R)*, so that biomass *(B)* accumulates in the system (9). After an early "bloom" at about 30 days, both rates decline, and they become approximately equal at 60 to 80 days, the *B/P* ratio, in terms of grams of carbon supported per gram of carbon production, increases from less than 20 to more than 100 as the steady state is reached. Not only are autotrophic and heterotrophic metabolism balanced in the climax, but a large organic structure is supported by small daily production and respiratory rates.

While direct projection from the small laboratory microecosystem to open nature may

Table 1. A tabular model of ecological succession: trends to be expected in the development of ecosystems.

	Ecosystem attributes	Developmental stages	Mature stages
	Community energetics		
1.	Gross production/community respiration (*P/R* ratio)	Greater or less than 1	Approaches 1
2.	Gross production/standing crop biomass (*P/B* ratio)	High	Low
3.	Biomass supported/unit energy flow (*B/E* ratio)	Low	High
4.	Net community production (yield)	High	Low
5.	Food chains	Linear, predominantly grazing	Weblike, predominantly detritus
	Community structure		
6.	Total organic matter	Small	Large
7.	Inorganic nutrients	Extrabiotic	Intrabiotic
8.	Species diversity—variety component	Low	High
9.	Species diversity—equitability component	Low	High
10.	Biochemical diversity	Low	High
11.	Stratification and spatial heterogeneity (pattern diversity)	Poorly organized	Well-organized
	Life history		
12.	Niche specialization	Broad	Narrow
13.	Size of organism	Small	Large
14.	Life cycles	Short, simple	Long, complex
	Nutrient cycling		
15.	Mineral cycles	Open	Closed
16.	Nutrient exchange rate, between organisms and environment	Rapid	Slow
17.	Role of detritus in nutrient regeneration	Unimportant	Important
	Selection pressure		
18.	Growth form	For rapid growth ("*r*-selection")	For feedback control ("*K*-selection")
19,	Production	Quantity	Quality
	Overall homeostasis		
20.	Internal symbiosis	Undeveloped	Developed
21.	Nutrient conservation	Poor	Good
22.	Stability (resistance to external perturbations)	Poor	Good
23.	Entropy	High	Low
24.	Information	Low	High

not be entirely valid, there is evidence that the same basic trends that are seen in the laboratory are characteristic of succession on land and in large bodies of water. Seasonal successions also often follow the same pattern, an early seasonal bloom characterized by rapid growth of a few dominant species being followed by the development later in the season of high *B/P* ratios, increased diversity, and a relatively steady, if temporary, state in terms of *P* and *R* (4). Open systems may not experience a decline, at maturity, in total or gross productivity, as the space-limited microcosms do, but the general pattern of bioenergetic change in the latter seems to mimic nature quite well.

These trends are not, as might at first seem to be the case, contrary to the classical limnological teaching which describes lakes as progressing in time from the less productive (oligotrophic) to the more productive (eutrophic) state. Table 1, as already emphasized, refers to changes which are brought about by biological processes *within* the ecosystem in question. Eutrophication, whether natural or cultural, results when nutrients are imported into the lake from *outside* the lake—that is, from the watershed. This is equivalent to adding nutrients to the laboratory microecosystem or fertilizing a field; the system is pushed back, in successional terms, to a younger or "bloom" state. Recent studies on lake sediments (10), as well as theoretical considerations (11), have indicated that lakes can and do progress to a more oligotrophic condition when the nutrient input from the watershed slows or ceases. Thus, there is hope that the troublesome cultural eutrophication of our waters can be reversed if the inflow of nutrients from the watershed can be greatly reduced. Most of all, however, this situation emphasizes that it is the entire drainage or catchment basin, not just the lake or stream, that must be considered the ecosystem unit if we are to deal successfully with our water pollution problems. Eco-systematic study of entire landscape catchment units is a major goal of the American plan for the proposed International Biological Program. Despite the obvious logic of such a

proposal, it is proving surprisingly difficult to get tradition-bound scientists and granting agencies to look beyond their specialties toward the support of functional studies of large units of the landscape.

Food Chains and Food Webs

As the ecosystem develops, subtle changes in the network pattern of food chains may be expected. The manner in which organisms are linked together through food tends to be relatively simple and linear in the very early stages of succession, as a consequence of low diversity. Furthermore, heterotrophic utilization of net production occurs predominantly by way of grazing food chains — that is, plant-herbivore-carnivore sequences. In contrast, food chains become complex webs in mature stages, with the bulk of biological energy flow following detritus pathways (Table 1, item 5). In a mature forest, for example, less than 10 percent of annual net production is consumed (that is, grazed) in the living state (12); most is utilized as dead matter (detritus) through delayed and complex pathways involving as yet little understood animal-microorganism interactions. The time involved in an uninterrupted succession allows for increasingly intimate associations and reciprocal adaptations between plants and animals, which lead to the development of many mechanisms that reduce grazing—such as the development of indigestible supporting tissues (cellulose, lignin, and so on), feedback control between plants and herbivores (13), and increasing predatory pressure on herbivores (14). Such mechanisms enable the biological community to maintain the large and complex organic structure that mitigates perturbations of the physical environment. Severe stress or rapid changes brought about by outside forces can, of course, rob the system of these protective mechanisms and allow irruptive, cancerous growths of certain species to occur, as man too often finds to his sorrow. An example of a stress-induced pest irruption occurred at Brookhaven National Laboratory, where oaks became vulnerable to aphids when translocation of sugars and amino acids was impaired by continuing gamma irradiation (15).

Radionuclide tracers are providing a means of charting food chains in the intact outdoor ecosystem to a degree that will permit analysis within the concepts of network or matrix algebra. For example, we have recently been able to map, by use of a radiophosphorus tracer, the open, relatively linear food linkage between plants and insects in an early old-field successional stage (16).

Diversity and Succession

Perhaps the most controversial of the successional trends pertain to the complex and much discussed subject of diversity (17). It is important to distinguish between different kinds of diversity indices, since they may not follow parallel trends in the same gradient or developmental series. Four components of diversity are listed in Table 1, items 8 through 11.

The variety of species, expressed as a species-number ratio or a species-area ratio, tends to increase during the early stages of community development. A second component of species diversity is what has been called equitability, or evenness (18), in the apportionment of individuals among the species. For example, two systems each containing 10 species and 100 individuals have the same diversity in terms of species-number ratio but could have widely different equitabilities depending on the apportionment of the 100 individuals among the 10 species—for example, 91-1-1-1-1-1-1-1-1-1 at one extreme or 10 individuals per species at the other. The Shannon formula,

$$ - \Sigma \frac{ni}{N} \log_2 \frac{ni}{N} $$

where ni is the number of individuals in each species and N is the total number of individuals, is widely used as a diversity index because it combines the variety and equitability components in one approximation. But, like all such lumping parameters, Shannon's formula may obscure the behavior of these two rather different aspects of diversity. For example, in

our most recent field experiments, an acute stress from insecticide reduced the number of species of insects relative to the number of individuals but increased the evenness in the relative abundances of the surviving species (19). Thus, in this case the "variety" and "evenness" components would tend to cancel each other in Shannon's formula.

While an increase in the variety of species together with reduced dominance by any one species or small group of species (that is, increased evenness) can be accepted as a general probability during succession (20), there are other community changes that may work against these trends. An increase in the size of organisms, an increase in the length and complexity of life histories, and an increase in interspecific competition that may result in competitive exclusion of species (Table 1, items 12-14) are trends that may reduce the number of species that can live in a given area. In the bloom stage of succession organisms tend to be small and to have simple life histories and rapid rates of reproduction. Changes in size appear to be a consequence of, or an adaptation to, a shift in nutrients from inorganic to organic (Table 1, item 7). In a mineral nutrient-rich environment, small size is of selective advantage, especially to autotrophs, because of the greater surface-to-volume ratio. As the ecosystem develops, however, inorganic nutrients tend to become more and more tied up in the biomass (that is, to become intrabiotic), so that the selective advantage shifts to larger organisms (either larger individuals of the same species or larger species, or both) which have greater storage capacities and more complex life histories, thus are adapted to exploiting seasonal or periodic releases of nutrients or other resources. The question of whether the seemingly direct relationship between organism size and stability is the result of positive feedback or is merely fortuitous remains unanswered (21).

Thus, whether or not species diversity continues to increase during succession will depend on whether the increase in potential niches resulting from increased biomass, stratification (Table 1, item 9), and other consequences of biological organization exceeds the counter-effects of increasing size and competition. No one has yet been able to catalogue all the species in any sizable area, much less follow total species diversity in a successional series. Data are so far available only for segments of the community (trees, birds, and so on). Margalef (4) postulates that diversity will tend to peak during the early or middle stages of succession and then decline in the climax. In a study of bird populations along a successional gradient we found a bimodal pattern (22); the number of species increased during the early stages of old-field succession, declined during the early forest stages, and then increased again in the mature forest.

Species variety, equitability, and stratification are only three aspects of diversity which change during succession. Perhaps an even more important trend is an increase in the diversity of organic compounds, not only of those within the biomass but also of those excreted and secreted into the media (air, soil, water) as by-products of the increasing community metabolism. An increase in such "biochemical diversity" (Table 1, item 10) is illustrated by the increase in the variety of plant pigments along a successional gradient in aquatic situations, as described by Margalef (4, 23). Biochemical diversity within populations, or within systems as a whole, has not yet been systematically studied to the degree the subject of species diversity has been. Consequently, few generalizations can be made, except that it seems safe to say that, as succession progresses, organic extrametabolites probably serve increasingly important functions as regulators which stabilize the growth and composition of the ecosystem. Such metabolites may, in fact, be extremely important in preventing populations from overshooting the equilibrial density, thus in reducing oscillations as the system develops stability.

The cause-and-effect relationship between diversity and stability is not clear and needs to be investigated from many angles. If it can be shown that biotic diversity does indeed enhance physical stability in the ecosystem, or is the result of it, then we would have an important guide for conservation practice. Preservation of hedgerows, woodlots, noneconomic species, noneutrophicated waters, and other biotic variety in man's landscape could then be justified on scientific as well as esthetic grounds, even though such preservation often must result in some reduction in the production of food or other immediate consumer needs. In other words, is variety only the spice of life, or is it a necessity for the long life of the total ecosystem comprising man and nature?

Nutrient Cycling

An important trend in successional development is the closing or "tightening" of the biogeochemical cycling of major nutrients, such as nitrogen, phosphorus, and calcium (Table 1, item 15-17). Mature systems, as compared to developing ones, have a greater capacity to entrap and hold nutrients for cycling within the system. For example, Bormann and Likens (24) have estimated that only 8 kilograms per hectare out of a total pool of exchangeable calcium of 365 kilograms per hectare is lost per year in stream outflow from a North Temperate watershed covered with a mature forest. Of this, about 3 kilograms per hectare is replaced by rainfall, leaving only 5 kilograms to be obtained from weathering of the underlying rocks in order for the system to maintain mineral balance. Reducing the volume of the vegetation, or otherwise setting the succession back to a younger state, results in increased water yield by way of stream outflow (25), but this greater outflow is accompanied by greater losses of nutrients, which may also produce downstream eutrophication. Unless there is a compensating increase in the rate of weathering, the exchangeable pool of nutrients suffers gradual depletion (not to mention possible effects on soil structure resulting from erosion). High fertility in "young systems" which have open nutrient cycles cannot be maintained without compensating inputs of new nutrients; examples of such practice are the continuous-flow culture of algae, or intensive agriculture where large amounts of fertilizer are imported into the system each year.

Because rates of leaching increase in latitudinal gradient from the poles to the equator, the role of the biotic community in nutrient retention is especially important in the high-rainfall areas of the subtropical latitudes, including not only land areas but also estuaries. Theoretically, as one goes equatorwards, a larger percentage of the available nutrient pool is tied up in the biomass and a correspondingly lower percentage is in the soil or sediment. This theory, however, needs testing, since data to show such a geographical trend are incomplete. It is perhaps significant that conventional North Temperate row-type agriculture, which represents a very youthful type of ecosystem, is successful in the humid tropics only if carried out in a system of "shifting agriculture" in which the crops alternate with periods of natural vegetative redevelopment. Tree culture and the semiaquatic culture of rice provide much better nutrient retention and consequently have a longer life expectancy on a given site in these warmer latitudes.

Selection Pressure: Quantity Versus Quality

MacArthur and Wilson (26) have reviewed stages of colonization of islands which provide direct parallels with stages in ecological succession on continents. Species with high rates of reproduction and growth, they find, are more likely to survive in the early uncrowded stages of island colonization. In contrast, selection pressure favors species with lower growth potential but better capabilities for competitive survival under the equilibrium density of late stages. Using the terminology of growth equations, where r is the intrinsic rate of increase and K is the upper asymptote or equilibrium population size, we may say that "r selection" predominates in early colonization, with "K selection" prevailing as more and more species and individuals attempt to colonize (Table 1, item 18). The same sort of thing is even seen within the species in certain "cyclic" northern insects in which "active" genetic strains found at low densities are replaced at high densities by "sluggish" strains that are adapted to crowding (27).

Genetic changes involving the whole biota may be presumed to accompany the successional gradient, since, as described above, quantity production characterizes the young ecosystem while quality production and feedback control are the trademarks of the mature system (Table 1, item 19). Selection at the ecosystem level may be primarily interspecific, since species replacement is a characteristic of successional series or seres. However, in most well-studied seres there seem to be a few early successional species that are able to persist through to late stages. Whether genetic changes contribute to adaptation in such species has not been determined, so far as I know, but studies on population genetics of *Drosophila* suggest that changes in genetic composition could be important in population regulation (28). Certainly, the human population, if it survives beyond its present rapid growth stage, is destined to be more and more affected by such selection pressures as adaptation to crowding becomes essential.

Overall Homeostasis

This brief review of ecosystem development emphasizes the complex nature of processes that interact. While one may well question whether all the trends described are characteristic of all types of ecosystems, there can be little doubt that the net result of community actions is symbiosis, nutrient conservation, stability, a decrease in entropy, and an increase in information (Table 1, items 20-24). The overall strategy is, as I stated at the beginning of this article, directed toward achieving as large and diverse an organic structure as is possible within the limits set by the available energy input and the prevailing physical conditions of existence (soil, water, climate, and so on). As studies of biotic communities become more functional and sophisticated, one is impressed with the importance of mutualism, parasitism, predation, commensalism, and other forms of symbiosis. Partnership between unrelated species is often noteworthy (for example, that between coral coelenterates and algae, or between mycorrhizae and trees). In many cases, at least, biotic control of grazing, population density, and nutrient cycling provide the chief positive-feedback mechanisms that contribute to stability in the mature system by preventing overshoots and destructive oscillations. The intriguing question is, Do mature ecosystems age, as organisms do? In other words, after a long period of relative stability or "adulthood," do ecosystems again develop unbalanced metabolism and become more vulnerable to diseases and other perturbations?

Relevance of Ecosystem Development Theory to Human Ecology

Figure 2-1 depicts a basic conflict between the strategies of man and of nature. The "bloom-type" relationships, as exhibited by the 30-day microcosm or the 30-year forest, illustrate man's present idea of how nature should be directed. For example, the goal of agriculture or intensive forestry, as now generally practiced, is to achieve high rates of production of readily harvestable products with little standing crop left to accumulate on the landscape—in other words, a high *P/B* efficiency. Nature's strategy, on the other hand, as seen in the outcome of the successional process, is directed towards the reverse efficiency—a high *B/P* ratio, as is depicted by the relationship at the right in Fig. 2-1. Man has generally been preoccupied with obtaining as much "production" from the landscape as possible, by developing and maintaining early successional types of ecosystems, usually monocultures. But, of course, man does not live by food and fiber alone; he also needs a balanced CO_2-O_2 atmosphere, the climatic buffer provided by oceans and masses of vegetation, and clean (that is, unproductive) water for cultural and industrial uses. Many essential life-cycle resources, not to mention recreational and esthetic needs, are best provided man by the less "productive" landscapes. In other words, the landscape is not just a supply depot but is also the *oikos*—the home—in which we must live. Until recently mankind has more or less taken for granted the gas-exchange,

water-purification, nutrient-cycling, and other protective functions of self-maintaining ecosystems, chiefly because neither his numbers nor his environmental manipulations have been great enough to affect regional and global balances. Now, of course, it is painfully evident that such balances are being affected, often detrimentally. The "one problem, one solution approach" is no longer adequate and must be replaced by some form of ecosystem analysis that considers man as a part of, not apart from, the environment.

The most pleasant and certainly the safest landscape to live in is one containing a variety of crops, forests, lakes, streams, roadsides, marshes, seashores, and "waste places"—in other words, a mixture of communities of different ecological ages. As individuals we more or less instinctively surround our houses with protective, nonedible cover (trees, shrubs, grass) at the same time that we strive to coax extra bushels from our cornfield. We all consider the cornfield a "good thing," of course, but most of us would not want to live there, and it would certainly be suicidal to cover the whole land area of the biosphere with cornfields, since the boom and bust oscillation in such a situation would be severe.

The basic problem facing organized society today boils down to determining in some objective manner when we are getting "too much of a good thing." This is a completely new challenge to mankind because, up until now, he has had to be concerned largely with too little rather than too much. Thus, concrete is a "good thing," but not if half the world is covered with it. Insecticides are "good things," but not when used, as they now are, in an indiscriminate and wholesale manner. Likewise water impoundments have proved to be very useful man-made additions to the landscape, but obviously we don't want the whole country inundated! Vast man-made lakes solve some problems, at least temporarily, but yield comparative little food or fiber, and, because of high evaporative losses, they may not even be the best device for storing water; it might better be stored in the watershed, or underground in aquafers. Also, the cost of building large dams is a drain on already overtaxed revenues.

Although as individuals we readily recognize that we can have too many dams or other large-scale environmental changes, governments are so fragmented and lacking in systems-analysis capabilities that there is no effective mechanism whereby negative feedback signals can be received and acted on before there has been a serious overshoot. Thus, today there are governmental agencies, spurred on by popular and political enthusiasm for dams, that are putting on the drawing boards plans for damming every river and stream in North America!

Society needs, and must find as quickly as possible, a way to deal with the landscape as a whole, so that manipulative skills (that is, technology) will not run too far ahead of our understanding of the impact of change. Recently a national ecological center outside of government and a coalition of governmental agencies have been proposed as two possible steps in the establishment of a political control mechanism for dealing with major environmental questions. The soil conservation movement in America is an excellent example of a program dedicated to the consideration of the whole farm or the whole watershed as an ecological unit. Soil conservation is well understood and supported by the public. However, soil conservation organizations have remained too exclusively farm-oriented, and have not yet risen to the challenge of the urban-rural landscape, where lies today's most serious problems. We do, then, have potential mechanisms in American society that could speak for the ecosystem as a whole, but none of them are really operational (29).

The general relevance of ecosystem development theory to landscape planning can, perhaps, be emphasized by the "mini-model" of Table 2, which contrasts the characteristics of young and mature-type ecosystems in more

Table 2. Contrasting characteristics of young and mature-type ecosystems.

Young	Mature
Production	Protection
Growth	Stability
Quantity	Quality

general terms than those provided by Table 1. It is mathematically impossible to obtain a maximum for more than one thing at a time, so one cannot have both extremes at the same time and place. Since all six characteristics listed in Table 2 are desirable in the aggregate, two possible solutions to the dilemma immediately suggest themselves. We can compromise so as to provide moderate quality and moderate yield on all the landscape, or we can deliberately plan to compartmentalize the landscape so as to simultaneously maintain highly productive and predominantly protective types as separate unities subject to different management strategies (strategies ranging, for example, from intensive cropping on the one hand to wilderness management on the other). If ecosystem development theory is valid and applicable to planning, then the so-called multiple-use strategy, about which we hear so much, will work only through one or both of these approaches, because, in most cases, the projected multiple uses conflict with one another. It is appropriate, then, to examine some examples of the compromise and the compartmental strategies.

Pulse Stability

A more or less regular but acute physical perturbation imposed from without can maintain an ecosystem at some intermediate point in the developmental sequence, resulting in, so to speak, a compromise between youth and maturity. What I would term "fluctuating water level ecosystems" are good examples. Estuaries, and intertidal zones in general, are maintained in an early, relatively fertile stage by the tides, which provide the energy for rapid nutrient cycling. Likewise, freshwater marshes, such as the Florida Everglades, are held at an early successional stage by the seasonal fluctuations in water levels. The dry-season drawdown speeds up aerobic decomposition of accumulated organic matter, releasing nutrients that, on reflooding, support a wet-season bloom in productivity. The life histories of many organisms are intimately coupled to this periodicity. The wood stork, for example, breeds when the water levels are falling and the small fish on which it feeds become concentrated and easy to catch in the drying pools. If the water level remains high during the usual dry season or fails to rise in the wet season, the stork will not nest (30). Stabilizing water levels in the Everglades by means of dikes, locks, and impoundments, as is now advocated by some, would, in my opinion, destroy rather than preserve the Everglades as we now know them just as surely as complete drainage would. Without periodic drawdowns and fires, the shallow basins would fill up with organic matter and succession would proceed from the present pond-and-prairie condition toward a scrub or swamp forest.

It is strange that man does not readily recognize the importance of recurrent changes in water level in a natural situation such as the Everglades when similar pulses are the basis for some of his most enduring food culture systems (31). Alternate filling and draining of ponds has been a standard procedure in fish culture for centuries in Europe and the Orient. The flooding, draining, and soil-aeration procedure in rice culture is another example. The rice paddy is thus the cultivated analogue of the natural marsh or the intertidal ecosystem.

Fire is another physical factor whose periodicity has been of vital importance to man and nature over the centuries. Whole biotas, such as those of the African grasslands and the California chaparral, have become adapted to periodic fires producing what ecologists often call "fire climaxes" (32). Man uses fire deliberately to maintain such climaxes or to set back succession to some desired point. In the southeastern coastal plain, for example, light fires of moderate frequency can maintain a pine forest against the encroachment of older successional stages which, at the present time at least, are considered economically less desirable. The fire-controlled forest yields less wood than a tree farm does (that is, young trees, all of about the same age, planted in rows and harvested on a short rotation schedule), but it provides a greater protective cover for the landscape, wood of higher quality, and a home for game birds (quail, wild turkey, and so on) which could not survive in a tree farm. The fire

climax, then, is an example of a compromise between production simplicity and protection diversity.

It should be emphasized that pulse stability works only if there is a complete community (including not only plants but animals and microorganisms) adapted to the particular intensity and frequency of the perturbation. Adaptation—operation of the selection process —requires time measurable on the evolutionary scale. Most physical stresses introduced by man are too sudden, too violent, or too arrhythmic for adaptation to occur at the ecosystem level, so severe oscillation rather than stability results. In many cases, at least, modification of naturally adapted ecosystems for cultural purposes would seem preferable to complete redesign.

Prospects for a Detritus Agriculture

As indicated above, heterotrophic utilization of primary production in mature ecosystems involves largely a delayed consumption of detritus. There is no reason why man cannot make greater use of detritus and thus obtain food or other products from the more protective type of ecosystem. Again, this would represent a compromise, since the short-term yield could not be as great as the yield obtained by direct exploitation of the grazing food chain. A detritus agriculture, however, would have some compensating advantages. Present agricultural strategy is based on selection for rapid growth and edibility in food plants, which, of course, make them vulnerable to attack by insects and disease. Consequently, the more we select for succulence and growth, the more effort we must invest in the chemical control of pests; this effort, in turn, increases the likelihood of our poisoning useful organisms, not to mention ourselves. Why not also practice the reverse strategy—that is, select plants which are essentially unpalatable, or which produce their own systemic insecticides while they are growing, and then convert the net production into edible products by microbial and chemical enrichment in food factories? We could then devote our biochemical genius to the enrichment process instead of fouling up our living space with chemical poisons! The production of silage by fermentation of low-grade fodder is an example of such a procedure already in widespread use. The cultivation of detritus-eating fishes in the Orient is another example.

By tapping the detritus food chain man can also obtain an appreciable harvest from many natural systems without greatly modifying them or destroying their protective and esthetic value. Oyster culture in estuaries is a good example. In Japan, raft and long-line culture of oysters has proved to be a very practical way to harvest the microbial products of estuaries and shallow bays. Furukawa (33) reports that the yield of cultured oysters in the Hiroshima Prefecture has increased tenfold since 1950, and that the yield of oysters (some 240,000 tons of meat) from this one district alone in 1965 was ten times the yield of natural oysters from the entire country. Such oyster culture is feasible along the entire Atlantic and Gulf coasts of the United States. A large investment in the culture of oysters and other seafoods would also provide the best possible deterrent against pollution, since the first threat of damage to the pollution-sensitive oyster industry would be immediately translated into political action!

The Compartment Model

Successful though they often are, compromise systems are not suitable nor desirable for the whole landscape. More emphasis needs to be placed on compartmentalization, so that growth-type, steady-state, and intermediate-type ecosystems can be linked with urban and industrial areas for mutual benefit. Knowing the transfer coefficients that define the flow of energy and the movement of materials and organisms (including man) between compartments, it should be possible to determine, through analog-computer manipulation, rational limits for the size and capacity of each compartment. We might start, for example, with a simplified model, shown in Fig. 2-2, consisting of four compartments of equal area, partitioned

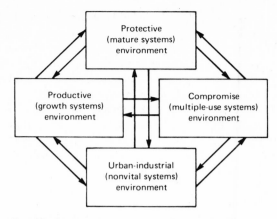

Fig. 2-2. Compartment model of the basic kinds of environment required by man, partitioned according to ecosystem development and life-cycle resource criteria.

according to the basic biotic-function criterion —that is, according to whether the area is (i) productive, (ii) protective, (iii) a compromise between (i) and (ii) or (iv), urban-industrial. By continually refining the transfer coefficents on the basis of real world situations, and by increasing and decreasing the size and capacity of each compartment through computer simulation, it would be possible to determine objectively the limits that must eventually be imposed on each compartment in order to maintain regional and global balances in the exchange of vital energy and of materials. A systems-analysis procedure provides at least one approach to the solution of the basic dilemma posed by the question "How do we determine when we are getting too much of a good thing?" Also it provides a means of evaluating the energy drains imposed on ecosystems by pollution, radiation, harvest, and other stresses (34).

Implementing any kind of compartmentalization plan, of course, would require procedures for zoning the landscape and restricting the use of some land and water areas. While the principle of zoning in cities is universally accepted, the procedures now followed do not work very well because zoning restrictions are too easily overturned by short-term economic and population pressures. Zoning the landscape would require a whole new order of thinking. Greater use of legal measures providing for tax relief, restrictions on use, scenic easements, and public ownership will be required if appreciable land and water areas are to be held in the "protective" categories. Several states (for example, New Jersey and California), where pollution and population pressure are beginning to hurt, have made a start in this direction by enacting "open space" legislation designed to get as much unoccupied land as possible into a "protective" status so that future uses can be planned on a rational and scientific basis. The United States as a whole is fortunate in that large areas of the country are in national forests, parks, wildlife refuges, and so on. The fact that such areas, as well as the bordering oceans, are not quickly exploitable gives us time for the accelerated ecological study and programming needed to determine what proportions of different types of landscape provide a safe balance between man and nature. The open oceans, for example, should forever be allowed to remain protective rather than productive territory, if Alfred Redfield's (35) assumptions are correct. Redfield views the oceans, the major part of the hydrosphere, as the biosphere's governor, which slows down and controls the rate of decomposition and nutrient regeneration, thereby creating and maintaining the highly aerobic terrestrial environment to which the higher forms of life, such as man, are adapted, Eutrophication of the ocean in a last-ditch effort to feed the populations of the land could well have an adverse effect on the oxygen reservoir in the atmosphere.

Until we can determine more precisely how far we may safely go in expanding intensive agriculture and urban sprawl at the expense of the protective landscape, it will be good insurance to hold inviolate as much of the latter as possible. Thus, the preservation of natural areas is not a peripheral luxury for society but a capital investment from which we expect to draw interest. Also, it may well be that restrictions in the use of land and water are our only practical means of avoiding overpopulation or too great an exploitation of resources, or both. Interestingly enough, restriction of land use is the analogue of a natural behavioral control mechanism known as "territoriality" by which many species of animals avoid crowding and social stress (36).

Since the legal and economic problems pertaining to zoning and compartmentalization are likely to be thorny, I urge law schools to establish departments, or institutes, of "landscape law" and to start training "landscape lawyers" who will be capable not only of clarifying existing procedures but also of drawing up new enabling legislation for consideration by state and national governing bodies. At present, society is concerned—and rightly so—with human rights, but environmental rights are equally vital. The "one man one vote" idea is important, but so also is a "one man one hectare" proposition.

Education, as always, must play a role in increasing man's awareness of his dependence on the natural environment. Perhaps we need to start teaching the principles of ecosystem in the third grade. A grammar school primer on man and his environment could logically consist of four chapters, one for each of the four essential kinds of environment, shown diagrammatically in Fig. 2-2.

Of the many books and articles that are being written these days about man's environmental crisis, I would like to cite two that go beyond "crying out in alarm" to suggestions for bringing about a reorientation of the goals of society. Garrett Hardin, in a recent article in *Science* (37), points out that, since the optimum population density is less than the maximum, there is no strictly technical solution to the problem of pollution caused by overpopulation; a solution he suggests, can only be achieved through moral and legal means of "mutual coercion, mutually agreed upon by the majority of people." Earl F. Murphy, in a book entitled *Governing Nature* (38), emphasizes that the regulatory approach alone is not enough to protect life-cycle resources, such as air and water, that cannot be allowed to deteriorate. He discusses permit systems, effluent charges, receptor levies, assessment, and cost-internalizing procedures as economic incentives for achieving Hardin's "mutually agreed upon coercion."

It goes without saying that the tabular model for ecosystem development which I have presented here has many parallels in the development of human society itself. In the pioneer society, as in the pioneer ecosystem, high birth rates, rapid growth, high economic profits, and exploitation of accessible and unused resources are advantageous, but, as the saturation level is approached, these drives must be shifted to considerations of symbiosis (that is, "civil rights," "law and order," "education," and "culture"), birth control, and the recycling of resources. A balance between youth and maturity in the socio-environmental system is, therefore, the really basic goal that must be achieved if man as a species is to successfully pass through the present rapid-growth stage, to which he is clearly well adapted, to the ultimate equilibrium-density stage, of which he as yet shows little understanding and to which he now shows little tendency to adapt.

References and Notes

1. E. P. Odum, *Ecology* (Holt, Rinehart and Winston, New York, 1963), chap. 6.
2. H. T. Odum and R. C. Pinkerton, *Amer. Scientist* 43, 331 (1955).
3. A. J. Lotka, *Elements of Physical Biology* (Williams and Wilkins, Baltimore, 1925).
4. R. Margalef, *Advan. Frontiers Plant Sci.* 2, 137 (1963); *Amer. Naturalist* 97, 357 (1963).
5. R. J. Beyers, *Ecol. Monographs* 33, 281 (1963).
6. The systems so far used to test ecological principles have been derived from sewage and farm ponds and are cultured in half-strength No. 36 Taub and Dollar medium [*Limnol. Oceanog.* 9, 61 (1964)]. They are closed to organic input or output but are open to the atmosphere through the cotton plug in the neck of the flask. Typically, liter-sized microecosystems contain two or three species of nonflagellated algae and one to three species each of flagellated protozoans, ciliated protozoans, rotifers, nematodes, and ostracods; a system derived from a sewage pond contained at least three species of fungi and 13 bacterial isolates [R. Gordon, thesis, University of Georgia (1967)]. These cultures are thus a kind of minimum ecosystem containing those small species originally found in the ancestral pond that are able to function together as a self-contained unit under the restricted conditions of the laboratory flask and the controlled environment of a growth chamber [temperature, 65° to 75°F (18° to 24°C); photoperiod, 12 hours; illumination, 100 to 1000 footcandles].
7. G. D. Cooke, *BioScience* 17, 717 (1967).
8. T. Kira and T. Shidei, *Japan J. Ecol.* 17, 70 (1967).
9. The metabolism of the microcosms was monitored by measuring diurnal pH changes, and the biomass (in terms of total organic matter and total carbon) was determined by periodic harvesting of replicate systems.
10. F. J. H. Mackereth, *Proc. Roy. Soc. London Ser. B* 161, 295 (1965); U. M. Cowgill and G. E. Hutchinson, *Proc. Intern. Limnol. Ass.* 15, 644 (1964); A. D. Harrison, *Trans. Roy. Soc. S. Africa* 36, 213 (1962).
11. R. Margalef, *Proc. Intern. Limnol. Ass.* 15, 169 (1964).
12. J. R. Bray, *Oikos* 12, 70 (1961).
13. D. Pimentel, *Amer. Naturalist* 95, 65 (1961).
14. R. T. Paine, *ibid.* 100, 65 (1966).
15. G. M. Woodwell, *Brookhaven Nat. Lab. Pub. 924)T-381)* (1965), pp. 1-15.
16. R. G. Wiegert, E. P. Odum, J. H. Schnell, *Ecology* 48, 75 (1967).
17. For selected general discussions of patterns of species diversity, see E. H. Simpson, *Nature,* 163, 688 (1949): C. B. Williams, *J. Animal Ecol.* 22, 14 (1953); G. E. Hutchinson, *Amer. Naturalist* 93, 145 (1959); R. Margalef, *Gen. Systems* 3, 36 (1958); R. MacArthur and J. MacArthur, *Ecology* 42, 594 (1961); N. G. Hairston, *ibid.* 40, 404 (1959); B. C. Patten, *J. Marine Res. (Sears Found. Marine Res.)* 20, 57 (1960); E. G. Leigh, *Proc. Nat. Acad. Sci. U.S.* 5, 777 (1965); E. R. Pianka, *Amer. Naturalist* 100, 33 (1966); E. C. Pielou, *J. Theoret. Biol.* 10, 370 (1966).
18. M. Lloyd and R. J. Ghelardi, *J. Animal Ecol.* 33, 217 (1964); E. C. Pielou, *J. Theoret. Bio.* 13, 131 (1966).
19. G. W. Barrett, *Ecology* 49, 1019 (1969).
20. In our studies of natural succession following grain culture, both the species-to-numbers and the equitability indices increased for all trophic levels but especially for predators and parasites. Only 44 percent of the species in the natural ecosystem were phytophagous, as compared to 77 percent in the grain field.
21. J. T. Bonner, *Size and Cycle* (Princeton Univ. Press, Princeton, N.J., 1963); P. Frank, *Ecology* 49, 355 (1968).
22. D. W. Johnston and E. P. Odum, *Ecology* 37, 50 (1956).
23. R. Margalef, *Oceanog. Marine Biol. Annu. Rev.* 5, 257 (1967).
24. F. H. Bormann and G. E. Likens, *Science* 155, 424 (1967).
25. Increased water yield following reduction of vegetative cover has been frequently demonstrated in experimental watersheds throughout the world [see A. R. Hibbert, in *International Symposium on Forest Hydrology* (Pergamon Press, New York, 1967), pp. 527-543]. Data on the long-term

hydrologic budget (rainfall input relative to stream outflow) are available at many of these sites, but mineral budgets have yet to be systematically studied. Again, this is a prime objective in the "ecosystem analysis" phase of the International Biological Program.

26. R. H. MacArthur and E. O. Wilson, *Theory of Island Biogeography* (Princeton Univ. Press, Princeton, N.J., 1967).

27. Examples are the tent caterpillar [see W. G. Wellington, *Can. J. Zool.* **35**, 293 (1957)] and the larch budworm [see W. Baltensweiler, *Can. Entomologist* **96**, 792 (1964)].

28. F. J. Ayala, *Science* **162**, 1453 (1968).

29. Ira Rubinoff, in discussing the proposed sea-level canal joining the Atlantic and Pacific oceans [*Science* **161**, 857 (1968)], calls for a "control commission for environmental manipulation" with "broad powers of approving, disapproving, or modifying all major alterations of the marine or terrestrial environments. . . ."

30. See M. P. Kahl, *Ecol. Monographs* **34**, 97 (1964).

31. The late Aldo Leopold remarked long ago [*Symposium on Hydrobiology* (Univ. of Wisconsin Press, Madison, 1941), p. 17] that man does not perceive organic behavior in systems unless he has built them himself. Let us hope it will not be necessary to rebuild the entire biosphere before we recognize the worth of natural systems!

32. See C. F. Cooper, *Sci. Amer.* **204**, 150 (April 1961).

33. See "Proceedings Oyster Culture Workshop, Marine Fisheries Division, Georgia Game and Fish Commission, Brunswick" (1968), pp.49-61.

34. See H. T. Odum, in *Symposium on Primary Productivity and Mineral Cycling in Natural Ecosystems,* H. E. Young, Ed. (Univ. of Maine Press, Orono, 1967), p. 81; ———, in *Pollution and Marine Ecology* (Wiley, New York, 1967), p. 99; K. E. F. Watt, *Ecology and Resource Management* (McGraw-Hill, New York, 1968).

35. A. C. Redfield, *Amer. Scientist* **46**, 205 (1958).

36. R. Ardrey, *The Territorial Imperative* (Atheneum, New York, 1967).

37. G. Hardin, *Science* **162**, 1243 (1968).

38. E. F. Murphy, *Governing Nature* (Quadrangle Books, Chicago, 1967).

3

NUTRIENT CYCLING

F. H. Bormann and G. E. Likens

Life on our planet is dependent upon the cycle of elements in the biosphere. Atmospheric carbon dioxide would be exhausted in a year or so by green plants were not the atmosphere continually recharged by CO_2 generated by respiration and fire *(1)*. Also, it is well known that life requires a constant cycling of nitrogen, oxygen, and water. These cycles include a gaseous phase and have self-regulating feedback mechanisms that make them relatively perfect *(2)*. Any increase in movement along one path is quickly compensated for by adjustments along other paths. Recently, however, concern has been expressed over the possible

Reprinted from *Science* 155: 424-29, 1967, with the permission of the publishers. Copyright 1967 by the American Association for the Advancement of Science.

disruption of the carbon cycle by the burning of fossil fuel *(3)* and of the nitrogen cycle by the thoughtless introduction of pesticides and other substances into the biosphere *(4)*.

Of no less importance to life are the elements with sedimentary cycles, such as phosphorus, calcium, and magnesium. With these cycles, there is a continual loss from biological systems in response to erosion, with ultimate deposition in the sea. Replacement or return of an element with a sedimentary cycle to terrestrial biological systems is dependent upon such processes as weathering of rocks, additions from volcanic gases, or the biological movement from the sea to the land. Sedimentary cycles are less perfect and more easily disrupted by man than carbon and nitrogen cycles *(2)*. Acceleration of losses or, more specifically, the disruption of local cycling patterns by the activities of man could reduce existing "pools" of an element in local ecosystems, restrict productivity, and consequently limit human population. For example, many agriculturalists, food scientists, and ecologists believe that man is accelerating losses of phosphorus and that this element will be a critical limiting resource for the functioning of the biosphere *(1, 5).*

Recognition of the importance of these biogeochemical processes to the welfare of mankind has generated intensive study of such cycles. Among ecologists and foresters working with natural terrestrial ecosystems, this interest has focused on those aspects of biogeochemical cycles that occur *within* particular ecosystems. Thus, information on the distribution of chemical elements and on rates of uptake, retention, and release in various ecosystems has been accumulating *(6).* Little has been done to establish the role that weathering and erosion play in these systems.

Yet, the rate of release of nutrients from minerals by weathering, the addition of nutrients by erosion, and the loss of nutrients by erosion are three primary determinants of structure and function in terrestrial ecosystems. Further, with this information it is possible to develop total chemical budgets for ecosystems and to relate these data to the larger biogeochemical cycles.

It is largely because of the complex natural interaction of the hydrologic cycle and nutrient cycles that it has not been possible to establish these relationships. In many ecosystems this interaction almost hopelessly complicates the measurement of weathering or erosion. Under certain conditions, however, these apparent hindrances can be turned to good advantage in an integrated study of biogeochemical cycling in small watershed ecosystems.

It is the function of this article (i) to develop the idea that small watersheds can be used to measure weathering and erosion, (ii) to describe the parameters of watersheds particularly suited for this type of study, and (iii) to discuss the types of nutrient-cycling problems that this model renders susceptible to attack. Finally (iv), the argument is developed that the watershed ecosystem provides an ideal setting for studies of ecosystem dynamics in general.

Ecosystem Defined

Communities such as fields and forests may be considered as ecological systems (7) in which living organisms and their physical and biological environments constitute a single interacting unit. These ecosystems occupy an arbitrarily defined volume of the biosphere at the earth-atmosphere interface.

Lateral boundaries of an ecosystem may be chosen to coincide with those of a biological community, such as the edges of a forest, or with the boundary of some pronounced characteristic of the physical environment, such as the shoreline of a small island. Most often, however, the continuous nature of vegetation and of the physical environment makes it difficult to establish exact lateral boundaries on the basis of "community" or "environmental discontinuity" *(8).* Often the investigator arbitrarily selects an area that may be conveniently studied.

From a functional point of view it is meaningless to include within the vertical limits of an ecosystem *all* of the column of air above and of soil and rock below the laterally defined ecosystem. For a working model of an ecosystem, it seems reasonable to include *only* that part of the column where atoms and molecules may participate in the chemical cycling that occurs within the system (see the "intrasystem cycle" of Fig. 3-1). When the biological community is taken as a determinant, the vertical extensions of the terrestrial ecosystem will be delimited by the top of the vegetation and the depth to which roots and other organisms penetrate into the regolith *(9).* Vertical dimensions, defined in this manner, can expand or contract depending on the growth potential of present or succeeding communities. Thus, volumetric changes with time can be considered—for example, those associated with primary and secondary succession or with cliseral changes.

The Ecosystem and Biogeochemical Cycling

The terrestrial ecosystem participates in the various larger biogeochemical cycles of the earth through a system of inputs and outputs. Biogeochemical input in forest or field ecosystems may be derived from three major sources: geologic, meteorologic, and biologic.

Fig. 3-1. Nutrient relationships of a terrestrial ecosystem, showing sites of accumulation and major pathways. Input and output may be composed of geologic, meteorologic, and biologic components, as described in the text.

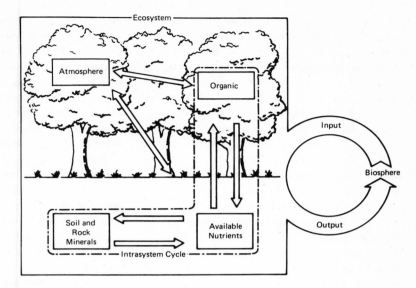

Geologic input is here defined as dissolved or particulate matter carried into the system by moving water or colluvial action, or both. Depositions of the products of erosion or mass wasting and ions dissolved in incoming seepage water are examples of geologic input. Meteorologic input enters the ecosystem through the atmosphere and is composed of additions of gaseous materials and of dissolved or particulate matter in precipitation, dust, and other wind-borne materials. Chemicals in gaseous form fixed by biologic activity within the ecosystem are considered to be meteorologic input. Biological input results from animal activity and is made up of depositions of materials originally gathered elsewhere; examples are fecal material of animals whose food was gathered outside the system, or fertilizers intentionally added by man.

Chemicals may leave the ecosystem in the form of dissolved or particulate matter in moving water or colluvium, or both (geologic output); through the diffusion or transport of gases or particulate matter by wind (meteorologic output); or as a result of the activity of animals, including man (biologic output).

Nutrients are found in four compartments within the terrestrial ecosystem: in the atmosphere, in the pool of available nutrients in the soil, in organic materials (biota and organic debris), and in soil and rock minerals (Fig 3-1). The atmospheric compartment includes all atoms or molecules in gaseous form in both the below-ground and the above-ground portions of the ecosystem. The pool of available nutrients in the soil consists of all ions absorbed on the clay-humus complex or dissolved in the soil solution. The organic compartment includes all atoms incorporated in living organisms and in their dead remains. (The distinction between living and dead is sometimes hard to make, particularly in the case of woody perennial plants.) The soil-rock compartment is comprised of elements incorporated in primary and secondary minerals, including the more readily decomposable minerals that enter into equilibrium reactions with the available nutrients.

The degree to which a nutrient circulates within a terrestrial ecosystem is determined, in part, by its physical state. Gases are easily moved by random forces of diffusion and air circulation; consequently, nutrients with a prominent gaseous phase tend not to cycle within the boundaries of a particular ecosystem but, rather, to be continually lost and replaced from outside. On the other hand, elements without a prominent gaseous phase may show considerable intrasystem cycling between the available-nutrient, organic, and soil-rock compartments (Fig. 3-1). This internal cycle results from (i) the uptake of nutrients by plants, (ii) the release of nutrients from plants by direct leaching, (iii) the release of nutrients from organic matter by biological decomposition, and (iv) equilibrium reactions that convert insoluble chemical forms in the soil-rock compartment to soluble forms in the available-nutrient compartment, and vice versa.

Available nutrients not only enter the ecosystem from outside but are added by the action of physical, chemical, and biological weathering of rock and soil minerals already within the system. Although some ions are continually withdrawn from the available-nutrient compartment, forming secondary minerals in the soil and rocks, for most nutrient elements there is a net movement out of the soil-rock compartment. As the ecosystem is gradually lowered in place by erosion or by the downward growth of roots, new supplies of residual rock or other parent material are included; in some systems these materials may also be added as geologic input.

Hydrologic-Cycle, Nutrient-Cycle Interaction

At many points, nutrient cycles may be strongly geared to the hydrologic cycle. Nutrient input and output are directly related to the amounts of water that move into and out of an ecosystem, as emphasized by the "leaching" and "flushing" concepts of Pearsall *(10)*, Dahl *(11)*, and Ratcliffe *(12)*, while temporal and absolute limits of biogeochemical activities within the system are markedly influenced by the hydrologic regime. Biologic uptake of nutrients by plants and release of nutrients by biological decomposition are closely related to the pattern of water availability. Potential levels of biomass within the system are determined in large measure by precipitation characteristics. Similarly, the nature and rate of weathering and soil formation are influenced by the hydrologic regime, since water is essential to the major chemical weathering processes [ion exchange, hydrolysis, solution, diffusion, oxidation-reduction, and adsorption and swelling *(13)*].

Biogeochemical Studies of Ecosystems

Although study of nutrient input, nutrient output, and weathering is necessary for an understanding of field and forest ecosystems *(6)*, ecologists, foresters, and pedologists have generally focused attention on the internal characteristics alone. Thus, considerable information has been accumulated on uptake, retention, and release of nutrients by the biota of ecosystems, and on soil-nutrient relationships (see, for example, *6, 14*). Rarely are these internal characteristics of the ecosystem correlated with input and output data, yet all these parameters are necessary for the construction of nutrient budgets of particular ecosystems, and for establishing the relationship of the smaller system to the biosphere.

Quantitative data on input-output relationships are at best spotty. There are many data on nutrient output due to harvesting of vegetation, but for particular natural ecosystems there are only sporadic data on nutrient input in precipitation, or on nutrient output in drainage waters *(6)*. Recently, small lysimeters have been used successfully in the measurement of nutrient dynamics within the soil profile and in the measurement of nutrient losses in drainage water *(15)*. The lysimeter technique seems to be well suited for studying ecosystems characterized by coarse textured soils with a relatively low field capacity *(16)*, high porosity, and no surface runoff. For most ecosystems, however, lysimeters are probably of limited value for measuring *total* nutrient output because (i) they are of questionable accuracy when used in rocky or markedly uneven ground, (ii) they cannot evaluate nutrient losses in surface waters, and (iii) their installation requires considerable disturbance of the soil profile.

The lack of information on the nutrient-input, nutrient-output relationships of ecosystems is apparently related to two considerations: (i) integrated studies of ecosystems tend to fall into an intellectual "no man's land" between traditional concepts of ecology, geology, and pedology; (ii) more important, the measurement of nutrient input and output requires measurement of hydrologic input and output. Unquestionably this lack of quantitative information is related to the difficulties encountered in measuring nutrients entering or leaving an ecosystem in seepage water or in sheet or rill flow, and to the high cost, in time and money, of obtaining continuous measurements of the more conventional hydrologic parameters of precipitation and stream flow. In many systems the problem is further complicated by the fact that much water may leave by way of deep seepage, eventually appearing in another drainage system: direct measurement of loss of water and nutrients by this route is virtually impossible.

Small-Watershed Approach to Biogeochemical Cycling

In some ecosystems the nutrient-cycle, hydrologic-cycle interaction can be turned to good advantage in the study of nutrient budgets, erosion, and weathering. This is particularly so if an ecosystem meets two specifications: (i) if the ecosystem is a watershed, and (ii) if the watershed is underlain by a tight bedrock or other impermeable base, such as permafrost. Given these conditions, for chemical elements without a gaseous form at biological temperatures, it is possible to construct nutrient budgets showing input, output, and net loss or gain from the system. These data provide estimates of weathering and erosion.

If the ecosystem were a small watershed, input would be limited to meteorologic and biologic origins. Geologic input, as defined above, need not be considered because there would be no transfer of alluvial or colluvial material between adjacent watersheds. Although materials might be moved within the ecosystem by alluvial or colluvial forces, these materials would originate within the ecosystem.

When the input and output of dust or windblown materials is negligible (this is certainly not the case in some systems), meteorologic input can be measured from a combination of hydrologic and precipitation-chemistry parameters. From periodic measurements of the elements contained in precipitation and from continuous measurements of precipitation entering a watershed of known area, one may calculate the temporal input of an element in terms of grams per hectare.

Noncoincidence of the topographic divide of the watershed and the phreatic divide may introduce a small error *(17)*.

Losses from this watershed ecosystem would be limited to geologic and biologic output. Given an impermeable base, geologic output (losses due to erosion) would consist of dissolved and particulate matter in either stream water or seepage water moving downhill above this impermeable base. Although downhill mass movement may occur within the system, the products of this movement are delivered to the stream bed, whence they are removed by erosion and stream transportation.

Geologic output can be estimated from hydrologic and chemical measurements. A weir, anchored to the bedrock (Fig. 3-2), will force all drainage water from the watershed to flow over the notch, where the volume and rate of flow can be measured. These data, in combination with periodic measures of dissolved and particulate matter in the outflowing water, provide an estimate of geologic output which may be expressed as grams of an element lost per hectare of watershed.

The nutrient budget for a single element in the watershed ecosystem may be expressed as follows: meteorologic input + biologic input) — (geologic output + biologic output) = net loss or gain. This equation may be futher simplified if the ecosystem meets a third specification—if it is part of a much larger, more or less homogeneous, vegetation unit. Biological output would tend to balance biological input if the ecosystem contained no special attraction or deterrent for animal populations moving at random through the larger vegetation system, randomly acquiring or discharging nutrients. On this assumption, the nutrient budget for a single system would become: (meteorologic input per hectare)—(geologic output per hectare) = net gain or loss per hectare. This fundamental relationship provides basic data for an integrated study of ecosystem dynamics.

Small Watersheds for Ecosystem Research

The relationship of the individual terrestrial ecosystem to biogeochemical cycles of the

Fig. 3-2. A weir showing the v-notch, recording house, and ponding basin. (Courtesy of the Northeastern Forest Experiment Station.)

biosphere can be established by the small-watershed approach. Data on input and output of nutrients provide direct measurements of this relationship, while data on net loss provide, as explained below, an indirect measure of weathering rates for soil and rock minerals in relatively undisturbed ecosystems.

The small watershed may be used for experiments at the ecosystem level. This has been shown by numerous experiments concerned with hydrologic relationships (see, for example, *18*). Thus, it is possible to test effects of various experimental treatments on the relationship of the individual ecosystem to the biospheric nutrient cycles. Experiments can be designed to determine whether logging, burning, or use of pesticides or herbicides have an appreciable effect on net nutrient losses from the system. This information is not generally available at the ecosystem level.

The small watershed, with its measured parameters of hydrologic and chemical input, output, and net change, is an excellent vehicle for the study of interrelationships within a single ecosystem. Nutrient output may be related to hydrologic parameters such as seasonal and diurnal variations in stream flow, seasonal patterns of precipitation, individual rainstorms, and variations in evapotranspiration. Characteristics of the nutrient cycle may also be related to phenological events occurring within the ecosystem, such as leaf development, initiation of root growth, leaf fall, and litter turnover. In combination with current methods of biomass and nutrient analysis (see, for example, *6*), the small-watershed approach provides a comprehensive view of the status and behavior of individual elements within an individual ecosystem.

Weathering, or the rate at which an element

bound in soil and rock minerals is made available, can be estimated from net losses of that element as calculated by the nutrient-budget method. Within the ecosystem (watershed), atoms of an element (one that lacks a gaseous form at ecosystem temperatures) may be located in (i) soil and rock minerals, (ii) the biota and organic debris, and (iii) the pool of available nutrients (Fig. 3-1). There is an intense intrasystem cycling between categories (ii) and (iii) as large quantities of ions are taken up by the vegetation each year and released by direct leaching or stepwise decomposition in the food chain. Ions are continually released to the intrasystem cycle by weathering of soil and rock material. Some of these ions, however, are reconstituted as secondary minerals. If an ecosystem is in a state of dynamic equilibrium, as the presence of climax forest would suggest *(19)*, ionic levels in the intrasystem cycle must remain about the same for many years. Thus, in the climax ecosystem, net ion losses (output minus input) must be balanced by equivalent additions derived from weathering of soil and rock materials. Thus, net ionic losses from an undisturbed, relatively stable terrestrial ecosystem are a measure of weathering within the system. In a successional ecosystem (in which nutrients are accumulating in biomass and organic debris over the course of years), the rate at which an ion is released by weathering must equal its rate of net loss from the ecosystem plus its rate of net accumulation in the biota and organic debris (Fig. 3-1).

Table 1. Budgets for dissolved cations in watershed No. 3 (42.4 hectares) for the period June 1963 to June 1964.

Cation	Input (kgl hectare)	Output (kgl hectare)	Net change (kgl hectare)
Calcium	3.0	7.7	−4.7
Sodium	1.0	6.3	−5.3
Magnesium	0.7	2.5	−1.8

The watershed model allows comparison in relative importance of solution and suspended bed load in removing nutrients from an ecosystem. Nutrient matter can be removed from an ecosystem by three forms of transportation in streams; in solution in the stream water, as inorganic and organic suspended load kept in motion by turbulent flow, and as inorganic and organic bed load slid or rolled along the stream bottom *(20)*. Solution losses may be measured, as described above, from stream-flow data and periodic measurements of dissolved substances in the stream. Part of the losses of suspended matter may be estimated from stream-flow data and periodic measurements of particulate matter obtained ' by straining or filtering stream water as it comes over the weir. The remaining suspended matter and all of the bed load may be measured above the weir, where these materials collect in the ponding basin (Fig. 3-2). These comparative measurements should be of interest not only to the ecologist concerned with ecosystem dynamics but also, since stream transportation is one of the important aspects of fluvial denudation, to geologists.

The small-watershed approach provides invaluable baseline information for the investigation of stream biology. Life-history studies of stream organisms, population studies, and shifts in community structure and diversity might be correlated with the measured physical and chemical parameters of drainage streams. Analyses of uptake, release, and transport of various nutrients by stream organisms could be made. Moreover, the vegetation of a watershed and the stream draining it are an inseparable unit functionally, and it would be of great interest to obtain information on the biological interaction between them.

Sites for Watershed Studies

Small watersheds meeting the conditions outlined above are probably common. However, even if the desired conditions are met, the investigator studying nutrient cycling is faced with the task of initiating a hydrologic study before he can attack his major problem. This is a time-consuming and expensive procedure, involving construction and maintenance of weirs, establishment of a precipitation network, and continuous collection of records, as well as land rental fees and possible road construction costs. A practical solution to this problem is inauguration of nutrient cycling studies at established hydrologic laboratories, where the required conditions exist and where hydrologic parameters are being measured and data are available.

The feasibility of this approach is demonstrated by our study at the Hubbard Brook Experimental Forest in West Thornton, New Hampshire. There, with the support of the National Science Foundation and the excellent cooperation of the Northeastern Forest Experiment Station, we are studying nutrient cycling and ecosystem dynamics on six small monitored watersheds. We have accumulated data on weathering rates, input, output, and the annual budget of several ions in this northern hardwood ecosystem. Also, studies of biomass, phenology, productivity, annual rates of nutrient turnover, and other factors are being made in one undisturbed watershed and in one in which conditions are being experimentally modified.

Preliminary data on input, output, and net change for three cations are presented in Table 1. These results allow us to add some numerical values to our ecosystem model (Fig. 3-3). For the calcium cycle, for example, input would be about 3 kilograms per hectare, while output (erosion) is estimated to be about 7.9 kilograms

per hectare. Of this latter amount, 98 percent (7.7 kilograms per hectare) is lost in the form of dissolved substances in the stream water, while first approximations indicate that 2 percent is lost as calcium incorporated in organic matter flushed out of the ecosystem. On the basis of assumptions discussed above, it is estimated that the net amount of calcium lost, approximately 5 kilograms per hectare, is replaced by calcium released from soil and rock minerals by weathering. Hence 5 kilograms of calcium per hectare is added to the system each year by weathering.

As yet we have not measured the calcium content of the soil and vegetation or the annual uptake and release of calcium by the biota. From Ovington's data *(6),* for a beech forest in West England, which must be of about the same magnitude as values for our forest in New Hampshire, we see that 203 kilograms of calcium per hectare are localized in the trees and litter, while 365 kilograms per hectare represent exchangeable calcium in the soil. This gives a total of 568 kilograms of calcium per hectare in organic matter or as available nutrient. Assuming that our forest (Fig. 3-3) contains a similar amount of calcium, we estimate that a net annual loss of 5 kilograms per hectare would represent only nine-tenths of 1 per cent of the total. This suggests a remarkable ability of these undisturbed systems to entrap and hold nutrients. However, if these

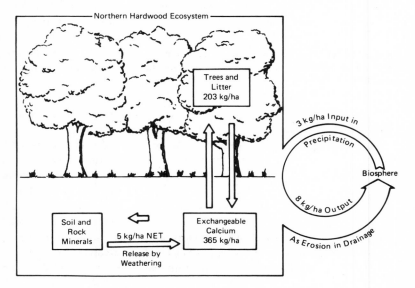

Fig. 3-3. Estimated parameters for the calcium cycle in an undisturbed northern hardwood ecosystem in central New Hampshire. [Data on trees, litter, and exchangeable calcium from Ovington (6).]

calculations were based on actual amounts of calcium circulated each year rather than on the total, the percentage losses would be higher.

On its completion, the Hubbard Brook study will have yielded estimates, for individual elements, of many of the parameters and flux rates represented in the nutrient cycle shown in Fig. 3-1. These data will increase our understanding of fundamental nutrient relationships of undisturbed northern hardwood forests, and they will provide baseline information from which we can judge the effects on nutrient cycling of such practices as cutting, burning, and the application of pesticides.

Studies similar to these at Hubbard Brook could be established elsewhere in the United States. There are thousands of gaged watersheds operated by private and public interests *(17)*, and some of these must meet the proposed requirements. On selected watersheds, cooperative studies could be made by the agencies or organizations controlling the watershed and university-based investigators interested in biogeochemical cycling. Just such cooperation, between federal agencies and universities, has been urged by the Task Group on Coordinated Water Resources Research *(21)*.

Cooperative studies of this type have the advantage of providing a useful exchange of ideas between scientists in diverse fields who are working on the same ecosystem. The studies would provide a larger yield of information on a single system, the prospect of new concepts arising from the available information, and a greater scientific yield per dollar invested. Finally, cooperative studies would make available, for interpretation from the standpoint of nutrient cycling, an invaluable record of past hydrologic performance and, in some cases, of the responses of watersheds to experimental manipulation.

Conclusion

The small-watershed approach to problems of nutrient cycling has these advantages. (i) The small watershed is a natural unit of suitable size for intensive study of nutrient cycling at the ecosystem level. (ii) It provides a means of reducing to a minimum, or virtually eliminating, the effect of the difficult-to-measure variables of geologic input and nutrient losses in deep seepage. Control of these variables makes possible accurate measurement of nutrient input and output (erosion) and therefore establishes the relationship of the smaller ecosystem to the larger biospheric cycles. (iii) The small-watershed approach provides a method whereby such important parameters as nutrient release from minerals (weathering) and annual nutrient budgets may be calculated. (iv) It provides a means of studying the interrelationships between the biota and the hydrologic cycle, various nutrient cycles, and energy flow in a single system. (v) Finally, with the small-watershed system we can test the effect of various land-management practices or environmental pollutants on nutrient cycling in natural systems.

References and Notes

1. L. C. Cole, *Sci. Amer.* **198**, 83 (Apr. 1958).
2. E. P. Odum, *Ecology* (Holt, Rinehart, and Winston, New York, 1963).
3. R. Revelle, W. Broecker, H. Craig, C. D. Keeling, J. Smargorinsky, in *Restoring the Quality of Our Environment* (Government Printing Office, Washington, D.C., 1965), pp. 111-133.
4. L. C. Cole, *Saturday Rev.* (7 May 1966).
5. E. P. Odum, *Fundamentals of Ecology* (Saunders, Philadelphia, 1959).
6. J. D. Ovington, in *Advances in Ecological Research*, J. B. Cragg, Ed. (Academic Press, New York, 1962), vol. 1.
7. A. G. Tansley, *Ecology* **16**, 284 (1935).
8. L. B. Slobodkin, *Growth and Regulation of Animal Populations* (Holt, Rinehart, and Winston, New York, 1961).
9. H. O. Buckman and N. C. Brady, *The Nature and Properties of Soils* (Macmillan, New York, 1960).
10. W. H. Pearsall, *Mountains and Moorlands* (Collins, London, 1950).
11. E. Dahl, "Rondane. Mountain vegetation in South Norway and its relation to the environment," *Skrifter Norske Videnskaps-Akad. Oslo I, Mat. Naturv. Kl. 1956* (1956).
12. D. A. Ratcliffe, *J. Ecol.* **47**, 371 (1959).
13. C. Bould, in *Plant Physiology, A Treatise*, F. C. Steward, Ed. (Academic Press, New York, 1963), vol. 3.
14. J. R. Bray and E. Gorham, in *Advances in Ecological Research*, J. B. Cragg, Ed. (Academic

Press, New York, 1964), vol. 2; K. J. Mustanoja and A. L. Leaf, *Botan. Rev.* 31, 151 (1965).

15. D. W. Cole and S. P. Gessel, *Soil Sci. Soc. Amer. Proc.* 25, 321 (1961); ——, in *Forest-Soil Relationships in North America*, C. T. Youngberg, Ed. (Oregon State Univ. Press, Corvallis, 1965).
16. D. W. Cole, *Soil Sc.* 85, 293 (1958).
17. C. O. Wisler and E. F. Brater, *Hydrology* (Wiley, New York, 1959).
18. R. E. Dils, *A Guide to the Coweeta Hydrologic Laboratory* (Southeastern Forest Experimental Station, Asheville, N. C., 1957).

19. R. H. Whattaker, *Ecol. Monographs* 23, 41 (1953).
20. A. N. Strahler, *The Earth Sciences* (Harper and Row, New York, 1963).
21. R. Revelle, *Science* 142, 1027 (1963).
22. Financial support was provided by National Science Foundation grants GB 1144 and GB 4169. We thank J. Cantlon, N. M. Johnson, R. C. Reynolds, R. H. Whittaker, and G. W. Woodwell for critical comments and suggestions during preparation of the manuscript.

4

WHATEVER HAPPENED TO HUMAN ECOLOGY?

Paul Shepard

The titles of the "New Book" shelf in the library suggest that we stand on the threshold of a new holistic vision. One sees there, for example, *The Ecological Perspective on Human Affairs* (Sprout, 1965). Upon examination, however, its only reference to nature is found to be an attack on environmental determinism. *The Ecology of Public Administration* (Riggs, 1962) would seem to be a bible for some future Secretary of the Interior, but it proves to be only a political text. We are attracted by a mysterious title, *The Discipline of the Cave* (Findlay, 1966). Is it Neanderthal ecology? It is an epistemology having nothing to do with caves. Still another, subtitled "Pastoral Ecology," is about the ministry instead of men and ungulates. It is evident that ecology has become an *in* word. *Environmentalism* swings. What is the half-life of fashionable words and what is their connection, if any, to the general intelligence?

There *is* increasing general ecological awareness. Air and water pollution are often considered in such a context. But there is also a

Reprinted from *Bioscience* 17: 891-94, 1967, with the permission of the publishers.

strong cultural resistance to the idea as a whole (White, 1967). Even Thomas Huxley's famous essay on "Man's Place in Nature" (Huxley, 1863) dealt with the question only of descent and morphology and set a precedent by which two generations of students of "man the animal" could elucidate primate anatomy and ignore primate ecology. The reaction of the conventional wisdom against the theory of evolution in the 19th Century was against its phylogenetic implications. Now it seems that much of the anguished a priori opposition to the biological creation and natural lineage of man has been redirected against ecological interdependence which links the living biota with mankind.

Development of Ecology

Efforts to include man in ecology took several directions as ecology itself developed in the United States. By 1930, for instance, Victor Shelford was putting two decades of reflection to work at Illinois, with graduate seminars on the subject of man's relationship to his environment. The framework was taxonomic community, dominance, succession, symbiosis, and niche. The subject was characterized by W. C. Van Deventer as "the man-dominated/man-influenced community of civilization" (Shelford, 1935). The idea is carried forth today as landscape ecology by Shelford's students. Van Deventer's course at Western Michigan University, for example, "Human Ecology, a Study of Man in Relation to His Living Environment," is a straightforward account of our familiar world as the product of human activity and ecological processes. It is a familiar theme of other ecologists as well, such as Edgar Anderson (1952) and Frank Fraser Darling (1955).

Meanwhile, the urban environment was scrutinized by sociologists. Robert Ezra Park (1936) explains that it was an attempt to operate between geography and economics and to apply to the interrelations of human beings the type of analysis developed in the study of plants and animals. He and E. W. Burgess are said by Hawley (1950) to have coined the phrase, "Human Ecology," in 1921, though it was also pioneered in the United States by R. D. McKenzie.

Gratified though the biologist may be by the vigor with which the sociologists embraced ecology, he is likely to read their papers with some uneasiness. Just as the demographers got the uses of "fertility" and "fecundity" backward, the sociologists transformed a terminology devised originally for describing interspecific processes as they applied it wholly within the human "community." From "dominance" and "symbiosis" to "territory" and "competition," nothing meant quite what it had. Forty years later, "Human Ecology" has become that branch of sociology dealing largely with urban geography. It has spawned its own raft of texts which testify to its essentially analogical character and restricted emphasis, narrower and less biological than Park's own original views. Some examples of the nature of scope of studies in this tradition may be seen in a current anthology (Theodorson, 1961).

Ecological Spin Off

The tendency for ecology to decentralize, to spin off independent systems and ideas, linked it to cultural demography by way of animal population studies, which continue to be one of the most vital areas in ecology. If those studies do not startle the actuarial world they at least reaffirm the reality of population limitation. What *Fortune* magazine was still calling "the Malthusian Mischief" (Winocour, 1952) was stirred up by a few outspoken ecologists and

like-minded humanists (the most cogent statements on human population ecology are probably those of Aldous Huxley in 1950 and 1963) in the years after World War II. Although human population saturation was not a new idea, it was still virtually subversive to declare that men must limit their numbers. *The Road to Survival* (Vogt, 1948) is a case in point, the contribution of a biologist to the creation of a public density sense. The biologists were strident when stridence was needed, while urbanity has lately marked the dialogue in the manner, for instance, of Edward Deevey's (1956, 1960) factual but far from feverish essays.

Animal behavior is another active field with roots in ecology. Its implications for the human situations are great, and great is the peril for any who attempt the bridge, for it is guarded not only by bulwarks of nonscientific indignation, but by scientific critics prepared to cut down anybody who is not as cautious (or as dull?) as themselves in translating the data from animal social life. Witness their treatment in reviews of *The Territorial Imperative* (Ardrey, 1966) and *On Aggression* (Lorenz, 1966).

There is a large body of cautionary literature stimulated by ecology which can only be suggested. It ranges from the preservation of species and species diversity (Elton, 1958) to the status of forests, water, and soil (Lowdermilk, 1952) and to the preservation of processes pertinent to the whole biosphere (Cole, 1966). The cautionary literature has been criticized (as a standard rejoinder by vested interests) for its pessimism, determinism, and primitivism. In the face of the destructive opportunism and technological fluidity which threaten to change the environment substantially before its ecology can be understood, most ecologists *are* discouraged. The forces poisoning the air and felling the trees around them are not merely the expedients of local self-seekers, but the visible front of a Cartesian-Hobbesian world view. In such a society the reaction to *Biology or Oblivion* (Hocking, 1965) is the frown of disapproval, for it adds the insult of ultimatum to the objectionable cry of Cassandra. A possible solution is implicit in the words of Alexander F. Skutch (1946), that we must go forward to Nature, not back to it. The ecologists' ability to untangle the meaning of that statement will determine their influence in the planning explosion which lies ahead.

Diverse other fields also make their humanizing claims on ecology, with occasional attempts at reconciliation (Quinn, 1940). "Geography as Human Ecology" (Barrows, 1923) is intermediate in time and by token representative of a range of interests going back to the 19th Century environmentalists and coming forward to the current outbreak of ecology in regional and urban design. Interest by historians in ecology is epitomized by the work of James Malin (1950). Anthropologists such as Laura Thompson (1949) and Betty Meggers (1954) represent a group of social scientists who do not believe with L. A. White (1949) that culture can be explained only in terms of itself. A recent symposium on man and animals (Leeds and Vayda, 1965) gives the impression that anthropology may be the generator of a true scientific discipline of human ecology in the future. Medical studies ranging from the ecology of the skin (Marples, 1965) to dissatisfaction with medical convention about cause and effect in disease (Dubos, 1966) are current topics indicating the inseparability of some kinds of physiology from ecology, tracing from the systems theory of Claude Bernard (1878) and pursuits of epidemiology (May, 1958). Other examples of this active field of research are to be found in current anthologies (Bresler, 1966) and in handbooks of physiology (Dill, 1964). The physiological approach to population densities (Christian and Davis, 1964) contacts the study of human stress (Selye, 1956) on one side and territoriality (Wynne-Edards, 1962) on the other.

Ecology and Man

If ecology applied to man seems to radiate into all aspects of human existence, its general principles become correspondingly more important. Its central concept is the ecosystem; the pathways of element, energy, and information flow. In controversial matters such as chemical pest control, the ecosystem idea is a useful framework for sorting the tangle of claims and counterclaims (Egler, 1964). The framework may emphasize the biotic pyramid (Leopold, 1949), biogeochemical cycles (Hutchinson, 1948), or energy in the ecosystem (Sears, 1959).

It seems that there are ecologies of man, but no definitive ecology in the sense that we have an ecology of the robin or of the pine tree. The situation is not altered by the large body of general perspective of man in the biosphere. Such comprehensive views, like those of C. C. Adams (1935), Lee Dice (1955), Marston Bates (1953), May Watts (1957), Sir George Stapledon (1964), and others attest a degree of predictability of the effects of human actions on other species and on the environment. The effects of the destruction of a pine forest, for example, on the local micro-climate, water supply, and biota can be seen and are crucial in the future of mankind. But the limitation of general ecology is that it throws no light on the question of whether men actually will or will not cut down the pine forest. Any number of other disciplines—humane, social, and scientific—would seem to have some part of an answer to that question, and the natural scientist's immediate reaction would be to leave the question to them.

The broad aspects of human ecology cannot be subdivided according to academic tradition. Committees seldom bridge interdisciplinary problems, but only confront each other at the borders. It is apparent that individual biologists and others must explore the man-nature interpenetration as a whole, as a cybernetic or functional system (Collins, 1965).

Abandonment of an Idea

It may be anticipated that one characteristic of such syntheses will be abandonment of the idea that culture is a superstructure. Led by Sir Julian Huxley (1941), biologists themselves were largely responsible for a view of human life as two-layered, one composed of vegetative functions and evolving genetically, the other, superimposed upon it, shaped independently by tradition and learning. Nonbiologists fastened only too gladly on a concept which freed them from having to learn biology and their special fields from what Albert Schweitzer called animal tracks on the clean kitchen floor of theology (Joy, 1951).

The general cultural resistance to the ideas of ecology is, in effect, a repudiation of the natural world itself. The answers to the question of what men will do with a pine forest are to be found in the working of history and prehistory, emerging from systems of psychic, biological, and environmental factors. "Cut the forest, there is no meat in it!" whispers the Australopithecene in our brain; "Cut the forest, there is no grass in it!" murmurs the pastoral memory; "Cut the forest, its soil needs sunlight!" cries the shade of the primeval farmer; "Cut the forest, for the wilderness is pagan!" thunders the Church; "Cut the forest, it blocks my view of the city!" cries the humanist; "Cut the forest, for the wood we can get!" pleads the haggler; "Cut the forest, to prove that ours is the choice!" howls the existentialist. All are one mind and many minds. In all the passion is complex, a swirling current of unconscious symbol and rational decision, of the most delicate feeling inseparable from the imprint of growth and perception. To cut the forest or not to cut it reflects a personal and social cosmology, not any aspect of which is free from the experience of gravity, earth, sky, air, sunlight, or the peculiar individual quirks of the unfolding of life in a natural world.

The Central Problem

Perhaps the central problem of human ecology may be characterized as the relationship of the mind to nature. Such a view was lucidly advanced by Sterling Lamprect (1938). His essay, "Man's Place in Nature," the same as Huxley's title, added thought to the phylogenetic and the ecological web-of-life perspectives. Some examples of the insight generated by such minding are to be found in the work of a biologist, an art historian, a theologian, a mythologist, and some anthropologists.

In *The Enchanted Voyage* (Hutchinson, 1962), a web of sea imagery is explored as an extension from terrestrial mythology. In the traditions of European seafaring the voyage is the discovery of forms and processes which seem to echo and yet to enlarge those of the land. Its symbols of fertility, the life cycle, and death not only enriched the art and imagination of Europe but stimulated the motive of discovery so that even the contemporary oceanographic voyage is a search in and for enchanted worlds. The study of such matters, in this instance by a biologist, illuminates the interpenetration of man and nature in such a way that we see mythologizing as a form of the perception of nature.

The Earth, the Temple and the Gods (Scully, 1962) examines the relationship of landform and religious architecture—which is inseparable from the ritual ceremony of early Greek temples. The Greeks have been rather generally looked upon as insensitive to the beauty of the landscape because the Classical period did not leave a great body of garden art, landscape painting, or the literary celebration of wild solitude. But Scully goes beyond those derivatives of the modern idea of scenery to show that the Greek response was not so abstract or superficial. The temple was built literally in the lap of the goddess, whose immediate local features were embodied in the morphology of the natural locale. The sanctuaries thus completed by architecture create a landscape art in which mind and physiography are inseparable, which are part of the feedback of a religious ceremony. Like the animal art of Paleolithic cave dwellers, the Greek temple sites are fossils of the functional genesis of art—so different from its modern civilized descendants, kept in our time by patrons as relict, domesticated curiosities for display or vicarious excitement.

The sacredness of space has been the subject of study elsewhere also. It comes at a time when the world is becoming notably homogenized. "The nonhomogeneity of space," says Mircea Eliade (1959), "is a primordial experience, homologizable to a founding of the world. It is not a matter of theoretical speculation, but of a primary religious experience that preceeds all reflection on the world." The process of homologizing is explored in a brilliant book by Joseph Campbell, *The Masks of God: Primitive Mythology* (1959). His thesis is derived directly from ethological concepts of the sign stimulus and of imprinting. He identifies the "imprints of experience—such events as birth, waking, sucking, perception of the face and sun—as structuring forms upon which ceremony and ritual build a wider reality. The ceremonial use of mask and environment of the Paleolithic cave rituals, for example, return the participating neophyte back into the womb to be reborn. The mask and pictures are supernormal re-creations. He is initiated into a metaphysical schema which is homologized by a re-enactment of his own biological experience.

In an essay of great insight and beauty, Edith Cobb (1958) reports on her study of autobiographical materials of the identification of "a special period, the little-understood, prepubertal, halcyon, middle age of childhood, approximately from five or six to eleven or twelve—between the strivings of animal infancy and the storms of adolescence—when the natural world is experienced in some highly evocative way, producing in the child a sense of some profound continuity with natural processes and presenting overt evidence of a biological basis of intuition." The development of the perceptual processes is inseparable from the child's activity in nature, an essential background to the ultimate and unique human types of creativity. She sees the "embryology of mind" as a genuinely ecological process and genius as recall based on the "child's early perceptual continuity with nature." This "deep need to make a world the way the world was made" is "the only truly effective counteragent to the forces of internal conflict which until recently were considered the major subjects of study, the main background to purpose in life." And she calls for a "redefinition of human relations in terms of man's total relations with 'outerness,' with nature itself."

The New Ecology

The new kind of ecology represented by Campbell and Cobb indicates that problems of identity and delinquency are more than social symptoms that will be solved by better urban planning, or even by "worthwhile" vocations (cf. Goodman, 1956). The processes of which they speak must be affirmed and nourished. The "crises of adolescence" can be like acute vitamin deficiencies. In contrast, among the Pueblo Indians, "the tribe knew that its hold upon the future, the persistence of its tradition, of its religion, of its emotional orientation, of its ancient soul which involved the world-soul, were dependent on the adolescent disciplines" (Collier, 1931). Building upon and coming after the "middle age of childhood," the early adolescent years fix the individual destiny. The Pueblo boys, returning to the community after a year's secret training, are "radiant of face, full-rounded and powerful of body, modest, detached: they were men now, keepers of the secrets, houses of the Spirit, reincarnations of the countless generations of their race; with 'reconditional reflexes,' with emotions organized toward their community, with a connection formed until death between their individual beings and that mythopoeic universe—that cosmic illusion—that real world—as the case may be, which both makes man through its dreams and is made by man's dreams."

Should our society settle for less? "The difference between primitive and civilized mentality is not absolute; there is no chasm between them, as some scholars have thought. We live in the same world as the savages. Our deepest experience, needs, and aspirations are the same, as surely as the crucial biological and psychic transitions occur in the life of every human being and force culture to take account of them in aesthetic forms" (Chase, 1949).

A final example is a group of studies which correlate anthropological, paleontological, and primate ethological evidence on the evolution of hominids leading to man (Washburn, 1961). On the whole, it seems to mark a return to a more fruitful exploration of instinct. It supports Julian Steward's (1936) contention that a large part of the human emergence, attitude towards nature, personality, and social organization were shaped by the conditions of social carnivorousness. The idea that the Pleistocene might hold the clues to the nature of man is not new, but the meaning of that experience in terms of the kinds of environments which men create, go to, and dream of remains to be discovered. Probably the reaction against the idea of human instinct (*qua* determinism) over the past 75 years crippled our awareness of the richness of innate human behavior and its interplay with learning. Now biology and psychology must confront the ecological function of the unconscious and anthropoid and primitive life as a frame of reference; in short, acknowledge the place of the primate soul and the hunting heart at the center of "the phenomenon of man."

Destiny

One might conclude that the destiny of human ecology is to accept its own eclectic nature. It would be impertinent to attempt to define it now so as to exclude its historical forms or its descendent and peripheral disciplines. The examples which I have given illustrating the kind of thinking and synthesis which seem to me to fulfill the great promise of human ecology are not research reports. They are works of art. Human ecology will probably never become the nucleus of a graduate department or governmental agency, except perhaps in one of its more restricted senses. There are at least three general approaches: a kind of extended individual physiology of the sort stimulated by space flight research and stress syndromes; the implications for man from general landscape and ecosystem ecology; and, finally, the exploration of nature and the human mind as a feedback system. The ecology of man has no sacred core to guard from Philistines. It will be healthiest perhaps when running out in all directions. Its practical significance may be the preservation of the earth and all its inhabitants.

References

Adams, C. C. 1935. The relation of general ecology to human ecology. *Ecology,* 16: 3.

Anderson, Edgar. 1952. *Plants, Man and Life,* Little Brown & Co., Boston, Mass.

Ardrey, Robert. 1966. *The Territorial Imperative.* Atheneum, New York.

Barrows, Harlan. 1923. Geography as human ecology. *Ann. Assoc. Am. Geograph.* 13: 1.

Bates, Marston. 1953. Human ecology, *Anthropology Today,* A. L. Kroeber (Ed.) University of Chicago Press, Chicago, Ill.

Bernard, Claud. 1878-79. *Leçons sur les Phénomènes de la Vie Commune aux Animaux et aux Végétaux,* J. B. Bailliere et Fils, Paris.

Bresler, Jack. 1966. *Human Ecology, Collected Readings.* Addison-Wesley Publishing Co., Reading, Mass.

Campbell, Joseph. 1959. *The Masks of God: Primitive Mythology.* Viking Press, New York.

Chase, Richard. 1949. *Quest for Myth.* Louisiana State University Press, Baton Rouge.

Christian, John J., and David E. Davis, 1964. Endocrines, behavior, and population, *Science,* 146: 3651.

Cobb, Edith. 1959. The ecology of imagination in childhood, *Daedalus,* Summer.

Cole, LaMont. 1966. Man's ecosystem, *BioScience,* 16: 4.

Collier, John. 1931. Fullness of life through leisure, *Mind-Body Relationship,* J. B. Nash (Ed.) A. S. Barnes & Co., New York.

Collins, Paul W. 1965. Functional analysis, *Man, Culture and Animals,* Anthony Leeds and Andrew P. Vayda. (Ed.) Pub. 78, American Association for the Advancement of Science, Washington, D.C.

Darling, Frank Frazer. 1955. *West Highland Survey, an Essay in Human Ecology.* Oxford University Press, London & New York.

Deevey, Edward. 1956. The human crop. *Sci. Am.,* 194: 34 1960. The human population, *Sci. Am.* 203: 3.

Dice, Lee Raymond. 1955. *Man's Nature and Nature's Man: The Ecology of Human Communities.* University of Michigan Press, Ann Arbor, Mich.

Dill, D. B., ed. 1964. *Handbook of Physiology, Section Four, Adaptation to Environment.* American Physiological Society, Washington, D.C.

Dubos, Rene. 1966. Second thoughts on the germ theory. *Sci. Am.* 192: 5.

Egler, Frank. 1964. Pesticides—in our ecosystem. *Am. Scientist,* 52: 110-136.

Eliade, Mircea. 1959. *The Sacred and the Profane,* Harcourt, Brace & World, New York.

Elton, Charles. 1958. *The Ecology of Invasions by Animals and Plants.* Methuen, London.

Findlay, John N. 1966. *The Discipline of the Cave,* Allen & Unwin, London.

Goodman, Paul. 1956. *Growing Up Absurd*. Random House, New York.

Hawley, Amos. 1950. *Human Ecology, a Theory of Community Structure*. Ronald Press, New York.

Hocking, Brian. 1965. *Biology or Oblivion*, Schenkman, Cambridge, Mass.

Hutchinson, G. E. 1949. On living in the biosphere. *Sci. Monthly*, 68: 6.

———1962. *The Enchanted Voyage*. Yale University Press, New Haven.

Huxley, Aldous. 1950. The double crisis, *Themes and Variations*. Harper, New York.

———1963. *The Politics of Ecology*. Center for the Study of Democratic Institutions, Santa Barbara, California.

Huxley, Julian. 1948. *Man in the Modern World*. Harper & Row, New York.

Huxley, Thomas Henry. 1863. *Man's Place in Nature*. London.

Joy, Charles R. 1951. *The Animal World of Albert Schweitzer, Jungle Insights into Reverence for Life*. Beacon, Boston, Mass., p. 165.

Lamprect, Sterling, 1938. Man's place in nature, *Am. Scholar*, Winter.

Leeds, Anthony, and Andrew P. Vayda. 1965. *Man, Culture, and Animals*. Pub. 78, American Association for the Advancement of Science, Washington, D.C.

Lorenz, Konrad. 1966. *On Aggression*. Harcourt, Brace & World, New York.

Lowdermilk, W. C. 1952. *Conquest of the Land Over 7000 Years*. USDA Agr. Inform. Bul. **99**, Washington, D.C.

Malin, James C. 1950. Ecology and history, *Sci. Monthly*, 70: 5.

Marples, Mary. 1965. *The Ecology of the Human Skin*. Charles C. Thomas, Springfield, Ill.

May, Jaques M. 1958. *The Ecology of Human Disease*. MD Publications, New York.

Meggers, Betty J. 1954. Environmental limitation on the development of culture. *Am. Anthropol.* 56: 803-804.

Park, Robert Ezra. 1936. Human ecology. *Am. J. Sociol.* 42: 1.

Quinn, J. A. 1940. Human ecology and interactional ecology. *Am. Sociol. Rev.* 5: 713-22.

Riggs, Fred Warren. 1962. *The Ecology of Public Administration*. Indian Institute for Public Affairs, New Delhi.

Scully, Vincent. 1962. *The Earth, the Temple and the Gods*. Yale University Press, New Haven, Conn.

Sears, Paul B. 1959. The steady state: physical law and moral choice. *The Key Reporter*, 34: 2.

Shelford, Victor, 1935. The physical environment, *A Handbook for Social Psychology*, Guy Murchison (Ed.) Clark University Press, Worcester, Mass.

Skutch, Alexander F. 1946. Back—or forward—to nature? *Nature*, 39: 9.

Sprout, Harold & Margaret. 1965. *The Ecological Perspective on Human Affairs*. Princeton University Press, Princeton, N.J.

Stapledon, Sir George, 1964. *Human Ecology*. Faber, London.

Steward, Julian H. 1936. The economic and social basis of primitive bands, *Essays in Honor of Alfred L. Kroeber*. University of California Press, Berkeley, Calif.

Theodorson, George A. 1961. *Studies in Human Ecology*. Harper, New York.

Thompson, Laura. 1949. The basic conservation problem. *Sci. Monthly*, 68: 2.

Vogt, William. 1948. *The Road to Survival*. Wm. Sloane Assoc., New York.

Washburn, Sherwood L. 1961. (Ed.). *Social Life of Early Man*. Wenner Gren, Chicago, Ill.

White, L. A. 1949. *The Science of Culture*. Farrar, Straus & Co., New York.

White, Lynn, Jr. 1967. The historical roots of our ecological crisis. *Science*, 155: 3767.

Winocour, Jack, 1952. The malthusian mischief. *Fortune*, May.

Wynne-Edwards, V. C. 1962. *Animal Dispersion in Relation to Social Behavior*. Stetchert-Hafner, New York.

5

HUMAN ENVIRONMENT AND WORLD ORDER

U Thant

Real life, in our time, has shown an alarming tendency to overtake science fiction, and this tendency is nowhere more evident than in the subject I am going to talk about here—the problem of the human environment. It is a problem which, although it is by no means new, has suddenly taken on the quality of a nightmare.

Although experts may disagree on this or that detail, there can be no doubt that we are faced with an unprecedented situation. This is the first time in its history that mankind faces not merely a threat, but an actual worldwide crisis involving all living creatures, all vegetable life, the entire system in which we live, and all nations large or small, advanced or developing. It is a crisis which concerns literally everyone, and involves, directly or indirectly, almost everything. It underlines, as no other phenomenon can, the fact that ours is the first global civilization and that, as such, it can make global mistakes which can wreck not just one nation or society, but the very Earth itself. We have, of course, also *invented* the means—nuclear, chemical and biological—of actually destroying our global society as well, but here, I shall concentrate on the ways in which we may wreck it not intentionally, but by mistake, by selfishness and by stupidity.

The exploration of outer space has given us a new appreciation of our planet and of its unique and bountiful nature. Through the eyes of space explorers we have seen the Earth as a jewel of the universe—with its great oceans, its incredible variety of terrain and vegetation, and its astonishing crew of animal and human life,

sailing in space and wreathed with the clouds and the air of its life-giving atmosphere. The Soviet cosmonauts movingly expressed our newly found Earth-patriotism when they wished their stricken American colleagues on Apollo 13 a safe return to "our native Earth."

The drama of Apollo 13 also gave us an exhibition on a small scale of what might easily become the problem of spaceship Earth. The problem in those agonizing days of Apollo 13's return from the Moon was basically the uncertain balance between the capacity of the spaceship to support life and the demands made on it by its inhabitants. Until recently, the Earth could, without difficulty, meet the needs of its passengers and could also absorb the various waste products which they produced. But now we face a rapidly increasing imbalance between the life-sustaining systems of the Earth and the demands, industrial, agricultural, technological, and demographic, which its inhabitants put upon it. This is an unprecedented challenge to all Earth-people here and now. If we fail to meet that challenge, it could become an unthinkable disaster for our children.

Apollo 13 had behind it a vast and brilliant research and planning organization and a dedicated and decisive Mission Control—stationed in Texas—whose authority was unquestioned. It also had a home base to return to. On spaceship Earth we do not as yet have any of these advantages. Indeed, it is strange that while we marvel at, and pride ourselves on, the miracles of invention, planning, technique, courage, and teamwork which sustain our space explorers, we still accept for our own spaceship Earth the most antiquated systems, the most wretched mismanagement and a level of profiteering, sabotage, self-seeking, and indiscipline which would not be tolerated for a second in the Manned Space Flight Center or at the Soviet Cosmodrome. Here I propose to consider briefly how we may begin to achieve for spaceship Earth, on the necessary scale, the kind of planning, organization, and authority which brought Apollo 13 safely home. Our problem, of course, is infinitely vaster and more complex, but the basic necessity is the same.

The symptoms of our problems are too well

Reprinted from the *International Journal of Environmental Studies* 1: 13-17, 1970, with the permission of the publishers, Gordon and Breach Science Publishers Ltd.

known to need description. We see, hear, and smell them all around us, and, belatedly perhaps, the environmental problem is becoming the most widely discussed and written about question of our time all over the world. This sudden interest and concern over the environment cannot be allowed to be merely a passing whim, and it is also essential to avoid any temptation to make the problem into some sort of cult. Clear and honest thinking, organization and hard work are vital. The environment must become a subject of lifelong dedication for many people everywhere, especially among our most promising young men and women. This is one branch of human endeavour in which we dare not permit ourselves to fail.

The causes of our problem are also generally well known. Man's technological achievements in the past two hundred years have allowed for, and encouraged a fantastic growth of population which has increased the number of the earth's inhabitants sevenfold since A.D.1600 and may well double it again in the next 38 years. This population increase has been accompanied by a process of urbanization which has already brought 40% of the world's people to live in cities and the urbanization process continues apace. Urbanization on this scale was neither foreseen nor planned by the presiding wizards of the industrial revolution—nor apparently did it worry them at all—and the appalling results are clear for all to see. Urbanization has become, in social and economic terms, an almost universal problem producing vast social and political difficulties as well as being a major source of pollution. At the same time the spread of industrialization and the inexorable advance of technology, of which the human and environmental consequences have so far been largely ignored, have produced a new and global range of problems which now threaten the very fabric and atmosphere of the earth itself.

We are all acquainted with striking examples of this horrible accident of history, and certainly we have already produced some irreversible disasters and have lost beyond redemption some precious parts of our common heritage. But there is no basic reason

why technology, urbanization, and industrialization, properly planned and controlled, should not be made to enrich the life of mankind rather than to deplete it, just as, at its best, the industrial revolution has, in some areas of the world, put an end to the drudgery and servility in which, for most of its history, a majority of the human race has lived. It is the aims, methods, and organization of technology, industrialization, and urbanization which must urgently be reviewed and, where necessary, changed, before we suffer larger and more fatally irreversible disasters.

Why has the environmental problem, which has been evident for so long in different ways and in different parts of the world, suddenly assumed the dramatic and global proportions of which men speak today? It is mainly, I suppose, because the accelerated growth of population and technology have compounded themselves in a progression which was mathematically predictable, but to which, until very recently, short-sightedness and self-interest blinded the authorities and interests mainly responsible. One statistic, quoted recently in *The New York Times*, may give an idea of the speed of this progression and of the size of the problems we face. In 1957 the gross national product of the United States was 453 billion dollars. In 1969 it was 728 billion dollars, an increase of 60%, and by 1980 it is estimated that it will again have increased by 50%. The output of goods and services in the United States grew as much between 1950 and 1970 as it did in the entire period between 1620, when the Pilgrims landed, and 1950. An increasing gross national product was, until recently, regarded as an entirely desirable goal, but now we must also see this goal in terms of demands on resources, in terms of waste disposal and pollution problems and of other serious consequences, social as well as economic.

The question of the growth of the gross national product as a national aim is only one of many areas in which a reconsideration of attitudes and ideas, which until lately have been generally accepted, is urgently required.

Obviously, the environmental problem looks very different according to the state of development of the country one happens to live in, and this makes a global approach all the more essential. A simple example is the question of DDT, the use of which is vitally important to the agricultural development of a number of developing countries at precisely the moment when some advanced countries are taking steps to curb, or even abolish, its use. It is clear also that the whole question of the pace and the goals of economic development must be examined in the light of environmental problems. The developing nations should not be encouraged to repeat the mistakes of the advanced countries. Nor should they be the victims either of the abuses of the environment committed by advanced countries, or of the measures which their new awareness of their mistakes may cause the advanced nations suddenly to take. In the interest of all peoples of the world, it is essential to evolve a new balance between economic development and the increase of the gross national product on the one hand and the human and social requirements of men and a reasonable use and conservation of the world's resources on the other.

This is only one of a whole range of broad questions which will need to be reexamined urgently in the light of the environmental crisis. On a national level there are many others. In some countries the whole system of profits, of sales promotion, and of the nature of commercial enterprise, as part of a national way of life, clearly have an important bearing on the environmental problem. The attitudes of consumers as well as of producers must be looked at anew from the environmental point of view. In other countries, which are not committed to the free enterprise system, national economic aims and policies will require a similar examination.

It also seems probable to me that the results of the habit of thinking primarily in national terms will be found to be closely connected with some of the problems of the environment. I think, for example, of the large numbers of aircraft from scores of national airlines which fly about the Earth, often with a small complement of passengers, and of the 35 tons of oxygen which each of them is said to replace with gases and fumes in every six-hour flight. One may be forgiven for wondering if a more

rational and efficient scheme of international civil aviation could not be devised which would reduce this major source of pollution, as well as lessening the overcrowding of the world's airports.

These are only a few of the general problems on which we urgently need a searching and responsible international dialogue. No one can say what the results of such a debate might be, but I believe that we should not be too pessimistic. Many of the questions to be discussed are overdue for discussion anyway, and it is even possible that out of this exchange we might evolve new aims, attitudes, and styles of life which would in themselves constitute a positive improvement in the human condition. We might, for example, begin to find a balance between the material cravings of man and other nobler aspirations which have tended to be overshadowed by the appetites cultivated by the technological age.

On more specific problems there is no shortage of evidence. The main areas of our concern are clear. The desperate conjunction of explosive population increase and food shortage has haunted us for many years. The effects of existing technology put an increasing strain on natural resources and now also threaten, through unabsorbable or undisposable waste products, not only the surface of the Earth but the very integrity of the atmospheric envelope in which we live. We now hear much, for example, of the "greenhouse effect" caused by the steadily increasing excess of unabsorbed carbon dioxide which we heedlessly release into the atmosphere each year. This could cause an increase in the mean annual temperature all over the world with a series of catastrophic results—the melting of the polar ice caps, radical changes in the ecology of the sea, and even floods on a scale hitherto undreamed of. There is also the emerging problem of new techniques which actually destroy the environment. The most dramatic of these is, of course, the thermonuclear explosion, but others less spectacular, and benevolent in the short-term, may prove to be long-term disasters. Some chemical pesticides, some fertilizers, and the internal combustion engine are obvious examples, not to mention the unknown effects on Earth and in the atmosphere of innovations such as the supersonic transport plane. Here again we have to reach a proper balance between new goals and real human requirements. To reach this balance we have to develop our knowledge of the results of technological change and our thinking as to what men really want and need.

There is indeed no shortage of problems to discuss, and it is my hope that the United Nations Conference on the Human Environment, which, at the initiative of the Government of Sweden, is to meet in Stockholm in 1972 and for which we are now actively preparing, may serve as an occasion for organizing, sharing, and deploying knowledge and expertise, identifying priority problems and coordinating national measures within an effective global framework. I do not propose to speak now in detail about the work of that conference. There is, however, one aspect of it which we must consider realistically and with care—I refer to the question of effective organization to meet this first truly global crisis. What is to be the nature of the institutional arrangements for planning, programming, and researching for the rescue of spaceship Earth? And who, if things go wrong, will be our Mission Control, with the wisdom and the authority to ensure that the agreed measures are the right ones and that they are actually carried out?

There is already a huge mass of information on the threat to the environment, and many organizations and governments all over the world are concerned with this or that aspect of the problem. There are even efforts to set international standards in some areas and to make international rules for the preservation of parts of our threatened environment. But the situation is now sufficiently urgent to demand a great deal more than this. The unthinking exploitation and abuse of the world's natural resources, and the plunder, befouling, and destruction of our native Earth, have already gone too far for us to rely any more on pious hopes, belated promises, and tardy efforts at self-discipline. Only last year Thor Heyerdahl, in his papyrus ship, encountered a 200-mile oil slick in the mid-equatorial Atlantic. It was the

contribution of countless tanker captains, and sometime soon it may begin to approach the shores of South America. There is no necessity for comment on an outrage such as this, but it underlines the fact that we do not have the time for an educational campaign to divert men from centuries of destructive or thoughtless habit.

If effective measures are to be taken in time, we need something new—and we need it speedily—a global authority with the support and agreement of governments and of other powerful interests, which can pull together all the piecemeal efforts now being made and which can fill in the gaps where something needs to be done. This authority must embark expeditiously, with the good of all men in mind, on the delicate process of reaching a workable compromise among governments and interests on matters affecting the environment. It should be able, if necessary, to police and enforce its decisions. Apart from the general support of governments, such an agency will have to rely, as Mr. George Kennan has rightly observed, on experts, scientists, and scholars who will be "true international servants, bound by no national or political mandate, by nothing, in fact, other than dedication to the work in hand." The immediate question is this: Do the sovereign nations of the world have the courage and the vision to set up and support such an agency *now*, and thus, in the interest of future generations of life on Earth, depart radically from the hitherto sacred paths of national sovereignty? I sincerely hope that they do have this courage and wisdom, for increasingly I doubt whether any lesser measures will suffice to meet the challenge which faces us. Certainly the clouds and currents of pollution ceased to respect national sovereignty long ago.

There is a secondary question which relates to the nature of this new global agency. Mr. Kennan has suggested, for reasons which he considers cogent and practical, that, to begin with at any rate, it should be constituted by a small group of leading industrial and maritime nations, whose economies are largely responsible for the environmental problem in the first place. With all respect for Mr. Kennan's judgement, I profoundly disagree with this idea. It has always seemed to me ironical that the Powers who had created, or who owned, nuclear weapons were precisely those who were so insistent that others should forswear them, although, from a practical point of view, they were unquestionably right in seeking to curb the spread of nuclear weapons. But in the matter of environmental pollution it seems to me to be absolutely essential that *all* countries and peoples should be associated from the outset with the effort to face what may well prove to be the gravest threat that mankind as a whole has ever encountered. As I said earlier, a balance has to be reached between economic development and human and social needs, and between population, development, and environmental control. The developing countries are intimately concerned in these problems, which are crucial both to their own future and to the future of the environment. Their voices must be heard, and listened to, even if at the outset their technical contribution may be relatively small. Their confidence and their cooperation, as representing the largest part of the world's population, are vital. Otherwise we shall once again increase the gap between advanced and developing nations which is already one of the major sources of tension in the world.

I further venture to say that I believe that a global authority for the protection of the environment should be closely associated with the United Nations. I hasten to add that in saying this I am motivated by no impulse for empire-building. The United Nations has no shortage of great and difficult problems on its agenda. But the United Nations, for all its shortcomings, is the nearest thing we have to a world organization, and it suffers from all the difficulties of a world organization. If the United Nations has so far failed to develop the degree of world order and the kind of international authority and responsibility which many of us believe the present state of the world demands, it is perhaps because the challenges it has faced hitherto have not seemed compelling enough to persuade its sovereign members to advance sufficiently fast from self-centered nationalism to internationalism. The fact remains, however, that the United Nations is still the only forum where the development of world order is continuously discussed and actively striven for. For the task of saving the environment, nothing less than a new step towards world order will do. Any new and separate universal agency set up for this purpose will have to face the same hard facts of international life which the United Nations faces, without the advantages of the accrued experience and existing organization of the United Nations.

One of the standard plots of science fiction is the overwhelming and mysterious threat from outer space which unites all men on Earth to defend their planet and which makes them forget at last their petty, Earthbound differences. If much of what we now hear about environmental problems is true, we may well, on our own, have provided the overriding incentive to unite and to cooperate, and we shall not be needing help from outer space. If that is so, I can only hope that we have the imagination and the strength to react in time and in a fitting manner. If we do, our present near-disaster could be turned, like the flight of Apollo 13, into a triumph of the human spirit and of human ingenuity. Every cloud, even if it consists of smog, may have a silver lining. The crisis of the environment could be the challenge which might show us the way forward to a responsible and a just world society—a path which, for all the efforts of the United Nations in the political crises of our time, has so far eluded us.

Is it wholly fantastic and utopian to ask that some of the ingenuity and the vast sums of money now spent on armaments might be diverted to the saving of our native Earth? Is it silly to believe that man can find within himself the generosity and the imagination to put the common good before self-interest? Is it naïve to hope that ideological struggles might give way to the struggle for survival and for a decent future? Is it unrealistic to suggest that the undoubted global challenge we now face might become the basis for a new start in world order and a more civilized and generous way of life for the peoples of the Earth?

A great American public servant recently observed that "invariably the right things get done for the wrong reasons, so the organizer looks for the wrong reasons to get the right things done." While this dictum may err on the side of scepticism, there is a great deal of wisdom in it. As Secretary-General of the United Nations, I am deeply concerned with the threat to the environment, but I cannot let this concern overshadow all of the other objectives for which the United Nations has striven and will strive. All of these aims—peace, disarmament, justice, human rights, world order, improved conditions for all peoples, the development of international law—are interrelated, and an advance in one area benefits all the others. If the threat to our environment proves to be as great and as imminent as many experts now say it is, and as I believe it to be, and if the concern now being expressed all over the world is sincere, I would hope with all my heart that the lessons we can learn from this bitter experience may also find a wider application. I would hope that in saving ourselves by preserving our environment, we might also find a new solidarity and a new spirit among the governments and peoples of the Earth, and so look to the future with greater courage and confidence.

PART TWO

Human Evolution

Our species is variously estimated to have been in existence for somewhere between one hundred thousand and a quarter of a million years. Not until the publication of Darwin's work a little more than a century ago was it realized that man has evolved by processes essentially similar to those that have produced all other living forms in our biosphere. Only within the last 20 or 30 years have we come to appreciate that, as with all other species, the life expectancy of the species *Homo sapiens* must be finite. No living species ever investigated has been found to survive a quarter of a billion years. However, extinction for our own species may well come suddenly and very short of this limiting period, as some of the selections in Part Five indicate.

Our own hominid line, it is generally believed, was derived by evolutionary processes from a primate stock. The conjectures and surmises necessary in providing an account of this progression are based especially on the imaginative interpretation of paleontological evidence. Many varying explanations of the origin of our species have been suggested on the basis of this evidence. Unfortunately, the fossil record of primates is not particularly good, and despite the patient efforts of numerous dedicated paleontologists, we do not yet have a complete understanding of the emergence of man. Yet investigation of many more hominid remains proceeds apace. Consequently, the next few years will see either the consolidation or rejection of many current theories of hominid evolution.

The most useful paleontological information regarding human evolution is derived from features of the skull. The size of the brain case can be measured to estimate cranial capacity and to gauge relative intelligence. Generally teeth are the most durable and best-preserved portions of the skull. Teeth offer what is often the best means of tracing and identifying evolutionary lineages and determining the evolutionary relationships among fossils. In addition, they provide information about the diet of a primate and its ecological role in the community. David L. Greene discusses the extent to which hominid dental evolution relates to the ecological niches of contemporary man (6). Additional information about these niches, including both trophic position in the community and social behavior, comes from an examination of the artifacts associated with hominid remains. Sally R. Binford discusses human evolution in the early Stone Age in terms of such artifacts (7).

The next two papers in this part deal with the exploration of skeletal material in relation to the associated artifacts. Although the widely scattered nature of the earliest finds suggested an Asian origin for man, the most complete hominid skeletal and artifact series are encountered in Africa. That continent is now considered the primary center of hominid evolution. When creatures morphologically indistinguishable from modern *Homo sapiens* had emerged, their social organization was probably into hunter-gatherer bands. James J. Hester outlines some of the possible ecological interactions of these early societies (8), and John R. Baker provides a description of the first identifiable European, Cro-Magnon man (9).

Our knowledge of hominid and human evolution, however, does not have to be constructed solely from interpretations of paleontological evidence such as these last four papers present. The comparative study of behavior in living primates can provide substantial if indirect evidence as to our ancestral behavioral patterns. During the last decade, many such investigations have been initiated; the current accounts of these investigations confirm the early promise of such work. In a survey paper (10), three eminent scholars in this area, S. L. Washburn, Phyllis C. Jay, and Jane B. Lancaster, describe some of the exciting prospects that can be anticipated from this line of study.

Through long biological evolution and a comparatively short social development, modern man has evolved a series of highly sophisticated cultural patterns. The nature of this cultural evolution is further explored in Part Three.

Additional Readings

Altmann, S. A. "Sociobiology of rhesus monkeys II: Stochastics of social communication," *J. Theor. Biol.* 8: 490-522, 1965.

Baird, D., and Carroll, R. L. "Romeriscus, the oldest known reptile," *Science* 157: 56-59, 1967.

Bajema, C. J., ed. *Natural Selection in Human Populations*, New York: Wiley, 1971.

Benedict, B. "Role analysis in animals and men," *Man* 4(2): 203-14, 1969.

Bilsborough, A. "Rates of evolutionary change in the hominid dentition," *Nature* 223: 146-49, 1969.

Binford, S. R., and Binford, L. R., "Stone tools and human behavior," *Scientific American* 220(4): 70-84, 1969.

Birdsell, J. B. "On population structure in generalized hunting and collecting populations," *Evolution* 12: 189-205, 1958.

Bishop, W. W., and Clark, J. D., eds. *Background to Evolution in Africa*, Chicago: University of Chicago Press, 1969.

Bishop, W. W., Moller, J. A., and Fitch, F. J. "New potassium-argon age determinations relevant to the Miocene fossil mammal sequence in East Africa," *Amer. J. Science* 267: 669-99, 1969.

Brace, C. L. "The origin of man," *Natural History* 79: 46-49, 1970.

Bramlette, M. N. "Massive extinctions in biota at the end of Mesozoic time," *Science* 148: 1969-99, 1965.

Buffington, J. D. "Predation, competition, and Pleistocene megafauna extinction," *Bioscience* 21: 167-70, 1971.

Carpenter, C. R. "A field study of the behavior and social relations of the gibbon," *Comparative Psychology Monographs, no. 16*, 1940 (republished in

Naturalistic Behavior of Nonhuman Primates, C. R. Carpenter, University Park, Pa: Pennsylvania State University Press, 1964).

Carpenter, C. R. "The howlers of Barro Colorada Island," in *Primate Behavior: Field Studies of Monkeys and Apes*, I. Devore, ed., New York: Holt, Rinehart and Winston, 1965, pp. 250-91.

Caspari, E. "Selective forces in the evolution of man," *Amer. Naturalist* 97: 5-14, 1963.

Clark, J. D. "Human ecology during Pleistocene and later times in Africa south of the Sahara," *Curr. Anthropol.* 1: 307-24, 1960.

Clarke, R. J., Howell, F. C., and Brain, C. K. "More evidence of an advanced hominid at Swartkrans," *Nature* 225: 1219-24, 1970.

Crook, J. H. "The socio-ecology of primates," in *Social Life in Animals and Man*, J. H. Crook, ed., London: Academic Press, 1970.

Day, M. H. "Omo human skeletal remains," *Nature* 222: 1135-38, 1969.

Delgado, J. M. R. "Brain research and behavioral activity," *Endeavour* 26(99): 149-54, 1967.

DeVore, I., ed. *Primate Behavior: Field Studies of Monkeys and Apes*, New York: Holt, Rinehart and Winston, 1965.

Dolhinow, P. "The living nonhuman primates," in *Background for Man*, P. Dolhinow and V. M. Sarich, eds., Boston: Little, Brown, 1971, pp. 261-84.

Emiliani, C. "The Pleistocene epoch and the evolution of man," *Curr. Anthropol.* 9: 27-47, 1968.

Fejfar, O. "Human remains from the early Pleistocene in Czechoslovakia," *Current Anthropology* 10: 170-73, 1969.

Gartlan, J. S., and Brain, C. K. "Ecology and social variability in *Cercopithecus aethiops and C. mitis*," in *Primates: Studies in Adaptation and Variability*, P. C. Jay, New York: Holt, Rinehart and Winston, 1968, pp. 253-92.

Goodall, J. M. "Tool-using and aimed throwing in a community of free-living chimpanzees," *Nature* 201: 1264, 1964.

———. "New discoveries among Africa's chimpanzees," *National Geographic* 128: 802-31, 1965.

Greenberg, J. H. "Language universals: A research frontier," *Science* 166: 473-78, 1969.

Haynes, C. V. "Elephant hunting in North America," *Scientific American* 214(6): 104-12, 1966.

Holloway, R. L. "Culture: A human domain," *Current Anthropology* 10: 395-412, 1969.

Howell, F. C. "Recent advances in human evolutionary studies," *Quart. Rev. Biol.* 42: 471-513, 1967.

———. "Remains of Hominidae from Plio-Pleistocene formations in the lower Omo basin, Ethiopia," *Nature* 223: 1234-39, 1969.

Howells, W. W. "*Homo erectus*," *Scientific American* 215(5): 46-53, 1966.

———. *Mankind in the Making*, rev. ed., New York: Doubleday, 1967.

Klein, R. G. "Mousterian cultures in European Russia," *Science* 165: 257-65, 1969.

Kummer, H. "Dimensions of a comparative biology of primate groups," *Amer. J. Phys. Anthropol.* 27(3): 357-66, 1967.

———. "Social organization of Hamadryas baboons: A field study," *Bibliotheca Primatologica* 6: 1-189, 1968.

Lancaster, J. B. "The evolution of tool-using behavior," *Amer. Anthropologist* 70: 56-66, 1968.

———. "Primate communication systems and the emergence of human language," in *Primates: Studies in Adaptation and Variability*, P. C. Jay, New York: Holt, Rinehart and Winston, 1968, pp. 483-557.

Leakey, L. S. B. *Olduvai Gorge 1951-1961, Fauna and Background*, Cambridge: Cambridge University Press, 1965.

Leakey, R. E. F. "In search of man's past at Lake Rudolf," *National Geographic* 137: 712-33, 1970.

Lederberg, J. "Experimental genetics and human evolution," *Bull. Atomic Scientists* 22: 1-11, 1966.

Lee, R. B., and DeVore, I. eds. *Man the Hunter*, Chicago: Aldine, 1968.

Livingstone, F. B. "Genetics, ecology, and the origin of incest and exogamy," *Curr. Anthropol.* 10: 45-61, 1969.

Loomis, W. F. "Skin-pigment regulation of vitamin D synthesis in man," *Science* 157: 501-6, 1967.

Mann, A. "Homo erectus," in *Background for Man*, P. Dolhinow and V. M. Sarich, eds., Boston: Little, Brown, 1971, pp. 166-77.

Menzel, E. W. "Naturalistic and experimental research on primates," *Human Development* 10: 170-86, 1967.

Mercer, J. H. "Glaciation in southern Argentina more than two million years ago," *Science* 164: 823-25, 1969.

Oakley, K. P. "Dating the emergence of man," *Advancement of Science* 18: 415-26, 1962.

Payne, M. M. "Family in search of prehistoric man," *National Geographic* 127: 194-231, 1965.

Robinson, J. T. "Homo 'habilis' and the Australopithecines," *Nature* 205: 121-24, 1965.

Romer, A. S. "Major steps in vertebrate evolution," *Science* 158: 1629-37, 1967.

Sarich, V. M. "Human variation in an evolutionary perspective," in *Background for Man*, P. Dolhinow and V. M. Sarich, eds., Boston: Little, Brown, 1971, pp. 182-91.

——, and Wilson, A. C. "Rate of albumin evolution in primates," *Proc. Nat. Acad. Sci. U.S.* 58: 142-148, 1967.

——. "A molecular approach to the question of human origins," in *Background for Man*, P. Dolhinow, and V. M. Sarich, eds., Boston: Little, Brown, 1971, pp. 60-81.

——. "Human variation in an evolutionary perspective," in *Background for Man*, P. Dolhinow, and V. M. Sarich, eds., Boston: Little, Brown, 1971. pp. 182-91.

Schaffer, W. M. "Character displacement and the evolution of the hominidae," *Amer. Naturalist* 102: 559-71, 1968.

Schreider, E. "Possible selective mechanisms of social differentation in biological traits," *Human Biol.* 39: 14-20, 1967.

Simons, E. L. "Some fallacies in the study of hominid phylogeny," *Science* 141: 879-89, 1963.

——. "Late Miocene hominid from Fort Ternan, Kenya," *Nature* 223: 687-89, 1969.

——. Pilbeam, D., and Ettel, P. C. "Controversial taxonomy of fossil hominids," *Science* 166: 258-59, 1969.

Tattersall, I. "Ecology of North Indian *Ramapithecus*," *Nature* 221: 451-52, 1969.

Tindale, N. B. "Ecology of primitive man in Australia," in *Biogeography and Ecology in Australia*, A. Keast, et al., eds., Monographiae Biologicae no. 8: 36-51, The Hague: Junk, 1959.

Tobias, P. V. "Early man in East Africa," *Science* 149: 22-33, 1965.

——. "The distinctiveness of Homo Habilis," *Nature* 209: 953-957, 1966.

Tuttle, R. H. "Knuckle-walking and the problem of human origins," *Science* 166: 953-61, 1969.

Uzzell, T., and Pilbeam, D. "Phyletic divergence dates of hominoid primates: A comparison of fossil and molecular data," *Evolution* 25(4): 615-35, 1971.

Van Lawick-Goodall, J. "The behavior of free-living chimpanzees in the Gombe Stream Reserve," *Animal Behavior Monographs* 1(3): 161-311, 1968.

Washburn, S. L. "Tools and human evolution," *Scientific American* 203(3): 62-75, 1960.

——, and DeVore, I. "The social life of baboons," *Scientific American* 204(6): 62-71, 1961.

——, Jay, P. C., and Lancaster, J. B., "Field studies of Old World monkeys and apes," *Science* 150: 1541-47, 1965.

——, and Lancaster, C. S. "The evolution of hunting," in *Man the Hunter*, R. B. Lee, and I. DeVore, eds., Chicago: Aldine, 1968, pp. 293-303.

——. "The study of human evolution," in *Background for Man*, P. Dolhinow and V. M. Sarich, eds., Boston: Little, Brown, 1971, pp. 82-117.

Weckler, J. E. "Neanderthal man," *Scientific American* 197(6): 89-96, 1957.

Workman, P. "Gene flow and the search for natural selection in man," *Human Biology* 40: 260-79, 1968.

Yoshiba, K. "Local and intertroop variability in ecology and social behavior of common Indian langurs," in *Primates: Studies in Adaptation and Variability*, P. C. Jay, ed., New York: Holt, Rinehart and Winston, 1968, pp. 217-42.

6

ENVIRONMENTAL INFLUENCES ON PLEISTOCENE HOMINID DENTAL EVOLUTION

David L. Greene

The object of this paper is to discuss two trends in the evolution of hominid teeth during the Pleistocene; a general reduction in size of teeth and a simplification in morphological complexity of the lower molars. These trends will be related to environmental factors found during the Pleistocene.

Mechanisms of evolution have been categorized by modern theorists. These are usually described as mutation, random genetic drift, nonrandom mating patterns within a population, and most important, natural selection. The first three mechanisms can produce short-term changes in the genetic constitution of populations; however, natural selection operates on these mechanisms to produce oriented change (Simpson, 1949). Long-term changes observed in the fossil record are the result of adaptation to particular environmental circumstances through natural selection.

Natural selection results from the differing degrees of fitness exhibited by different individuals in environmental situations. Those individuals most fit because of the possession of certain features will survive more often than less fit individuals and thereby potentially make a greater contribution to the genetic constitution of the next generation. Environmental variability is obviously very important for evolution through natural selection.

When dealing with the hominid environment during the Pleistocene, we must realize that during this epoch the development and elaboration of human cultural behavior modified the

Reprinted from *Bioscience* 20: 276-79, 1970, with the permission of the publishers.

effect of the natural environment. Culture began to take on two roles in the evolutionary process. One of these roles was as a buffer between man and the natural environment. Numerous examples come to mind from the Pleistocene record. The development of simple stone tools by Villafranchian times ultimately led to efficient pursuit and utilization of large wild game animals. During the Middle Pleistocene, the documented control and use of fire most likely enabled hominids to move out of the tropics and extend their range into moderate temperate areas like northern China. By Upper Pleistocene times, some Neanderthal hominids were undoubtedly using skins for protection from the elements in their very harsh subarctic environment. These cultural artifacts reduced the effect of natural selection. Many anthropologists feel that there is good evidence to indicate that by Middle Pleistocene times, if not before, the buffering effect of culture was so great as to limit the diversifying effect of natural selection in the different environments represented by the hominid range to a degree that eliminated speciation. From that time on it is felt that only one contemporaneous species of hominid existed (Lancaster, 1968).

The other role played by culture is that not only does it buffer some of the effects of the natural environment but that it also becomes part of the hominid environment. After the inception of culture, hominids not only had to adapt to the natural environment but also to the new environment that they created. In a hominid group where cultural behavior plays an important role in overall adaptation, selection would favor improvement in characteristics relating to increasing efficiency of cultural utilization. Few anthropologists doubt that the rapid increase in total brain capacity observed in fossils from different levels in the Pleistocene is a result of selection for increasing cultural capacity.

Aside from the complicating nature of the role of culture in hominid evolution, there are a number of problems relating to an analysis of dental evolution. One of these is that we must be aware of the possibility that the characteristics under consideration may not be directly selected for, but may be part of some major complex that is important to evolution. The features of the dentition considered in this paper might be nothing more than minor parts of the total facial complex (Osborne, 1967). Another way of putting this is to say that perhaps a major gene complex determines facial size and that the size of teeth and molar cusp variations are due to secondary pleiotropic effects. Selection for major aspects of the face such as overall size, shape of the nasal opening, or a variety of other possible factors might be the guiding force in determining the changes in tooth size and configuration noted in the fossil record. They might have been carried along by evolution for major features of facial structure. If this is the case, we will never be able to answer our questions by looking at the teeth themselves, but should turn our attention to the face.

Recent research (Greene, 1967) indicates that many features of the dentition show high degrees of genetic independence, while other features are complexly related. However, if evolution has operated through natural selection directly upon the dental characteristics under consideration, one would expect to see fairly long-term trends of change in the fossil record since natural selection is the only mechanism that produces orientation in the evolutionary process. As will be shown, both tooth size reduction and cusp simplification show long-term trends. For this reason, it is believed that these are not secondary pleiotropic changes, but are the result of direct selection for these reductions.

Another problem in analyzing dental evolution in terms of selection is that many investigations find it difficult to assume that what seem to be minor differences in tooth size and morphology could possibly lead to differential survival and reproduction (Osborne, 1967). They also assume that even if these factors could lead to differential survival, the morphological variations are usually worn away by reproductive age due to the extreme dental attrition common to most Pleistocene hominid groups.

In answer to the above objections, in some nonhominid mammalian groups paleontologists have demonstrated through careful study of variation in different age groups in the same species—in particular, Pleistocene bear populations—that selection for tooth size and morphology was operative. It has also been noted that 70% of the mortality in mammalian groups occurs before cusp variation is worn away (Kurten, 1967). This mortality might be related to selection for variations in dental morphology. It is thought that the rest of this paper will indicate factors of differential survival relating to differences in size and morphology of hominid teeth.

A number of authors have documented the fact that tooth dimensions have decreased in size from populations in Villafranchian (*Australopithecus* and *Paranthropus*), through Middle Pleistocene populations (*Homo erectus*), to Upper Pleistocene populations (Neanderthal and modern man) (Brace, 1967; Dahlberg, 1963). If this sequence represents an evolving lineage, as many anthropologists believe, then there is reason to suspect that the consistent size change through time is due to selection.

Weidenreich (1947) explained this reduction in the size of teeth and the loss of cusp complexity as a secondary result of the expansion of the brain. As the brain case increased in size, he postulated that jaw size and consequently the size of the teeth had to decrease because of growth relationships between parts of the skull. As teeth became smaller, they could accommodate fewer cusps leading to a reduction in molar crown complexity. This is an argument dependent upon the total skull being the evolving unit—each part somehow being functionally related to the other parts.

Unfortunately, because Weidenreich's argument is so simple and therefore appealing, there is evidence that indicates jaw size, tooth size, and skull size are not correlated to the degree necessary for this argument (Abbie, 1947). Within living *Homo sapiens,* and most likely in past hominid groups, large brains and skulls are not necessarily found along with large teeth and jaws. Consequently, we must turn to a consideration of reductions in the dentition in terms of the teeth themselves.

It is reasonable to assume that large teeth are

advantageous in situations of intensive dental attrition. Many of the largest-toothed Recent populations such as Australian aborigines exist under conditions of severe dental wear. Selection favored even larger teeth in early Pleistocene populations such as the Australopithecus group. These populations had simple stone tools to cope with the environment to a limited degree, but were still probably very dependent upon their teeth for chewing and tearing food and other substances. As culture increased in complexity throughout the Pleistocene, tools took over more and more of the functions of the dentition. Under these conditions, selection for large teeth and jaws was relaxed (Dahlberg, 1963; Brace and Montagu, 1965).

Given such a situation, it is difficult to explain the reductions in non-Lamarckian ways. Or to put it another way, why would large teeth and jaws be disadvantageous to modern man? It is difficult to think of an explanation based upon selection for this situation. Large-toothed individuals would have an excess of dental material, more than enough for an average lifetime of modern attrition.

Brace (1963; Brace and Montagu, 1965) offers a theoretical explanation in terms of his "Probable Mutation Effect" which is a revival of some of Wright's ideas about the effect of mutations under conditions of relaxed selective pressure along with the incorporation of new data about the structure of DNA derived from recent biochemical studies. He argues that if selective pressures for complex stuctures such as large teeth and jaws are relaxed, then due to the complex series of genetic and developmental events that have occurred to produce such structures, random mutations will tend to disrupt the final result leading eventually to simplification. Complex structures dependent upon complex gene action can only be maintained in the face of his postulated effect on mutations by strong positive selective pressures. As selection for big jaws and teeth was removed by the substitution of cultural ways of softening food and rending and tearing substances, Brace feels that the "Probable Mutation Effect" led to a reduction in size and structure of the dentition.

Even though Brace's formulations have met with criticism, it should be pointed out as one critic (Holloway, 1967) has, that it is a hypothetical attempt to explain a reduction in structure in terms of established principles. Explaining such reductions is a problem that has to be solved when dealing with the buffering effect of man's cultural environment. There are few good alternatives to Brace's explanation. One could resort to explanation in terms of pleiotropic effect, but as has already been indicated, this seems to be insufficient.

One reasonable alternative to the "Probable Mutation Effect" is as follows. The survival of an individual in a deme is dependent upon all of its characteristics (the total organism). Selection operates to favor that combination of total characteristics which is most efficient in a particular environment (Campbell, 1966). The maintenance of complex structures such as large and morphologically intricate teeth requires the expenditure of a certain amount of energy. When selective pressure is removed for these structures, those individuals that retain them will be at a disadvantage in terms of total organism energy utilization. Any mutations which would lead to a reduction in structure would be selected for in this situation, since they would ultimately lead to a conservation of organism energy. This explanation, like Brace's, is an extension of accepted theory, but it has the advantage of substituting a positive selective pressure for increasing efficiency in place of the accumulation of random mutations.

Both the random mutation and the organism efficiency theories might be criticized by reference to the relatively short time period (Pleistocene) that was available for the documented evolutionary changes in size and complexity of teeth. Both theories rely upon very gradual rates of change and it might seem improbable that they can account for the observed changes that occurred in a relatively short time. In answer to this possible criticism, it should be noted that while the changes seem great within the hominid line, they are, in absolute terms and using the Primate Order as a standard, not so great. All hominid dentitions, including the various varieties of Australopithecus, are more similar to one another than they are to any of the pongid dentitions (Kustaloglu, 1961). The reductions observed in the hominid line, while very important to an understanding of Pleistocene evolution, are in terms of macroevolutionary perspective relatively slight.

So far we have discussed decreases in size and structures as related phenomena. An examination of the changes in the structure of hominid lower molar teeth during the Pleistocene will clarify this relationship and perhaps add further insight into the responsible selective mechanisms. Various dental anthropologists and paleontologists (Dahlberg, 1945; Hellman, 1928) felt, a number of years ago, that the evolution of hominid lower molars followed a definite pattern. The earliest dentitions were thought to be characterized by a high frequency of the dryopithecus pattern, five cusps arranged in a Y pattern. As dental evolution progressed, there was a reduction in this basic pattern with an increase in four cusped teeth and a change to a cruciform pattern. They argued that the first lower molar was most stable and should retain a higher frequency of the dryopithecus pattern than the second or third molar. Fossil evidence basically supports this sequence (Kustaloglu, 1961; Broom and Robinson, 1952; Weidenreich, 1937). Australopithecus fossils have the highest frequency of the dryopithecine pattern, *Homo erectus* shows a slight reduction in number of cusps and a change toward the cruciform pattern, while Neanderthal and modern populations show extreme variation away from the dryopithecine pattern. Many modern man populations show very high frequencies of the four cusped cruciform pattern (Greene, 1967).

As well as having a high frequency of the dryopithecine pattern, the Australopithecus group, in addition, has a high frequency of a sixth supernumerary cusp. None of the other fossil or modern populations shows it to such levels. It would appear that the greatest reduction in morphological complexity is between Australopithecus and *Homo erectus.* This transition also produced the greatest reduction in tooth size (Brace, 1967).

These changes in cusp morphology can be related to the decrease in tooth size. As cultural devices removed selective pressures for large teeth, evolution favored a decrease in tooth size as already outlined. One very rapid way of reducing tooth size is by the removal of cusps since tooth size and cusp number are significantly related (Garn et al., 1966). The trend towards smaller teeth would favor mutations leading to a loss of cusps.

The greatest change, that between Australopithecus and *Homo erectus,* is probably related to the introduction of the control of fire that is documented archaeologically by Middle Pleistocene times. The cooking and subsequent softening of food might very well have removed selective pressures for large teeth and then selection for organism efficiency would have produced the reductions. The continuing reductions through Neanderthal and up to modern man are probably the result of increasing cultural complexity removing more and more selective pressure on the dentition and further operation of evolution toward reduction.

Toward the end of the Pleistocene, another event occurred that may have accelerated the trend toward a reduction in size and complexity of the lower molars. Around 10,000 years ago in the Mideast, man began to control the domestication of plants and animals. Correlated with the development and improvement of this Neolithic way of life is an increasing incidence of carious pathologies in the fossil record. The introduction of cariogenic carbohydrate-cooked foods in quantity in man's diet apparently led to an increase in caries incidence (Brothwell, 1963). Recent studies indicate that teeth with complex fissure patterns and five cusps have a higher incidence of lesions in a caries-producing environment than simpler teeth (Reenan, 1966; Armelagos, 1968). Those areas of the world, such as the Mideast and Europe, where today are found the smallest and simplest teeth (Dahlberg, 1963) have been exposed to the effects of the Neolithic Revolution for the longest time span (Braidwood, 1967). Hypothetically, it seems that selection for caries-resistant teeth, those with simpler morphology, accelerated the trend initiated by selection for organism efficiency toward a reduction of teeth in Europe and the Mideast.

There are some possible objections to this last hypothesis. For example, the dentitions of the Jarmo inhabitants, one of the earliest fully Neolithic sites in the Mideast, show the modern pattern of reduction in tooth size and cusp complexity (Dahlberg, 1960). In considering this data, it must be remembered that there are earlier cultural developments which are, in Braidwood's terminology, Incipient Neolithics (Braidwood, 1967). These represent that time when the Neolithic Revolution was beginning. The initial selective effect of caries in a Neolithic environment would have been felt in these Incipient Neolithic cultures. Unfortunately, we have little evidence as to the nature of the dentitions found in these cultures. There is some evidence that indicates that some of the Incipient Neolithic peoples associated in particular with the Natufian culture had larger teeth than the people at Jarmo (Braidwood, 1967), but little is known about the dental morphology and pathology of the Natufian peoples.

Another possible objection to the hypothesis relating caries to a reduction in morphology and size of teeth is that even if caries were instrumental in changing tooth morphology, its effect could not have operated over the short time span represented by the Neolithic in the Mideast. In answer to this, do we know what effect the first introduction of caries and concomitant oral infection might have had initially? The relatively minor effect of caries observed today upon differential mortality might be, in part, the result of care and prevention of further infection and also, in part, to the action of acquired genetic immunity. Those individuals who were constitutionally most susceptible to serious infection would have rapidly been eliminated from the populations under consideration. Those who were relatively immune would make a greater contribution to the genetic constitution of later generations. It is possible that selection under these circumstances would have been rapid.

In summary, this paper has considered the theoretical and empirical problems involved in an evolutionary analysis of hominid dentition during the Pleistocene epoch. The complicating nature of human cultural behavior upon the analysis has been presented. Any adequate theoretical formulation dealing with evolutionary trends in the dentition must take into account the buffering effects of man's culture. Theoretical formulations that consider what happens when positive selection for particular structures is removed must be expanded and refined. In this context, an alternative explanation for reductions in the size of teeth and complexity of molar patterns during the Pleistocene has been offered. This is an extension of established evolutionary principles and has been called selection for total organism efficiency.

Another effect of man's culture has been considered in connection with the possible result of the Neolithic upon caries incidence and perhaps differential mortality. If this example proves to be valid, it demonstrates how man has had to adapt to his cultural environment as well as to the natural environment during the Pleistocene.

References

Abbie, A. A. 1947. Headform and human evolution. *J. Anat.*, 81: 233-258.

Armelagos, G. L. 1968. The paleopathology of three archaeological populations from Sudanese Nubia. Doctoral Dissertation, University of Colorado.

Brace, C. L. 1963. Structural reduction in evolution. *Amer. Natur.*, 97: 39-49.

—— 1967. Environment, tooth form and size in the Pleistocene. *J. Dent. Res.*, 46, Part 1: 809-816.

Brace, C. L., and M. F. A. Montagu. 1965. *Man's Evolution.* Macmillan Co., New York.

Braidwood, R. J. 1967. *Prehistoric Men.* Scott, Foresman & Company, Glenview, Ill.

Broom, R., and J. T. Robinson, 1952. *Swartkrans Ape-Man.* Transvaal Museum, Pretoria.

Brothwell, D. R. 1963. *Digging Up Bones.* British Museum (Natural History).

Campbell, B. G. 1966. *Human Evolution.* Aldine Publishing Co., Chicago, Ill.

Dahlberg, A. A. 1945. The changing dentition of man. *J. Amer. Dent. Assoc.*, 32: 676-690.

—— 1960. The dentition of the first agriculturists. *Amer. J. Phys. Anthropol.*, 18: 243-256.

—— 1963. Dental evolution and culture. *Hum. Biol.*, 35: 237-249.

Garn, S. M., A. B. Lewis, A. A. Dahlberg, and R. S. Kerewsky, 1966. Interaction between relative molar size and relative number of cusps. *J. Dent. Res.,* 45: 1240.

Greene, D. L. 1967. Genetics, dentition and taxonomy. *U. Wyo. Publ. 33,* No. 2: 93-168.

Hellman, M. 1928. Racial characters in the human dentition. *Proc. Amer. Phil. Soc.,* 67: 157-174.

Holloway, R. L., Jr. 1967. Tools and teeth: some speculations regarding canine reduction. *Amer. Anthropol.,* 69: 63-67.

Kurten, B. 1967. Some quantitative approaches to dental microevolution. *J. Dent. Res.,* 46, Part 1: 817-828.

Kustaloglu, O. A. 1961. Australopithecus and Paranthropus dentitions. *S. W. J. Anthropol.,* 17: 226-237.

Lancaster, J. B. 1968. On the evolution of tool-using behavior. *Amer. Anthropol.,* 70: 56-66.

Osborne, R. H. 1967. Some genetic problems in interpreting the evolution of the human dentition. *J. Dent. Res.,* 46, Part 1: 945-948

Reenan, J. F. Van. 1966. Dental features of a low-caries primitive population. *J. Dent. Res.,* 45: 703-713.

Simpson, G. G. 1949. *The Meaning of Evolution.* Yale University Press, New Haven, Conn.

Weidenreich, F. 1937. The dentition of *Sinanthropus pekinensis. Palaeon. Sincia,* New Series D. No. 1.

—— 1947. The trend of human evolution. *Evolution,* 1: 221-236.

7

LATE MIDDLE PALEOLITHIC ADAPTATIONS AND THEIR POSSIBLE CONSEQUENCES

Sally R. Binford

In a recent paper (S. R. Binford, 1968), I proposed a model based on certain empirical generalizations drawn from the extant lithic and paleontological data of the early Würm of the Levant—a model which, it was hoped, could explain the distributions observed. Means were proposed for testing the adequacy of the sample on which the generalizations were made, although testing the model itself would involve a more complex and sophisticated series of tests.

What I propose to do in this paper can only be termed speculation; my justification for this rather dangerous game is my understanding of the purpose of this symposium—to explore in a free-wheeling fashion the implications of some current notions on human evolution. I will summarize briefly the substance of my earlier paper, and then explore some related problems dealing with the nature of the biological and

Reprinted from *Bioscience* 20: 280-83, 1970, with the permission of the publishers.

cultural changes from Neanderthal to fully modern man.

Anyone rash enough to engage in this game of speculation had best make explicit the assumptions and theoretical underpinnings of his argument; the following paragraphs are designed to do just that. In most general terms, the theoretical approach used here is the application of general systems theory to human evolution. The study of human evolution is the study of the development of human behavioral systems; and the human behavioral system is composed of two necessarily related subsystems: the biological and the cultural. Culture is defined in Leslie White's terms as man's extra-somatic means of adaptation (White, 1959)—all those means of coping with the external world that are learned and not genetically determined. Culture in this sense is predicated on the capacity to symbol, and fully human culture must be distinguished from the protoculture observed by Goodall and others in the behavior of the nonhuman primates. It is clear that culture has been the principal means of human adaptation for at least half a million years; it is culture and the consistent use of cultural means for solving problems of environmental differences that have allowed man to remain the highly generalized single species he is.

Man is viewed as one component in an ecosystem, and the nature of the linkages between the human species and the environment are complex. Like all other forms of life, man survives by capturing free energy from the environment and harnessing it for his own needs of nourishment, heat retention, and the like. It can be demonstrated that the history of the evolution of human cultural systems is the history of increasingly efficient means of capturing and harnessing energy. In so doing, man has brought into being a highly complex information system based on the use of symbols—language—and has developed many sophisticated means for extending the range of symbolic communication. Within this frame-work, evolutionary change is viewed as structural change in the matter/energy relations obtaining between the human species and its environment; such structural change can bring about new and more complex kinds of or-ganization both between the human species and its environment and among members of the human species themselves. The former kind of change occurs within the economic system, and the latter within the social system. At a higher level of analysis, both of these systems can be viewed as subsystems of the cultural system.

All this defining of subsystems and their interrelationships is intended as more than just a new and complicated verbiage; it is intended to convey the idea that culture is embedded in man's ecological relationships and cannot fruit-fully be dealt with, as is so often attempted in anthropology, only as a system of ideas or of kinship terms. Changes in cultural systems are *necessarily* related to changes in ecological relationships, and our task as paleoan-thropologists is to pinpoint those moments in time and space where such changing ecological relationships can be observed. Only then can we explain culture change without the distasteful necessity of postulating untestable propositions about territorial or other imperatives, or some innate, orthogenetic desire on the part of man to improve himself. The series of linkages involved in moving from a change in ecological relationships to specific, observable changes in archaeological assemblages is very complex, and it should be stressed here that simple-minded environmental determinism is to be sharply distinguished from the approach advocated here.

In the paper referred to above, my purpose

was to account for some of the variability noted by Howell (1957) among Neanderthal populations. Howell has divided the early Würm populations of Europe and the Near East into three groups: the Persistent Neanderthals of the Near East and eastern Europe, the Classic Neanderthals of western Europe, and the group that are thus far known only from the Levant, the Progressive Neanderthals. Howell went on to propose that the Progressive Neanderthals were a transitional population, on their way toward becoming anatomically modern man. The variability exhibited between the eastern and western groups during the glacial maxima of early Würm was accounted for by Howell by the presence of an isolating mechanism—a continental ice sheet across east-central Europe that restricted population movements and hence gene flow. Howell made a series of arguments that the Progressive Neanderthals of the Levant provided the principal (but not the exclusive) gene pool from which fully modern man descended. This formulation is generally, although by no means universally, accepted, and most human paleontologists today assign Neanderthal remains to our own genus and species, giving them the status of an historical race or subspecies. The purpose of this research has been to elucidate the nature of early Upper Pleistocene ecosystems in the Levant to try to account for the presence there of forms that appear to be transitional between Neanderthal and fully modern man.

The human paleontological and archeo-logical remains of the Near East, and espe-cially of the Levant, have occasioned a long, often bitter debate in the literature—the debate centering on the chronological relation-ship between the Mousterian and western Europe and the Near East (Bordes, 1955, 1960; Garrod, 1956). It is my opinion that while this question cannot be satisfactorily settled on the basis of the extant data, a new order of question asked of the same data can produce provocative results. The question being asked is: Do the archeological data from the late Mousterian of the Levant suggest a shift in adaptation—a change in the way in which man exploited the resources in his environ-ment—that might account for the kind of evolutionary change observed in the group of fossils classifed as Progressive Neanderthals? These fossils are known from Skhūl, a cave site in a valley south of present-day Haifa, from Qafzeh, a cave overlooking a mountain pass south of Nazareth, and most recently from a maxilla from Ksâr 'Akil, in a wadi near the coast of Lebanon.

Three Zones of the Levant

In order to gain a first understanding of patterns of prehistoric land use in the Levant, all known Mousterian sites were plotted on a large-scale contour map to determine if differences in land form or biome could be related to differences in archaeological deposits. The Levant is divided by most physical geographers into three district zones: the coastal plain, the mountains that rise just east of the coast, and the interior (Jordan) valley; each of these provinces has its typical plant and animal associations and climatic regime. Summarized very briefly, the coastal plain is well watered, with rains concentrated in the winter months, and the climatic regime is not unlike that of the coast of southern California today. The mountains serve as a break against which most of the winter rains are dumped, so that the western slopes are much better watered than are the eastern slopes. It is generally quite cool in the mountains during the winter months, with the upland meadows turning green with the arrival of the rain and drying out by May or June. The Jordan Valley, a deep trough that is 600 ft below sea level at Lake Tiberias and rapidly plunges deeper to the south, receives much more isolation and less rainfall than the other two areas. Plant and animal life is less rich and varied in this interior valley than it is on the coast or on the western slopes of the coastal mountains.

When the known Mousterian sites were plotted, some interesting differences with respect to these three zones could be noted:

Coastal Plain Sites

These are poorly known, perhaps as a function of the rising sea levels at the end of the Würm having drowned most of the Pleistocene plain. In present-day Lebanon, the coastal plain can scarcely be said to exist; in most places the mountains rise almost directly out of the sea. Those few sites that have been investigated both in Lebanon and in Israel appear to contain thin, discontinuous occupational horizons, with no single horizon of more than 20-30 cm in depth.

Jordan Valley Sites

Two main sub-areas have received archaeological attention: caves and shelters in Wadi Amud, near Lake Tiberias, and a series of caves and shelters in the southern Judean Hills, in valleys that drain eastward into the Jordan Valley. These sites have cultural deposits ranging from about 0.50-1.50 m in depth with a rather generalized fauna consisting of gazelle, fallow deer, wild cattle, pig, etc., with no indication of heavy reliance on any single species. Except for one site in the Judean Hills, none contains Upper Paleolithic deposits over-lying the Mousterian. The human remains recovered from two locations (Zuttiyeh and Amud Cave) are not of the Progressive type but appear to conform more to the Persistent form of Neanderthal.

Sites on the Western Slopes of the Coastal Mountains

These caves contain Mousterian deposits very much thicker than those in the other two zones, in some cases (Ksâr 'Akil and Tabūn) of over 20 m in depth. At two of these locations (Ksâr 'Akil and Skhūl,) in the terminal Mousterian deposits there has been noted a marked increase in frequencies of *Bos primigenius*—wild cattle. In the case of Skhūl, *Bos* make up 85% of the fauna. Three of these sites (Skhūl, Ksâr 'Akil, and Qafzeh) have yielded human remains which display characteristics intermediate between those of Neanderthal and fully modern man. Many of the sites in this zone also contain substantial Upper Paleolithic deposits overlying the Mousterian.

Climate

It should be stressed here that there is no evidence to suggest major climatic changes in the Levant between the Würm and the present; the proposed series of pluvials and interpluvials for this region has recently been seriously questioned and has been abandoned even by its former proponents. According to Butzer (1958) and others, there is some evidence to suggest a slight drying trend towards the end of early Würm, one which probably brought more marked seasonality of rainfall, resulting in the highly seasonal rainfall pattern observed today. Palynological indications are that the entire Levant was more heavily wooded than it is today, but it must be remembered that we are seeing the area today after 5000 years or more of grazing by sheep and goats.

Given the above data base, the following interpretation was proposed: Toward the end of early Würm, with its more highly seasonal rainfall pattern, seasonal movement of large herd animals, such as wild cattle and fallow deer, would have been intensified. Herd mammals generally have three kinds of feeding grounds: summer pasture, winter pasture, and the zones between these. In areas of highly seasonal rainfall and broken topography, the regular spring and fall migrations of herd mammals are well known. The adaptations of fully modern man during the second half of the Würm were based on the specialized hunting of migratory herd animals, with intensive exploitation of single species. The well-known Upper Paleolithic sites of southwestern France are situated in or above valleys that apparently served as migration routes for reindeer herds; the eastern Gravettian mammoth hunters also appear to have engaged in the seasonal harvesting of huge numbers of beasts along major waterways.

I have suggested that this Upper Paleolithic way of life can be seen in the terminal Mousterian of the Levant in those sites that occur in the wadis on the western slopes of the coastal mountains where the frequencies of wild cattle show an enormous increase. This interpretation is supported by the fact that many early Upper Paleolithic sites in the Levant display the same distribution as do these terminal Mousterian sites. Earlier Mousterian adaptations in the same area appear to have been based on the hunting of single animals, or small numbers of animals, with no heavy reliance on any single species. The organizational base for the proposed shift in hunting pattern must be considered also.

Social Hunting

Bernard Campbell (1966) has presented us with an elegant series of arguments on social hunting in the early Middle Pleistocene; man for some hundreds of thousands of years gained his livelihood by the cooperation of small groups of men hunting together and sharing the results of their combined efforts. This kind of hunting can be seen in its modern form in the Marshalls' film "The Hunters." The kind of hunting pattern I wish to contrast with this is the harvesting of what Birdsell (1953) has termed unearned resources—that is, forms that pass through the environment but gain most of their energy (food) from other areas. The herds of wild cattle whose remains appear in such high frequencies in the terminal Mousterian deposits of Ksâr 'Akil and Skhūl are an excellent example of an unearned resource since the valleys in which these sites are situated served as migration routes from summer to winter grazing grounds.

If man were to benefit from large quantities of beef on the hoof through known valleys at predictable times of the year, a much larger labor would have been required than in the case where a few men stalk a single animal. In ethnographically known societies such labor forces are obtained through ties of kinship. What I am suggesting is that while his hunting pattern conformed to the small-group-hunting-single-animal pattern, man's largest social unit need only have been the rather small exogamous local band. However, when a newer and more efficient means of exploiting game resources in the environment was developed, one that required much larger groups of cooperating males, the units between which mating occurred increased both in number and in size. Such a change in mating pattern would have substantially increased rates of gene flow, one of the conditions that can produce evolutionary change.

All of the above points were made in greater detail (and are certainly better documented) in my earlier paper, and perhaps it might be circumspect to warn the reader that what follows must be labeled pure speculation.

One of the imponderables of prehistory over which much ink has been spilled is the question of why the initial appearance of anatomically modern man appears to coincide with widespread use of indirect percussion and lithic industries with very high frequencies of punch-blades. If there were rather sizable groups, assembling twice a year to take advantage of large numbers of animals passing through limited areas, it would seem reasonable to expect that man prepared for several weeks of intensive hunting activity by making and stockpiling tools before they were actually needed. In the terminal Mousterian of the Levant, and even in the early Upper Paleolithic of the area, there was widespread use of the Levallois technique. Anyone who has seen tools made by this technique knows that it is a wasteful one, in the sense that the number of finished implements per unit weight of flint is low, especially if one desires rather uniformly shaped implements such as points for thrusting spears. With a punch-blade technology, however, many more standardized tools per unit weight of flint can be produced. I would like to suggest that the change from Levallois technique to punch-blade technique appeared as an adaptive response to the need for large numbers of implements produced in a limited area, the punch-blade technique being less likely to exhaust the supply of good-sized flint nodules in any given part of a valley. It is interesting to note that in many cases, both in western Europe and in the Near East, the shift from Middle to Upper Paleolithic is characterized first by changes in frequencies of tool forms and only later by the appearance of new techniques for their manufacture. It is proposed here that a major change in hunting pattern occurred *within the terminal Mousterian itself*, and that many of the formal and technological changes we can observe between the Middle and Upper Paleolithic occurred as adaptive responses to this major ecological change.

Changes in Man

What of the changes in the men themselves? What explanation can we offer for the differences between Neanderthal and fully modern man? The changes are limited almost exclusively to the skull: an elevation of the cranial vault, a relative shortening of the face, and an enlargement of the frontal area. If man was, for the first time, having to cope with large numbers of his fellow men, and if the continuance of good hunting depended on the maintenance of good social relations, then controlling aggression would be highly adaptive. So far as we can tell, the changes in skull structure in the frontal area involve those parts of the brain that are concerned with rational control of behavior. Cortical control of aggression can be seen as the outcome of the change in hunting pattern outlined above. In a lecture some 10 years ago, Washburn observed that all domesticated animals (cats, dogs, horses, cattle, etc.) have relatively shorter faces than their wild cousins; perhaps it is not too far-fetched to point out that the domestication of man had the same consequences.

Many ecologists, among whom Deevey (1968) has been very articulate, have raised rather basic questions about the validity of the frequent assertion by prehistorians that human populations in the past have been limited in size by the scarcity of food. Birdsell (1968) and others have suggested that the mobility imposed upon hunters who employ techniques requiring the pursuit of game resources has been the principal limiting factor in that women who must move their household every season have few compunctions about practicing birth control in the form of lactation taboos, abortion, and infanticide to avoid having to carry numbers of small children with them. The very rapid radiation of fully modern man to all parts of the world and the rate of population growth that this implies are seen here not as the direct consequence of a more abundant food supply, but as the result of the increased sedentism permitted by knowing where and when large supplies of food would be available and of having the means to exploit them. Such sedentism is documented as early as 29,000 B.C. at Dolni Vestonice and many other Upper Paleolithic sites.

Sedentism in the context of the regular exploitation of migratory herd mammals must also be predicated upon some means of gaining what L. R. Binford (1968) has called time utility from the resources exploited. If the principal protein source in the diet is captured twice a year, then both in the terminal Mousterian and throughout the Upper Paleolithic man must have developed means for storing the fruits of his biennial harvest—smoking or drying meat—and the archaeological discovery of these means is still a major task before prehistorians.

In summary, I have attempted to point out some of the possible causal linkages between changes in archaeological and human paleontological remains documented for the transition from Middle to Upper Paleolithic. The evolutionary changes noted are seen as the result of a complex of positive feedback relations between the cultural and biological subsystems; these changes are, in turn, explained by changes in man's relationship to his environment, both natural and social.

References

Binford, L. R. 1968. Post-Pleistocene adaptations. In: *New Perspectives in Archeology*, S. R. Binford and L. R. Binford (eds.). Aldine Publishing Co., Chicago, p. 318-341.

Binford, S. R. 1968. Early Upper Pleistocene adaptations in the Levant. *Amer. Anthropol.*, 70: 707-717.

Birdsell, J. B. 1953. Some environmental and cultural factors influencing the structuring of Australian Aboriginal populations. *Amer. Nat.* (Supp.; May-June) 87 (834); 171-207.

—— 1968. Some predictions for the Pleistocene based upon equilibrium systems among recent hunter-gatherers. In: *Man the Hunter*, R. B. Lee and I. DeVore (eds.). Aldine Publishing Co., Chicago, p. 229-240.

Bordes, F. H. 1955. Le paléolithique inférieur et moyen de Jabrud (Syrie) et la question du pré-Aurignacien. *l'Anthropol.*, 59 (5-6); 486-507.

—— 1960. Le pré-Aurignacien de Yabroud (Syrie) et son incidence sur la chronologie quaternaire du Moyen-Orient. *Bull. Res. Coun. Israel*, 9 (2-3): 91-103.

Butzer, K. B. 1958. Quaternary stratigraphy and climate in the Near East. *Bonner Geo. Abhand.* 24.

Campbell, B. G. 1966. *Human Evolution.* Aldine Publishing Co., Chicago.

Deevey, E. S. 1968. Pleistocene family planning: A discussion. In: *Man the Hunter*, R. B. Lee and I. DeVore (eds.). Aldine Publishing Co., Chicago, p. 248-9.

Garrod, D. A. E. 1956. Acheuléo-Jabroudien et pré-Aurignacien' de la grotte de Taboun (Mont Carmel): étude stratigraphique et chronologique. *Quaternaria*, 3: 39-59.

Howell, F. C. 1957. The evolutionary significance of variation and varieties of 'Neanderthal' man. *Quart. Rev. Biol.*, 32: 330-347.

White, L. A. 1959. *The Evolution of Culture.* McGraw-Hill Book Co., New York.

8

ECOLOGY OF THE NORTH AMERICAN PALEO-INDIAN

James J. Hester

Environmental studies carried out in conjunction with archaeological research on early sites was initiated by Howard (1935) at the Clovis site. At Clovis, the artifact- and fossil-bearing beds were studied as to sedimentary history, the nature of the associated vertebrate and invertebrate faunas, and the diatom flora. From these data the nature of the past environments of the site were inferred. Following this pioneer work, environmental studies of early man sites lapsed to some degree until the excavation of the Haco site in southern Arizona (Haury et al., 1953). Since that date, archaeologists have become increasingly aware of the wealth of information to be obtained from environmental research. Today, such interdisciplinary studies are typical of the research on Paleo-Indian sites.

Simultaneously, we have seen the development of full-scale studies of the past environments of specific regions of North America. Beginning with Sears' pioneering, the work has focused on bog sediments utilizing the preserved fossil pollen as a basis from which to infer the nature of past vegetation communities. From the composition of these communities, the accompanying temperature and precipitation have been inferred. Work in this field has provided detailed reconstructions for a few regions: the Southwest, Great Lakes, New England, the prairie Midwest, the Appalachians, Pacific Northwest, and the High Plains of West Texas (Wright and Frey, 1965; Cushing and Wright, 1967; Wendorf et al., 1961).

These regional reconstructions are continually being revised with new pollen and

Reprinted from *Bioscience* 20: 213-17, 1970, with the permission of the publishers.

radiocarbon data. In addition, there are disagreements as to the meaning of the data recovered. For example, Cushing (1967) states that the glacial and pollen evidence from Minnesota dated 10,000 to 15,000 years ago fail to support the hypothesis that vegetal succession was closely coordinated with phases of glacial activity. On the other hand, Ogden (1967) found that conifers in Western Ohio were replaced by deciduous forest just after 10,600 B.P. He states this change is too great and the time too short to permit gradual replacement. Therefore he infers that a dramatic and unique change in temperature and precipitation occurred about 10,000 years ago, a change which must have been reflected in glacial movements. In summary, current environmental studies suggest that comprehensive regional reconstructions of the late glacial-postglacial environments are somewhat premature. Thus, we will use the reconstructions available in our discussion of early man's environmental adaptation with full knowledge that they are in a constant state of change.

The Problem

Within the context of the historical development of the environmental studies condensed above, the major ecological problems of the North American Paleo-Indian are seen as follows:

1. The time and place of the peopling of North America.

2. The human response to the presence of continental glaciers.

3. Specific economic adaptations to the regional environments within North America.

4. Man's influence on components of these environments, especially the magafauna that became extinct within the time period under discussion.

5. The transition to an Archaic way of life with its emphasis on food collecting and small animal hunting.

These problems are examined in light of the following basic premises:

1. The earliest migrants to North America were of *Homo sapiens* type.

2. The continent at the time provided a series of empty ecological niches which man occupied.

3. With no competitors to impede him, man spread rapidly throughout most of the continent.

4. The early migrants brought with them a big-game hunting economy of Upper Paleolithic type.

5. The continent was well supplied with game suitable for exploitation by such an economy.

6. The time period pertinent to our study dates between 12,000 and 7500 years before present. These dates are selected on the basis of the compilations of radiocarbon dates by Haynes (1964, 1967a) which clearly indicate that associations of cultural materials with early C-14 dated materials cannot be established prior to 12,000 years before present. Some earlier sites may well exist, such as the Tlapacoya Site in Mexico (Haynes, 1967b). However, for purposes of the following discussion, I wish to limit our inquiries to the period for which the presence of early man in North America is an undisputed fact. After 7500 years B.P., changes in the economy signal the transition to the next major stage, the Archaic.

The Basic Ecological Pattern

The earliest Paleo-Indian cultural pattern defined in North America, the Clovis Culture, has strong affinities with a generalized Upper Paleolithic industry of the Old World (Hester, 1966). It is assumed that the bearers of this tradition migrated into Siberia following herds of mammoths and other late Pleistocene mammals, bringing with them a generalized Levalloisi-Mousterian unifacial stone industry and a simple bone-working technology. As they preyed upon the mammoths, these early peoples probably followed a life of restricted wandering in response to the movements of the mammoth herds. Analysis of stomach contents of mammoths preserved in Siberia (Wright, 1903; Farrand, 1961) indicates that these mammoths were subsisting on a diet of young shoots and cones of fir, pine, birch, and willow trees as well as a variety of boreal meadow and tundra herbs, mosses, and grasses. Presumably, the mammoth followed this environmental zone from Siberia through Alaska and Canada into the northern United States. Hunters following such game herds would have thus occupied the North American continent.

It has been assumed by researchers that this big-game hunting economy, typified by numerous outstanding sites in the Great Plains such as Clovis, Dent, and Lindenmeier, represented the basic environmental adaptation of the Paleo-Indians. For this reason we will quote from a description of this economy.

The Paleo-Indian cultural tradition in the Great Plains

was adapted to the utilization and exploitation of a savanna grassland with abundant permanent water in small ponds and streams. . . . The stream valleys sheltered galleries of juniper and oak in the valleys and along the bottoms. On this savanna landscape moved large herds of giant bison and smaller groups of other Pleistocene forms now extinct (Wendorf and Hester, 1962).

The correlation between type of site and site situation is striking . . . campsites tend to occur on ridges, dunes, or hills which overlook either a stream channel or a pond at a distance of several hundred yards to a mile. Kill sites tend to occur either at the edge of former ponds or stream channels (Wendorf and Hester, 1962).

Attributes of a campsite include hearths, discarded food bones, chipping debris, and a full chipped and flaked tool complex. . . . The food bones are normally disarticulated and are occasionally split and charred. Seeds, grinding stones, and storage or cooking pits are rarely present. Activities identified with campsites include food preparation, working of hides, and tool manufacture. The high proportion of point bases over point tips, a common attribute of campsite lithic collections, is suggestive of repair of weapons.

Kill sites are characterized by animal skeletons, frequently in high numbers, with the associated projectile points utilized to kill them plus a limited number of chipped and flaked butchering tools. Often preferred portions of the animals are missing. These body parts, presumably were cut out and taken back to nearby campsites, though hearths are occasionally present indicating that some of the kill was consumed or smoked on the spot (Wendorf and Hester, 1962).

One basic hunting pattern, reconstructed as follows, represents a majority of all the sites surveyed. The campsite was situated so that animals in the vicinity could be observed as they came for water. Once observed, the animals were stalked and killed as they were drinking in a stream or pond. The number of animals killed by this technique ranged from one to about thirty. Both mammoth and bison were hunted by this method.

A second pattern is the stampede . . . the animals in this case being bison which were driven into an arroyo, stream or over a cliff, where many of the animals were crushed or drowned. The number of animals killed by this technique occasionally was as high as several hundred. . . .

The location of the projectile points in the carcasses indicates an identical method of killing for both mammoth and bison. The spears were aimed at the thoracic region with the intent to penetrate the heart, spinal cord or other vital parts. . . .

The absence of an emphasis on the hunting of horses and the absence of mammoth traps suggest that we are studying hunting techniques specifically adapted to New World conditions, rather than techniques transferred from an Old World tradition (Wendorf and Hester, 1962).

A detailed pattern of bison butchering is known from the Olsen-Chubbock site in Colorado (*Ibid*) but is too lengthy to be repeated here.

A study of sites by time period for the Llano Estacado (Texas and New Mexico) revealed 13 Clovis components, 29 Folsom components, and 39 of the Parallel Flaked or Plano horizon. Many of these were multi-component sites suggesting a continuance of the same land use pattern through several thousand years. The site data also imply a steady population increase through time.

Analysis of stone types utilized for tool manufacture at Blackwater Draw, N.M., and the location of the stone quarries has led me to infer that the Paleo-Indian social group— probably a small band or extended kin group— wandered over an area some 100 to 200 miles in diameter. According to Haynes (1967a), the time period as established by C-14 for the earliest occupation in the Plains is between 12,650 ± 250 and 11,630 ± 400 B.P. However, he believes the main Clovis occupation to data ca. 11,200 B.P.

It seems pertinent here to examine the data from other regions to determine how generally or specifically the Plains reconstruction presented above may be applied to these other regions.

The Northeastern United States

The vegetation of the late glacial period from New England to Minnesota may be summarized from the writings of Davis (1967), Watts (1967), and Ogden (1967).

According to their interpretations, the succession of vegetal communities in a north-south transect south of the ice margin consisted of a tundra zone (although evidence for a continuous tundra zone is absent in the Great Lakes region), a zone of open spruce woodland or fir-spruce forest, a mixed forest zone of pine, oak, and elm, and finally a deciduous forest. Through time in association with deglaciation in the period 12,000 to 10,000 years ago, these zones were shifting northwards with the result that the vegetal communities requiring cool and moist conditions were being replaced by communities with warmer and drier requirements. Throughout this interval of deglaciation the trend of replacement shows no evidence of reversal.

Large mammals inhabiting these environments included the musk-ox, mammoth, mastodon, bison, *Cervalces*—the extinct moose *Castoroides*—the giant beaver, and *Platygonus* and *Mylohyus*—extinct peccaries. Also of possible significance to human existence at this time were the marine mammals in the Great Lakes which included whales, walrus, and seals (Griffin, 1965).

The archaeological evidence from the northeastern United States consists of frequent but isolated surface finds of fluted points and rare occurrences of concentrated campsite debris such as that at Shoop, Pennsylvania; Debert, Nova Scotia; and Bull Brook, Massachusetts. The artifactual assemblages are quite similar to those known from fluted point sites in the west such as Clovis and Lindenmeier (Hester, 1966; Byers, 1966). On the basis of these similarities both Byers and I have reached the conclusion that these eastern and western fluted points assemblages are closely related in a cultural sense and also in time. The latter is substantiated by radiocarbon dates. If these artifactual assemblages are similar, can we also assume the economies were similar? Faunal associations at the campsites in the northeast are totally lacking. Bone preservation is poor in these sites with the result that archaeologists have postulated big-game hunting of whatever animals were known to have been in the vicinity. In the case of the Debert site, these were caribou, and in the Great Lakes region, the mastodon. Although the distribution of fluted points and fossil mastodons in Michigan is essentially identical (Martin, 1967), we lack the kind of conclusive killsite associations so typical of the Plains. To my knowledge only one mastodon, currently being studied in Michigan, shows evidence of having been killed and butchered. On the other hand, remains of hundreds of mastodons have been found without any evidence of man,

According to recent opinions, the mastodon and other members of the late glacial megafauna seem to have become extinct during this interval (12,000-10,000 B.P.) Martin (1968) has plotted the northern distribution limits of species of this fauna and found it to lie south of the Valders ice margin. Therefore, he argues that if these species survived any later than 10,000 B.P., they would have undoubtedly moved north of this line.

McMillan[1] has reviewed the evidence for mastodons in association with Archaic materials and in every case has found the evidence to be suspect. He concludes that the mastodon became extinct prior to the advent of Archaic culture ca. 8000-8500 B.P. While all of this circumstantial evidence is impressive, that the extinction of the mastodon and other species was quite likely man's responsibility (Martin, 1967), the cultural evidence for "overkill" is lacking. We are left rather unpleasantly with Griffin's "tongue in cheek" hypothesis (1965) that man used "magic" as his primary weapon.

[1] McMillan, R. B., 1968. *The relationship of man to the mastodon in eastern North America.* Unpublished manuscript.

Evidence documenting man's disturbance of the flora has not yet been systematically collected.

Some authors (Mason, 1962; Griffin, 1965) have suggested that the Paleo-Indians arrived in the eastern United States some 12,000-15,000 years ago. Mason (1962) has even hypothesized that owing to the great numbers and widespread distribution of fluted points in the East, the Paleo-Indian culture originated there and spread to the West. There is currently no radiocarbon evidence to support these views of eastern primacy. The only securely dated site is that at Debert, Nova Scotia, with 13 dates from the archaeological horizon. The dates cluster closely and average 8635 ± 47 B.C. or 10,585 ± 47 B.P. (Stuckenrath, 1966), thus indicating an occupation some 600 to 1000 years later than established occupation in the Great Plains.

Evidence from Debert indicates that the local environment was quite cold. Borns (1966) states "by the time of the occupation of the Debert site all of the continental ice had dissipated from northern Nova Scotia, and that a Valders-age ice cap, the margin of which was probably less than 60 miles to the southwest, occupied the South Mountain area, while a snow cover more extensive and persistent than presently exists covered the Cobequid Mountains approximately 5 miles to the north." Borns (1966) goes on to postulate that the environment probably supported permafrost, thus implying arctic or subarctic temperatures. Of course, areas in the Northeast farther removed from the glacial margin would have featured a more moderate climate.

The Southeastern United States

The environment of the southeastern United States has been reconstructed by Whitehead (1965). Late glacial (15,000-10,000 B.P.) vegetation in the Chesapeake Bay and southeastern North Carolina regions is described as a spruce, fir, pine, and birch forest, shifting to a pine dominance with spruce, birch, and alder, with oak and hickory becoming more important. The postglacial environment (10,000 B.P.-Present) featured a gradual transformation of the "northern hardwood" forest type into a forest dominated by oak, hickory, sweet gum, and many other deciduous forest species which reached a maximum about 7000 years ago.

The archaeological sites are similar to those in the northeastern United States; isolated finds of fluted points are common and concentrations of occupational debris are rare. Associations with extinct fauna do not occur in these sites. The fluted points fall into a number of categories based on typological considerations. Williams and Stoltman (1965) discuss the form and chronological position of these variants (Redstone, Cumberland, Quad, Suwanee, and Dalton points) but admit that chronological controls are as yet inadequate.

The evidence for the economy practiced is also scanty. Willams and Stoltman (1965) hypothesize that the fluted point distribution is understandable if we assume that their makers roved the countryside hunting big game, primarily mastodon. They then "prove" their hypothesis by plotting the occurrence of mastodon remains and fluted points (Williams and Stoltman, 1965). Their survey does indicate regional concentrations of both mastodons and fluted points. Favored areas include the Appalachian chain, southeastern Virginia, western Kentucky and Tennessee, and north central Florida. However, the evidence is again circumstantial and does not really "prove" that the Paleo-Indians subsisted by big-game hunting.

Dates of this occupation are equivocal. The earliest radiocarbon dates accepted by Haynes (1967a), those from Modoc Roch Shelter, Illinois; Graham Cave, Missouri; Stanfield-Worley Rockshelter, Alabama; and Russell Cave, Alabama, all fall in the interval between 9000 and 10,000 B.P. These dates primarily pertain to Archaic materials and thus only indicate a possible terminal date for the Paleo-Indian occupation.

One item of significance is that by 9000-10,000 B.P. or slightly earlier there are several variants of fluted points within the Southeast, with differing geographic distributions. This fact suggests that specific regional adaptations reflected in the cultural inventory had already occurred.

The Great Basin

Man's appearance in the Great Basin was first evidenced 10,000-11,000 years ago in Danger Cave, Utah; Leonard Rockshelter, Fishbone Cave, Guano Cave, and Tule Springs, Nevada; Fort Rock Cave, Oregon; and Naco and Lehner, Arizona (Baumhoff and Heizer, 1965). These sites included both campsites and killsites. What is most distinctive, with the exception of the Naco and Lehner sites, is the general absence of bones of extinct fauna in the levels containing artifacts. Radiocarbon dates indicate the Great Basin to have been initially occupied by man between 10,000 and 11,000 years ago or slightly earlier. Dates from Tule Springs suggest the late glacial megafauna became extinct there by 11,500 B.P. (Haynes, 1967c). Abundant small bones and remains of plants indicate that food collecting and hunting was the primary economy. Quite likely seasonal wandering was the residence pattern as the inhabitants moved from one harvest to another.

The full glacial climate ca. 20,000 B.P. resulted in a biotic zone depression of 900-1200 m, but the change to a warm-dry postglacial grass and sagebrush environment seems to have occurred rather rapidly around 12,000 B.P. (Martin and Mehringer 1965 p. 451). As a result of this early shift to postglacial climate, Mehringer (1967) states that the environment of the Southwest, inhabited by mammoths and other large herbivores, was little different from that of today. Martin and Mehringer also find little evidence in the pollen record for late glacial oscillations of the type recorded in the northeastern United States and the High Plains of West Texas.

Shortly after 11,000 P.B., we may conclude that the Paleo-Indians of the Great Basin gave up the hunting of big game for a food-collecting economy featuring widespread use of grinding stones.

The West Coast

According to Heigham (1965), the oldest sites in the West are difficult to find. Many provide nothing datable and the cultural inventory is crude and limited. It is believed that the coast was settled from the inland prior to 8000 B.P. by big-game hunters who had no interest in the food resources of the sea. The primary culture material identified is the San Dieguito complex consisting of leaf-shaped points, cutting and scraping tools, and a few grinding stones. The primary extinct animal species thought to have been man's prey is the dwarf mammoth, known from Santa Rosa Island. It appears that men may have hunted these animals between 9500 and 12,500 B.P. After 7500 B.P., earlier peoples were succeeded by the La Jolla culture—a seed-grinding, small-game hunting, shellfish-gathering culture. To my knowledge there is no reconstruction of the environment. The paper by Adam (1967) refers to the environment of the Sierra, an area from which early archaeological materials are lacking.

The Columbia Plateau

Three major sites in the plateau region possess cultural and environmental materials associated with radiocarbon dates. The Five Mile Rapids site at the Dalles, Oregon, has a date of 9785 ± 220 B.P. from the lowest level. The economy was of riverine type, featuring salmon fishing and bird and mammal hunting. No extinct species occur. The artifactual complex, termed the Old Cordilleran tradition, featured leaf-shaped bipoints, bolas, burins, and heavy cobble choppers. One date associated with a point of this tradition from Wilson Butte Cave in Idaho has the surprising antiquity of 14,500 ± 500 B.P.

A similar site located on the Fraser River in British Columbia, the Yale site, has been dated 8150 ± 300 and 900 ± 150 B.P.

The environment east of the Cascades, as reconstructed by Heusser (1965), included a lodgepole pine parkland during the late glacial, succeeded by grasses, chenopods, and composites. This transition occurred about 8000 B.P. and undoubtedly was influential in the shift to a greater reliance on fishing recorded in the later archaeological levels.

Other Areas

Evidence from other areas in North America is little known; hence, only the most outstanding examples will be cited.

The plains region of southern Canada featured a bison-hunting economy with artifacts of the Plano horizon, probably dating 7000-8000 B.P. (Wormington and Forbis, 1965). Almost certainly this evidence records a late northward expansion of the economy developed in the Central Plains region.

One site, Onion Portage (currently being investigated) in northern Alaska, is of interest because of the early radiocarbon dates ranging from 8100 to 7180 B.P. In general, sites from Alaska have failed to suggest great antiquity and the extinct faunal remains have not had associated cultural materials.

Several sites in Mexico are of importance. The sites at Valsequillo and Talpacoya may pertain to an entirely earlier horizon than the sites discussed so far in this paper. A date at Tlapacoya from a hearth is 24,000 ± 4000 B.P. (Haynes, 1967b). More evidence is obviously needed before the importance of these finds can be evaluated. Later sites in Mexico record mammoth kills in the time range of 9500 to 11,000 B.P. These kills are similar in many ways to those known from the Great Plains.

Additional areas in North America have revealed little in the way of Paleo-Indian materials. In many cases these areas were covered with ice until well into the postglacial period.

Conclusions

General conclusions are limited to those aspects of widespread occurrence. The earliest established remains are those in the Great Plains dated 12,000-11,000 B.P., although most other areas record human habitation within the next thousand years. The big-game hunting economy established in the Plains is thought to have been practiced from the West Coast to the East Coast and south to the valley of Mexico. A detailed consideration of the data reveals little evidence outside of the Plains to "prove" this assumption. Much circumstantial evidence exists but validated killsites are rare.

The environmental reconstructions are quite variable not only in their specific ecological make-up but also in their indicated response to glacial fluctuations.

The major conclusion resulting from this survey is the fact that in every area for which we have data, at the earliest level, these data record cultural adaptations to local environments which included desert grassland, savanna grassland with gallery forests, pine parkland, boreal forest, deciduous forest, and even tundra. These adaptations record both differences in artifactual inventory and, where the evidence is present, in the nature of the food resources utilized.

References

Adam, D. P. 1967. Late-Pleistocene and Recent palynology in the central Sierra Nevada, California. In: *Quaternary Paleoecology*, E. J. Cushing and H. E. Wright, Jr. (eds.). Yale University Press, New Haven, Conn., p. 275-302.

Baumhoff, M. A., and R. F. Heizer. 1965. Post-glacial climate and archaeology in the desert west. In: *The Quaternary of the United States*, H. E. Wright, Jr., and D. G. Frey (eds.). Princeton University Press, Princeton, N.J., p. 697-707.

Borns, H. W., Jr. 1966. The geography of Paleo-Indian occupation in Nova Scotia. *Quaternaria*, **VIII**: 49-57.

Byers, D. S. 1966. The Debert archaeological project: The position of Debert with respect to the Paleo-Indian tradition: *Quarternaria*, **VIII**: 33-47.

Cushing, E. J. 1967. Late-Wisconsin pollen stratigraphy and the glacial sequence in Minnesota. In: *Quaternary Paleoecology*, E. J. Cushing and H. E. Wright, Jr. (eds.). Yale University Press, New Haven, Conn, p. 59-88.

Cushing, E. J., and H. E. Wright, Jr. (eds.). 1967. *Quaternary Paleoecology.* Yale University Press, New Haven, Conn.

Davis, M. B. 1967. Late-Glacial climate in northern United States: A comparison of New England and the Great Lakes region. In: *Quaternary Paleoecology*, E. J. Cushing and H. E. Wright Jr. (eds.). Yale University Press, New Haven, Conn., p. 11-44.

Farrand, W. R. 1961. Frozen mammoths and modern geology. *Science*, 133: 729-735.

Griffin, J. B. 1965. Late Quaternary prehistory in the northeastern woodlands. In: *Quaternary of the United States*, H. E. Wright, Jr., and D. G. Frey (eds.). Princeton University Press, Princeton, N.J., p. 655-667.

Haury, E. W. E. Antevs, and J. F. Lance, 1953. Artifacts with mammoth remains, Naco, Arizona. *Amer. Antiqu.*, 25 : 1-24.

Haynes, C. V., Jr. 1964. Fluted projectile points: Their age and dispersion. *Science*, **145**: 1408-1413.

—— 1967a. Carbon-14 dates and early man in the New World. In: *Pleistocene Extinctions.* P. S. Martin and H. E. Wright, Jr. (eds.). Yale University Press, New Haven, Conn., p. 267-286.

——, 1967b. *Carbon-14 sampling of the Tlapacoya site, Mexico.* dittoed. (Spanish translation appeared in *INAH Bull.* 29 Mexico City.)

——. 1967c. Quarternary geology of the Tule Springs area. Clark County, Nevada. *Nev. State Mus. Anthropol.* 13: part I.

Hester, J. J. 1966. Origins of the Clovis culture. *XXXVI Congress. Intern. Amer., actas y memorias,* p. 129-142.

Heusser, C. J. 1965. A Pleistocene phytogeographical sketch of the Pacific Northwest. In: *The Quaternary of the United States*, H. E. Wright, Jr., and D. G. Frey (eds.). Princeton University Press, Princeton, N.J., p. 469-483.

Howard, E. B. 1935. Evidence of early man in North America. *The Mus. J.*, 24: 61-175.

Martin, P. S. 1967. Prehistoric overkill. In: *Pleistocene Extinctions*, P. S. Martin and H. E. Wright, Jr. (eds.). Yale University Press, New Haven, Conn., p. 75-120.

——. 1968. Mastodons, mammoths, muskoxen and man. Abstract of paper, 33rd Annual Meeting Soc. Amer. Arch., p. 27.

Martin P. S., and P. J. Mehringer, Jr. 1965. Pleistocene pollen analysis and biogeography of the Southwest. In: *The Quaternary of the United States*, H. E. Wright, Jr., and D. G. Frey (eds.). Princeton University Press, Princeton, N.J., p. 433-451.

Mason, R. J. 1962. The Paleo-Indian tradition in eastern North America. *Curr. Anthropol.*, **3**: 227-246.

Mehringer, P. J., Jr. 1967. The environment of extinction of the Late-Pleistocene megafauna in the arid southwestern United States. In: *Pleistocene Extinctions*, P. S. Martin and H. E. Wright, Jr. (eds.). Yale University Press, New Haven, Conn., p. 247-266.

Meighan, C. W. 1965. Pacific coast archaeology. In: *The Quaternary of the United States*, H. E. Wright, Jr., and D. G. Frey (eds.). Princeton University Press, Princeton, N.J., p. 709-720.

Odgen, J. G., III. 1967. Radiocarbon and pollen evidence for a sudden change in climate in the Great Lakes region approximately 10,000 years ago. In: *Quaternary Paleoecology*, E. J. Cushing and H. E. Wright, Jr. (eds.). Yale University Press, New Haven, Conn., p. 117-127.

Stuchenrath, R., Jr. 1966. The Debert archaeological project, Nova Scotia: Radiocarbon dating. *Quaternaria*, **VIII**: 75-80.

Watts, W. A. 1967. Late-Glacial plant macrofossils

from Minnesota. In: *Quaternary Paleoecology*, E. J. Cushing and H. E. Wright, Jr. (eds.). Yale University Press, New Haven, Conn., p. 89-97.

Wendorf, D. F. (assembler). 1961. Paleoecology of the Llano Estacado, Vol., 1, *Papers of Ft. Burgwin Research Center*, 1.

Wendorf, D. F., and J. J. Hester. 1962. Early man's utilization of the Great Plains environment. *Amer. Anthropol.*, 18(28): 159-171.

Whitehead, D. R. 1965. Palynology and Pleistocene phytogeography of unglaciated eastern North America. In: *The Quaternary of the United States*, H. E. Wright, Jr., and D. G. Frey (eds.). Princeton University Press, Princeton, N.J., p. 417-432.

Williams, S., and J. B. Stoltman, 1965. An outline of

southeastern United States prehistory with particular emphasis on the Paleo-Indian era. In: *The Quaternary of the United States*, H. E. Wright, Jr., and D. G. Frey (eds.). Princeton University Press, Princeton, N.J., p. 669-683.

Wormington, H. M., and R. G. Forbis. 1965. An introduction to the archaeology of Alberta, Canada. *Dev. Mus. Natl. Hist. Proc.*, 11.

Wright, F. B. 1903. The mastodon and mammoth contemporary with man. *Rec. of the Past.* II: 243-253.

Wright, H. E., Jr., and D. G. Frey (eds.). 1965. *The Quaternary of the United States*. Princeton University Press, Princeton, N.J.

9

CRO-MAGNON MAN, 1868-1968

John R. Baker

The great rock, or 'Cro-Magnon,' is situated on the outskirts of the village of Les Eyzies in Dordogne, south-central France. It is actually a small hill of Cretaceous limestone. The weathering of this formation, and the underground flow of water through it, have produced shelters and tunnel-like caves in which Palaeolithic man lived and painted, and which have made the valley of the Vézère world-famous in prehistory.

The fall of an enormous quantity of rock debris over long ages covered up the shelter of Cro-Magnon, and no one guessed its existence. It was at last disclosed towards the end of March 1868, when some of the debris was being removed for use in the construction of a neighbouring road. The men engaged in removing loose material that had accumulated below a huge projecting shelf of rock soon discovered shaped flints, broken bones, and finally human skulls. By great good fortune those in charge of the work, MM. François

Reprinted from *Endeavour* 27: 87-90, 1968, with the permission of the publishers.

Berthoumeyrou and Delmarès, were men of high intelligence, who recognized the antiquity and scientific interest of the find. They at once stopped the excavation and informed local prehistorians, who removed parts of the skeletons and some of the artifacts to ensure their safety. The Minister of Public Instruction entrusted the geologist, Louis Lartet, with the task of verifying the authenticity of the discovery (22, 23).

The shelter was of considerable size. The thick stratum of hard rock that formed its roof was 17 metres long and projected nearly 10 metres in front of its deepest recess. The excavators built a pillar (seen in Fig. 9-1) to support this roof, but eventually it fell and was cleared away, and only the recess remains today. It was in this recess that the human skeletons were found. The shelter was nearly filled with deposits when the men began work, and the skeletons rested on a layer less than a metre from the roof. It follows that the bodies were placed there when that part of the cave was no longer inhabited. D. Peyrony's researches (32) show that human beings had already occupied it in Aurignacian I. In an authoritative article covering many aspects of the Cro-Magnon discovery, J. Bouchud (3) concludes that the skeletons date from Perigordian IV, that is, Gravettian. This implies that they belong to people who lived about 22,000 B.C., before the maximum of the Middle Würm glaciation (28).

Skeletons belonging unquestionably to

Fig. 9-1. Cro-Magnon, showing the shelter, the pillar built to support the roof, and the mushroom-shaped rock above (which is still there today): a rough sketch accompanying L. Lartet's description of the site. (a) The road rising to the NNW, (b) Les Eyzies. (From Reliquiae aquitanicae *[19].)*

Homo sapiens (in the stricter sense that excludes the Neanderthalians) had not previously been found in Palaeolithic deposits. The discovery showed that a modern type of man was much more ancient than had been supposed.

The Anatomy of the Cromagnids

The human skeletons were sent to Paris without delay, and shortly afterwards were described in separate publications by P. Broca (6, 7) and F. Pruner-Bey (33, 34). From the time of publication of de Quatrefages and Hamy's *'Crania ethnica'* (38) in 1882, no further report on the actual specimens was published, apart from certain measurements incorporated by G. M. Morant in a statistical paper (27), until in 1965 there appeared the detailed description by H. V. Vallois and G. Billy (43), which is now the standard monograph on the human skeletons of the Cro-Magnon shelter. These are preserved in the *Musée de l'Homme* in Paris. There are parts of at least five persons, of which one, designated No. 1 by both Broca and Pruner-Bey, is represented by a male skull with vertebrae, sacrum, ilia, and various limb-bones. Broca named this specimen *'le vieillard'*, but in fact he was at most 50 years old (43).

Broca thought the specimens sufficiently similar to one another and different from other known human types to justify their classification in a separate 'race', which he called *'la race des Eyzies'*. Broca himself (7), E. T. Hamy (14, 15), and de Quatrefages soon realized that this group, named by the latter (35) *'la race de Cro-Magnon'*, was of wide distribution. It constitutes, however, only a sub-race of the Europid ('Caucasian') race, and it is convenient to refer to the members of it as Cromagnids (12).

By a strange chance, the *vieillard* shows many of the characteristics of the Cromagnids in an exaggerated form. Broca himself already recognized this in 1873 (7). In the following two paragraphs an attempt is made to induce the skeletal characters[1] of a typical Cromagnid of the Upper Palaeolithic and Mesolithic from the available information about the original specimens and others that have been found over a wide area of Europe and in Algeria (1, 5, 6, 8, 15, 17, 20, 27, 30, 33, 34, 38, 43, 46, 47).

The skull is long, with somewhat bulging occiput. Viewed from on top, it approximates in shape to a drawn-out pentagon (with rounded corners), with the rather straight forehead as base. The skull also approximates to a pentagon when viewed from in front (Fig. 9-2(a)) or behind, since the side-walls are somewhat flattened where they slope up to meet in the median sagittal plane. The attachments of the masticatory muscles on the skull are large and much roughened. The skull is markedly low in relation to its length. Long skulls are usually

---

[1] Certain of the structures referred to are indicated in Fig. 9-3(b). Some other relevant anatomical terms that may not be generally familiar are: *hypotrochanteric fossa*, a pit sometimes present on the posterior side of the femur (thigh bone), besides the linea aspera; *linea aspera*, a ridge on the posterior side of the femur, roughened for muscle attachments; *orthognathous* (of the jaw), not projecting forward; *pilaster*, an extremely developed linea aspera (projecting from the femur like an architectural pilaster from a wall); *platycnemia*, flattening of the tibia (to a defined degree); *platymeria*, flattening of the femur (to a defined degree); *prosthion*, (as the term is used in measurements of facial height), the lowest point on the bony process between the two upper central incisor teeth.

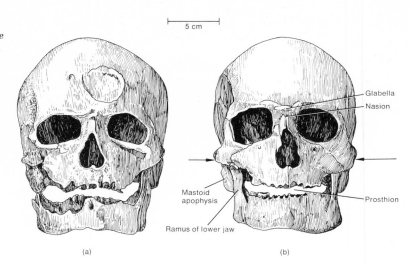

Fig. 9.2. (a) Skull of the vieillard of Cro-Magnon. (The right and left sides have been reversed by the diagraph used in making the figure.) (b) Ancient skull of a guanche, brought to France by Bouglinval [4]. The arrows indicate the points between which the bizygomatic width is measured. (Both figures from Crania ethnica *[38].)*

5 cm

Glabella
Nasion

Mastoid
apophysis

Ramus of lower jaw

Prosthion

(a)   (b)

accompanied by narrow faces, but the facial skeleton of the Cromagnids is 'disharmonic', for it is very wide (that is, the bizygomatic breadth is great in relation to the distance from nasion to prosthion). This 'disharmony' is one of the most distinctive features of the Cromagnids. Another is the shape of the orbits, which, at their entrances, are very long from side to side; their upper and lower borders are close to one another and almost parallel, and the inner nearly straight and at right angles to the upper and lower. The brow-ridges are short but moderately prominent, and confluent across the glabella. The forehead rises fairly steeply. The nasal aperture is of moderate width, or narrow (as in Cro-Magnon I); the nasal bones project strongly from a deeply sunk root. The face as a whole is orthognathous, but there is some projection of the part below the nose. The mastoid apophyses are very large (Fig. 9-2(a)). The lower jaw is wide at the angles, which flare outwards (Fig. 9-2(a)); the ramus is massive, with strongly developed muscle-attachments.

The stature is moderate or tall, and the whole skeleton rather massive and suggestive of strong muscular development. The forearm is long in relation to the upper (which is not short), and so is the lower leg in relation to the thigh. The hand (unfortunately very poorly represented at Cro-Magnon) is large. The platymeric femur shows some distinctive characters. The linea aspera is so prominent as

to form a pilaster; at its upper end it is raised into a large gluteal tuberosity, and laterally to this there is a hypotrochanteric fossa. The tibia is platycnemic.

The Cromagnids were naturally not everywhere exactly similar during Upper Palaeolithic and Mesolithic times. This could not be expected of a group that spread over nearly the whole of Europe [17] and into North Africa. The male specimen from Obercassel (near Bonn), for instance, has particularly well-developed brow-ridges, though R. Bonnet (48) greatly exaggerated the resemblances to the Neanderthalians in this and other parts of the skeleton. The Algerian specimens also have prominent brow-ridges, and the nose is wider and the skull somewhat higher than in the typical Cromagnid; but in general the resemblance is close, not only in the skull but also in the extremities (1).

From the studies of Morant (27), devoted entirely to the cranium, it has been widely concluded that all Upper Palaeolithic men of Europe belong to a single group, but in fact Morant himself recognized that his statistical treatment might obscure certain ethnic relationships of great evolutionary importance. No one who has studied the Chancelade skeleton, excellently displayed in the Museum of Périgueux, is likely to agree that this was a Cromagnid, and the so-called '*négroïdes*' of the *Grotte des Enfants*, near Menton, are even more distinct, in quite a different way (47).

At the time of the Cro-Magnon discovery certain very incomplete skeletons had already been unearthed that may perhaps have belonged to Upper Palaeolithic Cromagnids. In 1823 the headless skeleton of the 'Red Lady of Paviland' (in fact probably a male) had been discovered by William Buckland, the Oxford geologist, in a cave on the Gower Peninsula of South Wales (9); it is preserved in the Oxford University Museum. It was regarded as Cromagnid by the authors of *'Crania ethnica'* (38) and also by W. J. Sollas (42), who examined it some 90 years after its discovery, and assigned it to Aurignacian times. The evidence as to date appears inconclusive and in the absence of a skull it is difficult to determine the taxonomic position, though the femur and tibia certainly show Cromagnid features. A calvarium and other human skeletal fragments were found by P.-C. Shmerling about 1829 in the caves of Engis and Engihoul, near Liège. They were carefully described by the discoverer (41) and thirty years later by T. H. Huxley (18). It is possible that they are Cromagnid, as de Quatrefages and Hamy claimed (35, 38), but the evidence is inconclusive. The fragments were associated, curiously enough, with Mousterian implements.

The earliest-discovered Palaeolithic bones that can be referred with some confidence to the Cromagnid sub-race were found in 1864 in the famous cave of La Madeleine. This cave, which gave its name to the Magdalenian culture, is only about 3½ km from Cro-Magnon, on the opposite side of the River Vézère. It was explored by Edouard Lartet (father of Louis) and his British companion, H. Christy (21). They had great difficulty in believing that the skeletal fragments (a frontal bone, part of the lower jaw, and certain bones of the trunk and extremities) could belong to the Upper Palaeolithic, because they thought it unlikely that men of that period would have buried one of their companions in the place in which they ate their food, and without the usual accessories for a funeral. Hamy's careful description of the skeletal fragments (15) suggests strongly that they are Cromagnid, and there seems to be no reason to doubt that they were contemporary with the Magdalenian artifacts in the cave.

The Fate of the Cromagnids

Four years after the discovery at Cro-Magnon, a chance observation opened up a new line of thought about the Cromagnids (14, 16). Hamy, then a young man, had been one of the first to examine (though not to report on) the Cro-Magnon skeletons. Subsequently he happened to notice, in rather a strange old dissertation on the cerebellum (24), two drawings of a modern skull that showed close resemblance to the Cromagnid type. The skull was that of a Dalarnian (*'Dalecarlien'*), or inhabitant of Dalarna, nowadays the province of Kopparberg in Sweden. At the time Hamy was working in Broca's laboratory, where there was the cast of a Dalarnian skull. It had been brought there by Gaimard, who had recognized the structural peculiarities of the people of this part of Sweden. Here again Hamy noticed strong resemblances to the Cromagnid type. He had also seen the Guanche skulls that had been brought back by Bouglinval (4) from Teneriffe twenty years earlier. It now struck him forcibly that certain members of the population of the Canary Islands, before the Spanish conquest, had also been very similar to the Palaeolithic Cromagnids (Fig 9-2(b)). There thus arose in his mind the hypothesis that the Cromagnids had not died out or become completely unrecognizable by crossing with other sub-races, but had persisted in a somewhat attenuated form into modern times. This hypothesis was mentioned by Broca (7), accepted by de Quatrefages (35-37), and made generally known in *'Crania ethnica'* (38).

If the Cromagnids have survived, one must expect to find them in the Neolithic. Already in the 1880s R. Verneau [44] had attributed to this sub-race fourteen skulls of Neolithic age that had been found in Spanish sites from Oviedo in the north to Andalusia in the south, and three others from the Bronze Age of Granada. G. Perret (30) found the same type, clearly differentiated, in skulls from a very large Neolithic *Steinkiste* at Altendorf, near Kassel in Lower Hesse, western Germany. The continuity of Cromagnid types in Lower Hesse is remarkable, for Perret found skeletons there that he referred to this *'Rasse'* not only in

Bronze Age tumuli, but in some (but by no means all) of the Iron Age *Reihengräber* of this district, and even in a deserted village of the thirteenth or fourteenth century A.D. This, however, was not all. Lower Hesse adjoins or forms part of the rather ill-defined region of Germany that used to be the Duchy of Westphalia. A special physique has long been attributed to many of the people in this region. This so called *'fälische Rasse'* is thought to include not only the Westphalians, but also the Dalarnians of Sweden, and E. von Eickstedt (11) writes of a *'dalisch-fälisch'* type (cf. 40, 29, 17, 31). The typical specimen of this type does show marked resemblance to the Cromagnid (11, 30).

Similar types have been reported in the modern populations of the Dordogne (10), where the original Cromagnids once flourished; among the Kabyles of North Africa (37, 38), whose territory extends over the area where the ancient Algerian skeletons were found; and even in the Plynlimon district of Wales (13), though here the evidence is weak.

The Guanches of the Canary Islands probably provide the best evidence that the Cromagnids survived into modern times, as Hamy first suggested. Many authors have supported this contention, from the time of de Quatrefages (35, 38) onwards, and it is accepted by some of the most reliable authorities of the present day (5). One of the most prominent students of Cromagnid survival was Verneau, whose work in Spain has already been mentioned. He made two very long visits to the Canary Islands, and convinced himself not only that the unaltered or scarcely altered Cromagnid type had survived in Teneriffe till the Spanish occupation in the fifteenth century, but that their hybridized descendants still formed a considerable element in the population of the islands (44, 45).

The original Guanches had blue eyes and were blond or had chestnut hair (44, 45), and the *'dalisch-fälisch'* type also tends to be fair-haired (29, 26; cf. 39). Other modern groups supposed to be Cromagnid, however, have dark hair and eyes (10, 13).

The problem of Cromagnid survival to the present day is one on which it would be wrong to dogmatize in the present state of knowledge. Admittedly there has been some tendency to postulate Cromagnid ancestry on the obviously insufficient evidence of 'disharmonic' facial features. One might wish that certain persons, thought to be particularly good representatives of the *'dalisch-fälisch'* type, could be persuaded to bequeath their skeletons, or at any rate their skulls and femora, for anatomical study. This, however, would not necessarily solve the problem. Random assortment of genes might result occasionally in the production of a person showing some resemblance to a Cromagnid, or a similar result might happen locally on a larger scale through the co-existence and intermarriage in a particular territory of two Europid sub-races, neither of them Cromagnid. There is, indeed, evidence that this may have happened in Thuringia (40). In trying to determine whether the various groups of supposed modern Cromagnids are related to one another and therefore, presumably, to those of the Palaeolithic, one realizes how unsatisfactory it is to do no more than describe the morphological characters, without being able to analyse genetically the causes that produced them. Yet the unfortunate paradox remains: the better the evidence of relationship, the less susceptible are the facts to genetic analysis. Most of the structural peculiarities that distinguished the Palaeolithic Cromagnids were presumably the produce of many genes having cumulative effects. Such characters afford better evidence of relationship than those dependent on a few genes or only one. In animals, where appropriate matings can be made, genetic and chromosomal analysis of polygenes is a possibility (25). In man it presents almost insuperable difficulties; and with the ever-increasing frequency of intermarriage between the Europid sub-races, the type may no longer exist when geneticists have thought of a method that might have analysed it.

Acknowledgments

For information and general helpfulness I am greatly indebted to the proprietors of the

Cro-Magnon site, Monsieur and Madame Minier le Clech; the latter is the granddaughter of Monsieur Francois Berthoumeyrou. I thank Professor E. B Ford, F.R.S., and Mr. D. A. Roe for advice on specific points.

References

1. Arambourg, C., Boule, M., Vallois, N., and Verneau, R. *Arch. Inst. Paléont. humaine,* 13, 1, 1934.
2. Bertrand, A. 'Nos Origines: la Gaule avant les Gaulois'. Leroux, Paris. 1891.
3. Bouchud, J. *Bull. Soc. Étud. Rech. préhist.,* Les Eyzies, 15, 28, 1965.
4. Bouglinval. *C.r. hebd. Séanc. Acad. Sci. Paris,* 32, 865, 1851.
5. Boule, M. and Vallois, H. V. 'Fossil Men: a Textbook of Human Palaeontology'. Thames and Hudson, London, 1957.
6. Broca, P. *Bull. Soc. Anthrop.,* Paris, 3, 350, 1868.
7. *Idem. Revue Anthrop.,* 2, 1, 1873.
8. *Idem.* Chapter IX in Jones, T. R. (19).
9. Buckland, W. 'Reliquiae diluvianae'. Murray, London, 1823.
10. Collignon, R. *Mém. Soc. Anthrop.,* Paris, I, (3), I, 1894.
11. Eickstedt, E. von. 'Rassenkunde und Rassengeschichte der Menschheit'. Enke, Stuttgart, 1934.
12. *Idem. Z. Rassenk.,* 6, 151, 1937.
13. Fleure, H. J. and James, T. C. *Fl R. anthrop. Inst.,* 46, 35, 1916.
14. Hamy, E. T. Observations quoted by Broca (7).
15. *Idem.* Chapter xxv in Jones (19).
16. *Idem.* Annexe B to Bertrand (2).
17. Hauschild, M. W. *Z. Ethnol.,* 50, 54, 1923.
18. Huxley, T. H. 'Evidence as to Man's Place in Nature'. Williams and Norgate, London, 1863.
19. Jones, T. R. (edited by). 'Reliquiae aquitanicae'. Williams and Norgate, 1875.
20. Kollmann, J. *Arch. Anthrop.,* 14, 1, 1883.
21. Lartet, E. and Christy, H. 'Cavernes du Périgord'. Didier, Paris, 1864.
22. Lartet, L. *Bull. Soc. Anthrop.,* Paris, 3, 335, 1868.
23. *Idem.* Chapter VI in Jones (19).
24. Liedbeck, J. P. 'Ueber die Funktion des kleinen Gehirns: eine medicinisch-physiologische Abhandlung'. Groos, Karlsruhe. 1846.
25. Mather, K. and Harrison, B. J. *Heredity, Lond.,* 3, 1949.
26. Miszkiewicz, B. *Homo,* 13, 181, 1962.
27. Morant, G. M. *Ann. Eugen.,* 4, 109, 1930-31.
28. Movius, H. L. *Curr. Anthrop.,* 1 355, 1960.
29. Paudler, F. *Anthropos,* 12-13, 641, 1917-18.
30. Perret, G. *Z. Morph. Anthrop.,* 37, I, 1937.
31. Peters, H. B. *Z. Rassenk.,* 6, 211, 1937.
32. Peyrony, D. 'Le Périgord préhistorique'. Societé historique et archéologique du Périgord. Périgueux. 1949.
33. Pruner-Bey, F. *Annls. Sci. nat., Zool,,* 10, 145, 1868.
34. *Idem.* Chapter vii in Jones (19).
35. Quatrefages, A. de. *C.r. hebd. Séanc. Acad. Sci.,* Paris, 78, 861, 1874.
36. *Idem.* 'L'espèce humaine' (second edition). Bailliére, Paris, 1877.
37. Quatrefages, A. de and Hamy, E. T. *Bull. Soc. Anthrop.,* Paris, 9, 260, 1874.
38. *Idem.* 'Crania ethnica: les Cranes des Races humaines'. Ballière. Paris, 1882.
39. Retzius, G. and Fürst, C. M. 'Anthropologia Suecica: Beiträge zur Anthropologie der Schweden'. Aftonbladet, Stockholm. 1902.
40. Röse, C. *Arch. Rass.-u. GesBiol.,* 3, 42, 1906.
41. Schmerling, P.-C. 'Recherches sur les ossemens fossiles decouverts dans les cavernes de la Province de Liege'. Collardin, Liege. 1833.
42. Sollas, W. J. *Fl R. anthrop. Inst.,* 43, 325, 1913.
43. Vallois, H. V. and Billy, G. *Anthropologie,* Paris, 69, 47, 1965.
44. Verneau, R. *Revue Anthrop.,* 1, 10, 1886.
45. *Idem.* 'Cinq Années de Séjour aux Iles Canaries'. Hennuyer, Paris. 1891.
46. *Idem. Anthropologie,* Paris, 3, 513, 1892.
47. *Idem.* 'Les Grottes de Grimaldi (Baoussé-Roussé: Anthropologie)'. Imprimerie de Monace, Monaco, 1906.
48. Verworn, M., Bonnet, R., and Steinman, G. 'Der diluviale Menschenfund von Obercassel bei Bonn'. Bergmann, Wiesbaden. 1919.

10

FIELD STUDIES OF OLD WORLD MONKEYS AND APES

S. L. Washburn, Phyllis C. Jay, and Jane B. Lancaster

For many years there has been interest in the evolutionary roots of human behavior, and discussions of human evolution frequently include theories on the origin of human customs. In view of the old and widespread interest in the behavior of our nearest relatives, it is surprising how little systematic information was collected until very recently. At the time (1929) Yerkes and Yerkes collected data for their book on the great apes (1), no one had devoted even one continuous month to the systematic study of the behavior of an undisturbed, free-ranging nonhuman primate. Apparently scientists believed that the behavior of monkeys and apes was so stereotyped and simple that travelers' tales or the casual observations of hunters formed a reliable basis for scientific conclusions and social theorizing. As a part of the program of the Yale Laboratories of Comparative Psychology, Yerkes encouraged a series of field studies of the chimpanzee (2), the mountain gorilla (3), and the howling monkey (4). These first studies proved so difficult that Yerkes could write, in the introduction to Carpenter's study, "His is the first reasonably reliable working analysis of the constitution of social groups in the infra-human primates, and of the relations between the sexes and between mature and immature individuals for monkey or ape" (4, p. 4). Zuckerman, quite independently, had realized the importance of field observations and had combined some field work with physiology and the older literature to produce two very influential volumes (5).

From this beginning, only Carpenter continued to make field studies of behavior, and his study of the gibbon (6) is the first successful study of the naturalistic behavior of a member of the family Pongidae. Hooton summarized (7) what was then known about the primates, particularly stressing the importance of behavior and the work of Carpenter and Zuckerman.

The war stopped field work, and no major studies were undertaken for some 15 years. Then, in the 1950's investigators in Japan, England, France, Switzerland, and the United States independently started studies on the behavior of a wide variety of free-ranging primates. For the history of science it would be interesting to examine the reasons for this burst of parallel activity. Field studies were undertaken at more or less the same time, and publications started in the late 1950's and accelerated rapidly in the 1960's. This trend is still continuing and is well shown by the pattern of frequency of citations in a recent review by Hall (8). The review cites the papers of Bingham, Carpenter, Köhler (9), Nissen, Yerkes, and Zuckerman, but there are no references to additional field studies in the period 1941-51, and most of the references are to papers appearing in 1960 or later.

The increased interest in primates, and particularly in the behavior of free-ranging primates, has given rise to several symposiums, and results of the new studies have been published almost as soon as they have been completed. Data from the recent field studies are included in volumes edited by Buettner-Janusch (10), Washburn (11), Napier and Barnicot (12), and, especially, DeVore (13). The volume edited by DeVore is devoted entirely to recent field studies and their evaluation. It includes accounts of the behavior of five kinds of monkeys, of chimpanzees, and of gorillas. Each chapter is by the person who did the field work, and in addition there are eight general chapters. Two new journals also are devoted to primates. *Primates*, published by the Japan Monkey Centre, is now in its 5th year, and *Folia Primatologica* has completed volume 3. Carpenter's field studies and general papers have been reprinted so that they are now easily available (14). Southwick has published a collection of readings in primate social behavior (15), and Eimerl and DeVore contributed a volume on the primates to the Life Nature Library (16). Field studies have recently been reviewed by Jay (17), and proceedings of a symposium organized and edited by Altmann (18). This abundance of published material makes it hard to believe that only 2 years ago a course on primate social behavior was difficult to teach because of the lack of easily available, suitable reading material.

The New Field Studies

Obviously, with so much new data a complete review is impossible, and readers wishing more information and bibliography are referred to Jay (17) and to the symposiums previously noted. Here we wish to direct attention to the nature of the recent field studies and to a few of their major contributions. Perhaps their greatest contribution is a demonstration that close, accurate observation for hundreds of hours is possible. Prior to Schaller's field work, reported in 1963 (19), it was by no means clear that this kind of observation of gorillas would be possible; previous investigators had conducted very fragmentary observations, and Emlen and Schaller deserve great credit for the planning and execution of their study. A field study of the chimpanzee that seemed adequate in the 1930's now seems totally inadequate, when compared to Goodall's results (20). Today a field study is planned to yield something of the order of 1000 hours of observations, and the observer is expected to be close to the animals and to recognize individuals. A few years ago observations of this length and quality were thought unnecessary, if not impossible.

The importance of studies in which groups are visited repeatedly and animals are recognized individually may be illustrated by the problems they make it possible to study. For example, during one season of the year chimpanzees "fish" for termites by breaking off sticks or stiff grasses and sticking the prepared implement into a termite hole (21), and this whole complex of nest examination, tool pre-

paration, and fishing is learned by the young chimpanzee. It can be seen at only one time of the year and can be appreciated only by an observer whose presence no longer disturbs the animals. Habituation to the observer is a slow and difficult process. Goodall reports (20) that after 8 months of observations she could approach to no closer than 50 meters of the chimpanzees and then only when they were in thick cover or up a tree; by 14 months she was able to get within 10 to 15 meters of them. The problem of tool use in nonhuman primates has been reviewed by Hall (22), but the essential point here is that the amount of throwing and object manipulation in the monkeys (Cercopitheoidae) was greatly exaggerated in travelers' tales, which were uncritically accepted, and it took years of observation in a favorable locality to reveal the complexity of this kind of behavior in the chimpanzee (23).

Predation

Another example of the value of continued observations is in the study of deliberate hunting by baboons. In three seasons of field work and more than 1500 hours of observation DeVore had seen baboons catch and eat small mammals, but apparently almost by chance, when the baboon virtually stepped on something like a newborn antelope and then killed it (24, 25). But in 1965 DeVore saw repeated incidents of baboons surrounding, hunting, and killing small mammals (26).

The whole matter of predation on primates has been difficult to study. Rare events, such as an attack by an eagle (27) may be very important in the survival of primates, but such attacks are seldom observed, because the presence of the human observer disturbs either the predator or the prey. We think that the present deemphasis of the importance of predation on primates arises from these difficulties of observation and from the fact that even today most studies of free-ranging primates are made in areas where predators have been reduced or eliminated by man. Most predators are active at night, and there is still no adequate study of the nocturnal behavior of any monkey or ape. Predation probably can best be measured by studying the predators rather than the prey.

Recognition of individual animals is necessary for the study of many problems, from the first stages of the analysis of a social system to observations of social continuity or constancy of group membership; such observations are exceedingly difficult under most field conditions. For example, understanding of the dominance system implies repeated recognition of a number of animals under sufficiently various conditions so that the patterns of interaction become clear. Again, to be sure that a group has lost or gained a member, the observer must know the whole composition of the group.

Long-continued observations have proved to be important in many unexpected ways. For example, rhesus monkeys have been observed in several of their many very different habitats, and it has been found that young rhesus play more in cities than in some kinds of forest and play in the forest more at some seasons than at others. These differences are due in part to the amount of time which must be spent in getting food; the same forest troop may play more when fruits are available and hunger may be rapidly satisfied than at times of the year when the diet is composed of tiny seeds which take a long time to pick. Extracting the small seeds of sheesham pods during the months when rhesus troops spend most of their time in the sheesham trees takes many hours of the day (28). What might easily have been described in a short-term study as a species-specific difference of considerable magnitude turns out to be the result of seasonal and local variations in food source. It is essential to sample behavior in several habitats to gain an understanding of the flexibility of the built-in behavior patterns of a species, flexibility which precludes the need for development of new forms of genetically determined behavior to cope successfully with different habitats.

The long-term study in which many groups of a species are observed in different, contrasting localities, and in which at least some groups are known so well that most of the individuals can be recognized, will correct many

false notions and will make valid generalizations possible. Although so far there have been only a few major investigations of this sort, some important generalizations seem possible.

Environment and Social Behavior

Nowhere is the extent to which the behavior of a species is adaptable and responsive to local conditions more apparent than among groups of rhesus living in India. Rhesus occur naturally in such diverse environments as cities, villages, roadsides, cultivated fields, and many types of forest ranging to altitudes of over 2400 meters. Contact with man varies in these habitats from constant and close to rare and incidental.

Where rhesus groups are subjected to pressures of trapping, harassment, and high incidence of infectious disease, groups are tense and aggression is high. These pressures are found in areas where there is most contact and interaction with man, such as in cities and at places of pilgrimage. The animals are in generally poor physical condition, and numerous old and new wounds are evidence of a high rate of intragroup fighting. Tension among groups occupying adjacent areas of land is similarly high where there is insufficient space for normal movement and behavior, and where there may be intense competition for a limited supply of food and water. This is in sharp contrast to those groups living away from man where normal spacing among groups can be effected by the means evolved by the species. In the latter environments, such as forests, the rhesus are in excellent physical condition and what aggressive behavior occurs functions to maintain stable social groups and relationships among the members of the group; wounds are substantially fewer, and disease appears to be rare.

There has been considerable controversy in discussions of the relationships among social groups of the same species as to whether or not the geographical area occupied by a group should be called a territory or a home range. The point we wish to emphasize is that, within one species, populations living in different habitats may act quite differently toward neighboring groups. Populations may be capable of a wide variety of behavior patterns ranging from exclusive occupation of an area which may be defended against neighboring groups to a peaceful coexistence with conspecifics in which wide overlap in home ranges is tolerated. Because local populations of a species may maintain their ranges in different ways it is necessary to investigate all variations in group spacing in diverse habitats before attempting to describe characteristic behavior patterns for any species.

Not unexpectedly, population and group composition reflect these differences in habitat and stress. Groups living on the Gangetic plains, where trapping, harassment, and disease are important factors, are smaller, and the proportion of young members is also significantly smaller (28, 29). The long-term effects of pressures on different rhesus populations in northern and central India are now being investigated by a team of anthropologists of the National Center for Primate Biology.

A city presents a very different set of challenges to a rhesus group than does a forest. Often there are no trees to sleep in; living space must be shared with man and his domestic animals. Food is not available in the form common to other habitats, and monkeys may have to depend on their skill in stealing food from man. Often the food has been prepared by man for his own consumption, or it consists of fruits and vegetables pilfered from houses, shops, and streets. Garbage is picked through and edible portions are consumed. It is essential that the monkeys learn to differentiate between those humans who represent a real threat to their safety and those who are safe to approach. They must react quickly and learn to manipulate doors, gates, and other elements of the physical environment unique to their urban habitat. This is a tremendously different setting from that in which most rhesus live. City rhesus are more manipulative, more active, and often more aggressive than are forest rhesus. Clearly, the same species develops quite different learned habits in different environments.

Annual Reproductive Cycle

The belief, which has been widely maintained, that there is no breeding season in monkeys and apes gave rise to the theory that the persistence throughout the year of groups, or highly organized troops, was due to continuous sexual attraction. The evidence for a breeding season has been reviewed by Lancaster and Lee (30) who found that in many species of monkeys there is a well-marked breeding season. For example, Mizuhara has presented data (31) on 545 births of Japanese macaques of Takasakiyama. There were on the average approximately 90 births per year over six consecutive years. The average length of the birth season was 125 days, but it varied from 95 to 176 days. The majority of the births occurred in June and July. Copulations were most frequent in November to March and were not observed during the birth season, and in spite of this the highly organized group continues as a social unit throughout the year.

The birth season has been studied in other groups of Japanese macaques, and in general the situation is similar. There is no doubt that both mating and birth seasons are highly restricted in the Japanese macaque. The birth season is spring and summer, but its onset and duration vary considerably. If observations were limited and combined for the whole species, as they were in early studies, the birth season would appear to be much longer than in fact it is for an individual group, and it is the events within the local group, not averages of events for the species, that bear upon the role of sexual attraction in holding primate society together.

Under very different climatic conditions, in India, rhesus macaques also have a birth season, but copulations were observed in all months of the year, although probably not with equal frequency (29). Among rhesus on a small island off Puerto Rico births occur from January to June, and copulations are restricted to July-January (32). These data confirm the point that a birth season will be more sharply defined in a local group than in a species as a whole. There is a mating season among rhesus introduced on the island, but only a peak of mating in the same species in their nativè India (29). It is clear that survey data drawn from many groups over a wide area must be used with caution when the aim is to interpret the behavior of a single group. Since the birth season is an adaptation to local conditions, there is no reason to expect it to be the same over the entire geographical distribution of a species, and under laboratory conditions rhesus macaques breed throughout the year.

No data comparable to those for the macaques exist for other primates, and, since accurate determination of mating and birth seasons requires that reasonable numbers of animals be observed in different localities, really adequate data exist for only the Japanese macaque. However, Lancaster and Lee were able to assemble data on 14 species of monkeys and apes. They found that probably the most common situation is a birth peak, a time of year at which births tend to be concentrated, rather than sharply limited mating and birth seasons. This is highly adaptive for widely distributed species, for it allows the majority of births to occur at the optimum time for each locality while maintaining a widely variable basic pattern. The birth season may be a more effective adaptation to extreme climatic conditions. There may be a birth peak in the chimpanzee (20), and there may be none in the mountain gorilla (19), but, since we have no more data than are necessary to clarify the reproductive pattern in a single species of macaque, we can conclude only that, while birth seasons are not present in either gorillas or chimpanzees, a peak is possible in chimpanzees, at least for those living near Lake Tanganyika.

Prior to the recent investigations there was a great deal of information on primate reproduction, and yet as late as 1960 it was still possible to maintain that there were no breeding seasons in primates and that this was the basis of primate society. Until recently the question of seasonality was raised without reference to a birth season as distinguished from a birth peak, or to a limited mating season as distinguished from matings throughout the year with a high frequency in a particular period.

Frequency of Mating

Obviously many more studies are needed, and one of the intriguing problems is the role of potency. Not only does the frequency of mating vary through the year, but also there appear to be enormous differences in potency between species that are reproducing at a normal rate. In nearly 500 hours of observation of gorillas, Schaller (19) saw only two matings, fewer than might be seen in a troop of baboons in almost any single morning. The redtail monkey *(Cercopithecus ascanius)* mates rarely (27), but the closely related vervet *(Cercopithecus aethiops)* does so frequently. To a considerable extent the observed differences are correlated with structure (33), such as size of testes, and all these species seem to be reproducing at an adequate and normal rate. There is no evidence that langurs *(Presbytis entellus)* are less successful breeders than rhesus, but the langurs copulate less frequently (34).

Now that more adequate data are becoming available, the social functions of sexual behavior should be reinvestigated. The dismissal of the theory that sexual attraction is *the* basis of primate society should open the way for a more careful study of the multiple functions of sexual behavior. The great differences among the primate species should provide data to prove or disprove new theories. In passing it might be noted that the human mating system without estrous cycles in the female and without marked seasonal variations is unique.

Systems of Mating

Mating systems, like the presence or absence of seasonality in breeding and the frequency of copulation, are extremely variable in monkeys and apes. Eventually the relation of these variations to species adaptations will be understandable; at present it is most important to note that monkeys do not necessarily live either in harems or in promiscuous hordes as was once assumed. Restrictive mating patterns such as the stable and exclusive pair-bond formed between adult gibbons (6) and the harem system of the Hamadryas baboon (35) are comparatively rare. The most common mating pattern of monkeys and apes is promiscuity more or less influenced by dominance relationships. In species in which dominance relations are not constantly at issue, such as langurs (34), chimpanzees (20), or bonnet macaques (36), matings appear to be relatively promiscuous and are often based on the personal inclination of the estrous female. When dominance relationships are constantly at issue, as in baboons (37), Japanese macaques (38), and rhesus macaques (39, 40), sex often becomes one of the prerogatives of dominant rank. In such species dominant males tend to do a larger share of the mating than do more subordinate animals, but it is only in unusual situations that subordinate animals are barred from the mating system altogether. Mating systems probably support the general adaptation of the species to its environment. In most baboons and macaques the tendency for a few males to do much of the mating may be partly a by-product of natural selection for a hierarchy of adult males which dominates the troop so that in a dangerous terrestrial habitat external dangers will be met in an orderly way. Selection is not only for a male which can impregnate many females but it may also have favored a dominance-oriented social organization in which sexual activity has become one of the expressions of that dominance.

Dominance Relationships

Long-term field studies of monkeys and apes in their natural habitats have emphasized that social relationships within a group are patterned and organized in very complex ways. There is no single "monkey pattern" or "ape pattern"; rather, there is great variability, both among different species and among different populations of the same species, in the organization and expression of social relationships. A difference in the relative dominance of individuals is one of the most common modes of social organization in monkey and ape societies. Dominance is not synonymous with aggression, and the way dominance is expressed varies

greatly between species. In the gorilla, for example, dominance is most often expressed by extremely attenuated gestures and signals (19); a gentle nudge from the dominant male is more than enough to elicit a submissive response from a subordinate, whereas, in baboons, chases, fights, and biting can be daily occurrences (37). In many primates there is a tendency for the major age-sex classes to be ranked in a dominance order; for example, in baboons, macaques, and gorillas, adult males as a class are usually dominant over adult females, and females are dominant over young. This may not always be true, for in several species of macaques some females may outrank some adult males (36), although groups dominated by a female (such as the Minoo-B troop of Japanese macaques) are extremely rare (41). Dominance relationships may be quite unstructured, as in the chimpanzee (20), where dominance is expressed in interactions between individuals but where these relationships are not organized into any sort of hierarchy. A much more common situation is one in which dominance relations, among males at least, are organized into linear hierarchies that are quite stable over time, as in baboons (37), langurs (34, 42), and macaques (43, 44). Sometimes these dominance hierarchies are complicated by alliances among several males who back each other up very effectively (37) or even by an alliance between a male and a female (36). Although dominance varies widely among monkeys and apes both in its form and function, it is certainly one of the most important axes of social organization to be found in primate societies.

Genealogical Relationships

Recognition of individual animals and repeated studies of the same groups have opened the way to the appreciation of other long-continuing social relationships in monkeys and apes which cannot be interpreted in terms of dominance alone. Long-term studies of free-ranging animals have been made on only two species of nonhuman primates, Japanese macaques, which have been studied since 1950 by members of the Japan Monkey Centre, and Indian rhesus macaques living free on Cayo Santiago, Puerto Rico, the island colony established by Carpenter in 1938. In these studies, when the genealogy of the animals has been known, it has been obvious that genetic relationships play a major role in determining the course and nature of social interactions (41, 45-47). It becomes clear that bonds between mother and infant may persist into adult life to form a nucleus from which many other social bonds ramify. When the genealogy of individual animals is known, members of commonly observed subgroupings, such as a cluster of four or five animals grooming or resting together, are likely to be uterine kin. For example, members of a subgroup composed of several adult animals, both male and female, as well as juveniles and infants, may all be offspring of the same female (47). These relations continue to be very important in adult life not only in relaxed affectional relationships but also in dominance interactions. Sade saw a female rhesus monkey divert the attack of a dominant male from her adult son and saw another adult female protect her juvenile half-sisters (paternity is not determinable in most monkey societies). There is a very high frequency of grooming between related animals, and many animals never seek grooming partners outside of their own genealogies.

It should be stressed that there is no information leading us to believe that these animals are either recognizing genetic relationships or responding to any sort of abstract concept of family. Rather these social relationships are determined by the necessarily close association of mother with newborn infant, which is extended through time and generations and which ramifies into close associations among siblings. We believe that this pattern of enduring social relations between a mother and her offspring will be found in other species of primates. Because of their dramatic character, the importance of dominance and aggression has been greatly exaggerated compared to that of continuing, positive, affectional relations between related animals as expressed by their sitting or feeding together, touching, and grooming. Much of this behavior can be ob-

served easily in the field, but the extent to which it is in fact an expression of social genealogies has been demonstrated only in the studies cited above.

Positive, affectional relations are not limited to relatives. Male Japanese macaques may take care of young by forming special protective relationships with particular infants (48), but whether these males have any special relationship to the infants as either father or brother is uncertain, and the mating system is such that paternity cannot be known either to the observer or to the monkeys. MacRoberts (49) has recorded a very high frequency of care of infants by males in the Gibraltar macaque. In addition, he has demonstrated that these positive protective relations are very beneficial to the juvenile. Two juveniles which had no such close relationship were forced to be peripheral, were at a great disadvantage in feeding, and were groomed much less than other juveniles in the group.

The status of the adult can be conferred on closely associated young (frequently an offspring when the adult is female), and for this reason the young of dominant animals are most likely to be dominant. This inheritance of rank has been discussed by Imanishi (45) for the Japanese macaque and by Koford (46) for the rhesus. Sons of very dominant females seem to have a great advantage over other males both because their mothers are able to back them up successfully in social interaction and because they stay with their mothers near the other dominant animals at the center of the group. They may never go through the stage of being socially and physically peripheral to the group which is typical for young males of these species. A male cannot simply "inherit" high rank; he must also win this position through his own abilities, but his chances of so doing are greatly increased if he has had these early experiences of associating with and being supported by very dominant animals.

There could hardly be a greater contrast than that between the emerging picture of an orderly society, based heavily on affectionate or cooperative social actions and structured by stable dominance relationships, and the old notion of an unruly horde of monkeys dominated by a tyrant. The 19th-century social evolutionists attributed less order to the societies of primitive man than is now known to exist in the societies of monkeys and apes living today.

Communication

Research on the communication systems of monkeys and apes through 1962 has been most ably summarized and interpreted by Marler (52). Most of the data represent work by field observers who were primarily interested in social structure, and the signals, and their meanings, used to implement and facilitate social interactions were more or less taken for granted. Only in the last year or so have communication systems themselves been the object of careful study and analysis (see, for example, 18). Marler has emphasized both the extraordinary complexity of the communication systems of primates and the heavy dependence of these systems on composite signals (50). Most frequently it is not a single signal that passes between two animals but a signal complex composed of auditory, visual, tactile, and, more rarely, olfactory signals.

Communication in some monkey species is based on a system of intergrading signals, whereas in others much more use is made of highly discrete signals. For example, most vervet sounds (described by Struhsaker, 51) are of the discrete type, there being some 36 different sounds that are comparatively distinct both to the human ear and when analyzed by a sound spectrograph. In contrast, Rowell and Hinde have analyzed the sounds of the rhesus monkey (52) and found that of 13 harsh noises, 9 belonged to a single intergrading subsystem expressing agonistic emotions.

As more and more study is done on primates it will probably be shown that their communication systems tend to be of mixed form in that both graded and discrete signals are used depending on the relative efficiency of one or the other form in serving a specific function. In concert this use of both discrete and intergrading signals and of composites from several sensory modes produces a rich potential for the expression of very slight but significant changes in the intensity and nature of mood in the signaling animal. Marler has emphasized (50) that, except for calls warning of danger, the communication system is little applied to events outside the group. Communication systems in monkeys and apes are highly evolved in their capacity to express motivation of individuals and to facilitate social relationships. Without this ability to express mood, monkeys and apes would not be able to engage in the subtle and complicated social interactions that are a major feature of their adaptations.

Social Learning

Harlow and Harlow's experiments (53) show the importance of learning in the development of social life; however, monkeys and apes are so constituted that, except in the laboratory, social learning is inevitable. They adapt by their social life, and the group provides the context of affection, protection, and stability in which learning occurs. No one factor can explain the importance of social behavior, because society is a major adaptive mechanism with many functions, but one of the most important of these functions is the provision of a rich and protected social context in which young mature. Field observations, although mainly observations of the results of learning rather than of the process itself, provide necessary clues as to the nature of the integration of relevant developmental and social factors. These factors can then be estimated and defined for subsequent intensive controlled research in a laboratory or colony.

It has become clear that, although learning has great importance in the normal development of nearly all phases of primate behavior, it is not a generalized ability; animals are able to learn some things with great ease and other things only with the greatest of difficulty. Learning is part of the adaptive pattern of a species and can be understood only when it is seen as the process of acquiring skills and attitudes that are of evolutionary significance to a species when living in the environment to which it is adapted.

There are important biological limitations which vary from species to species and which do not reflect differences in intelligence so much as differences in specializations. For example, Goodall (21) has observed young chimpanzees learning to fish for termites both by their observation of older chimpanzees and by practice. It takes time for the chimpanzee to become proficient with these tools, and many mistakes are made. Chimpanzees are not the only primates that like termites, and Goodall has observed baboons sitting near chimpanzees watching and waiting while the latter are getting termites. The baboons are just as eager as the chimpanzees to eat termites but are unable to learn how to fish for termites for themselves.

It is likely that there are important variables among groups of a single species that make it possible for the acquisition of new patterns of behavior or the expression of basic learned species patterns to vary from group to group and from one habitat to another. For example, the nature of the integration and operation of a social unit varies in the extent to which it depends on the personalities of individuals in the group—this is another dimension of our understanding of how social behavior may affect species survival. Particularly aggressive adult males can make the behavior of their groups relative to that of adjacent groups with less assertive males substantially different. For example, a group with very aggressive males can control a larger geographic area than is occupied by a group with much less aggressive males. The tenor of life within a group may be tenser or more relaxed depending on personalities of adults in the group.

Imprinting has traditionally been distinguished from other learning processes by the fact that in imprinting the young animal will learn to follow, to be social (54), without an external or immediate reward (55). However, among monkeys and apes, simply being with other animals is a reward, and learning is reinforced by the affectional, attentive, supportive social context of the group (56). Butler was the first to use the sight of another monkey as a reward in psychological experiments (57). The field worker sees sick and practically disabled animals making great efforts to stay with their group. Among ground-living forms, animals that have lost or broken limbs or are so sick that they collapse as soon as the group stops moving, all walk along as the troop moves. Instances of wounded rhesus macaques moving into langur groups after the rhesus have left or have been forced out of their own group have been recorded. Clearly, it is essential for the young monkey or ape to mature in a social setting in which it learns appropriate skills and relationships during early years and in which it continues to learn during adulthood. "Where the individual primate is, in temporary isolation, learning a task without reference to any other member of its species, the learning is not normal" (58).

Future Primate Studies

At present many long-term studies are in process and major films are being edited (Goodall on chimpanzee and DeVore on baboon). There will be about twice as many accounts available in 2 years as there are now. Since it is now clear that detailed descriptive studies of undisturbed free-ranging primates can be made, and since available data show that there are substantial differences in the behavior of the different species, more species should be investigated. So far studies have concentrated for the most part on the larger ground-living forms which are easier to study. There is no study of *Cercocebus*, little on *Colobus* (59), and nothing on the numerous langurs *(Presbytis)* of southeast Asia. New World monkeys have been investigated very little, and there are numerous genera that have not been the subjects of a major field study. Also, since local variation is important, forms such as the chimpanzee and gorilla should be studied in more and contrasting localities.

Once the general characteristics of the behaviors of several species are known, then interest can shift to topics such as detailed ecology, birth, infant behavior, peer groups, affectionate behaviors, sex, or dominance, to mention only a few. The behavior of a whole species is a large problem, and description has to be at a very general level when the goal is a first general statement. A problem-oriented study permits choice of species and elaboration of techniques. A further advantage of the problem-oriented approach is that it allows the close coordination of the field work with experimental work in the laboratory. Fortunately, no division has developed between those doing the field work and those involved in the experimental analysis of behavior. Many scientists have done both controlled experiments and field studies. The interplay between naturalistic observation and controlled experiment is the essential key to the understanding of behavior (60). The character of the natural adaptation of the species and the dimensions of the society can be determined only in the field. Many topics, such as geographic range, food, predation, group size, aggression, and the like, can be seen only under field conditions. But the mechanisms of the observed behavior can be determined only in the laboratory, and this is the more complicated task. The relation of a field study to scientific understanding is like the relation of the observation that a man walks or runs to the whole analysis of locomotion. The field worker lists what the animals eat, but this gives no understanding of nutrition. The kinds of interactions may be charted in the field, but their interpretation requires the laboratory. Field workers saw hours devoted to play, but it was Harlow's experiments that showed how essential this activity was to the development of behavior. As the field studies develop it is to be hoped that they will maintain a close relation to controlled experiment. It is most fortunate that the present studies are being carried on by anthropologists, psychologists, and zoologists. An understanding of behavior is most likely to come from the bringing together of the methods and interests of many sciences, and we hope that the field studies remain a part of general behavioral science and do not become independent as workers and problems become more and more numerous.

Even now, in their preliminary state, the field studies can offer some conclusions that might be pondered by students in the multiplicity of departments now dividing up the study of human behavior. Behavior is profoundly influenced by the biology of the species, and problems of perception, emotion, aggression, and many others cannot be divorced from the biology of the actors in the social system. Early learning is important, and an understanding of the preschool years is essential to an understanding of behavior. Play is tremendously important, and a species that wastes the emotions and energies of its young by divorcing play from education has forfeited its evolutionary heritage—the biological motivation of learning. Social behavior is relatively simple compared to the biological mechanisms that make the behavior possible. Ultimately a science of human behavior must include both biological and social factors, and there is no more reason to separate the study of human behavior into many compartments than there would be to separate the field studies from the intellectual enrichment coming from the laboratory.

References

1. R. M. Yerkes and A. W. Yerkes, *The Great Apes, A Study of Anthropoid Life* (New Haven: Yale Univ. Press, 1929).
2. H. W. Nissen, "A Field Study of the Chimpanzee," *Comp. Psychol. Monogr. No. 8* (1931).
3. H. C. Bingham, "Gorillas in a Native Habitat," *Carnegie Inst. Wash. Publ. No. 426* (1932).
4. C. R. Carpenter, "A Field Study of the Behavior and Social Relations of Howling Monkeys," *Comp. Psych. Monogr. No. 10* (1934).
5. S. Zuckerman, *The Social Life of Monkeys and Apes* (London: Routledge and Kegan Paul, 1932); *Functional Affinities and Man, Monkeys and Apes* (London: Routledge and Kegan Paul, 1933).
6. C. R. Carpenter, "A Field Study in Siam of the Behavior and Social Relations of the Gibbon, *Hylobates lar.*," *Comp. Psychol. Monogr. No. 16* (1940).
7. E. A. Hooton, *Man's Poor Relations* (Garden City, N.Y.: Doubleday, 1942).
8. K. R. L. Hall, *Proc. Zool. Soc. London 14:265* (1965).
9. W. Köhler, *The Mentality of Apes* (New York: Harcourt Brace, 1925).
10. J. Buettner-Janusch, ed., "The Relatives of Man," *Ann. N.Y. Acad. Sci.* 102:181-514 (1962); J. Buettner-Janusch, ed., *Evolutionary and Genetic Biology of Primates* (New York: Academic Press, 1963-1964).

11. S. L. Washburn, ed., *Classification and Human Evolution,* Viking Fund Publications in Anthropology No. 37 (Aldine, New York, 1963).

12. J. Napier and N. Barnicot, eds., "The Primates," *Symp. Zool. Soc. London No. 10* (1963).

13. I. DeVore, ed., *Primate Behavior: Field Studies of Monkeys and Apes* (New York: Holt, Rinehart and Winston, 1965).

14. C. R. Carpenter, *Naturalistic Behavior of Nonhuman Primates* (University Park: Pennsylvania State Univ. Press, 1964).

15. C. H. Southwick, ed., *Primate Social Behavior* (Princeton: Van Nostrand, 1963).

16. S. Eimerl and I. DeVore, *The Primates* (New York: Time, Inc., 1965).

17. P. Jay, in *Behavior of Nonhuman Primates,* A. M. Schrier, H. F. Harlow, F. Stollnitz, eds. (New York: Academic Press, 1965), pp. 525-591.

18. S. A. Altmann, ed., "Social Communication among Primates" (Chicago: Univ. of Chicago Press, 1963).

19. G. Schaller, *The Mountain Gorilla: Ecology and Behavior* (Chicago: Univ. of Chicago Press, 1963).

20. J. Goodall, *Primate Behavior: Field Studies of Monkeys and Apes,* I. DeVore, ed. (New York: Holt, Rinehart and Winston, 1965), pp. 425-473.

21. ———, *Nature 201:1264* (1964).

22. K. R. L. Hall, *Current Anthropol.* 4(5):479 (1963).

23. J. B. Lancaster, "Chimpanzee Tool Use," paper presented at Southwestern Anthropological Association annual meeting, Los Angeles, Calif. (Apr. 1965).

24. I. DeVore and K. R. L. Hall, in *Primate Behavior: Field Studies of Monkeys and Apes* (New York: Holt, Rinehart and Winston, 1965), pp. 20-22.

25. "Baboon Behavior," motion picture produced by I. DeVore and S. L. Washburn, University Extension, Univ. Of California, Berkeley (1961).

26. I. DeVore, personal communication (1965).

27. A. J. Haddow, *Proc. Zool. Soc. London 122* (II):297 (1952).

28. P. Jay and D. Lindburg, "The Indian Primate Ecology Project (September 1964-June 1965)," unpublished manuscript.

29. C. H. Southwick, M. A. Beg, M. R. Siddiqi, *Ecology* 42:538 (1961); *ibid.,* p. 698.

30. J. B. Lancaster and R. B. Lee, in *Primate Behavior: Field Studies of Monkeys and Apes,* I. DeVore, ed. (New York: Holt, Rinehart and Winston, 1965), pp 486-513.

31. M. Mizuhara, personal communication (1965), quoted by Lancaster and Lee (30).

32. C. B. Koford, in *Primate Behavior: Field Studies of Monkeys and Apes,* I. DeVore, ed. (New York: Holt, Rinehart and Winston, 1965), pp. 160-174.

33. A. H. Schultz, *Anat. Rec.* 72:387 (1938).

34. P. Jay in *Primate Behavior: Field Studies of Monkeys and Apes,* I. DeVore, ed. (New York: Holt, Rinehart and Winston, 1965), pp. 197-249.

35. H. Kummer and F. Kurt, *Folia Primatologica* 1:4 (1963).

36. P. E. Simonds, in *Primate Behavior: Field Studies of Monkeys and Apes,* I. DeVore, ed. (New York: Holt, Rinehart and Winston, 1965), pp. 175-196.

37. K. R. L. Hall and I. DeVore, in *Primate Behavior: Field Studies of Monkeys and Apes,* I. DeVore, ed. (New York, Holt, Rinehart and Winston, 1965), pp. 53-110.

38. K. Tojuda, *Primates* 3:1 (1961-62).

39. C. H. Conaway and C. B. Koford, *J. Mammal.* 45:577 (1965).

40. C. Southwick, in *Primate Behavior: Field Studies of Monkeys and Apes,* I. DeVore, ed. (New York: Holt, Rinehart and Winston, 1965) pp. 111-159.

41. M. Yamada, *Primates* 4:45 (1963).

42. S. Ripley, in "Social Communication among Primates," S. Altmann, ed. (Chicago: Univ. of Chicago Press, 1967).

43. S. A. Altmann, *Ann. N.Y. Acad. Sci.* 102:338 (1962).

44. J. Itani, R. Tokuda, Y. Furuya, K. Kano, Y. Shin, *Primates* 4:1 (1963).

45. K. Imanishi, *Current Anthropol.* 1:393 (1960).

46. C. B. Koford, *Science* 141:356 (1963).

47. D. S. Sade, *Am. J. Phys. Anthropol.* 23:1 (1965).

48. J. Itani, *Primates* 4:1 (1959).

49. M. MacRoberts, "Gibralter macaques," paper presented at Southwestern Anthropological Association annual meeting, Los Angeles, Calif. (Apr. 1965).

50. P. Marler, in *Primate Behavior: Field Studies of Monkeys and Apes,* I. DeVore, ed. (New York: Holt, Rinehart, and Winston, 1965) , pp. 544-584.

51. T. T. Struhsaker, in "Social Communication among Primates," S. A. Altmann, ed. (Chicago: Univ. of Chicago Press, 1967).

52. T. E. Rowell and R. A. Hinde, *Proc. Zool. Soc. London* 138:279 (1962); T. E. Rowell, *Symp. Zool. Soc. London* 8:91 (1962).

53. H. F. Harlow and M. K. Harlow, in *Behavior of Nonhuman Primates,* A. M. Schrier, H. F. Harlow, F. Stollnitz, eds. (New York: Academic Press, 1965); vol. 2, pp. 287-334.

54. N. E. Collias, in *Roots of Behavior,* E. L. Bliss, ed. (New York: Harper, 1962), pp. 264-273.

55. W. Sluckin, *Imprinting and Early Learning* (Chicago: Aldine, 1965).

56. K. R. L. Hall, *Brit. J. Psychol.* 54:201 (1963).

57. R. A. Bulter, *J. Exp. Psychol.* 48:19 (1954).

58. K. R. L. Hall, unpublished manuscript.

59. W. Ulrich, *Zool. Garten* 25:305 (1961).

60. W. A. Mason, in *Primate Behavior: Field Studies of Monkeys and Apes,* I. DeVore, ed. (New York: Holt, Rinehart and Winston, 1965), pp. 514-543.

PART THREE

The Origins of Society

The hunter-gathering bands described in several papers in Part Two left scanty evidence of their existence by way of skeletal remains, tool kits, or other artifacts. From what little knowledge we have, it is surmised that a hunter-gathering stage of our ancestral human species populated the greater part of the Old World, segmenting it into a series of more-or-less stable territories. They were probably comparable in size and function to the aborigine territories that European explorers found established on the continent of Australia some hundred years ago. It is only from the time of the adoption of permanent settlements by our forebears that we begin to find a significantly increased number of human remains and artifacts, and from them, conjectures as to the ecology of past human life patterns can have a more substantial factual basis.

Without the establishment of permanent settlements, it seems probable that the cultural evolution of our species in its hunter-gathering bands would have continued at an extremely slow pace. Permanent settlements offered vast opportunities both for the exchange of information and for an increased division of labor. The possibilities they provided for the spread of new artifacts, sociofacts, and mentifacts were very much higher than in nomadic hunter-gathering bands. Each male or female no longer had to be a jack-of-all-trades, but could specialize in particular activities according to his or her aptitudes, inclinations, and abilities. Cultural advances developing specialist skills could more easily and more rapidly be disseminated in these settlement concentrations. Moreover, the possession of a permanent location permitted the accumulation of a far greater store of artifacts than could ever be transported by a nomadic band. It also set the scene for the Agricultural Revolution, which isolated groups of nomadic hunter-gatherers were apparently never able to achieve, as witness the contemporary Australian aborigines and Kalahari Bushmen.

Several of the papers in this part describe the nature of the earliest settlements and the possible reasons for their development. Other papers deal with the evolution of the structure of such settlements through the Agricultural Revolution to the Industrial Revolution, and some survey the basic functions of modern urban ecosystems and the diversity of human form that is encountered there. Although the patterns of urban civilization have been established for an estimated twelve or thirteen thousand years, something like two-thirds of our contemporary world population is still not completely urbanized. Nor have we all entirely abandoned a nomadic, or at least a migratory, way of life.

Some of the favorable situations that may have encouraged the establishment of permanent settlements in Central America are described by Michael D. Coe and Kent V. Flannery in the first selection here (11). Charles B. Heiser, Jr., discusses such early settlements in relation to initial plant domestication (12). D. K. Belyaev provides a similar account of animal domestication (13), outlining the probable sequence of events that followed the domestication of a species. Apparently such agricultural innovations were occurring spontaneously and simultaneously in several independent areas around the world approximately 15,000 BP. C. A. Doxiadis provides a stimulating theory as to how urban development proceeded from this time in terms of the mode of transportation (14). Athalstan Spilhaus relates how an ideal city is currently being planned and tells of the basic features that are considered necessary to its well-being (15).

Urban development could not have proceeded at its present rate without a compelling urge toward migration into urban centers. Possible effects of such in-migration are discussed in a short and controversial presentation by Richard Lynn (16) on a selective modern expression of such mass movement, "the brain drain." The basic need for instrumental learning is apparently one of the major forces that make us cluster in our urban areas, and cause this brain drain. The extent to which global aboriginal dispersal patterns may thereby have been disrupted within the last three centuries is illustrated by the concluding paper (17) in this section by T. Edward Reed, "Caucasian Genes in American Negroes." This paper illustrates two major themes of great significance in contemporary societies, *mobility* and *diversification*. A number of the papers listed in the Additional Readings for this section discuss these two phenomena.

We began to adopt the settlement patterns and urban society structures described in these selections a mere 15 millenia ago. Against the total one hundred thousand to one quarter million year history of our species, this can represent no more than the final 15 per cent of our evolutionary span. The other 85 to 94 per cent of the time, we were hunter-gatherers—as some of us still remain. It is not surprising then that while our cultural patterns have often acquired a veneer of sophistication, our innate behavior, our instincts (if this now somewhat outmoded word is still used) are basically those of a hunter-gatherer. One of these instincts, the desire to reproduce ourselves to the limits of our cultural capacity, has now landed us in an era that future historians may well label the Age of Overpopulation. This is the topic of Part Four.

Additional Readings

Adams, R. M. "The origin of cities," *Scientific American* 203 (3): 153-68, 1960.

Barry, J. "France's planners draw blue prints of an urban dream," *Smithsonian* 2(4): 40-45, 1971.

Bartlett, A. S., Barghoorn, E. S., and Berger, R. "Fossil maize from Panama," *Science* 165: 389-90, 1969.

Beale, C. L. "Rural depopulation in the United States," *Demography* 1: 264-72, 1964.

Bloom, H. F. "Does the melanin pigment of human skin have adaptive value?" *Quart. Rev. Biol.* 36: 50-63, 1961.

Borchert, J. R. "American metropolitan evolution," *Geographical Review* 57: 301-32, 1967.

Brace, C. L. "A non-racial approach towards the understanding of human diversity," in *The Concept of Race*, M. F. Ashley-Montagu, ed., New York: The Free Press, 1962.

Braidwood, R. J. "The agricultural revolution," *Scientific American* 203(3): 130-48, 1960.

——, Cambel, H., and Watson, P. J. "Prehistoric investigations in Southeastern Turkey," *Science* 164: 1275-76, 1969.

Cain, S. A. "Man and his environment," *Bulletin* 22: 96-103, 1966.

Cambel, H., and Braidwood, R. J. "An early farming village in Turkey," *Scientific American* 222(3): 50-56, 1970.

Cockrill, W. R. "The water buffalo," *Scientific American* 217(6): 118-25, 1967.

Court-Brown, W. M. "Heredity and responsibility," *New Scientist* 40: 235-36, 1968.

Crow, J. F. "The quality of people: human evolutionary changes," *Bioscience* 16: 863-67, 1966.

Curry, L. "Landscape as system," *Geographical Review* 54: 121-24, 1964.

Deevey, E. S. "The human population," *Scientific American* 203(3): 194-204, 1960.

Denevan, W. M. "Aboriginal drained-field cultivation in the Americas," *Science* 169: 647-54, 1970.

Dobzansky, T. "Genetics of race equality," *Eugenics Quart.* 10: 151-60, 1963.

Doxiadis, C. A. "Ekistics, the science of human settlements," *Science* 170: 393-404, 1970.

Duncan, O. D. "Occupation trends and patterns of net mobility," *Demography* 3: 444-55, 1965.

Dyer, K. F, "Hidden variability in man," *New Scientist* 44: 72-74, 1969.

Emden, J. M. "Natural selection and human behavior," *J. Theor. Biol.* 12: 410-18, 1966.

Flannery, K. V. "The ecology of early food production in Mesopotamia," *Science* 147: 1247-56, 1965.

Giula, M. F., and Daniels, D. N. "Violence and man's struggle to adapt," *Science* 164: 396-409, 1969.

Goldstein, S., and Mayer, K. B. "The impact of migration on the socioeconomic structure of cities and suburbs," *Sociology and Social Research* 50: 5-23, 1965.

Guildford, J. P. "Intelligence has three facets," *Science* 160: 615-20, 1968.

Harlan, J. R., and Zachary, D. "Distribution of wild wheats and barley," *Science* 153: 1074-80, 1966.

Harris, B. "City of the future," *Papers and Proceedings of the Regional Science Association* 19: 185-98, 1967.

Harris, D. R., "New light on plant domestication and the origin of agriculture: A review, "*Geograph Rev.* 57: 90-107, 1967.

Harris, M. "The cultural ecology of India's sacred cattle," *Curr. Anthropol.* 7: 51-56, 1966.

Haynes, C. V. "The earliest Americans," *Science* 166: 709-15, 1969.

Helback, H. "Ecological effects of irrigation in ancient Mesopotamia," *Iraq* 22: 186-96, 1960.

Helbark, R. "Domestication of food plants in the Old World," *Science* 130: 365-72, 1959.

Higgs, E. S., and Jarman, M. R. "The origins of agriculture: A reconsideration," *Antiquity* 43: 31-41, 1969.

Higham, C. F. W., and Leach, B. F. "An early center of bovine husbandry in Southeast Asia," *Science* 172: 54-56, 1971.

Hutchins, J. G. B. "The motor vehicle and the return of personalized transport," *Intern. J. Environ. Studies* 3: 173-79, 1972.

Isaac, E. "On the domestication of cattle," *Science* 137: 195-204, 1962.

Jacobsen, T., and Adams, R. M. "Salt and silt in ancient Mesopotamian agriculture," *Science* 128: 1251-58, 1958.

Jensen, A. "How much can we boost IQ and scholastic achievement?" *Harvard Educ. Rev.* 39(1): 1-123, 1969.

Johnson-Marshall, P. "The urban environment and the motor vehicle," *Intern. J. Environ. Studies* 3: 167-71, 1972.

Krantz, G. S. "Human activities and megafauna extinctions" *Amer. Scientist* 58(2): 164-70, 1970.

Krech, D. "The chemistry of learning," *Saturday Review*, January 20, 1968.

Lamberg-Karlovsky, C. C., and Lamberg-Karlovsky, M. "An early city in Iran," *Scientific American* 224(6): 102-11, 1971.

Laughlin, W. S. "Race: A population concept," *Eugenics Quart.* 13: 326-40, 1966.

Lederberg, J. "Experimental genetics and human evolution," *Amer. Naturalist* 100: 519-31, 1966.

Lee, E. S. "A theory of migration," *Demography* 3: 7-57, 1966.

Lowry, W. P. "The climate of cities," *Scientific American* 217(2): 15-23, 1967.

Lubove, R. "Urbanization process," *J. Amer. Inst. Planners* 33: 33-38, 1967.

McClure, H. M., Belden, K. H., Peiper, W. A., and Jacobsen, C. B. "Autosomal trisomy in a chimpanzee: Resemblance to Down's syndrome," *Science* 165: 1010-12, 1969.

MacNeish, R. S. "Early man in the Andes," *Scientific American* 224(4): 36-46, 1971.

Mangelsdorf, P. C., MacNeish, R. S., and Galinat, W. C. "Domestication of corn," *Science* 143: 538-45, 1961.

Mead, M. "The generation gap," *Science* 164: April 11, 1969.

Mellaart, J. "A Neolithic city in Turkey," *Scientific American* 210(4): 94-104, 1964.

———, "Deities and shrines of neolithic Anatolia: Excavations at Catal Hüyük, 1962," *Archeology* 16: 28-38, 1963.

Millon, R. "Teotihuacan: Completion of map of giant ancient city in the valley of Mexico," *Science* 172: 1077-82, 1971.

Mines, S. "Did you say *ekistics?*" *Ecology Today* 1(5): 21-24, 1971.

Newling, B. E. "Urban growth and spatial structure," *Geog. Rev.* 56: 213-25, 1966.

Northam, R. "Declining urban centers in the United States 1940-1960," *Annals Assoc. Amer. Geographers* 53: 50-59, 1963.

Northam, R. "Population size, relative location, and declining urban centers in the U.S.," *Land Economics* 45: 313-22, 1969.

O'Flaherty, C. A. "People, transport systems, and the urban scene: An overview," *Intern. J. Environ. Studies* 3: 265-85, 1972.

Parr, J. B. "City hierarchies and the distribution of city sizes," *J. Regional Science* 9: 239-54, 1969.

Perkins, D., and Daly, P. "A hunter's village in Neolithic Turkey," *Scientific American* 219(5): 98-106, 1968.

Reed, C. A. "Extinction of mammalian megafauna in the Old World late quaternary," *Bioscience* 20: 284-88, 1970.

Roberts, D. F., and Bainbridge, D. R. "Nilotic physique," *Amer. J. Phys. Anthropol.* 21: 341-70, 1963.

Russell, M. M. S. "The slash and burn technique," *Natural History* 77: 58-65, 1968.

Sahlins, M. D. "The origin of society," *Scientific American* 203(3): 76-87, 1960.

Sauer, C. O. "Seashore—primitive home of man?" *Amer. Philosoph. Soc. Proc.* 106: 41-47, 1962.

Schreider, E. "Ecological rules, body-heat regulation, and human evolution," *Evolution* 18: 1-9, 1964.

Sheppard, P. M. "Blood groups and natural selection," *Brit. Med. Bull.* 15: 134-39, 1969.

Soleri, P. *Arcology: The City in the Image of Man*, Cambridge, Mass.: MIT Press, 1969.

Stearns, F. W. "Wildlife habitat in urban and suburban environments," *Trans. N. A. Wildlife and Nat. Res. Conf.* 32: 61-69, 1967.

Street, J. M. "Evaluation of the concept of carrying capacity," *Professional Geographer* 21: 104-107, 1969.

Tijio, J. H., and Levan, A. "The chromosome number of man," *Hereditas* 4: 1, 1959.

Ucko, P. J., and Dimbleby, G. W., eds. *The Domestication and Exploitation of Plants and Animals*, Chicago: Aldine, 1969.

Ugent, D. "The potato," *Science* 170: 1161-66, 1970.

Wright, H. E. "Environmental changes and the origin of agriculture in the Near East," *Bioscience* 20: 210-12, 1970.

11

MICROENVIRONMENTS AND MESOAMERICAN PREHISTORY

Michael D. Coe and Kent V. Flannery

A crucial period in the story of the pre-Columbian cultures of the New World is the transition from a hunting-and-collecting way of life to effective village farming. We are now fairly certain that Mesoamerica (1) is the area in which this took place, and that the time span involved is from approximately 6500 to 1000 B.C., a period during which a kind of "incipient cultivation" based on a few domesticated plants, mainly maize, gradually supplemented and eventually replaced wild foods (2). Beginning probably about 1500 B.C., and definitely by 1000 B.C., villages with all of the signs of the settled arts, such as pottery and loom-weaving, appear throughout Mesoamerica, and the foundations of pre-Columbian civilization may be said to have been established.

Much has been written about food-producing "revolutions" in both hemispheres. There is now good evidence both in the Near East and in Mesoamerica that food production was part of a relatively slow *evolution*, but there still remain several problems related to the process of settling down. For the New World, there are three questions which we would like to answer.

1. What factors favored the early development of food production in Mesoamerica as compared with other regions of this hemisphere?

2. What was the mode of life of the earlier hunting-and-collecting peoples in Mesoamerica, and in exactly what ways was it changed by the addition of cultivated plants?

3. When, where, and how did food production make it possible for the first truly sedentary villages to be established in Mesoamerica?

The first of these questions cannot be answered until botanists determine the habits and preferred habitats of the wild ancestors of maize, beans, and the various cucurbits which were domesticated. To answer the other questions, we must reconstruct the human-ecological situations which prevailed.

Some remarkably sophisticated, multidisciplinary projects have been and still are being carried out elsewhere in the world, aimed at reconstructing prehistoric human ecology. However, for the most part they have been concerned with the adaptations of past human communities to large-scale changes in the environment over very long periods—that is, to alterations in the *macroenvironment*, generally caused by climatic fluctuations. Such alterations include the shift from tundra to boreal conditions in northern Europe. Nevertheless, there has been a growing suspicion among prehistorians that macroenvironmental changes are insufficient as an explanation of the possible causes of food production and its effects (3) regardless of what has been written to the contrary.

Ethnography and Microenvironments

We have been impressed, in reading anthropologists' accounts of simple societies, with the fact that human communities, while in some senses limited by the macroenvironment—for instance, by deserts or by tropical forests (4) usually exploit several or even a whole series of well-defined *microenvironments* in their quest for food (5). These microenvironments might be defined as smaller subdivisions of large ecological zones; examples are the immediate surroundings of the ancient archeological site itself, the bank of a nearby stream, or a distant patch of forest.

An interesting case is provided by the Shoshonean bands which, until the mid-19th century, occupied territories within the Great Basin of the American West (6). These extremely primitive peoples had a mode of life quite similar to that of the peoples of Mesoamerica of the 5th millennium B.C., who were the first to domesticate maize. The broadly limiting effects of the Great Basin (which, generally speaking, is a desert) and the lack of knowledge of irrigation precluded any effective form of agriculture, even though some bands actually sowed wild grasses and one group tried an ineffective watering of wild crops. Consequently, the Great Basin aborigines remained on a hunting and plant-collecting level, with extremely low population densities and a very simple social organization. However, Steward's study (6) shows that each band was not inhabiting a mere desert but moved on a strictly followed seasonal round among a vertically and horizontally differentiated set of microenvironments, from the lowest salt flats up to piñon forest, which were "niches" in a human-ecological sense.

The Great Basin environment supplied the potential for cultural development or lack of it, but the men who lived there selected this or that microenvironment. Steward clearly shows that *how* and *to what* they adapted influenced many other aspects of their culture, from their technology to their settlement pattern, which was necessarily one of restricted wandering from one seasonally occupied camp to another.

Seasonal wandering would appear to be about the only possible response of a people without animal or plant husbandry to the problem of getting enough food throughout the year. Even the relatively rich salmon-fishing cultures of the Northwest Coast (British Columbia and southern Alaska) were without permanently occupied villages. Contrariwise, it has seemed to us that only a drastic reduction of the number of niches to be exploited, and a concentration of these in space, would have permitted the establishment of full-time village life. The ethnographic data suggest that an analysis of microenvironments or niches would throw much light on the processes by which the Mesoamerican peoples settled down.

Methodology

If the environment in which an ancient people lived was radically different from any

known today, and especially if it included animal and plant species which are now extinct and whose behavior is consequently unknown, then any reconstruction of the subsistence activities of the people is going to be difficult. All one could hope for would be a more-or-less sound reconstruction of general ecological conditions, while a breakdown of the environment into smaller ecological niches would be impossible. However, much if not most archeological research concerns periods so recent in comparison with the million or so years of human prehistory that in most instances local conditions have not changed greatly in the interval between the periods investigated and the present.

If we assume that there is a continuity between the ancient and the modern macro-environments in the area of interest, there are three steps which we must take in tracing the role of microenvironments.

1. Analysis of the present-day microecology (from the human point of view) of the archeological zone. Archeological research is often carried out in remote and little known parts of the earth, which have not been studied from the point of view of natural history. Hence, the active participation of botanists, zoologists, and other natural scientists is highly recommended.

The modern ethnology of the region should never be neglected, for all kinds of highly relevant data on the use of surrounding niches by local people often lie immediately at hand. We have found in Mesoamerica that the workmen on the "dig" are a mine of such information. There may be little need to thumb through weighty reports on the Australian aborigines or South African Bushmen when the analogous custom can be found right under one's nose (7). The end result of the analysis should be a map of the microenvironments defined (here aerial photographs are a great use), with detailed data on the seasonal possibilities each offers human communities on certain technological levels of development,

2. Quantitative analysis of food remains in the archeological sites, and of the technical equipment (arrow or spear points, grinding stones for seeds, baskets and other containers, and so on) related to food-getting. It is a rare

site report that treats of bones and plant remains in any but the most perfunctory way. It might seem a simple thing to ship animal bones from a site to a specialist for identification, but most archeologists know that many zoologists consider identification of recent faunal remains a waste of time (8). Because of this, and because many museum collections do not include postcranial skeletons that could be used for identification, the archeologist must arrange to secure his own comparative collection. If this collection is assembled by a zoologist on the project, a by-product of the investigation would be a faunal study of microenvironments. Similarly, identification of floral and other specimens from the site would lead to other specialized studies.

3. Correlation of the archeological with the microenvironmental study in an overall analysis of the ancient human ecology.

The Tehuacán Valley

An archeological project undertaken by R. S. MacNeish, with such a strategy in mind, has been located since 1961 in the dry Tehuacán Valley of southern Puebla, Mexico (2, 9). The valley is fringed with bone-dry caves in which the food remains of early peoples have been preserved to a remarkable degree in stratified deposits. For a number of reasons, including the results of his past archeological work in

Mesoamerica, MacNeish believed that he would find here the origins of maize agriculture in the New World, and he has been proved right. It now seems certain that the wild ancestor of maize was domesticated in the Tehuacán area some time around the beginning of the 5th millennium B.C.

While the Tehuacán environment is in general a desert, the natural scientists of the project have defined within it four microenvironments. (Fig. 11-1).

1. *Alluvial valley floor,* a level plain sparsely covered with mesquite, grasses, and cacti, offering fairly good possibilities, especially along the Rio Salado, for primitive maize agriculture dependent on rainfall.

2. *Travertine slopes,* on the west side of the valley. This would have been a niche useful for growing maize and tomatoes and for trapping cottontail rabbits.

3. *Coxcatlán thorn forest,* with abundant seasonal crops of wild fruits, such as various species of *Opuntia,* pitahaya, and so on. There is also a seasonal abundance of whitetail deer, cottontail rabbits, and skunks, and there are some peccaries.

4. *Eroded canyons,* unsuitable for exploitation except for limited hunting of deer and as routes up to maguey fields for those peoples who chewed the leaves of that plant.

The correlation of this study with the analysis, by specialists, of the plant and animal remains (these include bones, maize cobs, chewed quids, and even feces) found in cave

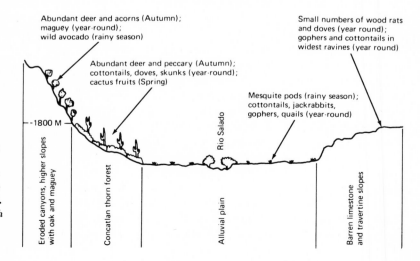

Fig. 11-1. An idealized east-west transection of the central part of the Tehuacán Valley, Puebla, Mexico, showing microenvironments and the seasons in which the food resources are exploited. East is to the left. The length of the area represented is about 20 kilometers.

Abundant deer and acorns (Autumn); maguey (year-round); wild avocado (rainy season)

Abundant deer and peccary (Autumn); cottontails, doves, skunks (year-round); cactus fruits (Spring)

Small numbers of wood rats and doves (year round); gophers and cottontails in widest ravines (year round)

Mesquite pods (rainy season); cottontails, jackrabbits, gophers, quails (year-round)

-1800 M

Rio Salado

Eroded canyons, higher slopes with oak and maguey

Concatlan thorn forest

Alluvial plain

Barren limestone and travertine slopes

deposits has shown that the way of life of the New World's first farmers was not very different from that of the Great Basin aborigines in the 19th century. Even the earliest inhabitants of the valley, prior to 6500 B.C., were more collectors of seasonally gathered wild plant foods than they were "big game hunters," and they traveled in microbands in an annual, wet-season-dry-season cycle (10). While slightly more sedentary macrobands appeared with the adoption of simple maize cultivation after 5000 B.C., these people nevertheless still followed the old pattern of moving from microenvironment to microenvironment, separating into microbands during the dry season.

The invention and gradual improvement of agriculture seem to have made few profound alterations in the settlement pattern of the valley for many millennia. Significantly, by the Formative period (from about 1500 B.C. to A.D. 200), when agriculture based on a hybridized maize was far more important than it had been in earlier periods as a source of food energy, the pattern was still one of part-time nomadism (11). In this part of the dry Mexican highlands , until the Classic period (about A.D. 200 to 900), when irrigation appears to have been introduced into Tehuacán, food production had still to be supplemented with extensive plant collecting and hunting.

Most of the peoples of the Formative period apparently lived in large villages on the alluvial valley floor during the wet season, from May through October of each year, for planting had to be done in May and June, and harvesting, in September and October. In the dry season, from November through February, when the trees and bushes had lost their leaves and the deer were easy to see and track, some of the population must have moved to hunting camps, principally in the Coxcatlán thorn forest. By February, hunting had become less rewarding as the now-wary deer moved as far as possible from human habitation; however, in April and May the thorn forest was still ripe for exploitation, as many kinds of wild fruit matured. In May it was again time to return to the villages on the valley floor for spring planting.

Now, in some other regions of Mesoamerica there were already, during the Formative period, fully sedentary village cultures in existence. It is clear that while the Tehuacán valley was the locus of the first domestication of maize, the origins of full-blown village life lie elsewhere. Because of the constraining effects of the macroenvironment, the Tehuacán people were exploiting, until relatively late in Mesoamerican prehistory, as widely spaced and as large a number of microenvironments as the Great Basin aborigines were exploiting in the 19th century.

Coastal Guatemala

Near the modern fishing port of Ocós, only a few kilometers from the Mexican border on the alluvial plain of the Pacific coast of Guatemala, we have found evidence for some of the oldest permanently occupied villages in Mesoamerica (12). We have also made an extensive study of the ecology and ethnology of the Ocós area.

From this study (13) we have defined no less than eight distinct microenvironments (Fig. 11-2) within an area of only about 90 square kilometers. These are as follows:

1. *Beach sand and low scrub.* A narrow, infertile strip from which the present-day villagers collect occasional mollusks, a beach crab called *chichimeco* and one known as *nazareño* and the sea turtle and its eggs.

2. *The marine estuary-and-lagoon system*, in places extending considerably inland and ultimately connecting with streams or rivers coming down from the Sierra Madre. The estuaries, with their mangrove-lined banks, make up the microenvironment richest in wild foods in the entire area. The brackish waters abound in catfish (*Arius* sp. and *Galeichthys* sp.), red snapper (*Lutjanus colorado*), several species of snook (*Centropomus* sp.), and many other kinds of fish. Within living memory, crocodiles (*Crocodylus astutus*) were common, but they have by now been hunted almost to extinction. The muddy banks of the estuaries are the habitat of many kinds of mollusks, including marsh clams (*Polymesoda radiata*), mussels (*Mytella falcata*), and oysters (*Ostrea columbiensis*), and they also support an extensive population of fiddler and mud crabs.

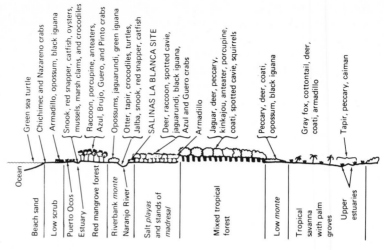

Fig. 11-2. Northeast-southwest transection of the Ocós area of coastal Guatemala, showing microenvironments in relation to the site of Salinas La Blanca. Northeast is to the right. The length of the area represented is about 15 kilometers.

3. *Mangrove forest,* consisting mainly of stilt-rooted red mangrove, which slowly gives way to white mangrove as one moves away from the estuary. We noted high populations of collared anteater *(Tamandua tetradactyla)* and arboreal porcupine *(Coendu mexicanus).* A large number of crabs (we did not determine the species) inhabit this microenvironment; these include, especially, one known locally as the *azul* (blue) crab, on which a large population of raccoons feeds.

4. *Riverine,* comprising the channels and banks of the sluggish Suchiate and Naranjo rivers, which connect with the lagoon-estuary system not far from their mouths. Freshwater turtles, catfish, snook, red snapper, and mojarra *(Cichlasoma* sp.) are found in these waters; the most common animal along the banks is the green iguana *(Iguana iguana).*

5. *Salt playas,* the dried remnants of ancient lagoon-and-estuary systems which are still subject to inundation during the wet season, with localized stands of a tree known as *madresal* ("mother of salt"). Here there is an abundance of game, including whitetail deer and the black iguana *(Ctenosaura similis),* as well as a rich supply of salt.

6. *Mixed tropical forest,* found a few kilometers inland, in slightly higher and better drained situations than the salt *playas.* This forest includes mostly tropical evergreens like the ceiba, as well as various zapote and fan palms, on the fruit of which a great variety of mammals thrive—the kinkajou, the spotted

cavy, the coatimundi, the raccoon, and even the gray fox. The soils here are highly suitable for maize agriculture.

7. *Tropical savannah,* occupying poorly drained patches along the upper stream and estuary systems of the area. This is the major habitat in the area for cottontail rabbits and gray foxes. Other common mammals are the coatimundi and armadillo.

8. *Cleared fields and second growth,* habitats which have been created by agriculturists, and which are generally confined to areas that were formerly mixed tropical forest.

Among the earliest formative cultures known thus far for the Ocós area is the Cuardos phase, dated by radiocarbon analysis at about 1000 to 850 B.C. and well represented in the site of Salinas La Blanca, which we excavated in 1962 (14). The site is on the banks of the Naranjo River among a variety of microenvironments; it consists of two flattish mounds built up from deeply stratified refuse layers representing house foundations of a succession of hamlets or small villages.

From our analysis of this refuse we have a good idea of the way in which the Cuadros people lived. Much of the refuse consists of potsherds from large, neckless jars, but very few of the clay figurines that abound in other Formative cultures of Mesoamerica were found. We discovered many plant remains; luckily these had been preserved or "fossilized" through replacement of the tissues by carbonates. From these we know that the people grew and ate a nonhybridized maize considerably more advanced than the maize which was then being grown in Tehuacán (15). The many impressions of leaves in clay floors in the site will, we hope, eventually make it possible to reconstruct the flora that immediately surrounded the village.

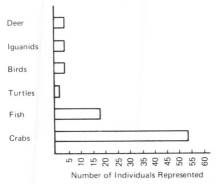

Deer

Iguanids

Birds

Turtles

Fish

Crabs

Number of Individuals Represented

Fig. 11-3. Animal remains, exclusive of mollusks, found in Cuadros phase levels at Salinas La Blanca.

The identification of animal remains (Fig. 11-3), together with our ecological study and with the knowledge that the people had a well-developed maize agriculture, gives a great deal of information on the subsistence activities of these early coastal villagers. First of all, we believe they had no interest whatever in hunting, a conclusion reinforced by our failure to find a single projectile point in the site. The few deer bones that have been recovered are all from immature individuals that could have been encountered by chance and clubbed to death. Most of the other remains are of animals that could have been collected by the environs of the village, specifically in the lagoon-estuary system and the flanking mangrove forest, where the people fished, dug for marsh clams, and, above all, caught crabs (primarily the *azul* crab, which is trapped at night). Entirely missing are many edible species found in other microenvironments, such as raccoon, cottontail rabbit, peccary, spotted cavy, and nine-banded armadillo.

There is no evidence at all that occupation of Salinas La Blanca was seasonal. An effective food production carried out on the rich, deep soils of the mixed tropical forest zone, together with the food resources of the lagoon-estuary system, made a permanently settled life possible. Looked at another way, developed maize agriculture had so reduced the number and spacing of the niches which had to be exploited that villages could be occupied the year round (16).

Conditions similar to those of the Ocós area are found all along the Pacific Coast of Guatemala and along the Gulf Coast of southern Veracruz and Tabasco in Mexico, and we suggest that the real transition to village life took place there and not in the dry Mexican highlands, where maize was domesticated initially (17).

Conclusion

The interpretation of archeological remains through a fine-scale analysis of small ecological zones throws new light on the move toward sedentary life in Mesoamerican prehistory. In our terms, the basic difference between peoples who subsist on wild foods and those who dwell in permanent villages is that the former must exploit a wide variety of small ecological niches in a seasonal pattern—niches which are usually scattered over a wide range of territory—while the latter may, because of an effective food production, concentrate on one or on only a few microenvironments which lie relatively close at hand.

Fine-scale ecological analysis indicates that there never was any such thing as an "agricultural revolution" in Mesoamerica, suddenly and almost miraculously resulting in village life. The gradual addition of domesticates such as maize, beans, and squash to the diet of wild plant and animal foods hardly changed the way of life of the Tehuacán people for many thousands of years, owing to a general paucity of the environment, and seasonal nomadism persisted until the introduction of irrigation. It probably was not until maize was taken to the alluvial, lowland littoral of Mesoamerica, perhaps around 1500 B.C., that permanently occupied villages became possible, through reduction of the number of microenvironments to which men had to adapt themselves.

References and Notes

1. Mesoamerica is the name given to that part of Mexico and Central America which was civilized in pre-Columbian times. For an excellent summary of its prehistory, see G. R. Willey, *Science* 131, 73 (1960).
2. R. S. MacNeish, *Science* 143, 531 (1964).
3. See C. A. Reed and R. J. Braidwood, "Toward the reconstruction of the environmental sequence of Northeastern Iraq," in R. J. Braidwood and B. Howe, "Prehistoric Investigations in Iraqi Kurdistan," *Oriental Institute, University of Chicago, Studies in Ancient Oriental Civilization No. 31* (1960), p. 163. Reed and Braidwood also convincingly reject the technological-deterministic approach of V. G. Childe and his followers.
4. See B. J. Meggers, *Am. Anthropologist* 56, 801 (1954), for an environmental-deterministic view of the constraining effects of tropical forests on human cultures.
5. See F. Barth, *ibid.* 58, 1079 (1956), for a microenvironmental approach by an ethnologist to the exceedingly complex interrelationships between sedentary agriculturalists, agriculturists practicing transhumant herding, and nomadic herders in the state of Swat, Pakistan.
6. J. H. Steward, "Basin-Plateau Aboriginal Sociopolitical Groups," *Smithsonian Inst. Bur. Am. Ethnol. Bull. 120* (1938).
7. The pitfalls of searching for ethnological data relevant to archeological problems among cultures far-flung in time and space are stressed by J. G. D. Clark, *Prehistoric Europe, The Economic Basis* (Philosophical Library, New York, 1952), p. 3.
8. See W. W. Taylor, Ed., "The identification of non-artifactual archaeological materials," Natl. Acad. Sci.–Natl. Res. Council Publ. 565 (1957). For a general article on the analysis of food remains in archeological deposits see R. F. Heizer in "Application of quantitative methods in archaeology," *Viking Fund Publications in Anthropology No. 28* (1960), pp. 93-157.
9. P. C. Mangelsdorf, R. S. MacNeish, W. C. Gallinat, *Science* 143, 538 (1964). We thank Dr. MacNeish for permission to use un-published data of the Tehuacán Archaeological-Botanical Project in this article.
10. R. S. MacNeish, *Second Annual Report of the Tehuacán Archaeological-Botanical Project* (Robert S. Peabody Foundation for Archaeology, Andover, Mass, 1962).
11. The research discussed in this and the following paragraph was carried out by Flannery as staff zoologist for the Tehuacán project during the field seasons of 1962 and 1963; see K. V. Flannery, "Vertebrate Fauna and Prehistoric Hunting Patterns in the Tehuacán Valley" (Robert S. Peabody Foundation for Archaeology, Andover, Mass., in press) ——, thesis, Univ. of Chicago, in preparation.
12. M. D. Coe, "La Victoria, an early site on the Pacific Coast of Guatemala," *Peabody Museum, Harvard, Papers No. 53* (1961).
13. The study was carried out largely by Flannery.
14. The final report on Salinas La Blanca by Coe and Flannery is in preparation. The research was supported by the National Science Foundation under a grant to the Institute of Andean Research, as part of the program "Interrelationships of New World Cultures." The oldest culture in the area is the Ocós phase, which has complex ceramics and figurines; the paleoecology of Ocós is less well known that that of Cuadros, which directly follows it in time.
15. P. C. Mangelsdorf, who has very kindly examined these maize specimens, informs us that they are uncontaminated with *Tripsacum*, and that probably all belong to the primitive lowland race, Nal-Tel.
16. To paraphrase the concept of "primary forest efficiency," developed by J. R. Caldwell (Trend and Tradition in the Eastern United States," *Am. Anthropol. Assoc. Mem. No. 88* (1958)), we might think of the Cuadros phase as leaning to a "primary lagoon-estuary efficiency." We might think the same of the Ocós phase of the same region, which may date back to 1500 B.C.
17. An additional factor which may in part account for the priority of coastal Guatemala over Tehuacán in the achievement of a sedentary mode of life is the presence of an extensive system of waterways in the former region, which might have made it less necessary for local communities to move to productive sources of food. By means of canoes, a few persons could have brought the products of other niches to the village. However, our evidence indicates that the Cuadros people largely ignored the possibilities of exploiting distant niches.

12

SOME CONSIDERATIONS OF EARLY PLANT DOMESTICATION

Charles B. Heiser, Jr.

Within the framework of this symposium it seems appropriate to give some consideration to early man and his environment. One of man's initial disturbances of that environment was to alter certain plants to fit his needs. This, in time, led to civilization which, in turn, led to some of the changes that have prompted this symposium. My principal concern will be with certain ecological and evolutionary principles relating to the initiation of plant domestication or incipient agriculture. Recent archaeological discoveries, particularly in the Near East, Mexico, and coastal Peru, bring about the need for a re-evaluation of earlier ideas concerning the origins of agriculture. I hesitate to speak on this subject for several reasons, not the least among them is that there may well be additional archaeological work unknown to me which has important bearings on the subject. Much of what I have to say is obvious, much is speculative, and very little is original. Moreover, this discussion may end up with more questions raised than answered.

The archaeological record (Braidwood and Willey, 1962; Flannery, 1965; MacNeish, 1964a; 1964b) indicates that plant domestication in both hemispheres had its beginnings in somewhat arid, hilly, or mountainous regions. Since plant remains are much more likely to be preserved in dry, rather than more humid, regions, there exists the possibility that we are reading too much into the archaeological record. There are, however, good ecological reasons to argue for the beginnings of agriculture in a semi-arid region of diversified terrain.

A region characterized by many micro-climates (Coe and Flannery, 1964) provides a diversity of plants from which man could select for his first domesticates. This is one of the reasons that impelled Vavilov (1926) to look for beginnings in mountainous or hilly country. Sauer (1952) maintains that some "leisure" time was necessary for man to experiment with growing plants, and an area of marked ecological contrasts within a limited zone would offer sufficient food at most times of the year to allow man the necessary time to attempt cultivation. Although Sauer has pointed to fishermen as meeting the requirements for the early cultivators since they would have had a dependable food supply, there is no archaeological evidence that the early cultivators of the Near East or Mexico depended heavily upon fish. Lanning (1965), moreover, has pointed out that certain early coastal inhabitants of Peru apparently gave up farming when an abundance of fish was available. In fact, one might ask, if sufficient food were available, why would man begin cultivation. Where an abundance of food was at hand, as, for example, in the northwest coast of North America, there would be no stimulus for agriculture. It might be suggested, therefore, that perhaps the food collectors of the semi-arid regions were not quite in the same position as the fishermen. Food was not so readily available that they would not be willing to search for a more dependable supply. Moreover, these people were primarily plant collectors who possessed more intimate knowledge of plants than might be expected of people more dependent on animal sources for their food.

Where did the first cultivators grow their plants? Several people have suggested grasslands, but Sauer (1952) has favored wooded areas, since primitive man could have killed trees more readily than he could have turned sod. But it is unlikely that the initial attempt at cultivation was in either of these areas. Anderson (1952) has suggested "dump-heaps" at the sites of human habitation. Certainly the idea that a seed of a plant produces another of its kind might have been fostered by observation of accidentally dropped seeds in such a place. In fact, such sites would have been suitable for some of the early American

Reprinted from *Bioscience* 19: 228-31, 1970, with the permission of the publishers.

domesticates, such as cucurbits, but they would hardly have served for growing enough of the cereals. Stream terraces, as have been suggested by several authors (Ames, 1939; Smith, 1965; and Flannery, 1965), may have provided an ideal place if they weren't subject to flash flooding during the growing season. Naturally disturbed areas about streams provide barren areas which require no extensive preparation of the soil and which also provide sufficient moisture. Another possible site offered by a semi-arid environment is one covered by annuals which could have been burnt off previous to planting. Since it may have been the annuals of these areas which were all-important wild sources of food, it is difficult to imagine why man would destroy a potential food source until he had dependable cultivated plants. Not only did the semi-arid region offer advantages in having a plant cover that might be easily removed for planting but also such a region would have fewer weeds, insect pests, and fungus diseases (Mangelsdorf et al., 1964a; Spinden, 1917) than would more mesic habitats.

We, of course, have no knowledge of how man first planted his seed. It would be interesting to know if one of the basic distinctions between Old and New World agriculture—broadcasting versus planting of individual seed—was established from the very beginning. Wheat, barley, and some of the pulses are suitable for broadcasting whereas the New World crops with their larger seeds—cucurbits, beans, and maize—are not. Broadcasting, however, usually follows soil preparation. Was there preparation of the soil, perhaps unintentional disturbances, that allowed some success near the outset?

Which plants did man pick for the first attempts at domestication—those available locally or those which he had to go some distance to acquire? Harlan and Zohary (1966) have asked why man would have cultivated those plants which were readily available. It would seem that there would have been a stimulus to cultivate those difficult to obtain and for the reason to be presented below we shall see that they might have also enjoyed greater success with plants not growing in the immediate environment. Although wild wheat

and barley, which apparently were some of the first plants domesticated, are now rather common in parts of the Near East (Harlan and Zohary, 1966), it does not necessarily follow that they were so common 10,000 years ago. As Zohary (1965) earlier pointed out, the original woody vegetation of this region has largely been destroyed by man's activities and the herbaceous plants have greatly increased their area. Once the idea of cultivation took hold, many different species would have been the subject for experimentation. Some species proved more successful than others. Those annual species which occur in open habitats in semi-arid regions would have been ideal candidates to become "colonizing species" as a result of man's disturbance of the environment and would have been subject to rapid evolution.

Mangelsdorf (1952) has suggested that the ancestors of cultivated plants were "more mutable" than species in general. He has postulated that the ancestors were poorly adaptive in the wild and points to the negative correlation between the distribution of a species in nature compared with the same species under domestication. I do not feel that this, however, necessarily destroys the idea that colonizing species were involved in the origin of many cultivated plants. It is true that the wild ancestors of some of our cultivated plants may be extinct, including wild maize, but for others there is good evidence that colonizing species were involved. My thoughts naturally turn to plants of which I have first-hand knowledge. Certainly the wild sunflower *(Helianthus annuus)* fits the category of a colonizing species as does the wild form of the chili pepper *(Capsicum annuum)*. The diploid forms of many of the cereals also qualify as colonizing species (Zohary, 1965).

Flannery (1965) has argued that "from an ecological standpoint the important point is not that man planted wheat but that he (1) moved it to niches to which it was not adapted, (2) removed pressures of natural selection which allowed more deviants from the normal phenotypes to survive, (3) eventually selected for characters not beneficial under conditions of natural selection." From an evolutionary, if not ecological, viewpoint these points deserve further consideration. In collecting from the wild, those plants with an imperfect method of dispersal would likely be included by chance in seed collected. That such seeds were intentionally saved for planting at the beginning seems unlikely, but the sample used for the later accidental or intentional planting would include such seed. Thus, an unconscious artificial selection would have been in operation very early. Although several people have stressed the importance of introducing plants into new environments, usually as a stimulus for mutation (Helbaek, 1959, 1960, for example), the actual significance is that the new environment might favor recombinants not possible in the original habitat (see Müntzing, 1959). In the movement to a new region, the plant might encounter other ecotypes of the species or other species with which hybridization could take place, allowing still greater possibilities for recombination. Other than Burkill (1953) no one has emphasized that in taking plants to a new area man might immediately be setting up isolation between the cultivated plants and the parent population. With the elimination of free intercrossing between the wild plant and the one being cultivated, the fixation of characters important to man could be more rapid. The importance of such geographical isolation in allowing the development of a new cultigen, of course, would depend upon the breeding system of the plant. Probably the majority of man's original cultigens were naturally cross-fertilized (see Hutchinson, 1958, 1965) so that some isolation would be desirable unless mutants for self-fertility occurred quite early. Although the distance involved did not necessarily need to be great—for example, plants growing naturally on the slopes of a hill might be effectively isolated if carried to the valley floor—it is entirely possible that plants got their start as cultigens after being carried some distance from the area where the plant grew wild. Thus we return to an earlier idea that those plants not available locally to man might have been the first domesticates, this time on the assumption that isolation would be important.

That most writers point to hybridization of a newly developing cultigen with other ecotypes of the species or with other species as important in its development may at first seem contradictory to the point I have made above, but unless the plant became self-pollinated, periods of isolation previous to and following such hybridization would be helpful in fixing desirable characters. Maize, as it so often does, requires special consideration. Mangelsdorf et al. (1964b) have presented a most interesting hypothesis that the newly developing cultivated maize may have hybridized wild maize out of existence. To me the idea of a cultivated plant swamping a wild one is difficult to accept, unless one assumes, as has been proposed, that the wild plant was on the verge of extinction or was a newly evolved species when man adopted it. If, however, as Mangelsdorf et al. (1964b) have suggested, maize was first cultivated in the very places where wild maize occurred, the alteration of the habitat by man could also have contributed to the disappearance of the wild plant. Fortunately, all of these difficulties disappear if one accepts the second hypothesis offered by these authors—that wild maize persisted until the Conquest, after which time the newly introduced domesticated animals of the Spanish ate it to extinction.

How much time did it take to make a domesticated plant out of a wild species? Once man plants seeds of a species one can speak of it as being cultivated, but this does not necessarily mean that the plant in question is "domesticated." The definition of a cultivated or domesticated plant often embodies the idea that it can no longer exist in the wild, but this would be difficult to determine from the archaeological record. Perhaps the best that we can do for most plants is to examine certain characters, such as the replacement of deciduous fruits by persistent ones or small seeds by large seeds, and assume, usually correctly, that these changes have come about through man's conscious or unconscious selection. Even where we have both wild and cultivated plants represented in archaeological sites, it is difficult to know whether the cultivated plants originated at that place or were introduced from some neighboring site after being partially or completely domesticated. Probably the best estimate of the time required for domestication comes from Helbaek's painstaking work on the wheat and barley of southwestern Asia. He points out that, based on the material he saw, all the principal changes from wild wheat and barley to the cultivated state were accomplished in some 1500 years (Helbaek, 1966). Another way of arriving at some idea of the amount of time required for domestication comes from estimates of the time involved in man's changing from a semi-sedentary way of life to village existence. Several archaeologists (Braidwood and Howe, 1962) have suggested a period of 2000 years for such a change. If this period of time is involved in reaching effective village life, then the development of a single species to a productive level is probably considerably less, since village life is usually based on several domesticates, some perhaps locally developed, others acquired from neighboring peoples. Thus I would suggest that for some annual plants a few hundred years or less might have been sufficient time to produce a fairly good domesticated plant; this contrasts with the vague "long time" required for domestication sometimes mentioned.

In the New World the transition from the beginning of agriculture to urbanization appears to have taken longer than in the Near East. Although Braidwood and Willey (1962) didn't offer explanations for this, several are possible. In the Near East wheat and barley apparently were among the first domesticates (Helbaek, 1960), whereas in the New World the basic cereal crop, maize is not among the first domesticates. Moreover, once maize had been acquired, its development to a truly productive stage may have taken far longer than did that of the Old World cereals. The differences between wild wheat and barley and the cultivated forms are probably not as great as those between wild maize and cultivated maize. Thus, fewer mutants would be needed to produce the cultivated wheat and barley, and it is possible that some of the characters needed to produce them could have been present in wild populations and only needed recombination and selection by man, whereas in maize the changes necessary to make a "good" cultigen may have had to await suitable mutations. Another factor not to be overlooked that could have contributed to a more rapid cultural advance in the Near East is that the people there had acquired domestic animals which could not be matched in the New World.

Sauer (1952) has presented logical reasons to support the hypothesis that the earliest agriculture was based on vegetative propagation. The recent archaeological discoveries indicate, however, that the first farmers in both the Old and New Worlds were entirely seed planters. It is apparent, though, that the areas where vegetative cultivation would have its greatest development are not favorable areas for the preservation of plant materials (von Wissmann, 1956), but the fact that there is no indirect evidence of early agricultural cultures known from such areas may be significant. Nevertheless, this still does not necessarily entirely rule out the possibility that vegetative cultivation is older than seed planting. First, the nature of the habitats and the plants themselves and the manner of propagation of vegetative cultigens would not allow for the rapid evolutionary advance through recombination that would occur with seed annuals. Therefore it might take much longer for vegetative cultigens to reach a productive level comparable to that of seed propagated plants.

Plant domestication appears to have begun in semi-arid regions of marked ecological diversity which provided sufficient wild food sources as well as a number of plants suitable for cultivation. Probably natural openings such as stream terraces as well as dump heaps provided early sites for artificially encouraging plants. Many of the plants that proved successful were of the colonizing sort—annuals subject to rapid evolutionary changes. The movement of plants to new habitats fostered the development of new types through recombination and may have been important also in providing isolation to allow fixation of desirable genes. The amount of time involved in a plant changing from wild to cultivated could have been in the order of a few hundred years. The transition from the beginnings of cultivation to effective village life was more rapid in the Old World than in the New since the cereals apparently were among the earliest cultivated plants of the Old but not of the New World.

Moreover, the cereals of the Old World were probably subject to more rapid improvement than was the New World cereal, maize.

This summary may give the impression that we now have some understanding of the origin of agriculture, but it must be remembered that it is based on systematic investigation of plant remains in relatively few areas. The actual situation is that we really know very little about the origin of plant domestication, particularly as to why man began cultivating plants.

Finally, I should say that while I have used "man" through this paper, I should point out that many have considered that plant domestication originated with woman. Thus, women were responsible for the development of civilization and so we must also hold them responsible for all its attendant ills—soil erosion, air and water pollution, and overpopulation (certainly they are responsible for this) that were to have been some of the subjects for this symposium. I was going to end with this statement, but Dr. Barbara Pickersgill, who has read this paper and while not necessarily agreeing with all my other conclusions, most strongly objected to the last statement and substituted the following: Women are responsible for the development of civilization and so we must hold them responsible for all its attendant benefits—spread of agriculture to hitherto unproductive areas, increased food production, and support of a larger population.

References

Ames, Oakes, 1939. *Economic Annuals and Human Cultures.* Botanical Museum of Harvard University, Cambridge, Mass.

Anderson, Edgar. 1952. *Plants, Man and Life.* Little, Brown & Co., Boston, Mass.

Braidwood, R. J., and Bruce Howe, 1962. Southwestern Asia beyond the lands of the Mediterranean littoral. In: *Courses Toward Urban Development,* Viking Fund Publ. Anthropol. No. 32, p. 132-146.

Braidwood, R. J., and G. R. Willey. 1962. Conclusions and afterthoughts. In: *Courses Toward Urban Development,* Viking Fund Publ. Anthropol. No. 32, p. 330-359.

Burkill, I. H. 1953. Habits of man and the origins of cultivated plants of the Old World. *Proc. Linn. Soc. London,* 164: 12-42.

Coe, M. D., and K. V. Flannery. 1964. Microenvironments and mesoamerican prehistory. *Science* 143: 650-654.

Flannery, K. V. 1965. The ecology of early food production in Mesopotamia. *Science,* 147: 1247-1256.

Harlan, Jack R., and Daniel Zohary. 1966. Distribution of wild wheats and barley. *Science,* 153: 1074-1080.

Helbaek, Hans. 1959. Domestication of food plants in the Old World. *Science,* 130: 365-372.

——. 1960. Ecological effects of irrigation in ancient Mesopotamia. *Iraq,* 22: 186-196.

——. 1966. 1966—Commentary on the phylogenesis of *Triticum* and *Hordeum.* *Econ. Botany,* 20: 350-360.

Hutchinson, Sir Joseph. 1958. *Genetics and the Improvement of Tropical Crops.* Cambridge University Press, Cambridge.

——. 1965. Crop plant evolution: A general discussion. In: *Crop Plant Evolution,* J. Hutchinson (ed.), Cambridge.

Lanning, Edward. 1965. Early man in Peru. *Sci. Am.,* 213: 68-76.

MacNeish, R. S. 1964a. The food gathering and incipient agriculture stage of prehistoric Middle America. In: *Handbook of Middle American Indians,* R. Wauchope (ed.), p. 413-426.

——. 1964b. Ancient Mesoamerican civilization. *Science,* 143: 531-537.

Mangelsdorf, Paul C. 1952. Evolution under domestication. *Am. Naturalist,* 86: 65-77.

Mangelsdorf, Paul C., R. S. MacNeish, and G. R. Willey. 1964a. Origins of agriculture in Middle America. In: *Handbook of Middle American Indians,* R. Wauchope (ed.), p. 427-445.

Mangelsdorf, Paul C., R. S. MacNeish, and W. C. Galinat. 1964b. Domestication of corn. *Science,* 143: 538-545.

Müntzing, Arne. 1959. Darwin's views on evolution under domestication in the light of present-day knowledge. *Proc. Am. Phil. Soc.,* 103: 190-220.

Sauer, Carl O. 1952. *Agricultural Origins and Dispersals.* Amer. Geog. Soc. N. Y.

Smith, C. Earle, Jr. 1965. Agriculture, Tehuacan Valley. *Fieldiana: Botany,* 31: 55-100.

Spinden, H. J. 1917. The origin and distribution of agriculture in America. *Proc. 19th Intern. Cong. Amer. 1915,* p. 269-276.

Vavilov, N. I. 1926. Studies on the origins of cultivated plants. *Bull. Appl. Botany, Genet., Plant Breeding,* 16: 139-248 (Eng. summary).

von Wissmann, Hermann. 1956. On the role of nature and man in changing the dry belt of Asia. In: *Man's Role in Changing the Face of the Earth,* W. L. Thomas, Jr. (ed.), p. 278-303, University of Chicago Press.

Zohary, Daniel. 1965. Colonizer species in the wheat group. In: *The Genetics of Colonizing Species,* H. G. Baker and G. L. Stebbins (eds.), p. 403-419, Academic Press, Inc., New York.

13

DOMESTICATION OF ANIMALS

D. K. Belyaev

A little more than 100 years ago Charles Darwin described the fundamental laws governing the evolution of organic life on the Earth. Having amassed an enormous store of factual material, which proved the creative role of natural selection guided by the blind forces of nature, Darwin wrote his major contribution to science, *The Origin of Species.* He began with an analysis of artificial selection motivated by the practical needs and whims of man to transform animals and plants into domesticated and cultured species. Nine years later he published *The Variation of Animals and Plants under Domestication,* which to this day remains a valuable account of the role of artificial selection in the creation of species of domesticated animals and plants.

Darwin's interest in domestication need not surprise us. Even a superficial comparison of modern domestic breeds with their wild ancestors shows the colossal differences between them. Many of our present domesticated species could no longer survive in a natural or wild condition. Dairy cattle, for example, even with a low level of milk yield would be condemned to extinction in natural conditions. It is impossible to imagine that even the most primitive breeds of domestic pig or the miniature toy dogs or huge St. Bernards could survive in natural conditions without the constant and special patronage of man. In short, domestication by artificial selection has produced large evolutionary changes. It therefore serves as a striking example of micro-evolution at work.

This process is distinctive not only because it has created forms of plants and animals, the specialization of which greatly harms their

Reprinted from *Science Journal* 5(1): 47-52, 1969, with the permission of the publishers.

biological adaptability, but also because of the impressive speed at which their evolution has taken place. The fact that selection is the primary force behind evolution is now widely known, but what forms of selection played the main part in the processes of domestication, what features of animals were selected and precisely what hereditary changes in these animals were the key ones are much less clear.

One of the main factors which makes this problem difficult to evaluate is that the main phenomena which led to the development of all basic domestic animals are lost in history and we do not possess, as it were, an entirely suitable laboratory model with which to study them. Nevertheless, thanks to progress in genetics and related sciences, we can now judge the mechanisms of the changes due to domestication with greater fullness and clarity than was possible in Darwin's time.

Domestic animals differ widely in colour and certain aspects of hair growth or plumage from their wild ancestors. The wild animals are characterized by protective colouring while their hair growth is adapted for thermal regulation. The domestic animals, on the other hand, have a great variety of colours, including piebald and brindled hues, and also structural changes in the hair such as much longer hair (the angora type), shorter hair (the rex type) or the formation of the curly hair characteristic of astrakhan sheep.

Mink (*Lutreola vison* Brisson) provide first class evidence of such changes which occurred soon after the animals were transferred from their natural environment. While minks living in natural surroundings (the so-called standard type) have brown fur, species with furs of light brown, beige, silvery-blue and white colour have appeared among the animals which began to be cultivated on farms only 30-35 years ago. Genetic analysis shows that most of the variations are conditioned by recessive mutations of separate genes which control the synthesis of the hair pigment or its distribution. On the basis of separate individual mutations there have been evolved, up to the present time, more than 100 complex forms. Such well known and widely spread mink colours as the sapphire, pearl, topaz, winter-blue and some others are conditioned by two, three or even four recessive mutations. Other mutations, also recessive, are known which change the structural form of the hair. Thus, for example, there is the "sami" mutation which develops in mink extra long hair of the angora type.

The effect of the mutations is not restricted to the fur. They also affect reproductive capacity, fertility and vitality. The great majority of the mutational forms of mink are characterized by reduced fertility and a decreased vitality, and can exist only in the conditions specially created for them by man. But even in those conditions some mutational forms are of so low a vitality that they are hardly ever used for breeding as a separate individual species, although they are used in combination with other mutated forms to create new color variations.

Thus in the first few years of mink cultivation by man, there occurred a differentiation of the wild form into a number of types, which represented, we must suppose, prototypes of future breeds. The variety of mink already developed does not of course represent the limit; it is certainly bound to increase as new mutations are drawn into the selection process. Thus in a short period of cultivation by man the natural mutation process has provided the necessary material for domestication changes which are fully comparable with analogous changes in such long since domesticated animals as rabbits, dogs and cats.

Why do these changes occur so quickly? Is this phenomenon connected with an increase in the rate of mutation of the genes of the animals during domestication, or is it due to the utilization of mutations stored up by the species in the wild and revealed later during the breeding of the animals by man?

There is no single answer. It is clear, however, that the differentiation of wild species during domestication has its origin in the utilization of mutations developed during their evolutionary history. In many cases this process is based on the utilization of recessive mutations which do not affect a species physically unless they are inherited from both parents. In the wild nearly all individuals are heterozygous, having inherited the gene from only one parent,

and the mutation exerts no physical effect. However, in small populations cultivated by man, with restricted freedom in cross-breeding and judiciously applied and random in-breedings, these mutations multiply and are 'chipped out' in animals which inherit the genes from both parents. Such homozygous individuals will have reduced vitality and fertility and would be eliminated in nature by natural selection. But in conditions controlled by man they survive and many of them, for one reason or another, become the objects of artificial selection. Thus restrictions in the freedom of cross-breeding and in-breeding create conditions which quickly bring to the surface types of mutations previously concealed in the wild animal.

This is precisely the position as far as mink is concerned, where changes in colour and other properties developed in captivity very quickly. A number of recessive mutations in the mink (for example of the silvery-blue colouring) were actually introduced into mink populations bred in farms by animals trapped in their natural surroundings. It would seem that the same mechanism operated during the domestication of the rabbit since the colour and structure of the fur, the hereditary changes of which constitute the basis of strain differentiation in this species, develop in most cases under the control of recessive mutations. Thus it is recessive genes which are responsible for the characteristics of such breeds as the chinchilla, the Vienna blue, the ermine and some other breeds of rabbits. The specific features of the fur covering of angora rabbits and rex rabbits are also developed under the control of recessive mutations. The saturation of natural populations of animals with recessive mutations was first revealed by the Soviet scientist Professor S. S. Chetverikov as early as 1926 in his experiments with the fruit fly *Drosophila*. It is quite clear that this discovery applies also to mammals.

The examples I have mentioned are by no means exclusive. I have the opportunity to observe daily from the window of my house in Akademgorodok, near Novosibirsk, white and black squirrels, the colouring of which also develops under the control of recessive genes. In the limited squirrel population of our Akademgorodok community the gene drift has transformed these mutations into the homozygous state and the animals, and their food supplies, have been artificially protected, especially during the long Siberian winter. This has saved them from the eliminating effect of natural selection.

But why are mutations which produce unfavourable biological effects in the homozygous state retained in the heterozygous state? The chief reason, apparently, is that many mutations which produce in the homozygous state a substantial depression of fertility and vitality (especially during the first few days after birth) produce a less severe or even reverse effect in the heterozygous state. In the latter case they may even produce an increase in adaptability, particularly with respect to fertility and vitality. Of course, it should be remembered that high fertility is evolutionarily profitable only under favourable conditions. In unfavourable conditions (especially during food shortage), it becomes a negative property, exposing to danger both the adult females and the young stock alike. In such conditions, obviously, the species with an average or even low fertility has a better chance of survival. The effects of heterozygosis are different for different genes but since natural conditions are also different, all these genes render a useful service to the species, regulating the fertility of the animals and consequently also their numbers in relation to given conditions.

Thus, for example, with mink the mutations of the genes of the silver-blue and especially the aleutian colour variety in the heterozygous state bring about a certain increase in the fertility of the females. The heterozygotes of the genes of the white (headlund) and beige (Swedish palamine) colour, on the other hand, are of decreased fertility.

However, mutations which appeared early on in wild animals are not the only source of variation during domestication. The mutational process goes on continuously and it is natural that artificial selection could depend on mutations which appeared in animals during later stages of domestication. These mutations are drawn into the selection process by the same mechanism of genetic drift as the mutations

stored by the wild species, and the conditions especially created by man for the animals, which protect the latter from the somewhat harsh effect of natural selection, ensure the survival of mutant forms which would be condemned to extinction in nature.

Obviously, the material for the differentiation of wild species in domestication was also provided by many dominant mutations, which were eliminated in nature for one reason or another by natural selection. For example, hairlessness characteristic of certain breeds of African dogs develops on the basis of the dominant mutation of one gene. Undoubtedly this mutation would be eliminated in nature by natural selection, whereas man has retained it and multiplied it.

Artificial selection carried out by man has thus drawn into the sphere of its activity an ever increasing variety of different mutations and has created new combinations of them, thus changing very markedly the genotype—the basic genetic constitution—of the wild species and creating new forms of animals unknown in nature. Let me cite an example of the creative activity of selection in the process of the domestication of animals, which is taking place under our very eyes. During the late 1930s and early 1940s there appeared in the populations of the silvery black foxes cultivated in farms in many countries the so-called platinum and white-faced foxes. They are characterized by a weakened pigmentation of the coat and the presence of a specific piebald pattern affecting the snout, neck, chest, belly and the paws of the foxes. Genetic analysis showed that the colouring of these foxes was controlled by dominant allelic genes, which if inherited from both parents caused the embryo to abort. Accordingly it was postulated that the new colouration was the result of newly developed mutations.

However, my research showed that this is not so. It transpired that the pigmentation and pattern characteristic of these platinum and white-nosed foxes appeared as a new manifestation of an old, widely spread mutation which produces a white patch on the paw of the animal. An intensive selection campaign had been carried out in the fox population of these farms to achieve a "purity of colouration" of the fur—an absence of yellow or brown hues which diminish sharply the price of the pelts— and also to increase the silveriness by increasing the quantity of partially or fully depigmented hair. Both these symptoms are polygenetic and artificial selection of them creates a new 'genotypic medium'. Analysis has shown that in this new genotypic medium the old mutation, manifested in the development of a white patch on the rear extremities of the animals, acquires a new form—more intense depigmentation of the coat and development of a specific pattern. In this particular case we see how selection, depending on the polygenetic system of one set of symptoms, literally brings to life a new pattern due to the change in the form of manifestation of the old mutation. Effects of this kind are probably very important in domestication.

However significant changes in physical appearance may be, of even greater biological importance are changes in physiological functions which develop during domestication. Many of these changes can be easily explained by the cumulative effect of artificial selection. It is quite clear that, even in the very first stages of domestication, the animals retained for further reproduction were those which satisfied the particular needs of man to the greatest extent. As human culture developed and the number of animals cultivated increased, the variety of these animals grew, and on this basis artificial selection led to sharp changes in such aspects as lactation, meat yield, fur yield, body build and other characteristics in which man was particularly interested. Although the share of hereditary changes in some of these symptoms, such as lactation, is comparatively small and they depend mainly on external conditions, nevertheless the methodical process of selection carried out from generation to generation did its work and produced considerable changes in the animals. This fact was repeatedly stressed by Darwin himself.

The evidence shows that the process of domestication has not only strengthened but also weakened some characteristics of animals which are very important to man. Thus alongside the increase in lactation there occurred also

a considerable decrease of the fat content in the milk of horned cattle. The reason for this is that lactation and the fat content of the milk are apparently, in all mammals, genetically related in such a way that any increase in lactation automatically leads to a decrease in the fat content of the milk.

This does not preclude, however, the possibility of a successful selection to increase the fat content in breeds with a high level of milk production. Special, sufficiently complicated methods of selection, which include an assessment of the hereditary qualities of animals, especially breeding bulls, while not entirely eliminating this negative correlation do nevertheless reduce it considerably. Of course the fat content does not attain the same level which characterized the wild ancestors of horned cattle (10-12 per cent) but it is considerably increased in comparison with animals producing a high yield of thin milk; today it is quite common to have large herds of animals which combine a milk yield of 5000 litres per lactation with a fat content of 4.5-4.8 per cent. Such high productivity indices are the result of very considerable changes in the heredity of animals, achieved by means of modern methods of selection.

Until recently it was more difficult to explain how, in the process of domestication, animals developed new properties which do not exhibit any hereditary variations and which therefore could not be changed by direct selection. Reproductive characteristics, for example, have undergone fundamental changes during domestication. These changes have been manifested by increased fertility, which can be explained by the cumulative effect of selection, and also in the loss by most species of domestic animals of strictly seasonal reproduction, which is characteristic of their wild ancestors.

The capacity to reproduce only during a definite sharply defined season is characteristic of the great majority of mammals in nature. The adaptive value of this most important biological property is quite clear: it ensures the birth of the young stock in conditions which are the most favourable for its nurture. Transgressing the limits of the seasonal period would be injurious or fatal to the species as a whole.

This explains the high stability of the hereditary systems on which the seasonal fluctuation of reproduction is based. As far as this property is concerned, we see no variations in wild animals. For example, the silver-black foxes have been bred in special farms, fully provided with food and under the constant care and protection of man, for about 70 years and have shown no signs at all of any tendency to reproduce outside their normal season. These animals mate between the end of January and the end of March and after 52-53 days of pregnancy produce their offspring; they do not mate or produce any offspring at any other time of the year.

Why is it, then, that in the process of domestication animals have lost the strictly seasonal fluctuations in reproduction and developed the capacity to reproduce at practically any time of the year, and in the case of some animals, such as dogs, twice a year? In order to answer this question, it is necessary to analyze the mechanisms controlling the processes of seasonal reproduction in animals. Research has shown that the seasonal fluctuation of reproduction in wild animals is controlled by the natural duration of daylight. With foxes, as with all other species with a short period of pregnancy, the mating season occurs at the time when the days begin to lengthen and with sheep, many species of which have retained the tendency to seasonal reproduction, it falls in the autumn period when the days are getting shorter. The duration of daylight constitutes that external signal which prompts or conditions the organism to reproductive activity and determines the boundaries of the reproductive season.

Thus the loss of strictly seasonal reproduction by animals in the process of domestication suggests the liquidation, weakening or at least a change in the form of control over this most important process. What is this change based on? Work in our laboratory gives reason to suppose that this process was the result of the selection of animals according to the character or nature of their defensive behaviour. There is no doubt that the change in the behaviour of animals is one of the foremost and most striking results of domestication. Everyone knows that a domestic animal differs

from a wild animal, in the first place, by its behaviour and especially by its reaction to man. There is also no doubt that the change in the behaviour of animals takes place on an hereditary basis and is the result of the unconscious selection carried out by man literally from the very first days of domestication. Only those animals came under man's sphere of influence which, on account of their behaviour, were able to coexist with him. All others were either destroyed by him or fled from him.

Selection by behaviour led to the hereditary reorganization of behaviour, with the result that previously wild animals became domesticated and some of them, for example dogs, even friendly to man. The fact that wild animals are genetically sufficiently varied for an hereditary reorganization of behaviour to be possible is corroborated by our experiment on the selection of silver-black foxes, bred in animal farms. Among the populations of these animals, which cannot be handled without special precautions against being bitten, have been found specimens of a quiet, timid, disposition. Genetic analysis has shown that this variety of behaviour is hereditary and is conditioned by heredity. About 15 years ago a programme was begun on the selection of these animals for a type of tranquil behaviour. The object of the project was to produce, by selection and equal treatment of the animals, foxes resembling the dog in behaviour. This problem is now largely solved and we have at the moment, in our experimental farm near Novosibirsk, a few score foxes the behaviour of which, although not as yet fully corresponding to the behaviour of dogs, is rapidly approaching it. I must stress that this result was produced by selection—by an hereditary reorganization of behaviour—and not by any training or coaching of the animals. This prolonged experiment was based on a hypothesis, formulated by me earlier, according to which behaviour selection must form the basis for the reorganization of reproduction, freeing the animals from the rigid photoperiodic control of their strictly seasonal reproduction.

The fact is that the daylight factor which controls the processes of seasonal reproduction exerts its influence on the organism through a special region of the brain—the hypothalamus—

which in conjunction with the hypophysis controls all the vital processes of animals. The hypothalamus performs its regulating functions in close liaison with the behaviour of animals. Due to this it was supposed that a change in behaviour cannot take place without a participation of hypothalamus hypophysis apparatus, or without producing a change in the functions regulated by this apparatus, including the function of reproduction. This hypothesis has now been justified to some extent. In the process of the investigation it has been established that there exists a definite genetically conditioned correlation between the nature of the defensive behaviour of foxes, the time of their reproduction and their fertility: foxes of tranquil behaviour reproduce much earlier within the reproductive season and their fertility is higher than that of aggressive or timid foxes.

The chief result, however, is that those foxes which behaved most like dogs showed signs of reproductive activity outside their characteristic season. Research has shown that their entire reproductive system is activated outside the reproduction season and this is never observed in wild foxes. Although we have not as yet observed the development of full sexual heat in tame females or sexual activity in tame males outside the reproductive season, it now seems probable that the selection of wild animals by behaviour leads to a reorganization of their reproduction, which suggests a fundamental change in the entire seasonal biology of animals. The physiological system created by centuries of natural selection in the interests of the natural species breaks down before our eyes.

The hereditary reorganization of the behaviour of wild animals and the conversion of them by selection into domestic and tame animals probably represents the most fundamental and most important result of domestication. It leads to a change in the functional state of the neuro-endocrinal mechanisms which regulate all the active processes of animals and determine the hormone status of the organism and all the processes of metabolism. The effect of this change embraces, it seems, not only the reproduction of the animals but also all the processes of individual develop-

ment. Not only are old mutations newly displayed, but mutations which in the old system of metabolism produced no physical effects are brought to the surface and influenced by artificial selection. This creates very real grounds for a greatly increased rate of forming new species and new possibilities for the differentiation of wild species.

It is thought, however, that the hereditary reorganization of behaviour has an even greater significance. It is known that the mutation processes in mammals depend largely on hormone balance, particularly between the adrenocorticotropic and sexual hormones. A decrease in the function of the suprarenal glands—glands lying over the upper end of the kidney—and correspondingly in the hormone that they produce, increases the frequency of mutations. But changes in behaviour in domestication lead to just such a decrease in the functional activity of the suprarenal glands. This therefore tends to increase the rate of mutation and consequently the variability of animals as a result of domestication.

The processes of domestication show most clearly that artificial selection differs very greatly from natural selection. One of the most essential functions of natural selection as the Soviet biologist I. I. Shmal'gauzen discovered, is that it leads to the stabilization of the processes of individual development and to the preservation of the 'wild' type as the optimum form of the organism in its external surroundings. Stabilizing selection dominates the other form of selection—motive selection—leading to the formation of species in nature.

Artificial selection, especially selection for behaviour, on the other hand favours the motive form of selection which 'breaks down' the control systems on the basis of which the wild phenotype was formed and reorganizes and varies the way in which mutations are expressed. This quite distinctive form of motive selection could well be called a destabilizing selection; it is the result of the selective accumulation of many mutations normally suppressed or eliminated in the process of natural selection and of changes in the systems of hormonal control. It is this which in turn leads to the spate of species formation which occurs in the domestication of animals.

14

MAN'S MOVEMENT AND HIS SETTLEMENTS

C. A. Doxiadis

Introduction

The Subject

Human settlements consist of the five elements nature, man, society, shells and networks, which form a system conditioning the type and quality of our life (1). The networks are mainly conditioned and created by man's movement in space. The subject of this text is to examine the relationship between networks for man's movement and human settlements as a whole. As we now live in an era of great confusion about human settlements and their nature, it is hoped that a study of this kind can contribute to a definition of the answers we need.

People form collective human settlements by meeting each other. This they do mainly by moving in space by means of different networks. The same networks are also used to visit places and to move goods. To understand the birth, formation, structure and function of these networks we have to understand man's *kinetic fields*, that is the fields within which man moves while living and forming his settlements. The fields which most condition his settlements are man's *daily kinetic fields*, or the ones he uses for his daily movement of life. All others, like the ones he uses on a weekly, monthly, or yearly basis play a much smaller role in the formation of his settlements.

The Nature of Human Settlements

The great confusion today about human settlements and their nature can be understood if we think of the many different ways in which

Reprinted from the *International Journal of Environmental Studies* 1: 19-30, 1970, with the permission of the publishers, Gordon and Breach Science Publishers Ltd.

they are conceived. From outside they can be described as built-up areas, or as administrative units, etc., while, from within, their inhabitants conceive them in ways which are influenced by their own movements and kinetic fields. No matter whether they live in a central city or a rural area, if they can easily visit other settlements daily for work or leisure, or if their children daily attend school in another settlement, their individual conception of their own human settlement goes far beyond a specific built-up area or administrative boundary.

At the present time it is difficult to find any city which operates as a self-contained settlement; the era of isolated cities is over. But in the past every human settlement was an isolated daily kinetic field. Human settlements have basically changed, not only because they cover much wider areas than at any time before, but because they have become systems of human settlements continuously subject to dynamic change. They are therefore different with every day that passes.

The nature of these changing human settlements is confusing because their dynamic growth appears completely different if it is regarded in terms of people and area—as is usual—or if it is regarded in terms of income, energy and complexity, which is less usual (2).

One of the most important of the many ways by which the nature of human settlements can be defined is as the spatial system of man's movement, or the kinetic field of man. This article makes an attempt to overcome the confusion that arises because of the constant changes of these movements and kinetic fields.

A Systematic Approach

A picture of the total kinetic fields in a contemporary human settlement would completely overwhelm us by its immense complexity. To organize this complexity, we have to go back to the beginnings of this phenomenon, as Aristotle so aptly recommends in his *Physics*

Here and elsewhere we shall not obtain the best insight into things until we actually see them growing from the beginning.

Aristotle, *Physics I*, 184a, 12.

Looking back, we find that the city was created by man's desire to overlap as many other personal kinetic fields as possible, in order to minimize his effort for contacts with the maximum number of people (3). In this way he serves, as best he can, the first two principles which guide him in the formation of his settlements—the maximum of contacts and the minimum of effort (4).

To understand what we can expect for the future, and thus define the actions necessary for the human settlements that we are now building, we have to examine the evolution of these kinetic fields from past to present. This is the course I follow here, and this presentation is a shortened form of lectures I have given during the last years at the Athens Center of Ekistics and in several Universities, as well as the analytical plans presented at the School of Geography of the University of Oxford.

The Past

The Beginnings

The first human settlements were non-permanent and thus man's daily movements did not lead to any permanent patterns of kinetic fields. Though it is very probable that, at times, the whole available space was covered by the kinetic fields of primitive groups of people, we have no reason to believe that the kinetic fields of each group of primitive hunters were the same every day, nor that they were not overlapping. On the contrary, as we know that several different groups used the same water-sources and the same hunting grounds, it is probable that their kinetic fields overlapped, but in non-regular patterns.

The Kinetic Fields of the Permanent Human Settlements

The situation changed completely when man created permanent human settlements. Though these are usually divided into rural and urban settlements, in practice each contained both farmers and urban dwellers in different percentages. To understand them we have to look at man's movements as a farmer and as an urban dweller and then at the combination of both functions. This shows that these settlements have the following characteristics:

1. They are simple daily systems: i.e., the daily movements of the inhabitants of one settlement do not overlap at all with the daily movements of people from other settlements.
2. In each settlement, the movements of its inhabitants overlap to a higher degree as they approach the most built-up area of the settlement.
3. The average maximum time-distance for the farmer to reach his fields (as a walking man) is 1 hr, or 5 km.
4. The average maximum time-distance for the urban dweller to reach urban functions on foot is 10 min, or 1 km.

Thus the kinetic fields form equal-size cells for farming or urban functions and, as a result, we see that human settlements form cells with a strong nucleus at their center.

This can be justified by looking at human settlements as patterns of consumption of human energy, in which a very small part of the total energy is spread over a wide area and by far the largest part is concentrated within the nucleus. This includes the entire energy of the children, old people, and the sick, and a large part of the energy of the remaining population.

In this way we find that simple settlements which live from farming and related functions, tend to have an optimum radius of between 1 or 2 and 5 km which allows for the formation of a nucleus of several hundred persons, depending on the type of land, irrigation, climate, and cultivation, and perhaps several other factors. This type of human settlement is usually described as a village and was probably the largest form of human settlement at the beginning of the agricultural revolution several thousand years ago.

During this phase, several regions of the surface of the Earth were occupied by such settlements, first separated by tracts of uncultivated land until gradually the increase of the population led to a complete coverage of the whole area by similar settlements. This gave occasion for more interaction between the settlements and the gradual formation of some more specialized settlements in the most central locations with a higher percentage of urban functions.

Such settlements were completely separate in the first phase but less so in the last phase of farming, as their kinetic fields gradually came together. After that they slowly developed physical and social connections, which held firm for a very long time if the conditions were favorable but easily broke down if they were not: for example, when mountains, rivers, or seas formed strong, physical boundaries or when there were strong social differences between the people.

The Structure

During this whole phase, the structure of human settlements can be characterized by two tendencies which led to two basically different forms. The first was an upward trend of synthesis leading to a radial form, the second a downward trend leading to an orthogonal form. The reason for the first is that a settlement grows slowly around a point of interest (crossroads, acropolis, palace, etc.); roads lead to it and people build along the roads. The settlement moves from a small start to an increasingly larger settlement, and the trend continues upward. In the second case somebody in authority recognizes the irrationality of the radial pattern and lays out an orthogonal design, which extends downward to the smallest units.

Three basically different types of human settlements result from the combinations of these two structural characteristics: they can be completely radial (Fig. 14-1a), orthogonal in their completely built-up area and radial beyond this (Fig. 14-1b) or completely orthogonal (Fig. 14-1c).

Most of the settlements around the world belong to the first type. A smaller number belong to the second one, and this includes such early settlements as the Hippodamian cities, like Miletus, or the Roman and other colonial settlements. A much smaller number belong to the third type, that is the completely orthogonal systems. Although several colonial

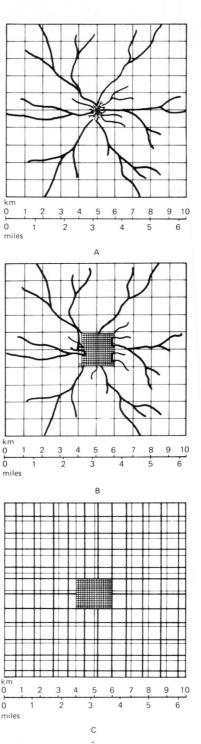

Fig. 14-1. *Village and small city. (a) Built-up area radial: non-built-up area radial. (b) Built-up area orthogonal: non-built-up area radial. (c) Built-up area orthogonal: non-built-up area orthogonal.*

Roman settlements originally had an orthogonal layout for both their built-up and non-built-up areas, the large scale implementation of this type of settlement appeared in the period of the organized settlement of the American middle-west, for example Michigan.

The question of the relative efficiency of the radial versus the orthogonal system can be answered by comparing patterns of the uses of space. This shows that while movement towards one center is best served by a radial system the sum-total of all movements from any point to any other one is irrational and that many problems of inequality are created in terms of inaccessibility and distance from roads, land development, cultivation, etc. It is thus clear that the radial system gives the best service to the inhabitants of the center, that is the few in control, whilst the orthogonal system corresponds to equal choices for all citizens, that is to the democratic concept of the city.

It is no coincidence that this system appeared in the era of the Greek republic. Human settlements based on the walking man grew to cities with a population of around 50,000 and an area of about 2000 x 2000 m: that is a city in which the maximum distance from the center is 10 min walking time (5, 6). The largest known of these settlements of the past covered an area that did not correspond to man's kinetic fields in this optimum city (1 km radius or 10 min walk) but to the maximum kinetic field of the walking man (that is a 5 km radius or 1 hr walk) and thus they could have up to 1 million inhabitants. Such settlements included Alexandria, and (later) Peking (Fig. 14-2) and (still later) Paris within its most expanded walls.

It is of interest to note that Peking, as well as the older capital of Chang'an, was divided into sectors which had their own structure and administration, and that Paris had to cut through its earlier orthogonal pattern to impose the new order of its grand boulevards, as was followed in new cities of the U.S.A., such as Washington or Chicago. The fact that these million cities were not the optimum, but the

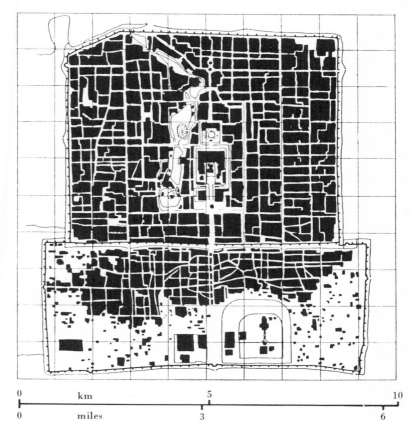

Fig. 14-2. Peking, China (A.D. 1409).

0	km	5	10
0	miles	3	6

maximum possible for the era of walking man, is made clear when we remember that imperial cities such as Rome and Constantinople, after rising up to one million inhabitants (in substance following a natural radial pattern) fell back to the optimum size when they lost their Empires. Only cities that remained capitals of empires (Peking, London, Paris) could survive with these large numbers of people before the beginning of the present era of human settlements.

The Present

The Beginnings

The next era of human settlements can be considered to open in 1802, when the first locomotive ran in Wales, although its preparation can be conceived as starting with Leonardo Da Vinci's conception of a self-propelled vehicle, or in 1769 when Cugnot of Lorraine built his model of a steam-powered tricycle. Similarly this phase can be considered to end in 1885 when Benz ran his first car. During this period, between the first railway (1804) and the first automobile (1885), the nature of our present human settlement was decided. They no longer relied on the natural movement of man and animal, but also on the mechanical movement of machines.

From the moment that people could use mechanical means of transportation of people and goods in urban and rural areas, as well as mechanical means for cultivation, human settlements entered a new era. It is this movement at many speeds which has completely changed their nature and has confused our minds about their basic characteristics, like their size and extent. We still live in an era of changing patterns of movement and therefore of changing human settlements. While the birth of the big city can be traced back to 1804, its growth still continues.

The Kinetic Fields of Human Settlements

The great changes that took place in human settlements affected many of their characteristics. Not only was contact between settlements easier but farmers could now reach their farms from different settlements. This led to a strengthening of some existing settlements as well as to changes in man's pattern of life, like living on the farm again. Similarly, farmers could now travel to larger settlements to make use of their more extensive urban functions, and new larger settlements could replace older and smaller ones.

If we now look at an area formerly inhabited by walking farmers and urban dwellers we can trace their changing kinetic fields which led to the replacement of the smaller settlements, and resulted in completely new patterns of life. For, while in the past every human settlement had its own territory, covered only by its own simple kinetic field, now, although some people might continue to move within a single settlement, others moved between several settlements. The kinetic fields of the settlements thus overlapped and led us towards complex daily systems.

How this is expressed in actual life can be seen in Brian Berry's map of the commuting fields of central cities in the U.S.A. for 1965 (Fig. 14-3). But the real complexity of the situation is only apparent when we recognize that this map only shows movements towards these central cities, and does not show the additional multitude of movements between all the settlements around.

The situation increases in complexity as people not only move about much more in their daily systems but they also have weekly systems as well as monthly, seasonal, and annual ones. If we superimpose all these kinetic fields, assigning each a value corresponding to its importance, we can observe the immense complexity of man's movement in contemporary human settlements compared to those of the past: with all the corresponding problems.

We can now state that, in comparison to settlements of the past, new types of movement and the corresponding new kinetic fields have made the human settlements of the present era:

1. Much larger in themselves.
2. Linked in continuous systems of settlements.

*Fig. 14-3. Commuting fields
of central cities.*

3. Much more complex:

(i) because of the possibility of many connections which did not exist in the past;

(ii) because of the possibility of many different types of connections (like for example, using the same road with the same type of automobile but at different speeds);

(iii) because of the desires of people for different types of settlements, which can now be fulfilled.

4. No longer clearly differentiated into rural and urban settlements, though each may contain rural and urban parts.

5. Continuously changing and therefore much more dynamic than at any time in the past.

We can observe that this change takes place through the advent of automobiles with slightly higher speeds or the introduction of a new road or of several new highways and an increasing number of automobiles. The effect of this situation upon a specific area is illustrated in a map of Michigan's Upper Peninsula (Fig. 14-4), which is now visited for recreational purposes by more and more people from increasingly distant areas. As such changes proceed continuously it is obvious that the system of human settlements must be continuously changing.

The Structure

As a result of the increasing complexity and continuous change of the human settlements of the present era, their structure is totally confused. What actually happens is that our new and changing functions are served by a structure which is the result of additions continuously being superimposed upon preexisting systems. Thus the contemporary human settlements do not have an order corresponding to their new nature and function, by which they could regain an organic structure such as they had in the past. This is their big problem: how to acquire a structure which can best serve their present functions.

During the last ten years this requirement is beginning to be faced by the development of expanding urban systems. Examples such as at Accra-Tema in Ghana and a new city like Islamabad show new types of orthogonal structure that correspond to the new functions.

Throughout human history, large regions, consisting of many urban and rural settlements have been developed on the basis of radial systems because:

1. They contained small settlements separated by large open areas, and direct connections were the obvious natural solution.

2. Very little energy was available per capita, thus every effort was made to avoid waste of energy or time and this resulted in direct, and therefore radial, connections between settlements.

3. They operated upon a hierarchical system of settlements which gave overriding importance to connections to a single center; not to connections between the lesser centers.

Fig. 14-4. Enlargement of recreation market in Northern Michigan.

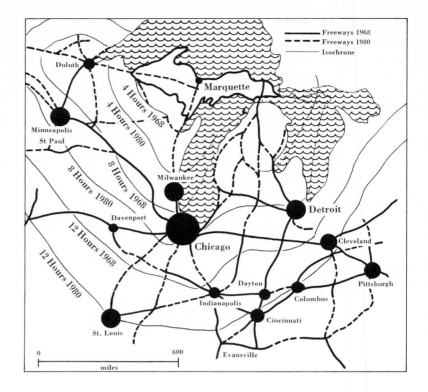

This situation still persists, although all three of these reasons are either no longer valid at all or are much less valid. *The Urban Detroit Area* (7) presents a characteristic example and its analysis shows that it has now to move from a radial towards an orthogonal pattern of organization. The old concept of growth by concentric circles is not possible any more and the earlier systems of natural settlements based on the walking man must move towards new types of human settlements.

The Theory

Evolution Up to Our Days

I repeat that the only way to understand our present human settlements is to follow their evolution and recognize their formation as an outcome of man's behavior. Some basic phases are presented in the following paragraphs.

In the first and very long hunting and food gathering phase, man's kinetic fields were large, ranging up to tens of kilometers in diameter. But his permanent settlements, as they began to

take shape, were very small; limited at first to a few tens of people.

In the second phase, man's kinetic fields grew continuously smaller as he produced more food through agriculture, until they led to the formation of isolated settlements—or villages—of a few hundred persons. These much smaller areas of cultivated land were surrounded by wider areas, which were probably still used for hunting and food gathering much as in the first phase.

In the third phase, the villages multiplied until they individually reached an optimum size. Then they gradually covered the whole available area until the boundaries of their kinetic fields met so that they formed a total system of non-connected settlements. Up to this stage there was no reason for connections, and probably also no reason for war, since there were no conflicting interests; for since their kinetic fields did not overlap there could be no conflicting territories.

In the fourth phase, interaction between neighbouring villages began. This started as soon as their daily kinetic fields actually touched one another and led to lines of connection between them. These connecting links gradually strengthened the functions of certain more central settlements and they acquired a greater percentage of non-farming functions and turned into urban settlements or cities. Thus the new urban settlements, which resulted from the interaction between villages, led to the formation of urban men—new types of people with new types of interests. As the kinetic fields of these new urban people did not touch those of other urban people, they tended to be isolated from other urban dwellers and to develop less ability for interaction with them. Thus they probably became more susceptible to the idea of war than farmers, whose kinetic fields touch and who by being directly exposed to their "adversaries" in good times and bad—in peace and at war—tend always to be in favour of peace, as we can see from Aristophanes' "Acharneans" in which, when Athens was threatened by invading armies of Laconians, an inhabitant of the adjacent rural community of Acharnae persuades his fellows to make peace.

In the fifth phase, the process towards inter-connections and formation of cities led to an optimum size of city-state and city, corresponding to the organizational ability of the society which established them. It is interesting to note that such city-states seldom covered an area larger than the area of the first phase of hunting and food gathering man (a diameter extending only to tens of kilometers), and that the city itself did not cover an area larger than that of the agricultural village (a diameter of up to 10 km). The characteristic feature of this stage is that the built-up part of the city reached an optimum of 2 km diameter, which is the size within which most of the cities that we now admire were developed.

A new and sixth phase then started, during which the expanding interconnections of human settlements led, as in other phenomena of evolution, to the formation of ever larger states, and to cities whose built-up area extended to a diameter of 10 km. However these cities never survived the decline of their empire states. They came into being as a result of vast interacting organizational networks and their physical structure (the roads of the Roman

Empire or the canals of the Babylonian Empire) collapsed with the collapse of the social system that created them.

The great change occurred in the seventh phase, when the introduction of a new technology caused the existing simple, loosely connected systems to become complex systems with overlapping kinetic fields, thus creating completely new situations from every point of view. From this moment human settlements entered a completely different phase of development and an ability to expand continuously with no apparent limit to this expansion.

We are now in the eighth phase. Man's kinetic fields have now expanded so much that everybody is confused about the nature of human settlements and the type of life within them; with the sole exception of those few people who still live in settlements of the third phase, without any overlapping kinetic fields. All the rest of us face continuous growth of man's kinetic fields and therefore of the operating human settlements. The extent of this growth can be observed by following the evolution of man's average daily journey to work (a daily, one-way, single trip) within built-up settlements throughout the ages (Fig. 14-5). In the village this was equal to 200 m

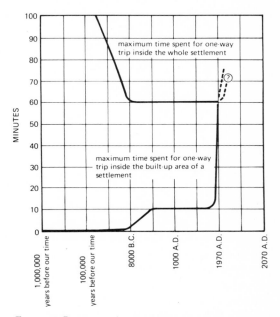

Fig. 14-5. Duration of one-way trips in human settlements.

and in the optimum city 1000 m. Its rapid growth only started in the seventh phase. In the U.S.A. it has now reached 9000 m and is continuing to grow at a pace of 120 m a year.

It is time to ask ourselves what kind of settlements we are now being led to.

The Lessons We Learn

Before trying to make projections for the future we must try to draw some conclusions from the evolutions up to the present day.

1. Human settlements follow certain laws which man has established through the long process of creating settlements to serve his biological needs. We have to recognize that human settlements are a biological extension of man, and for this reason they can be considered as macrobiological systems (8).

2. It is clear that man moves daily as far as he reasonably can and that the basic characteristics of his settlements (which in every phase have almost always first been built without any overall plan) result from these daily movements. We can safely say that man moves in space on the basis of those patterns that best serve him. How else could it be? He can afford to make a mistake once or twice, but he will certainly not repeat it continuously. Changes in man's daily kinetic fields are therefore the clearest expression of his need for and experience of a better way of life under existing conditions. It takes him some time to understand this but in the end he always does.

3. As time passes, man recognizes that certain new conditions have been created by his daily movement. It is then that he tries to organize the physical structure of his settlements in a way corresponding to the actions he has already taken. If his actions have added many more houses to an existing small settlement, he gradually recognizes that he needs wider streets and he begins to widen them. He may also recognize the need of larger public areas, such as space for the public market, and he either enlarges the existing one or creates a new one in the new areas of the expanded settlement. In other words, we can say that after man's first instinctive actions to change the existing settlement, man-the-engineer (man-the-builder) takes over to serve the new type of settlement.

4. Later man begins to think about the social and political structure of his settlements. Theseus is the symbol for the creation of the city of Athens but (whether Theseus is a real or a mythical figure) we have no reason to believe that he invented Athens. It is much more probable that he institutionalized it after more and more people had started to build on and around the Acropolis. It was much later that Hippodamus conceived the proper physical form of the city and that philosophers like Plato and Aristotle wrote about it.

5. Unlike the shells—the houses and buildings—of our settlements which follow a specific concept and plan (how else could a man build a hut and put a roof on it?), the networks of man's movements seem to have grown by constant small additions to an existing situation and it took a long time before they became recognized and expressed by concepts of the whole structure of the city. Historically, it appears that man has always begun by creating a radial network for his movements, whether he is dealing with a village, a city, a region or the world. Later he comes to recognize that this radial network is not the most rational. It does not lead to the most economic uses of the land, nor does it give equal opportunities to everyone to reach every location. As a result, man turns to a squared, grid-iron network, which does not have these weaknesses. We can see examples of this in many villages and cities; in the division of fields in rural areas and, on a regional scale, in some systems of colonization.

6. A study of the maximum times spent by man upon his daily movements shows that, as a hunter, movement occupied many hours each day; as a farmer, he decreased his travelling time to 2 hr a day; as an urbanized citizen to half-an-hour. This seems to be man's optimum, because he held to it for some thousands of years, only abandoning it gradually around A.D. 1800 under the pressure of a growing urban population and insufficient means of rapid transport. Today, we find ourselves back at the point of spending as much time on daily travel as when the hunter was turning into a farmer around 8000 B.C. (Fig. 14-6a).

Fig. 14-6. (a) Time spent for man's daily movements. (b) Human muscular energy spent for man's daily movement. (c) Energy spent for total movement and transportation as a percentage of total available energy to man. (d) Energy spent for daily movement as a percentage of total available energy to man.

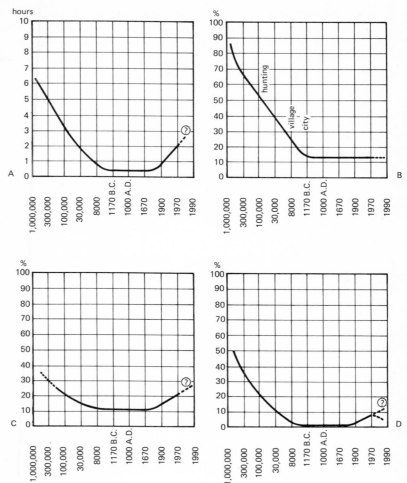

7. In the process of forming human settlements, man started by spending almost his whole available muscular energy on movement and then gradually reduced this to a lower percentage. This is part of the reason why man turned from hunter to farmer, to urban dweller. As a hunter, spending several hours walking per day, he probably used 50% of his whole muscular energy for movement. As a farmer, he walked up to 2 hr, using up 25% of his available muscular energy. As a citizen, he walked about 30 min, using 12.5% of his muscular energy. This last percentage seems to have remained constant from the formation of the first cities to recent times, because as man walked less his available muscular energy was also reduced, leaving the percentage approximately the same.

We can therefore say that, in terms of man's personal biological energy spent upon daily movement, the average healthy male citizen reached his optimum in the city in which civilization was created and developed (Fig. 14-6b).

8. It also appears that the percentage of all available energy used for all types of movement and transportation of people and goods started at a high level: it was about 20% for the organized hunter, and dropped to about 12.5% for both farmers and urban dwellers before the era of mechanical means of transportation. From then on it began to grow until it is now 20% for the whole world and 25% for the United States (Fig. 14-6c). As the United States with its high level of income and technology indicates trends for the future of the world, we can perhaps

foresee a new era during which the optimum of human and total energy spent for transportation within the traditional city (12.5%) for thousands of years changes because man has changed the economy and the technology of the world.

9. The percentage of the whole energy available to man spent on daily movement (after deducting the basic metabolic energy which keeps him alive) shows that man the hunter used up more than 20% of it, man the farmer about 4-5%, and man the urban dweller 1.5%-2%. This percentage began to increase as cities grew, and it now fluctuates between 2.5% and 8.0%. The latter is the probable average for the whole world in 1970. It is probably about 4.8% both in the United States as well as in some lower income cities (for different reasons). This means that there is today no clear trend corresponding to a systematic evolution of the urban systems (Fig. 14-6d).

These statements lead us to the following conclusions:

a. Man has always endeavoured to create an optimum type of settlement, corresponding to the time and energy available to him.

b. The time spent upon daily movement indicates that man established an optimum level of half an hour a day—or a maximum of 10 minutes time distance for a single journey—when he founded the first cities, and he held to this level for several thousand years. This optimum no longer exists in the cities of the present. As man does not easily change his optimum, something has gone wrong in his cities (see Fig. 14-6a).

c. Man reached the optimum of personal muscular energy expendable for movement and he held to this until recent times (see Fig. 14-6b).

d. As greater total energy became available to him, man increased the percentage spent upon movement and transportation in order to create a world economy (see Fig. 14-6c).

e. Man did not follow the same trend for his daily movement (see Fig. 14-6d) partly because this involved the limitation of time, which is not the case in (d) above; but also because of the absence of a specific technology which could give him a system of personal movement corresponding to the possibilities of modern technology and economy.

f. It is obvious that man *has not solved the problem of contemporary daily urban movement in a satisfactory way.* It occupies more than the optimum time and it does not make full use of the energy available to him, which could bring the time back to the optimum. But if he could use for his daily movement (see Fig. 14-6d) an amount equivalent to the percentage of energy spent for total movement and transportation (see Fig. 14-6d), he could again reduce his daily travelling time to the optimum (see Fig. 14-6a).

We can now project into the future and state that in the long run we should reckon with man's desire not to spend more than 30 minutes a day in travel—or 10 minutes for his longest journey—and that he can achieve this by devoting more and more of the total energy available to him upon means of personal transportation.

We can therefore expect a ninth phase in the evolution of human settlements with settlements growing in terms of people, in which a minimum amount of time and an increasing amount of energy is spent upon movement; also a tenth phase in which we will find a stable population on the earth and ameliorated movements that will tend to reduce time even more, and thus make it possible to achieve more contacts to all points at a minimum expenditure of the total energy available, even though the actual amount will be very much greater than at present.

Thinking of this tenth phase—the final phase we can foresee in the evolution of human settlements—we have to remember that densities will tend to increase up to the point at which man reacts to control the situation. It is necessary to state this because, throughout the history of the evolution of human settlements densities have been low at the start and have gradually got higher until man, by having exceeded the optimum for that period, learns what it was and tries to settle back to it. This is a phenomenon for which humanity has to be prepared, so that man can be in control of the situation before it becomes very dangerous.

The Future

The Inevitable Dimensions

The processes of the formation of human settlements indicate that their growth is going to continue, not only as long as world population continues to grow (that is for at least two or three generations), but as long as technology can provide better connections at higher speeds. These considerations, together with the analysis of how the processes take place, lead to the conclusion that it is inevitable that human settlements are going to grow into continuous interconnected networks.

The history of human settlements has moved from camp to village, to city, to metropolis, to megalopolis, and now we are moving towards the universal city or Ecumenopolis (9) whose anticipated shape can already be discerned in Europe, in the U.S.A. and in the world.

The Need of Order

The inevitable growth of human settlements must lead to more problems for each of their elements and to many more for the whole system. The only way to handle this situation is to create an orderly system to replace the chaotic one which now exists. Order in human settlements requires first a clear understanding of their problems, then an effective hierarchy and an effective structure.

Small cities have always needed, and still need, a hierarchical structure of at least home, block, neighbourhood and city. In the same way, but at a different scale, larger human settlements need a hierarchical order of sectors of different levels, as can be seen in the plans worked out for the future of the Urban Detroit Area for the year 2000 and for the 21st century.

The question immediately arises about what structure is going to facilitate this order, and the problem is again whether to select the radial or the orthogonal pattern as the basic one. If we turn back, we find that the solution for a city is undoubtedly an orthogonal system (Fig. 14-1) but the solution for a greater area may have to be re-examined for every specific case. In general, we can say that the reason for the

selection of the radial system in the past, although it has many structural disadvantages, was to conserve the maximum economy of energy, but that now and in the future, with more energy available and many more connections to be made, it is probable that orthogonal systems will prevail.

However, when we reach urban regions of the order of hundreds of kilometers (in at least one dimension) we may notice that throughout human history national states and the empires were always conceived as radial systems, focussing upon a single center, or upon a hierarchical system of centers, which were sufficiently far apart for each to operate as the center of its own radial system. A clear example is the statement that *"all roads lead to Rome"*, which is characteristic of the empire concept of organization in space.

The *empires of the oceans* were similarly conceived with a structure leading to a single center. As a characteristic example, connections by telephone between India and Pakistan, or between East and West Pakistan, passed through London.

Now we are in the phase in which we have many interwoven radial systems. The most characteristic example is offered by the *airlines* (Fig. 14-7). Each has a radial system, and together they form a multicenter system which is not coordinated. It is like the system which finally led the city to the gridiron concept; but when dealing with airlines, unlike the city, we do not face the disadvantages of an irrational use of triangular areas (or are they also irrational in the air?). If surface networks are leading to a gridiron organization, will not the air connections also be influenced towards the gridiron? Or shall we have a gridiron system on the surface of the Earth and a radial one in the air? It is too early to answer this question.

The Need of Quality

Whilst order is needed for the function of human settlements, quality is needed for the complete satisfaction of man. This is a principle of human settlements (10). This imperative need for quality is greatest in the residential urban units, which correspond in size to the cities of

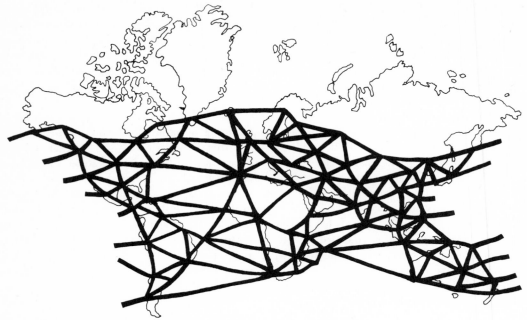

Fig. 14-7. Multicenter network of the future.

the past. These are the units within which people spend much of their lives; the units they can see as a whole, sense and enjoy. The overall size of these units should correspond with the optimum size of man's simple non-overlapping kinetic fields of the past, with a radius of 2 km and a maximum walking time of 10 minutes. In other words the cities of quality created by man over thousands of years correspond in scale with today's human communities in the cities of human development, which man so desperately needs (11).

References

1. C. A. Doxiadis, *Ekistics: An Introduction to the Science of Human Settlements* (Hutchinson, London, 1968; Oxford University Press, New York, 1968).
2. C. A. Doxiadis, "The future of human settlements", Nobel Symposium on "The Place of Value in a World of Facts", Stockholm, September 19, 1969; document R-GEN-A 443 printed by Doxiadis Associates.
3. C. A. Doxiadis, "Man's movement and his city", *Science* 326-334 (1968); *Ekistics* **159**, 88-94 (1969).
4. C. A. Doxiadis, "Ekistics: an attempt at a scientific approach to the problems of human settlements". This paper was prepared for the Committee on Science and Astronautics, House of Representatives, Washington, D.C., February 4, 1969 and was abstracted in *Ekistics* **163**, 359-360 (1969).
5. C. A. Doxiadis, "Ecumenopolis: tomorrow's city", 1968 *Britannica Book of the Year* (The University of Chicago, Chicago, 1968), pp. 16-38.
6. See Ref. 3.
7. *Emergence and Growth of an Urban Region, the Developing Urban Detroit Area*, Vol. 1, 1966; Vol. 2, 1967. A project of the Detroit Edison Company, Wayne State University and Doxiadis Associates under the chairmanship of W. L. Cisler, Chairman of the Board, the Detroit Edison Company, directed by C. A. Doxiadis, and published by the Detroit Edison Company.
8. C. A. Doxiadis, "Ekistic synthesis of structure and form", *Ekistics* **155**, 395-415 (1968).
9. "Ecumenopolis: The coming world-city", *Cities of Destiny*, edited by Arnold Toynbee (Thames and Hudson, 1967), pp. 336-358; "Ecumenopolis, world city of tomorrow", *Impact of Science on Society*, **XIX**, No. 2, 179-193 (1969).
10. See Ref. 4.
11. C. A. Doxiadis, "A city for human development", *Ekistics* **151**, 374-394 (1968).

15

THE EXPERIMENTAL CITY

Athelstan Spilhaus

A federal commissioner recently expressed an opinion typical of the "hopelessness approach" to city problems when he said, "We cannot, even if we would, dismantle the urban complex." I disagree completely. The overgrown urban complex must be selectively dismantled and dispersed if we are to cure the ills of the megalopolis.

Half of the people in the United States live on 1 percent of the land, and there is a continual drift to the big cities. Urban renewal encourages the increase in the size of the cities. Two or three-story slum buildings are torn down, and sterile, high-rise, so-called low-cost housing brings more people into the center of the city than ever before, compounding the problem.

Secretary of the Interior Stewart Udall, in an article which appeared in the September 1967 issue of the *Saturday Review*, addressed himself to the fundamental problem, that of controlling the population, and took a stand that must be considered courageous for a man in his position. If we consider that *any* excess that is harmful to decent living is a pollutant, then the prime pollutant on earth is too many people. But until we have the sense to control population, something has to be done for all these people, and here I discuss the question of what is to be done.

In his article, Udall goes on to say:

Our annual population growth of 4,000,000 people increases the physical and social pressures, causes us to seek quick remedies, leads us to waste too much wealth on quick-fix projects that provide at best a temporary respite from yesterday's mistakes. The razing of tenements, their instant replacement by high-rise slums, changes the facade—not the features—of the ghetto.

I agree completely, and propose, as a corrective, development of a system of dispersed cities of controlled size, differing in many respects from conventional cities, and surrounded by ample areas of open land. The proposed Minnesota Experimental City will be a prototype.

The initial group that planned the Experimental City project in Minnesota consisted of Otto Silha, Wayne Thompson, Walter Vivrett, Max Feldman, and myself, representing local business leaders, the University of Minnesota, and industry. Three departments of the federal government—Housing and Urban Development (HUD), Health, Education and Welfare (HEW), and Commerce—together with ten leading industrial firms, financed the first year's study at the University. This first phase concludes this spring. The state legislature has endorsed the project.

Dispersal

People like to live in cities. *Dispersal* does not mean that the whole United States is to become a single sprawling suburb, such as California is becoming. *Dispersal* refers to cities big enough to offer the advantages of city living yet small enough not to be subject to unplanned overgrowth. Each, with its surrounding reserved land, would be a separate unit. According to the Minnesota plan there would ultimately be many of these units, spread across the United States.

If the present 200 million people in the United States were living in 800 cities with a population of a quarter of a million each, and if these cities were scattered evenly across the United States, we would not have the pollution, the traffic congestion, the riots, and many of the other ills that develop when cities become too large.

In industry we already see trends toward dispersal. Industries are leading the way, by seeking small-town locations away from the large cities. Unfortunately, this migration has created a competition between Chambers of Commerce to retain industry or attract it to their present jurisdictions. Chambers of Commerce are strongest in the great overgrown cities. They are, therefore, a powerful force against urban dispersal. In large urban complexes two Chambers of Commerce may operate within one metropolitan area, with divided municipal responsibilities. Thus, if the competitor across the river brings in something big, the other side must do likewise, and the result is continual growth of the oversized city.

Buckminster Fuller, architect and imaginative member of our Experimental City Steering Committee, feels that industry of the future, largely automated, will be located outside the cities, and that the many functions of the city which in the past were directed toward facilitating the exchange of physical goods will in the future be directed toward the exchange of what he calls metaphysical values—ideas, learning, and culture.

Building from Scratch

Planning, constructing, populating, and managing a dispersed city highly suitable for industry, commerce, and human occupation will require the leadership, imagination, and enthusiasm of scientists, industrialists, and educators alike. We must be prepared to discard convention and to experiment with new and radical ideas. We must utilize the most advanced methods of construction, transportation, communications, waste removal, and city management.

The project simply could not be accomplished through any attempt to rebuild a present city, regardless of its size or location, for, without exception, our cities are bound by tradition, outmoded building codes, restrictive legislation, and the consequences of unplanned, unhealthy growth.

For these reasons the Experimental City Steering Committee has begun to work on the organization and financing of a scheme to build an experimental city from scratch, to house a quarter of a million people and the industry and commerce needed to support them.

The need for an experimental city was first impressed upon me after the year-long discus-sions conducted by the Committee on Pollution of the National Academy of Sciences—National Research Council, of which I was chairman. In the final report, "Waste Management and Control" (1), the first recommendation was:

That a full-scale experimental residue-control system be planned, designed, and constructed in a new city—this system to embody the newest and best principles of recycling, re-using, and recovering residues, and to serve as a demonstration model.

If this was necessary for waste management, why not for other new technologies in transportation, communications, and total city services? I was in Minnesota at the time and found staunch supporters there for the idea of an experimental city (2). As a result, the Experimental City Project in Minnesota came about. However, the need for experimental cities of this kind is a national need, and the Minnesota experiment must be considered only the prototype.

Urgent Need

Suppose we built an experimental city in every one of our 50 states. If each such city were populated by a quarter of a million people, we could care for only 12½ million people, barely the predicted increase of population in the United States in 3 years. Yet, according to our most optimistic estimates, just the building of an experimental city will take longer than 3 years, and if we merely keep up with the increase in population we will do nothing to alleviate the problems of overgrowth in our existing cities.

The problems of our large cities indicate an urgent need to move toward the dispersal concept immediately. If the need is urgent in the United States, it is even more urgent in the world as a whole, especially in those countries where the birthrate is much higher than ours.

Let us look ahead and suppose that the world population, if we do nothing about population control, reaches 15 billion by A.D. 2068. And let us assume that our technology permits us to build cities on any solid land, from Antarctica to the tropics, from desert to rain forest. The area of all the continents is about 2.3 billion acres. If we built cities of controlled size, dispersed throughout the world, there would be 60 thousand cities of a quarter of a million people each, and each such city would be surrounded by 40 thousand acres, or 64 square miles, of open land. The alternative of allowing the present big cities to grow unplanned, or to accelerate their growth through so-called urban renewal, would mean that vast tracts of the earth's surface would be uninhabited and the urban complexes would be intolerable.

(There is no magic in the figure of a quarter of a million. It may be that a city of half a million would better provide the choices that people want, or it may be that cities of different sizes would be needed. The important thing is that the size be controlled and that the cities be kept within a small area, with bounds, so that they would remain surrounded by open land.)

The advent of atomic power opens up the possibility of building verdant cities even in desert areas, if these areas are near the sea. An atomic plant which would generate a million kilowatts of electricity could distill half a billion gallons of freshwater from seawater and, from the residue, make enough fertilizer to grow the food to feed the entire populations of ten cities the size of the proposed experimental city.

We must try these schemes and others that will emerge. The place to try them is in new experimental, dispersed cities, such as that envisioned in the Minnesota plan.

The Minnesota Experimental City

Early in planning the Minnesota Experimental City we set some guidelines. (i) The ultimate maximum population would be a quarter of a million. The community would be (ii) economically viable as a unit of the U.S. economy, (iii) truly experimental, (iv) at least 100 miles from any major existing urban center, and (v) a densely populated center surrounded by open land. This surrounding land, which would have an area perhaps 100 times that of the densely populated center,

would be used for forests, outdoor museums, recreation, or agriculture, or just left as a rural area.

The idea would be to populate the experimental city in the shortest possible time by attracting people from the overcrowded urban complexes, in contrast to the past practice of letting the city slowly grow by drawing people from the immediately surrounding region. We must get away from what Fuller calls the "local focus" situation, wherein the city relates itself specifically to the needs, resources, and desires of people in its immediate vicinity.

Plans for building the Experimental City differ in many respects from plans for building other kinds of cities. Conventional cities grow above the ground, and as they grow, and as people demand transportation, power, water, gas, and sewers, the ground and rock underneath the city are tunneled for subways or the streets are dug up and the utility lines are buried. In the Experimental City the whole substructure will be planned and excavated, and the power lines and utility lines will be installed, before the city is built. Knowledge that the city is to be of a certain size will make this possible.

Costs of all city services will be part of the rental, occupancy charges—the "hotel bill"—for individuals, businesses, or industry in the city. Much of the equipment for servicing the city will be invisible and inaudible underground. Water and building materials can be stored there. Heating plants and cold-storage facilities can be located there. Underground pipelines can carry out solid wastes conventionally carried by trucks. Snow or rainwater from the streets can be channeled to underground reservoirs.

Pollution-producing vehicles can come in underground, and fume sewers can take the gases out to scrubbing and processing plants in the surrounding open-land area. Air-burning vehicles that connect the city with the rest of the nation can be parked underground. Police, ambulance, and emergency vehicles will all have underground throughways. By eliminating the need for some service vehicles, restricting those that are needed to the substructure, and providing a free above-the-ground transportation system (discussed below), we hope to eliminate all vehicles from ground-level streets.

A lawyer at one of our planning sessions asked whether the Experimental City might not eventually disintegrate and become merely a more modern, but no more effective, city complex. "If Chicago, Minneapolis, New York, and St. Paul are willing to allow smoke to billow from new factories," he said, "if they permit automobiles to crowd their streets, and if they do not restrict building construction from occurring in illogical patterns, why should we expect anything different in the Experimental City?"

The answer is simple. Industries, before they are selected or approved for participation in the Experimental City, must agree to abide by the city's building programs. They will be required to conform to certain waste-disposal methods. Presumably they will be willing to do so because they will benefit from the City's central waste-processing facilities, smoke sewers, and other underground disposal facilities.

Construction and Disassembly

All the buildings in the Experimental City will be constructed of the newest lightweight materials, and modular techniques of assembly will be used. Thus buildings can be easily erected and quickly disassembled as we learn what is needed, and as needs change.

The average useful life of a building has been estimated to be between 20 and 30 years. All buildings in the Experimental City will be designed with this in mind, and methods of construction that leave permanent outmoded monuments or later require the services of the wrecking crew will be abandoned. We will get away from the idea of building forever and, instead, will build for living, recognizing that people have continually changing desires.

With new building materials and freedom from obsolete codes and building practices, both public buildings and commercial structures can be made extremely flexible, with adjustable floors, curtain-walls and ceiling heights. It may even be possible to use inflat-

able buildings, which can be instantly deflated. Housing units may be precast, even pre-furnished, in the manner of Expo's Habitat, with units put together like building blocks and arranged and rearranged as desired. Practical application of this idea is no dream. Precast rooms were used months ago in building San Antonio's Hilton Hotel.

The disassembly of buildings will resemble the disassembly of an erector set. Reusable components of the building will be swallowed by the city's substructure. There will be no cluttering of streets with cranes and other moving equipment. An obsolete building will disappear like ice cream that melts and drains out through the truncated bottom of the cone. In building new structures, the process will be the reverse. Materials will be lifted from the substructure into the middle of the site, and adjacent activities will not be disturbed.

Certain parts of the Experimental City probably will be domed, so that the advantages and disadvantages of totally enclosed cities can be determined. It is our current view that not all of the city should be domed. Doming only a part of it will enable us to determine the extremes of climate under which total enclosure is economical and acceptable.

In the domed portion of the Experimental City, which may enclose a medical complex, we can undertake experiments on allergy control, and studies of acoustics, ventilation, and maintenance of a clean atmosphere.

A dome 2 miles in diameter, made of glass, would cost an estimated $80 million, but it would eliminate the need for snow removal and would make heating more efficient and less costly. Savings equivalent to the cost of its construction could be achieved in a 10-year period.

Waste Collection and Recycling

With a controlled city, savings can be realized, too, through new methods of waste collection and through use, reuse, and recycling of wastes. It may not be possible to achieve complete recycling immediately, although the objective would always be borne in mind in our planning. Total recycling is the ultimate answer to the waste problem for a closed-system earth.

One step toward recycling is the collection of waste at the source, whether or not it is reused. Another is the redesign of many systems, so that there is less waste. For example, a sterile pneumatic system for delivering foods might reduce the vast quantities of wrapping paper and containers that are now needed.

The very things we do today in our cities to dispose of wastes constitute pollution. Garbage cans litter the sidewalks, garbage trucks clog the streets, dumps of solid wastes insult our nostrils and esthetic sensibilities. The burning of land fills in municipal dumps pollutes the air, and green slime grows on the sewage- and detergent-filled waters.

In the pollution-free Experimental City the utility tunnels would carry away the liquid and gaseous wastes, and many of the solid wastes, to the processing plants. New systems for moving wastes may be used—pneumatic, hydraulic conveyors or unitized trains. If we can reduce the bulk of solid wastes and package them suitably, deadheading trains and trucks can take them away from the city to the open-land area, where they can be processed and then stored or reused, perhaps to build ski slopes, arenas, or other recreation facilities. Wastes that are not immediately reused can be sorted and stored in "mountains," to be mined when reuse becomes economically desirable.

In water-rich areas, water can be used first for drinking and then reused at least twice, for cooling and then for purposes of recreation. But if the Experimental City is to show the way for cities in arid areas, complete recycling of part of the water should be attempted.

Transportation

One of the most pressing problems of our urban living is transportation and the use, care, parking, and garaging of the private automobile.

Doxiadis recognizes that it is a tragedy when our city buildings are primarily designed to accommodate cars, both stationary and moving, and to destroy the "human scale." Lewis Mumford recognizes that the private car no longer performs the role of "facilitating meeting and sociability" and that its "assumed right" is a "license to destroy a city."

How can we provide people with a transportation system that facilitates the desirable social relationships which constitute the joy of city living yet does not have undesirable side effects?

We must remember not to force people into what is technologically easy but to find a technological solution which is practical and closely meets their desires. What people basically like about the private automobile is the fact that it is a small pod and gives them a sense of privacy in a world where any kind of privacy is becoming a scarce luxury. They also like the automobile because it takes them from where they are to where they want to go without stopping where everybody else wants to stop. But when so many automobiles crowd the streets that we cannot move because of traffic jams, and when our average speed in a pollution-producing, many-hundred-horsepower vehicle is 8 miles an hour, it is time to look at the alternatives.

Now in the process of design are many systems that can move people in motorless, driverless, noiseless, semi-private pods, computer-controlled so that the passengers travel from where they are to where they want to go without stopping. If you want to go to the store you don't go to the station and then walk to the store; your pod is sidetracked right into the store. The various systems have a common denominator: they are driven by a propulsion system built into the track. The pods are inexpensive, thus many of them can be used at the same time. Moving sidewalks, moving platforms, and other wheelless systems are all technically feasible. One important concept that has emerged in our discussions is this: if we are to use mass transportation in the Experimental City it should be free, like elevator service. You don't pay a fare to ride vertically in an elevator. Why should you pay a fare to ride horizontally? The cost can be embodied in the service costs of the city.

Eliminating the automobile by means of a modern transport system of this kind does away with the need for freeways and traffic control, eliminates smog, saves lives, lessens stress, and saves valuable space. Making the transit system free saves the costs otherwise associated with ticket-selling and ticket-taking. Because free transportation would reduce or eliminate the sale of automobiles, the parking-lot business, and other businesses basic to the economy of older cities, it can be introduced readily only in a newly planned, centrally governed city such as the Experimental City.

Communications

Among the greatest innovations that can be tried in the Experimental City are the new technologies in communications that have been developed but not yet put to practical use.

The current view is that radio frequencies should be reserved for purposes, such as communication to or from a vehicle in motion, where wires are not feasible. The substructure of the Experimental City would be wired, and coaxial cable would reach to every point where, conventionally, there would be a telephone. These wires and cables can be planned and located in the substructure even before we have a clear-cut idea of what terminals, picture-phones, computers, facsimile machines, and the like may ultimately be needed. (Because broad-band communications open up so many uses, the magnitude of the prospective network may be much greater than that required for ordinary telephone service. Consequently, special attention will have to be given to connection with the normal communication channels outside the Experimental City.)

Such a communication system can provide access from any point to large highspeed digital computers, for purposes of city management (on the basis of real information), crime prevention through the use of video monitors, and maintenance of up-to-the-minute data banks for the social experiment that the city constitutes. The same lines, in conjunction with smaller computers and other video terminals, can provide a means of decentralizing schools and hospitals and of bringing together electronically the now separated functions of shopping, charging, banking, credit, and business. Video ter-

minals can even provide "tele-babysitting." The advanced system will provide an ideal laboratory for determining how to insure privacy of computer use yet insure that computers are used to the maximum benefit of society.

In the Experimental City we will have a large pilot plant in which to develop a modern library along the lines suggested by M.I.T.'s Project Intrex. The medical extensions of the advanced system may make it possible to set up a series of care centers providing different degrees of medical care, and thus to make available appropriate care at minimum cost. The various care centers would be in touch with each other through a communications system insuring instant access to specialists in case of emergency.

Populating the City

How will the Experimental City be populated? Politicians say you can't move people. Many sociologists who are more interested in studying what is happening and predicting doom than in taking the steps necessary to avert it, agree. But the fact is that, with our existing legal and governmental structure, we do move people. We push people around everywhere, always with the excuse that it is for their own good. We move them in wars; we displace them when we build highways; and we move them when we clear slums and build much larger buildings than were there before. We move them, but often in the wrong direction, into the already overgrown cities.

Urban renewal in its worst manifestations is the construction of the slums of the future. Many people in the present overgrown cities might like to move out into new complexes which provided the advantages of city life without the physical and social distress. Many others whom the authorities say they cannot move have never contemplated moving because they have been trapped, lacking the opportunity to go anywhere else. The fact is that most of those who can afford to do so have already fled the cities, to suburbs that will become the slums of tomorrow.

We must build a city for today's city-dwellers and suburb-dwellers to go to. We must provide people with a different choice, not just that between life in a dirty overgrown city with suburbs or a completely rural existence. We can provide a middle choice—clean cities of controlled size, with plenty of space and an exciting new environment.

Population balance for the Experimental City will be achieved through careful selection of the type of industry that will be invited to participate and of the commercial operations that will be established.

Management and Cost

Now for two most important decisions: (i) Who will manage the Experimental City? (ii) How much will it cost?

The management of a typical city involves thousands of individuals. Many students of political science and law feel that this spreading of authority is basic to the democratic government of the city. There is, however, reason to believe that, with the changes in size of our cities and their merging together in huge complexes, this arrangement is no longer workable. For example, if one jurisdiction allows pollution, it will affect its neighbor. To resolve this conflict it has been necessary to establish federal standards and controls.

It would seem that the idea of running a city as a public utility by a quasi-public, quasi-private corporation should be tried. Present-day hotel complexes, with their associated shops, restaurants, transportation facilities, and so on, are growing larger and larger. Many of them are run very well. It is not much of a jump to think of experimental cities of controlled size as huge hotels. It seems to me that management of the city-hotel-corporation type should be tried.

Daniel Moynihan, director of the Harvard-M.I.T. Joint Center for Urban Studies, says realistically that the government cannot do everything well, and that many public services are best contracted to private enterprises. In the Experimental City, contracts for many such services would be let on a performance basis.

The federal government, too, is beginning to move in this direction. Agencies have let contracts to private enterprise for carrying out social work programs. Why not go the whole way and have responsible corporations provide all the services needed in the Experimental City?

As to the cost of building facilities for an Experimental City of a quarter of a million inhabitants, some simple arithmetic provides a reasonable estimate.

If we take 2.5 people as an average family unit, we will need 100,000 units. Taking $20,000 as the average cost per unit, we arrive at a figure of $2 billion. But because this city will be planned from scratch and have a large substructure housing all the equipment for city services, and because it will be experimental, we should probably double this figure. So we arrive at a guess of $4 billion.

It is important to stress that these costs are not an additional burden on the national economy. New housing and new factories and businesses will be built in any case, somewhere. We will merely concentrate the activity by attracting them to the Experimental City. The city must be built as any city is built. The plan must prove attractive to the industries that will come to the city to build new plants. If they are attracted to the Experimental City, they will bear part of the costs of construction and operation.

But it is realistic to recognize that a large sum of money is needed for planning and building the services substructure, which will utilize new technologies involving costly experimentation and research. Part of the construction costs could legitimately be funded by an FHA mortgage. Part of the costs of experimentation and research would be met by the private sector. Imaginative American industry needs a place, a city laboratory, in which to try out new technologies of waste management, communication, transportation, and construction. Industries are at present investing large sums in elements of these areas. Our plan for the Experimental City must show that it is the best place to do this research and to try out new developments.

At present, new systems for urban development must be tried piecemeal—a new transportation system here, a sewage system there, a communications system elsewhere. But a city is a complex system, and everything one does has an impact on other parts of the system. If we clean up the noise, take the waste heat out of the city, and control the filth of factories at the source, there will be no need for zoning. Factories, schools, and homes will all be in one complex. This will reduce the need for transportation. Reduced transportation further reduces pollution, and the combination of these technological improvements will have a profound influence on the city systems for health care, education, police surveillance, and other services.

I would expect that the Experimental City will be of interest as a laboratory to those of our industries that are getting heavily into the urban problem.

Other Approaches

Other approaches to the problems of today's cities are being tried. The government's Model City program, an urban renewal program administered by the Department of Housing and Urban Development, is an attempt to alleviate the overwhelming problems of the overgrown cities. The objective is a most important one, but, in general, the means used are the tearing out of slums and their replacement with new construction. The government is becoming the new slum landlord.

Worthwhile experiments in the building of new cities are being made by private enterprise. Examples are Columbia, Maryland; Disneyworld's experimental prototype city in Florida; and Westinghouse's community proving ground in Florida. More than 200 "new cities" are either in the design stage or under construction in the United States.

Some of the new towns are being built exclusively for the "senior citizen." In this country we are working hard at the problem of integrating people of different races, yet we segregate people of different ages. We must integrate people of all ages, income levels and interests, to achieve the total mixture which makes up the stimulating society of a city.

The government-financed and privately financed "new cities" are similar to the Minnesota Experimental City in one respect: they are built from scratch. On the other hand they are, in the best meaning of the term, real estate developments, and consequently they tend to be satellites of existing urban complexes—communities where people live and from which they commute to work. That this is the case may be seen from the fact that almost all of the "new cities" are growing along the coastlines—East, West, and Gulf—where the overgrown cities already are. Generally their size is not controlled, and one can anticipate that even the best of them, such as Reston (Virginia) and Columbia, will be swallowed up as the nearby urban complexes—in this case Washington and Baltimore—expand. Because they do not have sufficient reserved open land around them, even the best of the "new cities" will become engulfed; moreover, since they are close to existing huge cities, they cannot develop with enough independence to try novel technologies.

Conclusion

It is obvious to me that we must use all of our land for living, not just tiny fractions of it. To do this we must look at solutions that envisage urban dispersal, and if we are to disperse into new planned cities, a national experimental cities program is an urgent must.

References and Notes

1. "Waste Management and Control: A Report to the Federal Council for Science and Technology," *Nat. Acad. Sci.—Nat. Res. Council Pub. 1400* (1966), p. 26; *Science* **152**, 329 (1966).
2. I am most grateful for the support that I found in Minnesota, particularly from Mr. Otto Silha, who worked on organizing and financing the Experimental City from the outset.

16

GENETIC IMPLICATIONS OF THE BRAIN DRAIN

Richard Lynn

Despite the prominence of the "brain drain" from Britain as a subject of news and discussion, there has been virtually no comment on its genetic implications. I should like in this article to draw attention to the serious danger which a prolonged brain drain could entail for the genetic quality of the population remaining in Britain.

The first important point is that intelligence is principally determined by inheritance. There are a number of ways of demonstrating this, but the most crucial is the study of identical twins reared in different families. These investigations have invariably revealed a high measure of agreement between the IQs of the pairs, even though they have been reared in families of different educational and cultural standards. The correlations between pairs found in four independent investigations are shown in Table 1. These are all high correlations, and these and other studies seem to indicate conclusively that intelligence is principally determined by inheritance. This is a conclusion on which virtually all psychologists who have paid serious attention to the matter are agreed.

Since intelligence is principally determined by heredity, inheritance would seem to be the most important reason that intelligent people tend to have intelligent children, though the environmental advantages which intelligent parents confer on their children reinforce the genetic effects. This suggests that if intelligent people emigrate in large numbers there is likely to be a diminution in the number of intelligent children born into the next generation.

Intelligence is closely associated with the type of occupation a person follows. People in professional and executive occupations generally have IQs of between 120 and 160, and it is doubtful whether it would be possible to do most professional or executive jobs with an IQ of less than around 115. This is about the level at which children pass the eleven-plus examination and about 20 per cent of the population have IQs above this figure. Some typical results of a study of the mean IQs of different occupations are shown in Table 2. (The exact figures vary a little according to the tests used and the exact definitions of the occupation.)

This close correlation between intelligence and occupation means that occupation can be used as a reasonably reliable index of intelligence. This, in turn, allows us to make some estimate of the intelligence lost in the brain drain. Occupational categories of immigrants are recorded by the immigration departments of the principal countries to which the British emigrate. These show that a large percentage of the emigrants belong to the higher occupational groups. A breakdown by occupation of British emigrants to the United States, Canada and Australia in 1967 is shown in Table 3.

All three countries show a high proportion of emigrants in the higher occupational categories. In Britain there are, in round figures, 1.5 million people with university degrees or equivalent qualifications in a working force of 25 million—i.e. six per cent of the labour force.

Table 1. Correlations between the IQs of identical twins reared apart.

Investigation	Country	Correlation
C. Burt	Britain	.87
H. H. Newman	USA	.77
A. Mogensen	Denmark	.79
J. Shields	Britain	.77

Table 2. Relation between IQ and occupation (from *Uses and Abuses of Psychology*, by H. J. Eysenck, Penguin, 1953).

Occupation	Mean IQ
Higher professional and executive	150
Lower professional and executive	130
Highly skilled and clerical	118
Skilled workers	108
Semi-skilled workers	97
Unskilled workers	86

Reprinted from the *New Scientist* 41: 622-25, 1969, with the permission of the publishers.

Table 3. British emigrants in 1967 belonging to different occupational categories. Housewives, children and other dependants are excluded.

					Occupational category					
	Profes- sional	*Managers*	*Clerical*	*Salesman*	*Skilled workers*	*Domestics*	*Service workers*	*Farm and other labourers*	*Other occupa- tions*	*Total*
Australia	3,606	1,625	4,544	1.845	12,017	971	—	3,815	539	28,962
Canada	9,660	877	6,929	—not listed separately—			2,021	1,207	11,602	32,296
USA	4,726	488	2,209	337	2,415	1,171	569	620	6	12,541

Yet among the emigrants the professionally qualified group constitute 24 per cent of the total. This percentage errs on the low side because it excludes managers, some of whom almost certainly have graduate or equivalent qualifications. It should also be noted that skilled workers outnumber labourers by about four to one. These figures suggest that among emigrants as a whole there is a fairly substantial bias towards the more intelligent.

How significant is this loss? Estimates of various groups suggest that the number of highly able people leaving Britain's shores is running at around 15 to 30 per cent of the annual output from universities. Dr. E. Rudd and Dr. S. Hatch have investigated all British students who began postgraduate work in 1957 and found that 15 per cent were working abroad in 1966. The number of doctors emigrating over the decade 1954-63 was about a quarter of the output from the medical schools. One-third of psychology graduates with Oxford firsts over the years 1949-64 have emigrated. In 1966, 2000 scientists emigrated, representing 23 per cent of the universities' output; the number of engineers was 4200, representing 42 per cent of the output from the universities. At least 2200 managers emigrated in 1966, when the numbers of graduates entering management was a little over 7000.

Of these results the lowest is the 15 per cent loss of 1957 postgraduates. This is no doubt partly explained by the exceptionally rapid expansion of British universities in the years following 1957, which allowed unusually large numbers to be absorbed into employment in Britain. This expansion is not expected to continue at the same rate, so that the emigration of postgraduates may well rise in the years to come. Taking these figures as a whole, they suggest that somewhere around 20 to 25 per cent of the graduate class is emigrating.

It would be hazardous to try to estimate too precisely the effect of this loss on the genetic quality of the population. But there seems a high probability that it will be substantial. If we assume that in a relatively stable population each occupational class broadly reproduces itself, then a 20 to 25 per cent loss of graduates would involve a corresponding loss of these proportions in the next generation. Two qualifications must be made to this estimate. In the first place, it is well established that the higher occupational groups tend to have small families, and the effect of this tendency would be to compound the genetic deterioration caused by the brain drain.

On the other hand, the phenomenon known as "regression to the mean" would counteract the loss. Parents at either extreme of the intelligence scale tend to have children whose intelligence lies somewhere between that of the parents and the mean for the population as a whole. Thus the children of very unintelligent parents have IQs a little higher than their parents, while the children of highly intelligent parents are a little less intelligent than their parents. This tendency is sometimes used to play down the damaging effects of a brain drain (or of a differential birth rate between people of high and low intelligence). However, the regression phenomenon is only an average, and there is always quite a large spread around an average. Parents with IQs of 150 may have one child with an IQ of 150 and another with an IQ of 120. The average of the children is below that of the parents, but the loss of a large number of families of this type would still be expected to reduce the genetic quality of the population.

Highly able people generally come from two groups. Many come from well-established elite families, such as the Darwins, the Huxleys and other less well-known families who produce very gifted people in generation after generation. In addition, many able people emerge from the much larger number of families in the middle section of society, say with IQs in the range of 100 to 120. This is, of course, due to the fairly wide range of IQs of children around the mean of their parents, so that from millions of parents with IQs in the 100 to 120 range, there will emerge several thousands of children with IQs around 150. This means that even if all graduates emigrated there would always be some highly able people in the next generation thrown up from the middle ranks of society.

However, it should be noted from the figures shown in Table 3 that large numbers of these families of good average intelligence are emigrating. The total number of emigrants in the middle 1960s has been around a quarter of a million a year, of whom the great majority are of good average intelligence or above. Thus Britain is losing substantial numbers of both types of family from whom highly intelligent children are born. Highly intelligent children very rarely come from families with IQs below 100—the one group which is not emigrating on any considerable scale.

The implication seems to be that the genetic quality of the population is likely to deteriorate. It may be wondered whether such a thing could actually happen. It is doubtful whether there has ever before been such a mass migration of talented people across national frontiers as has occurred in the post-war decades. Even so, there have certainly been cases where the emigration of intellectual elites has had severely damaging effects. The sack of Constantinople in 1453, and the ensuing exodus of scholars to the West, effectively ended 1000 years of civilization and brought corresponding benefits to western Europe. At the end of the fifteenth century the Spanish expulsion of the Jews and the Moors, who were the backbone of the trading community, had severely detrimental effects on the commercial strength of the

country. In more recent times, it seems certain the German scientific achievement has been impaired by the loss of the large numbers of able scientists who fled from Hitler.

In spite of these emigrations, it is doubtful whether there is any historical parallel to the scale of the present brain drain. What has been more typical is the migration of talented families within nations from the country districts to the cities, especially the capital. It has frequently been found that the IQs of children in country districts are well below those in cities. This difference is often interpreted as an environmental effect of the limited experience of country living, or of bias in the tests favouring town children. These interpretations may be doubted. The main environmental effect of intelligence is the quality of the family and there seems no reason why this should differ between country and town, unless there is already a genetic difference. Examination of the content of intelligence tests makes it unlikely that they would favour town children, to any significant degree.

The most important reason for the country-city differences is surely selective migration of the more intelligent families into the cities. For example, it has been reported that children in the western islands of Scotland have an average IQ of around 85, which is very substantially below that found in cities. Many of the more able islanders, such as the Macmillans, have left these desolate parts over the course of the last two centuries and established themselves as leading metropolitan families. This selective emigration is sufficient to explain the low intelligence of the residue.

It is possible that whole provinces may have deteriorated genetically as a result of a brain drain. In his book *Secular Changes in Scottish Genius* (Mankind Monographs, 1962) Mr. R. Robertson has argued that Scotland has suffered in this way. There seems little doubt that Scottish achievements have fallen over the last century or so. In the eighteenth and early nineteenth century Scotland was a leading cultural centre and Havelock Ellis and others recorded that Scots were exceptionally prominent in all branches of learning and business. Today, Scotland is an economically depressed area, and the English have to be offered financial inducements from the government to go there and run businesses. Scottish universities in the 1950s had 18.6 per cent of the students at British universities, but less than half this percentage of Scots passed into the administrative grade of the civil service or were taken into the great national companies. The percentage of fellows of the Royal Society who were Scots declined from 10 per cent in 1850 to three per cent in 1950.

Thus in many of the important areas of life the achievements of the Scots are now below the national average. Admittedly, intelligence tests on Scottish children do not indicate that they have lower IQs than children in the rest of Britain, but the proportion of highly intelligent families is so small that a significant reduction in their number would not necessarily show up in national averages. Families with IQs of 150 comprise around one per cent of the population proportion and if this one per cent were halved in any particular province there would be little effect on the average IQ of the population as a whole.

I suggest that we should regard Scotland as a warning. The deterioration it has suffered in both cultural achievement and economic prosperity could well be due to a prolonged brain drain, and the next victim could be Britain as a whole.

17

CAUCASIAN GENES IN AMERICAN NEGROES

T. Edward Reed

It is very difficult to describe the genetic history of a large, defined human population in a meaningful way. As a result there have been few opportunities, at the population level, to study the consequences of known genetic events in the recent past of modern populations. The Negro population of the United States, however, is one of the exceptions to these generalizations. The American individual to whom the term *Negro* is applied is almost always a biracial hybrid. Usually between 2 and 50 percent of his genes are derived from Caucasian ancestors, and these genes were very probably received after 1700. While it is obviously of social and cultural importance to understand Negro hybridity, it is less obvious that there are several pertinent genetic reasons

Reprinted from *Science* 165: 762-68, 1969, with the permission of the publishers. Copyright 1969 by the American Association for the Advancement of Science.

for wishing to know about the magnitude and nature of Caucasian ancestry in Negroes. Recent data, both genetic and historical, now make possible a better understanding of American Negro genetic history than has been possible heretofore. Here I review and criticize the published data on this subject, present new data, and interpret the genetic significance of the evidence.

In order to put the genetic data in proper context, I must first give a little of the history of American slavery. The first slaves were brought to what is now the United States in 1619. Importation of slaves before 1700 was negligible, however, but after that date it proceeded at a high rate for most of the 18th century. Importation became illegal after 1808 but in fact continued at a low rate for several more decades (1, 2). The total number of slaves brought into the United States was probably somewhat less than 400,000 (3). Charleston, South Carolina, was the most important port of entry, receiving 30 to 40 percent of the total number (4). More than 98 percent of the slaves came from a very extensive area of West Africa and west-central Africa—from Senegal to Angola—and, in these areas, from both coastal and inland regions. Shipping lists of ships that brought slaves to the United States—and to the West Indies, often to be sent later to the United

States—provide a fairly detailed picture of the geographic origins of the slaves and a less complete picture of their ethnic origins. Table 1 gives the approximate proportions of American slaves brought from the eight major slaving areas of Africa. The contribution from East Africa is seen to be negligible, whereas the area from Senegal to western Nigeria contributed about half the total and the region from eastern Nigeria to Angola contributed the other half. An earlier tabulation for entry at Charleston alone (5) is quite similar, except that the contribution from the Bight of Biafra is much less (0.021 as compared to 0.233) and that from "Angola" is appreciably greater (0.396 as compared to 0.245).

At some early point in American slavery, matings between slaves and Caucasians began to occur. Quantitative data are lacking, and we can say only that most of these matings occurred after 1700. Our concern here is the genetic consequences of the matings—the introduction of Caucasian genes into the genome (or total complement of genetic material) of the American Negro. We could, in theory, estimate

the Caucasian contribution to American Negro ancestry in a very simple way *if* certain strict criteria were met. In practice it is not possible to show that all these criteria are met, but this fact has not stopped geneticists, including myself, from making estimates.

The usual estimation procedure is simple and direct. Consider some gene—say that allele A of the ABO blood group locus, whose frequency was q_a in the African ancestors of American Negroes and q_c in the Caucasian ancestors, while in modern American Negroes the frequency is q_n. If M is the present proportion of genes at this genetic locus (and, ideally, at every other locus too) which are derived from Caucasians, and if race mixture is the only process affecting q_n, then, by definition,

$$q_n = Mq_c + (1 - M)q_a \qquad (1)$$

and therefore

$$M = (q_n - q_a)/(q_c - q_a) \qquad (2)$$

This formula for M, or an algebraic equivalent, was used for all estimates of M given in Table 2 except one. [This one differed only in

Table 1. African origins of slaves imported into the North American mainland [data of Curtin (37)]. Distribution by areas is approximate and is an average of data for Virginia (1710-1769), for South Carolina (1773-1807), and for the British slave trade (1690-1807).

Coastal region of origin	Approximate present area	Peoples	Approximate proportion from region
Senegambia	Senegal and Gambia	Mainly Bambara and Malinke (from interior)	0.133
Sierra Leone	Sierra Leone	Sierra Leone, Guinea, Portugese Guinea peoples, plus Bambara and Malinke	.055
Windward Coast	Ivory Coast, Liberia	Various peoples of area	.144
Gold Coast	Ghana	About ¾ Akan people from southern part, the rest from northern part	.159
Bight of Benin	Togo, Dahomey, Nigeria west of Benin river	Peoples of Togo, southern Dahomey, and western Nigeria	.043
Bight of Biafra	Nigeria (east of Benin river) to 1°S (Gabon)	About ¾ Ibo, the rest Ibibio and people from Cameroon	.233
"Angola"	1°S to southwest Africa (Gabon, Congo, Angola)	Many peoples of the area, from the coast to far inland	.245
Mozambique and Madagascar			.016
Region unknown			.002

Table 2. Published estimates of the proportion (M), in American Negroes, of genes that are of Caucasian origin. All estimates except those based on genes Fy^a, Gm^1, $Gm^{1,2}$, or Gm^5 (and perhaps AK^2) require an estimate of African gene frequency appreciably different from zero. Within regions, localities are listed in chronological order of the estimates. Standard errors for M were not given (except for reference 6).

Region and locality	Gene(s)†	Sample size Negro	Caucasian	M	Reference
Estimates for M presumed by their authors to be valid					
Non-southern					
Baltimore	R^0	907	7,317	0.306	(7)
Baltimore	R^0	907	7,317	.216	(15)
Five areas	R^0, R^1, Jk^b, T, S	96 to 3.156	189 to 7,317	~.20	(16)
Cleveland and Baltimore	Gm^1, Gm^5	623	249	.310	(11)
Various	$R^0, R^1, R^2, r, M,$ S, Jk^b, k, Fy^b			.232-.261	(17)
Chicago	AK^2 ‡	1,063	1,315	.13	(14)
Washington, D.C., Baltimore, New York City	R^0, R^1, Fy^a			,20-.24	(8)
Oakland Calif.	$Gm^1, Gm^{1,2}, Gm^5$	260	478	.273 ± .037	(6)
Southern					
Evans and Bullock counties, Ga.	R^0, R^1	340	331	.104	(9)
Evans and Bullock counties, Ga.	$Gm^1, Gm^{1,5}$	189	295	.073	(12)
	Gc^1	231	292	~.10	
Charleston, S.C.	R^0, R^1, Fy^a	515		.04-.08	(8)
James Island, S.C. and Evans and Bullock counties, Ga.	R^0, R^1, Fy^a	394		.09-.12	(8)
Estimates of M presumed by their authors to indicate selection					
Non-southern					
Four areas, mainly Seattle	Hp^1	936	865(?)	~.40	(21)
Seattle	Hp^1	1,675	?	.478	(8)
Seattle	Gd^{A-}	658♂♂		.490	(8)
Southern					
Evans and Bullock counties, Ga.	T	285	314	.466	(9)
	Hp^1‖	167	145	.42-.70	
	Gd^{A-}	76♂♂		.34-.44	
	Hb^s	247		.46-.69	
	Tf^{D1}‖	133	107	.495	
	Gd^{A-}	97♂♂		.175	(8)

*An estimate of 0.34, from Hb^s data on 10,858 Negroes, is based on 11 sources in both the North and the South (38). It is therefore not placed in a regional category.   †Locus and alleles used are as follows. Blood groups: Rh (R^0, R^1, R^2, r), Kidd (Jk^b). M-N-S-s (M, S), Kell, (k), Duffy (Fy^a, Fy^b); serum protein genes; Gm (Gm^1,$Gm^{1,2}$,Gm^5), haptoglobin (Hp^1), Ge (Gc^1), transferrin (Tf^{D1}); hemoglobin; HbS (Hb^s); red cell enzymes; adenylate kinase (AK^2), glucose-6-phosphate dehydrogenase deficiency (Gd^{A-}); phenylthiocarbamide tasting (T);   ‡Newly investigated gene. The African frequency of AK^2 is poorly known, but it is assumed to be zero. The 95-percent confidence interval for M is 0.03-0.23, according to my calculation.   §Seven non-southern estimates ranging from 0.270 to 0.685, obtained by Workman (8) (using Hp^1 or Gd^{A-}) on small samples (79 to 238 Negroes) are omitted here.   ‖"Possibly" reflecting selection.

that three alleles were used simultaneously at one locus to obtain a maximum likelihood estimate for M; for each allele an equation of the type of Eq. 1 could be written and be used to estimate M (6).] We see that if we know q_a, q_e, and q_n (for a defined area) without error and if there were no factors affecting q_n other

than race crossing, estimation of M would be simple. Unfortunately, such is not the case.

Criteria for Critical Estimation of M

Critical evaluation of estimates of M requires complete specification of the needed criteria and judgment on the degree to which these criteria are met. These criteria are simple and obvious, but the demands they make have not always been appreciated. They are as follows.

1. The exact ethnic compositions of the two ancestral populations, African Negro and Caucasian, are known.
2. No change in gene frequency (for the gene in question) between ancestral and modern populations either of African Negroes or of American Caucasians has occurred.
3. Interbreeding of the two ancestral populations is the only factor affecting gene frequency in U.S. Negroes—that is, there has been no selection, mutation, or genetic drift.
4. Adequate samples (that is, samples that are unbiased, from correct populations with small standard error) of the modern descendants of the ancestral African Negroes and U.S. Caucasians, and of modern U.S. Negroes, are available.

It should be said immediately that none of these criteria has been shown to be fully met in any study. In particular, point 1 is not met, because the detailed ethnic origins of slaves from the various slaving areas are unknown (4). Point 2 can never be met because ancestral gene frequencies are unknown and point 3, at best, can only be inferred from indirect evidence. Point 4 cannot be fully met for African Negroes, since the proportions of various ethnic contributions are only roughly known. The problem is simpler for U.S. Negroes and Caucasians, although marked heterogeneity in values of M between different Negro populations is now known to complicate the matter.

Somewhat more affirmative views on these criteria can also be given, however. *If* it can be shown that gene frequencies in neighboring modern tribes and in populations of adjacent former slaving areas do not differ appreciably, point 1 becomes less important. For example, this appears to be the situation for the ABO blood groups, the best-known genetic system throughout the slaving area. With regard to point 2, since the populations concerned usually were, and are, large, it is probable that this criterion is quite well satisfied. If point 1 is satisfied in the way suggested, point 4 may be

met by using large, carefully collected samples. Unfortunately, it is less easy to overcome the problem posed by point 3. This is discussed below.

Review of Published Estimates of M

Table 2 is a tabulation of published estimates of M for American Negroes, beginning with the well-known estimate of 0.31 for Baltimore Negroes given by Glass and Li in 1953 (7). The estimates are grouped according to the authors' statements as to their validity or lack of validity (due to selection) as estimates of M. They are further classified as "southern" (estimates for Georgia, South Carolina, and Tennessee) or "non-southern." As has been noted elsewhere (6, 8, 9), among the presumed valid estimates, all "non-southern" estimates are greater than "southern" estimates. Also, the estimates presumed to indicate selection are usually appreciably higher than the estimates presumed to be valid. Among the "valid" estimates of M, that of Glass and Li (7) is by far the best known, and is often quoted as "the" estimate for the amount of Caucasian ancestry in "the" American Negro (see, for example, 10-14). A revision of this estimate from 0.31 to 0.216 (15) appears to have escaped general notice.

The estimates of Table 2 must be considered in the light of the four criteria given above. As already noted, criterion 1 cannot be strictly satisfied for any estimate because the detailed ethnic origins of the slaves are unknown. The estimates for M in Table 2, however, do not even roughly meet criterion 1, since none of them is based on quantitative information on distribution of origins, such as is given in Table 1. Typically, data from only one or two regions of West Africa are taken to represent the whole slaving area. Ironically, for the best-known estimate, that of Glass and Li (7), Rh blood group data from East and South Africa, as well as from Ghana, were used to represent ancestral Rh blood group frequencies because better data were not then available. Glass, for his revised estimate (15), used only Rh data from Nigeria and Ghana. Of the 540 individuals from Nigeria studied (15), 105 were Ibos, who may be representative of ancestral inhabitants of the Bight of Biafra region, the area of origin of about 23 percent of American slaves (Table 1); the remaining 435 individuals from Nigeria may be representative of the slaves (4 percent) who came from the Bight of Benin. The 274 individuals from Ghana studied (15) may be representative of the slaves (16 percent) from that region. The slaves (57 percent) from areas other than Nigeria and Ghana are unrepresented in Glass's revised estimate. These same Rh blood group data were used by later investigators in arriving at their own estimates (8, 9, 16, 17). These critical comments on the best-known estimate are made to illustrate the nature of the problem; similar comments could be made about each of the other estimates of Table 2.

With regard to criterion 4 (adequacy of samples), one can distinguish between (i) adequate representation (by the mean gene frequency used) of the entire slaving area and (ii) adequate sample size (as shown by a small standard error for M). If the gene used has a uniform frequency over the entire slaving area, any large sample from one part of the area could adequately represent the whole. The problem, of course, is to demonstrate uniformity. If, as one would expect, gene frequencies vary from region to region of the slaving area, appropriate samples over the whole area are needed if one is to obtain a properly weighted mean frequency. Neither of these approaches has been used in making any of the estimates. [I made an attempt to confirm the belief that the frequency of certain Gm alleles is near zero in African populations (6) but found that not enough surveys had been made.]

To make the problem more concrete, let us consider Glass's estimate of M (15) in the light of more recent Rh data. For the R^0 allele of the Rh locus, he used 0.5512 for the frequency in West Africa (on the basis of the data from Nigeria and Ghana). The frequencies in present-day U.S. Negroes and Caucasians were found to be 0.4381 and 0.0279, respectively, so that, from Eq. 2, we estimate M to be $(0.5512-0.4381)/(0.5512-0.0279)$, or 0.216. However, the frequency of R^0 in Liberia is 0.60

(18), and in Bantu of the Congo (Leopoldville) it is also about 0.60 (19). If the true overall value for the slaving area were 0.60, the estimate for M would be 0.283.

With regard to the purely statistical accuracy of the estimates of M, as shown by standard errors, calculation of the standard errors for several pertinent estimates indicates that they may be much larger than the authors may have suspected (20). The standard error for Glass's estimate (15), for example, is 0.042, giving a 95-percent confidence interval of 0.133 to 0.299. The estimate in Table 2, of 0.13 for M for gene AK^2 (the lowest estimate for the non-southern region) has a standard error of 0.053, producing a 95-percent confidence interval of 0.025-0.234, overlapping Glass's estimate. This large error seems particularly surprising at first, in view of the large sample sizes, but it is explained by the very low AK^2 gene frequencies (<5 percent). The standard errors of the other estimates appear to be of comparable size or larger (due to smaller sample sizes).

I have said enough to show the deficiencies of most of the estimates of Table 2 with regard to both African gene frequency and statistical accuracy. I should also comment on the classification of M estimates as "valid" (not affected by selection) or as indicating the effects of selection. Classification of an estimate in this way requires a "standard" M that is thought to be free from the effects of selection. Such a "standard" can then be used to determine whether an M estimated for some other gene demonstrates selection. The M estimates from Rh genes R^0 and R^1 have been assigned this role of "standard" by various investigators [Parker *et al.* (21) chose R^0 alone; Workman and his associates (8, 9) chose R^0 and R^1 in combination]. In addition, M estimates from frequencies of the Fy^a allele of the Duffy blood group locus (8) and the Gm^1 and Gm^5 alleles of the Gm serum group locus (21) have been considered as possible standards. Yet, as discussed above, it is not possible to prove directly that selection has not affected a particular gene frequency in American Negroes, and no evidence in support of the belief that it has not has been offered. We can only draw inferences of varying degrees of rigor as suitable data become available. I attempt in the remainder of this article to draw and apply such inferences.

An Approach to a More Critical Estimate of M

To constitute a critical estimate in the light of the four criteria listed above, an estimate of M should substantially meet three of them—1, 3, and 4 (2 is, of course, untestable). This means that we should (i) have good survey data on gene frequency from most or all of the seven West African and west-central African slaving areas of Table 1; (ii) be able to calculate a mean African gene frequency properly weighted according to the origins shown in Table 1; (iii) have adequate data on Caucasians and U.S. Negroes; (iv) have samples large enough to give an acceptably small standard error for M; and, very importantly, (v) have some evidence that in U.S. Negroes the gene in question is not subject to strong selection. With regard to points (i) and (ii), an ideal situation is to have a gene which can be shown to be absent or rare in all parts of the slaving area but common in Caucasians. The problem of finding "the" African-ancestor gene frequency is then eliminated, and M is simply q_n/q_c. The Caucasian gene contribution is then directly determinable. It has been claimed that Gm alleles Gm^1, $Gm^{1,2}$, and Gm^5 are of this type (22); it is quite likely that they are, but not enough of the slaving area has been surveyed for Gm alleles for us to be sure (6).

The Fy^a gene may be almost an ideal "Caucasian gene" for estimating M. Available survey data for regions from Liberia to the Congo (Leopoldville), presented in Table 3, show that in this region (from which about 56 percent of the ancestral slaves came) the mean frequency of Fy^a is probably not over about 0.02. The mean frequency for all Africans of the slave area is probably less than 0.03. The frequency for U.S. Caucasians is about 0.43 (Table 4). Moreover, recent extensive studies in a population of California Negroes revealed no evidence for natural selection (evidence pertaining to fetal and infant growth and viability and to adult growth and fertility) associated

Table 3. Frequencies of Duffy blood group Fy (a+) in West African and Congo (Leopoldville) populations.

Region	Sample size (N)	Proportion of Fy (a+)*	Reference
Liberia (many tribes)	661	0.00	(18)
Ivory Coast	163	.43†	(18)
Upper Volta	75	.00	(18)
Dahomey	20	.00	(18)
Ghana (Accra) and Nigeria (Lagos)	37	.00	(39)
Congo (Bantu)	501	.078‡	(40)

* Reacting positively with anti-Fy^a, indicating a genotype of Fy^aFy (most likely), or Fy^aFy^b, or Fy^aFy^a (rare) (39).   † The true proportion is probably zero because the Ivory Coast positive reactions with anti-Fy^a are believed to be incorrect.   ‡ The gene frequency for Fy^a is 0.040.

with Duffy blood group pheno-types (23). Strong selection due to this locus seems excluded, so there is some protection against bias in the estimation of M. Table 4 presents available Fy^a frequency data for U.S. Negroes and for some U.S. Caucasians, and the resulting M estimates. The M estimates for the three non-southern regions studied do not differ significantly, so the estimate 0.2195 ± 0.0093 for California Negroes—the largest of the three samples—may tentatively be used as the best estimate of M for a non-southern area. The very small standard error of this estimate reflects both the discrimination power of this "Caucasian gene" and the large sample sizes for the Negro and Caucasian populations. The two estimates from the "Deep South" do differ significantly and should be kept separate. The smaller one, 0.0366 ± 0.0091 from Charleston, appears to justify the statement that these Gullah Negroes have an unusually small amount of Caucasian ancestry (5). It is clear that the data of Table 4 are especially useful in comparing M for different U.S. Negro populations, because the same gene, Fy^a, is used as the basis for all estimates. Any bias due to selection should operate quite similarly in the different Negro populations. The difference between "southern" and "non-southern" M values evident in Table 2 is also marked in Table 4 and must be regarded as real.

Table 4. Estimates of M derived from Fy^a gene frequencies for American Negroes from various areas. The frequency of this gene in the African ancestors of American Negroes is assumed here to be zero; if it is not zero, these are *maximum* estimates. N = number in sample, q = Fy^a gene frequency, S.E. = standard error of q (all estimates by T. E. Reed).

Region and locality	Negroes		Caucasians		$M \pm S.E.$ *	Reference
	N	$q \pm S.E.$	N	$q \pm S.E.$		
Non-southern						
New York City	179	0.0809 ± 0.0147			0.189 ± 0.034	(39)†
Detroit	404	.1114 ± .0114			.260 ± .027	(41)
Oakland, Calif.	3146	.0941 ± .0038	5046	0.4286 ± 0.0058	.2195 ± .0093‡	(25)
Southern						
Charleston, S.C.	515	.0157 ± .0039‡			.0366 ± .0091	(5)
Evans and Bullock counties, Ga.	304	.0454 ± .0086	322	.422 ± .0224	.160 ± .020	(9)

* The q for Oakland Caucasians (who are of West European ancestry) was used in all estimates. $M = q_n/q_c$.
† Two other New York City studies (42) are omitted because they involved selection for dark skin color. The data used here were grouped with both anti-Fy^a and anti-Fy^b. The observed distribution of four Duffy phenotypes differs from the Hardy-Weinberg expectation at the 0.025 level of significance.   ‡ If the frequency of Fy^a in the African ancestors were 0.02, this estimate would be 0.181.

Thus Fy^a, for the reasons given, may be the best gene presently available for estimating M. When more African survey data are available, the "Caucasian" alleles Gm^1, $Gm^{1,2}$, and Gm^5 of the Gm locus, used jointly, may be as good. The AK^2 gene (Table 2) may be of some use if further African data establish a general zero frequency, but the low frequency, 0.047, of the AK^2 gene in Caucasians considerably reduces its discrimination power. The K gene of the Kell blood group system is sometimes thought of as a "Caucasian gene," but this is not strictly the case. This gene was present in 8 of 1202 Africans from the Liberia-Dahomey (18) and western Nigeria (24) region, at a mean frequency of 0.0033. The California Negroes of Table 4 (N = 3146) have a K gene frequency of about 0.0083, and the California Caucasians, a K gene frequency of about 0.046 (25). If we consider q_a to be zero, we obtain an estimate of 0.181 ± 0.026 for M for this population—clearly a maximum estimate and not reliable. This maximum does not differ significantly from the Fy^a estimate for this same population. The relatively large standard error here again reflects the low Caucasian gene frequency.

Although a zero q_a is generally preferable, there is one situation where a q_a value appreciably different from zero might yield a useful estimate of M. This could occur when there are sufficiently extensive and detailed

data on African gene frequency to make it possible to calculate a mean African gene frequency, with weighting of regional gene frequencies according to the proportions of Table 1. At present, the ABO blood groups provide the only such usable genetic marker [the gene for hemoglobin S is known to be affected by selection, and much less information is available for other loci (26); for selection data on hemoglobin S, see (27)]. Table 5 gives the gene frequencies for genes A and B of the ABO system from relevant surveys in the seven major slaving areas of Table 1.

These extensive surveys reveal an overall uniformity in gene frequency, with the one exception of a somewhat low B frequency for the Bight of Biafra (Ibos). From these mean values for African frequencies of genes A and B and from extensive data on ABO-system distribution in California Negroes and Caucasians (25), a maximum likelihood estimate for M of 0.200 ± 0.044 was obtained (28). This estimate is not greatly affected by the accuracy of the proportions given in Table 1 or by the exactness of the values for individual regional gene frequencies (29). A good fit of the observed number of individuals in each of the eight race and blood-group classes with the corresponding number expected from the estimated parameters (gene frequencies and M values) tested by the chi-square method, indicates both that

Table 5. Frequencies of genes *A* and *B* of the ABO blood-group system in surveys in the major slaving areas of Africa (see Table 1); p = frequency of *A* gene, q = frequency of *B* gene.

Region	Peoples or population	Sample size (N)	$p \pm S.E.$*	$q \pm S.E.$*	Refer-ence
Senegambia	Bambara, Malinke	2,210	0.159 ± .006	0.174 ± .006	(43)
Sierra Leone	Gbah-Mende	1,015	.159 ± .009	.151 ± .008	(44)
Liberia	>18 tribes†	2,337	.143 ± .005	.148 ± .006	(18)
Gold Coast	Unspecified, from Accra	1,540	.130 ± .006	.122 ± .006	(45)
Bight of Benin	Yoruba of Lagos, Ibadan	1,003	.130 ± .008	.141 ± .008	(46)
Bight of Biafra	Ibo ("Eastern")	572	.161 ± .011	.089 ± .009	(47)
"Angola"	"Bantu"–8,000 (mainly Bakongo) near Leopold-ville and 8,000 from Angola	16,000	.152 ± .002	.138 ± .002	(48)
Mean frequencies‡ over the entire slaving area			.150	.131	

* Maximum-likelihood estimate (49).   † Exclusive of Americo-Liberians.   ‡ Calculated from values for p and q given in the body of the table, weighted by the proportions of Table 1 (after the removal of values for Mozambique, Madagascar, and "region unknown").

the estimation is reasonable and that there are no large selective differences between genes *A* and *B* in U.S. Negroes (28). This procedure therefore seems justified for the case of ABO blood groups. Practically, however, the large standard error for *M* indicates that, in spite of large samples, the estimate for this locus is too imprecise to be very useful.

Since there are now three different estimates of *M*, and since extensive data on other aspects of the problem, including selection, are available for this one large California population of Negroes, these estimates are presented in a single table, Table 6. We note that they do not differ significantly from each other; this is due at least in part to the relatively large standard errors for the Gm and ABO estimates. The marked superiority, for estimating *M* of *Fy*a over *A* and *B* for samples of equal size is evident (30), whereas, if the sample sizes were

the same for *Fy*a and the three Gm alleles, it would be found that these are equally efficient for estimating *M*. An extensive search for evidence of natural selection due to the presence of ABO blood groups in these Negroes, similar to the search reported above for the Duffy blood group, also failed to reveal any consistent selective effect (23). This finding, plus the good chi-square fit in the estimation of *M*, which implies that the *A* and *B* genes are not very different with respect to their selective values in U.S. Negroes, gives some assurance that the ABO estimate is not greatly disturbed by selection (28). No selection studies for Gm were made on these California Negroes, but extensive studies on a Brazilian population which was about 30 percent Negro, 11 percent Indian, and 59 percent Caucasian (13) revealed no evidence of selective effect (31). Further evidence is provided by the good chi-square fit

Table 6. Estimates of *M* calculated from data of Gm serum groups, Duffy blood group, and ABO blood group from Negroes and Caucasians of the Oakland, California, area. [Data of the Child Health and Developmental Studies (6, 25).]

Locus	Alleles used	Sample size (N)		M
		Negroes	Caucasians	
Gm	$Gm^1, Gm^{1, 5}, Gm^5$	260	478	0.273 ± 0.037*
Duffy	Fy^a	3146	5046	.220 ± .009†
ABO	*A, B*	3146	5046	.200 ± .044†

* See (6).   † See text.

in the multi-allelic estimation obtained with the three Gm alleles (6). It seems reasonable to conclude that strong selective effects on these three estimates of M may be excluded. The existence of weaker effects, however, still sufficient to bias these estimates appreciably, cannot be ruled out. As more independent estimates on these and other genes become available, each having regard to the criteria listed above and including some safeguard against a strong bias due to selection and having a relatively small standard error (say, less than 0.02), it should become possible to obtain a "consensus" on the true value of M (for specified Negroes). Estimates biased upward or downward by selection will be separated from those little affected by selection, and so, in time, the former can be identified and rejected.

Use of M to Detect Selection

Several investigators (8, 9, 21, 32) have argued that selection for or against a gene may be clearly inferred from the M value that the gene produces. From the foregoing section it is clear that if (i) the true (unbiased) value of M (say, M_0) is known, (ii) the estimate in question (M_e) is calculated with regard to the criteria given above, and (iii) M_e differs significantly from M_0, then we may reasonably suspect that selection has caused the observed deviation. These conditions have not been met. In particular, we have no M_0. The M estimates obtained with R^0 (8, 9, 21), R^1 (8, 9), and Fy^a (8) were considered to be valid estimates unbiased by selection, but no objective evidence was offered to support these views. With one or more of these M estimates used as reference standards, it has been claimed that the deviant M estimates of the following genes demonstrate selection on these genes in U.S. Negroes: Hp^1, T, Gd^{A-}, Hb^S, and Tf^{D1} (see Table 2). These results can, at present, be considered only suggestive, but it must be admitted that the usually high M estimates obtained with Hp^1 and Gd^{A-} argue for an effect of selection (27).

A different approach was used to show that M estimates obtained with r, R^0, and R^1 alleles

of the Rh locus ranked in this (decreasing) order of size for a Georgia population and also for two Brazilian populations (32). Accepted at face value, this is evidence of differences between M values from different Rh alleles. The investigators attribute these differences to selection. This same approach in these populations also indicates that M for the B allele is greater than $1.5M$ for the A allele (32). African Rh and ABO gene frequencies, weighted by slaving-area origins, were not used, however, although the African areas of origin of Brazilian Negroes are known (2). Again, these findings are interesting and suggestive but far from conclusive.

Workman (8), from inspection of A_1, A_2, and B allele frequencies in various West African, U.S. Negro, and U.S. Caucasian populations, concludes that there has been strong selection in U.S. Negroes against A_1 and for A_2. He identifies the various African data only as "West Africa," and does not use significance tests. Since Workman and also Hertzog and Johnson claim to find selection in the ABO system, it is pertinent here to recall that the M estimate obtained from ABO-system distributions that is discussed earlier in this article (an estimate based on *large* populations and good estimates for African gene frequency) did not suggest selective differences between the A and B alleles.

This critical review of claims for selection would be incomplete if I did not mention that there *is* an important theoretical reason to look for selection in hybrid populations such as the American Negro. As has been previously recognized (6, 8, 32), selection in U.S. Negroes over several generations can produce a cumulative effect in present-day individuals appreciably greater than the effect of a single generation of selection—the type of data usually available. There is thus a possibility of detecting, in hybrids, selection due to common polymorphisms which is too small [usually less than 5 to 10 percent of the mean (23)] to be detectable by ordinary one-generation studies. This possibility, together with the probability that some of the genes are selective [because it is most unlikely that a new genotype (the hybrid) in a new environment would be exactly neutral in selective value], makes the search for selection here especially worthwhile. Some of these selective genes may already have been identified.

Other Uses of *M* Estimates

In addition to the definite likelihood of their yielding valuable information on the action of natural selection in human populations, good estimates of the amount of Caucasian ancestry in U.S. Negro populations have at least two other "uses."

1. They provide objective information about the genetic heterogeneity among various populations of U.S. Negroes. Evidence of marked differences between southern and non-southern Negroes with respect to the amount of Caucasian ancestry, as shown in Tables 2 and 4, is the first clear result from this use of *M* estimates. As more good estimates from defined U.S. Negro populations become available, we may expect further heterogeneity to be revealed.

2. They provide an understanding of the distribution in American Negroes of those genetic traits, including diseases, that are due primarily to genes of Caucasian origin. There are few examples of such genes at present. but, aside from common genetic polymorphisms, like blood groups, few genes have been sufficiently studied to permit possible identification of racial differences in gene frequency. One probable example of such a genetic trait is phenylketonuria—a condition resulting from homozygosity for a rare autosomal recessive gene, producing a deficiency of phenylalanine hydroxylase and resulting (if untreated) in severe mental defect. This occurs in about 1 in 10,000 births of persons of North European ancestry (33) but appears to be much rarer in U.S. Negroes (34). This rarity is understandable if the gene frequency in African Negroes is much lower than that in Caucasians (about 0.01). For example, if U.S. Negroes have, on the average, 20-percent Caucasian ancestry, the frequency of occurrence of phenylketonuria at birth in U.S. Negroes would be only 1/25th that in Caucasians, or roughly 1 in 250,000— rare indeed.

An example of a disease which is not simply inherited but which may show a similar racial distribution is cirrhosis of the liver. A study in Baltimore Negro cirrhotics revealed, relative to Negro controls, a significant increase in Fy (a+b+) Duffy blood group phenotype and a decrease in Fy (a—b—) phenotype, whereas Caucasian cirrhotics showed no such difference from Caucasian controls (35). The simplest interpretation is that the disease is more frequent in Caucasians, and that Negroes with some degree of Caucasian ancestry, as shown by their Duffy blood group, are more likely to develop the disease than those lacking such ancestry (35). Other examples of traits whose frequency of occurrence in U.S. Negroes is affected by the amount of their Caucasian ancestry will surely be reported (36). Accurate information on *M* will be clinically useful here.

Summary

Published estimates of the proportion, in American Negroes, of genes which are of Caucasian origin are critically reviewed. The criteria for estimating this proportion *(M)* are discussed, and it is argued that all estimates published to date have either deficiencies pertaining to the African-gene-frequency data used or statistical inaccuracies, or both. Other sources of error may also exist.

Evidence is presented that the *Fy*a gene of the Duffy blood group system may be the best gene now available for estimating *M*. Estimates based on *Fy*a frequencies have been obtained for Negroes in three non-southern and two southern areas. The value of *M* is found to be appreciably greater in non-southern areas, the best estimate being 0.2195 ± 0.0093 (Oakland, California). This estimate is still subject to some uncertainty. The value of *M* in the South is appreciably less.

Natural selection can introduce a bias in the estimate of *M*. Claims that selection acting on certain genes in American Negroes have been demonstrated are reviewed, and it is concluded that they are not yet proved. The approach discussed here may be valuable in the future as a sensitive method for detecting the action of natural selection. In addition, knowledge of the amount of Caucasian ancestry may be of medical value in explaining the frequencies of occurrence of certain hereditary diseases in Negroes.

References and Notes

1. J. H. Franklin and T. Marshall, in *World Book Encyclopedia* (Field Enterprises Educational Corporation, Chicago, 1966), vol. 14, p. 106.
2. P. D. Curtin, personal communication (1969).
3. J. Potter, in *Population in History: Essays in Historical Demography*, D. V. Glass and D. E. Eversley, Eds. (Univ. of Chicago Press, Chicago, 1965), p. 641.
4. P. D. Curtin, personal communication (1968).
5. W. S. Pollitzer, *Amer. J. Phys. Anthropol.* **16**, 241 (1958).
6. T. E. Reed, *Amer. J. Hum. Genet.* **21**. 71 (1969).
7. B. Glass and C. C. Li, *ibid.*, 5, 1 (1953).
8. P. L. Workman, *Hum. Biol.* **40**, 260 (1968).
9. ——, B. S. Blumberg, A. J. Cooper, *Amer. J. Hum. Genet.* 15, 429 (1963).
10. C. Stern, *Principles of Human Genetics* (Freeman, San Francisco, ed. 2, 1960), p. 356.
11. A. G. Steinberg, R. Stauffer, S. H. Boyer, *Nature* **188**, 169 (1960).
12. B. S. Blumberg, P. L. Workman, J. Hirschfeld, *ibid.* **202**, 561 (1964).
13. H. Krieger, N. E. Morton, M. P. Mi, E. Azevedo, A. Freire-Maia, N. Yasuda, *Ann. Hum. Genet.* 29, 113 (1965).
14. J. E. Bowman, H. Frischer, F. Ajmar, P. E. Carson, M. K. Gower, *Nature* 214, 1156 (1967).
15. B. Glass, *Amer. J. Hum. Genet.* 7, 368 (1955) (non-D^u-tested data for Africans, Negroes, and Caucasians; use of D^u-tested data for Africans and non D^u-tested data for others gives $M = 0.281$).
16. D. F. Roberts, *ibid.*, p. 361, The estimate is "provisional"; 66 separate estimates were made, ranging from 0.0404 to 0.3341.
17. —— and R. W. Hiorns, *ibid.* 14, 261 (1962). No sample sizes are specified.
18. F. B. Livingstone, H. Gershowitz, J. V. Neel, W. W. Zeulzer, M. D. Solomon, *Amer. J. Phys. Anthropol*, 18, 161 (1960).
19. P. V. Tobias, in *The Biology of Human Adaptability*, P. T. Baker and J. S. Weiner, Eds. (Clarendon Press, Oxford, 1966), p. 161.
20. The following formula for the standard error (S.E.) of a ratio $R = y/x$ was used:

$$\text{S.E. } R = R \left[\frac{V_y}{y^2} + \frac{V_x}{x^2} - \frac{2C_{xy}}{xy} \right]^{1/2}$$

where the variance of y is V_y, that of x is V_x and the covariance between x and y is C_{xy} [see, for example, L. Kish, *Survey Sampling* (Wiley, New York, 1965), p. 207]. This formula is adequate for large or moderate-sized samples when it is unlikely that x is near zero. In terms of Eq. 2 for M,

$$\text{S.E. } M = M \left[\frac{V(q_a - q_n)}{(q_a - q_n)^2} + \frac{V(q_a - q_c)}{(q_a - q_c)^2} - \frac{2V(q_a)}{(q_a - q_n)(q_a - q_c)} \right]^{1/2}$$

where V represents the variance of the adjoining quantity in parentheses. The covariance between numerator and denominator of Eq. 2, due to the presence of q_a in both, is allowed for in this standard error.
21. W. C. Parker and A. G. Bearn, *Ann. Hum. Genet. London* 25, 227 (1961). The total number of American, Canadian and British individuals tested in the study reported is 865. A weighted estimate for the frequency of gene Hp^1 in U.S. Negroes, based on the data of Parker and Bearn, is 0.55; this value gives an M of 0.53.
22. A. G. Steinberg, in *Symposium on Immunogenetics*, T. J. Greenwait, Ed. (Lippincott, Philadelphia, 1967), pp. 75-98.
23. T. E. Reed, *Amer. J. Hum. Genet.* 19, 732 (1967); *ibid.* 20, 119 (1968); *ibid.*, p. 129.
24. B. S. Blumberg, E. W. Ikin, A. E. Mourant, *Amer. J. Phys. Anthropol.* 19, 195 (1961).
25. T. E. Reed, *Amer. J. Hum. Genet.* 20, 142 (1968).
26. For gene distributions, see J. Hiernaux, *La Diversité Humaine en Afrique Subsaharienne* (Institut de Sociologie, Université Libre de Bruxelles, Brussels, 1968), figs. 2, 3, 7, 8, 12, 14.
27. There are good a priori reasons, entirely separate from M values, for expecting, in U.S. Negroes, a decrease in the frequency of the genes for sickle-cell hemoglobin. Hb^s, and for glucose-6-phosphate dehydrogenase deficiency, Gd^{A-}. (i) There is good evidence that in Africa the high frequency of the Hb^s gene is due to a selective advantage of heterozygotes for Hb^s in regions where malaria is endemic [see, for example, F. B. Livingstone, *Abnormal Hemoglobins in Human Populations* (Aldine, Chicago, 1967), pp. 105-107; A. C. Allison, in *Abnormal Haemoglobins in Africa*, J. H. P. Jonxis, Ed. (Davis, Philadelphia, 1965), pp. 369-371; D. L. Rucknagel and J. V. Neel, in *Progress in Medical Genetics*, A. G. Steinberg, Ed. (Grune & Stratton, New York, 1961), vol. 1. pp. 158-260]. There is strongly suggestive evidence that the Gd^{A-} gene in Africa is similarly kept at high frequencies due to selective advantage in malarious areas [see F. B. Livingstone, *Abnormal Hemoglobins in Human Populations* (Aldine, Chicago, 1967); A. G. Motulsky, in *Abnormal Haemoglobins in Africa*, J. H. P. Jonxis, Ed., (Davis, Philadelphia, 1965), pp. 181-185)]. (ii) Both

genes are known to have selective disadvantages which can explain their rarity in nonmalarious areas. It is therefore to be expected that Negroes moved from their highly malarious homelands to the less malarious, and now nonmalarious, regions of North America would have lower frequencies of these two genes. This selective decrease would raise M estimates above the true value,

28. The computer program [see T. E. Reed and W. J. Schull, *Amer. J. Hum. Genet.* **20**, 579 (1968)] estimated M and Caucasian A and B gene frequencies, given the two African mean frequencies as constants and the two California populations determined by the gene frequencies to be estimated, subject to the constraints that, for *both A and B*, $q_n = Mq_e + (1 - M)q_a$. This equation is Eq. 1 applied to both alleles and is true when there is simple gene mixture without selection (see 6). Comparison of the observed numbers of the eight race and blood-group classes (2 races x 4 groups) with the corresponding numbers expected on the basis of parameter estimates gives a chi-square value of 5.910 for 3 d.f., $P > .10$.

29. When the negligible contribution from Mozambique, Madagascar, and "Unknown" is excluded, the proportions of Table 1, column 4, become (in order): 0.135, 0.056, 0.116, 0.162, 0.044, 0.237, and 0.249. The corresponding proportions for South Carolina (1773-1807) are 0.197, 0.068, 0.164, 0.134, 0.016, 0.021, and 0.399 [data of Curtin (4)], yielding overall African mean values of 0.149 and 0.144 for p and q. These two series differ appreciably with respect to the final two values, yet when the South Carolina series is used the estimate of M is 0.256 ± 0.042, a difference of just over one standard error. Also, q for the Bight of Biafra is the only markedly variant gene frequency among the frequencies for the seven regions, but replacing the p and q for this region by the p and q for the Bight of Benin or for "Angola" does not significantly change M (0.281 ± 0.040 or 0.251 ± 0.042, respectively, when corrected proportions of Table 1 are used).

30. The Fy^a estimate is based on $(0.044)^2 / (0.0093)^2$, or 22 times as much statistical information as the ABO estimate.

31. N. E. Morton, H. Krieger, M. P. Mi, *Amer. J. Hum. Genet.* **18**, 153 (1966).

32. K. P. Hertzog and F. E. Johnston, *Hum. Biol.* **40**, 86 (1968).

33. V. A. McKusick, *Mendelian Inheritance in Man* (Johns Hopkins Press, Baltimore, ed. 2, 1968), p. 346.

34. For example, H. P. Katz and J. H. Menkes [*J. Pediat.* **65**, 71 (1964)] report the first definite case of phenylketonuria in a U.S. Negro, R. G. Graw and R. Koch [*Amer. J. Dis. Child.* **114**, 412 (1967)] report two "pale skinned" Negro brothers with phenylketonuria, bringing the total for U.S. Negroes at that time to five.

35. N. C. R. W. Reid, P. W. Brunt, W. B. Bias, W. C. Maddrey, B. A. Alonso, F. L. Iber, *Brit. Med. J.* **2**, 463 (1968).

36. Differences between Caucasians and Japanese with respect to gene frequency are instructive here. Phenylketonuria appears to be much rarer (perhaps a tenth as frequent) among Japanese than among Caucasians [K. Tanaka, E. Matsunaga, Y. Hanada, T. Murata, K. Takehara, *Jap. J. Hum. Genet,* **6**, 65 (1961)]. Another single-gene trait, Huntington's chorea, also appears to be about ten times as frequent in Caucasians as in Japanese, according to T. E. Reed and J. H. Chandler, *Amer. J. Hum. Genet.* **10**, 201 (1958). Examples of congenital abnormalities which are commoner in Caucasians than in Japanese, and vice versa, are given by J. V. Neel, *Amer. J. Hum. Genet.* **10**, 398 (1958).

37. P. D. Curtin, *The Atlantic Slave Trade: A Census* (Univ. of Wisconsin Press, Madison, in press).

38. J. V. Neel and W. J. Schull, *Human Heredity* (Univ. of Chicago Press, Chicago. 1954), p. 255; J. V. Neel, personal communication (1969). The estimate refers to "non-Negro" ancestry.

39. R. R. Race and R. Sanger, *Blood Groups in Man* (Blackwell, Oxford, ed. 5, 1968).

40. M. Shapiro and J. M. Vandepitte, *Int. Congr. Blood Transfusion, 5th.* Paris (1955), p. 243; M. Shapiro, personal communication (1969).

41. H. Gershowitz, unpublished data.

42. E. B. Miller, R. E. Rosenfield, P. Vogel, *Amer. J. Phys. Anthropol.* **9**, 115 (1951); R. Sanger, R. R. Race, J. Jack, *Brit J. Haematol.* **1**, 370 (1955).

43. R. Koerber, *C. R. Seances Soc. Biol.* **141**, 1013 (1947); R. Koerber and J. Linhard, *Bull. Soc. Anthropol, Paris* **2**, 158 (1951). The frequencies for Bambara and Malinke do not differ significantly.

44. P. Julien, *Z. Rassenphysiol.* **9**, 146 (1937).

45. G. M. Edington, *West Afr. Med. J.* **5**, 71 (1956).

46. H. R. Muller, *Proc. Soc. Exp. Biol.* **24**, 437 (1927); J. P. Garlick, quoted in A. E. Mourant, A. C. Kopeć, K. Domaniewska-Sobczak, *The ABO Blood Groups* (Blackwell, Oxford, 1958), p. 173; J. P. Garlick and N. A. Barnicot, *Ann. Hum. Genet.* **21**, 420 (1957). The frequencies in these three surveys do not differ significantly from each other.

47. J. Hardy, *Roy. Anthropol. Inst.* **92**, 223 (1962). I have not used Hardy's data on "Onitsha Ibo" (sample size, 228) because I consider the subjects to be probably not of Ibo origin. I have not used data of J. N. M. Chalmers, E. W. Ikin, and A. E. Mourant [*Ann. Eugenics* **17**, 168 (1953)] on "southeastern" Nigeria (105 Ibo and 1 Tiv) because information on the type of Ibo was not given. Table 1 describes this region as "about ¾ Ibo," and I could find no suitable data for the remaining quarter.

48. G. van Ros and R. Jourdain, *Ann. Soc. Belge Med. Trop.* **36**, 307 (1956); L. Mayor, *Bull. Clin.*

Statistics 7, No. 3, suppl. 126 (1954). The first study (for the Congo) gave values of 0.156 ± 0.0030 for *p* and 0.1244 ± 0.0027 for *q*. The second (for Angola) gave values of 0.1486 ± 0.0029 and 0.1514 ± 0.0030, respectively. An unweighted average of these values was used. The values for Angola do not differ significantly from the mean *p* and *q* values for seven central-coastal named tribes in Angola (total population 1285) tabulated by Hiernaux (see 26).

49. T. E. Reed and W. J. Schull, *Amer. J. Hum. Genet.* 20, 579 (1968).

50. Preparation of this article was begun while I was engaged in work for the Child Health and Development Studies (Division of Biostatistics, School of Public Health, University of California, Berkeley, and the Kaiser Foundation Research Institute, Oakland, California), on leave from the University of Toronto, and was supported there by U.S. Public Health Service research grants HD 00718 and HD 00720 from the National Institutes of Health. The analysis was supported in part by a grant from the Medical Research Council of Canada. I thank Professor Philip D. Curtin for making unpublished data available and for commenting on the manuscript, Dr. Arthur E. Mourant and Mrs. K. Domaniewska-Sobczak for recent references to African blood group distributions, and Professors Curt Stern, Donald Rucknagel, and Peter Carstens for their comments. Dr. H. Gershowitz and Dr. M. Shapiro made available unpublished data on Duffy blood groups in Negroes.

PART FOUR

Demography and Population Density

Most investigators who have explored this subject believe that in the hunting-gathering stage of human society, various environmental or cultural factors held the total population in a steady state. In the last few millenia of this long stationary phase, the global population began to increase, but it did not do so continuously or simultaneously in all occupied regions. Various cultural advances that led to a greater "extractive efficiency" periodically permitted a breakthrough from one plateau of population density to another. Thus gradually regional populations grew step by step and the total population density steadily increased. This fact is discussed by Nathan Keyfitz in the first paper (18) in this part.

The improvements in *extractive efficiency* that produced this incremental progress in regional population size operated essentially through changes in what may be termed a "density dependent factor"—food. Expressed in demographic terms, population size at this time was positively correlated with the amount of food available. The second paper (19) in this part, by Ivan L. Bennett, Jr., examines the question of food supply and its effect on present world populations. The first warnings of potential catastrophe, which were sounded some thirty years ago, were based on estimates of our ability to supply food for ever-increasing world populations. As variously related in the nine papers on food production, agriculturalists for some years have been protesting that they do not have the *sole* responsibility of ensuring that there is sufficient food to feed every mouth. They have emphasized the global limits of agricultural production and have demanded that some control be applied to the other side of the ledger. That is, they ask and sometimes insist that consideration be given to restricting the numbers of mouths that have to be fed.

Much has been written about the "green revolution" and its effects on food production; this topic is the subject of a paper (20) by Clifton R. Wharton. The specific techniques involved in improving one of the two major cereal grains of the world (wheat) are discussed by L. P. Reitz and S. C. Salmon (21), and Robert F. Chandler explains how immense advances have been achieved in the cultivation of the other principal grain (rice) (22). T. R. Preston and G. B. Hagelberg describe how carbohydrates can be converted into protein (23). Alternative food supplies from

149

nontraditional plant sources are considered by N. W. Pirie (24). Apart from the simple issue of food and famine, there is the perhaps even more important consideration of malnutrition. Graham Chedd considers this aspect in surveying international plans for food production (25).

Once we start to examine the limitations that food supplies impose on population size, we can immediately identify some potential restrictions on food production. One of these is the availability of water for agriculture. While it is possible that we could never exhaust supplies of drinking water before other limiting factors had long since intervened, several papers here—and particularly the one by Gale Young (26)—emphasize that in terms of agricultural water we are already coming to the end of our available resources. This is before we have even taken into account the vast amounts of industrial water that our most affluent societies require. The economics of utilizing in agricultural production desalted water as a possible alternative source are discussed by Marion Clawson et al. (27).

Of the so-called Malthusian factors affecting population density—which include food, and like food may be regarded as density dependent—*disease* is the next most important. George J. Armelagos and John R. Dewey discuss evolutionary responses in terms of the effect that disease has had, or may be expected to have, in the control of the size of human populations (28). The last major Malthusian factor, that of *war*, now threatens to become an all-or-nothing affair. If conflicts break out on a global scale and involve the widespread use of atomic weapons, the entire population of our species will probably perish. This possible calamity is discussed in a paper by Ernest J. Sternglass in Part Five. If, as now, war is confined to local situations and conventional weaponry, it would appear to be without any major effect on the total global population size.

Aside from these Malthusian factors, control of population density resolves itself into the use and impact of various *cultural* population controls. This is the most crucial matter raised in this section. Indeed it is the most critical and most controversial problem that now confronts us as we contemplate the future of our species. The seven papers that deal with this topic were selected because they provide views that represent various aspects of social population control. Paul R. Ehrlich presents the urgent reality of this situation in simple, unequivocal terms (29). The cultural adjustment of the birth rate until it balances the death rate—the *demographic transition*—is vital for all countries. Harold Frederiksen (30) and David M. Heer (31) describe this adjustment in population dynamics and in economic terms, respectively. In a major survey statement, Bernard Berelson examines all the methods presently available for achieving the desired social population control (32). Contrasting views of this process in current practice are provided in papers by Judith Blake (33) and Oscar Harkavey et al. (34). That economic factors strongly motivate demographic behavior in industrial societies is emphasized in several of the selections. It is also very much stressed in Joseph J. Spengler's paper (35), which concludes this section.

Additional Readings

Abelson, P. H. "Malnutrition, learning, and behavior," editorial in *Science* 164:17, 1969.
Adams, E. S. "Unwanted births and poverty in the United States," *Conference Board Record* 6(4): 10-17, 1969.

Bajema, C. J. "The genetic implications of population control," *Bioscience* 21: 71-75, 1971.

Birdsell, J. B. "On population structure in generalised hunting and collecting populations," *Evolution* 12:189-205, 1958.

Blake, J. "Reproductive motivation and population policy," *Bioscience* 21: 215-24, 1971.

Borgstrom, G. *Too Many: A Story of Earth's Biological Limitations*, New York: Macmillan, 1969.

Boyko, H. "Salt-water agriculture," *Scientific American* 216(3): 89-96, 1967.

Braidwood, R. J., and Reed, C. A. "The achievement and early consequences of food production," *Cold Spring Harbor Symp. Quant. Biol.* 22: 19,029, 1957.

Brown, L. R. "The world outlook for conventional agriculture," *Science* 158: 604-11, 1967.

Clark, J. D. "The evolution of culture in Africa," *Amer. Naturalist* 97: 15-28, 1963.

Clarkson, F. E., Vogel, S. R., Broverman, I. K., Broverman, D. M., and Rosenkrantz, P. S. "Family size and sex-role stereotypes," *Science* 167: 390-92, 1970.

Cook, R. C. "California after 19 million what?" *Population Bull.* 22: 29-57, 1962.

Coyle, D. C. "Japan's population," *Population Bull.* 15(7): 119-36, 1959.

Dalrymple, D. G. "The Soviet famine of 1932-34," *Soviet Studies* 14: 250-84, 1964.

Davis, Kingsley. "Population," *Scientific American* 209(3): 62-71, 1963.

——. "The population impact on children in the world's agrarian countries," *Population Review* 9: 17-31, 1965.

——. "Population policy: Will current trends succeed?" *Science* 158: 730-39, 1967.

Demko, G. J. Rose, H. M. and Schnell, G. A. eds. *Population Geography: A Reader*, New York: McGraw-Hill, 1970.

Dickson, E. M. "Model for zero population growth," *Bioscience* 20: 1245-46, 1970.

Djerassi, C. "Prognosis for the development of new birth-control agents," *Science* 166: 486-73, 1969.

Dobzansky, T. "The present evolution of man," *Scientific American* 203(3): 206-17, 1960.

Dorn, H. F. "World population growth: An international dilemma," *Science* 135: 283-90, 1962.

Dumont, R., and Rosier, B. *The Angry Future*, New York: Praeger, 1969.

Durand, J. D. "The modern expansion of world population," *Amer. Philosoph. Soc. Proc.* 3(3): 136-45, 1967.

Dykes, D. R., Bry, T. S., and Kliner, C. H. "Water management: A fashionable topic," *Environ. Sci. Technol.* 1(10): 780-84, 1967.

Ehrlich, P. R. "Population, food, and environment: Is the battle lost?" *Texas Quart.* 11(2): 43-54, 1968.

——. *The Population Bomb*, New York: Ballantine, 1968.

Eichenwald, H. F., and Fry, P. C. "Nutrition and learning," *Science* 163: 644-48, 1969.

Eisner, T., van Tienhoren, A., and Rosenblatt, F. "Population control, sterilization, and ignorance," editorial in *Science* 167:337, 1970.

Enke, S. "The economics of having children," *Policy Sciences* 1: 16-30, 1970.

Feiss, J. W. "Minerals," *Scientific American* 209(3): 128-36, 1963.

Fischer, A. "Community psychiatry and the population explosion," *Calif. Med.* 106: 189-95, 1967.

Frankel, O., Agble, W. K., Harlan, J. B., and Bennett, E. "Genetic dangers in the green revolution," *Ares* FAO 2(5): 35-37, 1969.

Friedlander, M. V., and Klarmov, J. "How many children?" *Environment* 11(10): 3-8, 1969.

Gerard, R. D., and Roels, D. A. "Deep ocean water as a resource," *Marine Tech. Soc. J.* 4(5): 69-78, 1970.

Hardin, G. "Birth control—the prospects," *Medicine Today* 1: 38-45, 1967.

——. "Abortion—or compulsory pregnancy?" *Marriage and the Family* 30: 246-51, 1968.

——. "Nobody ever dies of overpopulation," editorial in *Science* 171, 1971.

Harpstead, D. D. "High-lysine corn," *Scientific American* 225(2): 34-42, 1971.

Harrar, J. G., and Wortman, S. "Expanding food production in hungry nations, the promise, the problems," in *Overcoming World Hunger,* C. M. Hardin (ed.), Englewood Cliffs, N.J.: Prentice-Hall, 1969, pp. 89-135.

Hauser, P. M. *The Population Dilemma,* 2nd ed., Englewood Cliffs, N.J.: Prentice-Hall, 1969.

——. "The census of 1970," *Scientific American* 225(1): 17-25, 1971.

Haynes, C. V. "Elephant hunting in North America," *Scientific American* 214(6): 104-12, 1966.

Hoagland, H. "Mechanisms of population control," *Daedalus,* Summer 1964, 812-29.

Holt, S. J. "The food resources of the ocean," *Scientific American* 221(3): 178-94, 1969.

Howard, J. "New proteins: Animal, vegetable, mineral," *New Scientist and Science Journal* 49: 438-39, 1971.

Howard, W. E. "The population crisis is here now," *Bioscience* 19: 779-84, 1969.

Hulett, H. R. "Optimum world population," *Bioscience* 20: 160-61, 1970.

Keyfitz, N. "On the momentum of population growth," *Demography* 8: 71-81. 1971.

Kirk, D. "The relation of employment levels to births in Germany," *Milbank Mem. Fund. Quart.* 28: 126-38, 1962.

——. "Prospects for reducing natality in the underdeveloped world," *Ann. Amer. Acad. Pol. Soc. Sci.* 396: 48-60, 1967.

Kristenson, T. "The approaches and findings of economists," *Internat. J. Agrarian Affairs* 5: 139, 1967.

Ladejinsky, W. "Ironies of India's green revolution," *Foreign Affairs* 48: 758-68, 1970.

Langer, W. L. "The black death," *Scientific American* 210(2): 114-21, 1964.

McElroy, W. D. "Biomedical aspects of population control," *Bioscience* 19: 9-23, 1969.

McNeil, W. J., ed. *Marine Aquaculture,* Corvalis: Oregon State University Press, 1970.

Markert, C. L. "Biological limits on population growth," *Bioscience* 16: 858-62, 1966.

Meier, R. L. "The social impact of a nuplex," *Bull. Atomic Scientists,* March 1969, pp. 16-21.

Okun, D. A. "The hierarchy of water quality," *Environ. Sci. Technol.* 2(9): 672-75, 1968.

Paarlberg, D. "Food for more people and better nutrition," in *Overcoming World Hunger,* C. M. Hardin (ed.), Englewood Cliffs, N.J.: Prentice-Hall, 1967 pp. 41-87.

Paddock, W., and Paddock, P. *Famine—1975: America's Decision: Who Will Survive?* Boston: Little, Brown, 1967.

Pinchot, G. B. "Marine Farming," *Scientific American* 223(6): 15-21, 1970.

Pincus, G. "Control of conception of hormonal steroids," *Science* 153: 493-500, 1966.

Pirie, N. W. "Food from forests," *New Scientist,* 40: 420-22, 1968.

——. "Orthodox and unorthodox methods of meeting world food needs," *Scientific American* 216(2): 27-35, 1967.

Revelle, R. "Water," *Scientific American* 209(3): 92-108, 1963.

Revelle, R. "Introduction to historical populations studies," *Daedalus* 97: 353-62, 1968.

Ritchie-Calder, Lord. "Oceanic farming surface to the deepest deep," *Smithsonian* 1(12): 8-15, 1971.

Robinson, H. F. "Dimensions of the world food crisis," *Bioscience* 19: 24-28, 1969.

Ryther, J. H. "Photosynthesis and fish production in the sea," *Science* 166: 72-76, 1969.

Schurr, S. H. "Energy," *Scientific American* 209(3): 110-26, 1963.

Scott, R. W., Millet, M. A., and Hajny, G. J. "Wood wastes for animal feeding," *For. Prod. J.* 19: 14-18, 1969.

Scrimshaw, N. S. "Food," *Scientific American* 209(3): 72-80, 1963.

Simpson, D. "The dimensions of the world food crisis," *Bioscience* 19: 24-29, 1969.

Taeuber, C. "Population and food supply," *Ann. Amer. Acad. Pol. and Soc. Sci.* 369: 73-83 1967.

Taylor, C. T., and Berelson, B. "Maternity care and family planning as a world problem," *Amer. J. Obstet. Gynecol.* 100: 885-93, 1968.

Thurston, H. D. "Tropical agriculture: a key to the world food crises," *Bioscience* 19: 29-34, 1969.

Ucko, P. J., and Dimbleby, G. W., eds. *The Domestication and Exploitation of Plants and Animals*, London: Duckworth, 1969.

Walle, E. van de. "Marriage and marital fertility," *Daedalus* 97: 486-501, 1968.

Williamson, F. S. L. "Population pollution," *Bioscience* 19: 979-83, 1969.

Wynne-Edwards, V. C. "Self-regulating systems in populations of animals," *Science* 147: 1543-48, 1965.

Young, V. R., and Scrimshaw, N. S. "The physiology of starvation," *Scientific American* 225(4): 14-21, 1971.

18

HOW MANY PEOPLE HAVE LIVED ON THE EARTH?

Nathan Keyfitz

An estimate of the number of people who have lived on the earth is readily made once we are given the births at a few points of time, and suppose uniform increase between those points of time.

If in year t_1 the births were n_1, and in year t_2 ($t_2 > t_1$) the births were n_2, then the average annual rate of growth r satisfies

$$\frac{n_2}{n_1} = e^{r(t_2 - t_1)}$$

or

$$r = \frac{\ln n_2 - \ln n_1}{t_2 - t_1} \qquad (1)$$

Suppose that during the interval from t_1 to t_2 the rate of increase was at all times exactly r, then in any intermediate year t the births were $n_1 \, e^{r(t-t_1)}$, and summing this gives the total births as

$$\int_{t_1}^{t_2} n_1 e^{r(t-t_1)}dt = \frac{n_1}{r}\left[e^{r(t_2-t_1)}-1\right]. \quad (2)$$

Substituting the value of r from equation (1) in equation (2) gives for the births that occurred in the interval, which is the same as total persons lived, the simple result

$$\text{persons lived} = \frac{n_2-n_1}{r} = \frac{(n_2-n_1)(t_2-t_1)}{\ln n_2 - \ln n_1} \quad (3)$$

A widely quoted article of the Population Reference Bureau (1962) estimated births at four points in the history of mankind as follows:

t	n
600,000 B. C.	1
6,000 B.C.	250,000
1650 A.D.	25,000,000
1962 A.D.	110,000,000

Includes material from *Demography* 3: 581-82, 1966, with the permission of the publishers.

For the first of the three intervals between these four points, that between 600,000 B.C. and 6,000 B.C., expression (3) is

$$\text{persons lived} = \frac{(n_2 - n_1)(t_2 - t_1)}{\ln n_2 - \ln n_1}$$

$$= \frac{(250,000 - 1)(600,000 - 6000)}{12.4292 - 0}$$

$$= 11.9 \times 10^9$$

and for the other two intervals we have similarly 41.1×10^9 and 17.9×10^9 respectively. Adding the three intervals gives $11.9 + 41.1 + 17.9 = 70.9$ billion. (The Population Reference Bureau made an arithmetic error, and using the same data and the same formula published the incorrect figure of 77 billion.)

We can check the reasonableness of the 70.9 billion by applying the same expression (3) to an independent estimate of the number of persons alive at each of five points of time. Now the total (3) must be reinterpreted; it is no longer births but person-years (Table 1). Supposing the numbers alive to be those of the table below provides a total of 1,722 billion person-years, or, on dividing by 25 as the average expectation of life, to 68.9 billion persons lived. This is in close agreement with the 70.9 billion obtained above. Either estimate is subject to addition of the 1 billion births of the 1960's. The present 3.6 billion are thus about 5% of the total who ever lived.

The result is only moderately sensitive to the expectation of life we assume, between 20 and 35 years, which seems to cover the range of possibilities. It is very sensitive, however, to the way in which we divide the total time to fit the successive geometric curves implicit in the method. If, for instance, we do not divide the interval at all but simply take it that two people living a million years ago have by 1960 increased to 3 billion, then the number of person-years becomes $142,000 \times 10^9$, or $5,680 \times 10^9$ births, about 80 times as many as our 70×10^9. Such a calculation, using one geometric progression for the whole span of man's life on earth, and with various starting numbers, was published by Winkler (1959), and he found a range from $3,390 \times 10^9$ to $5,260 \times 10^9$ births; these, as he says, are outside figures.

Table 1. Calculation of person-years lived, when period is in four intervals.

t by calendar years of the Christian Era	n	$\ln n$	$\dfrac{(n_2-n_1)(t_2-t_1)}{\ln n_2 - \ln n_1}$
−1,000,000	2	0.693	338×10^9
−5,000	5,000,000	15.425	313×10^9
0	250,000,000	19.337	625×10^9
1650	545,000,000	20.116	446×10^9
1960	3,000,000,000	21.822	
Total person-years lived			$1,722 \times 10^9$

If we had more points at which population could be reasonably assessed the estimate might be lower. To assume a longer stretch of time than a million years would raise the number. The few facts at our disposal suggest the estimate 70 billion for the number of people who have ever lived. With the high mortality prevailing in most times only about half of those lived beyond childhood.

References

1. Robert C. Cook (ed.), "How many people have ever lived on earth?" *Population Bulletin,* XVIII (1962), 1-19.
2. Wilhelm Winkler, "Wieviele Menschen haben bisher auf der Erde gelebt?" *International Population Conference, Vienna 1959* (Vienna: Union Internationale pour l'Etude Scientifique de la Population, 1959), 73-76.

19

PROBLEMS OF
WORLD FOOD SUPPLY

Ivan L. Bennett, Jr.

It is my task on this program to provide an overview of the world food problem and to place it in context and perspective. My general remarks concerning world hunger are intended to give point and emphasis to the more specific presentations by the distinguished speakers who will follow me. Hunger is surely one of the pressing world issues of our time and it is an exceedingly complex issue. Indeed, world hunger is one of a series of interrelated problems, none of which can be solved, or indeed, even

Reprinted from the *XIth International Botanical Congress,* Seattle, Washington, All Congress Symposium, World Food Supply, August 28, 1969, with the permission of the author.

defined properly in isolation. S. S. Rosenfeld of the *Washington Post,* last year commented on the reaction to the starvation of children in the Nigerian civil war and, in so doing, he summarized exactly my own view of world hunger:

... The world's response to the Nigerian tragedy is relief, a quick burst of humanitarianism. ... Yet, however emotionally necessary the provision of relief is to the donors, it is physically inadequate to the recipients. Hunger in Nigeria, like hunger everywhere, is too profound to be left to the intermittent impulse of charity. It can be properly approached only in institutional ways: more food, more population control, more development, more self help, more aid.

You should know that, despite Dr. Van Overbeek's flattering introduction, I am not a food production scientist but a medical scientist and not even a specialist in nutrition. My excuse for being here is that three years ago, I was appointed Chairman of a Panel of the President's Science Advisory Committee, instructed by President Johnson to conduct a comprehensive study of the World Food Problem. My only qualification at that time was that being unencumbered by factual knowledge, I would embark on the task without preconceived notions.

More than 100 knowledgeable and experienced specialists, including Dr. Van Overbeek, participated in the study which was finally published in three volumes totalling 1320 pages. I will endeavor to summarize some of the conclusions of the study.

It is now very clear that if present trends continue, the size and severity of the world food problem will be apparent to all within, at most, 15 years—at which time it may be too late to provide a solution. There are some who believe that the crucial time for decision has already passed. The exact date itself is not really worth arguing about because it depends heavily upon the assumptions that one makes in forecasting rather than any real event—it has been placed at 1984 by the Department of Agriculture, at 1980 by Dr. Raymond Ewell of the State University of New York at Buffalo, and in the mid-1970's by the Paddock brothers in their recent book called *Famine 1975*. Most agree, however, on the following:

1. *Unless the situation changes markedly*, food shortages and actual famine will occur and with these, civil strife and political upheaval of unprecedented proportions will sweep through the developing nations. These consequences must occur when aid, in the form of food shipments from the developed nations will no longer buffer the needs of the hungry countries, and if they continue to be incapable of providing food for their peoples.

2. *Present efforts will not do the job.* Various types of foreign assistance by the U.S., other developed nations, international agencies, and voluntary organizations are "directed" to solving the food shortage but the present size and scope and type of these activities are inadequate. Hence, the problem worsens each year.

3. *Increased food must come from farming.* Although non-agricultural sources of food cannot be overlooked, the bulk of the increased food needs for the developing countries will have to come from agricultural production within these countries themselves. They cannot afford to import food and the rest of the world will be unable to give it to them in the needed amounts.

4. *There is still hope.* If agricultural technology is improved in the hungry nations, the situation is still reversible. This can result only from crop-oriented programs of technical assistance, designed around adaptive research, to produce a "package of practices," including improved seeds, physical inputs and cropping techniques that will improve yields per acre of land. This hope is critically dependent on the development of agricultural resources in the hungry countries which, in turn, must be tied to overall economic development. The ultimate solution will depend upon the amount of assistance, capital and technical, which can be applied to the task by the developed countries.

5. *Population control alone is not a solution.* During the next 20 years, food needs will more than double in the developing countries if present rates of population growth continue. Optimistic estimates of success in family planning in the next 20 years will only reduce food needs by 20 per cent—a significant fraction, but not a solution. The effects of successful family planning will become more apparent in the last years of this century if programs are initiated now. In short, the impact of population control will be realized over a period of many years but there is an immediate and increasing need for food regardless of what happens ultimately in programs of population control.

The critical need for food can be illustrated by pointing out that even to feed the people already born in the developing countries will be an enormous problem because of the large proportion of children in their populations. The amount of food required increases steadily from the time of birth to about 19 years of age. Half of those living in the developing countries are less than 15 years old. To maintain the Indian population at its *present level* of nutrition would require 20 per cent more food in 1975 than in 1965 *if no new children were added during this 10 year period*. To elevate the diet to the minimal standard recommended by the United Nations Food and Agricultural Organization, a 30 per cent increase would be required. In terms of wheat, these caloric increases represent 20 and 30 million metric tons annually in 1975—more than twice the amount of our annual food shipments to India and about the increase that can be expected from present favorable trends in Indian agricultural production.

Hunger and malnutrition and the population explosion are not primary diseases of the developing countries—rather they are the symptoms of an underlying malady, lagging economic development.

Economic assistance to developing countries by the United States began in earnest under President Truman's famous Point Four. We were full of confidence and enthusiasm, fresh from the heady successes of the Marshall Plan in Europe. In Europe, however, there already existed long-established, highly developed credit institutions for banking, marketing, transportation, and agriculture. There was no shortage of seasoned managerial talent and there was a large reservoir of skilled workmen ready to man the machines as soon as they could be provided.

In the developing nations, however, we have found that the job is tough, incredibly more complicated, difficult, and prolonged than anyone imagined in the beginning. This new task, we found, did not entail merely the restoration of a bruised economy like our own but required the building of a new structure from the ground up.

It is almost impossible to devise any new or original statement of the general problem of the World Food Supply. The subject has been treated so thoroughly in orations and editorials during the past two decades that both its size and significance tend to be obscured by rhetorical overkill. All has been said before and said extremely well; all has been repeated, reiterated, and rephrased. The stark misery of hunger, the ravages of malnutrition, the threats of civil strife, social unrest, and political upheaval posed by food shortages, and the shadow cast by impending famine have all been portrayed in urgent and compelling terms. So repetitively has the problem been brought to the attention of the American public that we seem almost to have lost the ability to respond to the stimulus; we are aware of the existence of the problem, we converse about it from time to time, but there is no longer any depth of understanding or concern. The situation has been aptly put by Norman Cousins:

A nation conditioned by affluence might possibly be suffering from compassion fatigue, or from conscience sickness, the peril of narrowing our field of vision to leave out the unpleasant view of life disfigured by hunger.

The hard fact remains that despite expenditures of billions of dollars for foreign aid; despite donations and concessional sales of millions of tons of food to developing nations; despite herculean efforts by numerous voluntary groups; despite examples of highly productive technical assistance programs by foundations; and despite years of activity by international organizations such as IBRD, FAO, WHO, UNESCO, and UNICEF, there are today in the world more hungry mouths than ever before in history.

There are several reasons for this apparent failure:

1. The overall problem of the world food supply is so large and so extremely complex that it is almost impossible for the casual or even the moderately concerned observer to comprehend its true dimensions or to grasp its intricate interrelationships with the many other aspects of economic growth and development.

2. Despite its true complexity, the problem, at first glance, seems deceptively straightforward and is, therefore, unusually susceptible to over-simplification. Because, farming seems readily understandable to the average citizen in a developed country such as the United States where the scientific base of modern agriculture is taken for granted, the temptation to act on the basis of superficial or incomplete information has been irresistible. This has led to seizure and overemphasis upon panaceas and piecemeal "solutions" which are inapplicable, ineffectual, or inadequate. The cumulative delays engendered by false starts and stop-gap measures have obscured the requirement for broad and effective programs, tailored to the demands and dimensions of the overall problem.

3. The details of the task involved in increasing food production to meet world needs have never been charted with the clarity and exactness that the available information will permit. The problem has been treated dramatically but incompletely—usually to incite short-term action for humanitarian reasons. A whole-

hearted response to an incomplete proposal, however, lulls the participants into an unjustified feeling of security that the problem is coming under control.

4. Food shortage and rapid population growth are separate, but interrelated problems. The solutions, likewise, are separate, but related. The choice is not to solve one or the other; to solve both is an absolute necessity. The popular tendency to think of food production and fertility control as alternative solutions to a common problem is dangerously misleading.

5. The twin problems of food and population imbalance have one feature in common that adds immeasurably to the difficulties of achieving control. Their eventual solution is crucially dependent upon success in convincing millions of citizens in the developing nations to take individual action. Fertility control cannot be achieved by declarations of government policy or by executive decree although adoption of a policy and the provision of information, instruction, and materials are obviously needed and are helpful. Similarly, political declarations concerning agricultural productivity are ineffective unless individual farmers can be convinced to adopt the necessary improved practices. The provision of these personal incentives is a task that encompasses a vast array of social, economic and political considerations which differ between countries and within countries. Indeed, the very fabric of traditional societies must be rewoven if the situation is to change permanently.

6. The eventual alleviation of world hunger will require many years. It is dependent on far-reaching social reforms and long-range programs of hard work which offer no promises of quick and dramatic results of the type so dear to politicians and so helpful in maintaining enthusiasm for a concerted, difficult undertaking. The results cannot be seen as the dedication of new buildings or dams, as a successful launching into space, or as other spectacular, "newsworthy" events to punctuate the year in and year out toil.

As H. E. Thomas has put it:

The chief handicap faced by all is the impatience of the modern fast moving world ... expressed in the desire of philanthropists (individual, foundation, national, and international) for concrete evidence of good they are doing; expressed in the hope of the specialist during a tour of 1½ or 2 years, to leave a permanent mark upon the culture that has been evolving for 1½ or 2 millenia.

In agricultural development as well as in other areas of assistance to a developing country, the political stability and predominant attitudes of the recipient government are of crucial importance. Most American citizens are thoroughly familiar with the constraints and disruptions that domestic political conditions within a developing country can create for aid programs. Recent history is replete with episodes which try our patience and frustrate our good intentions.

In contrast to these more obvious and better publicized difficulties at the political level, the obstacles posed by traditional culture, social structure, religious beliefs, and the long-established habits and customs of many developing countries are rarely considered in truly realistic terms. To understand, much less to accept these constraints is particularly difficult for Americans who remain among the citizens of Western Nations the least cosmopolitan and least tolerant of delay.

The key man in this discussion is the farmer. He buys the inputs of seeds, fertilizer, and pesticides and produces the outputs, the food with which we are concerned. Unless farmers in a traditional subsistence agriculture can be persuaded (that is, can be supplied with incentives) to use inputs to increase output *all other efforts to increase food production will fail.* Until a "cash flow" can be generated at farm level, agricultural development will be stymied. Inputs cost money; farmers need credit to buy them; farmers need to be able to sell their products at a price that will enable them to pay for inputs and have something left besides. When price policy holds down food costs for the consumer, the producer may not get his share and hence, may see no reason to produce beyond the immediate needs of his family. In many of the developing countries, the lands are cultivated by tradition-bound peasants who are controlled by a political system which has its power base in cities and is unfamiliar or unconcerned with problems of farming or with the measures, including price incentives, needed to increase agricultural productivity.

There are relationships between the demand for foodstuffs and the overall demand for goods and services in any economy. In order for "effective demand" for food to exist, the means of buying the food—purchasing power—must be available.

Likewise, on the supply or production side, there are relationships which link agricultural food production to overall production. Farms require manufactured inputs such as fertilizer, pesticides, and machinery which must be imported or produced domestically. If they are imported, the overall economy must generate sufficient exports or rely on a net inflow of foreign assistance or private capital to pay for the imports. If these inputs are produced domestically or paid for by industrial exports, the non-agricultural sectors must expand at the rates consistent with the need of the agricultural sector. Various non-agricultural sectors are dependent on agricultural raw materials, and in some cases, food products.

Because of the interdependence which exists among food need, food demand, overall income, agricultural output, and total output (which is GNP), *it is meaningless to consider a nation's demand and supply of foodstuffs independently from overall economic growth.*

Even when farmers can make a profit, unless consumer goods which they wish to purchase are available, the money means little to them and one of the persisting problems is to make consumer goods available in the rural areas. This need is but one of the many reasons that the agricultural and industrial sectors must grow together in developing countries; they are complementary, not competitive.

The very nature of farming must be understood if appropriate measures are to be developed in the hungry nations. Farm production is based upon the growth processes of plants that utilize solar energy through photosynthesis. Because the basic process of farming depends upon solar energy, it must always remain widely distributed over the face of the earth so the sunlight can be utilized where it falls. No other single fact has greater significance for agricultural development.

On the one hand, it requires an extensive and well-articulated transportation system to move the production inputs which a progressive agriculture needs from distant points of manufacture to each farm and to move farm products to ultimate consumers. Furthermore, it denies to farming two opportunities that are available to many other industries. One of these is the opportunity to concentrate activities in order that industries geographically adjacent can exchange products, avoiding major transportation costs or time-lags. The other is the opportunity to create favorable working conditions without transforming an entire society. A steel or textile mill can establish working conditions in a plant which, during working hours, will separate laborers from the demands, customs and traditions of their families. Agriculture cannot do this since farming must be carried on in widely dispersed village settings, in the midst of family influences and traditional social pressures. Agricultural development, by virtue of this inherent dispersal, requires a major social transformation. It cannot create in part-time oases the new sets of working conditions appropriate to its production needs.

The private enterprise community and, in particular, the agribusiness group of companies which includes fertilizers, agricultural chemicals, implements, seeds, irrigation equipment, food processing, and food marketing companies have shown a responsible and growing interest in participating in the war on hunger. To take advantage of this reservoir of interest and purpose, governments must accelerate efforts to work with the private sector in the developing countries. Measures such as liberalized loan policy, investment guarantees and other facilitation of investment must be supplemented by cutting red tape and allowing for operation of the profit motive.

The most important ingredient in mounting a strategy to meet the World Food Problem will be the provision of long-range, continuous programs of both capital and technical assistance from the U.S. and other developed countries.

From the point of view of donors and recipients and of planners and implementers, and for the sake of ultimate success, long-term commitment of substantial resources is an absolute necessity.

Particularly in the field of agricultural development, technical assistance is essential to achieving the ultimate objective of foreign aid, namely, self-sustaining economic growth.

There still persists in many quarters the feeling that research or science is a sort of luxury or prestige activity which has no substantial place in a program of aid to developing countries. Quite apart from the fact that adaptive research is an absolute prerequisite to the use of modern agricultural systems in different regions of the world, the basis for continuing agricultural development in any country, including the United States, is continuing research. Research in modern agriculture is a never-ending task.

Improvement of agricultural production by modern scientific methods consists of adapting plant varieties, pesticides, fertilizer usage, and cropping techniques to the local soil and climate. In other words, a "package" is tailor-made for the locality by applying scientific principles to find the answers to local problems. Just as one size of uniform cannot be expected to fit all soldiers, the final fit depending upon tailoring the garment to the individual, no single set of agricultural technology can be transferred successfully to another country without tailoring it by adaptive research. Furthermore, the adaptive research and testing must be carried out in the country or region where crop improvement is desired.

The failure of most of us, including policy-makers in government, to distinguish between the ability of agriculture science to find answers and already knowing the answers has led to insufficient emphasis upon technical assistance as opposed to "practical assistance." For example, a so-called farmer-to-farmer program has been proposed and enacted into law in the well-intentioned but quite erroneous belief that American farmers could be sent overseas to teach farmers in the developing countries how to increase farm production. Without the scientific and technological back-up routinely available to them in the U.S., these farmers would be helpless to change conditions elsewhere.

Many have tried to correct this know-how, show-how fallacy by saying that what works in Kansas won't work in Karachi but the message has not yet penetrated foreign aid policy to the required extent and the notion that research is an absolute necessity rather than an academic diversion is very slow to disappear from popular thinking.

At the risk of being somewhat inaccurate as to details, I would like to illustrate the absolute necessity for overseas research and the pitfalls in direct transfer of U.S. practices to other regions by citing a specific example.

Genetic improvement of quality and quantity of corn in the United States has been remarkably successful as evidenced by the rapid adoption of hybrid strains by farmers and the striking increase in yields per acre during the past 40 years. Corn-breeding in the United States has developed around the inbreeding and hybridization concept. There were two basic reasons for this:

1. The belief that mass selection techniques were ineffective.
2. The absence of heterosis (a fancy term for "hybrid vigor") in hybrids among American varieties of corn.

The alternative approach which was adopted in this country was varietal inbreeding followed by single- or double-cross hybridization.

Because of the great success of this approach in the United States, other countries have followed the same pattern. Indeed, this technique became a sort of status symbol, adopted by other countries without questioning its necessity or desirability under conditions quite different from those in the United States.

During the past decade, however, we have learned that both of the initial justifications for the inbreeding-hybridization approach were not universally applicable. Simple selection procedures can be highly effective and in Latin America, India, Thailand, the Philippines, and Kenya, varietal hybrids have been identified with marked heterosis or vigor which are higher yielding than the best available double-crosses. Kenya has made the best commercial use of such varieties. All of the current information indicates that the most rapid and substantial progress would be made if corn-breeding programs in most of the developing countries did not follow the United States pattern.

In the Kenya program, initiated by British scientists in 1958, a double-cross hybrid which produced yield increases of 25% was developed. When American agriculturalists entered the program in 1964, they found varietal hybrids with marked heterosis which increased yields by 50 per cent and determined that the yield variance was additive.

This meant that simple selection schemes were worthwhile and these were immediately instituted. As a result, varietal hybrids are now in use which give yield increases of another 50 per cent above the original varietal hybrid.

The adoption of these improved varieties of corn by the farmers in Kenya has been very rapid. The acreage planted in hybrid corn increased from 400 in 1963 to 450,000 in 1967.

This Kenyan "success story," however, remains an exception rather than the rule. We must find ways in which this success can be replicated.

An editorial in the *Christian Science Monitor*, entitled "World Poverty Circle," epitomized what is perhaps the greatest obstacle of all to economic development in the poor nations. Quoting a recent statement by John Kenneth Galbraith that economic expansion in the U.S. no longer is hampered by a shortage of capital resources, but rather by a shortage of qualified manpower, the article goes on to say:

It is, however, in weighing America's problems in this direction that one gets a clearer picture of the difficult situation which faces so many nations today as they seek to propel themselves forward economically. For, while American establishments sometimes find themselves short of trained personnel, how infinitely better off are they than those establishments in so many other lands which have neither trained personnel nor the hope of adequate financing.

With either trained personnel or sufficient financing, a country is able to begin that self-perpetuating upward spiral of development which leads to a steadily broadening economy and rising standard of living. Trained manpower always generates money. And money can greatly ease the task of producing trained manpower.

But without either, a country often does little more than go round and round on the same dead-level circle, producing neither wealth nor a class of citizenry

well enough educated and skilled to break out of the circle. In most of Africa, throughout much of Latin America and over wide areas of Asia this is the situation which prevails today.

The Afro-Asian-Latin American problem is compounded by the fact that, even when progress is made in either accumulating investable wealth or in enlarging the reservoir of educated men and women, this is offset by the increase in population, which, in turn, creates new problems.

At some point a means must be found to break up the self-perpetuating circle of poverty—too many people, too few skills, too little money.

Until technical assistance programs have been successful in establishing within the developing countries the institutional and manpower bases for continued research in agriculture, in health, in all aspects of physical, biological and social sciences, and in administration, management and techniques of diffusing knowledge, no amount of capital investment alone will succeed in bringing about self-sustained economic growth in these nations.

Congressional authorization for foreign aid is now almost entirely on a year-to-year basis. Budgets are dealt with more ruthlessly each year and the annual passage of the foreign assistance act is the most tedious and agonizing process in Washington.

The hard-won experience of the past two decades and the urgent problem of feeding the burgeoning millions in the underdeveloped countries, taken together, signal the need and the opportunity for a reorientation and expansion of the U.S. program of economic assistance. We should minimize the errors of the past, and in concert with other nations, apply the knowledge that we have acquired by strenuous and dedicated effort.

There are four distinct but related reasons for programs to assist overseas economic development:

1. *A humanitarian reason* which may be served by channeling additional capital, technical assistance, and food aid through international agencies. The increasing use of multilateral assistance is not a new idea, of course. The size and duration of the effort that will be required to cope with the problem of world food supply will necessitate a strengthening and restructuring of the existing United Nations

agencies, many of which are not geared to operational efforts on the scale that will be required. Bilateral effort should be maintained and expanded by the developed countries, particularly in technical assistance and in programs involving the private sector of the economy. The willingness of universities and business firms to increase their activities in the developing countries will be better preserved and expanded through bilateral programs.

Such efforts should be planned on a basis of long-term strategy. Their continuity should not be subject to threat from episodic disagreements among nations and withdrawal or curtailment should not be employed as a foreign policy sanction except under the gravest of international crises.

The agencies charged with this task must have a new capacity to measure economic and agricultural development and hence the food supply problem. It is essential to develop a system to examine all the elements required to deal with this complex situation and permit the drafting of coordinated programs to be carried on throughout the world. One way in which this critically important function could be accomplished would be through a nonprofit international planning organization. Such a group could undertake this task of measurement, appraisal, planning, programming and monitoring results. The extraordinary technological resources now available in developed countries can be creatively applied to this immense problem.

2. *A tactical foreign policy reason, primarily for improving bilateral relationships. This could encompass the whole range of capital assistance* and technical assistance. It could and should include the financing of projects intended for prestige (ranging from airlines to palaces). Foreign aid is not a substitute for diplomacy, but it can supplement and enhance its effectiveness. There is, of course, an inseparable overlap in these tactical and strategic programs. Recognition of humanitarian purpose as opposed to diplomatic purpose does not imply that any final separation into two distinct programs is necessary or feasible.

3. *A security reason* because military assistance, obviously, can also play a major role in the bilateral relationships mentioned under diplomatic and foreign policy functions.

In a larger sense, however, humanitarian, long-range economic assistance will contribute to national and world security. The importance of insulating that (as opposed to the strictly military) form of assistance is nowhere better described than in the words of former Secretary of Defense Robert McNamara:

Our security is related directly to the security of the newly developing world. In a modernizing society, security is not military force—though it may involve it. Security is not traditional military activity—though it may encompass it. Security is development.

Again, the idea that security is more than military might is not a new one. Seneca, nearly two thousand years ago, warned the Roman Senate:

A hungry people listens not to reason nor is its demand turned aside by prayers.

4. *A long-range economic reason*, involving the eventual creation of additional markets for goods and products. This aim is not entirely self-serving for the achievement of sustained economic growth by the developing countries will be dependent upon their participation in world markets on a competitive basis.

This last goal of foreign aid has important implications for the inclusion of trade concession in the humanitarian and strategic programs of assistance discussed above.

Trade adjustments which appear to involve immediate sacrifices may, in the longer view, be far less costly than capital assistance given in traditional fashion. It is highly likely, in most instances, that provision of export markets based upon competitive advantage will be a most effective stimulus to development.

All too often, the wealthy nations have seemed to regard economic assistance as a short-term relief to countries which are temporarily poor. The experience of the past two decades indicates that aid should become a part of a concept of the economic relations between unequally developed countries, which will last for many decades to come.

Finally, if the United States is to deal seriously and productively with international development, three conditions must be fulfilled:

1. The American people must be convinced that the efforts merit investment of their taxes and that the efforts will be effective in meeting the overall problem.

2. The American people must have confidence in the substance of the programs which are implemented and in the arm of the government which is responsible for administration of those programs.

3. Foreign aid must be placed on a long-range basis, not budgeted and funded hand-to-mouth, from year to year. Foreign economic assistance is doomed to frustration and failure as long as the responsible agency is forced by Congress to deal only with quick payoff projects and to show results tomorrow in order to survive the next set of hearings on Capitol Hill.

20

THE GREEN REVOLUTION: CORNUCOPIA OR PANDORA'S BOX?

Clifton R. Wharton, Jr.

The application of science and technology to traditional agriculture has begun to produce dramatic results, above all in Asia. The rapid expansion of certain food grains in the developing world is being particularly widely heralded, and justly so, as the "Green Revolution." The discussion of the phenomenon tends to cluster around two views. On the one hand, some observers now believe that the race between food and population is over, that the new agricultural technology constitutes a cornucopia for the developing world, and that victory is in sight in the "War on Hunger." Others see this development as opening a Pandora's box; its very success will produce a number of new problems which are far more subtle and difficult than those faced during the development of the new technology. It is important to give careful attention and critical analysis to both interpretations in order to be optimistic about the promise of the Green Revolution where justified, and at the same time to prepare for

Reprinted from *Foreign Affairs* 47: 464-76, 1969. Reprinted by permission from *Foreign Affairs*, April 1969, copyright held by the Council on Foreign Relations, Inc., New York.

the problems that are now emerging. The Green Revolution offers an unparalleled opportunity to break the chains of rural poverty in important parts of the world. Success will depend upon how well the opportunity is handled and upon how alert we are to the inherent consequences.

It is now generally known that major technological breakthroughs in food production are believed to have lifted the spectre of famine in the immediate future and to have postponed the prospect of Malthusian population disaster. Startling developments have been accomplished in wheat, rice and corn—major food staples in much of the developing world. The possibilities for doubling or even tripling production are based upon new high-yield varieties coupled with adequate supplies of water, fertilizer, pesticides and modern equipment. Overnight, the image of agriculture in the developing countries has changed from that of an economic backwater to that of a major potential contributor to overall development. The new varieties are rapidly spreading both within countries and across national boundaries. A recent estimate of the International Agricultural Development Service of the U.S. Department of Agriculture reveals that in Asia alone the estimated acreage planted with these new high-yield varieties rose from 200 acres in 1964-65 to 20 million in 1967-68. Traditional food-importing nations like the Philippines and Pakistan are becoming self-sufficient and have the prospect of becoming net food exporters.

It will be no easy task to achieve the potential increased production offered by the new technology, particularly when it involves millions upon millions of diverse farms and farmers scattered over the countryside. If the increased production is in fact obtained, this will automatically produce a whole new set of second-generation problems which must be faced if development is to be sustained and accelerated. Therefore, two considerations need to be borne in mind. First, there is reason to believe that the further spread of new varieties will not be as fast as early successes might suggest. Second, the new problems arising out of the spread of the new technology, whatever its speed, need to be foreseen and acted upon now. The probable developments in each case have the greatest significance for economic growth and for the conduct of international relations.

II

The reasons for believing that the new technology will not in fact spread nearly as widely or as rapidly as supposed and predicted include, first, the fact that the availability of irrigated land imposes at least a short-run limit to the spread of the new high-yield varieties. Most of these require irrigation and careful water control throughout the growing cycle. In most Asian countries about one-fourth to one-half of the rice lands are irrigated; the remainder are dependent upon monsoons and seasonal rains. The speed with which additional land can be converted to the new technology depends on the rapidity with which new irrigation facilities can be constructed; and here the high capital costs are likely to be a retarding factor.

Large-scale irrigation projects can seriously strain the investment capacity of developing nations. For example, the massive Mekong River development scheme, involving Laos, Cambodia, Viet Nam and Thailand, has been estimated to require a capital investment over the next 20 years of about $2 billion, roughly 35 percent of the annual national income of the four countries involved and exceeding the annual net new investment of all the countries of Southeast Asia combined. Further, significant additional costs are involved in converting existing irrigation systems to the requirements of modern agriculture. Many of the old gravity irrigation systems were not designed to provide the sophisticated water controls demanded by the new varieties. (For example, each plot must be controlled separately throughout the growing season.)

Second, there are doubts about the ability of existing markets to handle the increased product. Storage facilities and transport are inadequate and crop grading often deficient. Not only must the marketing system be expanded to handle a larger output; there also is an increased need for farm supplies and equipment. Fertilizers, pesticides and insecticides must be available in the right quantities, at the right times, and in the right places. Given the inadequacy of the agricultural infrastructure, the need to expand and modernize marketing systems is likely to reduce the pace of the Revolution.

Because many of the new varieties, especially rice, do not appeal to the tastes of most consumers, it is difficult to calculate the size of the market. Some argue that until newer varieties which are closer to popular tastes are developed, the market will be limited.

Third, the adoption of the new technology is likely to be much slower where the crop is a basic food staple, grown by a farmer for family consumption. Such farmers are understandably reluctant to experiment with the very survival of their families. Peasant producers are obviously far more numerous in the developing world than are commercial farmers and the task of converting them to a more modern technology is considerably more difficult. So far, spectacular results have been achieved primarily among the relatively large commercial farmers. Some semi-subsistence farmers have begun to grow the new varieties, but the rate at which they adopt them may be slower.

Fourth, farmers must learn new farming skills and expertise of a higher order than was needed in traditional methods of cultivation. The new agronomic requirements are quite different as regards planting dates and planting depths; fertilizer rates and timing; insecticide, pesticide and fungicide applications; watering and many others. Unless appropriate extension measures are taken to educate farmers with respect to these new farming complexities the higher yields will not be obtained.

Fifth, many of the new varieties are non-photosensitive and the shorter term will allow two or three crops per year instead of one. Multiple cropping is good, but there may be difficulties if the new harvest comes during the wet season without provision having been made for mechanical drying of the crop to replace the traditional sun drying. In addition, there may be resistance if the new harvest pattern conflicts with religious or traditional holidays which have grown up around the customary agricultural cycles.

Sixth, failure to make significant institutional reforms may well be a handicap. There is evidence in several Latin American countries that a failure to make needed changes in policies now detrimental to agriculture, or a reluctance to effectuate the institutional reforms required to give real economic incentives to small farmers and tenants, has been primarily responsible for the very slow spread of Mexico's success with new varieties of wheat and corn to its neighbors to the south.

From all this one may deduce that the "first" or "early" adopters of the new technology will be in regions which are already more advanced, literate, responsive and progressive and which have better soil, better water management, closer access to roads and markets—in sum, the wealthier, more modern farmers. For them, it is easier to adopt the new higher-yield varieties since the financial risk is less and they already have better managerial skills. When they do adopt them, the doubling and trebling of yields mean a corresponding increase in their incomes. One indication of this is the large number of new private farm-management consultant firms in the Philippines which are advising large landlords on the use of the new seed varieties and making handsome profits out of their share of the increased output.

As a result of different rates in the diffusion of the new technology, the richer farmers will become richer. In fact, it may be possible that the more progressive farmers will capture food markets previously served by the smaller semi-subsistence producer. In India, only 20 percent

of the total area planted to wheat in 1967-68 consisted of the new dwarf wheats, but they contributed to 34 percent of the total production. Such a development could well lead to a net reduction in the income of the smaller, poorer and less venturesome farmers. This raises massive problems of welfare and equity. If only a small fraction of the rural population moves into the modern century while the bulk remains behind, or perhaps even goes backward, the situation will be highly explosive. For example, Tanjore district in Madras, India, has been one of the prize areas where the new high-yield varieties have been successfully promoted. Yet one day last December, 43 persons were killed in a clash there between the landlords and their landless workers, who felt that they were not receiving their proper share of the increased prosperity brought by the Green Revolution.

III

Other experts argue that the new technology's stimulus to production and income cannot be stemmed. It is true that the rapidity with which the new seed varieties have spread in country after country belies the customary view of an inert, unresponsive peasantry. In 1965, India began a program of high-yield varieties which set a goal of 32.5 million acres by 1970-71; last year's crop season saw 18 million acres already planted, which contributed to the most successful year in recent Indian agricultural history (some 100 million tons of food grains, 11 million over the previous record year of 1964-65). Self-sufficiency in food grains is predicted in three or four years. Other countries are experiencing similar situations where the demand for the new seeds is outstripping the available supplies and black markets are even developing in seeds and fertilizer.

Nevertheless, if we assume that the new varieties will continue to live up to expectations and spread rapidly and widely, the increased production will in turn lead to a new set of difficulties. First, large tracts planted in one of the new varieties may be susceptible to disease and infestation which could cause massive losses. Heretofore, reliance upon seed selected by individual farmers meant that neighboring farms growing the same crop usually planted two or more different varieties or strains. This heterogeneity provided a built-in protection against widespread plant diseases, since not all varieties are equally susceptible. But where a single variety is introduced, covering large contiguous areas, the dangers of pathologic susceptibility are multiplied. For example, the new wheat introduced from Mexico into the Indo-Gangetic belt in India and Pakistan has involved a small range of genotypes—and the same has been true in Iran, Turkey and certain Middle Eastern countries. Any change in the spectrum of races of wheat rust in any of these countries could threaten the wheat crop on a massive scale, since it would involve the entire area.

Two steps are necessary to avoid these dangers: first, a diversified breeding program which can continually produce new varieties; second, an able and well-organized plant protection service which can quickly identify dangerous outbreaks and initiate prompt steps to combat them. Both activities must rely primarily upon national organizations rather than the regional or international ones. Both demand a skilled, well-trained staff. Some nations have recognized these dangers and are taking steps to meet them, but others still have not been made sufficiently aware. Aid givers—public and private—who are responsible for promoting the new varieties bear an equal responsibility to promote indigenous research and plant protection services. The outbreak of any major disease which wipes out the harvest of thousands of farmers is far more likely to be blamed on the producers and spreaders of the miracle seed than on Fate. Agricultural development could be set back several decades.

Second, it is vitally important to expand the entire complex of services and industries required to achieve the higher production. Any government or foreign-aid agency which distributes the "miracle" seed but fails to provide the insecticide and fertilizer in the appropriate quantities when and where needed is courting political disaster; unless these inputs are available and used, some local, traditional varieties

will outyield the new ones. A seed industry, agricultural chemical plants, processing and storage firms, factories producing hand sprayers, dusters, water pumps and engines—these are just a few of the agriculturally related industries which must develop if the Revolution is to take hold.

The skills and the capital needed cannot be provided solely by the public sector. Private capital must also be utilized. In a few countries the spread of the new technologies has already forced an abrupt departure from the previous practice of having government agencies serve as the major or sole distributor of the required inputs. Private industry, especially American, has stepped in to provide a new, more dynamic pattern of distribution. In the Philippines, for example, EESO has become a major distributor of fertilizer and agricultural chemicals. Frequently, such ventures have involved links with local firms. In India, the International Minerals and Chemicals Corporation, with the Standard Oil Company of California, built a fertilizer plant with a yearly capacity of 365,000 tons; the U.S. firms provide the management but control is held by an Indian firm. Storage silos, seed multiplication firms and even integrated farm-to-retail firms are just a few of the activities where private U.S. resources are being harnessed to serve the Green Revolution.

Equally important are the increased farm services which are required, particularly agricultural credit. For example, from studies conducted at the International Rice Research Institute, it is estimated that whereas the total cash costs of production for the average Filipino rice farmer using traditional methods and varieties is about $20 per hectare, the cost rises to $220 when the new, high-yielding IR-8 is grown. Although the yield may increase threefold, leading to a net return four times greater than with traditional varieties, the farmer must have access to substantially greater credit to finance his operations. Especially for the poorer farmers with low cash reserves, who may want to adopt the new varieties, the village moneylender and merchant will not be adequate unless they in turn have access to additional funds. Indeed, the Green Revolution must be accompanied both by an increase in the amount of credit available and by the expansion and modernization of credit institutions and mechanisms. Tapping the capital markets in the modern urban sector must be encouraged, and ways must be found at the village level to mobilize local capital, especially the increased savings which are possible from higher farm incomes. The Green Revolution will generate increased cash which, if properly marshalled, can contribute to capital formation and agricultural progress.

Third, much more attention must be devoted to marketing the increased output. Where there has been semi-subsistence agriculture, the impact of the new technology upon the *marketed* product is even greater than on total production. If the crop is a food staple and if the peasant farm family traditionally consumes some 70 to 80 percent of its total product each year, a doubling of output does not lead to a doubling in the amount retained for family consumption. Some modest increase in consumption is likely, but the bulk of the increased production will enter the market. Thus a doubling in yields in a semi-subsistence agriculture usually leads to much more than a doubling of the amount sold.

The impact of this explosive increase upon the traditional marketing network and storage capacity can be calamitous. The case of India is illustrative. During the past crop year, India experienced a marvelous increase in food-grain production, but the marketing network and storage facilities were not prepared to cope with it. The result can be seen in the mountains of food-grain stored in schools and in the open air under conditions which are apt to reduce if not negate the grains. The food-deficit psychology which underlies the failure of planners and policy-makers to anticipate these results is not limited to the developing nations. Aid givers were equally surprised. Strangely, the lessons of the Indian experience do not yet seem to have affected the thinking and planning of other nations which are promoting the new technology.

Fourth, the slowness with which the food-deficit psychology dies also has an important consequence in terms of government pricing policies. The fact that agriculture, even

semi-subsistence agriculture, does respond to price, is only gradually becoming accepted. But the shock which quantum jumps in food production may have on domestic prices has not been sufficiently appreciated. The downward pressure on prices, especially where transport is deficient and storage is inadequate, may in fact be so severe as to have a disincentive effect upon producers. Unless adequate attention is given to developing a sound pricing policy to prevent excessive dampening of incentives, the spread of the new technology may in fact be cut short before any "takeoff" has occurred. Premature discouragement could produce a reversion leading to a slowing up in food production or even a rejection of the new technology.

It has been amply demonstrated throughout the world that peasant and subsistence farmers are responsive to favorable prices, provided the return is real and they receive the benefit. For example, from 1951-53 through 1961-63, the farmers of Thailand in response to favorable prices increased their exports of corn at an average annual compounded rate of 35.8 percent; casava, 25.0 percent; and kenaf, 43.8 percent. Filipino farmers responded to a governmental price-support program for tobacco by changing from native to Virginia tobacco and then booming production from 3 million kilos in 1954 to over 30 million kilos in 1962. The list of crops where peasant farmers have responded to favorable prices is large—rubber, oil palm, coffee, jute, wheat, barley, sorghum, millet, gram, cotton. Thus, if the full potential offered by the new technology is to be realized, every effort must be made to insure that there is in fact a significant return to the producer and that the rapid rise in output does not lead to a counter-productive slump in prices.

Fifth, the goals of increased food production are frequently couched in terms of some desirable, minimal standards of nutrition. Such nutritional goals are commendable, but they can be attained only by individuals who have the income with which to purchase the better diet. Effective demand for food depends upon both the income of the demanders and the price of the food. If the increased production leads to lower costs and prices, then consumers will be able to increase their food purchase and hopefully to raise their levels of nutrition. Equally important is the need to increase incomes so that the greater production entering the market can be purchased. The food problem in a developing world is both a problem of production and supply and a problem of demand and income. Unless the higher levels of effective demand materialize, the prospect will be market gluts, price depression and, in certain cases, shifts by the farmers away from the higher-yielding varieties. Hence, every effort must be made both to reduce the unit costs of the increased food output and to augment the incomes of consumers who purchase food; otherwise, the second bowl of rice will not be bought—despite the technical feasibility of producing it.

Sixth, one of the major avowed aims of most nations which are eagerly promoting the Green Revolution is to achieve self-sufficiency in food production. In Southeast Asia, for example, the Philippines already claims to have become self-sufficient. Malaysia predicts that she will be self-sufficient by 1971; Indonesia by 1973. Some believe that these target dates are overly optimistic. But if the rice-deficit nations of the region such as Malaysia, Indonesia and the Philippines eventually become self-sufficient by successfully adopting the new technology, what will happen to the rice-surplus nations like Burma and Thailand whose economies are heavily dependent upon rice export? To whom will they sell their rice? Self-sufficiency will not only be detrimental to the rice-exporting nations, but will reduce one of the few areas of economic interdependence in the region. Unless action is taken in advance to offset the predictable impact of the new technology, hopes of promoting regional economic integration will be substantially reduced. Whether or not one agrees with the goal of self-sufficiency for these nations, the policies have been adopted and will be pursued. Many developing nations spend some 30 percent of their foreign exchange on food imports and wish to eliminate this drain as well as the irritation of chronic deficits in domestic production. We should anticipate the predictable consequences of these policies—in this case major economic dislocations in trade—

so that we can be equally ready with developmental efforts or foreign assistance to reduce the dimensions of the problem. Unless the exporting nations take immediate stock of their prospects and seek to diversify their agriculture, the impact of such trade distortions could have major consequences for their economies and pace of development.

Seventh, a critical question is whether these technological developments are a "once-and-for-all" phenomenon. How likely is it that new technological improvement will continue to be made? The application of science to agriculture over the last 300 years has resulted in a tenfold increase in yield per acre on the best farmed lands in the temperate zone. This expansion is what led to the production controls introduced by the surplus nations, such as the United States, to keep demand and supply in reasonable balance. Today's Green Revolution is the result of a similar application of science to agriculture in the developing world. But it should be noted that the institutionalized application of science is largely concentrated at present in food crops. Before World War II, primary attention in agricultural research in the developing world was devoted to the major crops—rubber in Malaysia, sugar in the Philippines, coffee in Kenya, palm oil in Nigeria, coffee in Brazil, bananas in Honduras. Staple food crops were either ignored or received scant attention. Thus the successes of the recent application of science to peasant agriculture could be interpreted as an exploitation of a "technical gap" in food crops left by years of neglect. If current developments merely represent a "catching-up," then as soon as population overtakes current developments, we are back to "square one."

Much will depend upon whether or not the necessary manpower is trained in each country to provide a continuing human resource which can produce a constant stream of new technology. The manpower trained in the Rockefeller Foundation's Mexican program has always been a greater contribution, in my view, than the new varieties. Successful adoption should not deflect attention from the importance and role of continuous agricultural research. The development of indigenous competence to engage in agricultural research is critical and becomes even more critical as the new varieties are adopted. The target should be not *a* new technology but ever-new technology, and this requires skilled manpower.

These are only a few of the possible consequences of the successful spread of the new technology. There are several broader consequences and issues which can be raised only as questions in this brief presentation:

To what extent will the diffusion of the new technology accentuate the displacement of rural people and heighten the pace of migration to the cities? If higher yields per acre, multiple cropping plus mechanization, force surplus manpower out of agriculture, what are the prospects for increased employment in industry and services to absorb this manpower?

For the average developing nation the Green Revolution means that instead of devoting two-thirds to three-fourths of its agricultural resources to food production, these resources may now be shifted to other higher paying crops. The question then becomes, what crops and for what markets?

If agriculture becomes more modern, dynamic and wealthy, will the non-agricultural sector allow agriculture to retain a significant share of this increased income or merely follow the previous patterns of taxing agriculture for non-agricultural development?

What will be the political significance of these changes if successful adoption of the new technology leads to an economically invigorated and strengthened rural population—almost invariably a large majority in developing nations? Will rural-based political parties and movements emerge to alter the recent dominance of urban centers?

What will be the global effect of a food explosion in the tropical and sub-tropical world? Will such developments lead to an improved reallocation of productive specialization among the developed and developing world, or will nationalistic trade barriers continue to flout natural comparative advantages?

One final danger lies in assuming that there is no longer an urgent need for measures to reduce rates of population growth. Quite the contrary. While the new developments are a splendid gift of time to allow a holding operation, effective population measures continue to be essential. Whether one assumes a growth rate of 2.5 or 3 percent, the inexorable fact is that, give or take a few years, the population of the developing world will double in about 25 years.

The significance of the food-population problem is more than humanitarian and developmental; it also has critical implications for the conduct of international relations. Relations between nations are often profoundly affected by long-run forces over which men can exercise only limited control in the short run. The food-population race is an excellent example of such a set of forces. Predictions regarding both population and food, as well as their interaction over varying lengths of time, must be taken into account in the conduct of developmental assistance, not only by aid-giving nations and international organizations, but by the governments of developing nations themselves. Policies and programs designed to win the race between food and population may have unintended, though often predictable, consequences which may have a very broad impact.

IV

Charles Malik once said that "one of the principal causes of both international conflict and internal strife is unfounded expectations. These are based ultimately either on deception or on a belief in magic."[1] What we have in hand seems to many people to approach magic; let us hope that it does not become the source of deception.

To speak of the possible consequences and problems associated with the next phase of the Green Revolution should not be misinterpreted as a plea for the suppression of the Revolution because, like Pandora's box, it will lead to even greater problems than those it was designed to eliminate. On the contrary, I would strongly argue that the list of second-generation problems is a measure of what great opportunities

[1] Charles H. Malik, "What Shall It Profit A Man?" *Columbia Journal of World Business*, Summer 1966.

exist for breaking the centuries-old chains of peasant poverty. They also demonstrate how closely interrelated are the various factors which impel or retard agricultural development. This complex interrelationship makes interdisciplinary research and coöperation vital if the current problems are to be solved and future ones anticipated. The most realistic prediction is that each country is likely to experience a different set of these problems and that there will be variations among countries between the two extremes of optimistic and pessimistic prognoses.

The quiet, passive peasant is already aware of the modern world—far more than we realize—and he is impatient to gain his share. The Green Revolution offers him the dramatic possibility of achieving his goal through peaceful means. It has burst with such suddenness that it has caught many unawares. Now is the time to place it in its long-range perspective and to engage in contingency planning so that we may respond flexibly and quickly as the Revolution proceeds. Perhaps in this way we can ensure that what we are providing becomes a cornucopia, not a Pandora's box.

21

ORIGIN, HISTORY, AND USE OF NORIN 10 WHEAT

L. P. Reitz and S. C. Salmon

New varieties of wheat (*Triticum aestivum* L. em Thell.) derived from the semidwarf 'Norin 10' and similar varieties from Japan have recently attracted much attention in most wheat growing countries of the world. It seems desirable to bring together the relevant facts regarding the origin and history of Norin 10 and some of the others. They are of interest mainly because of their short, stiff straw and resistance to lodging under conditions of climate and soil especially favorable for vegetative growth and high yield. Some of the new varieties have been so successful in so many countries that their performance has been characterized by such words as "sensational," "revolutionary," and a "breakthrough" in production. Although these may well be regarded as exaggerations, it is nevertheless a fact that for many countries Norin 10 derivatives have been responsible for, or promise, improvements in wheat production scarcely dreamed of a few

Reprinted from *Crop Science* 8: 686-689, 1968, with the permission of the publishers.

years ago. We estimate that between 15 and 18 million acres of Norin 10 derivatives were seeded in 1968.

Origin and History

The word "Norin" is an acronym made up of the first letter of each word in the Romanized title of the Japanese Agricultural Experiment Station. The numerals are selection numbers; hence, we have Norin 10, Norin 33, etc.

Through the courtesy of Dr. Torao Gotoh, Ministry of Agriculture and Forestry, Fukuyama-Shi, Hiroshima-Ken, Japan (personal communication), we have learned more about the origin of Norin 10. Japanese records show that the variety included two U.S. wheats in its lineage, namely 'Fultz' and 'Turkey Red.' The first was exported to Japan sometime before 1892; the date of acquisition of the other presumably was about the same. By pedigree selection at Nishigawa, Tokyo, a form called "Glassy Fultz' was isolated and crossed in 1917 with 'Daruma,' a native variety of Japan. Daruma, in Japanese, means a kind of tumbler doll and the name is applied to a group of several varieties native to the country. In 1924, Fultz-Daruma was crossed with Turkey Red at the same station. The F_2 was grown and selected at the Konosu Branch Station in 1926. Seed was sent to the Iwate-Ken Prefectural Station in northeastern Japan where the F_3

was grown and final selections were made. The selection known as Tohoku No. 34 was named Norin 10, registered and released in 1935. The pedigree is shown graphically in Fig. 21-1. Records at Iwate show that in 1935 Norin 10 was 55 cm. tall, 13 cm. shorter than the control variety Norin 1. Dr. Gotoh has forwarded seed of Fultz-Daruma, Aka-Daruma (red) and Shiro-Daruma (white) for inclusion in the USDA World Collection. In the greenhouse at Beltsville, Maryland, the first of these was medium in height whereas the others were typical of our semidwarfs in plant height.

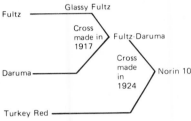

Fultz

Glassy Fultz

Cross made in 1917

Fultz-Daruma

Cross made in 1924

Norin 10

Daruma

Turkey Red

Fig. 21-1. Pedigree of Norin 10.

Fig. 21-2. Four distinct height classes in common wheat: triple dwarf, 40 cm. (left); Lemhi, 66-100 cm.; Gaines, 75 cm.; and double dwarf, 60 cm.

Norin 10 and similar Japanese wheats resemble ordinary wheat except for short, stiff straw and an ability to produce more tillers than is usual for varieties with stiff straw. They range in height from 60 to 80 cm. or about 1/2 to 2/3 that of ordinary varieties (Fig. 21-2).

The semidwarfs first attracted attention in the United States soon after one of us (S. C. Salmon), who was then Agricultural Advisor to the Occupation Army in Japan, brought back to the United States seed of Norin 10 and 15 other varieties of this type in 1946.

Norin 10 was seen near harvest time at the Morioka Branch Station in Northern Honshu. It had been seeded in rows approximately 50 cm. (20 in.) apart in accord with the Japanese practice and on land that had been heavily fertilized and irrigated. In spite of these very favorable conditions for vegetative growth, the plants were only about 60 cm. high and there was no tendency to lodge. Also, they had tillered so much and there were so many large heads, a second look was necessary to verify the fact that the seeding had been in wide-spaced rows instead of the common 15-25 cm. in the United States. Through the kind assistance of Japanese officials, seed of Norin 10 and 15 others was obtained, brought to the United States, grown in a detention nursery for a year to avoid the possible introduction of new disease or insect pests, and in subsequent years distributed to wheat breeders in various States.

Other semidwarfs have attracted attention. One is 'Seu Seun 27,' seed of which was imported from Korea by H. Florell to B. B. Bayles and grown at Lincoln, Nebraska, in 1949. Suwon 92, also from Korea, and numerous varieties from Italy have been observed. None of these semidwarfs has been useful in the United States as such; they have been a source of short, stiff straw, tillering capacity and, in the case of Suwon 92, powdery mildew resistance in crosses with other varieties.

Use of Norin and Other Semidwarfs

The first wheat breeder in North America to use the semidwarfs extensively was O. A. Vogel, U.S. Department of Agriculture Agronomist at the Washington Agricultural Experiment Station, Pullman, Wash. A series of crosses including Norin 10 X Brevor and Norin 10 X Baart were made by the State-Federal co-operating wheat research group at Pullman in 1949. Progeny from the Brevor cross was featured in later aspects of Vogel's program. The variety 'Gaines' was bred from these crosses and was released cooperatively by the Crops Research Division, ARS, USDA, and the Washington, Oregon, and Idaho Agricultural Experiment Stations in 1961. Another deriv-ative, 'Nugaines,' was distributed in 1965 by the same agencies. These varieties comprised about 1,012,500 ha (2,500,000 acres) of the Pacific Northwest wheat acreage in 1967 and 1968. Individual farmers have obtained yields exceeding 130 hl/ha (150 bu/acre) and one obtained 183 hl/ha (209 bu/acre) (12).

A soft red winter wheat called 'Blueboy' was developed by the North Carolina Experimental Station and released in 1966. It was derived from the cross Norin 10 X Brevor 2x Anderson X Coker 55-9 made in South Carolina. In 1967, it surpassed the 100 bu/acre mark in North Carolina and was the first variety ever to do this on a farm scale east of the Continental Divide.

'Yorkstar' was bred from the cross Genesee 3 *3x Yorkwin 2x Norin 10 X Brevor. It is a short straw and white-grain winter type. It was developed at the Cornell University Agricultural Experiment Station and released in 1966.

'Maricopa' is a semidwarf white, spring wheat well adapted to fall seeding in Arizona where it was developed by the Agricultural Experiment Station and the Crops Research Division. It was released in 1961 and was bred from the cross Ramona 50 3x Ramona 44 2x Norin 10 X Brevor-14.

'Timwin' is a semidwarf, soft red winter wheat developed cooperatively by the Wisconsin Agricultural Experiment Station and the Crops Research Division from the cross Knox 3x Norin 10 X Brevor 2x H483a-3-5. It was released in 1967.

The most extensive use of Norin 10 genes outside Japan and the United States has been by N. E. Borlaug and associates in Mexico. An extensive breeding program was initiated in 1954 by crossing important Mexican varieties

with Norin 10 X Brevor, Norin 10 X Baart, and other descendants of Norin 10 from the Washington Station. Semidwarfs derived from these crosses were distributed to Mexican farm-ers in 1962 (The Farm Quarterly. Fall 1965. p. 62) Also, derivatives of crosses between Indiana varieties of Norin 33 were brought to Mexico from Purdue in 1957 by Ignacio Narvaesz and crossed with Mexican varieties (Rockefeller Report 1962-63).

An important characteristic bred into many of the Mexican semidwarfs is relative insensi-tivity to length of day which means they can be grown successfully in any latitude if satis-factory in other respects (The Farm Quarterly. Fall 1965. p. 67).

Semidwarfs, principally from Mexico, have been and are being grown in California and some 20 or more foreign countries in South America, Africa, the Mediterranean Basin and the India-Pakistan Subcontinent, principally through the initiative of the Rockefeller Foun-dation. The U.S. Department of Agriculture, the Agency for International Development of the U.S. Department of State, and the Ford Foun-dation have played important roles in providing seed and information regarding these semi-dwarfs. Results in Pakistan, India, and Turkey have been so promising that large quantities of seed of certain derivatives of Norin 10 crosses have been imported from Mexico for direct use by farmers pending the creation of varieties especially suited for their countries. The gov-ernment of Pakistan imported 350 tons of seed in 1965 and an additional 42,000 tons in 1967. The Government of India imported 250 tons in 1965-66 and obtained 18,000 tons of seed in May of 1966. Turkey obtained 60 tons of seed in 1966 and 22,000 tons in April of 1967. These shipments total 82,660 tons and together comprise the largest international shipment of seed for seed purposes of any major grain in history. (1966-67 Report of CIMMYT. Inter-national Maize and Wheat Improvement Center, Londres 40, Mexico 6, D.F., Mexico. 103 p. illus). Authorities in Pakistan and India have predicted that wheat production in their coun-tries will be doubled within five years through the use of semidwarfs combined with other improved practices including a more extensive use of commercial fertilizer.

Discussion

Dwarf and semidwarf wheats have been known for many years, certainly since Farrer (3) in 1891 observed dwarfs in certain progenies and in 1895 observed "grass clumps" in the F_2, and rarely F_1, generations of some crosses. These are often called a type of hybrid weakness (5). McMillan (6) investigated the phenomenon rather thoroughly and his basic hypothesis of three additive interacting genes was greatly extended by Hermsen (5). Percival (11) gave an account of the sphaerococcum type of short-straw wheats called 'Indian Dwarf' or 'shot,' because of their small, nearly round kernels. Morris and Sears (8) place shot wheat with *Triticum aestivum* L. em Thell. as a variety group. Morrison (9) gave a chronological list of reports on genetic dwarfs and concluded that most of them involve a 2-gene system of a dominant for dwarfism and an inhibitor resulting in F_2 ratios of 13-3. Pao et al. (10) postulated six genes in the inheritance of dwarfness. Allan and Vogel (1) found that at least 11 chromosomes influenced culm length expression in their Norin 10 crosses but they did not locate the two major genes believed to be carried by the Norin 10 parent. The genes for semidwarfism in Norin 10 are recessive. It is a familiar experience of most wheat breeders that a number of genes modify plant height and that transgressive segregation often occurs. Some varieties without known Japanese ancestry fall into the range of Norin 10 derivatives in culm length.

Whereas the three groupings of short-straw wheats overlap, (i.e., shot, grass clumps, and Norin 10) and the taller ones overlap the height range of standard varieties, no evolutionary connection has been established among them. Some dwarf types die and others mature seed; grass clumps occasionally reach 25 cm. and some may be over 35 cm. in height under conditions when normal plants grow 1 m. tall (5, 6). The sphaerococcum effect seen in shot wheat has been described as a pleiotropic effect of a single locus (8) to give the type and thereby can be set apart as altogether different from grass clumps or the Norin 10 type. Another short-culm type is 'Tom Thumb' (C.I. 13563), which has one or more dominant genes

for short culm (1966-67 Report, CIMMYT). At this time it is speculative whether a variant (or a mutant) of the grass clump dwarf type is the ancestor of the Japanese semidwarfs but this hypothesis is worthy of study. In fact, Hermsen (5) outlines the potential of certain types of dwarfs for use in wheat breeding programs.

As a corollary to these enquiries about the use of Japanese semidwarfs in America, several sources of evidence indicate that ancestry of the short, stiff-strawed wheats of Italy and the Balkan countries can be traced to Japan. Strampelli (13, 14) and Forlani (4) in Italy show several Japanese wheats in their pedigrees from 1911 onward from which early maturing, short-culm, non-lodging varieties were selected. Italian wheats have subsequently been bred with culm length of less than 40 cm (7). Borojevic and Mikic (2) of Yugoslavia reported transgressive segregation in their materials in which two Japanese sources were involved, one by way of Italy and the other by way of South Africa.

Genetic studies (R. E. Allan, personal communication) show that major genes for semidwarfness in Norin 10 derivatives are in part the same as those found in Suwon 92 and Seu Seun 27, Korean wheats. Hence, circumstantial evidence points to numerous benefits by various routes from this now-famous group of Japanese varieties.

Literature Cited

1. Allan, R. E., and O. A. Vogel. 1963. Monosomic analysis of culm length in wheat crosses involving semidwarf Norin 10-Brevor 14 and the Chinese Spring Series. Crop Sc. 3: 538-540.
2. Borojevic, S., and D. Mikic. 1965. The occurrence and characteristics of dwarf lines in wheat obtained by transgressive segregation. Arhiv Za Poljoprivredne Nauke (J. Sci. Agr. Res.) 18:3-15.
3. Farrer, W. 1898. The making and improvement of wheats for Australian conditions. Misc. Publ. 206, Dept. of Agr., Sydney, N.S.W., 57 p.
4. Forlani, Roberto, 1954. Il Freumento: Aspetti genetici e agronomici del miglioramento della cultura granaria. Monografie di Genetica Agraria. Tipografia del Libro, Pavia. 315 p. illus.
5. Hermsen, J. G. Th. 1967. Hybrid dwarfness in wheat. Euphytica 16:134-162.
6. McMillan, J. R. A. 1937. Investigations on the

occurrence and inheritance of the grass clump character in crosses between varieties of *Triticum vulgare* (Vill.). Bull. 104. Council Sc. and Ind. Res., Melbourne, Australia. 68 p.

7. Mairo, Bonvicini. 1954. Indirizzi della genetica agraria per la resistenza all'allettamento in *Triticum vulgare.* Caryologia, Vol. Suppl. Atti del IX Congresso Internazional di Genetica. p. 738-743.

8. Morris, R., and E. R. Sears. 1967. The cytogenetics of wheat and its relatives. Chap. 2. *In* Wheat and wheat improvement. ASA Monograph 13. Madison, Wis.

9. Morrison, J. W. 1957. Dwarfs, semi-lethals, and lethals in wheat. Euphytica 6:213-223.

10. Pao, W. K., C. H. Li, C. W. Chen, and H. W. Li. 1944. Inheritance of dwarfness in common wheat. Agron. J. 36: 417-428.

11. Percival, J. 1921. The wheat plant. A monograph. E. P. Dutton and Co. 463 p.

12. Reitz, L. P. 1967. World distribution and importance of wheat. Chap. 1. *In* Wheat and wheat improvement. ASA Monograph 13, Madison, Wis.

13. Strampelli, Nazareno. 1933. Early ripening wheats and the advance of Italian wheat cultivation. Tipografia Failli. Rome 26 p.

14. Strampelli, Nazareno. 1932. I miei lavori: origini e sviluppi—I grani della vittoria. p. 47-100. *In* Origini, sviluppi Lavori e risultati, Parte seconda. Illus. S. A. Stab. Arti Grafiche Alfieri & Lacrois, Milano.

22

NEW HORIZONS FOR AN ANCIENT CROP

Robert F. Chandler, Jr.

Introduction

Rice has been man's major food staple in tropical and subtropical Asia for thousands of years, its cultivation a continuing concern from age to age. Yet, taking place only today is some of the most significant research work ever done on the improvement of this ancient crop.

The purpose of this paper is to present a few high points of that breakthrough and to indicate some of the components deemed responsible for and perhaps even essential to such accomplishment.

Let us first review several of the more dramatic research achievements in tropical rice, then—in the case of the institution selected here because of the writer's close connection with its program—examine the background and approach that made these successes possible. Accordingly, in support of the main points of

Reprinted from the *XIth International Botanical Congress*, Seattle, Washington, All-Congress Symposium on World Food Supply, August 28, 1969, with the permission of the author.

this paper are cited the activities of the International Rice Research Institute, an organization established in the Philippines by the Ford and Rockefeller Foundations.

Varietal Improvement

In 1962, when the Institute started its research program, the average yield of rice in tropical Asia was about 1,500 kilograms per hectare, whereas Japan was producing over three times as much, with an average yield of about 5,000 kilograms per hectare.

In examining the differences between the rice of Japan (and other temperate zone countries where yields are high) and of the tropics, Institute scientists readily observed that the tropical rice plant characteristically is tall, has overly long, drooping leaves and, as a significant consequence of its structure, when fertilization and other modern cultural and management practices are applied, tends to lodge or fall over before harvest. Indeed, earlier research already had established a direct correlation between grain yield and the number of days before harvest that a rice plant lodges: the earlier the lodging, the lower the yield.

This knowledge led plant breeders at the Institute to seek to develop rice varieties that were short and stiff-strawed, with relatively narrow, upright leaves—plants that would resist lodging even when heavily fertilized and intensely managed.

As genetic sources of short stature, three varieties from Taiwan were used; namely, Dee-geo-woo-gen, I-geo-tze and Taichung (Native) One (a short, improved variety with Dee-geo-woo-gen as the short parent). These varieties were crossed with such tall vigorous, heavy-tillering and disease-resistant tropical varieties as Peta and Signadis from Indonesia, H-105 from Ceylon and BPI-76 from the Philippines.

During 1962, Institute plant breeders made 38 crosses, 11 of them involving either Dee-geo-woo-gen or I-geo-tze as one of the parents. Other crosses were largely between tall tropical indica varieties and the so-called Ponlai varieties from Taiwan, which are actually japonica varieties developed from the tropics and sub-tropics.

Several crosses made in 1962 were successful; others were soon discarded because of such inferior characteristics as disease susceptibility and poor plant type. The eighth cross, however, proved exceptional. From it came a variety, now named IR8, which has opened new vistas of rice yields and has given added hope for food sufficiency to the vast number of Asians dependent upon rice for their staple food.

This dramatically different rice plant was obtained by crossing Peta, a tall Indonesian variety that has disease resistance, heavy-tillering ability, seedling vigor and seed dormancy, with Dee-geo-woo-gen, a short-statured Chinese variety. Of about 10,000 plants grown in each of the second and third generations, only a few hundred were retained for further testing. In the fourth generation, plant No. 3 in row 288 was among those selected out and was appropriately designated IR8-288-3.

After further purification in the fifth and sixth generations, IR8-288-3 was planted in its first trial. That was in March 1965, less than 3 years from the date the cross was made. In July, during the rainy season, it surprisingly produced a computed yield of about 6,000 kilograms per hectare. In the cloudy monsoon season in the humid tropics when plant performance is seriously limited by insufficient solar radiation, a yield of that magnitude is excellent. Later, we found that in the dry season and under high-level management, this strain could produce over 9,000 kg/ha and

would regularly yield between 6,000 and 8,000 kilograms.

Moreover, we soon learned that high yield records for the new variety were being established not only in the Philippines and Southeast Asia generally, but in Latin America and Africa as well. Widespread adoption of this promising new rice plant seemed assured. In recognition of its general acceptance, the International Rice Research Institute, in November 1966, announced that henceforth IR8-288-3 would be known simply as IR8.

Figure 22-1 is a photograph of IR8 just before harvest. Evident are its excellent plant type with short upright leaves, sturdy stems and high tillering capacity. This particular stand, during the dry season in the Philippines, produced a grain yield of 8,500 kg/ha.

Figure 22-2 shows the nitrogen responsiveness of IR8, as compared with that of its tall parent Peta, in the dry and wet seasons. As is evident, on the naturally rather fertile soil of the area, fertilizer applications for the traditional tropical varieties are not economically profitable, whereas the new short, upright-leaved varieties are remarkably responsive to the input.

Emphatically, IR8 is far from being an ideal variety. Because of its high yield potential and nitrogen responsiveness, it nevertheless represents the first major stride in tropical rice improvement. The IR8 plant type is judged to be here to stay; the variety itself, however, will soon be replaced by others having better grain appearance and milling qualities, superior cooking and eating characteristics, increased resistance to insect and disease attack, and such other beneficial characteristics as leaf toughness and slower senescence. In fact, one or more improved varieties are expected to be named by the Institute in late 1969.

Solar Radiation and Yield

The graphs in Fig 22-2 demonstrate that yields in the dry season are much greater than those in the wet season. Before the Institute started its program, little notice had been taken of the possible causes for this difference.

Fig. 22-1. Stand of the IR8 variety of rice ready for harvest. This actual field yielded 8,500 kg/ha of grain during the dry season. Note the upright leaves, the short sturdy stems, and the high tillering capacity.

Fig. 22-2. The nitrogen responsiveness of two contrasting plant types in the sunny, dry season and in the cloudy monsoon season in the Philippines. IR8 is a short, stiff-strawed variety, while Peta is a typical tall variety. (Data are 3-year averages for experiments conducted in 1966, 1967, and 1968. Please note that the scales for the two seasons are different.)

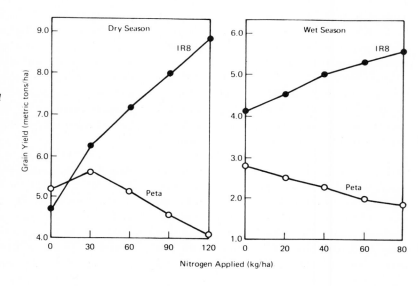

Starting in 1963, our plant physiologists, agronomists and agricultural engineers turned their attention to this problem and soon concluded that grain yield (other factors not being limiting, of course) is closely correlated with the solar radiation received by the rice crop, especially during the last 45 days the crop is in the field, i.e., the period from panicle initiation to harvest.

Of the many studies (all published in Institute annual reports) conducted to prove this point, a vivid example is presented in Fig. 22-3, which shows the average grain yields for monthly plantings of IR8 and IR5 and the cumulative solar energy for the last 45 days before each of the monthly harvests from May through August. In Los Baños, the Philippines, where these studies were made, May is the last month of the dry season and August the height of the rainy season.

The establishment of this relationship between solar radiation and grain yield, while naturally of interest from the viewpoint of understanding the response of the rice plant to its environment is, in addition, of considerable practical use in predicting the value of irrigation during the dry sunny season in monsoon Asia and, of course, in any season in arid regions whenever and wherever temperatures are favorable for rice production.

Chemical Weed Control

The Institute has been working on herbicides for the past seven years and has learned much about the effectiveness of various chemicals and about their toxicity to the rice plant in relation to the time and amount of application. It was not until 1968, however, that sufficient progress had been made to reveal the fact that a single application of a combination of two herbicides, applied in granular form just after transplanting, could provide almost 100 per cent control of weeds for the duration of the crop.

Several combinations of chemicals have proved to be highly effective, and undoubtedly new and superior ones will continually appear on the market. Furthermore, chemicals now available but not yet adopted for rice may prove quite useful after more research on their concentration and timing.

Simply as an example of current results in this area of research, yield data from a cooperative experiment conducted during the 1968 wet season at the Visayas Rice Experimental Station of the Bureau of Plant Industry at Iloilo, the Philippines, are presented in Table 1.

None of the treatments shown in Table 1 gave a yield significantly different from that of

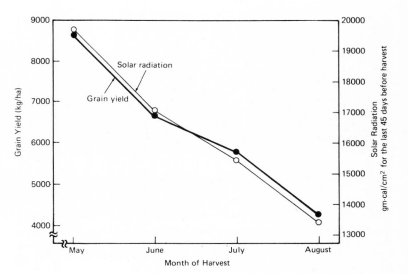

Fig. 22-3. Average grain yield for IR8 and IR5 rice varieties and the solar radiation for the last 45 days before each of the four monthly harvests from May through August. (120 kg/ha of nitrogen was applied. Phosphorus and potassium were in abundant supply.)

Table 1. Effect of granular herbicides on the grain yield of rice when only one application was made 3 days after transplanting.

Treatment	Rate of application kg/ha of active ingredients	Grain yield kg/ha
Trifluralin plus MCPA	0.7 + 0.4	6,831
Nitrofen plus 2, 4-D	2.0 + 0.5	6,778
EPTC plus MCPA	1.75 + 0.7	6,725
TCE-Styrene + 2,4-D	1.00 + 0.5	6,575
Two handweedings	25 and 40 days after transplanting	6,924
Untreated	———	4,328

the others, but each produced significantly more grain than did the unweeded control plot.

Figure 22-4 is a photograph of a treated and an untreated plot side by side. In this particular case the chemical used was EPTC plus MCPA, which is marketed in the Philippines as EPTAM-M. Before the experiment was started, barnyard grass seed *(Echinochloa crusgalli)* was broadcast over the entire area to assure the presence of a weed crop. Obviously, the profitability of using a chemical depends not only upon the cost of the herbicide itself, but upon the intensity of the weed population. In the Philippines, if handweeding is done with hired help, the cost is about ₱80.00 per hectare. Some of the chemical herbicides can be bought and applied for ₱70.00 per hectare.

Varietal Resistance to Insect Attack

Since the first years of its establishment, the Institute's entomology department has been screening the world rice collection of more than

Fig. 22-4. Photograph of adjacent plots of the IR8 variety of rice, the one on the right receiving one application of EPTAM-M and the one on the left receiving no chemical and no handweeding. The tall grassy weeds are mostly Echinochloa crus-galli, *commonly known as barnyard grass.*

8,000 varieties for resistance to attack by the major insect pests of rice that are present in the Philippines *viz.*, rice stem borers, green leafhoppers and brown planthoppers.

Although considerable progress is being made in breeding for resistance to the several species of rice stem borers, the most striking results have come from the project to develop varieties with resistance to leafhoppers and planthoppers, and only that work will be described here.

To identify the more promising varieties in the world collection, the entire set was given a preliminary screening in the field at the rate of about 2,000 varieties each growing season. After this rough field screening, approximately 1,000 varieties were chosen for more careful tests. This was done by placing 20-day-old seedlings in screened cages (measuring 12 feet x 12 feet and extending to the roof of the greenhouse) in which were trapped large numbers of the green leafhopper *(Nephotettix impicticeps)* or the brown planthopper *(Nilaparvata lugens)*. The population level of the insects was such as to kill within 10 days at least 90 per cent of the seedlings of a susceptible variety. Those varieties that survived this test were then further evaluated by being caged separately with a given number of insects.

In these tests, two varieties consistently showed exceptionally high resistance. Pankhari 203 from India and Mudgo, also from India, proved to be highly resistant to the green leafhopper and to the brown planthopper, respectively.

Crosses between Pankhari 203 (which also has considerable resistance to the tungro virus disease, of which the green leafhopper is a vector) and several of the better modern varieties with good plant type have already been made. Similar crosses have been made with Mudgo in an effort to develop acceptable varieties with high resistance to the brown planthopper, a pest which not only can cause direct damage to the rice plant but also is a vector of the grassy stunt virus disease.

The photograph in Fig. 22-5 shows a row of the IR8 variety largely destroyed by the brown planthopper and surrounded by planting of the F_2 generation of a cross between IR8 and Mudgo. By actual count approximately 75 per cent of the F_2 progeny were resistant and 25 per cent were susceptible, indicating that resistance is controlled by a single dominant gene. Although that point obviously needs verification by further studies, these results are notable examples of what entomologists and plant breeders can do in developing varieties with high insect resistance. Furthermore, preliminary studies strongly indicate the possibility of developing single varieties with resistance to both green leafhoppers and brown planthoppers—to the extent, indeed, that the use of chemical insecticides for the control of those two insects may no longer be necessary.

Developing Rice with a Higher Protein Content

Essentially half the world's population depends upon rice for its staple food. Asians, in particular, even get much of their protein from rice, simply because rice constitutes such a large proportion of their diet. The average protein content of polished rice is considered to be about 7.5 per cent. The variety IR8 under good management contains about 8 per cent. Although environmental factors strongly influence the protein content of rice grain, the Institute has recently obtained evidence that protein content is heritable and thus can be passed on to succeeding generations.

In arriving at this finding, first all 8,000 entries in the Institutes world collection of rice varieties were analyzed for protein content (Total N x 6.95) and those varieties with a content of more than 13.5 per cent in the unpolished (brown) rice grain were planted again; then those still showing the same high level were planted once more. A few of these final selections were used as parents and crossed with IR8. The protein content of the F_3 and F_4 grain of several of these crosses, separated into low and high protein groups, is shown in Table 2.

Preliminary though they are, these results represent concrete evidence that protein content is a heritable character and indicate that increasing the protein content of the rice grain by an actual 2 per cent is a distinct probability.

Fig. 22-5. *Many of the plants in the center row are dead from planthopper burn due to the high susceptibility of IR8 to brown planthopper (*Nilaparvata lugens*) attack. When IR8 was crossed with Mudgo, a highly resistant variety, approximately three-quarters of the plants in the F_2 generation were healthy, indicating that resistance may be controlled by a single dominant gene.*

Table 2. **The protein content of the F_3 and F_4 seed (brown rice) of the progeny of crosses between IR8 and six high-protein varieties.**

	Protein content of grain (per cent of grain with 12 per cent moisture content)			
	Selections containing 11% or more protein in the F_3 seed		Selections with less than 10% protein in the F_3 seed	
Cross	*F_3 seed*	*F_4 seed*	*F_3 seed*	*F_4 seed*
IR8 x Rikuto Norin 20	12.1	12.1	7.8	8.6
IR8 x Omirt 39	11.7	11.6	7.5	8.7
IR8 x Santo	11.2	12.4	7.1	8.7
IR8 x Chow Sung	11.6	11.9	7.1	9.0
IR8 x Crythrocerus Korn	11.3	11.7	8.1	9.0
IR8 x Cho-jye-bichal	13.1	11.9	7.4	9.2
Average	11.8	11.9	7.5	8.8

Some nutritionists feel that, considering the natural high lysine content of rice, this difference will be sufficient to protect growing children, in affected populations, from the ravages of "kwashiorkor," the disease caused by protein deficiency.

Varietal Differences in the Rate of Photosynthesis

As implied earlier in this paper, it appears that there is little room for additional improvement in plant type, *per se*. If, however, marked differences among varieties in the rate of photosynthesis per unit leaf area were to exist, a further advance in yield potential might be possible.

Studying this possibility Institute plant physiologists, during 1968, measured the photosynthetic rate of 50 different varieties and found considerable variation. The results for 12 of the varieties tested, including the lowest and highest values, are presented in Table 3.

The range of nearly 100 per cent in photosynthetic rates among varieties indicates the importance of this factor in rice breeding. An early though unwitting practical application may already have taken place in India, for among the hundreds of selections under trial in the All-India Coordinated Rice Improvement Project, the two high-yielding selections re-

leased as varieties in 1968 had T-141 as one of the parents. As can be seen in Table 3, this variety had the highest photosynthetic efficiency of any of those tried—a fact, however, that was unknown in India when the crosses were made or when the varieties were selected.

Developing a Simple but Efficient Thresher for Rice

In the tropics the threshing of rice is usually accomplished manually, by pounding it over wooden slats or across a log or stone. In some countries, however, the most common method of separating the grain from the straw is by the tramping of work animals driven in circles over the harvested rice.

In most areas, regardless of the threshing method, the rice is cut in the field with hand sickles and is brought to a central platform for threshing. The need, therefore, without changing the current harvesting practices, is for a low-cost power-operated thresher to meet the requirements of small farmers and custom operators in the tropical countries. For year-round use in high rainfall area, such a machine should handle wet grain as well as dry.

Institute engineers have developed a thresher utilizing a Japanese-style wire loop threshing drum that has been widely used and has proved highly effective as a threshing device with low power requirements. The new design, however,

Table 3. The rate of carbon fixation by photosynthesis of isolated leaves of 12 rice varieties, exposed to a light intensity of 60 K lux.

Variety and country of origin		Photosynthetic rate (mg of CO_2 fixed per 100 cm of leaf area per hour)
Hoyoku	Japan	34.5
Tainan 3	Taiwan	35.3
Wagwag	Philippines	42.1
H-4	Ceylon	44.9
ADT 27	India	47.0
IR8	Philippines (IRRI)	47.0
Leuang Yai 36	Thailand	47.2
Suwedee	Nigeria	51.1
Basmati	India	52.7
Dee-geo-woo-gen	Taiwan	53.0
BJ 1	India	55.6
Lab Mue Nhang III	Thailand	57.8
T-141	India	62.1

departs considerably from existing practices for conveying, separating and cleaning the harvested materials.

A 6-foot-long, hollow threshing drum is mounted within a sheet-metal trough. Rubber flaps mounted spirally on the drum sweep the trough bottom to deliver the threshed materials to the rear-end mounted rotary screen separator. An axially mounted fan blows an air stream through the hollow threshing drum and the rotary screen separator. The air stream blows the light straw, leaves and chaff to the rear and out of the machine, leaving the heavier grain to fall through the rotating screen. The tumbling action results in a more aggressive sieve separation under wet conditions. A photograph of this machine in use is shown in Fig. 22-6. Note that four men simultaneously can feed bundles of harvested rice for continuous

threshing. The machine can be powered either by an independent 4-hp air-cooled engine or by the small tractor engine used for towing the thresher. Other than the engine there is little to wear out on the thresher, the entire drum being supported on two lubricated bearings.

The machine is now manufactured commercially in the Philippines and is being tried in several countries. Early tests in the Philippines have been quite satisfactory and have shown that four men can thresh more than 250 kg of grain an hour.

Discussion of Important Ingredients for Rapid Progress in Agricultural Research

The projects described above are but examples of achievements, in a seven-year period,

Fig. 22-6. The new drum-type threshing machine in use.

of a not large group of scientists working together to study and improve the rice plant and its management, with the objective constantly before them of increasing the yield potential of tropical rice.

People have asked what the principal factors are that have enabled such rapid progress to be made in so short a time. Naturally, the factors are many. Their identification and relative importance probably would vary according to the viewpoint of the individual making the judgment. As Director of the Institute, the writer has the limitation of close involvement with the project. Despite the unavoidable biases of such an association, however, enumerated below are what he considers to be some of the more important factors contributing to the quite rapid progress that has been made. Hopefully, such principles would be applicable to any similar research institution. They are as follows:

1. Adequate financial support and the freedom to make local decisions within the framework of the total allocation of funds

Certainly at the outset when the Institute was being planned, built and staffed, no single factor seemed more important for progress than that the two foundations provided the necessary funds in accordance with the cost estimates submitted, then allowed the principal officers of the Institute to make day-to-day decisions regarding construction of buildings and selection of staff. The whole project went ahead in an atmosphere of mutual confidence between the foundations and the Institute, the latter, of course, making every effort to keep the foundations well informed of plans and progress as the buildings were going up and as prospective staff members were being interviewed. Communication and accord were facilitated by the fact that before construction started the final plans had been submitted for and had received foundation approval.

Such advance approval, indeed, is a condition of any major commitment by the foundations. The Institute's well designed and well equipped buildings create the impression among some visitors that the Ford and Rockefeller Foundations give the organization whatever it wants simply for the asking. This is decidedly not the case. Each Institute request must be justified, first in words and later in deeds. In fact, no major grant—from any source—has yet been made to the Institute without our initially presenting an acceptable plan for use of the funds. Furthermore, since such proposals must be implemented successfully before additional grants can be expected it is upon the solid achievements of its scientists that the year-to-year support for the Institute unquestionably depends.

2. The existence of clearly defined objectives for the Institute

Although every research organization has a reason for being, unless its objects are well specified and continuously kept in mind the efforts of its scientists may be dissipated by lack of coordination and of a common direction.

The International Rice Research Institute has had from the start the primary objective of increasing the yield potential of tropical rice through the study and improvement of the plant itself and of its management. In order to make rapid and steady progress toward this goal, Institute scientists have had to keep in mind, no matter what their discipline, that all research ultimately should contribute toward increased grain yield and improved quality. This meant that in the majority of the research programs, field studies played a continuous and integral part and grain yield was the final criterion of success. An examination of the Institute's annual reports would reveal that grain yields are recorded in many field experiments whether conducted by entomologists or agronomists, by rice breeders or agricultural engineers.

In spite of the generally practical objectives of the Institute's program, we seek also to understand the rice plant as a biological organism and to that end are conducting some rather fundamental studies. Most of these investigations, however, have been prompted by the lack of an adequate explanation for the results of the more applied research.

The writer by no means suggests that because the International Rice Research Institute confines itself largely to problem-oriented research, all research institutions should do the same. Undeniably there is an essential place for basic research conducted for the sole purpose of increasing man's understanding of the nature of the universe. This is the area in which the Nobel prizes and other distinguished awards are rightful recognition for those who have made historic contributions toward expanding human knowledge, through efforts requiring such an exceptional degree of intelligence, imagination and ingenuity as to constitute genius.

Contributing to the work of those rare minds, however, are cadres of eminently qualified scientists and research personnel whose efforts are more urgently needed in less theoretical fields. In the world's developing regions, therefore, scientific brainpower and manpower, except for the talent uniquely adapted to basic studies, would be better directed toward the solution of the population's crucial practical problems.

3. The selection of highly qualified staff

This ingredient for success in a research program is so obvious as really to need no expansion here. Nevertheless, in the writer's view, the selection of staff for foreign assignments involves certain special considerations worthy of mention.

In an international institute, and indeed in any other research effort in a foreign country, it seems best generally to have young but well-trained scientists and to engage them on a career basis of no predetermined duration—or, in Institute terms, "for as long as there is mutual satisfaction."

Young men, carefully selected, have abundant energy and unflagging enthusiasm. They have yet to establish a reputation among their colleagues and, in the right environment combining challenge with security, they are intent on doing so. In the process they elevate equally the reputation of the organization with which they are associated.

If, on the other hand, a staff member brought into a foreign environment knows from the start that his assignment is, say, for only two years, he cannot be expected to make significant contributions. One year is spent in adjusting to the new conditions; and before the second year is half over his thoughts stray increasingly to the furtherance of his career elsewhere.

In contrast, The Rockefeller Foundation's agricultural programs of the past twenty years owe their successes in large part to a personnel policy much as is recommended above—hiring bright young men with no definite time limit to their appointments.

Another consideration, the writer feels, is that a research organization of international scope—regardless of the source of its funds—should engage scientists from several countries, rather than from just one. The Institute, for instance, long has had a corps of senior scientists from seven nations, *viz.*, Ceylon, China, India, Japan, the Philippines, Thailand and the United States. In our experience, when the scientific staff is provided with an environment for productive research, one nationality is as effective as another. The significant differences are in the qualifications, capacity and performance of the scientists as individuals, quite apart from their national origins. This is not to imply that ethnic and cultural distinctions are suppressed nor indeed that they do not enrich and enliven the general environment.

In fact, many of us feel that one of the finest things about the International Rice Research Institute has been the *international* character of its scientific staff, which has demonstrated that a seemingly disparate group of scientists and their families—varying in race, color, creed and national origin—can work and live together in an exceedingly congenial, co-operative and productive manner.

The scientist selected for a post in a foreign country needs certain attributes to enable him to work there effectively and happily. Beyond the essentials of high basic intelligence and good training, he should have drive and enthusiasm for his work. Such qualities obviously are needed in any important position anywhere, yet for successful work abroad they often do not suffice. Away from his own country, a scientist needs in addition to be as free as possible of pride and prejudice with respect to his own culture, nationality and race, so that simply as a member of the human species he can work for mankind's betterment.

Professionally, the international scientist needs similar flexibility. He should be as adaptable as possible with regard to his own research program and be ready to attack problems he never before encountered.

The International Rice Research Institute takes some pride in the fact that on the whole its staff meets well the standards described above.

4. Provision of adequate facilities for the scientists

To perform at his best, a scientist must be provided with the full facilities of his discipline. He must have access to a good library. He must have adequate funds for supplies, travel and equipment. Naturally, his needs must be justified and should not represent an extravagant and inconsiderate use of available advantages. On the other hand, particularly in Asia one often sees research organizations with an oversupply of men and an undersupply of financial support. Since the scarcity of funds generally cannot be remedied, it seems more logical to hire fewer people and to provide them with adequate support.

The International Rice Research Institute had 17 senior scientists (those in charge of research programs) in 1963; today six years later, it has exactly the same number. This is not a highly significant point perhaps, yet it does reflect in part a desire not to sacrifice quality for quantity (as evidenced by the fact that although the top scientists have remained the same in number, the total employees and the annual budget have increased).

5. Sound and flexible administrative policies

This is a difficult topic for the writer, as Director of the International Rice Research Institute, to take up. Realizing the likelihood that both right and wrong administrative policies are being followed, he still must feel that the former prevail, for naturally one believes in what one practices.

Eric Ashby, Master of Clare College in Cambridge, England, describes the administrator as "a man who precipitates out decisions on behalf of units of society." Primarily, the administrator is a decision maker, but he acts in consultation with others, for his decisions must be predominantly wise ones that can stand the test of time.

To the writer, the good administrator leads and attempts to inspire his staff; he seldom if ever commands them. The principal day-to-day task of the research administrator is to facilitate and coordinate the program. He "facilitates" by representing the institution to the public (whose interest and understanding are an asset to any endeavor) and particularly to those organizations from which financial support is derived or sought. He attempts to find the best scientists available and then to provide them with an environment conducive to high achievement. This means not only decent working and living conditions, but an atmosphere of concerned and often excited interest in what each scientist is attempting to accomplish.

An important part of the building of individual morale and of *esprit de corps* consists in granting the scientists the widest reasonable degree of freedom. Some decisions belong to chief administration, but many others rightly belong to the scientist. In the words of Dr. George Warren, the renowned agricultural economist at Cornell University some 30 years ago, "The way to get a job done is to hire a truly able person and then turn him loose." Overmuch supervision smothers initiative; responsibility and freedom nourish it. If the administrator, then, is to facilitate the work of the organization effectively, he must be prepared to delegate cheerfully such responsibilities and decisions as can fittingly be handled by others.

A complex research program requires coordination. This function, too, devolves upon the administrative officers, who are in a position to see the program as a whole, to note any overlapping and any gaps. In its effort to consolidate the research work the Institute has found its annual program review of immense benefit. During the conference, which lasts five days, each senior scientist is given an opportunity to present his accomplishments of the past year and to describe his plans for the next. He solicits the comments of his colleagues and engages in uninhibited discussion with fellow scientists and administrators alike. This has turned out to be one of the most important annual events at the Institute, a source of guidance and satisfaction to all who participate.

The Impact of the Program

Obviously, the evidence of the worth of a problem-oriented agricultural research program lies in the changes it produces on farms. It is still too early to make a valid analysis of the impact of the work of the International Rice Research Institute on the rice-growing world. Nevertheless, enough evidence is at hand to show that sweeping changes are taking place and that the impetus given to the ancient crop of rice is here to stay. Not again need the rice grower return to the tall, lodging-susceptible varieties. He is now assured that with reasonably good water control and a source of fertilizers and insecticides he consistently can at least double the yields he obtained before the advent of this new era in tropical rice growing.

The new varieties and methods of management are being adopted by farmers in many countries of the tropics and subtropics. It is estimated that in 1968 India planted more than six million acres to the new rice varieties and that Pakistan had more than a million acres of IR8. Burma reportedly devoted over 600,000 acres to IR8 and IR5 last year (1968), and the Philippines planted a total of more than 750,000 acres to the new varieties. (Figure 22-7 is a photograph of the fields of two Filipino farmers, one who changed to growing IR8 and one who continued to grow a traditional, tall tropical variety.)

Many other countries of Southeast Asia, such as Malaysia, Indonesia, Laos, Cambodia and Thailand, are making rapid progress in replacing the traditional varieties with the modern. Cuba, Mexico and certain South American countries are fast following suit.

More importantly, many of these countries have put new vigor and effort into their old rice breeding programs and are developing varieties of their own that combine the favorable characteristics of the local varieties with the short stature and fertilizer-responsive qualities of the new ones.

Only recently has man adequately demonstrated the true food-production potential of the tropics. Now, through actual experimentation, we know that the annual food-grain producing capacity of the tropics, where temperatures favorable to crop production prevail throughout the year, exceeds 20 metric tons per hectare. Such yields can be obtained with three crops of rice a year, for example, or by growing rice in the rainy season and such crops as sorghum, millet and maize in the drier months. The nutritive value of the crops can be increased by substituting for part of the cereal grains such high-protein crops as soybeans and other grain legumes, or—as a source of vitamin A—sweet potatoes.

So great has been the impact of the new rice varieties and management practices that agricultural economists and other experts are now concerned about the problems emerging from the application of the new technology. Questions of drying, storage, shipping, marketing and, of course, price now come to the fore. Though none of these problems is insurmountable, all need to be recognized and studied so that remedies can quickly be found.

Regardless of the problems presented by the new high rice yields, efforts to increase production still further must continue. The greater, more critical problem of population control which, despite world attention and intention, remains largely unsolved to date, makes imperative the provision of more and more food. It is therefore the responsibility of those concerned with food-crop production to continue unabated the efforts to develop higher-yielding varieties, to increase the nutritive value of the edible parts of the plants, and to devise more efficient methods of crop management. Only thus—until we learn to control our own numbers—will it be possible to feed the additional millions of human beings being added to the world population each year.

Fig. 22-7. Photograph taken at the boundary of the land of two rice farmers in the Philippines. The field on the left is planted to IR8 and the one on the right to Intan, a traditional tall lodging-susceptible variety. The yield of the IR8 was about twice that of the Intan.

Summary

This paper reviews several of the more significant research achievements of the International Rice Research Institute and examines some of the conditions which made those advances possible.

The examples of research accomplishments cited are as follows:

1. The development of a new short-statured, stiff-strawed, fertilizer-responsive tropical rice plant with a yield potential twice that of the traditional varieties.
2. Proof of the close correlation between solar energy and rice grain yield.
3. Disclosure of the fact that weeds in transplanted rice fields can be controlled effectively by a single application of one of several mixtures of herbicides in granular form at costs competitive with those of hand-weeding.
4. Progress toward the development of rice varieties with such high resistance to green leafhoppers and brown planthoppers as to suggest that before many years chemicals no longer may be necessary for the control of those particular insects.
5. The finding that the protein content of the rice grain is a heritable character and that

there is a possibility of increasing the actual protein content of polished rice by 2 per cent.

6. Demonstration of the fact that rice varieties differ in the photosynthetic rate of their leaves by nearly 100 per cent, thus indicating the possibility of further increases in yield potential by introducing into the improved varieties the character for high photosynthetic efficiency.

7. The design of a simple, relatively inexpensive but efficient rice threshing machine.

A discussion of the ingredients for rapid progress in agricultural research programs stresses the need for a clearly defined purpose, a capable and dedicated staff, the necessary financial support, and the freedom, both intra— and extra—organizational, to pursue the desired objectives.

23

TURNING SUGAR INTO MEAT

T. R. Preston and G. Bernardo Hagelberg

FAO studies predict that food supplies in developing countries must quadruple by the year 2000 in order to overcome present hunger and malnutrition and furnish an adequate diet for a rapidly growing population. The urgency of the problem was highlighted by the poor world harvest of 1965-66, the effects of which were alleviated only at the expense of already dwindling reserves. According to B. R. Sen, FAO's director general, the present world food situation is more precarious than it has been since the period of acute shortage following the Second World War. Due to the reduction of reserves, the world now depends much more on current production and is thus at the mercy of vagaries of climate.

While much research has been directed towards the development of unconventional foods—cultivation of microorganisms on oil derivates, growing of algae and extraction of vegetable protein from green material—this is at best a long-term proposition. In the final analysis, the fundamental solution of the problem must rest with the exploitation of

Reprinted from the *New Scientist* 36: 31-33, 1967, with the permission of the publishers.

the agricultural potential of each and every country.

At this point it is opportune to consider what is meant by world hunger. Man's basic requirements are energy and protein. Animal protein is both more valuable nutritionally and more sought after by the consumer in comparison with that of vegetable origin. Countries with high standards of living consume from one-half to two-thirds of their protein in the form of meat, milk and eggs.

Per Caput Needs of Energy

FAO statistics show that developing countries in tropical and subtropical areas have met or soon may be expected to meet their per caput needs of energy. Existing deficiencies should be considered against the background of the sizeable exports of energy by these countries. For example, Latin America was in 1965 a net exporter of close to 9.2 million tons of sugar (excluding trade between the United States and its territories) and of 2.2 million tons of maize. Although the Far East (without Mainland China) was a large importer of cereals, four countries of the region—India, Indonesia, Philippines and Taiwan—exported 2.3 million tons of sugar.

As to protein, the situation is quite different. Even in those countries which have sufficient total protein, the proportion of animal protein is very much lower than that in the developed areas of the world. To cite an extreme case, India and Pakistan, with nearly one-fifth the world's population, in 1963/64 almost met their caloric requirements, but their per caput supplies of animal protein were only 10 and 15 per cent, respectively, of the US level.

It is legitimate to infer that at their present stage of development tropical countries find it easier to produce energy than protein. The question arises whether this potential for energy can be exploited to solve the scarcity of protein.

Pigs and poultry produce protein palatable to man starting from energy in the form of highly digestible carbohydrates and proteins unacceptable to man, such as fish meal, yeasts and oil seeds. Cattle, by virtue of their rumen microorganisms, can break down fibrous material and thus exist on low-grade forages not suitable for pigs and poultry. An even more valuable characteristic—especially where proteins of any sort are scarce—is their capacity to synthesize good-quality protein from cheap nitrogenous chemicals, such as urea. But for this they require that the major proportion of their diet should consist of readily available carbohydrates, such as starch or sugar.

Thus, in designing systems for producing animal protein, consideration must be given to the overall energetic efficiency of the process and the nature and availability of the raw materials. With respect to pigs and poultry, the best feed conversions have been obtained from cereals, such as maize, sorghum, barley and wheat. With cattle, it has also been found that although they can digest very fibrous feeds, the most efficient feed conversion for meat is obtained with the highest possible proportion of cereals in the ration. For milk production, efficiency is best with approximately two-thirds cereals and only one-third forage.

Theoretical Refinements

In developing tropical countries, however, such refinements are somewhat theoretical. Not only are yields of cereals generally low, but such as are grown must first satisfy the needs of the human population. On the other hand, cereals are not the sole source of readily digestible carbohydrates, and tropical countries do have both relatively high yields and large volumes of carbohydrates in the form of sugar and its by-products.

Certainly the potential of sugar as an energy source for animals has not so far been fully exploited. There has been little incentive for research and development along these lines primarily because of the apparently unfavourable price relation between sugar and animal products.

However, the economic situation has changed substantially in the past few years. As the accompanying trend lines show, the gap between meat and sugar export prices is steadily widening. Whereas in 1948 the relation of beef to sugar prices was little more than three to one, the predicted 1970 ratio will be 6.5 to 1 for all sugar exports (including preferential markets) and nine to one in the case of free world market prices. The significance of this development for animal production will depend upon the extent to which sugar in its various forms—juice, syrup, invert molasses or centrifuged—can serve as an alternative to cereals, and the efficiency with which it can be utilized.

The use of final or blackstrap molasses in animal feeds has been increasing in recent years, but unrestricted utilization has been hampered by the belief that more than 10 to 15 per cent of molasses in the diet would be detrimental because of its laxative effect. Granulated sugar has been employed in relatively small quantities and mainly to enhance palatability, rather than as a prime source of energy.

Now, however, there promise to be technical changes in the utilization of sugar to match the changing economics. The nutritional problems of employing sugar in animal feeds are turning out to be less formidable than was once thought and we can begin to evaluate sugar not just as a marginal supplement, but rather as a major source of energy for intensive animal production.

In France, D. Fromageot has successfully used up to 54 per cent of sucrose in broiler diets, achieving feed conversions comparable to those obtained with cereals. More recently, an important advance has been made in the feeding of final molasses to beef cattle (Preston,

Elias, Willis and Sutherland, 1967 *Rev. cubana Cienc. Agric.* Vol. 1, in press).

The essential features of this work are:

1. Final molasses contributed 73 per cent of the dry matter in the diet.
2. Urea provided 59 per cent of the total dietary nitrogen.
3. Daily gains averaged 0.78 kg.
4. Carcass yield was 56 to 57 per cent of live weight and, like feed conversion and meat quality, comparable to grain-fed cattle and much superior to that obtained with forage as the major ingredient of the diet.

These data relate to 48 unimproved commercial Zebu bulls starting at 244 kg live weight and fed over a period of 168 days to a slaughter weight of 370 kg. The average daily ration was 6.13 kg of molasses (containing 3 per cent urea) diluted with water to 14 per cent solids and offered *ad libitum*, 4.50 kg green maize and either 0.46 or 1.18 kg protein/mineral/vitamin supplement according to treatment. The molasses was diluted in order to avoid the risk of toxicity sometimes associated with a high consumption.

These results, which are now being tested on an even wider scale, are much superior to those obtained previously when molasses was fed undiluted and forage given *ad libitum*, i.e. up to 30 kg per day. For example, feed conversion has been improved for 40 Mcal metabolizable energy per kg of gain to 25, while on a carcass basis the increase in efficiency is even more marked.

The economics of this system can be expressed in the following terms: on the average, one kilogram of weight gain required about 8.3 kg of molasses, 5.5 kg of forage and 1 kg of protein supplement. The cost of these ingredients, conservatively calculated, represents 60-65 per cent of the value of the weight gain.

These data refer to final molasses. It is likely that similar results will be obtained with invert molasses and even cane juice, although the economics will clearly be different. In any event, the possibilities are sufficiently interesting to warrant further investigation.

The social and economic implications of this research could be far-reaching. The use of sugar in animal feeds, either centrifuged or better still as juice, syrup or molasses, could go a long way towards providing an adequate level of protein nutrition in those countries which are traditional cane producers. Moreover, increased domestic use of sugar will act as a support for the national sugar industries—an important consideration in certain Central and South American countries in which per caput sugar consumption is already high. The economic feasibility of feeding sugar to livestock in Europe and North America is also bound to alleviate the traditional conflict between cane and beet, thus opening up greater possibilities of exports by the developing tropical countries to those economically advanced (Fig. 23-1).

Fig. 23-1. The economics of using sugar in animal production. (Sources: FAO and the International Sugar Council.)

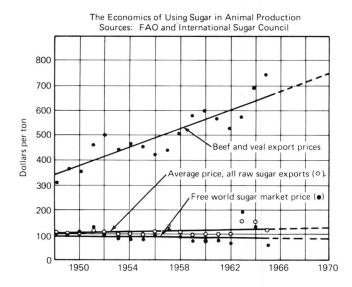

The Economics of Using Sugar in Animal Production
Sources: FAO and International Sugar Council

As has been pointed out, at the present time cane far surpasses cereals as a producer of energy in tropical countries. This is not necessarily a reflection of underdevelopment, but may be due to climatic factors as well. The average sugar cane yields in Hawaii and Peru are of the order of 100 tons per hectare per year, equivalent to around 20 tons of invert molasses. No country has yet produced an equivalent yield of readily available carbohydrate in the form of cereal grain. The maximum national averages for maize and barley are four to five t/ha in developed countries. Even in temperate climates, sugar outyields cereals, albeit in the form of beet instead of cane. Thus, advanced Western European countries produce on average

42 tons of beet, yielding about 6 tons of sugar per hectare.

Applying the best conversion rates and yields so far demonstrated, three cattle can be fattened from a starting weight of 90 kg to slaughter at 400 kg on one hectare yielding four to five tons of maize. By comparison, one hectare can produce 20 tons of invert molasses to fatten nine cattle. (This assumes proportionately the same degree of supplementation with forage, protein, minerals and vitamins as for a cereal diet.) Even taking average yields, of the order of two tons of maize and 10 tons of invert molasses per hectare, the respective fattening capacities would be 1.3 animals on maize, compared with 4.5 animals on sugar cane.

24

PLANTS AS SOURCES OF UNCONVENTIONAL PROTEIN FOODS

N. W. Pirie

Estimates of world population are reasonably trustworthy and all forecasts agree that it will increase. Obviously, there is disagreement about the rate and extent of the increase, but few would be so bold as to predict anything less than a doubling in the next 30 to 40 years.

Estimates of the amount of food eaten are much less trustworthy. Even in a country such as Britain, with a reasonably effective service for collecting statistics, there is a 20% discrepancy between the amount of food apparently going into households and the amount that is actually eaten. The latter figure is derived (Greaves & Hollingsworth, 1966) from calculations of the amount of work done by the population and the rate at which it is putting

Reprinted from the *XIth International Botanical Congress,* Seattle, Washington, All-Congress Symposium on World Food Supply, August 28, 1969, with the permission of the author.

on weight. Discrepancies of this sort have embarrassed surveyors for many years because it is difficult to account for them completely by invoking waste, the feeding of pets, etc. They suggest that we should be wary of accepting at their face value figures coming from countries with less trustworthy statistical services. We do not therefore know how much most of the world's inhabitants eat. Estimates, or guesses, that they eat too little are confirmed by the impression that any observant traveller forms, and that the more reliable statistics for such things as height, weight and death-rate between the ages of 1 and 5, suggest. It seems that we have a food problem now and that it is likely to get worse.

There is a substantial unanimity that shortage of protein is the main dietary deficiency (UN, 1968). This had seemed obvious to many of us 30 years ago but the idea was resisted by those who argued that it was wasteful to increase the amount of protein eaten, if so little food was being eaten that the protein had simply to be used as an energy source. Coping with hunger should take precedence over balancing the diet. This argument paid insufficient attention to the fact that only administrative action was needed to produce as much starch, and other energy sources, as the world needed. In putting it thus I do not wish to minimize the magnitude of the administrative task; it would entail a committment by one half of the world to supply cereals free to the other half for an indefinite period and to do this not only at the expense of existing surpluses but also by a change in agricultural policy so that more cereals would be grown. All that is formidable; nevertheless, it does not involve new research. That is why it can be called administrative. Protein cannot be supplied in the same way. The surpluses are trivial, the well-fed countries are already importing protein concentrates, and we do not know how to produce enough of the conventional protein concentrates in wet tropical regions.

The amount of protein that will be needed depends not only on the unknown number of people to be fed but also on the disputed amount of protein that each needs. Some experts put requirements as low as 40 g a day. I think it is unrealistic to put the average requirement much lower than 100 g a day (Pirie, 1969a). If the experts should happen to be right, cereals should suffice; a predominantly cereal diet supplying 11 M joules (2700 kcal) a day would supply more than 40 g of protein. There would not be trouble unless the main energy source were cassava, banana, or some other protein-deficient food. If 100 g of protein a day is the desirable intake, and if any significant amount of sugar or fat is being eaten, cereals will not supply the necessary protein. Some form of protein concentrate is needed.

Animal products are the most commonly eaten protein concentrates in the well-fed countries. The supply is partly maintained by massive imports of fodder in the form of fishmeal and plant protein concentrates; often from countries such as Peru, Nigeria and even India that suffer from a protein shortage. This arrangement is traditional and, like many traditional arrangements, absurd. Those protein concentrates that cannot be used as human food in the countries where they are produced should at least be used as fodder there. That would leave the well-fed countries searching for new protein sources. It is very unlikely, though one cannot be dogmatic on the subject, that any mere rearrangement of the existing supplies of animal fodder could produce enough protein to meet the world's present needs: it is certain that this would not meet the impending needs. That is why new sources of protein are needed—preferably in forms that can be made locally by simple techniques and that can be used directly as human food.

A world that takes its protein supplies seriously, and tries to distribute them equitably, will use each region in such a way that it is producing optimally, and will use each type of organism in such a way that its peculiar merits or capacities are fully exploited. Such a policy necessitates the abandonment of many preconceptions: a preconception cannot be abandoned until it has been recognized. The most obstructive preconception is that we, in the humid temperate zone, have discovered the ideal techniques of agriculture and that the world's food problems will be solved by adopting these techniques more intensively and introducing them into increasingly improbable climatic zones. In the wake of European engineering skill and knowledge, European domestic animals have spread all over the world. Engineering techniques have universal applicability. There is more specificity about animals.

Ruminant animals are such inefficient converters of forage into food that potential arable land is not used efficiently when it produces fodder in a protein deficient region. Ruminants should be restricted to land that is not arable, or is deliberately retained in a semi-wild state for the sake of the amenities. But that does not necessarily imply that it should be left to grow whatever climax vegetation its climate and the unrestrained grazing and browsing of animals produces.

In a country like Britain, "unspoiled" or "natural" scenery is almost entirely manmade. It can be remade. To a lesser extent the same applies elsewhere. Experiment is needed to find what vegetative cover would be most productive in each region classified as non-arable, what intensity of grazing, browsing, and reseeding will maintain it in that state, and what animal, or mixture of animals, will make optimal use of it. Systematic work along these lines has hardly begun but is being discussed in the International Biological Program (IBP).

Fermentation of forage is sometimes suggested as alternative to feeding it to a ruminant. In certain circumstances this course might be preferable, but it is most unlikely that it would be in all circumstances. An animal collects its own forage and can do this on terrain where mechanical harvesting would be difficult if not impossible. Furthermore, it is a self-reproducing fermentation tank with automatic temperature and pH control, and it will be many years before most people will reject animal products in favour of the microbial harvest from a fermenter.

The problems raised by non-ruminant animals are somewhat different. They can be maintained to a limited extent only on "natural" vegetation and its invertebrate animal associates. In protein-deficient regions, the only sensible role for pigs and chickens is to consume wastes, by-products and other material that is not too fibrous and that people cannot eat, or prefer not to eat. What is often miscalled "efficient" production—in which one pound of dry fodder can produce 2 pounds of wet chicken, including guts, head, and other inedible parts—is achieved by using as fodder much material that could have been used as human food, or that is grown on land that could have grown human food. This is a pleasant luxury in affluent countries but misguided in protein-deficient ones.

The conclusion is therefore that in this hypothetical, rationally run world, the meat and milk products of ruminants may remain abundant because there is much non-arable land and all systems of agriculture (including sophisticated methods of handling its products) will produce fibrous by-products on which ruminants can be maintained with the help of N supplements such as urea. But the use of non-ruminants is likely to decline because of its inherent inefficiency.

Before leaving animals, a word may be said about the aquatic environment. Without a radical change in technique, the sea could produce 2 or 3 times as much fish as we now get out of it. That would be useful but would not solve the problem—especially if the present-day trend continues and an increasing proportion of what is caught is used as fodder in the well-fed countries. Obviously, fish depend ultimately on plants but most of the fish we eat are the wasteful end-product of a three or four membered food chain. There would be greater production if some method could be devised for encouraging marine herbivorous fish such as the mullet. It may be easier to exploit instead, static converters such as shell fish. A great deal of money is now spent on the control of weeds in fresh water; very little is spent on finding uses for them (Little, 1968). This is perverse. The encouragement of herbivorous fish such as carp and *Tilapia* gets a little attention. The encouragements of herbivorous edible mammals e.g. the dugong and manatee, gets much less but these potentially useful sources of meat have at least achieved the status of mention by the IBP.

Animal conversion is a traditional, and widely relished, means for turning plants into protein concentrates. Several types of plant produce protein concentrates that can be eaten directly without conversion or intensive sophistication. Outstanding among these are the peas and beans on which such countries as India and Mexico rely heavily. Unfortunately, they suffer from ill-merited neglect by plant breeders. Attention should be directed not only to yield, protein content and resistance to disease, but also to the quality of the protein, freedom from toxic components and ease of cooking. There is, for example, still some uncertainty about the nature of lathyrism and the circumstances in which dangerous levels of nitriles and oxalyl amino acids accumulate.

The rejection of a new variety of bean in Mexico was interpreted as mere conservative prejudice until it was discovered that, though admirable at sea level, it would not cook at high altitudes. These points are now gaining recognition. The Protein Advisory Group, reporting to the U.N. Economic and Social Council in 1968, remarked "In agricultural planning attention should be given to the production of protein as well as total yield, since an increase in yield may often result in a decrease in protein content per unit of production. Attention should also be given to the quality of the protein in the crops produced."

Hitherto it has been assumed that the legumes were the most promising source of protein-rich seeds that could be eaten without extensive pretreatment. The newly awakened interest in protein concentrates has produced some encouraging results in other plant families. There are sorghums with 3% to 4% of N in the grain and a wheat with 3.8% (Johnson *et al.*, 1968). A recently discovered variety of oat contains 4.8% (Murphy *et al.*, 1969). It is too early to tell how well these varieties will stand up to commercial production, what effect diseases will have on them and how restricted their climatic requirements are. It would be unwise therefore to assume, as some officials have done, that there is now no need for further work on protein concentrates because a community that used one of the new varieties as its main energy source would get sufficient protein. Even in cereal-growing regions there is no certainty about this, and there are other regions.

People eat food—not nutrients. They therefore judge foods by taste and appearance and not by analytical composition. This method works fairly well with the meats and fish; one can see how much bone, fat and inedible material there is and the mixture of proteins in meat has such a similar composition throughout the animal kingdom that animals may, to a first approximation, be regarded as nutritionally equivalent. The position is very different with plant products. Without access to a laboratory, not even the protein content can be determined; a very well-equipped laboratory is needed to measure the amino acid distribution in that protein.

Animal-feeding experiments showed half a century ago that the legume seed proteins differed and it has therefore become economically important to measure systematically the amino acid composition of those seeds that are used as fodder. Brewing requirements and bread-making led to an interest in the protein content of barley and wheat. These interests stimulated systematic amino acid analyses of these two cereals; the interest spread to the others very recently. Everyone interested in the nutritional value of foodstuffs should be constantly reminded that the strains of maize with enhanced lysine, which have recently been greeted with such justified enthusiasm, were isolated 35 years ago and lay on the shelf

unanalyzed. It is now conventional, perhaps because automatic amino acid analysers make the process easy, to determine the amino acid composition of every species and variety of seed that could be used as a food. That is excellent—but it is not enough. The vegetables are neglected.

Most people eat fruits and vegetables for their flavour and appearance though they may justify their diet by referring to them as sources of minerals and vitamins. Enthusiasm for minerals and vitamins is not, however, strong enough to make people logical about this. For a fraction of the cost they could get, as inorganic chemicals, all the minerals they get from plant food. The great variation in the average ascorbic acid content of different varieties of apple does not seem significantly to affect their sales. With this degree of unawareness of what one is actually buying and eating in fruits and vegetables, it is perhaps not surprising that little attention is paid to their protein content and scarcely any to the amino acid composition of that protein. This is the justification for including vegetables among the unconventional protein foods.

The parts of broccoli, cauliflower and brussels sprouts that are actually eaten contain 5 to 5.5% of N; that is also the amount present in several tropical vegetables, e.g. the immature flowers of *Saccharum edule* and the leaves of *Moringa oleifera* (drumstick) and the *Amaranths*. Much, probably most, of this N is protein-N, but there are few systematic analyses bearing on this very important point. These leaves and immature flowers are metabolically active, it is therefore reasonable to assume that they contain an immense array of enzymes, each with a different amino acid composition, so that the protein in all of them will be similar in composition to the preparations of leaf protein that have been made in bulk.

Table 1 compares the range of these amino acid analyses with FAO "reference protein." If the supposition is justified that the protein in many vegetables comes in these ranges also, they are obviously valuable protein supplements. But the supposition needs experimental confirmation: that is to say, horticultural research should be nudged gently into the 20th

Table 1. Essential amino acids in bulk preparations of leaf protein and in FAO reference protein.

Amino acid	Ranges %	FAO
Isoleucine	4.7-5.2	4.2
Leucine	8.8-10.0	4.8
Lysine	5.6-7.1	4.2
Methionine	1.7-2.8	2.2
Phenylalanine	5.5-6.4	2.8
Threonine	4.8-5.7	2.8
Tryptophan	1.7-2.3	1.4
Tyrosine	3.9-4.6	2.8
Valine	6.0-7.2	4.2

century. Even in such authoritative works as *Horticulture in Britain, I, Vegetables* (1967) it is usually impossible to find out just what was being weighed when yields were assessed. Presumably it was the weight "as harvested" rather than "as presented on the table." The one value may be twice the other. And composition is not recorded at all. This is an important issue because the cultivation of some vegetables produces, as a concentrate, more edible protein than any other conventional method of using land. In Britain, brussels sprouts can yield 30 tons (as marketed) per hectare which probably means a little more than a ton of edible protein per hectare. Suitably chosen vegetables should give twice that yield in the tropics. The point is gaining recognition: the acreage of vegetables, other than roots, more than doubled in Trinidad between 1965 and 1967. It is to be hoped that the extra space is used for protein-rich crops and not just for okra and tomatoes.

It may be argued that, with a comparable amount of agricultural effort the yield of protein can be as great as this when the conventional varieties of wheat or potatoes are grown. We can harvest 3.5 tons of wheat per acre at Rothamsted and that is a ton of protein per hectare; more than 20 tons of potatoes per acre would be needed for this protein yield—that is a large crop, but attainable with skill. These crops do not meet the need for protein concentrates. That need can however be met if part of the starch in wheat, potatoes and similar crops is removed either by extraction with water, as in the Chinese method of making *mien chin* that Beccari used when he characterized gluten in 1728, or by "air classification"

and sifting. These methods are already used for making protein-enriched, or starch-depleted, bread. Rice seems to be particularly well adapted to treatments such as this because the outer layer of the grain can be ground off as a protein-enriched flour. Even if the starch-rich fraction is discarded, these processes are not as wasteful of protein as the more conventional process of using an animal to concentrate protein. A pig or chicken gives back only a quarter of the protein it eats. The discarded starch need not be wasted; if fortified with urea, it can be used as ruminant fodder.

Soya and groundnut are accepted foods in several parts of the world and there are traditional methods for removing the trypsin inhibitor and part of the oil from soya by fermentation and extraction. Although Sun Yat-sen, in 1921, advocated the use of soya as a food in regions other than the Far East (Aziz, 1965) the suggestion was acted on slowly. At that time soya was regarded as a forage crop in the U.S.A. and was almost unknown in other parts of the industrialized world. During the past 10 to 15 years there has been increasing recognition that the residue left when oil is expressed from cottonseed, soya or groundnut, which used to be regarded as cattle fodder or fertilizer, is a potential human food. This recognition has been accompanied by an economic change—soya residue is now as financially important as the oil, and production of most of the oilseeds has increased. Production of groundnuts has more than doubled in 10 years.

Recent production figures and an estimate of what they mean in terms of protein are given in Table 2. The total 21 M tons, is about a fifth of the amount needed to give everyone in the world 100 g of protein a day, and it is more than the FAO estimate of the existing world

Table 2. World production of oilseeds 1964-1965.

	Million tons	
Soya	32 =	12.0 protein
Cottonseed	19	3.8
Groundnut	14	3.6
Sunflower	6	0.9
Copra	3.3	0.7
Sesame	1.6	0.3
Total		21.3

protein deficit. The residue, as normally prepared, cannot be used as food because it is apt
to be contaminated with dirt and to have been
damaged by overheating during the oil-extrac-
tion. Sometimes, especially with groundnuts,
there is contamination from toxic products
produced by funguses such as *Aspergillus
flavus*. It may be that alarm about this fungus
contamination has become directed too specifically. Any moist foodstuff can become contaminated if stored in unsuitable conditions.
The full potential of the oilseed residues as
human foods will not be realized until they are
harvested, stored and processed with the same
meticulous care that we have come to accept as
a routine with the cereals.

The trypsin inhibitors in soya are now
usually destroyed by heating, and soya flour is
increasingly used to fortify foods and to give
them a desirable texture. It is a pity that the
carbohydrate that accompanies the protein is,
for the most part, indigestible by people. There
is scope for research here both on methods
of enzymic predigestion to get metabolisable
sugars and on a search for soya varieties containing a more useful carbohydrate. In India,
groundnut meal is proving an acceptable addition to many foods and in Guatemala cottonseed is used as the main protein component of
Incaparina. Incaparina is produced commercially in several Latin American countries.
Dimino (1969) describes the continuing success
of the Quaker Oats Company in making and
marketing it in Colombia.

Most varieties of cotton give seed that
contains gossypol, which is both unattractive
and makes the lysine in the protein unavailable.
There are strains of cotton that contain little or
no gossypol but they are said to be specially
subject to insect attack. Gossypol can be
removed by solvent extraction and in other
ways. The need for this treatment, before
cottonseed residue can be used as food, coupled
with the need to remove bitter substances and
trypsin inhibitors from soya and the fear that it
may be necessary to remove fungal toxins from
groundnuts, makes one wonder whether more
complex methods of processing might be advantageous. The simple methods depend on the
concept that, when an oilseed contains little

fibre, and when the carbohydrate in it is either
useful or harmless, it can be used as a protein
concentrate if it is harvested cleanly, separated
from the shell and testa, freed from excessive
components such as oil and from deleterious
ones such as gossypol. That is to say the
product eaten is made by stripping unwanted
material away. The alternative concept is to
separate the protein from the other substances
by methods which are essentially the same as
those used to make textile fibres in the late 30s;
this extraction was discontinued when wholly
synthetic fibres were produced (Trail, 1945). If
the protein is to be used in the medical
treatment of extreme malnutrition, perhaps by
injection, a purified and uniform isolate has
obvious advantages. But if it is to be eaten as a
regular part of the diet of the community, the
advantages of isolation have to be demonstrated
rather than assumed. Present experience suggests that protein isolated from an oilseed
would cost five times as much as the same
amount of unextracted oilseed protein but
given the minimal treatment needed to make it
safe and palatable. There is no general rule:
each protein source and each use raises different issues.

When a protein source is fibrous there is
little room for argument. The protein has to be
extracted or the quantity eaten will necessarily
be limited by the limited capacity of the human
gut to handle fibre. This is the position with
leafy vegetables. Very few communities now
eat them to the extent that would be desirable
and, as already pointed out, they are one of the
more productive ways of using land. But few
people could cope with a quantity that would
supply more than 3 g of protein a day. It is,
however, easy to extract protein from leaves by
the method outlined in Table 3 (Pirie, 1942;
1952; 1966; 1969b). Machinery suitable for
processing about a ton (fresh weight) of crop
per hour has been gradually improved at Rothamsted. . . .

The advantages of growing a crop to make
leaf protein, rather than using the land in a
more conventional way, are that leaves flourish
in the wet tropics where the worst malnutrition
exists and where many seed crops are difficult
to grow, and that the yield is unprecedently

Table 3. Outline of the method by which leaf protein is extracted.

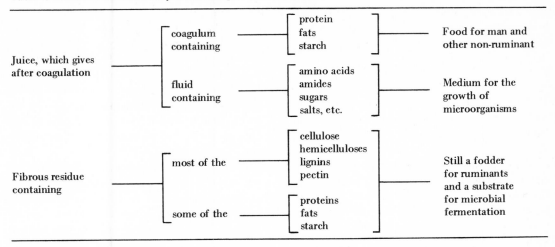

great. The results of one experiment are set out in Table 4. As well as getting two tons of extracted protein from a hectare within the year, nearly one ton of protein remains unextracted in the fibre and can be used as ruminant fodder. The liquor could be used as a culture medium for microorganisms and so yield a further supply of protein. In Mysore, with no winter cessation of growth, the yield is three tons of extracted protein per hectare.

Table 4. Extracted protein yields in kilos/hectare/year.

Winter wheat sown 20/10/67, cut 1/5/68: 819; *regrowth cut 18/6/68: 284 followed by either* *Mustard or fodder*		*Fodder radish*	
1st crop cut 1/8/68:	426	12/8/68:	460
2nd crop cut 20/9/68:	490	15/10/68:	461
Total yield:	2019		2024

So far we have separated protein in bulk from conventional agricultural crops only, but more than 100 species of leaf have given satisfactory results on a laboratory scale. Ideally, leaf protein would be made from leaves that are the by-product of some other operation. There is, for example, more extractable protein in the leaves, stems and pods of a pea crop than in the peas, and we have extracted protein from sugar beet at the rate of 830 kg per hectare. Protein has been extracted in India

from the leaves of cotton and it could probably be extracted from jute and ramie. Some other possibilities are summarized in Table 5.

Table 5. Sources of leaf for protein production.

Crops grown specially because the protein yield per acre-year is exceptionally great
By-product leaves, e.g., cotton, jute, sugar beet, sweet potato and vegetable discards
Leaves that are not now harvested but that could be, e.g., floating or palustrine plants
Inadequately or incompletely used crops, e.g., green manures and cover crops
Crops from land too briefly moist for normal farming, e.g., shores of seasonal lakes and rivers

I have discussed the potentialities of tree leaves elsewhere (Pirie, 1968). The mixture of weeds growing on unused land is not a probable source. If the land is of such character that mechanical harvesting is feasible, it could be ploughed, fertilized, and sown with a desirable crop. Water weeds are different. Usually, each area is dominated by a single species and collection, with a barge-mounted extraction unit, would be simple. It is a pity that so much effort is put into attempts to control water weeds with herbicides and so little into attempts to use them.

To facilitate quantitative work on species that might at first be difficult to grow in bulk, and for experiments on the optimal seeding rate, fertilizer treatment and time of harvest with crops that seem promising, we have made a laboratory-scale extraction unit that simulates the action of the large unit closely (Davys, Pirie & Street, 1969; Davys & Pirie, 1969). These laboratory-scale extraction units have already been sent to, or been made in, Biafra, Canada, Ceylon, Eire, India, New Zealand, Nigeria and Sweden. Most of these were made under our supervision and paid for by committees of the I.B.P.

Table 2 shows that coconuts could be an important source of protein. This protein, like that in leaves, can be eaten only sparingly because of the amount of fibre with which it is accompanied. As normally prepared, the protein in the residue after oil expulsion is seriously damaged (Butterworth & Fox, 1963) because of the combined effects of the archaic process of making copra and the brutal treatment it gets during pressing. When carefully made it has good nutritional value (Snyderman, Boyer & Holt, 1961; Rao *et al.*, 1967) and progress is being made in devising methods for separating it from the fibre mechanically, by acid extraction (Chelliah & Baptist, 1969) and by fermentation (Ramamurti & Johar, 1963; Chandrasekaran & King, 1967).

There are several other unused or underused sources of plant protein; only two need be mentioned as examples. Guar *(Sesbania aculeata)* is extensively grown in countries such as Pakistan because the seed pods contain a gum that is outstanding as a means of stabilizing oil-drilling mud. The Wheat Research Unit of the Australian CSIRO finds that the protein in the by-product seed meal is nutritionally valuable and that 8% of it can be added to bread without damaging the texture. Although there is very little protein in that part of a sugar cane crop that is crushed in the factory, the tonnage handled is so large that many thousands of tons of protein are present in the "filter mud"—the heat coagulum from the juice. It contains too much wax to be used directly as a food or fodder but both the protein and the wax would probably be valuable if they were separated.

When leaf protein begins to be taken seriously as a food, many species that are not now thought of as crop-plants will come into use.

But they are likely to be angiosperms similar to those with which farmers are familiar. Some years ago the illusion was widespread that algae such as *Chlorella* were more productive than higher plants and that agriculture was likely to be replaced by the cultivation of algae in tanks. This illusion arose because the conditions being compared were not comparable: pampered algae on the one hand and conventional crops exposed to the vicissitudes of normal agriculture on the other.

In short-term experiments at the time of year when growth is most rapid (these are conditions comparable to those in which large yields are claimed for the algae) corn cockle *(Agrostemma githago)* accumulates dry matter at the rate of 0.62 tons per hectare per day in Britain (Blackman, 1962) and bulrush millet *(Pennisetum typhoides)* in Northern Australia at the rate of 0.54 tons (Begg, 1965). The latter crop was using the visible component of sunlight with 9.5% efficiency. In the neighbourhood of Turin, in August, maize achieves 8.2% efficiency (Gibbon, Luppi & Mattei, 1968). These values are as great as those claimed for algae.

Algae do however have an important role in the treatment of sewage coming from residential communities where it is not contaminated by toxic industrial effluents. Bacteria destroy the organic matter in the sewage and produce CO_2 on which algae thrive and make the O_2 that the bacteria need. The mixed mass of bacterial residues and algae can be used as fodder and the water is left ready for reuse. This system works well in California (Oswald & Golueke, 1969) and has the great merit that the algae grow under control in tanks whence they can be recovered, whereas when sewage is discharged into a river, after a little treatment in a sewage works, it promotes uncontrolled algal growth in many regions and fouls the river.

All the novel protein sources that have been mentioned have been amply tested for safety and nutritional value by experiments on animals. There have been fewer human trials but they are equally convincing. Early results were reviewed at a symposium in 1960 (Washington, 1961) and progress has been reviewed from time to time at other symposia, e.g. in Mysore in 1967 and Stockholm in 1968 (not yet published). The conclusion is that these proteins are valuable though not as good as the proteins in milk and egg, which are exceptional because they are the end product of a vast period of selection for the feeding of young animals. The forms in which the seed proteins are available are surveyed by Orr & Adair (1967).

Much less work has been done on the production and use of leaf protein than on any of the others, but interest in it is increasing. When the N intake was 500 mg per kg body weight per day, infants retained as much N on a diet containing equal amounts of leaf protein and milk as on one containing milk alone (Waterlow, 1962) and, in a six month trial, children grew more on a ragi diet supplemented with 10 g leaf protein per day than on diets supplemented with sesame meal or with lysine (Doraiswamy, Singh & Daniel, 1969).

Any novel protein, whether it is wheat gluten, yeast, leaf protein, an oilseed residue, or a fish flour, raises significant but surmountable problems in presentation. The product can be masked by putting it into sausages or pies where its presence will not be noticed: in some quarters the immediate reaction to almost any desired innovation seems to be "Let's shove it in the bread." Neither approach is wise when the daily use of 5 to 10 g of the product per head is envisaged as a permanent feature of the dietary scene. Ultimately the novelty will have to be knowingly used and an effort to gain acceptance for it might as well be made at the start. The rules are simple. The innovator must be patient, must manifestly eat the product, must resist attempts to use it on underprivileged groups or it will acquire a stigma, and must discourage publicity until the supply is adequate. These points are universal.

Each product also raises its own specific difficulties. Leaf protein can, by solvent extraction, easily be made as a pale brown powder but we prefer to use it as a green cake because that is the form in which it would most easily be made in the regions where it is needed. In countries with a predominantly vegetarian diet, such as New Guinea, Nigeria and South India,

the colour is not objectionable and even in Harpenden it is, with experience, accepted. Coconut protein would probably be readily accepted; people like the flavour and it will probably be nearly white. Foods based on fermented soya, or soya partly freed from flavour and antitryptic factors by various traditional methods, are already extensively eaten in South-east Asia. These methods would repay sophisticated research for they may prove preferable to the processes, mainly dependent on heating, now used in the West. I have discussed the technique of presentation more fully elsewhere (Pirie, 1969c).

Many of the opinions expressed, and the lines of research advocated, in this paper are unorthodox. This does not necessarily mean that they are unsound, for novelty is usually damned at first; equally, the unpopularity of an idea cannot be taken as evidence for its soundness. Ibsen's contention that "minorities are always right" cannot be correct, for there are conflicting minority views on most subjects. They cannot all be right. By inversion we get a much more nearly tenable contention— majorities are always wrong. They may not be totally wrong, but they are wrong in detail or there would be no progress. The majority tends to be conservative and to think, or assume, that orthodox methods will solve current problems if a little more effort is put into their use. It is conceivable, though unlikely, that this is so, but it would be prudent to heed minority opinion, at least to the extent of getting the necessary research done.

Well-informed people will find nothing new in the proposals made in this paper—most of them have been with us for a generation. That is why there is now cause for hope. Gradually people who heard these ideas when they were students are coming into influential positions in the national and international bodies that are concerned with our food supplies. The ideas no longer arouse the automatic antagonism that really novel ideas are apt to excite in senior officials. Intellectual acceptance may have been won for the idea that radically new methods may ultimately be needed; a great deal of work remains to be done before this is translated into practical action.

References

Aziz, U. A. (1965). Poverty, proteins and disguised starvation. *Kajian Ekonomi Malaysia, 2,* 7.

Begg, J. E. (1965). **High photosynthetic efficiency in a** low-latitude environment. *Nature, Lond. 205,* 1025.

Blackman, G. E. (1962). The limit of plant productivity. *Ann. Rep. of the East Malling Res. Sta. for 1961,* p. 39.

Butterworth, M. H. & Fox, H. C. (1963). The effects of heat treatment on the nutritive value of coconut meal, and the prediction of nutritive value by chemical methods. *Brit. J. Nutr. 17,* 445.

Chandrasekaran, A. & King, K. W. (1967). Enzymic modification of the extractability of protein from coconuts *(Cocos nucifera). J. Agric. Fd. Chem. 15,* 305.

Chelliah, J. & Baptist, N. G. (1969). Extraction of protein from expeller- and solvent-extracted coconut meal by dilute acid, alkali and salt solutions. *J. Sci. Fd. Agric. 20* 49.

Davys, M. N. G. & Pirie, N. W. (1969). A laboratory-scale pulper for leafy plant material. *Biotech. Bioengng* (in the press).

Davys, M. N. G., Pirie, N. W. & Street, G. (1969). A laboratory-scale press for extracting juice from leaf pulp. *Biotech, Bioengng* (in the press).

Dimino, A. J. (1968). Factors in industrial participation. In *Single-Cell-Protein,* p. 444. Ed. by Mateles, R. I. & Tannenbaum, S. R. Massachusetts: London: The M.I.T. Press.

Doraiswamy, T. R., Singh, N. & Daniel, V. A. (1969). Effect of lysine or leaf protein supplementation of ragi *(Eleusine coracana)* diets on growth and nitrogen retention in children. *Brit. J. Nutr.* (in the press).

Gibbon, D. P., Luppi, G. & Mattei, F. (1968). The agronomic potential of an environment and its measurement. *Ricerca Scientifica, 38,* 579.

Greaves, J. P. & Hollingsworth, D. F. (1966). Trends in food consumption in the United Kingdom. *World Review of Nutrition and Dietetics, 6,* 34.

Horticulture in Britain. I. Vegetables. (1967) HMSO London.

Johnson, V. A., Schmidt, J. W. & Mattern, P. J. (1968). Cereal breeding for better protein impact. *Econ. Bot. 22,* 16.

Little, E. C. S. (1968). Handbook of utilization of aquatic plants. F.A.O. Rome PL:CP/20.

Murphy, H. C., Sadanaga, K., Zillinsky, F. J., Terrell, E. E. & Smith R. T. (1968). *Avena magna:* an important new tetraploid species of oats. *Science, 159,* 103.

Orr, E. & Adair, D. (1967). The production of protein foods and concentrates from oilseeds. Report G 31 of the Tropical Products Institute, London.

Oswald, W. J. & Golueke, C. G. (1968). Large-scale production of algae. In *Single-Cell Protein,* p. 271. Ed. by Mateles, R. I. & Tannenbaum, S. R. Massachusetts: London: The M.I.T. Press.

Pirie, N. W. (1942). Direct use of leaf protein in human nutrition. *Chemy & Ind. 61,* 45.

Pirie, N. W. (1952). Large scale production of edible protein from fresh leaves. *Ann. Rep. Rothamsted Exp. Sta.* p. 173.

Pirie, N. W. (1966). Leaf protein as a human food. *Science, 152,* 1701.

Pirie, N. W. (1968). Food from forests. *New Scientist, 40,* 420.

Pirie, N. W. (1969 a). Complementary ways of meeting the world's protein needs. *Proc. Nutr. Soc.* (in the press).

Pirie, N. W. (1969 b). The production and use of leaf protein. *Proc. Nutr. Soc, 28,* 85.

Pirie, N. W. (1969 c). *Food Resources: Conventional and Novel.* Penguin Books: London.

Ramamurti, J. & Johar, D. S. (1963). Enzymatic digestion of fibre in coconut cake. *Nature, Lond. 198,* 481.

Rao, G. R., Ramanatham, G., Indira, K., Rao, U. S. B., Chandrasekhara, M. R., Carpenter, J. J. & Bhatia, D. S. (1967). Nutritive value of coconut protein concentrates obtained by wet processing. *Indian J. Experimental Biology, 5,* 114.

Snyderman, S. E., Boyer, A. & Holt, Jr., L. E. (1961). Evaluation of protein foods in premature infants. In *Progress in Meeting Protein Needs of Infants and Preschool Children.* p. 331. Publ. 843, National Academy of Sciences—National Research Council: Washington D.C.

Trail, D. (1945). Vegetable proteins and synthetic fibres. *Chemy. & Ind.* p. 58.

United Nations (1968). International action to avert the impending protein crisis. New York.

Washington (1961). Meeting protein needs of infants and children. Publ. 843 National Academy of Sciences—National Research Council.

Waterlow, J. C. (1962). The absorption and retention of nitrogen from leaf protein by infants recovering from malnutrition. *Brit. J. Nutr. 16,* 531.

25

FAMINE OR SANITY?

Graham Chedd

The most dispiriting thing about the human race is its refusal to consider the precipice around the corner while it is picking its way myopically over the pebbles at its feet. It knows, of course, that the precipice is there; men like Paul Ehrlich have repeatedly hammered home (as he did again at the Institute of Biology symposium in London a few weeks ago) the inevitability of the plunge into unprecedented disaster unless—and even if—drastic action on population control and new efforts to feed the world's hungry are undertaken immediately. Yet our political parties spend their holidays in Brighton discussing the postures to strike in order to win the election next year or the year after, while the churches appear to be more concerned with their own survival than with the future of the race. Next month, a mile or two from the Vatican, delegates from some 117 nations will sit down to give their governments' verdicts on a dramatic attempt to smash this apathy. Inevitably, there will be bickering and quibbling and posturing. But it seems equally certain that the document they will be debating will be accepted more or less in its entirety.

The document is a plan; or rather, a Plan—probably the most ambitious and almost certainly the most presumptuous Plan ever devised. It sets out to provide a clearly defined set of difficult (but feasible) and realistic (but optimistic) targets for the agricultural sector of the world's economy between now and 1985. Its full title is the Indicative World Plan for Agricultural Development—though until FAO's 117 member nations debate it at the biannual conference between 8 and 27 November, the Plan is, strictly speaking, merely provisional.

The Indicative World Plan (IWP) has had a

Reprinted from the *New Scientist* 44: 178-82, 1969, with the permission of the publishers.

curious gestation. Conceived in 1963, the original idea was to produce a survey of the world food situation in relation to population and overall development, and a plan of action to counter the widening food gap. But it soon became apparent that to look at the food problem alone ignored the enormous economic and social implications of agricultural development. Accordingly, the scope of the Plan was broadened into an analysis of the major issues that are likely to be facing world agriculture in the 1970s and early 1980s, together with recommendations regarding the most important directions in which efforts will need to be made—not only to feed people, but to contribute also to their economic and social well-being.

As the Plan became more ambitious, something of a crisis of confidence took place even among its progenitors, the FAO. Many sceptics thought that the Plan was over-reaching itself. This scepticism is easy enough to understand, when the difficulties involved in formulating such a plan are considered. First there was the massive problem of simply collecting statistics for the chosen base year, 1962—statistics such as the cattle population or the area under maize or the egg production, which in many cases just did not exist and had to be prised out of the nations concerned, often with no real guarantee as to their accuracy. Then assessments had to be made of demands in a world where not only is population rising, but where social and economic conditions are changing too and affecting the things people want to be able to buy.

Probably most difficult of all, projections had finally to be drawn of the production potentials of the various regions and individual nations. This task involved the review and assessment of national plans for the development of resources, an examination of the new possibilities created by scientific research and technology, and a study of the main physical, institutional and economic constraints upon the potential for agricultural production. Complicating these predictions were the perturbations to the system that the Plan itself hopes to introduce. And there still remained the unpredictable—the disastrous failure of a harvest, or the outbreak of a new plant disease or the achievement of a totally unforeseen scientific or technological breakthrough. The people at FAO and elsewhere who thought the whole Plan to be pie-in-the-sky had a pretty solid case. But as the formulation of the Plan progressed, the crisis of confidence eased. Despite all these provisos, the general feeling at FAO headquarters now is that what many people were regarding as a rather embarrassing ugly duckling has mysteriously mutated into a swan.

The Challenge of 1985

For the purposes of the IWP, the countries of the world were divided under three headings: Zone A, developed market economies (for example, the USA and the European countries); Zone B, centrally planned economies (a euphemism for nations in the Communist bloc); and Zone C, "developing" countries. The Plan is largely concerned with Zone C nations, in the economies of which agriculture has an overwhelming role. In the base year, 1962 for instance, the agricultural sector contributed around 30 per cent of a typical Zone C country's GNP, provided over 40 per cent of total exports and supported directly over 70 per cent of the population. (In African countries south of the Sahara this last figure reaches an average of 82 per cent.)

Unfortunately, as the IWP points out, the weight of agriculture in the developing nations has not been matched by its performance. Over the decade 1955-65, the gross value of agricultural production in Zone C countries rose at 2.8 per cent per annum, as against a population rise of 2.6 per cent. The result was a *per capita* rise in food production of only 0.4 per cent. (The annual growth in developed countries, largely as a result of slower population increase, was 1.5 per cent.)

The IWP has set, in what it calls its "macro-model," what it considers to be feasible, if optimistic, growth rates for the GNPs of Zone C countries. These work out to be between 4.9 and 5.9 per cent from 1962 to 1985, depending on the region (compared with 3.8 to 4.8 per cent if past trends are continued). If the

agricultural sector is to fulfil its allotted role in this growth, and not to act as a brake on overall development, agricultural production has to increase from its 1962 figure of 2.8 per cent per annum to between 3.2 and 3.8 per cent. At first sight, this might seem a small enough increment; but in Asia and Africa in particular it would require a very considerable improvement over past performances—more so because in the five years from 1962 to 1967 growth rates in this region failed to increase significantly. Already leeway must be made up.

The Indicative World Plan identifies five objectives of key importance if these growth rates are to be achieved. They are as follows:

1. Securing staple food supplies with populations typically growing at 2.5 to 3 per cent a year. Here a faster rate of growth in cereal production is the single most important factor.
2. Providing the type of food that rising incomes and an increasingly urbanized population demands, and which present-day dietary deficiencies indicate are clearly lacking. Fundamentally, this is a matter of producing more protein, particularly animal protein.
3. Earning and saving foreign exchange, a shortage of which is one of the most serious bottlenecks to economic growth in the majority of Zone C countries.
4. Providing employment within agriculture, and at the same time helping to stimulate the creation of jobs off the land, for instance, in "agro-allied" industries.
5. Increasing the productivity of agriculture through intensification.

Let Them Eat Bread

It was the alarming prospect of a continually widening gap between food and population that led to the original proposal for the IWP. In its attempt to propose policies for narrowing that gap, the Plan has adopted what at first sight may seem a cold-blooded statistician's approach. Rather than rely on what are "desirable nutritional requirements," the FAO have chosen instead to project the effective *economic* demand for food. In other words, hard cash, not rumbling bellies or crippling protein malnutrition, is the parameter they juggle. But their decision was not made solely because it comes more easily to planners to balance cashbooks; they have on their side powerful human arguments, too. For instance, it is market demand in relation to supply that determines either whether prices will rise, causing the poor to suffer most; or whether surpluses will be created, with subsequent crises for the farmers (who, in developing nations, are also the poor). Moreover, the monetary approach takes account of the fact that as incomes rise people not only buy more food, but they seek to buy *better* food; and that money is a powerful incentive to encourage changes in production policies aimed toward improving the quality of the diet.

Nevertheless, by far the greater part of the additional demand for food in the period covered by the Plan will come about simply as a result of population increase. In 1965, there were about 1500 million people living in Zone C countries. It is practically inevitable, saving war or mass famine, that by 1985 the population of these countries—which spread in a densely populated belt from West Pakistan to Korea, and also include most of those in Latin America, Africa and the Middle East—will have risen to 2500 million. In fact, 85 out of every 100 people born between now and 1985 will live in the developing nations, most of which are already over-burdened with their present populations. Simply to maintain the present nutrition levels and patterns of consumption of people in these countries—implying total stagnation both in calorie intake and quality— would require Zone C countries to increase their food supplies by over 80 per cent.

If now the income rise postulated in the IWP's macro-model is considered, FAO calculates a further 33 per cent rise in demand caused by people being richer. The total increase in demand for food in the years 1962 to 1985 for Zone C countries therefore works out at 142 per cent—an annual increase of 3.9 per cent.

The implications of a continuance of the past trend for food production in the light of the 3.9 per cent per year increase in demand are staggering. IWP calculates that by 1985, to balance their food "budget", the countries in Zone C would need to import from the developed nations some 26,000 million dollars of food (as against 2000 million dollars in 1962). This situation could, of course, never actually come about; people would starve instead. To avoid this alternative, and achieve a 3.9 per cent per annum increase, means that food production in Zone C countries needs to grow about 45 per cent faster from 1962 to 1985 than it did before 1962. As some of this period has already elapsed with little improvement, the situation now is that the period 1967 to 1985 needs to show an increase of 4.3 per cent per annum, or nearly *60 per cent* higher than the past trend.

The IWP argues that the only way this target will be achieved is by a doubling of production of staple grains in Zone C countries, from 231 million tons in 1962 to 509 million tons in 1985. And it is here that the world has had its first, and perhaps all-important, lucky break. While the IWP was being formulated, the so-called "high yielding varieties" of cereals were coming into commercial use (see *New Scientist*, vol. 39, p. 438). With these varieties, it is technically possible for a grower to double or treble yields from one planting, and to reap two harvests a year instead of one. The IWP has made the wider adaptation of the new varieties —supported by the complementary measures essential for their successful use—the spearhead of its attack on the world food problem.

One can only hope that IWP's faith in the high yielding varieties is justified. Although the high yielding varieties of wheat have so far lived up to their promise, experience with the high yielding varieties of rice in Asia has until now been little short of disastrous. The new varieties have proved highly susceptible to pests and diseases, and have produced crops of inferior quality to the traditional types. The rice behaves poorly in the milling machine, tending to break up more easily than the old varieties. Most important of all, it doesn't taste so good. The IWP acknowledges most of these drawbacks, and emphasizes that a great deal more research is needed.

Table 1. Even though, in 1985, the number of people on the land will represent a lower percentage of the total population of Zone C countries, they will number almost half as many again as the 1962 agricultural population. This will cause a large drop in the area of land per person, emphasizing the urgent need for more intensive farming methods.

	Agricultural population 1962 1985		Agricultural population as per cent of total population 1962 1985		Arable land per unit of:			
					Agricult. 1962	Population 1985	Total 1962	Population 1985
	Millions		Per cent		Hectares			
Africa, south of Sahara	165	250	82	70	1.10	0.89	0.90	0.62
Asia and Far East	583	880	70	60	0.45	0.31	0.31	0.19
Latin America	99	144	44	33	1.49	1.32	0.64	0.43
Near East and North Africa	88	144	65	45	0.83	0.72	0.54	0.32
Total Zone C	935	1388	67	55	0.72	0.56	0.48	0.31

It proposes that by 1985, about one-third of the world's total cereal area will be under high yielding varieties, as against the 5 per cent a recent FAO survey showed for 1968. The Plan works through in detail the implications of this target, in terms of seed production (a requirement of 900 million dollars by 1985), the improvement necessary in the land in order to support the heavy cropping (detailed plans for the introduction of small-scale irrigation projects in the early years of the Plan; more grandiose schemes as the increasing area under high yielding varieties pushes up the need for water; training in water management for farmers), and the demand for and supply of fertilizer, pesticides and machinery. All these requirements have been worked out on a regional basis, as have those for increased storage and processing facilities.

The IWP also considers the likely effect of immense increases in cereal supply upon the pricing structure for crops. The new technology has made cereal production so profitable in some countries that farmers are considering changing from high value crops like sugar cane or citrus fruits to cereals. The Plan therefore explores the possibility of a gradual decrease in cereal price at a rate such that cereal production remains attractive but not too tempting. The most important outcome of this study is that eventually the price of cereals would be reduced to the level at which it could be fed economically to livestock, for conversion into animal protein. This brings us to the next of the Plan's key objectives.

Bridging the Protein Gap

The IWP stresses that, at the moment, much of the world's population is not only underfed in terms of calories, but is also badly nourished in respect of the composition of the diet. The most serious shortage is of protein, especially animal protein in the shape of meat, fish, milk and eggs. If past production trends in this sector (estimated to be growing at about 1.5 per cent per annum) were to be continued, only *one quarter* of the extra demand for animal protein could be produced domestically in developing countries over the period of the IWP. There would either be a drastic fall in per capita intakes of animal protein (for instance, from 14.4 grammes per day in the Near East in 1962 to only 9.6 grammes per day in 1985), or a massive rise in import requirements. In its detailed regional plans, the IWP reckons that it would just be possible to raise the *average* per capita intake of animal protein from 10.9 grammes in 1962 to 12.7 grammes in 1985. But the income effect mentioned earlier would in the same period in fact *widen* the gap between supply and demand to some 23 per cent in 1985. The result would be that the poorer sections of the community would not get the extra protein.

From this apparently hopeless situation, the breakthrough in cereal production and subsequent drop in cereal prices provides a possible escape. The IWP therefore re-examined its regional studies in the livestock sector with a view to the feasibility of achieving a very rapid expansion of poultry and pig production using grain as food. The conclusion is that, given an all-out effort and the large-scale adoption of "factory farming" techniques, the gap between supply and demand for meat could, technically be closed.

Even if the rapid growth of pig and poultry production could be achieved, however, ruminant meat such as beef would still supply around 50 per cent of all meat supplies. The main constraint to the growth of livestock production remains with ruminant meat and milk, because the reproductive cycle of the animals involved is so long. The IWP therefore proposes that during the early years of the Plan, meat production from ruminants be deliberately held down (pigs and poultry should be used to fill the resulting gap) in order to build up the ruminant population to allow for an expansion of supply from this sector in the later years. The IWP also gives detailed plans by which the productivity of ruminants could be improved, one of which also involves the use of surplus grain in feed lots.

Milk presents a rather special problem. The Plan points out that rising incomes and increasing urbanization will lead to enormous increases in demand for milk. It recommends that Zone C countries should provide "package" support in the form of veterinary services, marketing and milk collection, and training, in an attempt to get the dairy industry off the ground. The dairy industry also lends itself well to international aid projects. But despite these efforts, IWP predicts a gap between demand and supply in the order of 34 million tons of milk by 1985. The Plan stresses that the way in which developed countries could help most in food aid during the 1970s is by the provision of processed milk on a massive scale.

Earning Foreign Exchange

A major brake on the economic advancement of developing countries is a crippling shortage of foreign exchange. Almost the only way they have of earning foreign currency is by the export of agricultural goods. IWP's projections of the rate of growth of these exports in the period covered by the Plan are bleak. Unlike the other areas covered, this is one in which the developed countries could play a major role. It has been the tendency of developed countries to produce for themselves many of the same goods that Zone C countries are best at exporting (for instance, sugar, edible oils, cotton, cereals), often with the benefit of protective tariffs. The IWP urges instead that very substantial concessions should be made in the production and trade policies of Zones A and B to benefit agricultural export earnings in developing countries. Indeed, ultimately such a policy would be in the developed countries' own interests, for the additional foreign exchange available to Zone C countries would provide an expanding market for the industrial produce of the developed nations.

The IWP also suggests ways in which trade *between* the developing countries could be increased, and points to the great potential—particularly of the River Plate countries of South America—for expanding their beef exports to Zone A and B nations.

The Employment Problem

The most dramatic and terrifying finding of the IWP studies concerns not so much feeding the extra population of the developing nations, but of finding them jobs to do. Already there is serious underemployment in the rural areas of all developing regions, especially during certain seasons of the year. The Plan has made a special study of the employment problem in Asia, where by 1985 it will have reached stunning dimensions. In Asian countries the IWP envisages the growth of the non-agricultural section of the community to be faster than the total population increase, at 3.8 per cent per year as against 2.5 per cent. But since the growth of the non-agricultural population starts from a relatively small base (250 out of 833 million) the differential in the rate of increase will not be enough to absorb all the extra people. In fact, nearly half the additional people between 1962 and 1985 would need to be absorbed into the agricultural sector.

But merely to examine the period covered by the IWP does not reveal the gravity of the problem. Further extrapolation of the trends discussed above reveals that the peak in agricultural population would not occur until about AD 2020, when 1300 million people—nearly double the present number—would be crowded on to the farms of Asia. And should the population increase at 2.8 per cent per year as against 2.5 per cent, the maximum agricultural population would not begin to decrease until after AD 2050, having reached 2800 million people!

Even the normally optimistic authors of the IWP are reduced almost to despair by the employment problem. Having estimated the maximum possible rate at which non-agricultural jobs could be created, the Plan concedes that a large increase in the already swollen numbers in agriculture appears practically inevitable unless the rate of growth of the total population can be slowed down appreciably (see Table). It then goes on thus: "In fact the main cause for concern over population growth rates in Asia stems not from the immediate prospects for the food supply, but from the long term implications for reduced efficiency as a result of shrinking farm size, lower farm income per capita, the relative shortage of urban employment, and all the tremendous economic and social pressures inherent in trying to cram still more people into the agricultural economy of the region". Elsewhere, the Plan states: "It may be that the greatest threat to the technological revolution which could solve the food problem—at least for the foreseeable future—lies in the social disorganization which could result from the ever-increasing millions dependent on a living from the agricultural economy".

A partial solution to the problem proposed by the Plan is the undertaking of major public work programmes in rural areas—the building of irrigation works, roads, communication systems, schools, hospitals and so on. Here again is a perfect target for international aid which, the Plan urges, "would yield a high return if it were making possible the fuller utilization of developing countries". Already, in fact, FAO—through its World Food Programme—is providing such aid, by arranging that food is supplied for the labour of such projects. A notable example is an afforestation project now being undertaken in Algeria.

The Need for Intensification

Many of the problems mentioned earlier converge on the urgent need for raising the productivity of agriculture in the developing countries. After considering the alternatives of expanding the existing area of cultivated lands or intensifying the use of existing resources, the IWP plumps very firmly for the latter. Indeed, it makes intensification the "cornerstone" of its entire plan. And by intensification it does not merely mean the development of better varieties, improving irrigation systems, or supplying fertilizers or pesticides (vital though these will of course be). As important, and undoubtedly more difficult to achieve, is a major social and economic revolution, by which, as the Plan puts it, "agriculture will have to be regarded more as a business and less merely a way of life".

The IWP here lays great emphasis on land reform, and above all upon the attitude the FAO planners themselves decided to adopt in formulating the Plan—namely the spread of the *monetary* economy into rural areas. Proper marketing is seen as one of the major keys to success: for instance, while overall production should rather more than double over the period covered by the Plan, marketing output is expected to increase three to fourfold.

By this time next month, we should have some idea as to how the IWP has been officially received by the 117 member governments of the FAO. If it can prompt them to lift their eyes from their feet, it will have done a great service. And if by some miracle the governments rise to the challenge of the targets and policies it proposes, then, who knows, the world in 1985 might yet be a tolerable place in which to live.

26

DRY LANDS AND DESALTED WATER

Gale Young

Men spread now, with the whole power of the race to aid them, into every available region of the earth. Their cities are no longer tethered to running water and the proximity of cultivation . . . they lie out in the former deserts, those long-wasted sun baths of the race, they tower amidst eternal snows. . . . One may live anywhere.

—H. G. Wells, *The World Set Free*
—A Story of Mankind

Mounting population and pollution exert pressure on man to enlarge his living space. At present, the most rapidly growing part of the United States is the desert of the Southwest, into which the Colorado and Rio Grande rivers have been largely diverted. Water from the Feather River will shortly be added, crossing over a mountain range 2000 feet (600 meters) high, by way of conveyance facilities now under construction.

The building of the Colorado Aqueduct of the Metropolitan Water District of Southern California was undertaken 40 years ago. Since then, the assessed valuation of the region served by this water supply has increased by $20 billion, or by $5 for each 1000 gallons of water that has flowed through the pipes.

These remarks are not intended to impute some exaggerated value to water, but are made, rather, to point out that people seem to like desert climates (better than, say, rain forests or frozen tundras) and that they will move into them and build vigorous societies. Since the water is essential to the welfare of all, whether they be large direct users or not, the cost of the water in arid areas is often carried in part as overhead. For example, the Metropolitan Water District derives funds to meet about half of its

Reprinted from *Science* 167: 339-43, 1970, with the permission of the publishers. Copyright 1970 by the American Association for the Advancement of Science.

costs from water revenues and levies taxes for the balance.

Water-supply projects tend to proceed by large steps. When they are first completed there is an excess of water, and this can be used for agriculture while population and land values build up (2). Later on, the suburban farmland and its water allotments are absorbed in urban growth. This process is now under way around the large cities in our dry Southwest.

A third of the world's land is dry and virtually unoccupied, while half of the world's people are jammed—impoverished and under-nourished—into a tenth of the land area. A major part of the coming increase in population will occur in the less-developed countries and, as *Nature* expressed it, (3), "This huge army of uneducated, untrained, underfed, underprivileged recruits to humanity is being bred at the very moment when science and technology are rapidly undermining the need for and the status of the unskilled. . . . What stands out most emphatically is in fact the insufficiency of economic factors or motives if the challenge is to be met."

The past decade has seen a quickening of interest in the large-scale desalting of seawater as another means of opening up dry areas of the earth for human occupancy. Thus, Jacob Bronowski writes (4), "let me ask first what is going to be the single greatest technological change in the physical sciences over the next twenty or thirty years. My guess is that desalting of seawater is going to be the most important advance for overall world development. Without this the whole complex program of bringing under-developed countries to an acceptable level of economics, education and political maturity is insoluble." And Charles Lowe writes (5), "The desert is man's future land bank. Fortunately, it is a wondrously rich bank, which may turn green when man someday taps distilled seawater for irrigation. Bridging the gap from sea to desert will be greatly facilitated by the geographical nearness of most of the world's deserts to the oceans. When this occurs it will surely be one of the greatest transformations made by man in his persistent and successful role in changing the face of the planet." As an example, imagine what changes would follow if Baja California were to be opened up for settlement with the help of desalting and power stations. What might another thousand miles of southern California be worth in a few generations?

This process has already begun to take place on a small scale in certain locations. Thus, Kuwait on the Persian Gulf and Shevchenko on the barren eastern shore of the Caspian Sea, where the Russians are building the world's largest desalting unit, are two oil field communities which depend upon desalination for their water supply. As in other locations where desalination would be employed, no cheaper sources of fresh water are available.

In general, desalination will be able to meet the freshwater needs of municipalities and industries located along the ocean shore, or in some interior regions having salty lakes or groundwater. And anywhere that cities go, some agriculture, for fresh fruits and vegetables at least, tends to follow. For example, Kuwait, in one of the most devilishly hot and sandridden environments on earth, has recently ordered acres of enclosed greenhouses at a cost of many thousands of dollars per acre to supply garden produce which will be fresher and reportedly cheaper than imported produce. But it is less clear whether agriculture that depends on desalted water ("desalination agriculture") may someday expand to include substantial production of staple foods as well. Here opinions differ, and, as the saying goes, the less light sometimes generates the more heat.

Water Requirements for Crops

In enclosed agriculture, such as Kuwait will have, so little fresh water escapes that its cost is not important. The situation is quite different in open-field agriculture, since the amount of water lost to the atmosphere in evapotranspiration is generally (6) many times that actually involved in the plant's growth reactions, and the cost of supplying this total by desalination is of prime importance.

Some authors have stated that the cost of desalted water will be for many years "at least one whole order of magnitude greater than the value of the water to agriculture" (7). Other writers have been more optimistic. Thus, the value of distilled water for agriculture in Israel has been estimated by MacAvoy and Peterson (8) to be about 27 cents per 100 gallons. A generalized study (9, p. 28) indicates that "arid tropical and semitropical regions with year-round growing climates appear potentially capable of growing food at costs in or near the world market import price range, using desalted water at prices like 20 cents per thousand gallons." Estimates have been made of the total (direct plus indirect) benefits of irrigation water in several U.S. locations. There is considerable variation, estimates of losses due to taking water away from crops being 25 to 36 cents per 100 gallons for the Texas High Plains and 32 to 44 cents for the Imperial Valley (10).

As noted above, the growing of some high-value crops tends to follow the occupation of a dry area, and an economic enterprise would, of course, first seek to saturate the market for this produce. But one is not going to feed the teeming millions on orchids or avocados, so the inquiry turns inevitably to the bulk staple foods. Of the staples, the grains are the most important, and, of the grains, rice is the staple and preferred food of half the human race. Rice, because of this demand, has a value double that of wheat on the world market—but it is not usually talked about in connection with desalination agriculture. Let us, therefore, talk about it.

Rice is indigenous to southern and eastern Asia, where much of the world's starvation occurs. In the monsoon countries, where fields are flooded periodically, the rice plant has the great virtue of being able to conduct oxygen to its roots through a hollow stem, and to flourish where other crops suffocate. Cultivation under such conditions leads to heavy use of water. In Table 1, from a talk by the dean of agriculture of the University of Sydney (11), it may be seen that in Australia, the most favorable of the instances shown, a price for water of 20 cents per 1000 gallons would add 10.6 cents per pound to the cost of rice. This is more than the rice is worth and provides little basis for enthusiasm about desalination.

Table 2 gives data on yield and water use for several other crops which are widely used. The

Table 1. Amount of water used in growing rice in various countries.

Location	Pounds of water per pound of paddy rice	Gallons of water used per pound of milled rice
Thailand	10,000	1,800
India	10,000	1,800
Japan	4,900	900
California	3,300	610
Australia	2,900	530

"Rice" row of Table 2 is left blank for the present. The water-use rates were estimated (and checked against measured rates for farms when these were available) for a coastal site in the southeastern Mediterranean area, an irrigation efficiency (the fraction of the applied water which is lost to the atmosphere in evapotranspiration) of 80 percent being assumed. The other 20 percent of the water is that part which evaporates before reaching the crop, or which is carried away by deep percolation below the root zone. With efficient sprinkler or soaker irrigation systems this efficiency can usually be bettered, even without allowing for partial recovery of the deep drainage water. The yields assumed are those obtained regularly today by efficient farmers in production areas specializing in the crops in question. Record yields are considerably higher—more than double in the case of wheat, potato, tomato, and maize and in the case of an assumed yield for rice, discussed below.

Table 1 shows that rice growers typically use several times as much water per pound of grain as is needed for the other grains of Table 2. While some people may have doubted that rice requires this much water, this is the way the picture has stood historically. Just recently, however, results have appeared which do not support the classical view of rice as a water hog. In an experiment with IR 8 rice at India's Central Rice Institute, in Cuttack, a good crop [6350 pounds (2900 kilograms) per acre as paddy rice] was obtained with consumption of only 16.7 inches (42 centimeters) of water, irrigation being applied only when the soil was completely crusted. This work was reviewed and reported by J. S. Kanwar, deputy director general of the Indian Council of Agriculture Research (12). Kanwar states, "The common notion that continuous submergence is essential for paddy is belied." In a corresponding experiment based on the classical practice of continuous submergence, six times as much water (100 inches) was used and the yield was 6 per cent higher. Obviously, most of the 100 inches of water was forced into the subsoil by the head of standing water.

If confirmed in subsequent tests and field experience, this finding may turn out to be one of the landmarks in the war against hunger. We add that rice can be grown the year round in warm climates; for example, in the Philippines three crops per year have been grown, yielding a total of 18,000 pounds of rice per acre.

If the results of the Indian experiment are

Table 2. Relation of yield to water use for various crops.

Crop	Yield (10^3 lb/acre)	Food value 10^2 Cal/lb	Water use		
			Inches	Gal/lb	Gal/10^3 Cal
Grain					
Wheat	6.0	14.8	20.0	91	61
Sorghum	8.0	15.1	27.6	94	62
Maize	9.0	15.8	27.6	83	53
Rice					
Vegetable					
Potato	48	2.79	16.0	9.0	32
Tomato	60	0.95	19.0	8.6	91
Citrus					
Orange	44	1.31	53.1	33	250

taken at face value, the missing numbers for rice, which can now be added to Table 2, are as follows: yield, 4.2 (103 pounds per acre); food value, 16.5 (102 Calories per pound); water use—16.7 inches, 108 gallons per pound, 65 gallons per 103 Calories. This puts rice right in among the other grains as a user of water. It may be seen that to supply a person a minimum adequate allowance of 2500 Calories per day (13) in this highly intensive and scientifically managed type of agriculture would require an average of 160 gallons of water per day in the case of grain, or half this in the case of potatoes.

Production Cost Estimates for Grain

For any selected price of water, Table 2 enables one to compute the cost of water per pound of product, as illustrated for rice in Table 1. However, water is only one component of the total cost. We have, therefore, made some illustrative estimates of the total production costs for grain for a large, intensively operated farm. These costs are not expected to vary greatly with farm size. The estimates were made for a farm of 300,000 acres (120,000 hectares) which uses about a billion gallons of water per day.

These estimates are summarized in Tables 3 to 5. Table 3 shows the capital investment per acre, while Table 4 gives annual out-of-pocket costs for items which cannot be allocated directly to specific crops in the year-round rotation. The costs which can be specifically assigned are shown in Table 5.

It should be noted that the water is priced at the farm inlet and that it is supplied to the farm at a rate that is constant throughout the year, except for the time when the desalting plant is shut down for maintenance or other reasons. Thus, because of seasonal variations in the requirement for irrigation water, it is necessary to resort to such measures as (i) making seasonal adjustments in the size of the irrigated area and (ii) storing water in underground aquifers at certain times of the year and pumping it back up at other times (10 percent of the stored water is assumed to be lost in this

process). Allowance for such storage has been made in Tables 3 and 4 (14).

An interest rate of 10 percent on the investment shown in Table 3 amounts to $95 per acre per year, and allowance for depreciation and for working-capital needs adds about $10 more. With the overhead costs shown in Table 4, the total fixed charges are thus $140 per acre per year. In regions where a second major crop, of the same or some other product,

Table 3. Estimated capital investment.

Item	Dollars per acre
Irrigation and storage-well system	375
Land, land development, and roads	85
Drainage system	110
Water for initial leaching	130
Grain storage	85
Machinery	115
Farm buildings	25
Interest during construction	25
Total	950

Table 4. Estimated overhead costs.

Item	Dollars per acre per year
Maintenance	14
Pumping power	1
Water losses in storage and canal leakage	12
Experimental station	1
Management and miscellaneous	7
Total	35

Table 5. Estimated direct costs for grain production.*

Item	Dollars per acre per crop
Fertilizer	11
Pumping power	6
Seed	5
Labor	2
Machine operation	2
Storage and marketing	3
Other chemicals	3
Miscellaneous	8
Total	40

* Exclusive of the cost of irrigation water.

can be grown in the same year on the same land and share fixed costs with the grain, the cost of an acre crop of grain would be ($140/2) + $40 + cost of water = $110 + cost of water. In some areas, such as parts of India, where it might be possible to grow three crops per year, the corresponding cost would be $87 + cost of water.

The resulting costs for milled rice and for wheat are plotted in Fig. 26-1, along with some representative prices.

In effect, what is here being contemplated is that the high cost of water may be at least partially offset by the opportunity to conduct intensive year-round "food factory" agriculture in favorable growing climates with many conditions under unusually good control. For example, recent observations suggest that very frequent or drip irrigation can cause substantial increases in the crop yield (15). In these experiments the nitrogen fertilizer was applied in the water. There is also speculation that slow release of carbon dioxide beneath the plant

canopy might enhance yields. Thus it is entirely possible that future yields may exceed those of Table 2.

Desalination

The newest United States desalting plant, at Key West, Florida, produces 2.5 million gallons of fresh water per day at a cost of about $1 per 1000 gallons. It is anticipated that the larger plants envisaged for future regional water supply will be able to attain lower costs through the economies of scale and the benefits of more advanced technology. A plant producing 8 million gallons per day (16), which will be built around a gas turbine, will have vapor-compressor heat pumps coupled to vertical-tube evaporators and will use the engine-rejected heat in flash evaporators, is expected to produce fresh water at a cost of about half that for the Key West plant (17).

Heat transfer enhancement is currently being

Fig. 26-1. The costs of growing grain (see 30). (Oak Ridge National Laboratory.)

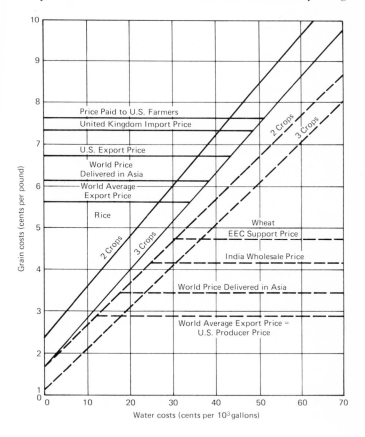

introduced into evaporator designs. For example, doubly finned or doubly fluted vertical tubes give several times the heat transfer of plain smooth tubes, and their use can considerably reduce the size and cost of a plant (18). To some degree the heat transfer in the horizontal tubes of a flash evaporator can be similarly augmented. Such advances are now being tried in test units and pilot plants. The preferred large-plant design at present is a combined flash and vertical-tube evaporator with heat transfer enhancement (19).

Economies can be achieved through the design and construction of dual-purpose plants which produce both power and water, as compared to single-purpose plants that produce only water. In terms of 1967 dollars at 10 percent interest (20), the cost of water at a large (billion gallons per day) single-purpose plant, in which most of the steam bypasses the turbine without generating any power, was estimated (9, pp. 3, 4, 19, 20; 21, p. 39) to be 26 to 32 cents per 1000 gallons, while at a dual-purpose station range for incremental cost of water was 16 to 24 cents. At an interest rate of 9 percent, another study (22) indicated 15 to 26 cents for the dual-purpose cost range. These large-plant studies were based on the use of reactor heat sources, with technology ranging from reactors of the type (light-water) and size being built in the United States today to advanced fast and thermal breeder reactors of the type that will be operational some two decades hence. Since these estimates were made there have been sharp increases in reactor prices, and it may turn out that the ·costs of water will have to be revised upward by 2 or 3 cents per 1000 (23). On the other hand, advanced · evaporator and agricultural technologies appear to be moving ahead more rapidly than had been expected.

The saving effected through dual-purpose operation works the other way as well. Once you have decided to build a single-purpose steam bypass water plant, the incremental cost of producing power also is very low—say, 1.5 mills per kilowatt-hour (21, p. 39) for reactor stations of the largest sizes being constructed today, such as Brown's Ferry (3000 electrical megawatts). This power may be transmitted to a network in some instances, or to adjacent industrial plants in a so-called agro-industrial complex, to help develop and build up the region. A number of industrial processes have been studied in this connection (9, 21, 24), as well as several possible locales (25) and some of the implementation problems (26). One of the large energy consumers is the production of ammonia for fertilizer by way of electrolytic hydrogen, with only air and water used as raw materials. Potassium fertilizer can be produced from the sea, as can other products, such as chlorine, magnesium, salt, and caustic. Hoyle writes (27):

> . . . the older established industries of Europe and America . . . grew up around specialized mineral deposits—coal, oil, metallic ores. Without these deposits the older style of industrialization was completely impossible. On the political and economic fronts, the world became divided into "haves" and "have nots," depending whereabouts on the earth's surface these specialized deposits happen to be situated. . . . In the second phase of industrialism, . . . no specialized deposits are needed at all. The key to this second phase lies in the possession of an effectively unlimited source of energy. . . . Low-grade ores can be smelted—and there is an ample supply of such ores to be found everywhere. Carbon can be taken from inorganic compounds, nitrogen from the air, a whole vast range of chemicals from seawater. So . . . a phase in which nothing is needed but the commonest materials—water, air and fairly common rocks. This was a phase that can be practiced by anybody, by any nation. . . . This second phase was clearly enormously more effective and powerful than the first.

Summary

The fastest-growing region in our country is the desert of the Southwest. This suggests that the vast, warm, dry areas of the world may be attractive for human occupancy as earth's population soars, if the water and power needs can be met. It may also be that nuclear energy—not tied by any umbilical cord to fossil deposits—will have a significant role in opening up these arid areas and creating usable land for human living space.

Since much arid land lies relatively near the sea and the aggregate length of the coastal deserts nearly equals the circumference of the globe, desalination is a freshwater source of broad potential applicability when cheaper alternative sources are not available. Cities and industries can now spread widely along the ocean shore, bringing with them some agriculture for garden produce.

A more difficult question concerns the extent to which desalination agriculture will be used in newly occupied arid lands for the production of staple foods. Since we cannot predict with any accuracy either the population growth or the increase in food production by various means, let alone the difference between these two large quantities, our knowledge of future food shortages is very poor indeed. It therefore appears prudent to conduct research, development, and pilot planting projects to investigate such potential methods for augmenting food production. These activities should be conducted on a scale sufficient to permit practical evaluation, so that the option of invoking such methods will be open, should circumstances require it. To quote R. R. R. Brooks (28) "The key to [the] ... future of two-thirds of the human species is rising productivity in agriculture. All political dogmas, party slogans, planning strategies, and models of economic growth shrivel to irrelevance in the face of this fact."

A preliminary and generalized study was conducted at the Oak Ridge National Laboratory with the collaboration of outstanding agricultural and engineering people from other countries and from U.S. government agencies, universities, foundations, and industries. This study considered intensive year-round farming in warm coastal deserts, based on the use of distilled seawater, in association with clustering industries. As indicated in Fig. 26-1, production costs for rice and wheat appear (29) to fall, for water costs of around 35 and 20 cents per 1000 gallons, respectively, in the general area of recent grain prices. These water prices, in turn, fall (barely) within the estimated future cost range for desalinated water.

The significant conclusion, we believe, is that desalination agriculture is in the realm of practical possibility, rather than being far afield. To our mind this appears of sufficient importance, in view of the population expansion and the interest in opening up new lands and communities, to warrant the development of advanced desalting plants and intensive scientifically managed agriculture. We hope that desert research farms running on distilled water, and controlled-environment agricultural test chambers, may become as well known to you on your TV screen in a few years as starving Biafran babies are today.

References and Notes

1. H. G. Wells, *The World Set Free—A Story of Mankind* (Dutton, New York, 1914), p. 241.
2. In Los Angeles some strawberry growers use land worth $10,000 per acre and pay city taxes on it.
3. *Nature* **199**, 411 (1963).
4. J. Bronowski, *Saturday Rev.* **1969**, 45 (5 July 1969).
5. C. H. Lowe, Jr., in A. S. Leopold, *The Desert* (Life Nature Library, New York, 1961), introduction.
6. There are xerophytic plants (such as pineapple) that carry on photosynthesis with closed stomata in the daytime, using stored carbon dioxide absorbed through open stomata at night. They thus transpire much less water per unit of plant matter produced than ordinary crops do.
7. M. Clawson, H. H. Landsberg, L. T. Alexander, *Science* **164**, 1141 (1969).
8. P. W. MacAvoy and D. F. Peterson, Jr., *The Engineering Economics of Large-Scale Desalting in the 1970's* (Praeger, New York, in press).
9. "Nuclear Energy Centers; Industrial and Agro-Industrial Complexes: Summary Report," *Oak Ridge Nat. Lab. Rep. ORNL4291* (1968).
10. C. W. Howe, in *Arid Lands in Perspective*, W. G. McGinnies and B. J. Goldman, Eds. (AAAS, Washington, D.C., 1969), p. 379.
11. J. R. A. McMillan, "Water, Agricultural Production and World Population" (Farrer Oration) (1965).
12. J. S. Kanwar, "From protective to productive irrigation," *Econ. Polit. Weekly Rev. Agr.* (29 March 1969). Data, cited from M. S. Chaudhury and R. G. Pandrey, are given in more detail in an article in *Indian Farming*, in press.
13. R. Revelle. *Proc. Nat. Acad. Sci. U.S.* **56**, 328 (1966).
14. If suitable aquifers are not present and an above-ground storage reservoir is constructed in the farming region, there is an increase in cost such that the value $140 in the next paragraph of the text changes to about $150 per acre per year, it being assumed that the reservoir is of a size adequate to supply a farm region with an intake of about 10^9 gallons of water per day.
15. D. Goldberg, B. Gornat, M. Shmueli, "Advances in irrigation in Israel's agriculture," paper presented at the 1st World Congress of Engineers and

Architects, Israel (1967). See also D. Goldberg and M. Shmueli, "Drip irrigation—a method used under arid and desert conditions of high water and soil salinity," unpublished.

16. This plant is now in the preliminary planning stage.

17. "Design and Economic Study of a Gas Turbine Powered Vapor Compression Plant for Evaporation of Seawater," *Office Saline Water Res. Develop. Progr. Rep. No. 377* (1968).

18. Such tubes are to be used in the gas turbine unit discussed in the preceding paragraph.

19. "Conceptual Design Study of a 250-Million Gallon per Day Combined Vertical Tube-Flash Evaporator Desalination Plant," *Office Saline Water Res. Develop. Progr. Rep. No. 391* (1968).

20. The cost of desalted water is sensitive to changes in interest rates because, like conventional means of providing new water supplies such as dams and aqueducts, the process requires a large capital outlay.

21. *Oak Ridge Nat. Lab. Rep. No. ORNL-4290* (1968).

22. "Nuclear Power and Water Desalting Plants for Southwest United States and Northwest Mexico" (1968), pp. 113 and 136; this is a preliminary assessment made by a joint United States-Mexico International Atomic Energy Agency study team.

23. This expectation is based on the assumption that combined flash and vertical-tube evaporators are adopted; otherwise, the increase in water costs would be expected to be larger.

24. A. M. Squires, "Steel making in an agro-industrial complex," in *Oak Ridge Nat. Lab. Rep. No. ORNL-4294* (1968); W. E. Lobo, "Acetyline production from naphtha by electric arc and by partial combustion," in *ibid.;* H. E. Goeller, "Tables for computing manufacturing costs of industrial products in an agro-industrial complex," *Oak Ridge Nat. Lab. Rep. No. ORNL-4296* (1969).

25. T. Tamura and W. J. Young, "Data Obtained on Several Possible Locales for the Agro-Industrial Complex," *Oak Ridge Nat. Lab. Rep. No. ORNL-4293* (1970).

26. J. A. Ritchey, "Problems in Implementation of an Agro-Industrial Complex," *Oak Ridge Nat. Lab. Rep. No. ORNL-4295* (1969); R. L. Meier, *Bull. At. Sci.* 1969, 16 (March 1969); R. D. Sharma, *ibid.* 1969, 31 (November 1969).

27. F. Hoyle, *Ossian's Ride* (Harper, New York, 1959), p. 146.

28. R. R. R. Brooks, *Saturday Rev.* 1969, 14 (9 August 1969).

29. The estimates are based on an interest rate of 10 percent.

30. Figure 26-1 is based on data and publications as follows. The average price paid the U.S. producer for wheat in the period 1956-65; the average price per pound of milled rice, at 0.65 paddy weight (0.65 pound of milled rice from each pound of paddy), paid the U.S. producer in the period 1950-65; the average price of Siam Patna No. 2 rice imported into the United Kingdom in the period 1955-65; the average wholesale price of wheat in India (the Punjab) in the period 1951-65 [*FAO (Food Agr. Organ. UN) Prod. Yearb.* 20 (1966)]; the world average export value of wheat in the period 1961-67; the world average export value of rice in the period 1955-67 [*The State of Food and Agriculture: 1968* (Food and Agriculture Organization of the United Nations, Rome, 1968)]; the average U.S. export value of rice in the period 1960-65; the European Economic Community's wheat support price [*The World Food Problem* (President's Science Advisory Committee, Washington, D.C., 1967), vol. 2, pp. 145-149]; recent world prices for wheat and rice delivered in Asia, as given by R. P. Hammond in a paper presented at the International Conference on Water for Peace, Washington, D.C., May 1967.

31. The research discussed here is sponsored by the U.S. Atomic Energy Commission under contract with the Union Carbide Corp.

27

DESALTED SEAWATER FOR AGRICULTURE: IS IT ECONOMIC?

Marion Clawson, Hans H. Landsberg, and Lyle T. Alexander

In the past decade, there has been mounting advocacy of desalting seawater for use in commercial agriculture in various locations of the world, especially in the Middle East. The process, it is contended, is both technically and economically feasible, or soon will be, and its application on a large scale can produce additional volumes of food at competitive prices—the desert will blossom like the rose—and at a profit.

Although research on desalting techniques had proceeded for many years in the Interior Department's Office of Saline Water supported by modest funds, and the Atomic Energy Commission had been exploring the role that nuclear energy might play in desalting, the entire matter suddenly acquired international interest after the 6-day Israeli-Arab war in June 1967.

Within days after the war, the London *Times* published two letters recommending desalting schemes in the Middle East. A detailed letter from Edmund de Rothschild suggested three nuclear desalting installations in Israel, Jordan, and the Gaza Strip, respectively. This provoked comments and questions in the House of Commons, which generally approved the idea or at least further exploration of it. On this side of the Atlantic the U.S. Senate in December 1967 passed Resolution 155 without a dissenting vote. It says in part:

Whereas the greatest bar to a long-term settlement of the differences between the Arab and Israeli people is the chronic shortage of fresh water, useful work, and an adequate food supply; and

Reprinted from *Science* 164: 1141-48, 1969, with the permission of the publishers. Copyright 1969 by the American Association for the Advancement of Science.

Whereas the United States now has available the technology and the resources to alleviate these shortages and to provide a base for peaceful cooperation between the countries involved:

Now, therefore, be it

Resolved, that it is the sense of the Senate that the prompt design, construction, and operation of nuclear desalting plants will provide large quantities of fresh water to both Arab and Israeli territories and, thereby, will result in

1. new jobs for many refugees;
2. an enormous increase in the agricultural productivity of existing wastelands;
3. a broad base for cooperation between the Israeli and Arab governments; and
4. a further demonstration of the United States efforts to find peaceful solutions to areas of conflict . . .

The resolution was a direct descendant of the "Strauss-Eisenhower Plan," a proposal by former AEC Chairman Lewis Strauss for which he obtained Eisenhower's backing. The proposal gained its greatest popularity through an article written by Eisenhower (1), which, with reference to the Middle East, states the proposition in its most optimistic form:

Now it looks as if we are on the threshold of a new breakthrough—the atomic desalting of sea water in vast quantities for making the desert lands of this earth bloom for human need . . . Since we now know that the cost of desalting water drops sharply and progressively as the size of the installation increases, it is probable that sweet water produced by these huge plants would cost no more than 15 cents per 1000 gallons—and possibly considerably less . . . There is every reason to suppose that it could be a successful, self-sustaining business enterprise, whose revenue would derive from the sale of its products—water and electricity—to the users . . . The purpose . . . is . . . to promote peace in a deeply troubled area of the world through a new cooperative venture among nations.

These and other basic documents, including Strauss' memorandum outlining the proposal, have provided not only a flood of newspaper stories and magazine articles, but have also accelerated government-sponsored efforts. Of the engineering studies, two are directed specifically to foreign areas. Following President Johnson's meeting with Israel Prime Minister Levi Eshkol in June 1964, the Kaiser company was commissioned to make an engineering study of the feasibility of seawater desalting in Israel (2). The Oak Ridge National Laboratory has produced a report on nuclear energy centers

215

and agro-industrial complexes to be established in various arid areas of the world (3). The tone of these two reports is cautiously optimistic, but a more careful review of their assumptions leads to quite opposite conclusions (4). Others have written uninhibitedly—as if sweet water were already flowing into the desert at low costs (5).

The Kaiser study was specifically concerned with a desalting plant in Israel; the contemplated location of the plant was on the Mediterranean seashore about 9 kilometers south of Ashdod. The power plant would be a nuclear steam-generating facility using a conventional light-water nuclear reactor with a thermal rating of 1250 megawatts. Essentially all of the steam generated in the reactor passes through the generator without condensation; the steam exhausted from the turbine is condensed in the shell side of the brine heaters of the desalting plant. The evaporator structures consist of heat recovery stages, heat reject, and heat reject-deaerator stages. A multiple seawater intake structure would be located 450 meters offshore and 7 meters deep. An outfall facility would consist of a buried concrete box culvert with transition to an open channel beyond the desalting plant limits. The plant would have a capacity of 100 million gallons of desalted water daily; a plant operating factor of 85 percent is assumed. The generator would produce 200 megawatts salable electrical power at an estimated price of 5.3 mills per kilowatt-hour and an 85 percent power plant operating factor. Total capital costs are estimated from $187 to $210 million, depending upon interest rate. Annual operating costs vary from $16.8 to $28.7 million, for interest rates of 1.9 percent and 8.0 percent, respectively. Crediting power sales against total costs, water costs per 1000 gallons—conceived as the residual costs—range from 28.6 cents if interest is calculated at 1.9 percent to 67.0 cents if the interest is 8.0 percent. Several variations in structure and methods of operation are possible without major effect upon water cost.

The Oak Ridge proposal is for a major nuclear energy center, with industrial and agro-industrial complexes, as well as desalting works. It was conceived to be broadly suitable for several locations in the world, subject to specific site planning and adaptation. The proposal is based upon technologies expected to be developed over the next decade or two, not upon technologies tested and in application today—and that reason makes it less suitable for rigorous review since at *some* time in the future costs of both power and water production will presumably be lower than they are now. "Near-term" light-water reactors and "far-term" advanced breeder reactors were considered as well as near- and far-term desalting equipment; a number of alternative layouts were included, with industrial electrical power ranging mostly from 1585 to 2070 megawatts. Most of the designs would produce 1 billion gallons of desalted water daily. Investment costs in the nuclear plant and desalting works would range from $1.5 to $2.0 billion for most designs. Various industrial processes, producing metals or chemicals and using large amounts of electricity, are considered. Alternative costs are estimated, with different interest rates and other cost factors. A highly advanced type of agriculture is assumed. The Oak Ridge complex would produce ten times as much water as the Kaiser proposal, at a cost at "near-term" technology of 17 cents per 1000 gallons at 5 percent interest, 24 cents at 10 percent interest, and 32 cents at 15 percent interest and about one-third lower at "far-term" technology. As pointed out in the report, these values are arbitrary, since the complexes are conceived as closed economies. They represent the incremental cost of adding one unit of water to an existing plant. But, in the size class here contemplated, these incremental costs will approximate the average cost sufficiently to stand as surrogates.

Currently, a second stage of research, which includes the outlook for marketing the expected increase in output, has been undertaken at Oak Ridge to adapt the general design specifically to conditions as they exist in a number of locations in the Middle East.

Our purpose in this article is to explore the economic feasibility of desalting seawater on a large scale for commercial agriculture in regions of extremely low rainfall. In preparation of the material on desalting costs we have made extensive use of the analysis by Paul Wolfowitz (6) of the University of Chicago and a report by W. E. Hoehn of the RAND Corporation (7).

Little will be said here of the political aspects of such ventures except to note that we see no reason to believe that the desalting of seawater in the Middle East would have the peacemaking effects that have been claimed for it. The struggles between Israel and its neighbors have not been over freshwater, and even where water has been at issue, as in the case of the Jordan River, the differences could be resolved readily if there were peace in the Middle East, or at least an atmosphere in which negotiations were possible. Indeed, in 1955 these differences were resolved on a technical level, but formal agreement was frustrated by political antagonism (8).

Desalting Seawater for Large-Scale Commercial Agriculture

Any program to desalt seawater for use in agriculture involves three closely interrelated components: (i) a source of energy; (ii) a process for producing sweet water out of seawater; and (iii) means for transporting the water, at the right time, to the place of its application for the growth of crops.

Each component is essential, and any part can set a technical or economic limit to the whole process. Much has been written about the first two components, but very little about the third.

Numerous sources of energy and methods of desalting exist, but we shall focus entirely upon nuclear power as the energy source and upon evaporation as the desalting method.

No persuasive case can be made for a preferred energy source. Indeed, one might simply stipulate a given cost of energy, from whatever source is locally most advantageous, and concentrate attention on the other two components. We are analyzing nuclear rather than fossil-fuel energy only because the proposals that have received most notice have been based on nuclear energy. First, the atom attracts both attention and funds. Second, there is a large well-funded atomic research establish-

ment, certainly in the United States, staffed with imaginative and highly skilled thinkers who do not shrink from the novel and spectacular. Third, the larger the proposed installation, the greater the advantage of nuclear energy. And fourth, there are arid areas in the vicinity of seacoasts that are remote from other fuel sources and to which nuclear energy may offer less expensive access to the new technology of sweet water production. For these and perhaps other reasons the packages offered so far have contained nuclear energy as the energy source.

Regarding desalting, it may safely be assumed that current technology offers no more feasible way to obtain freshwater from the sea on a large scale. Even the so-called "far-off," 20-years-in-the-future, technology used in the more favorable of the two Oak Ridge variants is based on evaporation. That a breakthrough—say a very efficient, stiff, membrane—could change the picture goes without saying. But such breakthroughs are not now in view, despite much effort in that direction. Nor would they have a necessary advantageous association with power generation.

In short, we discuss the merits of the programs in the terms chosen by their proponents. Although costs would vary with the location of the plant and other environmental factors, it is possible to consider the problem in general and to reach conclusions which no specific application could significantly change. This is true even for the third component—the conveyance of the water once produced—provided that areas are eliminated which do not have suitable soils, or are too remote from the seacoast, or do not in other ways qualify.

Nuclear Energy

The reputation of nuclear power as a cheap source of energy understandably has reached the desalting field, once it was realized that the addition of power production (from any fuel) to a desalting plant represented a logical combination, wherever raising of steam was part of the desalting process. Nobody now doubts that electricity from nuclear power plants can indeed be fully competitive with that from fossil-fuel plants under certain conditions in certain areas. But it is also true that some of the enthusiasm of recent years was based upon circumstances unlikely to be repeated in this country or to be found at all in less-developed regions of the world. These include the large funds furnished by the government for R&D, and the initial input made by suppliers who quoted highly attractive prices for their generating equipment when it seemed essential to the spread of the new technology. For these and other reasons, some sober criticism has been directed at the evaluation of the outlook for nuclear energy (7, 9). This does not cast doubt on its basic competitive position but does question the extent of this advantage. These are major considerations:

1. It will be a year or two before even one U.S. nuclear plant designed to be competitive with fossil-fuel plants has been in operation long enough to establish a performance record that would substantiate expectations. The large scaling-up in size of the equipment ordered for nuclear plants in 1967 and 1968 and the reliance placed in all cost estimates on minimum downtime make this especially significant. What little experience has accumulated from demonstration plants in the United States indicates that the high rates of availability, a *sine qua non* of low power cost assumptions, will not be easy to attain.

2. The cost of nuclear generating equipment for the long run is far from settled. Past reductions in equipment prices by manufacturers have turned out to be more in the nature of initial lures. Costs in 1967 and early 1968 were $30 or more per kilowatt installed above those of 1965 and 1966, allowing for differences in size (7). Nor has the trend abated (10). Costs of conventional equipment have also risen, but less steeply.

3. There is some uncertainty regarding the future costs of nuclear fuel, once the increased power generation begins to reduce the uranium supply and forces a diversion to higher cost sources of the mineral. But prices of competitive fuels cannot be assumed as constant either, so that uncertainty is the real problem.

4. Nuclear power plants, owing partly to the heavy cost of shielding and containment, require more capital than conventional plants do (11). Whenever a portion of the fuel is awaiting enrichment (or being enriched), being fabricated into fuel elements, awaiting loading, or undergoing cooling, it still represents capital investment and thus carries interest charges, no matter whether the utility or the supplier manages the fuel cycle. The recent steep rise in interest rates has been penalizing nuclear more than conventionally fired plants. No one knows whether, to what level and and how soon, rates will begin to decline, but while rates are high they blunt the competitive edge of nuclear plants.

In addition to the factors cited which tend to make themselves felt in aggravated form in less-developed countries, there are some elements that apply especially to them.

Economies of Scale

Electric power generation is a classic example of economics of scale: unit cost drops as size of the plant rises. This is especially marked for nuclear power plants, partly because the absolute cost of shielding and containment increases relatively little with reactor size.

Information available for 1967 shows a rise in capital costs per kilowatt capacity from about $130 for plants of 1200 megawatts to about $180 per kilowatt for plants in the 400-megawatt range. This explains why no nuclear power plant smaller than 450 megawatts has been ordered in the United States since 1963, and why the smallest size plant which a utility can now order from a major U.S. supplier is 480 megawatts (12).

However, these economies can be realized only when certain other favorable factors are also present. In the less-developed countries they are usually absent. Chief among them are a large market for electricity, that can accommodate a very large plant, and a well-developed power grid.

An engineering rule of thumb calls for reserve capacity equal to at least the largest single generator in the system to assure continued supply when that unit is out. In fact, to keep the system from collapsing in case the nuclear plant trips out, prudent engineers advise against installing in a small isolated system a nuclear plant that is larger than 10 percent of the peak load.

How many countries are there that fulfill the conditions which permit them to benefit from the economies offered by large nuclear reactors? To be competitive with power from conventional sources, "... a reactor of 500 Mw, now about the lower limit in size, would ... have to produce not less than 3.5 billion kwh per year. Presently, there is only a handful of countries outside of North America, Europe, and Oceania that consume that much electric energy per year *altogether*. And, of these, only Argentina, Brazil, Japan, India, North Korea, and the Republic of South Africa consume greatly more" (13). Even though power markets will, of course be larger 10 and 20 years from now, it is precisely this circumstance, the "low-demand trap," that has led to the search for an adequate and reliable market, hence the recent work on agro-industrial complexes as built-in consumers.

Availability of Capital

Because nuclear power plants require a large capital outlay per kilowatt of installed capacity, the availability of capital is of great importance. Most of the countries which could best use additional power—and water—are seriously short of capital; alternative investment opportunities exist which can earn interest at much higher rates than are customary in the United States even now. Israel, for instance, permits a legal maximum of 11 percent, and the demand for loans is usually greater than can be supplied at this rate (14). Higher rates are paid in various ways. It is certainly doubtful if any country which could use a large desalting project based on nuclear power should count on having to pay less than 10 percent interest per year. If for political or other noneconomic reasons the United States should decide to provide a plant in a country on a subsidized basis, any interest rate could be used in the calculations. Without

discussing the merits of subsidization, however, current efforts to portray nuclear desalting as having come or about to come "of age" are based not on subsidized but on market conditions.

Cost of Equipment

Power plant costs would almost surely be higher outside the United States, especially in countries that have been mentioned as candidates for desalting plants (7, p. 165). The reasons include costs of shipment of equipment, lack of supporting industries and their production, shortage of national specialists and construction crews, and longer construction time. Only a small portion of these increases might be made up by procurement of some of the equipment from lower cost sources abroad.

Operating Performance

The cost of servicing a nuclear power plant is likely to be higher than in the United States for reasons very similar to those just cited. The intrusion of a highly complex technology into an environment that is not geared to it is bound to result in lessened effectiveness and higher cost of maintenance and operations generally. Although the record of power availability of nuclear plants is anything but good in the few plants that have so far operated in the United States, it is likely to be poorer in the less-developed areas of the world unless the plant can be run as a virtual enclave, and even then a good record is by no means certain. This is not to say that improvements would not gradually be attained, as they are bound to be attained in the United States. It is reasonable to believe that the economics of nuclear desalting, examined alone, would make the first plant ordered in any less-developed country disproportionately large, and it would be a long time before a second and a third could be built. Thus the initial plant would for years bear the burden and cost of serving both as an economic input and as a training and experimental facility.

We do not wish to appear unduly pessimistic. Not all of the adverse factors need come true, but some are sure to be felt. And there is little in the picture that points to the emergence of unforeseen favorable elements, at least not without consideration of other energy sources. A good deal of what has been said above would not be true of fossil fuels, abundantly available in the Middle East, where vast amounts of natural gas are flared, and where the marginal cost of crude oil is extremely low. Moreover, the economies of scale would be less pronounced and size problems somewhat alleviated.

But for the moment no such proposals have caught the public fancy, although there is no generally valid technical, economic, or other connection between nuclear energy and desalting. Indeed, from the viewpoint of international complications, the association of desalting with nuclear energy probably represents an obstacle rather than an aid to achievement of the economic objectives in some parts of the world. A first indication of change in that direction could be the proposed bill transmitted to the Senate by the Department of the Interior on 17 January 1969, 3 days prior to the Adminstration changeover. It would authorize U.S. participation in a dual-purpose plant to be erected in Israel. An upper limit of $40 million would be placed on any grant made to help finance the desalting techniques and necessary modifications in the power production of the plant. Financing of the balance as well as the choice of energy source would be determined by the Israeli government.

Efforts to overcome the difficulties briefly described above have taken two forms. One has been to present an optimistic picture of the expected costs of water by making highly favorable assumptions for cost and output factors. The other has been to broaden the scope of operations beyond production of power and water and to test the feasibility of a large agro-industrial complex in which the large volume of electricity that cannot be absorbed by the ordinary demand of the country can find a ready market.

First Kaiser used plant costs based upon a price schedule that became quickly outmoded,

as we have pointed out above, and has led to later revisions (15). This would matter less if prices of crops had undergone similar increases, but they have not. Second, interest charges, and fixed charges based upon that interest, are unrealistically low. Even the highest variant has an interest charge of only 8 percent. The assumed downtime for the generating plant is 10 percent, certainly a highly optimistic assumption over the lifetime of the plant (6). And since the cost of water is arrived at by deducting from the total costs of the dual plant the income from selling the large amounts of electricity that are not consumed internally, a constant price of that electricity is assumed for the lifetime of the plant. This method discounts the possibility of slowly falling revenue stemming from a declining power-cost level in the economy as a whole. To the extent that the income from electricity sales is maximized, the "cost" of water, as the residual, is minimized.

The Oak Ridge study does make some allowance for higher costs outside of the United States, and sets out a wide range of possible interest rates. But in terms of the Oak Ridge concept, there is no need (and perhaps no basis for doing so) to determine separately the cost of either power or water, since it is the returns for the operation as a whole that measure the profitability of this closed complex.

We shall deal later with the various assumptions, but one needs mentioning here. In both studies joint production economies are reflected in the cost of water. While such a subsidy from one part of joint production to the other may be wholly desirable in a given case, it is apt to mislead those who are interested in the cost of desalted water regardless of its association with power production. In fact, the popular discussion has fastened on precisely the costs of water that have emerged from such studies without awareness that water cost is to a substantial degree a function of the price at which power can be sold. In this connection, the Oak Ridge study straddles the fence. Although its basic concept of an integrated complex renders the costing of either power or water meaningless, it fails to exploit this advantage in a consistent way and presents both costs separately, albeit in a somewhat offhand manner, and, it must be said, to the decided detriment of the entire exercise; for it leads the reader to marvel at the agricultural sector calculations being based predominantly on water at 10 cents per thousand gallons, when the rest of the study clearly spells out that no such water is in the offing, not even in the "far-term" model 20 years hence.

The same phenomenon has turned up in the case of the dual plant in the Los Angeles area, discussed briefly below. Before it was tentatively shelved in mid-'68, the estimated cost of water at the plant had risen from 22 to nearer 40 cents per thousand gallons. But "20 cents per thousand gallons" has left a lasting impression with well-intentioned but ill-informed writers and speakers.

Desalting Process

Much of the uncertainty to which we have drawn attention in the discussion of the energy-producing component is present in aggravated form in the desalting component. Here too, the scale of operations proposed in each instance is greatly in excess of anything that has so far been tried, although in the Kaiser proposal the large capacity is reached by replication of small, basic modules that are only five times the size of anything now in operation.

In each proposal the nuclear power plant and the distillation plant would be closely linked. Anything which led to a shutdown in one would force an early shutdown in the other, although planned maintenance in either process might be carried out during forced shutdowns of the other process. The schedule for a power and distillation plant in the Kaiser proposal calls for a demanding availability of 85 percent jointly, or a downtime of 15 percent. There is little on which to base an appraisal of this assumption. But it may be noted that the Point Loma demonstration plant of the Department of the Interior, prior to its transfer to Guantanamo Bay in Cuba, had an availability of only 70 percent (6). Since this was an early plant, one would expect later ones to operate more continuously, if it were not for the type of difficulties that the Point Loma plant ex-

perienced. A serious one that the Kaiser plant does not seem to have adequately taken into account was the problem of drawing water out of the ocean. Many materials obstructed the intake pipe—kelp, sand and silt, fish, even large stones. Large and expensive stilling basins must be installed if such difficulties are to be avoided, and one may assume that the type of difficulty will vary from one location to another. "It is evident from our observations both at San Diego and elsewhere," an engineering evaluation states, "that the importance of trouble-free intake systems either does not get through to those responsible for the design of the system or that there exists a tendency to skimp in the design in order to reduce costs" (16).

Another unknown is the discharge of hot and bitter brines in volumes 100 times and more than that of existing plants. This could present awkward problems. At the minimum, the discharge point must be removed by considerable distance from the intake point to prevent even partial recirculation of even saltier water; expensive piping out to sea may be required (17). Adverse ecological consequences of dumping these wastes are inevitable. Neither they nor the possible costs of dealing with them have received attention.

Although each report is concerned with the future, some comparison with present plants is sobering. The lowest cost plant operating today (providing water for Key West, Florida) produces water for 83 cents per 1000 gallons, but with a subsidized interest rate loan from the federal government; without it the cost would have been very close to $1 per 1000 gallons. In 1966, two private utilities in Southern California, the City of Los Angeles, and the Metropolitan Water District of Southern California, assisted by funds from the U.S. Department of the Interior and the Atomic Energy Commission, entered into an agreement to build a desalting plant on man-made Bolsa Island in Southern California to serve an urban area with a high demand for both electricity and water. The plant was to produce 150 million gallons of desalted water daily and have a generating capacity of 1.8 million kilowatts of electricity. The originally estimated cost including water conveyance and power transmission was $444 million; by the summer of 1968 estimated costs had escalated to $765 million, owing to a greatly lengthened construction period, increased equipment and interest cost, stricter design criteria, and, one of the smallest items, a 10 percent larger power output. The project is uneconomic at this price, and the proposal in its present form has been shelved.

If desalting of seawater is not economic in Southern California today—where alternative water must be brought long distances at high cost, where electricity surely has a ready market, and where much of the water would not go to agriculture—then where is large-scale desalting of seawater economic? If it is not economic at an interest rate of 3.5 percent, and at the lifetime capacity factor for both water and power of 90 percent, assumed for this venture, then what are the prospects under less generous assumptions?

These recent experiences may not apply to desalting costs in the more distant future, but they are at least sobering. This is particularly true when one attempts to make corrections both for the unrealistically low fixed charges, and especially the interest rate (the Oak Ridge proposal is the more realistic in that respect), and some allowance also for the optimism incorporated into the estimates at various stages. Wolfowitz has tried to make adjustments for the proposed Israeli plant (6). Using as his point of departure the lowest estimated cost of 28.6 cents, based on an interest charge of 1.9 percent, he demonstrates persuasively that the likely contingent expenses not included would bring the cost to 40 cents per 1000 gallons at the farm. If adjustment is then made to a more realistic but still modest fixed charge such as 10 percent, the resulting cost of water at the farm would rise to somewhere between 90 cents and $1 per 1000 gallons.

Application of Desalted Seawater to the Land

The third, and most generally neglected, aspect of desalting seawater for use in large-scale agriculture is the conveyance of the water from where it is produced at the edge of the sea to the land, which may be some distance inland and at a much higher elevation. The desalting plants discussed above will produce water in a constant stream (except when shut down for repairs or servicing), but the farmer wants water in a different time sequence during the year. In some way, water must be stored and transported, from one time and place pattern to another, and substantial costs will be incurred in doing so. Much of the discussion of the economics of desalting seawater overlooks this point; someone will compare the costs of water at the plant (usually grossly underestimated) with the value of the water at the farm (usually grossly overestimated).

In an arid region, irrigation water is essential for successful production of most crops, but so are several other inputs. The farmer combines them all into the farm operation program for production of crops and livestock which, in view of prices, costs, and markets, seems to him most likely to produce the greatest net income. The resulting time sequence of irrigation-water use is usually highly seasonal in character, its exact pattern depending upon climatic factors as well as upon choice of crops and methods of crop production. Modifying the farming program to smooth out the seasonal demand somewhat for irrigation water is possible in some areas and under some circumstances, but this modification is very likely to reduce income, sometimes substantially, from the whole farm operation. By and large, for desert and arid areas where desalted water might be used, a markedly seasonal demand for irrigation water is certain, if the farmer is free to choose when he takes water; demand for off-season water may be low.

The problem of storing and conveying water from desalting plant to farm will vary greatly from one location to another, but some generalizations may be made. Desalted water, in excess of immediate need, might be stored in surface reservoirs or underground aquifers located en route or not too distant from the place of either production or application, or in the soil of the farm. In each case, some water—often a great deal—will be lost through evaporation or percolation, or both; water stored in the soil may pick up salt—a great deal in most desert soils. Evaporation in most desert areas is high, often 10 feet or more annually from a water surface. There may be no suitable reservoir site; in any event, dams cost money to build. Soils and aquifers may have a low water-holding capacity or intake rate. Also, some means must be provided for carrying water by large conduits, pipes, or canals from the desalting plant or storage site to the border of each farm. In the United States, this has proven rather costly even when the water source was available by gravity flow. If the arable lands lie at some elevation, pumping costs will be considerable.

In the Kaiser report, the water-conveyance facilities and electrical transmission lines are not included. It is stated that they would add more than 15 percent to the investment. The water cost estimates are based upon 310 days annual operation of the desalting plant but no provision is made for storing this water at times of slack demand and no allowance is made for pumping costs. There are few good surface reservoir sites in Israel. The same limestone formations which allow infiltration of natural precipitation that could later be salvaged as groundwater also are the cause of leaky reservoirs. The most suitable lands in Israel near the proposed desalting plant lie at an elevation of 500 feet or more; pumping costs, even with relatively cheap electricity, would be considerable. The cost of taking desalted water from the plant to the field includes (i) losses in transport; (ii) pumping costs; and (iii) costs of conveyance to the farm, including distribution canals or pipes. By far the greatest of these is likely to be water loss. A 10 percent loss of water would raise the cost of the remaining water by 11 percent, a 20 percent loss by 25 percent, and a 30 percent loss by 43 percent. The more costly the desalting process, the more costly the loss of water in storage or in conveyance.

Pumping costs depend primarily upon lift and distance. Even with high pump efficiency, lifting water requires somewhat more than one kilowatt-hour for each foot of lift for an acre-foot of water (enough water to cover an acre one foot deep, or 326,000 gallons). A 500-foot lift, as would be necessary at the most frequently mentioned Israeli site, would require about 640 kilowatt-hours of electricity; at 5.3 mills per kilowatt-hour, the rate at which the Kaiser report estimates electricity can be disposed of, this would still mean nearly $3.50 per acre-foot of energy; depreciation, maintenance, and interest on pumping equipment would probably add as much again. Finally, there are the costs of construction, maintenance, and operation of a canal or pipe system. The annual cost, including interest on capital, could hardly be less than $3 per acre-foot.

The Kaiser report, on the basis of 8 percent interest on invested capital, arrives at a cost of 67 cents per 1000 gallons at the plant, or $218 per acre-foot. On the basis of the foregoing calculations, an overall loss of water of 10 percent (representing a much higher loss on the volumes actually stored), plus the other costs, would add about $34 per acre-foot to the cost, or 14 percent. If the overall loss were 20 percent, the lost water would add $55 per acre-foot to the cost of the delivered water; with the other costs, total costs incurred between distillation plant and field would be $65, or a 30 percent increase.

If all calculations in the Kaiser report were retained, but the interest rate raised to 12 percent, the costs of desalted water would be in excess of 75 cents per 1000 gallons. If 20 percent were added for conveyance costs and losses, the delivered cost at the farmer's field, on the time schedule he wants the water, rises to 90 cents or more per 1000 gallons.

If one accepts the Oak Ridge calculations, but uses an interest rate of 12 percent, the cost of desalted water at the plant is 28 cents per 1000 gallons; if 20 percent were added for conveyance costs and losses, the delivered price becomes 34 cents; and taking into account all the variables discussed, it seems realistic to count on a delivered cost of at least 40 cents per 1000 gallons, or $130 per acre-foot. It should be noted that some of these additional costs, here incorporated in the cost of irrigation water, are allowed for in various ways in the Oak Ridge scheme under various capital charges of the farm enterprise. Thus, comparisons are difficult because the cost of the water remains unchanged from its cost at the outlet of the desalting plant. But primarily, it is larger size and assumptions of less costly future technology that explain the lower costs of the Oak Ridge study as compared to the Kaiser study.

Value of Irrigation Water

The value of water for irrigation, whatever its source, is affected by many variables—climate, soils, associated inputs such as fertilizer, markets, efficiency of farmers, competition from other producing areas, and many others. Throughout the whole world, water is rarely sold on a market, hence one must estimate "shadow prices" for the irrigation-water supply. It is extremely difficult to determine the *actual* value of irrigation water, but not difficult to say how it should *not* be determined.

First, the value of irrigation water to be developed by the two desalting projects cannot be determined on the basis of what a few farmers could pay to produce a highly specialized crop for a special market. There has been much loose talk about production of "winter vegetables," for instance; aside from the fact that this type of agriculture has never been the gold mine that some think it is, and that competition among producing areas in the future will reduce whatever large profits may have existed in the past (it is hardly legitimate to assume that the advantages of new technology will not be available to other, similarly situated areas), the scale of the Kaiser and Oak Ridge projects preclude this type of agriculture for more than a small fraction of the water to be produced. One hundred million gallons a day for 310 days in the year—85 percent availability—in the Kaiser project, are nearly 100,000 acre-feet annually, or irrigation water for perhaps 35,000 acres of summer crops and much more of winter crops; the Oak Ridge project is ten times as large. Even 35,000 acres is not much less than the total acreage of all vegetables grown annually in Israel, of which only a small fraction are exported. Such an acreage of winter vegetables could not be grown at any single location for the home market and if exported would have disastrous results in terms

of prices of products. True, tomatoes—greatly desired as a leading export—are grown in Egypt on some 200,000 acres but exports in 1965 were the equivalent, at prevailing yields, of the harvest from 40 acres! Even in 1960, the best recent export year, exports came from the equivalent of 700 acres. The task of escalating from such levels to those appropriate to the magnitude of the desalting plants is truly overwhelming. Such comparisons and our ignorance concerning the characteristics of the specialty markets lead one to conclude that crop production from large-scale desalting works must be primarily staple, not specialty, crops.

Second, one cannot safely assume that all the increase in value of output resulting from irrigation will, or can be made to, accrue to the irrigation water; this is a trap into which economists around the world have fallen repeatedly. The quality of the labor and the management which will be required under the more intensive irrigation farming will demand, and can get, higher returns than the kind of labor and management which sufficed for the less intensive agriculture that the new irrigation replaced. Moreover, farmers and other landowners the world over have demanded and have secured some part of the increased production resulting from irrigation as a reward for their land. Further, to attract the capital needed for the new irrigated agriculture, adequate rewards must be in prospect, including a generous allowance for risk. Some of the farm programs or budgets prepared for proposed new irrigation seem to show that very large sums can be paid for irrigation water. On closer examination, these have a fatal flaw; if the intended crop production is so profitable that very large sums can be paid for water, then it is profitable enough so that other extensive areas of the world, including those that need not pay high prices for water, can undertake such production—and the estimated price then quickly drops. Furthermore, the costs of other inputs rise rapidly, as the high yields conventionally assumed on irrigated acreage in these studies demand greatly increased applications of fertilizer, pesticides, and so forth, with attendant employment of sophisticated skills and machinery. In irrigated cotton-growing in California, for example, other costs are so high that water costs typically constitute only 10 to 15 percent of total operating cost.

Third, it is easy to develop plans which embody a wholly new order of magnitude in farm efficiency—crop yields much higher than those obtained by farmers in other irrigation projects in the region, fertilizer inputs several times as great as now practiced, new crop varieties that lead to much higher yields, and many others. By comparing irrigation agriculture on this new higher plane of efficiency with nonirrigated agriculture (or even with present irrigation) on the older, lower level of efficiency, some very high values of water can be estimated. Irrigation does indeed open up new production opportunities, but realism is called for in estimating just how much advantage can and will be taken of these opportunities, and how soon. If the new system of agriculture is possible with new irrigation, why is it not feasible with old irrigation? What reason is there to expect that provision of irrigation water will immediately transform a backward, traditional agriculture into a modern or futuristic efficient one?

Fourth, the agro-industrial complex has been offered as an answer to the last question asked. But is it? Such complexes as sketched by their proponents employ currently unknown or untested methods in industry and agriculture, produce for unspecified markets, and appear to justify very high costs for irrigation water. The prime example here is the Oak Ridge project. Although comprehensive in the scope of things to be considered, it tends to assume optimistic outcomes, uses low costs, and fails to allow for unexpected difficulties and costs. Above all, it fails to supply a satisfactory answer to the question: if these great agro-industrial complexes are economically feasible with desalted water, why are they not feasible with natural flow or groundwater? There is nothing magical about desalted water: it is simply water.

The agro-industrial complexes of the Oak Ridge type have been defended on the ground that they would constitute a new order of technology and organization, freed of all the inhibitions of restrictive institutions, cultural values, modes of living, and so forth, which impede agricultural and industrial development in some countries. This is a dubious argument if applied to Australia, Israel, and possibly to Mexico and India. Moreover, this proposal is futuristic plantation philosophy. In many colonies of the world before World War II, there were plantation economies, using outside capital, outside management, and producing for an export market; often they were highly efficient. Most are now liquidated as foreign enterprises; there is little reason to expect that the countries would welcome them back. The very isolation of the proposed agro-industrial complex from the mainstream of the country's culture is its most devastating weakness, regardless of the efficiency it might attain. The Oak Ridge study comments on this by contemplating that the food factory concept ". . . would appear to be the reverse of agrarian reform programs in many countries. On the other hand, setting up an operation in a sparsely populated area might be effective in avoiding complications of existing social organizations and customs" (3, p. 27). One can only comment that it would save even more trouble if one were to select a less difficult geographic, social, and political setting and then find a way of letting the country to be aided share in the fruits of production by assigning to it the plant's net return.

But ignoring these broader-based considerations and insisting only that the large-scale desalting projects planned by Kaiser and Oak Ridge must produce predominantly staple crops, such as grains and cotton, for domestic and export markets, one can judge the economic feasibility from a number of recent American studies that provide estimates of the value of irrigation water for such crops. Since the contemplated farming ventures discussed above are based on highly advanced technologies and must to a large extent be competitive with world market prices, such studies are not as inappropriate a criterion as one might first think.

Young and Martin provide information and analyses to indicate that the value of irrigation water in central Arizona is less than $21 per acre-foot (18); Stults, considering the situation in Pinal Country, Arizona, makes analyses which imply that the value of the water is about $9 per acre-foot (19); Grubb estimated the ability to pay for irrigation water in the High Plains of Texas ranged from $27 to $36 an acre-foot, even in 1990 (20); and Brown and McGuire found that the marginal value productivity of irrigation water in Kern County, California, was about $19 per acre-foot (21). These are all in fairly good farming areas, where the growing season is rather long, cropping patterns can be rather intensive, and crop yields are relatively high. In irrigated areas where farming is somewhat less intensive, due in part to differences in climate, Hartman and Anderson concluded that the value of supplementary water was from $1.50 to $3 per acre-foot (22); and Fullerton found that in a fairly active water-rental area, the price was about $8.75 per acre-foot (23). All of these examples involve rather high-level managerial competence (which is more easily hypothesized) unlike that found in some of the countries under study; the same is true of the availability of farm machinery, fertilizer, insecticides, and other inputs. It is important to note that they do not focus on the subsidized price of water, but on what users can afford to pay. Thus they are directly relevant to the hypothetical cost of desalted (or any other) water. Moreover, they escape the frequent criticism that the cost of desalted water should not be compared with the actual price currently paid for water, or that the present price of water is an irrelevant object of comparison, since it must be judged in a multi-purpose use context.

On the basis of this range of American experience, it seems most unlikely that irrigation water delivered to the farm on the schedule the farmer wants it, for the production of staple crops, can attain a value greater than $30 per acre-foot (10 cents per 1000 gallons), and a value of $10 per acre-foot (3 cents per 1000 gallons) is a much more reasonable planning standard.

The conclusion is inescapable: the full and true costs of the proposed desalting projects, now and for the next 20 years, are at least one whole order of magnitude greater than the value of the water to agriculture. The specifics of both cost and value will vary, depending upon the location of the plant and the myriad of factors associated with that location, upon what desalting costs actually are in practice, upon crop possibilities (costs and markets, especially), and upon other variables. But it is impossible to bring planned costs and prospective values for agriculture together or even close.

Nothing we have said with regard to the prospects for desalting seawater should be construed as an argument against continued research, including the construction of a rather large pilot plant. The Oak Ridge study both merits and needs attentive reading and critical review. Such research must not stop at the farm gate nor bypass the broader implications of such programs with a few passing sentences. There is more involved here than either "truth in advertising," the discovery of a new input, or a new means of fighting hunger. The present mirage may indeed have an oasis within it, and we as a nation have the resources to pursue the matter much further. But let us not delude ourselves or the rest of the world that an early and practical solution is at hand.

References and Notes

1. D. D. Eisenhower, *Reader's Digest*, June 1968. By "huge" plants, he means a billion gallon daily capacity.
2. Kaiser Engineers and Catalytic Construction Co., *Engineering Feasibility and Economic Study for Dual-Purpose Electric Power-Water Desalting Plant for Israel*, January 1966. The study has been revised twice since, and may be secured from Kaiser Engineers, Oakland, California.
3. *Nuclear Energy Center, Industrial and Agro-Industrial Complexes*, ORNL-4290, UC-80-Reactor Technology (Oak Ridge National Laboratory, Oak Ridge, Tenn., November, 1968). The full report was not available at the time of writing, but has since been published.
4. See our letter to the editor, *Environ. Sci. Technol.* 2, 648 (1968).
5. An example of this sort of writing is an article by V. Nikitopoulos, *Ekistics* 26, 14 (July 1968), in which the author presents a map showing the land areas of the world which *cannot* be served by desalinated water, namely those more than 1000 kilometers from any ocean.
6. P. Wolfowitz, *Middle East Nuclear Desalting: Economic and Political Considerations*,

RM-6019—FF (RAND Corp., Santa Monica, Calif., 1969).

7. W. E. Hoehn, *The Economics of Nuclear Reactors for Power and Desalting*, RM-5227-PR/ISA (RAND Corp., Santa Monica, Calif., 1967).

8. G. G. Stevens, *Jordan River Partition* (Hoover Institution on War, Revolution, and Peace, Stanford Univ., Stanford, Calif., 1965).

9. See P. Sporn in *Nuclear Power Economics—1962 through 1967*, report of Joint Committee on Atomic Energy, U.S. Congress (Government Printing Office, Washington, D.C., 1968), p. 2.

10. The Atomic Industry Forum ["The Nuclear Energy Industry—The U.S. Highlights of 1968" (1968), mimeographed] puts the case even more strongly: "The direct costs of constructing nuclear generating plants rose significantly in 1968. From a low in 1966 of about $100 they had increased some 30-40 per cent in 1967, and there seemed to be a strong consensus that this year's increase was also 30-40 percent. While the costs of comparable fossil-fueled units also rose, the increase was apparently less abrupt."

11. Interestingly, the same is true for the desalting phases. The "far-term" technology (combined flash-vertical-tube requires more capital than the "near-term" (multistage flash) does.

12. The pessimistic outlook for the emergence of smaller but still low-cost reactors was presented in a paper given at the 1968 World Power Conference in Moscow, and entitled "Prospects for Small- and Medium-Sized Nuclear Reactor Plants," by W. Buenlich and P. H. Kruck (Central Office of World Power Conference, London, England).

13. H. H. Landsberg, in *World Population—The View Ahead* (International Development Research Center Ser. No. 1) R. N. Farmer, J. D. Long, G. J. Stolnitz, Eds. (Bureau of Business Research, In-

diana School of Business, Bloomington, 1968), p. 138.

14. *The Economist* (London), "Quarterly Economic Review: Israel," annual supplement, 1966 [cited in Wolfowitz (6)].

15. For a detailed review of the Kaiser Engineering proposal see Hoehn (7). We have not so far seen any similarly careful review of the Oak Ridge study.

16. A. C. Foster and J. P. Herlihy, "Operating Experience at San Diego Flash Distillation Plant," in *Proc. First Inst. Symp. Water Desalination* (Government Printing Office, Washington, D.C., 1965 [cited by Wolfowitz (6)].

17. S. T. Powell, "Factors Involved in the Economic Production of Usable Fresh Water from Saline Sources," in *Proc. First Inst. Symp. Water Desalination* [cited by Wolfowitz (6)].

18. R. A. Young and W. E. Martin, *Ariz. Rev.* **16,** 9 (March 1967).

19. H. M. Stults, *Water Resources and Economic Development of the West, Rep. No. 15, Conf. Proc.* of the Committee of the Economics of Water Resource Development of the Western Agricultural Economic Research Council, 7-9 December, 1966, Las Vegas, Nevada.

20. H. W. Grubb, *Importance of Irrigation Water to the Economy of the Texas High Plains, Texas Water Development Board Rep. 11* (Austin, Texas, January 1966).

21. G. M. Brown and C. B. McGuire, *Water Resources Res.* **3,** 33 (1967).

22. L. M. Hartman and R. L. Anderson, *J. Farm Econ.* **44,** 207 (1962).

23. H. H. Fullerton, "Transfer Restrictions and Misallocation of Irrigation Water," thesis, Utah State University (1965).

28

EVOLUTIONARY RESPONSE TO HUMAN INFECTIOUS DISEASES

George J. Armelagos and John R. Dewey

The study of the evolution of man seldom takes into consideration the role of disease in this development. This is understandable since the evidence available is essentially inferential and consequently open to interpretation. These inferences are based on the actual paleontological record with additional information provided by the historical accounts of disease. We are also able to speculate on the occurrence of disease in prehistoric populations from the disease patterns in contemporary *Homo sapiens* and nonhominid populations. This study is an attempt to discuss infectious diseases in human evolution.

There are three variables which we must consider in the study of infectious diseases—the host, the pathogen, and the environment (Cockburn, 1963). The study of diseases in man, then, would involve the interrelationship of these variables. Although there have been changes in the host (in this case, man) and the pathogen, some of the most significant changes are those in the environment (Armelagos, 1967). It is important to note that the environment of man includes all aspects of his culture (Bates, 1953). This presents somewhat of a dilemma, since man has used culture as his major mode of adaptation in an attempt to control the other aspects of his environment. The study of man's culture—his technology, social system, and even his ideology—must be considered if we are to understand the disease patterns of man.

The role of culture is so significant in understanding the disease process that May (1960) constructed a model in which culture is dealt with as a separate factor, as are the

Reprinted from *Bioscience* 20: 271-75, 1970, with the permission of the publishers.

environment (which includes the pathogen) and the host. May illustrates the role of culture with particular disease patterns in North Vietnam. North Vietnam has two relevant geomorphological features: fertile delta and the fertile hills. Although rice is grown in the hills, the major area of rice cultivation is in the delta. The rice growers in the delta build houses on the ground, with a stable on one side and a kitchen on the other. The hill people, on the other hand, build houses on stilts with living rooms about 8 to 10 ft above the ground. The animals are kept underneath the houses, while the cooking is done in the living room.

The vector for malaria, *Anopheles minimus*, occurs in the hills, but the flight ceiling of this vector is about 8 or 9 ft and, consequently, the *Anopheles* encounter only the animals under the house. If the vector were to stray to the living room, fumes from the cooking would tend to drive it away. The malaria vector does not occur in the delta.

Some people have been forced to move to the hills under pressure of overpopulation in the delta. Typically, movement of the delta people to the hills has not resulted in the acceptance of the culture of the hill people. The delta tribes still build their houses on the ground, with the animals kept in the stables on the side. Food is cooked outside and brought into the house to be eaten in the smoke-free living room. This results in the *Anopheles minimus* feeding on the humans, whom they prefer to the nonhuman animals. This transfer results in the transmission of malaria to the new inhabitants. According to May, the people of the delta have been discouraged from relocating, feeling that the evil spirits in the hills do not like them. The intimate relationship between disease and culture noted by May is not unique; others (Hackett, 1937; Livingston, 1958; Lambrecht, 1964; Alland, 1967; and Hudson, 1965) have presented similar interactions.

The Cultural Adaptation

The beginning of the cultural adaptation began about 2 million years ago with the emergence of man. During the Paleolithic, which lasted for 99% of human history, man was essentially a hunter and gatherer. Cultural development was excruciatingly slow. Pebble tools of the Oldowan culture persisted over a million years. The more refined hand axes and flake tools of the Abbervillian and Acheulian periods lasted another half-million years. There were other changes during the Lower Paleolithic which are relevant. The Australopithecines, the original hominids, were restricted to the tropical grasslands and exploited only a small portion of the available habitat. Although the diet of the Australopithecines, according to Howell (1964), consisted of a small amount of meat from fish, amphibians, reptiles, small mammals, and moderate-sized herbivorous ungulates, the major proportion was made up of gathered vegetal material.

During the latter part of the Lower Paleolithic, a period in which the hominids reached the *Homo erectus* stage of development, there was an increase in hunting ability. There are archeological sites which indicate preferential hunting. Seventy per cent of a large sample of bones found at Choukoutien, near Peking, China, belong to two species of deer (Howell, 1964). It is from this same site that the first evidence of fire is found. The major consequence of the cultural adaptation was an expansion of populations into the temperate zone. It is important to note that in our model we emphasize an expansion, rather than a migration, of population.

The changes during the latter part of the Lower Paleolithic, the Middle Paleolithic (130,000-40,000 B.P.), and Upper Paleolithic (40,000-12,000 B.P.) were variations of the same theme. The adaptation of intensive hunting persists, with specialization in the Upper Paleolithic to differing environments. Again expansion is noted, this time into the tundra zone. It is during this period that we have the arrival of the first hominids into the New World (Griffin, 1964).

The close of the Pleistocene was marked by significant climatic changes in both the Old and New Worlds. The disappearance of the last glacier and a general warming trend caused significant changes in the distribution of large animals. Added to the apparent migration, the efficiency of Upper Paleolithic hunters led to the disappearance of many of the large animals in many areas. The hunting continued, but fishing and collecting became more important. Regional specialization continued in this period, the Mesolithic (12,000-8,000 B.P.).

In the Near East, these changes were responsible for an increased dependence on wild cereal which eventually led to semi-sedentary adaptation. This increased sedentarism, diversification of food sources, and decreased dependency on large animals were prerequisite to the domestication of plants and animals (Adams, 1964).

Although Neolithic development in the New World and Old World were independent, the consequences were similar. Sedentary villages were built to protect and care for the fields. There was a substantial increase in the size of residential units and total population. Increased food supply and the economic importance of children were causal factors for these increases. The agricultural adaptation led quickly to the development of sedentary villages in the Near East (4200 B.C.), urban centers (3100 B.C.), and preindustrial cities and industrial cities (1800 A.D.).

Neolithic development resulted in drastic shifts in the ecological balance. Prior to the Neolithic, man had little observable effect on the environment (Sears, 1956). The utilization of fire (Stewart, 1956) represents one cultural practice which could have altered the landscape. In addition, the improvement of hunting techniques late in the Lower Paleolithic may have led to the extinction of the megafauna (Martin, 1967).

The adaptation we have been talking about is better reflected in population figures computed by Deevey (1960). By the end of the Lower Paleolithic, total population was 125,000 with a density of $0.00425/km^2$. This increased to 1,000,000 (density $0.012/km^2$.) in the Middle Paleolithic and to 5,320,000 (0.04 people/km^2) in the Mesolithic. Following the Neolithic Revolution, there was nearly a sixteenfold increase over the Mesolithic population to 86,500,000 (1.4 people/km^2). The increase in population, it is sad to say, continues.

Another factor which is relevant is the size of the social unit. A group of hunters and gatherers is not likely to increase much over 100 people and a more likely figure is 50-75 before fission occurs. The early agricultural villages at Jarmo, which were quite small, had over 150 people. Other agricultural villages would likely have had 300 or 400 people, but urban centers which followed far outshadowed this. Ur, according to Woolley (1965), had a population of 350,000, while Sjoberg (1965) estimates a population of 100,000 people for the Valley of Mexico. By 1500 A.D. only 1.6% of the total European population was living in centers of 100,000 or more people. By 1700 A.D. this increased to 1.9%, and by 1800 A.D., to 2.2%. Following the Industrial Revolution, in Great Britain alone 10% of the population was living in centers of over 100,000. By 1990, Davis (1965) estimates that half the world will be living in urban areas of this size or larger.

The changes in cultural adaptation, with the resulting increases in population size, population density, and changes in the ecological balance, altered the disease pattern of man. Polgar (1964) suggests five stages in the disease history of mankind: hunting and gathering, settled villages, preindustrial cities, industrial cities, and the present. Our discussion of infectious disease in human evolution will utilize Polgar's description of these stages.

The Hunting and Gathering Stage

For almost 2 million years man has subsisted on the animals he could hunt and on the edible plants he could gather. As one would expect, populations adapted to a hunting and gathering subsistence are small and are distributed over a wide area. In addition to their low density, these groups would have led a seminomadic existence. Small population size and low density would restrict the types of infectious disease which would have plagued them. Contagious diseases, for example, would not have had a large enough population base to have an impact on the evolution of these populations. Polgar suggests that the hunter and gatherers would have been afflicted with two types of

disease—those which had adapted to the pre-hominids and persisted to infest them after speciation of the hominids, and those (zoonoses) which did not have human hosts but were accidentally transmitted to man. Such parasites as the head and body louse *(Pediculus humanus)*, pinworms, yaws, and malaria would fall into the first category. Cockburn (1967b) would add that most of the internal protozoa found in modern man and bacteria such as *Salmonella typhi* and staphylococci would have been present. It is interesting to note that Livingston (1958) would argue against malarial infections in early man. The small population size and bipedalism indicating a savannah adaptation would preclude the presence of malaria.

The second type of disease is that which has adapted to another host and is transmitted to man accidentally by insect bite, wounds, or from consuming meat of the infected animal. Sleeping sickness, scrub typhus, relapsing fever, tetanus, trichinosis, tularemia, leptospirosis, and schistosomiasis are examples of diseases which, Polgar speculates, may have been transmitted accidentally to man.

The range of the hunters and gatherers is a limiting factor for the kinds of parasites which would have been present. During the earlier period of the hunting and gathering stage, the hominids were restricted to the tropical zone. With an expansion of hominids into the temperate zone (by the time of *Homo erectus*), new and different parasites would have been present. It is important to note that by this time some food was being cooked, a process which would kill some of the parasites present.

Missing from the list of diseases which would have involved man prior to the Neolithic are contagious community diseases such as measles, influenza, smallpox, and mumps (Polgar, 1964). Burnet (1962) goes further and suggests that few viruses would have infected early man. Cockburn (1967a) disagrees strongly, since there are a number of viral infections found in monkeys. Although it is possible that monkeys studied may have contracted the viruses in captivity, the differences in the form of these viruses, according to Cockburn, are enough to argue against this.

The Settled Village Stage

The semi-sedentary encampments of the Mesolithic and sedentary villages of the Neolithic resulted in the concentration of populations in relatively small areas. As one could expect, this would create new and different problems. In hunting and gathering societies, the disposal of human excrement presents no great problem since nomadic travel would preclude the accumulation of human waste (Heinz, 1961). It should be pointed out that in some cases, hunters and gatherers living in caves were forced to abandon them as the debris accumulated.

The sedentarism which is characteristic of the Mesolithic and Neolithic would provide new breeding places for many forms of life which harbor disease. In addition, domestication would have led to the herding of animals near the areas of habitation. Prior to this time, the dog was the only domesticated animal. *Salmonella* and *Ascaris* are carried by domesticated animals such as pigs, sheep, cattle, and fowl. C. A. Hoare (1957) has suggested that the trypanosomes were spread beyond the range of the normal host by domesticated animals. Polgar (1964) also suggests that the products of domesticated animals (milk, skin, hair) and the dust raised by the animals provide for the transmission of anthrax, Q Fever, brucellosis, and tuberculosis.

The expansion of agricultural societies into new environments created other problems. Audy (1961) has demonstrated that as new ground is broken for cultivation, scrub typhus increases. In this case, the agriculturalists exposed themselves to the bites of insects as they toiled in the fields. Livingston (1958) has impressively illustrated the relationship between the spread of agriculture, malaria, and sickle cell anemia. As the West African agriculturalists expanded into the forest and destroyed the trees in the preparation of ground for cultivation, they encroached on the environment of the pongids. The pongids, which were the primary host of the *Plasmodium falciparum* carried by *Anopheles gambiae*, were exterminated or forced further into the forest. The mosquitoes quickly transferred to the hominids for their meals. Livingstone points out that agricultural activity, which provides new breeding areas for mosquitoes and provides a large population for the mosquitoes to feed, led to malaria becoming an endemic disease. Populations in this area have developed a genetic polymorphism—sickle cell trait—which gives those individual heterozygotes for the trait immunity to malaria. In other words, as the agriculturalists expanded, malaria would increase. In response to the increase in malaria, the frequency of the abnormal sickle cell hemoglobin would increase.

Preindustrial Cities

The expansion of the population which began in the Neolithic continued with the development of large urban centers in the preindustrial cities. The problem which faced the settled communities of the Neolithic are present but are significantly more difficult to control. The concentration of a large population in a small area creates problems in supplying food and water and removing human waste. Since many cities dispose of waste via their water supply, serious health hazards developed. Cholera, for example, was transmitted by polluted water. Even with our advanced technology, pollution is still a serious concern.

The increased frequency of contact between members of the population resulted in the transmission of disease by contact. Typhus was transmitted by lice which moved from person to person. Plague bacillus which was originally spread by rodents could, with the high population density, be transmitted by inhalation. During the preindustrial stage, viral diseases such as measles, mumps, chickenpox, and smallpox were also transmitted by contact.

Social change resulting from urbanization was responsible for alteration in the expression of some of the disease. Prior to urbanization, syphilis was a nonvenereal disease, but with the changes in family structure, crowding, and sexual promiscuity, syphilis became a venereal disease (Hudson, 1965).

It was during this period that exploration resulted in the introduction of disease into new areas.

Population during this period approached a size for the maintenance of diseases in an endemic form. Cockburn (1967b) has suggested that a population of about one million is necessary for measles to be maintained as an endemic disease.

Industrial Cities

Increase in population size and density was again a consequence of the cultural advances of the industrial revolution. The social and environmental changes were important. Industrial wastes increased pollution of water and air. Unsanitary conditions in the slums were ideal focal points for the spread of infectious diseases, and imperialistic expansion transported disease into new areas.

Epidemics also created havoc in the industrial populations. Typhus, typhoid, smallpox, diphtheria, measles, malaria, and yellow fever epidemics are well documented for the late 18th and early 19th centuries (Polgar, 1964). Tuberculosis and respiratory diseases such as pneumonia and bronchitis were enhanced by the crowding and harsh working conditions.

Perhaps the saddest consequence of the industrial period was the spread of epidemic diseases to populations which had not developed an immunity to them. Although contact had occurred earlier, in the preindustrial period, the impact was greater during the industrial period.

Present

The advances that have been made in recent times have been quite remarkable; our understanding of the relevant features of infectious diseases has allowed us to make significant strides in preventing and controlling some infectious diseases. Even with these advances, infectious diseases are still prevalent in many areas. Attempts to control disease are more difficult with rapid transportation. Infectious diseases may be transmitted in hours to populations which, 50 years ago, were 2 weeks distant.

The Evolutionary Response

The study of infectious diseases and their impact on human development is the host and the parasite (Motulsky, 1960). The duration of a human generation is much longer than that of the parasites which feed on man. This would favor evolutionary changes in the parasites leading to less severe manifestations of the disease. This is understandable since a parasite which causes the death of the host can then die from lack of a host.

The responses in the host were also significant. Haldane (1949) suggests that infectious diseases have been the most important selective factor in human evolution. Since the factors (i.e., large, dense population) which led to epidemic infectious diseases arose rapidly following the Neolithic revolution, the genetic factors would not have been present to provide immunity against these infectious diseases. In other words, the genotypes that were selected during the hunting and gathering stage would have provided little protection against the infectious diseases, but the genetic heterogeneity of the population would have been adequate to protect some individuals from the diseases. Lederberg (1963) disagrees, since many of the diseases which have animal reservoirs would be important in an epidemic sense. Instead of rapid selection acting on a large population, Lederberg suggests that the persistent applications of small differentials over a long period of time, as characteristic of "reservoir disease," could have developed factors of genetic immunity.

Motulsky (1963) states that there are three areas of concern in disease-susceptibility and resistance: (1) factors of immunity in the conventional antigen-antibody reaction; (2) generalized host factors; and (3) highly specific gene-determined factors which provide resistance.

Motulsky points out that there may be a genetic potential for antibody production, but it would be difficult to demonstrate in man. Lederberg (1959) has provided other data which would suggest a possible genetic variation in the response to antibody protection. Although not much is known about the inheritance of the nonspecific host factors in the response to infectious disease, they do appear to have a genetic basis. Efficiency of phagocytosis, levels of complements, antimicrobial factors in tissue, and serum inhibitors of microbial growth may have been important in providing immunity to diseases (Motulsky, 1963).

The highly specific genetic factors may have had a key role in the evolutionary response to infectious diseases. Although it would be impossible to demonstrate the genetic factors involved, populations appear to have developed a genetic immunity to disease. Motulsky (1960) states that when tuberculosis strikes a population which was not previously exposed to the disease, the mortality is high and the infection is acute. The individuals which are most susceptible to the disease would perish, while those with genetic characteristics which provide some resistance would survive. In subsequent episodes, the mortality is lower and infection is less severe. The differential susceptibility in different populations could result from a genetic difference. For example, American Indians and Eskimos developed a more acute tubercular infection. The evidence for genetic immunity is suggestive, however, since environmental differences in nutrition and sanitation may explain some of the population differences.

The evidence for highly specific genetic factors is more convincing in the metabolic polymorphisms which have evolved in response to disease (Motulsky, 1960). For example, the sickle cell trait, which provides resistance to malaria, has been discussed. Other polymorphisms have evolved in areas where malaria is endemic. The hemoglobinopathy thalassemia and glucose-6-phosphate dehydrogenase deficiency also appear to provide protection against malaria (Motulsky, 1963).

The evolution of genetic protection against infectious disease would have been essential for the survival of a population, since epidemic diseases could destroy large segments of the population. In some instances, infectious diseases may act as a factor inhibiting population growth. In those populations in which epidemic diseases are still an important factor, increases in population are evidence. Cultural practices tend to maintain population size. As cultural groups are better able to prevent and control infectious disease, the population increases at an alarming rate. In order to combat this increase in population. Polgar (1964) suggests that public health programs which are designed to control and prevent infectious diseases in countries with high fertility rates should include programs to limit population increase.

In addition to the problem of the exploding population, the control of infectious diseases has helped to increase life expectancy. The increase in longevity would have created new problems for the older segments of the population; increase in degenerative disease would have been a consequence. In a population in which the oldest individuals live to 60 years of age, degenerative diseases are relatively unimportant. Nell (1958) states that in the state of Michigan, of the deaths in 1953 from arteriosclerotic, hypertensive, or degenerative heart disease (which constituted 33.1% of all deaths), 7.4% occurred prior to age 50. By the 60th year, approximately 25% have died of degenerative heart disease. The remaining 75% of deaths due to degenerative heart disease occur after 60 years of age.

Recently, we are able to demonstrate that osteoporosis (loss of bone mass with age) occurs earlier and is more severe in prehistoric Nubian populations when compared to bone loss in a modern population. In the prehistoric Nubian population, the frequency of fractures due to severe bone loss was not evident. An examination of the mortality pattern would indicate why this should be the case. Approximately 40% of the population die before their 40th year. Only 15% live past 40 years and all are dead before age 60. In the United States, 91% live past their 40th year, 75% past their 60th, 29% past their 80th, and 6% past their 90th year. Since many individuals live past age 60 and osteoporosis continues, the decrease in bone mass becomes great enough to predispose the neck of the femur to pathological fracture. It should be pointed out that since these degenerative conditions occur in that segment of the population which is past reproductive age, selective responses to degenerative conditions could not occur.

With the possibility that we may be able to control infectious diseases in some populations, concern with degenerative conditions (Spiegelman, 1956) and population control should be two areas of future research.

Acknowledgment

Partial support was received from a grant (H. D. AM02771-01) from the National Institute of Child Health and Human Development, United States Public Health Service.

References

Adams, R. M. 1964. The origin of agriculture. In: *Horizons in Anthropology*, S. Tas (ed.). The Johns Hopkins Press, Baltimore, Md., p. 120-131.

Alland, A., Jr. 1967. War and disease: An anthropological perspective. *Natur. Hist.*, 76: 58-61.

Armelagos, C. J. 1967. Man's changing environment. In: *Infectious Diseases: Their Evolution and Eradication*, A Cockburn (ed.). Charles C. Thomas, Springfield, Ill., p. 66-83.

Audy, J. R. 1961. The ecology of scrub typhus. In: *Studies in Disease Ecology*, J. M. May (ed.). Hafner Publishing Co., New York, p. 387-433.

Bates, M. 1953. Human ecology. In: *Anthropology Today*. A L. Kroeber (ed.). University of Chicago Press, Chicago, Ill., p. 700-713.

Burnet, Sir. F. M. 1962. *Natural History of Infectious Disease*. Cambridge University Press, England.

Cockburn, T. A. 1963. *The Evolution and Eradication of Diseases*. The Johns Hopkins Press, Baltimore, Md.

—— 1967a. Infections of the order Primates. In: *Infectious Diseases: Their Evolution and Eradication*, T. A. Cockburn (ed.). Charles C. Thomas, Springfield, Ill., p. 38-107.

—— 1967b. The evolution of human infectious diseases. In: *Infectious Diseases: Their Evolution and Eradication*, T. A. Cockburn (ed.). Charles C. Thomas, Springfield, Ill., p. 84-107.

Davis, K. 1965. The urbanization of human population. *Sci. Amer.*, 213: 40-54.

Deevey, E. W., Jr. 1960. The human population. *Sci. Amer.*, 208: 48, 194-198.

Griffin, J. B. 1960. Some connections between Siberia and America. *Science* 131: 801-812.

Hackett, L. W. 1937. *Malaria in Europe*. Oxford University Press, London.

Haldane, J. B. S. 1949. Disease and evolution. Supplement to *La Ricerca Scientifica*. 19: 68-76.

Heinz, H. J. 1961. Factors governing the survival of bushmen worm parasites in the Kalahari. *S. Afr. J. Sci.*, 8: 207-213.

Hoare, C. A. 1957. The spread of African trypanosomes beyond their natural range. *Z. Tropenmed. Parasitol.*, 8: 1-6.

Howell, F. C. 1964. The hominization process. In: *Horizons of Anthropology*, S. Tax (ed.). Aldine Publishing Co., Chicago, Ill., p. 49-59.

Hudson, E. H. 1965. Treponematosis and man's social evolution. *Amer. Anthropol.*, 67: 885-902.

Lambrecht, F. L. 1964. Aspects of evolution and ecology of tsetse flies and trypanosomiasis in prehistoric African environments. *J. Afr. Hist.*, 5: 1-24

Lederberg, J. 1959. Genes and antibodies. *Science*, 129: 1649-1653.

—— 1963. Comments on A. Motulsky's *Genetic Systems in Disease Susceptibility in Mammals*. In: *Genetic Selection in Man*, W. J. Schull (ed.). University of Michigan Press, Ann Arbor, p. 112-260. (The comments are interspersed with Motulsky's text.)

Livingstone, F. B. 1958. Anthropological implication of sickle cell gene distribution in West Africa. *Amer. Antropol.*, 60: 533-562.

Martin, P. S. 1967. Pleistocene overkill. In: *Pleistocene Extinction: The Search for a Cause*, P. S. Martin and H. E. Wright (eds.). Yale University Press, New Haven & London, p. 75-120.

May, J. M. 1960. The ecology of human disease. *Ann. N.Y. Acad. Sci.* 84: 789-794.

Motulsky, A. G. 1960. Metabolic polymorphism and the role of infectious diseases. *Hum. Biol.*, 32: 28-63.

—— 1963. Genetic systems involved in disease susceptibility in mammals. In: *Genetic Selection in Man*, W. J. Schull (ed.). University of Michigan Press, Ann Arbor, p. 112-260.

Neel, J. V. 1958. The study of natural selection in primitive and civilized human populations. *Amer. Anthropol. Assoc. Mem.*, 86: 43-72.

Polgar, S. 1964. Evolution and the ills of mankind In: *Horizons of Anthropology*, S. Tax (ed.). Aldine Publishing Co. Chicago, Ill., p. 200-211.

Sears, P. B. 1956. The processes of environmental changes by man. In: *Man's Role in Changing the Face of the Earth*, W. L. Thomas (ed.). University of Chicago Press, Chicago, Ill., p. 471-484.

Sjoberg, G. 1965. The origin and evolution of cities. *Sci. Amer.*, 213: 55-63.

Spiegelman, M. 1956. Recent trends and determinants of mortality in highly developed countries. In: *Trends and Differentials in Mortality*, F. C. Boudreau and C. V. Kiser (eds.). Milbank Memorial Fund, New York, p. 51-60.

Stewart, O. C. 1956. Fire as the first great force employed by man. In: *Man's Role in Changing the Face of the Earth*. W. C. Thomas (ed.). University of Chicago Press, Chicago, Ill.

Woolley, L. 1965. *Beginnings of Civilization, History of Mankind*. Vol. 1. Part II. The New American Library. Mentor Books, New York & Toronto.

29

ALL THAT EMPTY SPACE

Paul R. Ehrlich

There was so much handwriting on the wall that
even the wall fell down . . .

—Christopher Morley

As they cruise at 35,000 feet, many air
travelers are impressed by the vast "empty"
stretches of such western U.S. states as Nevada
and Utah. Even over areas of the Midwest,
South, and East, they notice large areas with
few buildings. It comes as a surprise, then, to
hear ecologists talk about the United States as
an "overpopulated country." What about "all
that empty space?"

It is a common confusion to think overpopulation means too many people for the
amount of space available. By that standard,
the United States, with some 55 persons per
square mile, is relatively underpopulated. There
is plenty of room for us to move around.
Except in the big cities, we're not yet so
overcrowded that we are stepping on each
other's toes.

By the same standard, the open oceans, the
Greenland Ice Cap, most of Antarctica, and the
moon, all with zero persons per square mile, are
even more underpopulated!

A Standard for Overpopulation Based Solely on People per Unit of Area Is Naïve and Relatively Meaningless

The most common forms of overpopulation
involve not too many people for the available
space, but too many people for the available
resources, or too many people for the efficient
functioning of society.

Southern California, for instance, has lots
and lots of open desert, but still is wildly

Reprinted with the permission of Paul R. Ehrlich
from the *TWO Ambassador* 3(7): 5-9, 1970.

overpopulated. It does not have enough water
to support its population and must go to
tremendous expense and trouble to import
water for its burgeoning millions. The capacity
of the atmosphere over the area to absorb
dangerous pollutants is clearly overtaxed, as
almost anyone who has flown into the Los
Angeles Basin can testify. And the huge, impersonal, smoggy cities of this area, like those
elsewhere, show signs of social decay. By itself,
halving the population would probably not
solve any of these problems, but it would make
all of them easier to solve.

We cannot, of course, consider an area that
is not entirely self-sufficient "overpopulated."
To do so would put all cities, which always
depend on hinterlands for food, in this category. Southern California draws food from
many areas, but neither extraordinary difficulty
in obtaining food nor severe competition with
the food needs of other areas of the United
States is involved. Shortage of food resources is
not, at the moment, a sign of Southern California's population crisis. On the other hand,
both extraordinary difficulty (and thus expense), as well as competition, are involved in
supplying water to this fundamentally desert
area. Water shortage is a sign of overpopulation
there.

No knowledgeable person will dispute that
some urban areas are overpopulated, but what
about the United States as a whole?

Consider our resource position: we represent
roughly six per cent of the population of the
world, but we consume some 35 per cent of
global resources used by man each year. Since
we are resource-poor (much of this material
comes from outside our borders), those who
shape our foreign policy must give high priority
to maintaining our influence at the sources of
the petroleum, asbestos, manganese, nickel,
tungsten, tin, platinum and other resources we
require. Not even our closest neighbors and
staunch allies are safe from our growing appetites: the United States is so short of water that
it has cooked up an economically and ecologically preposterous scheme—the North American Water and Power Alliance—to grab what
we can of Canada's supply.

At the moment, the United States could in

theory feed herself without outside help. However, the quality of our diet would change if we tried it, since we depend on imports (including fish catches) for part of the high-quality protein we presently consume. Moreover, our present food reserves are insufficient to last for more than a year—an uncomfortable situation when one considers the potential for agricultural disaster in the next decade. Changes in our weather, brought on by the veil of air pollution now covering the earth, could seriously reduce our agricultural production and lead to serious food crisis.

We travel together, passengers on a little spaceship; dependent on its vulnerable reserve of air and soil; all committed for our safety to its security and peace; preserved from annihilation only by the care, the work, and the love we give to our craft.

—Adlai Stevenson

Obviously, then, we are overpopulated in the sense that our standard of living cannot be maintained on our own resource base. Even using all the resources of the entire world (that is, giving none to anyone else), we would run out of many critical ones in the next century or so.

Today, the United States and the other overdeveloped countries not only are using more than their share of resources, they also are mismanaging those they use, wastefully dispersing irreplaceable materials which would have made the lives of their descendents easier. We are committing, as David Brower has said, "grand larceny against the future."

Our population size is pressing hard not just against our resources, but against our values as well. Peace, quiet, tranquility, and a joyous life seem harder and harder to obtain.

In Spite of Our Vaunted Affluence, Tens of Millions of Americans Are Hungry, and Many More Are Denied a Full Share of Our Affluence

Equal rights for all Americans remains a seemingly unattainable dream. While many

white Americans think of environmental deterioration in terms of polluted trout streams and crowded national parks, many black citizens face a degraded environment in the form of dilapidated slums filled with cockroaches and rats. All Americans face serious threats to their health and survival from air and water pollution, increased chances of vast plagues and increased chances of thermonuclear war. None of these problems would *disappear* if our population were smaller, but they all can be shown to be related to and aggravated by overpopulation. All would be more readily solved in a less crowded world.

Because there are disproportionately many young people in the United States and in the world as a whole, measures to bring population growth under control will take decades to be effective (there will be large numbers of people in the child-bearing age group for a long time to come). It is therefore imperative that population control start among the affluent peoples of the overdeveloped nations. We, and our European, Soviet and Japanese colleagues, are the prime looters and polluters of the globe. We are the ones who must lead the way, moving to reduce our numbers and "de-develop." By "de-develop," I mean to move to an economic system appropriate for the crew of a finite spaceship. We must learn to recycle everything and waste nothing. We must acquire a life style which has as its goal maximum freedom and happiness for the individual, not a maximum Gross National Product. As the overdeveloped countries de-develop, they must also stop exploiting the hungry countries of the world and start aiding them to achieve a level of development that will let their citizens lead a high-quality life.

Far out and idealistic you say? You bet it is! But it is also the only way out of our current bind. Mankind's present course leads straight down the drain. Our species will either adjust its behavior to the realities of today's world, or it will lose its dominant position and perhaps suffer the fate of the dinosaurs.

30

FEEDBACKS IN ECONOMIC AND DEMOGRAPHIC TRANSITION

Harald Frederiksen

Demographic transition and economic development are not independent phenomena. If there is such a thing as a "population problem," it cannot be understood and solved in isolation from the complex process of national development, of which economic development is but one aspect.

Needs and resources for health and family-planning programs evolve in the context of the successive stages of demographic transition and economic development. We have to agree on the nature and magnitude of the interactions between population and economic phenomena at the various stages of national development (called simply "development" hereafter) before we can agree on how much of what is most appropriate and effective in the circumstances in question.

Neo-Malthusian Model

A neo-Malthusian school believes that the process of development is impeded when the rate of population growth is high, and that this high rate of growth is the result of a rapid reduction in mortality, which in turn is the result of alien technology's increasing the effectiveness and efficiency of health services quite independently of levels of production and consumption. Let me quote from some writers who belong to this school.

The death rate in less-developed areas is dropping very rapidly ... and without regard to economic change. ...

Reprinted from *Science* 166: 837-47, 1969, with the permission of the publishers. Copyright 1969 by the American Association for the Advancement of Science.

The less-developed areas have been able to import low-cost measures of controlling disease, measures developed for the most part in the highly industrialized societies. The use of residual insecticides to provide effective protection against malaria at a cost of no more than 25 cents per capita per annum is an outstanding example. ...

The death rate in Ceylon was cut in half in less than a decade and declines approaching this rapidity are almost commonplace. The result of a precipitous decline in mortality while birth rate remains essentially unchanged is, of course, a very rapid acceleration in population growth. ...

In the longer run, economic progress will eventually be stopped and reversed unless the birth rate declines *or the death rate increases* (1).

The higher the population growth, the harder becomes the task of breaking through the Malthusian trap. A vicious spiral is set into operation. Because of a high rate of population growth, industrialization is difficult to attain. Because there is no industrialization, the birth rate and the rate of population growth remain high (2).

It may seem indecent to some to suggest that medical research first be concentrated on those diseases whose control will do most to improve the happiness and ability to work of people without reducing infant mortality ... (3).

... Public health measures which can save millions of lives should not be practiced in China on a nationwide scale until the stage is set for a concurrent reduction in the birth rate (4).

Another 10 to 15 points of the initial death rate of 40 per thousand may be attributable to inadequate diet, clothing and shelter, with malnutrition the primary cause. This is of direct concern to economic policy makers because it suggests that extra investments that do *not* increase the food supply, whether directly through international trade, may temporarily be preferred to those that do (5).

Thus, a neo-Malthusian model of economic and demographic transition may seem quite plausible, at least when used to explain failure or to predict the probability of failure (Fig. 30-1). But in order to explain successful development, we have to explain how countries proceed from low to high levels of production and consumption, and from high to low levels of mortality and fertility.

A more humanitarian version of a neo-Malthusian model of successful development would allow some reduction in mortality, but not too rapid a reduction, so that a concurrent and commensurate reduction in fertility would keep population growth to a minimum and raise the formation of capital to a maximum

Fig. 30-1. Neo-Malthusian model of failure of economic and demographic transition.

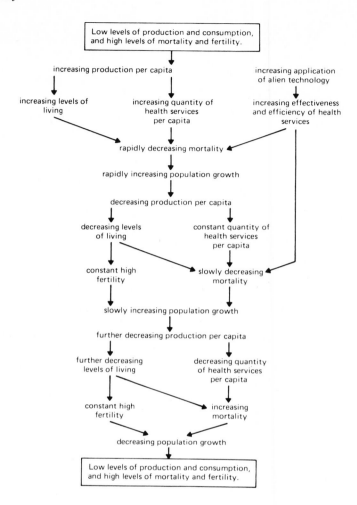

(Fig. 30-2). Such a model of economic and demographic transition implies that high levels of production could be achieved when consumption, mortality, and fertility are, at best, still at intermediate levels.

Even if it were feasible to achieve high levels of production by some such shortcut, bypassing commensurate improvements in the levels of living and health and commensurate reductions in mortality and fertility, high levels of production alone would hardly meet the criteria for successful development. It remains to be seen, in the real world, whether the neo-Malthusian model is a shortcut to successful development. Yet, as a possible result of uncritical acceptance of the neo-Malthusian model, with its explanation of failure in development,

"health programs," says Taylor (6), "which once represented a major effort in American technical assistance, are now being quietly downgraded or phased out in more [underdeveloped] countries except those that are obviously under-populated, such as Ethiopia."

Alternative Model

An alternative model of successful economic and demographic transition would seem to explain more readily the transition from low to high levels of production and consumption, and from high to low levels of mortality and fertility (Fig. 30-3).

This alternative model assumes that improve-

Fig. 30-2. Neo-Malthusian model of successful takeoff in economic and demographic transition.

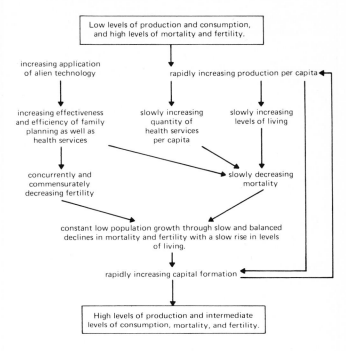

ments in the standard of living and decreases in the mortality and fertility rates are linked in a process of "concurrent, circular, and cumulative causation" (to use the language of Gunnar Mydral). This model stresses the human factor in development and views a drop in the mortality rate as part of the solution of the population problem, not as a cause.

A reduction in mortality is considered a necessary, although insufficient, condition for a reduction in fertility. Mortality trends may influence fertility trends by way of two mechanisms: (i) with reductions in mortality, compensatory reductions in fertility are required if the desired family size is to be achieved; (ii) when there is less uncertainty about survival, the desired family size may be reduced.

In regions where there had been considerable variation in the number of child deaths from family to family, a reduction in overall mortality might result in a reduction in fertility larger than that required to offset the reduced probability of child loss. Thus, a reduction, at the family level, in uncertainty concerning the survival of children might tend to make people want smaller families.

Let me quote from some of the writers who have arrived at similar conclusions.

. . . The removal of any of the particular causes of mortality can have no further effect upon population than the means of subsistence will allow. . . . Of its operation in tending to prevent marriage, by diminishing the demand for fresh supplies of children, I have no doubt (7).

To some extent the birth rate is influenced by the death rates in the lower age groups. . . . A reduction in child mortality would probably reduce birth rates after a lag of several decades (5).

Low death rates, or conditions underlying low death rates, merit consideration as contributory factors, if not as prerequisites, for low birth rates (8).

No efforts of social-economic development can be successful in a disease-ridden population, nor will a desire for small families be likely to emerge (9).

Mortality varies inversely with economic indicators of the levels of living. In a balancing movement, fertility tends toward approximate equilibrium with mortality. . . . a deliberate reduction in fertility is a sequel to a reduction in mortality which develops individual and collective motivations as well as the need for a commensurate restraint of fertility (10).

High fertility has been an adjustment to high and unpredictable mortality. . . . Availability of birth control is largely irrelevant until the desired number of living children is secured (11).

Fig. 30-3. Alternative model of successful economic and demographic transition from low to high levels of production and consumption, and from high to low levels of mortality and fertility.

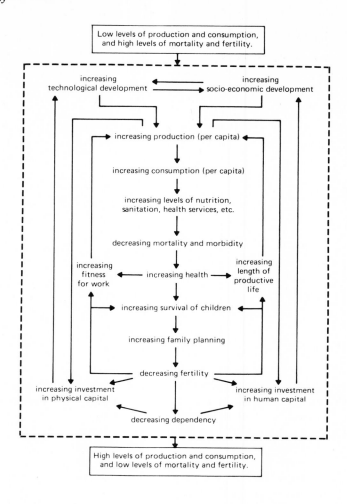

The frequency of births in a population can be understood in terms of three groups of factors that influence parents' desires for births. First there is a family size goal or a number of surviving children that parents want. This goal is determined by a host of environmental factors that modify the relative attractiveness of many versus few children. Second is the incidence of death, mainly among offspring, which necessitates a compensating adjustment in birth rates to achieve any specific family size goal. Third is the effect of uncertainty in the family formation process where births, deaths, and remarriage are unpredictable (12).

In nations with traditionally high child mortality, this desire of fathers to have sons who will outlive them acts as a deterrent to restriction of family size (13).

It was generally agreed that in high mortality countries, the thing *not* to do is blanket the country with a massive family planning program. . . . programs will usually not emerge in countries where the population perceives that the high rate of infant mortality is either high by their standards or is not declining (14).

Although the world-wide population explosion has been created by a decline in death rates paradoxically a further decline in mortality in the less developed nations may be an invaluable aid for curbing the current rate of population growth (15).

The authors quoted above seem to support one or other of the basic assumptions (concerning the interactions between mortality, fertility, and levels of living) which underlie the alternative model of successful development. But those authors may or may not support the alternative model, which puts these basic interactions together in a concurrent, circular, and cumulative process of transition from low to high levels of production and consumption, and from high to low levels of mortality and fertility (Fig. 30-3).

Neo-Malthusian Model

Dependent Variables	Independent Variables		
	Levels of Living	Mortality	Fertility
Levels of living	▨	⊕	−
Mortality	○	▨	+
Fertility	−	○	▨

Alternative Model

Dependent Variables	Independent Variables		
	Levels of Living	Mortality	Fertility
Levels of living	▨	⊖	−
Mortality	⊖	▨	+
Fertility	−	⊕	▨

Fig. 30-4. Neo-Malthusian and alternative models of demographic and economic interaction. The circles focus attention on interactions which are essentially different in the two models. Plus or minus signs indicate a positive or negative association.

Comparison of the Models

Comparison (Fig. 30-4) of the neo-Malthusian model (Fig. 30-2) and the alternative model (Fig. 30-3) indicates three essential differences.

The neo-Malthusian model views a reduction in mortality as an increase in population growth, whereas the alternative model notes the transitory nature of the "population explosion" and emphasizes the improvement in health, productivity, and longevity.

The neo-Malthusian model explicitly or implicitly assumes that levels of mortality are now *quite independent* of levels of living, whereas the alternative model assumes that levels of mortality are still *quite dependent* on levels of living, although the relative effectiveness of health services increases with increasing levels of living.

The neo-Malthusian model ignores any dependence of fertility trends on mortality trends, whereas the alternative model assumes that reductions in mortality develop the need and desire for family planning.

Empirical Test of the Models

At any given point of development, the economic growth rate per capita approximates the economic growth rate minus the population growth rate. This may have led some to equate the population problem with excessive population growth. But it does not follow that a decrease in the population growth rate would be associated with a commensurate increase in the economic growth rate per capita.

Cross-sectional comparison of nonlinear regression lines for population growth rates, economic growth rates, and economic growth rates per capita, for 67 countries, plotted by gross national product per capita, indicates no obvious correlation between population growth rates and economic growth rates per capita (Fig. 30-5).

The *linear* correlation of the rate of population growth with the rate of economic growth *per capita* for the 67 countries was only weakly negative ($r = 0.32$), even though the population growth rate serves as denominator for the dependent variable. In contrast, the linear correlation of the rate of economic growth was only slightly positive ($r = 0.15$).

A statistical significance test was performed only for the latter correlation—that between the rates of population growth and of economic growth—since only these two variables are not algebraically related to each other. The correlation ($r = 0.15$) was not significant even at the 5 percent level of probability.

Actually, the rate of *per capita* economic growth is a poor indicator of development. A low rate of economic growth per capita can be the result of a balance between high or low rates of economic and population growth and thus may be found in countries with *any* rate of economic growth, and with any rate, and at any level, of development.

Moreover, the rate of population growth is a poor indicator of the "population problem," or of its solution, since this rate tends first to rise and then to fall in the course of the modernization process.

Rather than rely exclusively or primarily on the population growth rate as a basis for understanding, measuring, and influencing the

Fig. 30-5. Nonlinear regression lines (third degree) for population growth rates (1958-1966), economic growth rates (1960-1965), and economic growth rates per capita (1960-1965), by gross national product per capita (1965), for 67 countries. (Sources of basic data, United Nations and World Bank.)

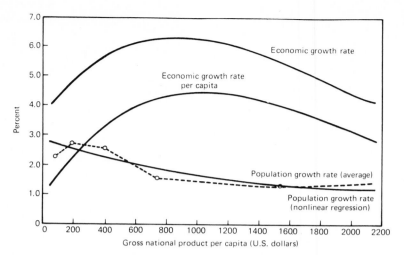

demographic transition, it would be better to rely on the birth rates and death rates from which the population growth rates are derived.

Thus, in the real world, successful development is associated with increasing levels of consumption and of capital formation and with decreasing levels of mortality and fertility—first mortality, then fertility (Fig. 30-6).

Incidentally, the rise in the crude death rates toward the higher values for gross national product per capita is a result of the aging of the populations, which in turn is a result of the declining birth rates. If the death rates could have been adjusted for the differences in age distributions, there would not have been such an apparent rise in the death rates at the higher values for gross national product per capita.

Unfortunately, not enough comparable detailed data were available to permit adjustment of the death rates for differences in the age distributions.

The objection might be raised that these comparisons are cross-sectional, and that these relationships that existed at a point in time would not hold true in longitudinal comparisons over a period of time.

The historical tendency for mortality trends to vary inversely with the standard of living and for fertility trends to maintain or restore approximate balance between mortality and fertility is indicated by the economic and demographic transition that has occurred in France over the past two centuries (Fig. 30-7).

A similar tendency toward approximate bal-

Fig. 30-6. Nonlinear regression lines (third degree) for economic and demographic variables by gross national product per capita (1965), for 67 countries. (Sources of basic data, United Nations and World Bank.)

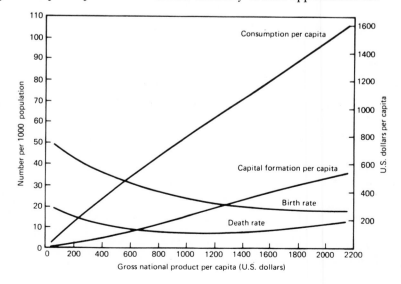

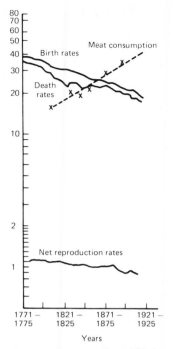

Fig. 30-7. Average annual number of births per 1000, number of deaths per 1000, and net reproduction rates in the 5-year periods 1771 to 1775 and 1906 to 1910, and annual consumption of meat and animal fat (in kilograms per capita) between 1812 and 1910, in France. [For sources of basic data, see (22).]

ance between mortality and fertility has been observed in Japan (Fig. 30-8), where the demographic transition began much later than it did in France. Whereas France was the first country to enter into the process of demographic transition, Japan was one of the latest countries to complete it.

When one compares the experience of France and of Japan, it seems that the process of transition has been accelerated. Whereas improvements in the standard of living and reductions in mortality have accelerated, the lag between mortality and fertility may have remained more or less constant. Thus, we are observing more violent, but transitory, "population explosions." Once the fertility trend turns downward, the reductions in fertility are also accelerated.

Japan, it might be argued, was a rapidly developing country at the time of its demographic transition, and it was for this reason that the transition could take place in Japan as

late as it did, but modern medicine has since changed the course of demographic transition and the prospects for development in the less developed world.

Kirk has noted (16) that the later phases of the demographic transition (that is, definitive declines in birth rates to low or moderate fertility) have now reached almost all people of European ethnic background, but that Costa Rica and, until recently, Chile have been exceptions. Kirk made his statement in 1967; information subsequently made available indicates that Costa Rica and Chile are beginning to complete the historic process of demographic transition first observed in Europe. Thus, in the 5 years between 1962 and 1967, Costa Rica experienced about a 10 percent reduction, and Chile about a 20 percent reduction in fertility.

It might be objected that Costa Rica and Chile, while they may be developing countries, are of European ethnic background, and that their experience may differ from that of countries of non-European background. It is for this reason that the case histories of Ceylon and of Mauritius are cited here, since these

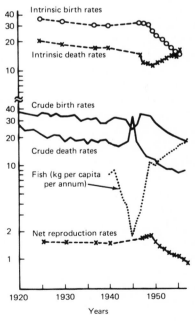

Fig. 30-8. Processed fishery products (in kilograms per capita per annum), crude and intrinsic birth rates and death rates (in number of births or deaths per 1000), and net reproduction rates, for Japan, for the period 1920 to 1957. [For sources, see (23).]

countries were first selected by the neo-Malthusian school to bolster their views.

Many writers—too many to be cited here—have attributed the dramatic postwar decline in mortality in Ceylon solely or largely to the eradication of malaria. Newman (17), who has studied the case history of Ceylon more than most, has concluded that eradication of malaria has accounted for 42 percent of the postwar decline in the death rate of Ceylon. Titmuss and Abel-Smith (18) have attributed most of the dramatic decline in mortality between 1946 and 1947 in Mauritius to eradication of malaria.

If the sequence of events in Ceylon and Mauritius had demonstrated that economic development is no longer a prerequisite for a decline in the death rate, it might have seemed plausible to postulate that modern public health measures would tend to reduce per capita income as well as mortality, should economic development lag; it might have seemed plausible to infer that per capita income would rise with a rise in mortality. But the postulation of such determinants and consequences of mortality trends is not confirmed by the experiences of Ceylon and Mauritius (10).

Although the postwar decline in the death rate in Ceylon, from 20 to 14 per 1000 in the single year from 1946 to 1947, approximately coincided with a campaign of spraying with insecticides, the spectacular decline in mortality was about the same for the area without malaria, not protected by insecticides, as for the area with malaria, protected by insecticides (19). It has also been shown (8) that the decline in mortality was associated with a commensurate development of the economy and rise in the standard of living.

Moreover, the birth rate declined from a postwar peak of 39.8 per 1000 in 1951 to 31.6 in 1967. In the 5 years between 1962 and 1967, Ceylon has experienced a greater than 10 percent decline in birth rate.

The postwar drop in the death rate in Mauritius, from 30 to 20 per 1000 in the single year from 1946 to 1947, was also attributed mainly to the use of insecticides. But the spraying campaign was started in 1949, 2 years after the dramatic 1947 decline in the death rate. Moreover, the per capita production of

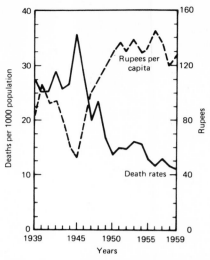

Fig. 30-9. Levels of mortality and levels of living, as indicated by the sales proceeds from sugar production (in constant rupees per capita) for Mauritius, for the period 1939 to 1959. (Constant rupees at 1939 prices were computed from the consumer price index for manual workers.) [Source of basic data, Yearbook of Statistics (Central Statistical Office, Colony of Mauritius, 1946-1959).]

sugar, virtually the sole export of the island, rose sharply as mortality declined.

Mauritius may follow the pattern of demographic transition displayed in the course of history in the West.

First, the inverse relationship between (i) the mortality rate and (ii) the standard of living indicated by the per capita proceeds (in 1939 rupees) from sale of the principal cash crop suggests that reductions in mortality are still dependent on commensurate improvements in the standard of living. Improvements in health services may be involved, but only as a part of general improvements in living standards (Fig. 30-9).

Second, the fertility trend has now turned downward, decisively so, about 20 years after the dramatic downturn in the death rate. From a postwar peak of 49.7 per thousand in 1950, the birth rate declined to 30.4 in 1967. In the 5 years between 1962 and 1967, Mauritius experienced about a 20 percent decline in the birth rate. This seems to confirm the experience of other countries: a reduction in mortality is a precursor of, and perhaps a prerequisite for, a reduction in fertility in the course of demographic transition (Fig. 30-10).

Thus, Mauritius experienced a population explosion. As the word implies, an explosion is a transitory phenomenon. The sharp increase in the rate of population growth calls for individual and collective decision making. With lower mortality, the traditional and practical family size can be achieved with lower fertility. Moreover, the lessening of uncertainty about whether one's children will survive, and the greater overall probability that they will, may induce parents to want fewer children than they have wanted in the past. Thus, reduction in mortality, by influencing the decision concerning family size as well as facilitating its realization, may operate by way of two mechanisms to develop motivation toward a reduction in fertility.

In the course of economic and demographic transition, a reduction in mortality induces a population explosion which may, in turn, induce a commensurate reduction in fertility, thereby restoring approximate balance between mortality and fertility.

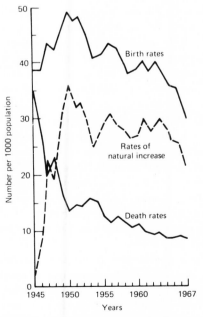

Fig. 30-10. Rates of birth, death, and natural increase for Mauritius, for the period 1945 to 1967. [Source of basic data, Demographic Yearbook (United Nations, New York, 1954-1967).]

The qualitative nature and directions of the feedbacks in the alternative model (Figs. 30-3 and 30-4) seem to be consistent with the relationships observed in the real world, as indicated by longitudinal as well as cross-sectional observations, and by historical as well as contemporary case histories (Figs. 30-5 and 30-10). Let me say again that case histories of Ceylon and Mauritius were first cited by those who wanted to bolster their neo-Malthusian views. But the actual events in these countries seem to refute the neo-Malthusian model and to support the alternative model of economic and demographic transition.

Additional empirical evidence for the alternative model has been presented elsewhere (10, 20).

Dynamics of Transition

The dynamic equilibrium of economic and demographic transition in the postwar era may be indicated by empirical equations describing the quantitative and qualitative relationships between changes in mortality, fertility, and living standards in 21 countries, for which comparable data were available.

The equations imply that the prospective rate of natural increase can be estimated on the basis of the rates of fertility and mortality in the base year and the relative change in per capita product at constant prices.

The relative change in natality n in year t can be expressed in terms of natality n and mortality m in the base year o:

$$\frac{n_t}{n_o} = \left[\frac{a}{(n_o - m_o)^b}\right]^{t-o}$$

(a and b are constants).

The relative change in mortality m in year t can be expressed in terms of the relative change in per capita product (at constant prices) p in year t:

$$\frac{m_t}{m_o} = \left[\frac{c}{\left(\frac{P_t}{P_o}\right)^d}\right]^{t-o}$$

(c and d are constants).

When the equations for relative changes in natality and mortality are combined, the rate of natural increase, $n-m$, in year t can be expressed in terms of natality n and mortality m in the based year o and the relative change in per capita product (at constant prices) p in year t:

$$n_t - m_t = n_o\left[\frac{a}{(n_o - m_o)^b}\right]^{t-o} - m_o\left[\frac{c}{\left(\frac{P_t}{P_o}\right)^d}\right]^{t-o}$$

The empirical derivation of the equations and of the constants $a (= 1.028)$, $b (= 0.016)$, $c (= 1.085)$, and $d (= 0.018)$ are described elsewhere (20). The parameters can hardly be expected to predict the trends in vital events in all countries at all times, at least with any great degree of accuracy. For one thing, the values of the constants were derived from data uncorrected for differences in the age distributions. Second, the process of economic and demographic transition is constantly accelerating, as indicated by comparisons of the tempo of transition in developing countries with the tempo of the historical process in Europe.

But the equations were remarkably accurate in predicting or explaining the recent changes in the levels of fertility, mortality, and natural increase in Chile and Costa Rica. The recent dramatic turn in the trends of vital events in Chile and Costa Rica would have been missed had it simply been assumed "that current trends continue."

The population projections for Costa Rica, published by the United Nations in 1966 but based on data available in 1963, implied a rate of population growth of 3.9 percent in 1965 (an average annual rate of 4.0 percent between 1965 and 1970). The United Nations has since reported that the actual rate of population growth in 1965 was 3.1 percent. By substituting, in the foregoing equations, the birth rate and the death rate in 1960 and the relative change in per capita gross national product at constant prices between 1960 and 1965, we would estimate the 1965 population growth rate to be 3.3 percent in 1965.

Of course, the estimate of the death rate, and the rate of population growth derived therefrom, require economic data first available sometime after 1965, and for this reason this part of the equation is explanatory rather than predictive. But the estimate of the birth rate (number of births per 1000 population) obtained by means of this equation can be based solely on demographic data available in the base year. Such an estimate, for Costa Rica, based on the 1960 birth rate of 48.4 per 1000 and the 1960 death rate of 41.3 in 1965, which quite closely approximates the actual birth rate of 40.5 for 1960.

Of course, no one factor in the equation can be successfully manipulated independently of the other factors, in the expectation that the other factors will automatically respond, as if this were simply a matter of arithmetic.

Demographic Policy for Demographic Transition

The solution of the "population problem" is not simply the achievement of a low rate of population growth, which could be the result of a balance between either high or low birth rates and death rates. All humanitarian considerations aside, only low death rates matched by low birth rates will provide maximum returns from investment in human resources and keep to a minimum the burdens of child dependency.

Of course, the desired demographic changes are no more automatic than the desired economic changes. The systematic extension of information and facilities favoring the use of efficient, effective, and acceptable methods of regulating family size is the appropriate response to spontaneous motivation to limit family size—motivation which increases as rates of survival increase.

Thus, improvements in the standard of living, as well as desired changes in mortality and fertility rates, will result from an interplay of effort in both the demographic and the economic aspects of economic and demographic transition.

Health measures and family planning, by their effects on morbidity, mortality, and fertility, can accelerate the economic transition from low to high levels of production and consumption. They can also accelerate the demographic transition from high to low levels of mortality and fertility by restoring the balance between mortality and fertility at the lowest level of mortality attainable with the available resources. With such understanding, the allocations for health services would be limited by the availability of resources rather than by a fear that health services might be too effective.

The availability of resources for competing sectors of development would be decided by empirical review of the combinations of allocations to determine which combination had achieved a given level of development in the past and seemed to be necessary and feasible for achieving the next level.

Relative Costs and Benefits

The question remains, How should we or can we plan optimum efforts in view of the unlimited needs competing for the limited resources available? If we are to set realistic health targets, we must consider political, social, economic, and demographic, as well as administrative, factors. We must consider non-economic as well as economic costs and benefits, and we must start with the given set of circumstances, not with rarefied abstractions.

Health planners can dream of comprehensive and integrated health services, both curative and preventive, for achieving the ideal state of health as defined by the World Health Organization. But in the real world, available resources are limited. Moreover, it is in the less developed parts of the world that the needs are greatest, and the resources least.

In planning health services as integral parts of national development, it would be necessary or desirable to compare the costs and benefits of alternative programs, having different objectives, in different sectors of the economy, as well as the costs and benefits of alternative programs, having the same objectives, within the health sector. We must determine the optimum allocations for all sectors in the context of multiple needs competing for inadequate resources.

But, in practice, cost-benefit analysis may be neither a practical nor a valid method of deciding whether a more efficient and more effective program is an appropriate alternative for a less efficient and less effective program when the two do not have the same objective.

For one thing, we may lack a common unit of measurement for comparing the costs and benefits of programs in the health sector with those of programs having different objectives, in other sectors. In theory it may seem possible to quantify the various benefits in dollars, but what seems possible in theory may not prove feasible in practice.

Moreover, we lack understanding of, or agreement on, the innumerable interactions of the multiple factors in the complex process of development. For example, death control and birth control programs may be placed in competition for limited funds. In such a predicament, the dilemma can be resolved neither by moral arguments nor by cost-benefit analysis. Simple comparisons of the ratios of the costs and benefits of these arbitrary alternatives would be meaningless and misleading.

On the basis of simple arithmetic, we find that either more deaths or fewer births would lower the rate of population growth. But a low rate of population growth may be the result of a balance between either high or low birth rates and death rates. Only a balance between low birth and death rates will give the highest possible ratio between producers and dependents. And, as discussed above, only a prior reduction of mortality will develop the motivation needed for limiting family size.

Thus it is clear that cost-benefit analyses must be based on valid alternatives and not on simple assumptions and speculations which tend to ignore the dynamic nature and sequence of the interactions between economic and demographic factors. We might feel assured that a good analyst would take second and third order benefits into account. Yet, again, what seems possible in theory may not prove feasible in practice.

Again (to cite a comparison of the costs and benefits of another popular pair of specious choices), it has been variously calculated that the expenditure on a program of birth control of either $1 or $5 from each $100 spent on development can double the rate of per capita economic growth achieved by the whole expenditure. But could we really double economic growth merely by increasing our investment in contraception? If that were possible, we might concentrate on contraception and eliminate investments in all other sectors of development. Although the popular notion that an ounce of contraception is worth a pound of development has some validity, this does not mean that birth-control programs could or should invariably be substituted for programs that have a less favorable cost-benefit ratio. The setting of priorities is not simply a mathematical problem.

Of course, within a given sector, a more effective and efficient program may be substituted for one that has the same objective but a less favorable cost-benefit ratio, provided the proposed alternative is otherwise appropriate and acceptable.

Actually, there is little need for complex and controversial economic and demographic arguments to justify appropriate action in response to spontaneous motivation to restore the balance between mortality and fertility. We all know the absurd consequences projected by extrapolations of imbalances between current mortality and fertility trends.

Although intersectoral cost-benefit analyses may not be particularly feasible, such analyses may be undertaken intrasectorally in conjunction with an empirical method, described next, for intersectoral linking of targeting and budgeting in a multisectoral system of development.

Profiles of Relative Development

So far, no comprehensive model of development for obtaining the best possible allocations among the innumerable needs competing for limited resources has been generally accepted and successfully applied. In the absence of such a model, analysis of national and sectoral "profiles of the relative development" of human and natural resources provides an ob-

jective and practical method for setting realistic, although tentative, targets and budgets (21). Such profiles facilitate comparison between countries or regions with respect to a number of variables, each of which can serve as an indicator of the level of development (Fig. 30-11).

Profiles of individual countries are entered on global grids of development, which are constructed by ranking any number of variables from all countries for which comparable data are available; the deciles thus obtained are used to construct the grids.

For example, the first indicator in the global grid is the product per capita. Data for this variable from 120 countries are ranked in the first two horizontal rows of Fig. 30-11, from left to right. The top entry in the first vertical column (the 0-percentile column) indicates that none of the 120 countries had a per capita product of less than $35 in 1965. The top entry in the second vertical column (the 10-percentile column) indicates that 12 countries (10 percent of 120) had a per capita product of no more than $70. And the top entry in the last vertical column (the 100-percentile column) indicates that all 120 countries had a per capita product lower than $3300. The profile of the relative development of a particular country (Nepal, the U.S.S.R., and the United States) is indicated by the histogram in the grid. For example, Nepal had a product per capita of less than $70.

Variables have been included in the grid without regard to any hierarchy or classification. The variables or indicators are simply a diverse collection of characteristics of a society or economy, some of which might be considered costs or benefits, inputs or outputs, causes or effects, needs or resources, means or ends. The preparation of development profiles requires neither classification of the variables nor understanding of the nature and extent of their interactions—neither explicit nor implicit assumptions other than recognition of a tendency toward balance or complementarity in the development of human and natural resources. Whether progress is the inevitable result of free enterprise or the intended result of a planned economy, if and when a system or policy or fortuitous combination of factors

Indicators of Development	No. of Countries	0	10	20	30	40	50	60	70	80	90	100
Product per capita ($U.S. per annum)	120	35	70	89	135	185	226	305	482	797	1615	3300
Agricultural occupation (percent)	110	93	72	60	56	51	42	38	28	8	11	5
Wheat yield (100 kg per hectare)	87	3	6	7	8	10	13	15	17	24	28	42
Rice yield (100 kg per hectare)	97	5	7	10	13	16	17	21	24	34	41	62
Maize yield (100 kg per hectare)	116	3	5	7	8	10	11	13	18	22	28	49
Calories (per capita per day)	76	1800	2000	2120	2200	2295	2430	2600	2695	2940	3110	3510
Total proteins (grams per capita per day)	52	42	48	52	59	72	78	80	85	90	94	112
Animal proteins (grams per capita per day)	52	6	10	14	17	20	25	32	47	53	57	77
Electricity generation (kwh per capita)	120	2	8	21	51	93	151	373	600	1240	2687	10961
Steel consumption (metric tons per 1000 pop.)	67	2	8	16	20	31	69	120	220	277	371	545
Literacy (percent)	113	3	8	12	25	35	55	75	85	96	99	99
Newspaper circulation (per 1000 pop. per day)	147	0	2	6	11	19	38	64	100	168	291	499
Primary school enrollment (percent of age group)	75	3	15	26	36	44	52	62	65	69	77	94
Secondary school enrollment (percent of age group)	75	0	2	5	8	12	17	22	29	35	57	95
Tertiary school enrollment (percent of age group)	75	0.0	0.1	0.3	0.7	2	3	4	5	8	9	33
Teachers, primary and secondary (per 10,000 pop.)	68	2	12	24	28	35	41	48	60	70	80	135
Crude birth rate (per 1000 pop.)	106	59	51	49	47	45	42	35	23	20	18	13
Infant mortality (per 1000 live births)	112	259	172	127	94	68	53	39	31	26	20	14
Life expectancy (years at birth)	73	26	35	37	43	46	50	58	62	67	70	73
Inhabitants per physician	126	189300	41400	25000	12600	7100	4600	2600	1610	910	760	1400

Column header: Nepal · USSR · USA · Percentile Rank (deciles 10, 30, 50, 70, 90 above; 0, 20, 40, 60, 80, 100 below)

Fig. 30-11. Profiles of the relative development of Nepal, the U.S.S.R., and the U.S. (indicated by the histogram) in comparison with ten levels in the global grid of sectoral development, indicated by the deciles in the rankings of indicators from the latest year, and the maximum number of countries, for which comparable data are available. [For sources, see (24).]

results in development, the balance in the development of human and of natural resources is remarkable.

For different countries, paths of development are usually and essentially the same, but the path may be followed with greater or lesser speed. Harmonizing the objectives and choosing the best possible targets may accelerate the passage from traditional to modern stages of society and economy.

Since grids such as Fig. 30-11 have no time scale, it is not possible to schedule the achievement of individual targets within fixed periods. Rather, the profiles suggest, for example, that it might be realistic to choose as a target reductions in infant mortality from 127 to 68 per 1000 live births coincidentally with an increase in the product per capita from $89 to $185 a year.

The observed balance in the development of

human and natural resources permits us to decide what is necessary or desirable and feasible at the various stages of development, even though we lack a comprehensive mathematical model of development. In effect, the open-ended nature of the grid permits approximation of a comprehensive model of development, albeit associatively rather than structurally.

The method of analysis is discussed more fully elsewhere (21).

Evolution of Goals and Services

Integration of planning, programming, and budgeting of health services into a system for accelerating development may confirm the belief that differences between a sound economic point of view and a bonafide humanitarian point of view are more apparent than real. Of course, there are situations where the two are irreconcilable. In such situations, the deliberate political decision may be to choose a humanitarian policy rather than the most economic alternative. However, in the long run it may not be politically opportune or economically feasible to consistently ignore either humanitarian or economic considerations.

Fortunately what is necessary or desirable from the economic and the humanitarian points of view may, and usually does, turn out to be essentially the same, when analyses of the relative costs and benefits are based on targets or budgets for programs that are possible and feasible, valid and appropriate in the context of the evolving needs and resources. And what is necessary or desirable and feasible from the economic and humanitarian point of view may, in the long run, be a safe and sound position from the political point of view as well.

Thus, the best or only way to obviate or resolve conflicts, apparent or real, between independently derived economic and health plans would be to devise and adopt a method of planning health services and investments as integral parts of a multisectoral system for accelerating the development of an economy and a society. Such planning must be based on an understanding of the quantitative evolution of feasible goals and optimum programs in the context of evolving needs and resources at successive stages of development.

Disease and reproduction tend to occur in definable patterns that closely reflect the degree of modernization of the society (Table 1). Where the patterns are not compatible with the process of modernization, we can attempt to modify the patterns and make them compatible.

The ideal health policy would be one of short-term and long-term planning such that the manpower and organization of the health services, designed to attack the most prevalent diseases that are amenable to attack, would evolve along with the needs and resources in the complex process of economic, social, and demographic transition.

There are various alternative strategies and tactics that might be pursued by the health services. Before we try to determine the relative cost effectiveness of alternatives we must decide which of the many alternative programs are valid paths to the agreed-upon objectives; this decision, in turn, must be based on consideration of what alternatives are both possible and feasible.

This requires, first, consideration of the nature of the problem, which may call for epidemiologic study. Then the possibilities of prevention must be determined; this involves determination of the link in the chain of transmission or causation that is most readily broken by the possible means of prevention.

But what is possible may not be feasible. The feasibility of goals and services evolves with the needs and the resources (Fig. 30-11 and Table 1). And once we decide which alternative is feasible, we still must set tentative targets or budgets for the alternative programs before we can analyze the relative costs and benefits.

The profiles of relative development permit the setting of tentative but realistic targets, as well as tentative but realistic budgets for health services. Such empirical targeting and budgeting makes it possible to keep costs to a minimum and to achieve maximum benefits, by permitting cost-effectiveness analyses to be based on the empirically derived targets as well as budgets.

Table 1. Evolution of environmental health problems; predominant patterns of disease, mortality, and fertility; goals, type and scope of health services; and the state of nutrition.

State of society	Environmental health problems	Predominant patterns of disease, mortality, and fertility	Goals, type and scope of health services	State of nutrition
Traditional	Largely rural environment with contamination of water and food; proliferation of insects and rodents; periodic food scarcities.	Endemic infections parasitisms, infestations, nutritional deficiencies. High death rate and high birth rate.	Indigenous systems of medicine based on traditional practices and beliefs.	Undernutrition as a result of food scarcities in a subsistence economy with practices and preferences of food production and consumption of a traditional, but youthful, society.
Early transitional	Largely rural environment with contamination of water and food; proliferation of insects and rodents; adulteration of foods and drugs; food scarcities.	Endemic infections, parasitisms, infestations, nutritional deficiencies. Intermediate death rate and high birth rate.	Medical relief and family planning in key centers; control of endemic diseases and environmental sanitation in selected areas; nationwide extension of categorical health services (malaria and smallpox eradication) requiring only minimal cooperation from the public and only minimal judgment from auxiliary staff with stereotype duties (residual spraying and vaccination).	Potential improvements in nutrition in areas of the monetary economy through possible modification of social, economic, and agricultural policies favoring the consumption of a variety of nutritious foods; facilitation of the extension of modern practices of agriculture, food technology and marketing, nutrition education, child-feeding and school lunch programs to the minority of the population within the scope of the nutrition programs of the health, education, and agricultural services.
Late transitional	Rural environment still resembles that of traditional society, whereas the urban environment resembles that of modern society.	Endemic diseases prevail at reduced levels in rural areas, whereas the disease patterns of urban areas resemble those of modern society. Low death rate and intermediate birth rate.	Comprehensive and integrated systems of preventive and curative health and medical services in key centers, with nationwide extension of medical relief, family planning, nutrition, basic sanitation, health education, and communicable disease control.	Continuing improvement of nutrition as a by-product of economic growth and as the result of progressive extension of nutrition programs nationwide, including the production of protein-rich foods and the fortification of staples.
Modern	Largely urban environment with pollution of air, water, and food, plus hazards from use of cigarettes, alcohol, food additives, new drugs, and narcotics.	Bronchopulmonary and cardiovascular disease, malignant neoplasias, mental illness, accidents, obesity. Low death rate and low birth rate.	Nationwide extension of complex systems of comprehensive and integrated preventive and curative health and medical services, requiring a prosperous society and an enlightened public, as well as ample health manpower, qualified to exercise independent judgment.	Overnutrition as a result of an abundance of foods in an industrial economy of an affluent, sedentary, and aging society.

Summary and Conclusions

The feedbacks in a neo-Malthusian and in an alternative model of economic and demographic transition are compared with each other and tested against the real world. On the basis of the empirical evidence, it is postulated that the population problem is not simply a high rate of growth. Nor is its solution simply a low rate of growth, which could be the result of a balance between either high or low rates of mortality and fertility.

Reductions in the mortality rate are part of the solution, rather than the cause, of the problem. Mortality rates tend to vary inversely with levels of consumption and production. Moreover, reductions in mortality seem to be prerequisites for compensating reductions in fertility to achieve the desired family size.

Of course, the desired demographic changes are no more automatic than the desired economic changes. The systematic extension of information and of facilities favoring the use of acceptable methods of regulating family size is the appropriate response to spontaneous motivation to limit family size.

Successful development results in, and from, a balance between mortality and fertility at the lowest mortality rate attainable with the resources available. With improved health and greater longevity increasing the returns from human resources, and with decreasing fertility decreasing the burdens of dependency, the maximum improvements in the standard of living and the desired changes in mortality and fertility will result from interplay of efforts in both the demographic and the economic areas.

Strategy and tactics for national development evolve with the needs and resources. "Profiles of relative development" in the multiple sectors of national development may indicate what targets and budgets are necessary or desirable and feasible at successive stages.

Paths of development may be usually and essentially the same for different countries, but the path may be followed with greater or lesser speed. Harmonization of the objectives and wise choice of targets may accelerate the passage from traditional to modern stages of society and economy.

Health measures and family planning, as integral parts of the complex process of modernization, can accelerate and must complete the economic and demographic transition from low to high levels of production and consumption, and from high to low levels of mortality and fertility.

References

1. "The Growth of the World Population," *Nat. Acad. Sci. Nat. Res. Counc. Publ. No. 1091* (1963).
2. C. M. Cipolla, *The Economic History of World Population* (Penguin, Baltimore, 1964).
3. I. M. D. Little, *Aid to Africa* (Pergamon, London, 1964).
4. G. Winfield, quoted by N. K. Sarkar in *China: The Land and the People* (Sloane, New York, 1948).
5. S. Enke, *Quart. J. Economics* 71, No. 1, 19 (1957).
6. C. E. Taylor, *Foreign Affairs* 43, 475 (1965).
7. T. R. Malthus, *An Essay on the Principle of Population* (ed. 7, 1872), bk. 4, chap. 5.
8. H. Frederiksen, *Public Health Rep.* 76, 659 (1961).
9. F. N. Notestein, D. Kirk, S. Segal, in *The Population Dilemma*, P. M. Hauser, Ed. (Prentice-Hall, Englewood Cliffs, N.J., 1963).
10. H. Frederiksen, *Public Health Rep.* 81, 727 (1966).
11. President's Science Advisory Committee, *The World Food Problem* (Government Printing Office, Washington, D.C., 1967) vol. 2, p. 34.
12. T. Schultz, "A Family Planning Hypothesis: Some Empirical Evidence from Puerto Rico," *Agency Int. Develop. Mem. RM-5405-RC/AID* (1967).
13. G. E. Immerwahr, *Demography* 4, 710 (1967).
14. Southeast Asia Development Advisory Groups (SEADAG) reports, Population Seminar, New York, March 1968.
15. D. N. Heer and D. O. Smith, *Demography* 5, 104 (1968).
16. D. Kirk, "Natality in the developing countries: recent trends and prospects," paper presented at the University of Michigan Sesquicentennial Conference on Fertility and Family Planning, November 1967.
17. P. Newman, "Malaria Eradication and Population Growth with Special Reference to Ceylon and British Guiana," *Univ. Mich. School Public Health Res. Ser. No. 10* (1965).
18. R. M. Titmuss and B. Abel-Smith, *Social Policies and Population Growth in Mauritius* (Methuen, London, 1961).
19. H. Frederiksen, *Public Health Rep.* 75, 865 (1960).
20. ——, *Econ. Develop. Cult. Change* 14, 316 (1966).

21. H. Frederiksen, *Int. Develop. Rev.* 11, No. 4, 27 (1967).

22. *Annuaires Statistiques de la France* (Institut National de la Statistique et des Etudes Economiques, Ministère des Finances et des Affaires Economiques, Republique Francaise); *Demographic and Statistical Yearbooks* (United Nations, New York); J. Bourgeois-Pichat, in *Population History* (Aldine, Chicago, 1965); C. Clark, *The Conditions of Economic Progress* (Macmillan, London, 1951).

23. *Statistical Yearbooks* (Prime Minister's Office, Japan); I. B. Taeuber, *The Population of Japan* (Princeton Univ. Press, Princeton, N.J., 1958).

24. Population Reference Bureau, December 1965; *U.N. Food & Agriculture Organization Production Yearbook* (1964); *U.N. Statistical Yearbook* (1964); N. Ginsburg, *Atlas of Economic Development* (Univ. of Chicago Press, Chicago, 1961); F. Harbison and C. A. Myers, *Education, Manpower and Economic Growth* (McGraw-Hill, New York, 1964); *U.N. Demographic Yearbook* (1964).

31

ECONOMIC DEVELOPMENT AND THE FERTILITY TRANSITION

David M. Heer

The developed nations have a long history of increasing per-capita monetary income. According to Simon Kuznets, the average decennial rate of growth per-capita national product in the United States between 1839 and 1960-62 was more than 17 per cent, a rate sufficient to increase per-capita product 4.9 times per century. The developed nations also have a long history of decreasing hours devoted to gainful employment and increasing amounts of leisure time. Had there been no change in either the price or preference system, one might have expected that the long-term trend in fertility would have been upward. Since fertility has tended over the long run to go down rather than up, changes in the preference and price system must have discouraged rather than encouraged fertility to an extent that they counterbalanced the elevating effects of increased money and leisure time. (See Fig. 31-1.)

On the other hand, the developed nations which did not suffer severely from World War II (United States, Canada, Australia, and New Zealand) underwent a substantial rise in fertility during the 1940's and 1950's. As I have noted earlier, Easterlin has provided extensive documentation that this period of rising fertility was also one of rapid rise in monetary income for young adults in the United States. During the period of the baby boom in the United States, the amount of time, money, and effort available for child-rearing activities was markedly expanded by the increased willingness and ability of grandparents to help their married children in child-care responsibilities. The grandparents of the postwar baby crop had had relatively few children themselves and, therefore, probably welcomed the chance to share in the work of raising their grandchildren. Moreover, even though the number of children per parent was quite high during the 1950's, the number per grandparent was not large since the number in the parental generation was so small. Thus, grandparents could make a large contribution to the rearing of each grandchild in a way that will not, for example, be possible for the grandparents of the 1970's. We may therefore presume that during the period of the baby boom the elevating effects of rising resources more than counterbalanced any depressing effects of changes in the preference or price system.

In the last hundred years or so, several changes in the preference system of the developed nations have undoubtedly tended to reduce family size. One of the most important of these is the decline in mortality, which has of course been pronounced. In the United States for example, the mean expectation of life at birth increased from 47.3 years in 1900 to 70.2 years in 1964. The secular (long-term) decline in mor-

Extract from *Daedalus* 97:447-62, 1968.
Reprinted by permission of *Daedalus,* Journal of the American Academy of Arts and Sciences, Boston, Massachusetts.

Fig. 31-1. Total fertility rate for the white population of the United States 1800-1965. Sources: Ansley J. Coale and Melvin Zelnik, New Estimates of Fertility and Population in the United States *(Princeton, 1963), p. 36; U.S. National Center for Health Statistics,* Monthly Vital Statistics Report, *Vol. 15, No. 11 Supplement (February 1967).*

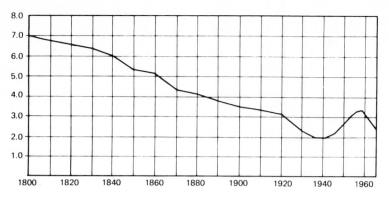

tality has had greater relative effect in infancy and childhood than adulthood. If fertility had not declined, the reduction in mortality would have tended to increase somewhat the number of living children per living parent. The United Nations estimates that for a population with high fertility (a Gross Reproduction Rate of 2.5) and very high mortality (life expectation at birth of twenty years), the ratio of population under fifteen years to that aged fifteen to fifty-nine years is 0.56. When the expectation of life at birth is increased to seventy years with no change in fertility the ratio is increased to 0.83. Thus one would expect the value of an additional birth to wane as the level of mortality declines.

There is also a possible connection between the level of mortality and the amount of emotional energy that parents invest in each of their children. It may be supposed that the pain of bereavement at a child's death is directly proportional to the amount of emotional energy that the parents have invested in the child. Where mortality levels are high, one might expect parents, in the interest of self-protection, to develop relatively little emotional involvement in any one child. A reduction in mortality encourages parents to place more libido in the existing children and thus should reduce their desire to have an additional child, since they have limited amounts of emotional energy.

Lowering the mortality level should also reduce the desire for additional children because parents can be more certain of having a specified minimum number of children survive to maturity. When mortality is high, one cannot be sure that any of one's existing children will

survive to maturity. When mortality is as low as it is in the developed nations, parents can be highly certain that their child will survive from birth to maturity. Thus, a decline in mortality reduces the value of an additional child as insurance against the possibility that one or more of the existing children may die. The effect of mortality reduction in this respect can be quantitatively measured. If one assumes that each couple is capable of bearing twelve children, that a perfect means of birth control is available and utilized, and that all couples want to be 95 per cent certain of having at least one son who will survive to the father's sixty-fifth birthday, the Gross Reproduction Rate will fall from 5.2 when the expectation of life at birth is twenty years to 0.95 when the expectation of life rises to seventy-four years.

A second long-term change in the preference system relates to the value which parents can derive from the productive labor of their children. In the agrarian society of the United States in the eighteenth century, when the supply of land was practically unlimited, children could be productive assets to their parents at a very early age. As the amount of land per capita declined, as it did in the United States during the nineteenth century, the value to the farmer of the labor of an additional child probably declined correspondingly. In all of the developed nations, industrialization substantially reduced the value of child labor. Although such labor was quite common in many of the early factories, the situation of the child in the factory was much less satisfactory than it was when he worked under the direction of his father on the family farm. As a result, strong moral sentiment developed against child labor, and legislation restricting it emerged in all of the developed nations. In each nation, the development of this legislation was very gradual, and the early regulations were much less restrictive than later laws. The first such legislation in England, passed in 1817, merely banned children under nine years of age from working in cotton mills. In the United States, the first mildly restrictive legislation appeared in a few northern states about the middle of the nineteenth century. Only in 1938 did the United States Federal Government enact child-labor regulations; these prohibited the employment of children under sixteen in manufacturing or mining and banned the employment of children under fourteen from all industry, except agriculture, which engaged in interstate commerce.

The utility of child labor was further reduced by compulsory education laws which, as they increased in severity, also lowered the productive value to the parents of an additional child. Prussia, under the leadership of Frederick the Great, became in 1763 the first nation to legislate compulsory attendance at schools for all persons five to fourteen years of age. The first law establishing compulsory school attendance in England was enacted in 1876. In the United States, Massachusetts became in 1852 the first state to demand school attendance; similar legislation did not become universal until 1918, when attendance was finally made compulsory in Mississippi.

The development of formal institutions to support the elderly has also brought about substantial changes in the value of an additional child. In the pre-industrial period and in the early stages of the Industrial Revolution, the elderly could expect to receive financial support only from their own kin—mainly from their sons. Gradually business corporations and governments developed social-security schemes for the aged and for widows. In the United Kingdom, legislation establishing old-age pensions for needy persons was first enacted in 1908, and in 1925 a contributory system covering all workers was established. In the United States, the first federal legislation concerning old-age, survivors', or disability pen-

sions dates from 1935, although many private corporations provided pensions and insurance systems much earlier. With the full development of social security, it became unnecessary for parents to bear children in sufficient number to assure that one or more sons would support them in their old age. Thus, the value to parents of additional children has been further diminished.

The preference system has also been altered by the decline in social rewards for bearing a large number of children. When mortality was high, a high rate of fertility was a positive necessity if the population was not to decline. Governmental and religious authorities who did not wish to see the nation's population reduced encouraged a high level of fertility. As mortality declined, however, a high level of fertility was no longer necessary to maintain the existing population level. As a result, many governments and religious bodies have shifted from a position favoring large families to one of neutrality or even opposition. A historic landmark was reached when the Church of England admitted at its Lambeth Conference of 1930 that mechanical or chemical means of contraception were not necessarily immoral. Since that time, the Protestant churches have, for the most part, ceased to extol the virtue of large families, and in the present decade the Roman Catholic Church has been faced with a great internal struggle, as yet unresolved, concerning this question. Although no European government has become alarmed about problems of excess fertility—all, in fact, encourage large families through their programs of family allowances—the United States has for the first time, under the Johnson Administration, provided federal funds for the establishment of family-planning clinics, thus indicating that it no longer wishes to encourage large families, at least among the poor.

A fifth possible change in the preference system may be the result of a tendency for economic development to shift the criteria for social status from ascribed characteristics (such as birth into a particular family) to achievement. Where status is ascribed at birth, one need spend little effort in advertising one's status to others; where status is achieved, its level tends to be transitory, and individuals may develop an intense need for conspicuous consumption to demonstrate their rank. If the preference for conspicuous consumption increases, the preference for children, who do little to publicize one's status, should decline. J. A. Banks has provided extensive documentation to show that during the latter years of the Victorian Era, the British middle class felt an increasing need to engage in conspicuous consumption and that English fertility first began its decline during this period.

The tremendous development of new and improved methods of birth control over the last century has not only reduced the relative preference for children, but has also increased their price relative to that of other goals. When available methods of birth control are crude and undeveloped, or knowledge of better methods is lacking, the decision not to have an additional child involves substantial inconvenience, interference with sexual pleasure, or even some hazard to health and life incurred by resort to a primitive means of abortion. Some of the major landmarks in the development of contraceptive technology during the last century were the manufacture of rubber condoms in the late-nineteenth century, the invention of a diaphragm by Mensinga in 1880, and in the 1930's the appearance of the latex condom, which was cheaper and better than its rubber predecessor. Increasing use of the highly effective oral contraceptives in the United States and other nations during the 1960's reduced the penalties in deciding against another child and may have been one of the major reasons for sharp fertility decline. Although the "pill" was placed on the United States market only in 1960, by 1965 it was the most popular contraceptive, the method used most recently by 24 per cent of white wives eighteen to thirty-nine years of age. Abortion has also been one of the principal means of birth control, and improvements in its technology have probably affected the preference for children. Little has been written about this, however, and it is difficult to ascertain the history of abortion techniques in those nations where the purposeful disruption of pregnancy is for the most part illegal.

Economic development has produced other changes in the price system affecting desired family size. Urbanization has been one of the most important concomitants of economic development. In the United States, the proportion of the population classified as urban increased from 5 to 70 per cent between 1790 and 1960. In general, urbanization results in a rise in the relative price of living space. Since rearing of children demands considerable living space, the relative cost of children no doubt rises with each increase in the relative price of living space. Although the relative cost of living space has in general been increasing over the last hundred years, the rise has, perhaps, not been invariant. One may speculate that the increasingly widespread use of the automobile in the United States during the 1940's and 1950's, together with governmental policies which subsidized home-ownership, made possible the acquisition of suburban houses at a relative cost probably substantially lower than prevailed during previous decades. Part of the American baby boom of the 1940's and 1950's may be explained by this short-term change in the relative cost of living space.

The tendency for the labor cost of child care to rise relative to the labor cost of producing material goods no doubt is a factor affecting desired family size. While economic development makes possible a much larger production of factor goods per man-hour of labor, the number of man-hours necessary to supervise and socialize a child has certainly not declined and most probably has risen. When a married couple are deciding whether to have another child, they can assume that an additional child will burden the wife with the responsibilities of child care for about three years. Moreover, with another child to supervise, she will have to work harder during the period when the older children are still under her care. This increased effort must be set against the possible remuneration from a job. Since the amount of material goods which can be bought with each hour of labor outside the home has steadily increased with each advance in national economic level, there has been a substantial long-term increase in the price of child-care services relative to the price of material goods.

A final long-term change in the price system affecting the decision to have children concerns the quality of education which parents demand for their children and which is socially imposed. A society more and more oriented to a complex technology requires that children be given an increasingly lengthy education. Parents recognize that their own child will be at a substantial disadvantage unless his education meets society's new norm. Even where the direct cost of education is met by the state, longer education increases the cost to the parent in terms of more years of child dependency. Hence the secular rise in the standard of education has no doubt helped to depress family size.

The factors connected with industrial development which I have listed have, in my opinion, tended to depress fertility to such an extent that the actual trend has usually been downward despite the elevating effect increased resources have had on fertility. It is not yet possible to evaluate the importance of the role each of these factors has played in the temporal changes in fertility in the developed nations during the past century or more. Although their relative importance may never be well established, further historical research may be of great value. I would recommend, in particular, detailed study correlating fertility change with such matters as the development of social-security systems, the decline in the prevalence of child labor, increases in the proportion of children attending school, changes in the relative cost of living space, and augmentation of the relative labor cost of child care.

32

BEYOND FAMILY PLANNING

Bernard Berelson

This article rests on four propositions: (i) among the great problems on the world agenda is the population problem; (ii) that problem is most urgent in the developing countries, where rapid population growth retards social and economic development; (iii) there is a time penalty on the problem in the sense that, other things being equal, anything not done sooner may be harder to do later, due to increased numbers; and accordingly (iv) everything that can properly be done to lower population growth rates should be done, now. The question is, what is to be done? There is a certain agreement on the general objective (that is, on the desirability of lowering birth rates, though not on how far and how fast), but there is disagreement as to means.

Reprinted from *Science* 163: 533-43, 1969, with the permission of the publishers. Copyright 1969 by the American Association for the Advancement of Science.

The first response to too high growth rates deriving from too high birth rates is to introduce voluntary contraception on a mass basis, or try to. Why is family planning the first step taken on the road to population control? Probably because, from a broad political standpoint, it is the most acceptable one; since it is closely tied to maternal and child care it can be perceived as a health measure beyond dispute, and since it is voluntary it can be justified as a contribution to the effective personal freedom of individual couples. On both scores, it ties into accepted values and thus achieves political viability. Moreover, it is a gradual effort and an inexpensive one, both of which features contribute to its political acceptability.

How effective have family-planning programs been as a means toward population control? There is currently some controversy among qualified observers as to its efficacy (1), and this is not the place to review that issue. There is agreement, however, that the problem is of such magnitude and consequence that additional efforts are needed to reach a "solution," however that is responsibly defined.

For the purpose of this article, then, let us

assume that today's national family-planning programs, mainly based on voluntary contraception, are not "enough"—where "enough" is defined not necessarily as achieving zero growth in some extended present but simply as lowering birth rates quickly and substantially. "Enough" begs the question of the ultimate goal and only asks that a faster decline in population growth rates be brought about than is presently being achieved or in prospect—and, within the range of the possible, the faster the better (2, 3). Just to indicate roughly the order of magnitude, let us say that the proximate goal is the halving of the birth rate in the developing countries in the next decade or two—from, say, over 40 births per thousand per year to 20 to 25 (4). For obvious reasons, both emigration and increased death rates are ruled out of consideration.

What is to be done to bring that reduction about, beyond present programs of voluntary family planning? I address that question in two ways: first, by listing the programs or policies more or less responsibly suggested in recent years for achieving this end; second, by reviewing the issues raised by the suggested approaches.

Proposals Beyond Family Planning

Here is a listing of the several proposals, arranged in descriptive categories. The list includes both proposals for consideration and proposals for action.

A. Extensions of Voluntary Fertility Control

1. Institutionalization of maternal care in rural areas of developing countries: a feasibility study of what would be required in order to bring some degreee of modern medical or paramedical attention to every pregnant woman in the rural areas of five developing countries, with professional backup for difficult cases and with family-planning education and services a central component of the program, aimed particularly at women of low parity (5).

2. Liberalization of induced abortion (6; 7, p. 139; 8).

B. Establishment of Involuntary Fertility Control

1. Mass use of a "fertility control agent" by the government to regulate births at an acceptable level. The "fertility control agent," designed to lower fertility in the society to a level 5 to 75 percent below the present birth rate, as needed, would be a substance now unknown but believed to be available for field testing after 5 to 15 years of research work. It would be included in the water supply in urban areas and administered by "other methods" elsewhere (9). A related suggestion is the "addition of temporary sterilants to water supplies or staple food" (10).

2. "Marketable licenses to have children," given to women and perhaps men in "whatever number would ensure a reproduction rate of one" (say, 2.2 children per couple). For example, "the unit certificate might be the 'deci-child,' and accumulation of ten of these units, by purchase, inheritance or gift, would permit a woman in maturity to have one legal child" (11).

3. Temporary sterilization of all girls by means of time-capsule contraceptives, and of girls and women after each delivery, with reversibility allowed only upon governmental approval. Certificates of approval would be distributed according to national popular vote on desired population growth, and saleable on the open market (12).

4. Compulsory sterilization of men with three or more living children (13); a requirement of induced abortion for all illegitimate pregnancies (6).

C. Intensified Educational Campaigns

1. Inclusion of educational materials on population in primary and secondary school systems (6, 14, 15).

2. Promotion of national satellite television systems for directly disseminating information on population and family planning and for indirectly promoting acceptance of modern attitudes and practices in general (7, p. 162; 16; 17, especially pp. 13–14; 18).

D. Incentive Programs

As used here, the term *incentive programs* refers to payments, or their equivalent, made directly to couples who use contraceptives or to couples who do not have children for specified periods. It does *not* refer to payments to field workers, medical personnel, volunteers, and others, for securing acceptance of contraceptive practice.

1. Payment, or the equivalent (for example, the gift of a transistor radio), for accepting sterilization (6, 19-21) or for the effective practice of contraception (21-24).

2. A bonus for child spacing or nonpregnancy (25-28); a savings certificate to couples for each 12-month period in which no child is born (29); a lottery scheme for preventing illegitimate births among teenagers in a small country (30); "responsibility prizes" for each 5 years of childless marriage or for vasectomy before the birth of a third child, and special lotteries, with tickets available to the childless (7, p. 138).

E. Tax and Welfare Benefits and Penalties

That is, a system of social services that would discourage childbearing rather than encourage it, as present systems tend to do.

1. Withdrawal of maternity benefits, perhaps after the birth of N (3?) children (6, 21, 26) or in cases where certain limiting conditions, such as adequate child spacing, knowledge of family planning, or attainment of a given level of income, have not been met (31, pp. 130-31).

2. Withdrawal of child or family allowances, perhaps after the birth of N children (6; 26; 31, pp. 131-136).

3. Levy of tax on births after the Nth child (21; 26; 28, p. 30).

4. Limitation of governmentally provided medical treatment, housing scholarships, loans, subsidies, and so on, to families with fewer than N children (6, 26).

5. Reversal of tax benefits, to favor the unmarried and the parents of fewer rather than more children (6; 7, pp. 136-37; 21; 26; 31, p. 137; 32).

6. Provision by the state of N years of free schooling, at all levels, to each family, to be allocated among the children as desired (33).

7. Pensions for poor parents with fewer than N children, as social security for their old age (21, 34, 35).

F. Shifts in Social and Economic Institutions

That is, broad changes in fundamental institutional arrangements that could have the effect of lowering fertility.

1. Raising the minimum age at marriage, through legislation or through imposition of a substantial fee for marriage license (6, 32); through direct payment of bonuses for delayed marriage (25); through payment of marriage benefits only to parents of brides over 21 years old (31, p. 130); through government loans for wedding ceremonies when the bride is over a given age or with the interest rate inversely related to the bride's age (36); through a "governmental 'first marriage grant' . . . awarded each couple in which the age of both [sic] partners was 25 or more" (7, p. 138); or through establishment of a domestic "national service" program for all men for the appropriate 2-year period in order to develop social services, inculcate modern attitudes toward (among other matters) family planning and population control, and delay marriage (37).

2. Measures to promote or require the participation of women in the labor force (outside the home), in order to provide roles and interests for women that are alternative or supplementary to marriage (6, 32, 38).

3. "Direct manipulation of family structure itself—planned efforts at deflecting the family's socializing function . . . or introducing nonfamilial distractions . . . into people's lives," specifically through employment of women outside the house (39); "selective restructuring of the family in relation to the rest of society" (6).

4. Promotion of "two types of marriage, one of them childless and readily dissolved, and the other licensed for children and designed to be stable"; marriages of the first type would have to constitute 20 to 40 percent of the total in order to allow free choice of family size for marriages of the second type (16, 40).

5. Encouragement of long-range s o c i a l trends leading toward lower fertility—for example, "improved and universal general education, or new roads facilitating communication, or improved agricultural methods, or a new industry that would increase productivity, or other types of innovation that may break the 'cake of custom' and produce social foment" (41); improvement in the status of women (42).

6. Efforts to lower death rates even further, particularly infant and child death rates, in the belief that lower birth rates will follow (43).

G. Political Channels and Organizations

1. U.S. insistence on "population control as the price of food aid," with highly selective assistance based thereon, and exertion of political pressures on governments or religious groups that impede "solution" of the population problem (7, pp. 161-66; 44).

2. Reorganization of national and international agencies to deal with the population problem: within the United States, "coordination by a powerful governmental agency, a Federal Department of Population and Environment ... with the power to take whatever steps are necessary to establish a reasonable population size" (7, p. 138; 45); within India, creation of "a separate Ministry of Population Control" (46, p. 96); development of an "international specialized agency larger than WHO to operate programs for extending family limitation techniques to the world ... charged with the responsibility of effecting the transfer to population equilibrium" (16).

3. Promotion of zero growth in population as the ultimate goal, and acceptance of this goal now in order to place intermediate goals of lowered fertility in proper context (6).

H. Augmented Research Efforts

1. More research on social means for achieving necessary fertility goals (6).

2. Focused research on practical methods of sex determination (47).

3. Increased research directed toward improvement of the contraceptive technology (48).

Proposals: Review of the Issues

Here are 29 proposals beyond family planning for dealing with the problem of undue population growth in the developing world. Naturally I cannot claim that these are all the proposals that have been made more or less responsibly toward that end, but my guess is that there are not many more and that these proposals are a reasonably good sample of the total list.

Since several of the proposals tend in the same direction, it seems appropriate to review them against the criteria that any such proposals might be required to meet. What are such criteria? There are at least six: (i) scientific, medical, and technological readiness; (ii) political viability; (iii) administrative feasibility; (iv) economic capability; (v) moral, ethical, and philosophical acceptability; and (vi) presumed effectiveness. In other words, the key questions are: Is the scientific, medical, technological base available or likely? Will governments approve? Can the proposal be administered? Can the society afford the proposal? Is it morally acceptable? And finally, will it work?

Scientific, Medical, Technological Readiness

Two questions are involved: (i) is the needed technology available? and (ii) are the medical or paramedical personnel needed in order to assure medical administration and safety available or readily trainable?

With regard to temporary contraception, sterilization, and abortion, not only is the needed technology available now, but it is being steadily improved and expanded. The intrauterine device (IUD) and the oral pill have been major contraceptive developments of the past decade, and several promising leads are now being followed up (49), though it cannot be said with much confidence that any of the efforts will produce measures suitable for mass use within the next few years (50). Improved technologies for sterilization, both male and female, are being worked on, and there has been a recent development in abortion technique, the so-called suction device.

However, neither Ehrlich's "temporary sterilants" nor Ketchel's "fertility control agent" (B-1) is now available or on the technological horizon, though that does not mean that the research task ought not to be pursued against a subsequent need especially since any such substance could be administered to individuals on a voluntary basis as well as to the population as a whole on an involuntary basis. In the latter case, if administered through the water supply or a similar source, the substance would have to be medically safe and free of side effects for men and women, young and old, well and ill, physiologically normal and physiologically marginal, as well as for animals and perhaps plants. As some people have remarked, the proposal that such a substance be added to a water supply would face far greater difficulties of acceptance, simply on medical grounds, than the far milder proposals with regard to fluoridation to prevent tooth decay.

Though a substantial technology in fertility control does exist, that does not necessarily mean that the techniques can be applied where they are most needed; this is true partly because of limitations in the number of trained personnel. In general, the more the technology requires the services of medical or paramedical personnel (or, what is much the same, is perceived as requiring them), the more difficult it is to administer in the developing countries. In the case of sterilization and abortion, the medical requirement becomes more severe. For example, when the policy of compulsory vasectomy of men with three or more children was first being considered in India (see 13), it was estimated that the policy would affect about 40 million males: "one thousand surgeons or parasurgeons each averaging 20 operations a day for five days a week would take eight years to cope with the existing candidates, and during this time of course a constant supply of new candidates would be coming along" (51)—at present birth rates, probably some 3.5 million a year. A program of large-scale abortion (provided such a program was legal and acceptable) might additionally require hospital beds, which are in particularly short supply in most developing countries. However, the newer abortion technique might not require hospitalization—theoretically, the abortion "camp" may be

feasible, as the vasectomy "camp" was, though the problems are substantially greater.

In short, the technology is available for some but not for all current proposals, and the case is similar for properly trained personnel.

Political Viability

The "population problem" has been increasingly recognized by national governments and international agencies over the past decade, and policies for dealing with it have been increasingly adopted: national family-planning programs in some 20 to 25 countries; positive resolutions and actions within the United Nations family; large programs of support by such developed countries as the United States and Sweden; the so-called World Leaders' Statement, in which 30 heads of governments endorsed efforts to limit population growth. There is no reason to think that the trend toward population limitation has run its course.

At the same time, the political picture is by no means unblemished. Some favorable policies are not strong enough to support a vigorous program, even one limited to family planning on health grounds; in national politics, "population control" can become a handy issue for a determined opposition; internal ethnic balances are sometimes delicately involved, with political ramifications; national size is often equated with national power, from the standpoint of international relations and regional military balances; the motives behind the support and encouragement of population control by the developed countries are sometimes perceived as neocolonialist or neoimperialist; and on the international front, as represented by the United Nations, there is still considerable reluctance based on both religious and political considerations. In short, ambivalence on the part of the elite and recognition of the issue as a political liability are not absent even in the countries that favor population limitation.

Any social policy adopted by government rests on some minimum consensus concerning goals and means. They need not be the ultimate goals or the final means; the socioeconomic plans of developing countries are typically 5-year plans, not 20- or 40- or 100-year plans.

Indeed, the ultimate goal of population policy —that is, zero growth—need not be agreed upon or even considered by officials who *can* agree upon the immediate goal of lowering growth by a specified amount or by "as much as possible" within a period of years. And since there are always goals beyond goals, one does not even need to know what the ultimate goal is—only the direction in which it will be found (which is usually more readily agreed upon). Would insistence *now* on the acknowledgement of an *ultimate* goal of zero growth advance the effort or change its direction?

To start with, the proposal of compulsory controls in India in 1967 (B-4) precipitated "a storm of questions in Parliament" (52); the proposal was withdrawn, and the issue resulted in a high-level shift of personnel within the family-planning organization. No other country has seriously entertained the idea. Other considerations aside, in many countries political instability would make implementation virtually impossible.

Social measures designed to affect the birth rate indirectly—for example, tax benefits, social security arrangements, and so on—have been proposed from time to time. In India there have been several such proposals: for example, by the United Nations mission (53, chap. 11), by the Small Family Norm Committee (26), by the Central Family Planning Council (54), and in almost every issue of such publications as *Family Planning News, Centre Calling,* and *Planned Parenthood.*

As Samuel reports, with accompanying documentation (21), "the desirability of imposing a tax on births of fourth or higher order has been afloat for some time. However, time and again, the suggestion has been rejected by the Government of India." In some cases action has been taken either by the central government [for example, income tax "deductions for dependent children are given for the first and second child only" (53, p. 87)] or by certain states ["Maharashtra and Uttar Pradesh have decided to grant educational concessions and benefits only to those children whose parents restrict the size of their families" (55)]. Indicative of political sensitivity is the fact that an order withdrawing maternity leave for non-industrial women employees with three or more living children—at best a tiny number of educated women—was revoked before it went into effect (56). There is a special political problem in many countries, in that economic constraints on fertility often turn out in practice to be selective on class, racial, or ethnic grounds, and thus exacerbate political tensions. Moreover, the promotion of female participation in the labor force runs up against the political problem that such employment would be competitive with men in situations of already high male unemployment and underemployment.

Whether programs for eliminating population growth are or are not politically acceptable appears to depend largely upon whether they are perceived as positive or negative; where "positive" means that they are seen as promoting not only population limitation but other social benefits as well, and where "negative" means that they are seen as limited to population control. For example, family planning programs, as noted above, are often rationalized as contributing to both maternal and child health and to the effective freedom of the individual family; a pension for the elderly would have social welfare benefits as well as indirect impact upon family size, in countries where a large family has been the traditional "social security system"; contraceptive programs in Latin America are promoted by the medical community as a medical and humanitarian answer not to the population problem but to the extensive illegal and dangerous practice of abortion. On the other hand, imposing tax liabilities or withdrawing benefits after the birth of the *N*th child, not to mention involuntary measures, can be attacked as punitive means whose only purpose is that of limiting population.

It would thus require great political courage, joined to very firm demographic convictions, for a national leader to move toward an unpopular and severe prescription designed to cure his country's population ills. Indeed, it is difficult to envisage such a political move in an open society where a political opposition could present a counter view and perhaps prevail.

The governmental decisions about measures to be taken to deal with undue population growth must be made mainly by the countries directly involved; after all, it is their people and their nation whose prospects are most centrally affected. But in an interconnected world, with peace and human welfare at issue, others are properly concerned, for reasons both of self-interest and of humanitarianism—other governments from the developed world, the international community, private groups. What of the political considerations in this connection?

A recommendation (G-1) that the United States exert strong political pressures to effect population control in developing countries seems more likely to generate political opposition abroad than acceptance. It is conceivable that such measures might be adopted here, but it is hardly conceivable that they would be agreed to by the proposed recipients. Such a policy seems likely to boomerang against its own objective, quite aside from ethical or political considerations.

The proposal (G-2) to create an international superagency seems more likely of success, but is not without its difficulties. The World Health Organization, UNICEF, and UNESCO have moved some distance toward family planning, if not population control, but only slowly and in the face of considerable political restraint on the international front (57). A new international agency would find the road easier only if its efforts were restricted to the convinced countries. Certainly the international organizations now concerned with this problem would not be expected to abdicate in favor of a new agency. If it could be brought into being and given a strong charter for action, then, almost by definition, the international political climate would be such as to favor action by the present agencies, and then efficiency and not political acceptability would be the issue.

Administrative Feasibility

Given technical availability and political acceptability, what can actually be done? This is where several "good ideas" run into difficulties in the developing world, in the translation of a theoretical idea into a practical program.

It is difficult to estimate the administrative feasibility of several of the proposals listed above, if for no other reason than that the proponents do not put forward the necessary organizational plans or details. How are "fertility control agents" or "sterilants" to be administered on an involuntary mass basis in the absence of a central water supply or a food-processing system? How are men with three or more children to be reliably identified in a peasant society and impelled to undergo sterilization against their will; and what is to be done if they decline, or if a fourth child is born? What is to be done with parents who evade the compulsory programs, or with the children born as a result of this evasion? How can an incentive system be honestly run in the absence of an organized network of offices positioned and staffed to carry out the regulatory activity? How can a system of social benefits and penalties, including incentives to postpone or forego marriage, be made to work in the absence of such a network?

These questions are meant only to suggest the kinds of difficulties that must be taken into account if proposals are to be translated into programs. It would seem desirable that every responsibly made proposal address itself to such administrative problems. Some proposals do move in that direction. The feasibility in administration, personnel, and costs of the plan (A-1) to institutionalize maternal care in rural areas, with family planning attached, is currently under study in several developing countries.

The plan (C-1) to include population as a subject in the school curriculum has been carried forward as far as the preparation of educational materials, and in a few cases beyond that (58). The plans for incentive programs sometimes come down to only the theoretical proposition that people will do anything for money (in this case refrain from having children), but in some cases the permissible payment is proposed on the basis of an economic analysis, and in a few cases an administrative means is also proposed (59). The plan for governmental wedding loans scaled to the bride's age recognizes that a birth-registration system might be needed to control against misreporting of age (6).

Thus the *why* of population control is easy, the *what* is not very hard, but the *how* is difficult. We may know that the extension of popular education or an increase in the number of women in the labor force or a later age at marriage would all contribute to population control in a significant way. But there remains the administrative question of how to bring those developments about. In short, several proposals assume workability of a complicated scheme in a country that cannot now collect its own vital statistics in a reliable manner. Moreover, there is a limit to how much administrative burden the typical developing country can carry: it cannot manage many large-scale developmental efforts at a time, either within the field of population or overall. After all, population is not the only effort; agriculture, industry, education, health, communications, the military—all are important claimants. And, within the field of population, a country that finds it difficult to organize and run a family-planning program will find that harder when other programs are added. So, difficult administrative choices must be made.

Economic Capability

From the standpoint of economic capability there are two questions: (i) is the program worthwhile when measured against the criterion of economic return, and (ii) if worthwhile, can it be afforded from present budgets?

Most of the proposals probably pass the second screen. If a fertility-control agent suitable for mass administration becomes available and politically and administratively acceptable, such a program would probably not be prohibitively expensive; incorporation of population materials into the school curriculum is not unduly expensive; imposing of taxes or withdrawing of benefits or increasing fees for marriage licenses might even return a net gain after administrative cost.

But a few proposals are costly in absolute if not relative terms. For example, the institutionalization of maternal care (proposal A-1) might cost some $500 million for construction and $200 million for annual operation in India, or, respectively, $25 million and $10 million in a country with population of 25 million (5) (although recent estimates are substantially lower). The plan for a "youth corps" in India

would cost upward of $450 million a year if the participants were paid only $50 annually. The plan for payment of pensions to elderly fathers without sons could cost from $400 million to $1 billion a year, plus administrative costs (35). The satellite television system for India would cost $50 million for capital costs only, on a restricted project (17, p. 23), with at least another $200 million needed for receiving sets, broadcast terminals, and programming costs if national coverage were to be secured. All of these proposals are intended to have beneficial consequences beyond population control and hence can be justified on multiple grounds, but they are still expensive in absolute amounts.

The broad social programs of popular education, improved methods of agriculture and increased industrialization (F-5) already absorb even larger sums, and they could no doubt utilize even more. Here the question is a different one. At present, in such countries as India, Pakistan, South Korea, and Turkey, the funds allocated to family-planning programs constitute less than 1 percent—in most cases, much less—of the total funds devoted to economic development. Would that tiny proportion make a greater contribution to population control, over some specified period, if given over to education or industrialization or road-building than it makes when utilized directly for family planning (60)? From what we now know, the answer is certainly "No."

Beyond family planning, the situation is still less clear. On the assumption that some level of incentive or benefit would have a demographic impact, what would the level have to be to cut the birth rate by, say, 20 percent? We simply do not know: the necessary experiments on administration and effectiveness have not been carried out. Let us review what has been proposed with respect to incentives. On the ground that incentives for vasectomy are better than incentives for contraception—since vasectomy is a one-time procedure and is likely to be more effective in preventing births—Pohlman (20) proposes for India a range of money benefits depending upon parity and degree of acceptance—from $7 to a father of four or more children if half the villagers in that category enter the program up to $40 to a father of three children if 75 percent enter. If the 50-percent criterion were met in both categories throughout India, the current plan would cost on the order of $260 million in incentives alone, apart from administrative costs. The decline in the birth rate would be slightly over a fourth, perhaps a third—roughly equivalent to $35 to $40 per prevented birth (61).

Simon proposes an incentive of half the per capita income "each year to each fertile woman who does not get pregnant" (23). Here a special problem arises. In a typical developing population of 1000, about 25 to 30 percent of the married women of reproductive age give birth each year: a population of 1000 means from 145 to 165 such women, and a birth rate of, say, 40. Thus, the incentives paid to about three-fourths of the married women of reproductive age would have no effect on the birth rate, since these women would not be having a child that year in any case; thus the cost could be three to four times the amount "needed" for a desired result. Even if the incentive were fully effective and really did prevent a birth, a cut of ten points in the Indian birth rate would cost the order of $250 million (or 5 million prevented births at $50 each). The cost would be substantially larger if the women (including the nonfecund or the semi-fecund) who would not have had a child that year in any case, could not be screened out effectively.

But these and other possibilities are only speculations: to date we simply do not know whether incentives will lower a birth rate, or, rather, we do not know how large the incentives would have to be in order to do so. These illustrations show only that an incentive program could be expensive. In any case, incentive systems would require a good amount of supervision and record-keeping; and, presumably, the higher the incentive (and hence the greater the chance of impact), the greater the risk of false reporting and the greater the need of supervision—which is not only expensive but difficult administratively.

Moral, Ethical, and Philosophical Acceptability

Next, is the proposal not only politically acceptable but considered right and proper—by the target population, government officials, professional or intellectual elites, and the outside agencies committed to aid in its administration?

Coale states (3, 62), "One reason the policy of seeking to make voluntary fertility universal is appealing—whether adequate or not—is that it is a natural extension of traditional democratic values: of providing each individual with the information he needs to make wise choices, and allowing the greatest freedom for each to work out his own destiny. The underlying rationale is that if every individual knowledgeably pursues his self-interest, the social interest will best be served." But what if "stressing the right of parents to have the number of children they want . . . evades the basic question of population policy, which is how to give societies the number of children they need" (6)? The issue rests at the center of political philosophy: how best to reconcile individual and collective interests.

Today, most observers would acknowledge that having a child is theoretically a free choice of the individual couple. However, for many couples, particularly among the poor of the world, the choice is not effectively free in the sense that the individual couple does not have the information, services, and supplies needed to implement a free wish in this regard. Such couples are restrained by ignorance, not only of contraceptive practice but of the consequences of high fertility for themselves, their children, and their country; they are restrained by religious doctrine, even though they may not accept the doctrine; they are restrained legally, as in the case of people who would choose abortion if that course were open to them; they are restrained culturally, as in the case of women subject to a tradition that reserves for them only the childbearing and childrearing roles. Hence effective freedom of choice in the matter of childbearing is by no means realized in the world today, as recent policy statements have remarked (63).

To what extent should a society be willing to compromise its ethical standards for the sake of solving a great social problem? Suppose a program for population control resulted in many more abortions in a society where abortion is morally repugnant and where, moreover, abortion by acceptable medical standards is widely unattainable; how much fertility decline would be "worth" the result? What of infanticide under the same conditions? How many innocent or unknowing men may be vasectomized for a fee (for themselves or for others who obtained their consent) before the practice calls for a moral restraint? How large an increase in the regulatory bureaucracy, or in systematic corruption through incentives, or in differential effect by social class to the disadvantage of the poor (64) is worth how much decrease in the birth rate? How much association of childbearing with monetary incentive is warranted before "bribing people not to have children" becomes contaminating, with adverse long-run effects on parental responsibility (65)? How much "immorality," locally defined as extramarital sex, outweighs the benefits of contraceptive practice (assuming that there is an association)? How much withholding of food aid is ethical, judged against degree of fertility decline? If it were possible to legislate a later age at marriage, would it be right to do so against the will of young women, in a society in which they have nothing else to do? In countries, like our own, where urbanization is a serious population problem, is it right to tell people *where* to live, or to impose heavy economic constraints that in effect "force" the desired migration? Is it right to withdraw educational benefits from children in "too large" families? Such withdrawal would not only be repressive from the standpoint of free education but in the long run would be unfortunate from the standpoint of fertility control. In the balance—and this is a question of great but neglected importance— what weight should be given to opportunities of future generations as against the ignorance, the prejudices, or the preferences of the present one?

Guidance on such ethical questions is needed. For further consideration, these propositions are put forward. (i) "An ideal policy would permit a maximum of individual freedom and diversity. It would not prescribe a precise number of children for each category of married couple, nor lay down a universal norm to which all couples should conform" (3). (ii) "An ideal program designed to affect the number of children people want would help promote other goals that are worth supporting on their own merits, or at least not conflict with such goals" (3). (iii) An ideal program would not burden the innocent in an attempt to penalize the guilty—for example, would not burden the *N*th child by denying him a free education simply because he *was* the *N*th child of irresponsible parents. (iv) An ideal program would not weigh heavily upon the already disadvantaged—for example, by withdrawing maternal or medical benefits or free education from large families, policies that would tend to further deprive the poor. (v) An ideal program would be comprehensible to those directly affected and hence subject to their response. (vi) An ideal program would respect present values concerning family and children, values which some people may not be willing to bargain away in a cost-benefit analysis. (vii) An ideal program would not rest upon the designation of population control as the final value justifying all others; "preoccupation with population growth should not serve to justify measures more dangerous or of higher social cost than population growth itself" (3).

Presumed Effectiveness

If proposals are scientifically ready to be implemented, politically and morally acceptable, and administratively and financially feasible, to what extent will they actually work in bringing population growth under control? That is the final question.

To begin with, the compulsory measures would probably be quite effective in lowering fertility. Inevitably in such schemes, strongly motivated people are ingenious enough to find ways "to beat the system"; if such people were numerous enough the system could not be enforced except under conditions of severe political repression (66). Otherwise, if the scheme was workable, compulsion could have its effect.

What about the proposals for the extension of voluntary contraception? Institutionalizing maternal care in the rural areas, with family planning attached, does promise to be effective within, say, 5 to 10 years, particularly in its potential for reaching younger women and women of lower parity. The International Postpartum Program did have that effect in the urban areas (67), and presumably the impact would extend to the rural areas, though probably not to the same degree because of the somewhat greater sophistication and modernization of the cities.

A liberalized abortion system—again, if workable—could also be effective in preventing unwanted births, but it would probably have to be associated with a contraceptive effort; otherwise there might be too many abortions for the system, as well as for the individual woman (who might need three a year to remain without issue).

Free abortion in cases where contraception had failed would probably make for a decline in fertility, but how large a one would depend upon the quality of the contraceptive program. With modern contraception (the IUD and the pill) the failure rates are quite small, but women who only marginally tolerate these two methods could fall back on abortion. Free abortion has certainly lowered fertility in Japan and in certain countries of eastern Europe (68) and, where medically feasible, would do so elsewhere as well; as a colleague observes, in this field one should not underestimate the attraction of a certainty as compared to a probability.

The large question of the impact of the various incentive and benefit or liability plans (D and E) simply cannot be answered; we have too little experience to know much about the conditions under which financial factors will affect childbearing to any substantial degree. Perhaps everyone has his price for everything; if so, we do not know what would have to be paid, directly or indirectly, to make people decide not to bear children.

Such as it is, the evidence from the pro-natalist side of the effectiveness of incentives is not encouraging. All the countries of Europe have family allowance programs of one kind or another (69), most of them legislated in the 1930's and 1940's to raise the birth rate; collectively Europe has the lowest birth rate of any continent. The consensus among demographers appears to be that such programs cannot be shown to have effected an upward trend in the birth rate where tried.

As in the case of abortion for illegitimate pregnancies, several of the benefit or liability proposals would affect only a trivial fraction of people in much of the developing world. However, because the impact of incentive and benefit or liability plans is uncertain and may become important, we need to become better informed on the possibilities and limitations, and this information can come only from experimentation under realistic circumstances and at realistic levels of payment.

A higher age of marriage and a greater participation of women in the labor force are generally credited with effecting fertility declines. In a recent Indian conference on raising the age at marriage, the specialists seemed to differ only on the magnitude of the fertility decline that would result: a decline of 30 percent in the birth rate in a generation of 28 years if the minimum age of the woman at marriage were raised to 20 (70), or a decline of not more than 15 percent in 10 years (71). I say "seemed to differ" since these figures are not necessarily incompatible. In either case, the decline is a valuable one. But an increase in the age at marriage is not easy to achieve, and that must come before the fertility effect.

Similarly, an increase in the proportion of working women would have its demographic effect, but could probably come about only in conjunction with other broad social trends like education and industrialization, which themselves would powerfully affect fertility, just as a decline in fertility would assist importantly in bringing these trends about (72). Both compulsory education and restrictions on child labor would lower the economic value of children, hence tend to produce a decline in fertility. The question is, how are they to be brought about?

Finally, whether or not research would affect fertility trends depends of course upon its nature and outcome. Most observers believe that, under the typical conditions of the developing society, any improvement in contraceptive technology would lead toward the realization of present fertility goals and might help turn the spiral down. Indeed, several observers believe that this is the single most important desideratum, over the short run. Easy means of determining sex should have some effect upon the "need for sons" and thus cut family size to some extent. Research on the social-economic side would probably have to take effect through programs of the kind discussed above.

The picture is not particularly encouraging. The measures that would work to sharply cut fertility are politically and morally unacceptable to the societies in question (as with coercion), and in any case unavailable; or they are difficult of attainment in any foreseeable future, as in the case of broad social trends or a shift in age at marriage. The measures that might possibly be tried in some settings, like some version of incentives or benefit or liability plans, give uncertain promise of results at the probable level of operation. Legalization of abortion, where the needed medical facilities are available, would almost certainly have a measurable effect, but acceptability is problematic.

Conclusion

This review leaves us with some conclusions concerning proposals that go beyond family planning.

1. There is no easy way to achieve population control. If this review has indicated nothing else, it has shown how many obstacles stand in the way of a solution to the population problem. Table 1 shows, by way of recapitulation, how the various proposals seem to fit the several criteria (73). That is only one observer's judgment of the present situation, but, whatever appraisal is made of specific items, it would appear that the overall picture is mixed.

2. Family-planning programs do not compare unfavorably with other specific proposals, especially when one considers that any *actual*

operating program is at a disadvantage when compared with any competitive *ideal* policy. Indeed, on this showing, if family-planning programs did not exist, they would have to be invented; it appears that they would be among the first proposals to be made and the first programs to be tried, given their generally acceptable characteristics.

In fact, when such proposals are made, it turns out that many of them call for *more* family planning, not less, but in a somewhat different form. In the present case, at least a third of the proposals listed above put forward, in effect, simply another approach to family planning, often accepting the existing motivation as to family size. In any case, family-planning programs are established, have some momentum, and, importantly, would be useful as the direct instrument through which other proposals would take effect. So, as a major critic (74) acknowledges (6), "there is no reason to abandon family-planning programs."

What is needed is the energetic and full implementation of present experience. Much more could be done on the informational side, on encouraging commercial distribution of contraceptives, on the use of paramedical personnel, on logistics and supply, on the training and supervision of field workers, on approaches to special groups of individuals, ranging from women after childbirth to young men drafted into the armed forces. If workers in this field did well what they know how to do, that in itself would in all likelihood make a measurable difference, competitive in magnitude with the probable effects of other specific proposals— not to mention the further impetus of any improved contraceptive technology.

3. Most of the proposed ideas are not new; they have been around for some time. So, if they are not being tried, it is not because they have not been known but because they have not been accepted—presumably, for reasons like those discussed above. In India, for example, several of the social measures being proposed have been, it would seem, under almost constant review by one or another committee for the past 10 to 15 years. So it is not correct to imply that it is only new ideas that are needed; the ideas are there, but their political,

Table 1. Illustrative appraisal of proposals, by criteria.

Proposal	Scientific readiness	Political viability	Administrative feasibility	Economic capability	Ethical acceptability	Presumed effectiveness
A. Extension of voluntary fertility control	High	High on maternal care, moderate-to-low on abortion	Uncertain in near future	Maternal care too costly for local budget, abortion feasible	High for maternal care, low for abortion	Moderately high
B. Establishment of involuntary fertility control	Low	Low	Low	High	Low	High
C. Intensified educational campaigns	High	Moderate-to-high	High	Probably high	Generally high	Moderate
D. Incentive programs	High	Moderately low	Low	Low-to-moderate	Low-to-high	Uncertain
E. Tax and welfare benefits and penalties	High	Moderately low	Low	Low-to-moderate	Low-to-moderate	Uncertain
F. Shifts in social and economic institutions	High	Generally high, but low on some specifics	Low	Generally low	Generally high, but uneven	High, over long run
G. Political channels and organizations	High	Low	Low	Moderate	Moderately low	Uncertain
H. Augmented research efforts	Moderate	High	Moderate-to-high	High	High	Uncertain
Family-planning programs	Generally high, but could use improved technology	Moderate-to-high	Moderate-to-high	High	Generally high, but uneven, on religious grounds	Moderately high

economic, or administrative feasibility are problematic.

4. All of the proposers are dissatisfied to some degree with present family-planning efforts, but that does not mean that they agree with one another's schemes for doing better. Thus, Ohlin believes that "the demographic significance of such measures [maternity benefits and tax deductions for children] would be limited" (34). Ketchel eloquently opposes several "possible alternatives to fertility control agents" (9). Meier argues against the tax on children on both humanitarian and political grounds (16). The U.N. Advisory Mission to India comments (53, p. 87), "it is realised that no major demographic effects can be expected from measures of this kind [maternity benefits], particularly as only a small proportion of families are covered . . . but they could contribute, together with the family planning program, to a general change in the social climate relating to childbearing." Earlier, in supporting a family-planning effort in India, Davis noted that "the reaction to the Sarda Act [the Child Marriage Restraint Act of 1929] prohibiting female marriage [below the age of 14] shows the difficulty of trying to regulate the age of marriage by direct legislation" (75). Myrdal warns against cash payments to parents in this connection and supports social awards in kind to the children (76). Kirk believes that "it might prove to be the height of folly to undermine the existing family structure, which continues to be a crucial institution for stability and socialization in an increasingly mobile and revolutionary society" (77). Finally, Ehrlich is contemptuous of the professors whose "ideas of 'action' is to form a committee or to urge 'more research.' Both courses are actually substitutes for action" (7, p. 191).

5. In a rough way, there appears to be a progression in national efforts to deal with the problem of population control. The first step is the theoretical recognition that population growth may have something to do with the prospects for economic development. Then, typically, comes an expert mission from abroad to make a survey and report to the government, as has occurred in India, Pakistan, South Korea, Turkey, Iran, Tunisia, Morocco, and Kenya,

among others. The first action program is in family planning, and most of the efforts are still at that level. Beyond that, it apparently takes (i) some degree of discouragement about progress combined with (ii) some heightened awareness of the seriousness of the problem to move the effort forward. To date, those conditions have been most prominently present in India—and that is the country that has gone farthest in the use of incentives and in at least consideration of further steps along the lines mentioned above.

6. Proposals need to be specific—proposals both for action and for further research. It is perhaps too much to ask advocates to spell out all the administrative details of the way their plan is to operate in the face of obstacles and difficulties, or even to spell out how it is to get permission to operate; the situations, settings, opportunities, and personalities are too diverse for that. But it does seem proper to ask for the fullest possible specification of actual plans, under realistic conditions, in order to test out their feasibility and likely effectiveness. Similarly, advocates of further research ought to spell out not only what would be studied, and how, but also how the results might be applied to action programs to affect fertility. Social research is not always readily translated into action, especially into administrative action; and the thrust of research is toward refinement, subtlety, precision, and qualification, whereas the administrator must act in the large. Short of such specification, the field remains confronted with potentially good ideas, such as "raise the age at marriage" or "use incentives" or "substitute pension systems for male children," without being able to move very far toward implementation.

7. Just as there is no easy way, there is no single way. Since population control will at best be difficult, it follows that every acceptable step that promises some measure of impact should be taken. The most likely prospect is that population control, to the degree it is realized, will be the result of a combination of efforts—economic, legal, social, medical—each of which has some effect but not an immediately overwhelming one (78). Accordingly, it is incumbent upon workers in the professional

fields concerned to look hard at various approaches, including family planning itself, in order to screen out what is potentially useful for application. In doing so, it may be the path of wisdom to move with the "natural" progression. Some important proposals seem reasonably likely of adoption—institutionalization of maternal care, population study in the schools, the TV satellite system for disseminating information, a better contraceptive technology, perhaps even liberalization of abortion laws in some settings—and we need to know not only how effective such efforts will be but, beyond them, how large a money incentive would have to be to effect a given amount of fertility control and how effective those indirect social measures are that are morally acceptable and capable of realization. It may be that some of these measures would be both feasible and effective—many observers 15 years ago thought that family-planning programs were neither—and a genuine effort needs to be made. The "heavy" measures—involuntary measures and political pressures—may be put aside for the time being, if not forever.

8. In the last analysis, what will be scientifically available, politically acceptable, administratively feasible, economically justifiable, and morally tolerated depends upon people's perceptions of consequences. If "the population problem" is considered relatively unimportant or only moderately important, that judgment will not support much investment of effort. If it is considered urgent, much more can and will be done. The fact is that, despite the large forward strides taken in international recognition of the problem in the 1960's, there still does not exist an informed, firm, and constant conviction in high circles that this is a matter with truly great implications for human welfare (79). Such convictions must be based on sound knowledge. Here it would appear that the demographers and economists have not sufficiently made their case to the world elite—or that, if made, the case has not sufficiently commanded their attention and support. Population pressures are not sharply visible on a day-to-day or even year-to-year basis, nor, short of major famine, do they show themselves in dramatic events. Moreover, the warnings of demographers are often dismissed, albeit unfairly and wrongly, on the basis of past forecasts that were not borne out (80). After all, only a generation ago we were being warned about a decline in population in the West. Asking government leaders to take steps toward population control is asking them to take very substantial steps indeed—substantial for their people as well as for their own political careers—hence the case must be virtually incontrovertible. Accordingly, the scientific base must be carefully prepared (and perhaps with some sense of humility about the ease of predicting or urging great events, for the record is not without blemishes). Greater measures to meet the problem—measures which exclude social repression and needless limitation of human freedom—must rely on heightened awareness of what is at stake, on the part of leaders and masses alike.

What is beyond family planning? Even if most of the specific plans are not particularly new, that in itself does not mean that they are to be disregarded. The questions are: Which plans can be effected, given such criteria? How can they be implemented? What will be the outcome?

This article is an effort to promote the discourse across the professional fields concerned with this important issue. Given the recent stress on family-planning programs as the "means of choice" in dealing with the problem, it is natural and desirable that counterpositions be put forward and reviewed. But that does not in itself settle the critical questions. What can we do now to advance the matter? Beyond family planning, what?

References and Notes

1. See, for example, K. Davis, *Science* **158**, 730 (1967); R. G. Potter, R. Freedman, L. P. Chow, *ibid.* **160**, 848 (1968); F. W. Notestein, "Population growth and its control," paper presented before the American Assembly on World Hunger, Fall 1968.
2. See, for example, the section on "Goals" in K. Davis, *Science* **158**, 730 (1967).
3. A. J. Coale, "Should the United States start a campaign for fewer births?," presidential address presented before the Population Association of America, 1968.

4. For current targets of some national family-planning programs, see B. Berelson, "National family planning programs: Where we stand," paper presented at the University of Michigan Sesquicentennial Celebration, November 1967; the paper concludes: "By and large, developing countries are now aiming at the birth rates of Western Europe 75 years ago or the United States 50 years ago."

5. H. C. Taylor, Jr., and B. Berelson, *Amer. J. Obstet. Gynecol.* 100, 885 (1968).

6. K. Davis, *Science* 158, 730 (1967).

7. P. R. Ehrlich, *The Population Bomb* (Ballantine, New York, 1968).

8. S. Chandrasekhar, *Population Rev.* 10, 17 (1966).

9. M. M. Ketchel, *Perspect. Biol. Med.* 11, 687 (1968); see also Ketchel's article in *Med. World News* (18 Oct. 1968), p. 66.

10. Ehrlich appears to dismiss the scheme as unworkable (7, p. 136), though two pages later he advocates "ample funds" to "promote intensive investigation of new techniques of birth control, possibly leading to the development of mass sterilizing agents such as were discussed above."

11. K. E. Boulding, *The Meaning of the Twentieth Century: The Great Transition* (Harper & Row, New York, 1964), pp. 135-36.

12. W. B. Schockley, in a lecture delivered at McMaster University, Hamilton, Ontario, December, 1967.

13. S. Chandrasekhar, as reported in the New York *Times* 24 July 1967. Just as the present article was being completed, Chandrasekhar proposed (*ibid.*, 21 Oct. 1968) "that every married couple in India deny themselves sexual intercourse for a year. . . . Abstinence for a year would do enormous good to the individual and the country." The reader may wish to consider this the 30th proposal and test it against the criteria that follow.

14. S. Wayland, in *Family Planning and Population Programs*, B. Berelson, R. K. Anderson, O. Harkavy, J. Maier, W. P. Mauldin, S. J. Segal, Eds. (Univ. of Chicago Press, Chicago, 1966), pp. 353-62: ———, in "Family Planning Programs: Administration, Education, Evaluation," J. Ross and J. Friesen, Eds., in preparation; "Teaching Population Dynamics: An Instructional Unit for Secondary School Students" (Columbia University, New York, 1965); "Critical Stages in Reproduction: Instruction Materials in General Science and Biology" (Columbia University, New York, 1965). The two last-named publications are pamphlets prepared under Wayland's direction at Teachers College.

15. P. Visaria, *Economic Weekly* (8 Aug. 1964), p. 1343.

16. R. L. Meier and G. Meier, "New Directions: A Population Policy for the Future," unpublished manuscript.

17. *Preparatory Study of a Pilot Project in the Use of Satellite Communication for National Develop-ment Purposes in India* (UNESCO Expert Mission, 1968).

18. W. Schramm and L. Nelson, *Communication Satellite for Education and Development—The Case of India* (Stanford Research Institute, Stanford, Calif., 1968), pp. 63-66.

19. S. Chandrasekhar, as reported in the New York *Times*, 19 July, 1967.

20. E. Pohlman (Central Family Planning Institute, India), "Incentives for 'Non-Maternity' Cannot 'Compete' with Incentives for Vasectomy," unpublished manuscript.

21. T. J. Samuel, *J. Family Welfare* 13, 11 (1966).

22. J. Simon, "Money Incentives to Reduce Birth Rates in Low-Income Countries: A Proposal to Determine the Effect Experimentally," unpublished manuscript; "The Role of Bonuses and Persuasive Propaganda in the Reduction of Birth Rates," unpublished manuscript.

23. ———, "Family Planning Prospects in Less-Developed Countries, and a Cost-Benefit Analysis of Various Alternatives," unpublished manuscript.

24. S. Enke, *Population Rev.* 4, 47 (1960).

25. M. Young, "The Behavioral Sciences and Family Planning Programs: Report on a Conference," *Studies in Family Planning*, No. 23 (1967), p. 10.

26. D. Bhatia, "Government of India Small Family Norm Committee Questionnaire," *Indian J. Med. Educ.* 6, 189 (1967). As the title indicates, this is not a proposal but a questionnaire soliciting opinions on various ideas put forward to promote "the small family norm."

27. S. Enke, "The Gains to India from Population Control," *Rev. Econ. Statist.* 42, 179, 180 (1960).

27a J. W. Leasure, *Milbank Mem. Fund Quart.* 45, 417 (1967).

28. J. J. Spengler, "Agricultural development is not enough," paper presented before the Conference on World Population Problems, Indiana University, May 1967.

29. M. C. Balfour, "A Scheme for Rewarding Successful Family Planners," *Population Council Mem.* (1962).

30. W. P. Mauldin, "Prevention of Illegitimate Births: A Bonus Scheme," *Population Council Mem.* (1967).

31. R. M. Titmuss and B. Abel-Smith, *Social Policies and Population Growth in Mauritius* (Methuen, London, 1960).

32. A. S. David, *National Development, Population and Family Planning in Nepal* (1968), pp. 53-54.

33. J. Fawcett, personal communication.

34. G. Ohlin, *Population Control and Economic Development* (Development Centre of the Organisation for Economic Co-operation and Development, New York, 1967), p. 104.

35. W. P. Davison, personal communication. Davison suggests a good pension (perhaps $400 a year) for men aged 60, married for at least 20 years, with no sons.

36. K. Davis, personal communication.

37. B. Berelson and A. Etzioni, brief formulations, 1962 and 1967, respectively.

38. P. M. Hauser, in "The Behavioral Sciences and Family Planning Programs: Report on a Conference," *Studies in Family Planning*, No. 23 (1967), p. 9.

39. J. Blake, in *Public Health and Population Change: Current Research Issues*, M. C. Sheps and J. C. Ridley, Eds. (Univ. of Pittsburgh Press, Pittsburgh, 1965), p. 62.

40. For the initial formulation of the proposal, see R. L. Meier, *Modern Science and the Human Fertility Problem* (Wiley, New York, 1959), chap. 7.

41. P. M. Hauser, *Demography* 4, 412 (1967).

42. "Family Planning and the Status of Women: Interim Report of the Secretary-General" (United Nations Economic and Social Council, Commission on the Status of Women, New York, 1968), especially p. 17 ff.

43. R. Revelle, quoted by M. Viorst, *Horizon* (summer 1968), p. 35; D. M. Heer and D. O. Smith, "Mortality level and desired family size," paper presented before the Population Association of America, April 1967.

44. Ehrlich makes the same point in *New Scientist* (14 Dec. 1967), p. 655: "Refuse all foreign aid to any country with an increasing population which we believe is not making a maximum effort to limit its population. . . . The United States should use its power and prestige to bring extreme diplomatic and/or economic pressure on any country or organization (the Roman Catholic Church?) impeding a solution to the world's most pressing problem."

45. In an earlier article Ehrlich calls for a "Federal Population Commission with a large budget for propaganda," presumably limited to the United States.

46. S. Chandrasekhar, in *Asia's Population Problems*, S. Chandrasekhar, Ed. (Allen & Unwin, New York, 1967), p. 96; Chandrasekhar cites a suggestion made in 1961 by Julian Huxley.

47. S. Polgar, in "The Behavioral Sciences and Family Planning Programs: Report on a Conference," *Studies in Family Planning*, No. 23 (1967), p. 10.

48. *The Growth of World Population* (National Academy of Sciences, Committee on Science and Public Policy, Washington, D.C., 1963), pp. 5, 28-36. This recommendation has of course been made on several occasions by several people. For an imaginative account of the impact of biological developments, see P. C. Berry, appendix to *The Next Thirty-Four Years: A Context for Speculation* (Hudson Institute, Croton-on-Hudson, New York, 1966).

49. See, for example, S. J. Segal, "Biological aspects of fertility regulation," paper presented at the University of Michigan Sesquicentennial Celebration, November, 1967.

50. It is worth noting that such expectations are not particularly reliable. For example, in 1952-53 a Working Group on Fertility Control was organized by the Conservation Foundation to review the most promising "leads to physiologic control of fertility," based on a survey conducted by Paul S. Henshaw and Kingsley Davis. This group did identify a "lead" that became the oral contraceptive (then already under investigation) but did not mention the intrauterine device. It was searching specifically for better ways to control fertility because of the population problem in the developing world, and considered the contraceptive approach essential to that end: "It thus appears imperative that an attempt be made to bring down fertility in overpopulated regions without waiting for a remote, hoped-for transformation of the entire society. . . . It seems plausible that acceptable birth control techniques might be found, and that the application of science to developing such techniques for peasant regions might yield revolutionary results" [*The Physiological Approach to Fertility Control, Report of the Working Group on Fertility Control* (Conservation Foundation, New York, 1953)].

51. A. S. Parkes, *New Scientist* 35, 186 (1967).

52. New York *Times* (17 Nov. 1967). The then Minister had earlier suggested a substantial bonus (100 rupees) for vasectomy, the funds to be taken from U.S. counterpart funds, "but both Governments are extremely sensitive in this area. Yet in a problem this crucial perhaps we need more action and less sensitivity" [S. Chandrasekhar (46)].

53. *Report on the Family Planning Programme in India* (United Nations Advisory Mission, New York, 1966).

54. *Implications of Raising the Female Age at Marriage in India* (Demographic Training and Research Centre, Chembur, India, 1968), p. 109; *Centre Calling* (May 1968), p. 4.

55. *Planned Parenthood* (Mar. 1968), p. 3.

56. *Ibid.* (Apr. 1968), p. 2.

57. For a review of this development see R. Symonds and M. Carder, *International Organisations and Population Control (1947-67)* (Institute of Development Studies, Univ. of Sussex, Brighton, England, 1968).

58. At present, population materials are being included in school programs in Pakistan, Iran, Taiwan, and elsewhere.

59. See, for example, Balfour (29), Mauldin (30), and Pohlman (20) and, for the economic analysis, Enke (27) and Simon (22).

60. For the negative answer, see Enke (27) and Simon (22). Data are from family-planning budgets and national development budgets contained in 5-year development plans.

61. E. Pohlman, "Incentives in birth planning," in preparation.

62. Coale, however, does point out that "it is clearly

fallacious to accept as optimal a growth that continues until overcrowding makes additional births intolerably expensive."

63. See, for example, the World Leaders' Statement [*Studies in Family Planning*, No. 26 (1968)] and the Resolution of the International Conference on Human Rights on "Human Rights Aspects of Family Planning," adopted 12 May 1968, reported in *Population Newsletter*, No. 2 (issued by the Population Division, United Nations) (1968), p. 21 ff. Incidentally, the issue of population policy was apparently a live one in classical times, and resolved by the great philosophers in ways not fully consonant with modern views. Plato, in the *Republic* (Modern Library edition, pp. 412, 414) says, "the number of weddings is a matter which must be left to the discretion of the rulers, whose aim will be to preserve the average of population and to prevent the State from becoming either too large or too small"—to which end certain marriages have strict orders to prevent any embryo which may come into being from seeing the light; and if any force a way to the birth, the parents must understand that the offspring of such a union cannot be maintained, and arrange accordingly." Aristotle, in *Politics* (Modern Library edition, p. 316) says, "on the ground of an excess in the number of children, if the established customs of the state forbid this (for in our state population has a limit), no child is to be exposed, but when couples have children in excess, let abortion be procured before sense and life have begun. . . ."

64. After noting that economic constraints have not been adopted in South Asia, though often proposed, Gunnar Myrdal continues: "The reason is not difficult to understand. Since having many children is a main cause of poverty, such measures would penalize the relatively poor and subsidize the relatively well off. Such a result would not only violate rules of equity but would be detrimental to the health of the poor families, and so of the growing generation" [*Asian Drama: An Inquiry into the Poverty of Nations* (Pantheon, New York, 1968), vol. 2, pp. 1502-03].

65. F. W. Notestein, in *Family Planning and Population Programs*, Berelson *et al.*, Eds. (University of Chicago Press, Chicago, 1966), pp. 828-29: "There is a real danger that sanctions, for example through taxation, would affect adversely the welfare of the children. There is also danger that incentives through bonuses will put the whole matter of family planning in a grossly commercial light. It is quite possible that to poor and harassed people financial inducements will amount to coercion and not to an enlargement of their freedom of choice. Family planning must be, and must seem to be, an extension of personal and familial freedom of choice and thereby an enrichment of life, not coercion toward its restriction."

66. In this connection see the novel by A. Burgess,

The Wanting Seed (Ballantine, New York, 1963). At the same time, Myrdal, a long-time observer of social affairs, remarks that "the South Asian countries . . . can, to begin with, have no other principle than that of voluntary parenthood. . . . State direction by compulsion in these personal matters is not effective. . ." [G. Myrdal, *Asian Drama: An Inquiry into the Poverty of Nations* (Pantheon, New York, 1968), p. 1501].

67. G. I. Zatuchni, "International Postpartum Family Planning Program: Report on the First Year," *Studies in Family Planning*, No. 22 (1967), p. 14 ff.

68. For example, the repeal of the free abortion law in Rumania resulted in an increase in the birth rate from 14 in the third quarter of 1966 to 38 in the third quarter of 1967. For an early report, see R. Pressat, *Population* 22, 1116 (1967).

69. *See Social Security Programs Throughout the World, 1964* (U.S. Department of Health, Education, and Welfare, Washington, D.C., 1964).

70. S. N. Agarwala in *Implications of Raising the Female Age at Marriage in India* (Demographic Training and Research Centre, Chembur, India, 1968), p. 21.

71. V. C. Chidambaram, *ibid.*, p. 47.

72. Actually, recent research is calling into question some of the received wisdom of the prior need of such broad institutional factors for fertility decline. If further study supports the new findings, that could have important implications for present strategy in the developing countries. See A. J. Coale, in *Proc. U.N. World Population Conf.* (1965), vol. 2, pp. 205-09, and ———, "The decline of fertility in Europe from the French Revolution to World War II," paper presented at the University of Michigan Sesquicentennial Celebration, 1967.

73. As the roughest sort of summary of Table 1, if one assigns values from 5 for "high" to 1 for "low," the various proposals rank as follows: family-planning programs 25; intensified educational campaigns, 25; augmented research efforts, 24; extension of voluntary fertility control, 20; shifts in social and economic institutions, 20; incentive programs, 14; tax and welfare benefits and penalties, 14; political channels and organizations. 14; establishment of involuntary fertility control, 14.

74. Davis was a strong advocate of family planning in India, and quite optimistic about its prospects even in the pre-IUD or pre-pill era. See K. Davis, in *The Interrelations of Demographic, Economic, and Social Problems in Selected Underdeveloped Areas* (Milbank Memorial Fund, New York, 1954). Davis concludes (pp. 87-88): "Although India is already well-launched in the rapid-growth phase of the demographic transition, there is no inherent reason why she should long continue in this phase. She need not necessarily wait patiently while the forces of urbanization, class mobility, and industrial development gradually build up to the

point where parents are forced to limit their offspring on their own initiative and without help, perhaps even in the face of official opposition. . . . Realistically appraising her situation, India has a chance to be the first country to achieve a major revolution in human life—the planned diffusion of fertility control in a peasant population prior to, and for the benefit of, the urban-industrial transition."

75. K. Davis, in *The Interrelations of Demographic, Economic, and Social Problems in Selected Underdeveloped Areas* (Milbank Memorial Fund, New York, 1954), p. 86.

76. G. Myrdal, *Asian Drama: An Inquiry into the Poverty of Nations* (Pantheon, New York, 1968), p. 1503.

77. D. Kirk, "Population research in relation to population policy and national family planning programs," paper presented before the American Sociological Association, August, 1968.

78. It begins to appear that the prospects for fertility control may be improving over the decades. Kirk, after reviewing several factors that "favor a much more rapid [demographic] transition than occurred in the West"—changed climate of opinion, religious doctrine, decline of infant mortality, modernization, fertility differentials, grass-roots concerned, and improved contraceptive technology—shows, in a remarkable tabulation, that the later a country begins the reduction of its birth rate from 35 to 20 births per thousand, the shorter the time it took to achieve this reduction: from 73 years (average) for the period 1831-60, for example, to 21 years after 1951; the trend has been consistently downward for over a century [D. Kirk, "Natality in the developing countries: recent trends and prospects," paper presented at the University of Michigan Sesquicentennial Celebration, 1967].

79. Nor, often, does such a conviction exist among the general public. For example, in midsummer of 1968 a national sample of adults was asked in a Gallup poll, "What do you think is the most important problem facing this country today?" Less than 1 percent mentioned population growth (Gallup release, 3 Aug. 1968, and personal communication).

80. For an old but enlightening review, see H. Dorn, *J. Amer. Statist. Ass.* 45, 311 (1950).

33

POPULATION POLICY FOR AMERICANS: IS THE GOVERNMENT BEING MISLED?

Judith Blake

Pressure on the federal government for "action" to limit population growth in the United States has intensified greatly during the past 10 years, and at present such action is virtually unchallenged as an official national goal. Given the goal, the question of means becomes crucial. Here I first evaluate the particular means being advocated and pursued in public policy, then I present alternative ways of possibly achieving the goal.

The prevailing view as to the best means is remarkably unanimous and abundantly documented. It is set forth in the 17 volumes of congressional hearings so far published on the "population crisis" (1); in "The Growth of U.S. Population," a report by the Committee on Population of the National Academy of Sciences (2); in a statement made by an officer of the Ford Foundation who was asked by the Department of Health, Education, and Welfare to make suggestions (3); and, finally, in the "Report of the President's Committee on Population and Family Planning," which was officially released this past January (4). The essential recommendation throughout is that the government should give highest priority to ghetto-oriented family-planning programs designed to "deliver" birth-control services to the poor and uneducated, among whom, it is claimed, there are at least 5 million women who are "in need" of such federally sponsored birth-control assistance.

By what logic have the proponents of control moved from a concern with population growth to a recommendation favoring highest

priority for poverty-oriented birth-control programs? First, they have assumed that fertility is
the only component of population growth
worthy of government attention. Second, they
have taken it for granted that, to reduce
fertility, one sponsors birth-control programs
("family planning"). Just why they have made
this assumption is not clear, but its logical
implication is that population growth is due to
births that couples would have preferred to
avoid. Furthermore, the reasoning confuses
couple control over births with societal control
over them (5). Third, the proponents of the
new policy have seized on the poor and
uneducated as the "target" group for birth-
control action because they see this group as
the only remaining target for a program of
voluntary family planning. The rest of the
population is handling its family planning
pretty well on its own: over 95 percent of
fecund U.S. couples already either use birth-
control methods or intend to do so. The poor,
on the other hand—at least those who are
fecund—have larger families than the advantaged; they not only use birth-control methods
less but they use them less effectively. The
family-planning movement's notion of "responsible parenthood" carries the implication
that family size should be directly, not inversely, related to social and economic advantage, and the poor are seen as constituting the
residual slack to be taken up by the movement's efforts. Why are the poor not con-
forming to the dictates of responsible parenthood? Given the movement's basic assumptions, there are only two answers: the poor are
irresponsible, or they have not had the opportunity. Since present-day leaders would abhor
labeling the poor irresponsible, they have
chosen to blame lack of opportunity as the
cause. Opportunity has been lacking, in their
eyes, either because the poor have not been
"educated" in family planning or because they
have not been "reached" by family-planning
services. In either case, as they see it, the poor
have been deprived of their "rights" (2, p. 22;
6). This deprivation has allegedly been due to
the prudery and hypocrisy of the affluent, who
have overtly tabooed discussion of birth control
and dissemination of birth-control materials

while, themselves, covertly enjoying the benefits of family planning (7).

So much for the logic underlying recent
proposals for controlling population growth in
the United States. But what is the evidence
on which this argument is based? On what
empirical grounds is the government being
asked to embark on a high-priority program of
providing contraceptive services to the poor?
Moreover, what, if any, are some of the
important public issues that the suggested
policy raises—what are its social and political
side effects? And, finally, is such a policy, even
if appropriate for the poor and even if relatively
unencumbered by public disapproval, relevant
to the problem of population growth in
America? If demographic curtailment is really
the objective, must alternative policies be considered and possibly given highest priority?

Turning to the alleged need for government-
sponsored birth-control services, one may ask
whether birth control has in fact been a
tabooed topic among the middle and upper
classes, so that the less advantaged could be said
to have suffered "deprivation" and consequently now to require government help. One
may then question whether there is a mandate
from the poor for the type of federally sponsored service that is now being urged, and
whether as many as 5 million women are "in
need" of such family-planning assistance.

Has Birth Control Been a Tabooed Topic?

The notion that the American public has
only recently become willing to tolerate open
discussion of birth control has been assiduously
cultivated by congressmen and others concerned with government policy on population.
For example, Senator Tydings credited Sena-
tors Gruening and Clark and President Johnson
with having almost single-handedly changed
American public attitudes toward birth control.
In 1966 he read the following statement into
the 28 February *Congressional Record* (8).

The time is ripe for positive action. Ten years ago,
even five years ago, this was a politically delicate
subject. Today the Nation has awakened to the need
for Government action.

This change in public attitude has come about through the efforts of men who had the courage to brook the tides of public opinion. Senator Clark is such a man. Senator Gruening is such a man. So is President Johnson. Because of their leadership it is no longer necessary for an elected official to speak with trepidation on this subject.

A year later, Senator Tydings reduced his estimate of the time required for the shift in public opinion to "3 or 4 years" (9, p. 12; 10). Senator Gruening maintained (11) that the "ninety-eight distinguished men and women" who testified at the public hearing on S. 1676 were "pioneers" whose "names comprise an important honor roll which historically bears an analogy to other famous lists; the signers of the Declaration of Independence, those who ratified the Constitution of the United States and others whose names were appended to and made possible some of the great turning points in history." Reasoning from the continued existence of old, and typically unenforced, laws concerning birth control (together with President Eisenhower's famous anti-birth-control statement), Stycos, in a recent article (12), stated:

The public reaction to family planning in the United States has varied between disgust and silent resignation to a necessary evil. At best it was viewed as so delicate and risky that it was a matter of "individual conscience." As such, it was a matter so totally private, so sacred (or profane), that no external agents, and certainly not the state, should have anything to do with it.

Does the evidence support such impressionistic claims? How did the general public regard government sponsorship of birth control long before it became a subject of congressional hearings, a National Academy report, and a Presidential Committee report? Fortunately, a question on this topic appeared in no less than 13 national polls and surveys conducted between 1937 and 1966. As part of a larger project concerned with public knowledge and opinions about demographic topics, I have gathered together the original data cards from these polls, prepared them for computer processing, and analyzed the results. The data are all from Gallup polls and are all from national samples of the white, adult population. Here I

Table 1. Percentages of white U.S. men and women between the ages of 21 and 44 who, in various national polls and surveys made between 1937 and 1964*, expressed the opinion that birth-control information should be made available to individuals who desired it.

Year	Men		Women	
	%	N	%	N
1937	66	1038	70	734
1938	67	1111	72	548
1939	74	1101	73	630
1940	72	1127	75	618
1943	67	628	73	866
1945	64	714	70	879
1947	76	353	75	405
1959	78	301	79	394
1961	82	336	81	394
1962	85	288	80	381
1963	78	323	79	373
1964	89	324	86	410

* The question asked of respondents concerning birth control were as follows. In 1937: Do you favor the birth control movement? In 1938, 1939, 1940, 1943, 1945, and 1947; Would you like to see a government agency (or "government health clinics") furnish birth-control information to married people who want it? In 1959, 1961, 1962, and 1963: In some places in the United States it is not legal to supply birth-control information. How do you feel about this—do you think birth-control information should be available to anyone who wants it, or not? In 1964: Do you think birth-control information should be available to anyone who wants it, or not?

concentrate on adults under 45—that is, on adults in the childbearing age group.

The data of Table 1 contradict the notion that Americans have only recently ceased to regard birth control as a tabooed topic. As far back as 30 years ago, almost three-quarters of the women questioned in these surveys actively approved having the *government* make birth-control information available to the married. By the early 1960's, 80 percent or more of women approved overcoming legal barriers and allowing "anyone who wants it" to have birth-control information. The figures for men are similar. The question asked in 1964—the one question in recent years that did not mention illegality—brought 86 percent of the women and 89 percent of the men into the category of those who approved availability of birth-control information for "anyone who wants it." Furthermore, in judging the level of disapproval, one should bear in mind that the remainder of the respondents, in all of these years, includes from 7 to 15 percent who claim that they have "no opinion" on the subject, not that they "disapprove."

An important difference of opinion corresponds to a difference in religious affiliation. Among non-Catholics (including those who have "no religion" and do not attend church) approval has been considerably higher than it has been among Catholics. Among non-Catholic women, over 80 percent approved as early as 1939, and among non-Catholic men the percentages were approximately the same. The 1964 poll showed that 90 percent of each sex approved. Among Catholics, in recent years about 60 percent have approved, and, in 1964, the question that mentioned neither the government nor legality brought opinions of approval from 77 percent of the women and 83 percent of the men.

Clearly, if birth-control information has in fact been unavailable to the poor, the cause has not been a generalized and pervasive attitude of prudery on the part of the American public. Although public officials may have misjudged American opinion (and may have mistakenly assumed that the Catholic Church "spoke for" a majority of Americans, or even for a majority of Catholics), most Americans of an age to be having children did not regard birth control as a subject that should be under a blanket of secrecy and, as far back as the 1930's, evinced a marked willingness to have their government make such information widely available. It seems unlikely, therefore, that poorer sectors of our population were "cut off" from birth-control knowledge primarily because informal channels of communication (the channels through which most people learn about birth control) were blocked by an upper- and middle-class conspiracy of silence.

What has happened, however, is that pressure groups for family planning, like the Catholic hierarchy they have been opposing, have been acting as self-designated spokesmen for "public opinion." By developing a cause as righteous as that of the Catholics (the "rights" of the poor as against the "rights" of a religious group), the family planners have used the American way of influencing official opinion.

Now public officials appear to believe that publicly supported birth-control services are what the poor have always wanted and needed, just as, in the past, official opinion acceded to the notion that such services would have been "offensive" to certain groups. Nonetheless, the question remains of whether or not publicly supported services are actually appropriate to the attitudes and objectives of the poor and uneducated in matters of reproduction. Is the government responding to a mandate from the poor or to an ill-concealed mandate from the well-to-do? If there is no mandate from the poor, the provision of birth-control services may prove a convenience for certain women but is likely to have little effect on the reproductive performance of the poor in general. Let us look at the evidence.

Is There a Mandate from the Poor?

The notion that the poor have larger families than the affluent only because they have less access to birth-control information implies that the poor *desire* families as small as, or smaller than, those of the well-to-do. The poor are simply unable to realize this desire, the argument goes, because of lack of access to birth-control information. The National Academy of Sciences Committee on Population stated the argument very well (2, p. 10).

The available evidence indicates that low-income families do not want more children than do families with higher incomes, but they have more because they do not have the information or the resources to plan their families effectively according to their own desires.

The committee, however, presents none of the "available evidence" that "low-income families do not want more children than do families with higher incomes." Actually, my data supply evidence that runs counter to the statement quoted above, both with respect to the desired or ideal number of children and with respect to attitudes toward birth control.

I shall begin with the preferred size of family. A number of national polls, conducted over some 25 years, provide data concerning opinions on ideal family size. In addition, I

Table 2. Mean number of children considered ideal by non-Catholic women, according to education and economic status, for selected years between 1943 and 1968.

Date	Age range	Level of education*			Income or economic status†				Total respondents	
		College	High school	Grade school	1	2	3	4	X	N
1943	20-34	2.8	2.6	2.6	2.9	2.7	2.7	2.5	2.7	1893
1952	21 +	3.3	3.1	3.6		3.3		3.3	3.3	3.3
1955‡	18-39	3.1	3.2	3.7	3.2	3.1	3.2	3.5	3.3	1905
1955 §	18-39	3.3	3.4	3.9	3.4	3.3	3.4	3.7	3.4	1905
1957	21 +	3.4	3.2	3.6		3.3	3.2	3.5	3.3	448
1959	21 +	3.5	3.4	3.9		3.5	3.5	3.6	3.5	472
1960‡	18-39	3.1	3.2	3.5	3.1	3.2	3.3	3.2	3.2	1728
1960 §	18-39	3.2	3.4	3.6	3.2	3.3	3.5	3.4	3.4	1728
1963	21 +	3.2	3.4	3.5	3.3	3.3	3.5	3.5	3.4	483
1966	21 +	3.1	3.3	3.7	3.2	3.2	3.4	3.7	3.3	374
1967	21 +	3.1	3.3	3.4	3.3	3.2	3.1	3.4	3.3	488
1968	21 +	3.2	3.3	3.7	3.2	3.0	3.4	3.6	3.3	539

* Level of education is measured by the highest grade completed.
† Levels 1 to 4 for economic status range in order from "high" to "low."
‡ Minimum ideal (results from coding range answers to the lowest figure).
§ Maximum ideal (results from coding range answers to the highest figure).

include tabulations of data from two national surveys on fertility (the "Growth of American Families Studies"), conducted in 1955 and 1960 (13, 14). My detailed analyses of the results of these polls and surveys are given elsewhere (15) and are only briefly summarized here. Table 2 gives mean values for the family size considered ideal by white, non-Catholic women, according to education and economic status.

The data lend little support to the hypothesis that the poor desire families as small as those desired by the middle and upper classes. Within both the educational and the economic categories, those on the lower rungs not only have larger families than those on the higher rungs (at least in the case of non-Catholics) but say they want larger families and consider them ideal. This differential has existed for as long as information on preferred family size in this country has been available, and it persists. It thus seems extremely hazardous to base a major governmental effort on the notion that, among individuals (white individuals, at least) at the lower social levels, there is a widespread and deeply held desire for families as small as, or smaller than, those desired by the well-to-do. No major survey shows this to be the case.

Not only do persons of lower socioeconomic status prefer larger families than the more affluent do, they also generally favor birth control less. Tables 3 and 4 show the percentages of white men and women who expressed approval of birth control in surveys made between 1937 and 1964, by educational level and economic status, respectively.

Looking at the educational differential (Table 3), one finds that, in general, the proportion of those who approve birth control drops precipitately between the college and grade school levels. As far back as the early 1940's, over 80 percent of women and 75 percent of men with some or more college education approved government action on birth control. By 1964, over 90 percent of both sexes approved. By contrast, only 60 percent of men and women with an elementary school education approved in the 1940's, and, despite a rise in approval, there is still a differential. When non-Catholics alone are considered, the educational difference is even more pronounced in many cases.

Turning to economic or income status (Table 4), one generally finds the same results. The high proportions (close to 100 percent) of women in the highest and next-to-highest

Table 3. Percentages of white U.S. men and women between the ages of 21 and 44 who, in various national polls taken between 1943 and 1964, expressed the opinion that birth-control information should be made available to individuals who desired it. The percentages are given by level of education;* the numbers in parentheses are total numbers of respondents in each category.

	Men			Women		
Year	College	High school	Grade school	College	High school	Grade school
1943	75 (184)	68 (284)	56 (157)	82 (216)	74 (442)	60 (207)
1945	74 (202)	62 (360)	58 (140)	83 (216)	68 (434)	56 (207)
1947	91 (84)	72 (199)	67 (66)	81 (89)	74 (228)	72 (81)
1959	88 (89)	76 (163)	65 (49)	91 (55)	79 (279)	68 (41)
1961	88 (102)	81 (188)	67 (46)	84 (81)	81 (265)	78 (50)
1962	91 (93)	85 (171)	61 (23)	84 (79)	82 (258)	66 (44)
1963	86 (105)	79 (178)	53 (40)	81 (80)	78 (251)	81 (42)
1964	92 (107)	88 (188)	83 (29)	94 (79)	86 (293)	74 (38)

* The level of education is measured by the last grade completed.

economic brackets who, in recent years, have approved birth-control efforts is noteworthy, as is the fact that approximately 80 percent of women in these brackets approved such efforts as far back as the 1930's. On the other hand, men and women in lower income brackets have been slower to approve birth-control policies.

Despite the inverse relationship just described, I may have overemphasized the lesser approval of birth-control programs on the part of persons of lower economic and social status.

After all, in recent years approval often has been high even among people at the lowest social levels. Among women with only a grade school education, the percentage of those favoring birth-control programs averaged 73 percent in polls taken between 1959 and 1964; among men at the lowest educational level, the corresponding average was 66 percent. Yet it is undeniably true that, throughout the period for which data are available, the people who needed birth-control information most, ac-

Table 4. Percentages of white U.S. men and women between the ages of 21 and 44 who, in various national polls taken betwen 1937 and 1964, expressed the opinion that birth-control information should be made available to individuals who desired it. The percentages are given by economic status (levels 1–4*); the numbers in parentheses are total numbers of respondents in each category.

	Men				Women			
Year	1	2	3	4	1	2	3	4
1937	78 (112)	70 (406)	61 (520)		67 (69)	78 (293)	64 (372)	
1938	65 (125)	74 (453)	62 (521)		80 (51)	73 (232)	70 (259)	
1939	78 (116)	75 (432)	73 (553)		71 (68)	77 (260)	71 (302)	
1940	79 (131)	75 (443)	68 (553)		80 (49)	78 (258)	71 (311)	
1943	76 (80)	72 (219)	62 (330)		80 (90)	79 (272)	68 (500)	
1945	73 (67)	66 (286)	62 (352)		83 (75)	77 (264)	64 (531)	
1947	86 (42)	77 (123)	72 (188)		92 (38)	71 (119)	73 (237)	
1959	83 (101)	76 (120)	73 (79)		83 (139)	82 (152)	72 (95)	
1961	93 (42)	85 (80)	87 (103)	69 (111)	88 (41)	80 (97)	80 (76)	81 (138)
1962	82 (45)	89 (71)	86 (94)	80 (74)	82 (51)	80 (75)	84 (110)	77 (140)
1963	88 (60)	84 (79)	76 (96)	61 (97)	87 (67)	79 (107)	79 (98)	75 (100)
1964	90 (67)	87 (26)	93 (82)	85 (79)	96 (90)	90 (87)	85 (104)	78 (120)

* Levels 1 to 4 for the years 1961-64 range from income of $10,000 and over down to incomes under $5000. Prior to 1961, levels 1 to 3 represent "upper," "middle," and "lower" income brackets.

cording to recent policy pronouncements, have been precisely the ones who were least in favor of a policy that would make it widely available.

The truth of this conclusion becomes more evident when we move to an analysis of a question asked on the 1966 Gallup poll: Do you think birth-control pills should be made available free to all women on relief who are of childbearing age? This question presents the public with the specific issue that is the focus of current policy—namely, birth control especially for the poor. A summary of the replies to this question is given in Table 5, together with average percentages of people who, in the five surveys made between 1959 and 1964, replied that they approved birth control generally.

It is clear that the overall level of approval drops when specific reference to a poverty-oriented birth-control policy is introduced. The decline is from an average of approximately 80 percent for each sex during the period 1959-64 to 65 percent for men and 71 percent for women in 1966. Of most significance, however, is the fact that the largest proportionate drop in approval occurs among members of the "target" groups themselves—the poor and uneducated. In particular, there is a remarkable drop in approval among men at this socio-economic level. There is a 42-percent decline in approval among men who have had only a grade school education and a 29-percent drop among those with a high school education. Among the college-educated men the drop in approval is only 6 percent. The results, by income, parallel those by education: there is a 47-percent drop for men in the lowest income group but only a 9-percent drop for those in the highest income bracket. Even if the tabulations are restricted to non-Catholics (data that are not presented here), the results are essentially the same.

If the ghetto-oriented birth-control policy urged on the federal government meets with limited public enthusiasm, how does the public view extension of that policy to teen-age girls? The question is of some importance because a notable aspect of the pressure for government-sponsored family-planning programs is advocacy of making birth-control information and materials available at the high school level.

The Committee on Population of the National Academy of Sciences urges early education in "family planning" in order to prevent illegitimacy (2, p. 13).

... government statistics show that the mothers of approximately 41 per cent of the 245,000 babies born illegitimately in the United States every year are women 19 years of age or younger. Thus a large

Table 5. Percentages of white U.S. men and women between the ages of 21 and 44 who, in a 1966 poll, expressed approval of free distribution of birth-control pills for women on relief, and average percentages of individuals in this age group who, in polls taken between 1959 and 1964, expressed approval of birth control. Percentages approving and numbers of individuals interviewed are given as totals and also by education and economic status of the respondents.

	Men			Women		
	1966		1959-64	1966		1959-64
Item	%	N	(av. %)	%	N	(av. %)
Total	65	264	82	71	385	81
Education						
College	82	98	87	75	197	87
High school	58	142	82	70	392	81
Grade school	38	24	66	59	32	73
Economic status						
1	79	80	89	70	110	87
2	69	75	84	76	99	82
3	59	65	83	70	91	80
4	39	41	74	67	76	78

proportion of all illegitimate children are progeny of teen-age mothers. To reduce the number of such children born to teen-age mothers, high-school education in family planning is essential.

Katherine B. Oettinger, Deputy Secretary for Family Planning of the Department of Health, Education, and Welfare, importunes us not to "demand the eligibility card of a first pregnancy before we admit vulnerable girls to family planning services" (16). The Harkavy report states (3, p. 29):

Eligibility requirements should be liberal with respect to marital status. Such services should be made available to the unmarried as well as the married. . . . Eligibility requirements should be liberal with respect to the age of unmarried women seeking help. This will undoubtedly pose some problems, but they may not be insurmountable. Some publically supported programs are already facing them (for example, in Baltimore).

Representative Scheuer from New York has berated the federal government for not "bringing family planning into the schools." He has cited the "desperate need for family planning by unmarried 14-, 15-, and 16-year-old girls in school [which] is so transparently evident that it almost boggles the imagination to realize that nothing has been done. Virtually no leadership has come from the federal government" (9, p. 18).

Obviously there is little recognition in these statements that such a policy might engender a negative public response. Yet such a possibility cannot be discounted. The results of the 1966 question "Do you think they [the pills] should be made available to teen-age girls?" suggests that a policy of pill distribution to female adolescents may be viewed by the public as involving more complex issues than the mere democratization of "medical" services. These results, tabulated by social level, are shown in Table 6.

It may be seen that, in general, a proposal for distribution of pills to teen-age girls meets with very little approval. There is more disapproval among women than among men. Even among women under the age of 30, only 17 percent approve; among men in this age group, 29 percent approve. At no age does feminine approval reach 20 percent, and in most cases it is below 15 percent. Furthermore, restriction of the results to non-Catholics does not raise the percentages of those who approve the policy. Most noteworthy is the socioeconomic gradient among men. Whereas 32 percent of college-educated men approve distribution of pills to young girls, only 13 percent of men with a

Table 6. Percentages of white U.S. men and women who, in a 1966 poll, expressed approval of making birth-control pills available to teen-age girls. Percentages approving and numbers of individuals interviewed are given by age group, by education, and by economic status.

Item	All religions				Non-Catholics			
	Men		Women		Men		Women	
	%	N	%	N	%	N	%	N
Age								
Under 30	29	86	17	149	34	65	19	102
30–44	19	172	8	238	20	133	7	169
Education								
College	32	98	15	100	36	75	13	71
High school	18	142	9	264	19	110	9	180
Grade school	13	24	11	35	6	17	14	28
Economic status								
1	33	80	11	113	35	58	11	75
2	20	75	13	105	24	58	14	72
3	19	65	7	94	18	50	5	64
4	13	41	16	82	15	33	14	66

grade school education do. Thirty-three percent of men in the highest income bracket approve, but only 13 percent in the lowest bracket do.

Clearly, the extension of "family planning" to poor, unmarried teen-agers is not regarded simply as "health care." Individuals may approve, in a general way, a wider availability of birth-control information without approving federal expenditure to facilitate a high level of activity by teen-age girls. One suspects that explicit recognition and implied approval of such activity still comes hard to our population, and that it comes hardest to the group most involved in the problems of illegitimacy and premarital conception—namely, the poor and uneducated themselves. The extreme disapproval of a policy of pill distribution to teen-age girls that is found in lower-class groups (particularly among lower-class men) suggests that a double standard of sexual behavior is operative in these groups—a standard that does not allow open toleration of the idea that the ordinary teen-age girl requires the pill, or that a part of her junior high school and high school education should include instruction in its use.

Can "Five Million Women" Be Wrong?

The most widely publicized argument favoring federal birth-control programs, and apparently the one that elected officials find most persuasive, is the claim that there are approximately "five million" poor women "in need" of publicly subsidized birth-control help (17). I list below some of the principal assumptions upon which this estimate is based—all of which introduce serious upward biases into the evidence.

1. It is claimed that women at the poverty and near-poverty levels desire families of 3.0 chidren. While this may be true of nonwhite wives at this economic level, it is not true, as we have seen, of white women, who comprise a major share of the "target" group and who, on the average, desire a number of children closer to 4 (especially if Catholics are included, as they are in the "five million").

2. It is assumed by the estimators that 82 percent of all poor women aged 15 to 44 are at risk of conception (that is, exposed sexually), in spite of the fact that only 45 percent of poor women in this age group are married and living with their husbands. In arriving at the figure of 82 percent, the estimators assumed that all women in the "married" category (including those who were separated from their husbands and those whose husbands were absent) were sexually exposed regularly, and that half of the women in the "nonmarried" category—that is, single, widowed, and divorced women—were exposed regularly. Information is scarce concerning the sexual behavior of widows and divorced women, but Kinsey's data on premarital coitus leads one to believe that the assumption of 50 percent for single women may be high. Among the women with a grade school education in Kinsey's sample, 38 percent had had coitus at some time between the ages of 16 and 20, and 26 percent, at some time between the ages of 21 and 25. Moreover, Kinsey emphasizes, these encounters were characteristically sporadic (18).

3. The proportion of sterile women among the poor is assumed to be 13 percent, although the Scripps 1960 "Growth of American Families Study" showed the proportion among white women of grade school education to be 22 percent (14, p. 159).

4. No allowance is made for less-than-normal fecundity, although the Scripps 1960 study (14, p. 159) had indicated that, among women of grade school education, an additional 10 percent (over and above the 22 percent) were subnormal in their ability to reproduce.

5. It is taken for granted by the estimators that no Catholic women would object, on religious grounds, to the use of modern methods, and no allowance is made for objection by non-Catholics, on religious or other grounds. In other words, it is assumed that all women "want" the service. Yet, in response to a question concerning the desirability of limiting or spacing pregnancies, 29 percent of the wives with grade school education who were interviewed in the Scripps 1960 study said they were "against" such limitation or spacing (14, p. 177). Among the Catholic wives with grade school education, the proportion "against" was 48 percent, although half of

these objectors were "for" the rhythm method. Similar objections among the disadvantaged have been revealed by many polls over a long period.

6. Perhaps most important, the estimate of 5 million women "wanting" and "in need of" birth-control information includes not only objectors but women who are already practicing birth control. Hence, in addition to all the other biases, the estimate represents a blanket decision by the estimators that the women require medical attention regarding birth control—particularly that they need the pill and the coil. In the words of the Harkavy report (2, attachment A, p. 19):

This may be considered a high estimate of the number of women who need to have family planning services made available to them in public clinics, because some of the couples among the poor and near poor are able to exercise satisfactory control over their fertility. However, even these couples do not have the same access as the non-poor to the more effective and acceptable methods of contraception, particularly the pill and the loop. So, simply in order to equalize the access of the methods of contraception under medical supervision, it is appropriate to try to make contraceptive services available to all who may need and want them.

Yet the 1960 Scripps study found that, among fecund women of grade school education, 79 percent used contraceptives (14, p. 159). The 21 percent who did not included young women who were building families and said they wanted to get pregnant, as well as Catholics who objected to birth control on religious grounds. As for the methods that women currently are using, it seems gratuitous for the federal government to decide that only medically supervised methods—the pill and the coil—are suitable for lower-income couples, and that a mammoth "service" program is therefore required. In fact, the implications of such a decision border on the fantastic—the implications that we should substitute scarce medical and paramedical attention for all contraceptive methods now being used by poor couples.

In sum, the argument supporting a "need" for nationwide, publicly sustained birth-control programs does not stand up under empirical scrutiny. Most fecund lower-class couples now use birth-control methods when they want to

prevent pregnancy; in the case of those who do not, the blame cannot simply be laid at the door of the affluent who have kept the subject of birth control under wraps, or of a government that has withheld services. As we have seen, opinion on birth control has been, and is, less favorable among the poor and the less well educated than among the well-to-do. In addition, the poor desire larger families. Although it may be argued that, at the public welfare level, birth control has, until recently, been taboo because of the "Catholic vote," most individuals at all social levels have learned about birth control *informally* and without medical attention. Furthermore, the most popular birth-control device, the condom, has long been as available as aspirin or cigarettes, and certainly has been used by men of all social classes. When one bears in mind the fact that the poor have no difficulty in gaining access to illegal narcotics (despite their obvious "unavailability"), and that the affluent had drastically reduced their fertility before present-day contraceptive methods were available, one must recognize and take into account a motivational component in nonuse and inefficient use of contraceptives. Indeed, were relative lack of demand on the part of the poor not a principal factor, it would be difficult to explain why such an important "market" for birth-control materials—legal or illegal—would have escaped the attention of enterprising businessmen or bootleggers. In any event, any estimate based on the assumption that all poor women in the reproductive group "want" birth-control information and materials and that virtually all "need" publicly supported services that will provide them—including women with impaired fecundity, women who have sexual intercourse rarely or not at all, women who object on religious grounds, and women who are already using birth-control methods—would seem to be seriously misleading as a guide for our government in its efforts to control population growth.

Moreover, the proposal for government sponsorship takes no account of the possible advantages of alternative means of reaching that part of the "market" that may not be optimally served at present. For example, competitive pricing, better marketing, and a program of advertising could make it possible for many groups in the population who are now being counted as "targets" for government efforts to purchase contraceptives of various kinds. When one bears in mind the fact that an important reason for nonuse or lack of access to contraceptives may be some sort of conflict situation (between husband and wife, adolescent child and parent, and so on), it becomes apparent that the impersonal and responsive marketplace is a far better agency for effecting smooth social change that is a far-flung national bureaucracy loaded with well-meaning but often blundering "health workers." The government could doubtless play an initial stimulating and facilitating role in relation to private industry, without duplicating, on a welfare basis, functions that might be more efficiently handled in the marketplace.

Would the Policy Have Side Effects?

The possible inadvisability of having the government become a direct purveyor of birth-control materials to poverty groups becomes more clear when we consider some of the risks involved in such a course of action.

Even if the goal of reducing family size were completely and widely accepted by the poorer and less well educated sectors of the population, we should not assume that the general public would necessarily view a policy concerned with the means and practice of birth control (in any social group) as it views ordinary medical care—that is, as being morally neutral and obviously "desirable." Birth control is related to sexual behavior, and, in all viable societies, sexual behavior is regulated by social institutions. It is thus an oversimplification to think that people will be unmindful of what are, for them at least, the moral implications of changes in the conditions under which sexual intercourse is possible, permissible, or likely. An issue such as distribution of pills to teen-age girls runs a collision course with norms about premarital relations for young girls—norms that, in turn, relate to the saliency of marriage and motherhood as a woman's principal career and

to the consequent need for socially created restrictions on free sexual access if an important inducement to marriage is not to be lost. Only if viable careers alternative to marriage existed for women would the lessening of controls over sexual behavior outside marriage be unrelated to women's lifetime opportunities, for such opportunities would be independent of the marriage market and, a fortiori, independent of sexual bargaining. But such independence clearly does not exist. Hence, when the government is told that it will be resolving a "medical" problem if it makes birth-control pills available to teen-agers, it is being misled into becoming the protagonist in a sociologically based conflict between short-run feminine interests—a conflict that is expressed both in relations between parents and children and in relations between the sexes. This sociological conflict far transcends the "medical" issue of whether or not birth-control services should be made widely available.

Actually, the issue of sexual morality is only one among many potentially explosive aspects of direct federal involvement in family-planning programs for the poor. Others come readily to mind, such as the possibility that the pill and other physiological methods could have long-run, serious side effects, or that racial organizations could seize on the existence of these programs as a prime example of "genocide." Eager promoters of the suggested programs tend to brush such problems aside as trivial, but the problems, like the issue of sexual morality, cannot be wished away, for they are quite patently there (9, p. 62). There *are* risks involved in all drug-taking, and it is recognized that many of the specific ones involved in long-term ingestion of the pill may not be discovered for many years. No one today can say that these are less than, equal to, or greater than the normal risks of pregnancy and childbirth. Equally, a class-directed birth-control program, whatever its intent, is open to charges of genocide that are difficult to refute. Such a program cannot fail to appear to single out the disadvantaged as the "goat," all the while implying that the very considerable "planned" fertility of most Americans inexplicably requires no government attention at all.

Population Policy for Americans

It seems clear that the suggested policy of poverty-oriented birth-control programs does not make sense as a welfare measure. It is also true that, as an inhibitor of population growth, it is inconsequential and trivial. It does not touch the principal cause of such growth in the United States—namely, the reproductive behavior of the majority of Americans who, under present conditions, want families of more than three children and thereby generate a growth rate far in excess of that required for population stability. Indeed, for most Americans the "family planning" approach, concentrating as it does on the distribution of contraceptive materials and services, is irrelevant, because they already know about efficient contraception and are already "planning" their families. It is thus apparent that any policy designed to influence reproductive behavior must not only concern itself with all fecund Americans (rather than just the poor) but must, as well, relate to family-size goals (rather than just to contraceptive means). In addition, such a policy cannot be limited to matters affecting contraception (or even to matters affecting gestation and parturition, such as abortion), but must, additionally, take into account influences on the formation and dissolution of heterosexual unions (19).

What kinds of reproductive policies can be pursued in an effort to reduce long-term population growth? The most important step towards developing such new policies is to recognize and understand the existing ones, for we already have influential and coercive policies regarding reproductive behavior. Furthermore, these existing policies relate not merely to proscriptions (legal or informal) regarding certain means of birth control (like abortion) but also to a definition of reproduction as a primary societal end and to an organization of social roles that draws most of the population into reproductive unions.

The existence of such pronatalist policies becomes apparent when we recall that, among human beings, population replacement would not occur at all were it not for the complex social organization and system of incentives that encourage mating, pregnancy, and the care, support, and rearing of children. These institutional mechanisms are the pronatalist "policies" evolved unconsciously over millennia to give societies a fertility sufficient to offset high mortality. The formation and implementation of antinatalist policies must be based, therefore, on an analysis and modification of the existing pronatalist policies. It follows, as well, that antinatalist policies will not necessarily involve the introduction of coercive measures. In fact, just the opposite is the case. Many of these new policies will entail a *lifting* of pressures *to* reproduce, rather than an *imposition* of pressures *not* to do so. In order to understand this point let us consider briefly our present-day pronatalism.

It is convenient to start with the family, because pronatalism finds its most obvious expression in this social institution. The pronatalism of the family has many manifestations, but among the most influential and universal are two: the standardization of both the male and the female sexual roles in terms of reproductive functions, obligations, and activities, and the standardization of the occupational role of women—half of the population—in terms of child-bearing, child-rearing, and complementary activities. These two "policies" insure that just about everyone will be propelled into reproductive unions, and that half of the population will enter such unions as a "career"—a life's work. Each of the two "policies" is worth considering.

With regard to sex roles, it is generally recognized that potential human variability is greater than is normally permitted *within* each sex category. Existing societies have tended to suppress and extinguish such variability and to standardize sexual roles in ways that imply that all "normal" persons will attain the status of parents. This coercion takes many forms, including one-sided indoctrination in schools, legal barriers and penalties for deviation, and the threats of loneliness, ostracism, and ridicule that are implied in the unavailability of alternatives. Individuals who—by temperament, health, or constitution—do not fit the ideal sex role pattern are nonetheless coerced into attempting to achieve it, and many of them do achieve it, at least to the extent of having demographic impact by becoming parents.

Therefore, a policy that sought out the ways in which coercion regarding sex roles is at present manifesting itself could find numerous avenues for relieving the coercion and for allowing life styles different from marriage and parenthood to find free and legitimatized expression. Such a policy would have an effect on the content of expectations regarding sex roles as presented and enforced in schools, on laws concerning sexual activity between consenting adults, on taxation with respect to marital status and number of children, on residential building policies, and on just about every facet of existence that is now organized so as exclusively to favor and reward a pattern of sex roles based on marriage and parenthood.

As for the occupational roles of women, existing pressures still attempt to make the reproductive and occupational roles coterminus for all women who elect to marry and have children. This rigid structure of the wife-mother position builds into the entire motivational pattern of women's lives a tendency to want at least a moderate-size family. To understand this point one must recognize that the desired number of children relates not simply to the wish for a family of a particular size but relates as well to a need for more than one or two children if one is going to enjoy "family life" over a significant portion of one's lifetime. This need is increased rather than lessened by improved life expectancy. Insofar as women focus their energies and emotions on their families, one cannot expect that they will be satisfied to play their only important role for a diminishing fraction of their lives, or that they will readily regard make-work and dead-end jobs as a substitute for "mothering." The notion that most women will "see the error of their ways" and decide to have two-child families is naive, since few healthy and energetic women will be so misguided as to deprive themselves of most of the rewards society has to offer them and choose a situation that allows them neither a life's work outside the home nor one within it. Those who do deprive themselves in this fashion are, in effect, taking the brunt of the still existing maladjustment between the

roles of women and the reproductive needs of society. In a society oriented around achievement and accomplishment, such women are exceptionally vulnerable to depression, frustration, and a sense of futility, because they are being blocked from a sense of fulfillment both at home and abroad.

In sum, the problem of inhibiting population growth in the United States cannot be dealt with in terms of "family-planning needs" because this country is well beyond the point of "needing" birth control methods. Indeed, even the poor seem not to be a last outpost for family-planning attention. If we wish to limit our growth, such a desire implies basic changes in the social organization of reproduction that will make nonmarriage, childlessness, and small (two-child) families far more prevalent than they are now. A new policy, to achieve such ends, can take advantage of the antinatalist tendencies that our present institutions have suppressed. This will involve the lifting of penalties for antinatalist behavior rather than the "creation" of new ways of life. This behavior already exists among us as part of our covert and deviant culture, on the one hand, and our elite and artistic culture, on the other. Such antinatalist tendencies have also found expression in feminism, which has been stifled in the United States by means of systematic legal, educational, and social pressures concerned with women's "obligations" to create and care for children. A fertility-control policy that does not take into account the need to alter the present structure of reproduction in these and other ways merely trivializes the problem of population control and misleads those who have the power to guide our country toward completing the vital revolution.

References and Notes

1. *Hearings on S. 1676, U.S. Senate Subcommittee on Foreign Aid Expenditures* (the 1965 and 1966 Hearings each comprise seven volumes; the 1967-68 Hearings, to date, comprise three volumes) (Government Printing Office, Washington, D.C.).
2. "The Growth of U.S. Population." *Nat. Acad. Sci.-Nat. Res. Council Pub. 1279* (1965).

3. O. Harkavy, F. S. Jaffe, S. S. Wishik, "Implementing DHEW Policy on Family Planning and Population" (mimeographed, 1967; available from the Ford Foundation, New York).

4. "Reporting of the President's Committee on Population and Family Planning: The Transition from Concern to Action" (Government Printing Office, Washington, D.C., 1968).

5. K. Davis, *Science* 158, 730 (1967); J. Blake, in *Public Health and Population Change*, M. C. Sheps and J. C. Ridley, Eds. (Univ. of Pittsburgh Press, Pittsburgh, Pa., 1965).

6. In the words of the Committee on Population, "The freedom to limit family size to the number of children wanted when they are wanted is, in our view, a basic human right . . . most Americans of higher income and better education exercise this right as a matter of course, but . . . many of the poor and uneducated are in fact deprived of the right."

7. W. J. Cohen, *Family Planning: One Aspect of Freedom to Choose* (Government Printing Office, Washington, D.C., 1966), p. 2. Cohen, former Secretary of Health, Education, and Welfare, says: "Until a few years ago, family planning and population problems were considered 'hush-hush' subjects. Public discussion was curtailed not only in polite society, but in the legislative and executive branches of the government as well."

8. *Hearings on S. 2993, U.S. Senate Subcommittee on Employment, Manpower, and Poverty, 89th Congress, Second Session, May 10* (Government Printing Office, Washington, D.C., 1966), p. 31.

9. *Hearings on S. 1676, U.S. Senate Subcommittee on Foreign Aid Expenditures, 90th Congress, First Session, November 2* (Government Printing Office, Washington, D.C., 1967), pt. 1.

10. Senator Tydings (D-Md). said at the Hearings on S. 1676 (see 9): "As recently as 3 or 4 years ago, the idea that Federal, State or local governments should make available family planning information and services to families who could not otherwise afford them was extremely controversial. But in a brief period of time there has been a substantial shift of opinion among the moral leadership of our country, brought about in large measure by the vigorous efforts of the distinguished Senator from Alaska, Ernest Gruening, the chairman of this subcommittee."

11. E. Gruening, "What the Federal Government Is Now Doing in the Field of Population Control and What Is Needed," speech presented before the U.S. Senate, 3 May 1967.

12. J. M. Stycos, in *World Population and U.S. Government Policy and Programs*, F. T. Brayer, Ed. (Georgetown Univ. Press, Washington, D.C., 1968).

13. R. Freedman, P. K. Whelpton, A. A. Campbell, *Family Planning, Sterility and Population Growth* (McGraw-Hill, New York, 1959).

14. P. K. Whelpton, A. A. Campbell, J. E. Patterson, *Fertility and Family Planning in the United States* (Princeton Univ. Press, Princeton, N.J., 1966).

15. J. Blake, *Demography* 3, 154 (1966); *Population Studies* 20, 27 (1966); *ibid.* 21, 159 (1967); *ibid.*, p. 185; *ibid.* 22, 5 (1968).

16. *Family Planner* 2, 3 (1968).

17. The estimate (by Arthur A. Campbell) under discussion here may be found in the Harkavy report (see 3, attachment A, pp. 4-19). Another estimate has been circulated by the Planned Parenthood Federation in a brochure entitled *Five Million Women* (Planned Parenthood, New York).

18. A. C. Kinsey, W. B. Pomeroy, C. E. Martin, P. B. Gebhard, *Sexual Behavior in the Human Female* (Saunders, Philadelphia, 1953), pp. 291 and 337.

19. K. Davis and J. Blake, *Econ. Develop. Cult. Change* 4, 211 (1956).

20. I make grateful acknowledgement to the Ford Foundation for support of the research presented in this article and to the National Institutes of Health (general research support grant 1501-TR-544104) for assistance to Statistical Services, School of Public Health, University of California, Berkeley. I am also indebted to Kingsley Davis, whose critical comments and helpful suggestions have greatly advanced my thinking. The Roper Center and the Gallup Poll kindly supplied me with polling data.

34

FAMILY PLANNING AND PUBLIC POLICY: WHO IS MISLEADING WHOM?

Oscar Harkavy, Frederick S. Jaffe, and Samuel M. Wishik

Federal policies on family planning services and population research are currently under review as a result of the report of the President's Committee on Population and Family Planning (1). Judith Blake's article, "Population policy for Americans: Is the government being misled?" (2), which is presumably intended to influence this review, contains numerous errors of fact and interpretation which it is important to clarify. To support her position, she knocks down several straw men; ignores the bulk of serious demographic research on U.S. fertility patterns in the last 15 years, as well as research on differential availability of health care and the relative effectiveness of various contraceptive methods; and cites opinion-poll data in a manner that distorts the overall picture. The article's methodological limitations alone are sufficient to suggest that the question raised in its subtitle may more appropriately be turned around and asked of the article itself.

The article is based on six principal propositions.

1. That the reduction of U.S. population growth—indeed, the achievement of "population stability"—is "virtually unchallenged as an official national goal."
2. That, in pursuit of *this* goal, the "essential recommendation" by official and private groups has been a program of publicly financed family planning services for the poor.
3. That this program of family planning for the poor will not achieve the goal of population stability.

4. That advocates of this policy contend that the poor have been denied access to family planning services because of "the prudery and hypocrisy of the affluent."
5. That the poor desire larger families than higher-income couples do and are significantly less inclined to favor birth control.
6. That the estimate of 5 million poor women as the approximate number in need of subsidized family planning services is exaggerated.

With the exception of proposition 3, each of these statements is seriously misleading or in error. Let us examine the evidence on each point.

A Consensus on U.S. Population Stability?

If the United States had as a national goal the reduction of its population growth and the achievement of population stability—and if the program of publicly funded family planning services for those who cannot afford private medical care had been advanced as the principal or only means of achieving population stability—Judith Blake's contention that the government is being misled would have much validity. However, neither proposition is sustained by the evidence.

We have individually and jointly been associated with the evolution of public policy in this field for more than a decade. To our knowledge, there has never been an official policy regarding the virtue or necessity of reducing U.S. population growth, much less achieving population stability. Nor has there emerged among Americans generally a "virtually unchallenged" consensus on what should constitute an official U.S. population policy.

The clearest statement of official U.S. *domestic* policy is contained in President Johnson's 1966 Health Message to Congress (3):
(3):

We have a growing concern to foster the integrity of the family and the opportunity for each child. It is essential that all families have access to information and services that will allow freedom to choose the number and spacing of their children within the dictates of individual conscience.

Neither in this or in any other statement did the President cite stabilization of U.S. growth as the objective of federal policy. Nor has such a goal been articulated by Congress or the federal agencies. In 1966, Secretary Gardner of the Department of Health, Education, and Welfare (HEW) stated (4) that the objectives of departmental policy are "to improve the health of the people, to strengthen the integrity of the family and to provide families the freedom of choice to determine the spacing of their children and the size of their families." In 1968 he reiterated (5) that "the immediate objective is to extend family planning services to all those desiring such services who would not otherwise have access to them."

It is clear that the federal program has been advanced, not for population control, but to improve health and reduce the impact of poverty and deprivation.

Goals of Federal Family Planning Policy

Given this unambiguous framework for federal policy, it is inexplicable how Blake could arrive at the statement that population limitation has become our national goal and that the "essential recommendation" for reaching *this* goal has been to extend family planning services to the poor. She attributes this "misleading" recommendation to a 1965 report by the National Academy of Sciences (6), a 1967 consultant's review of HEW programs written by us (7), and the report of the President's Committee (1), despite the fact that each of these reports clearly distinguishes a family planning program for the poor from an overall U.S. population control program or policy. For example, the National Academy of Sciences report stated explicitly (6, p. 6) that U.S. population growth "is caused more by the preference for larger families among those who consciously choose the number of children they have than by high fertility in the impoverished segments of the population. The importance of high fertility among the underprivileged lies not so much in its contribution to the national birth rate as in the difficulties that excessive

fertility imposes on the impoverished themselves."

The 1967 HEW review sought to determine how well the department's stated policy was being implemented. It found the department's efforts lagging and recommended higher priority in staff and budget for family planning services and population research programs. It also distinguished this effort from an overall U.S. population policy and program (7, pp. 23-24):

While study should be given to the present and future implications of the growth of the Nation's population as a whole—perhaps through a series of university studies sponsored by a Presidential commission—the Federal government should at present focus its *family planning assistance* on the disadvantaged segments of the population. The great majority of non-poor American couples have access to competent medical guidance in family planning and are able to control their fertility with remarkable effectiveness. The poor lack such access and have more children than they want. It should be the goal of Federal policy to provide the poor with the same opportunity to plan their families that most other Americans have long enjoyed. Public financing of family planning for the disadvantaged is clearly justified for health reasons alone, particularly for its potential influence in reducing current rates of maternal and infant mortality and morbidity. Additionally, there are excellent humanitarian and economic justifications for a major directed program to serve the poor.

The President's Committee did not concentrate on family planning alone but made numerous recommendations for short-and long-term programs of domestic and international services, research, and education. Its recommendation on domestic family planning services again was justified, not in terms of population control, but as a health and social measure (1, pp. 15-16):

Excessive fertility can drive a family into poverty as well as reduce its chances of escaping it. The frequency of maternal deaths, the level of infant mortality, and the number of children who are chronically handicapped are all markedly greater among the poor than in the rest of the population. One of the most effective measures that could be taken to lower mortality and morbidity rates among mothers and children would be to help the poor to have the number of children they desire.

As for immediate programs to further reduce the incidence of unwanted pregnancy among the rest of the population, the committee recommended (1, p. 15) expansion of bio-medical research for improved contraceptive techniques and expansion of social research; increased education in population dynamics, sex, and human reproduction, and improved training programs for physicians and other relevant professionals. It stated explicitly (1, p. 37) that these recommended programs "are only *one* of the important factors that influence population trends," and called for a Presidential Commission on Population to, among other things, "assess the social and economic consequences of population trends in the U.S. . . . [and] consider the consequences of alternative population policies" (1, pp. 37-38).

These reports only reiterate what has been the basic justification for publicly funded family planning services for the poor for more than a decade. The leaders of the U.S. family planning movement have not advanced this program as a means of achieving population stability, because it has been evident that the poor and near-poor, who constitute only about one-quarter of the U.S. population, are not the major contributors to U.S. population growth, despite their higher fertility.

Blake believes the U.S. policy should aim toward a zero rate of population growth, as is her right. But she has no right to accuse family planners of misleading the public into believing that extension of family planning to the poor would bring about such population stability—a claim they have never made. Of course, any reduction in births, wanted or unwanted, will result in *less* natural increase and, other things being equal, *less* population growth. Elimination or reduction of unwanted pregnancies among the poor and near-poor would thus reduce *somewhat* the rate of population growth, though not eliminate it entirely (8).

Prudery—or Politics?

Another straw man erected by Blake is the assertion that denial of birth control services to the poor has been attributed by advocates of family planning to the "prudery and hypocrisy of the affluent, who have overtly tabooed discussion of birth control and dissemination of birth control materials." As proof that this has not been the case, she cites opinion polls going back to 1937 showing majority support for making birth control information available to those who desire it.

The proof is irrelevant in two major respects. First, the issue is not *information* about birth control, but *availability of services* (a distinction which Blake obscures throughout her article). And second, the operative factor in regard to the poor has not been generalized approval or disapproval, but the policies in regard to provision of contraceptive services of public health and welfare institutions on which the poor depend for medical care. As she notes, it was evident as long ago as the 1930's that most Americans approved of birth control and practiced it in some form (although it was not until the late 1950's that the mass media began to carry relatively explicit birth control material). But this public-opinion base did not control the policies of public institutions or the attitudes of political leaders. In most tax-supported hospitals and health departments there were explicit or implicit prohibitions on the prescription of contraceptive methods and materials, and many states had legislative restrictions which were enforced primarily in public agencies. To change these policies required protracted campaigns, which began in the New York municipal hospitals in 1958 (9), continued in Illinois, Maryland, Pennsylvania, and other states in the early 1960's, and culminated in legislative actions in 1965 and 1966 in at least 15 states and congressional action in 1967 in the Social Security and Poverty legislation.

The family planning movement has not ascribed the denial of birth control services to the poor to a generalized "taboo" but, rather, has ascribed it to concrete prohibitions on provision of services which stemmed from fear on the part of political leaders of the presumed controversial nature of the subject. The fears were perhaps exaggerated, but nevertheless real.

The result was that very few poor women received contraceptive guidance and prescription in tax-supported agencies at times in their lives when it would have been of most importance to them—at the premarital examination and after the birth of the child, for example. It was not until the years 1964 to 1966 that several hundred public hospitals and health departments began providing family planning services, and it was not until 1967 that as much as $10 million in federal funds became available to finance identifiable family planning programs.

Family Size Desired by the Poor

Judith Blake contends that her data show that the poor desire larger families than the non-poor. She bases her assertion on responses to opinion polls and ignores the three major national studies conducted since 1955, covering larger and properly structured random samples of the U.S. population, which have probed these issues in depth. Even when the poll responses are accepted at face value, it is of interest to note that the "larger" family said to be desired by those in the lowest economic status group was larger by as much as 0.4 of a child in only 2 of the 12 years cited (10).

Also of interest is the fact that Blake treats responses to questions on *ideal* family size as evidence of the number of children the poor *want*. At various points in the text she refers to the data she cites as demonstrating "*desired* or ideal" number of children or "*preferred* family size," or states that the poor "say they *want* larger families" (emphasis added). The dubiousness of this methodology is revealed by the very different treatment of responses on *ideal* and *wanted* family size in the 1955 and 1960 Growth of American Families Studies (11, 12) and in the 1965 National Fertility study (13, 14-16).

In the 1955 study, Freedman and his co-workers stated that the question on ideal family size "was not designed to discover the wife's personal ideal but sought a picture of her more stereotyped impressions on what family size should be" (11, p. 221). "The more

realistic question about desired . . . family size," they concluded, "is that regarding the number of children wanted at the time of the interview" (11, p. 224). They found that the stereotyped "ideal" generally was higher than the number wanted. In the 1960 study, Whelpton and his colleagues came to the same conclusion (12, p. 37). In the 1965 study, Ryder and Westoff expressed "profound reservations" about the usefulness of the "ideal" question and found that it "lacks face validity . . . is relatively unreliable and has a small variance" (13).

The poll responses cited by Blake appear to show that *ideal* family size varies inversely, among non-Catholic white women, with education and economic status. Responses to detailed surveys on *wanted* family size, however, either show insignificant differences between lower-and higher-status non-Catholic white respondents or *reverse the direction*. The data for 1960 show no difference in the number of children wanted by highest-status and lowest-status non-Catholic whites, and the data for 1965 show a very small increase in the number wanted by the group with only grade school education. (The pattern for Catholics was, of course, different.) Other measures of socioeconomic status show either no difference in the number of children wanted or, in the case of the measure of income, a smaller number for those with income below $3000 than for those with income above $10,000 (Table 1).

Judith Blake also uses opinion-poll responses, rather than the results of in-depth studies, to measure approval of birth control in the different socioeconomic groups. The result is, again, an overstatement of the differences between the highest and lowest social groups. In Table 2 are given excerpts from findings for 1960 and 1965 on approval of the practice of fertility control (including the rhythm method). The only deviation from the near-universal approval of fertility control is in the group with only grade school education, which is rapidly becoming a smaller proportion of all U.S. women and is hardly coterminous with the poor and near poor. [Among all poor and near-poor women aged 18 to 44 in 1966, only

Table 1. Number of children wanted, by education, color or race, income, and occupational status of respondents, as shown by studies made in 1960 and 1965.

Education, income, and occupational status	1960				1965‡			
	White*			Non-white†	White			Negro
	Total	Protes-tant	Cath-olic		Total	Non-Catholic	Cath-olic	
Education								
College	3.3	3.1	4.8	2.4	3.22	3.03	3.86	2.70
High school (4 yr)	3.2	3.0	3.9	2.7	3.21	3.01	3.65	2.89
High school (1-3 yr)	3.3	3.2	3.6	2.7				
Grade school	3.5	3.1	4.3	3.5				
High school (1-3 yr) or grade school					3.46	3.30	3.83	3.48
Husband's income§								
> $10,000	3.3							
$7,000-9,000	3.2							
$6,000-6,999	3.3							
$5,000-5,999	3.3							
$4,000-4,999	3.4							
$3,000-3,999	3.4							
< $3,000	3.2							
Occupation‖								
Upper white-collar	3.3							
Lower white-collar	3.3							
Upper blue-collar	3.3							
Lower blue-collar	3.3							
Farm	3.5							
Other	3.0							
Total	3.3	3.1	4.0	2.9	3.29	3.11	3.74	3.21

*From 12, Table 54.
†From 12, Table 189.
‡From 13, Table 4.
§Unpublished data from the 1960 "Growth of American Families Studies," made available by A. A. Campbell.
‖From 12, Table 71.

Table 2. Percentages (by education and color of respondents) of women who favored fertility control, as shown by studies made in 1960 and 1965.*

	White		Nonwhite	
Education	1960*	1965†	1960†	1965†
College	97	97	97	94
High school (4 yr)	95	97	90	94
High school (1-3 yr)	93	94	78	90
Grade school	82	82	67	84

*Data from 12, Table 102.
†Data from 17a, table 7.

26.1 percent had grade school education or less; 31.9 percent had completed from 1 to 3 years of high school, and 42.1 percent had been graduated from high school; some of the latter had attended college (17).] Even in the grade-school group, however, more than four-fifths of white women approved of birth control in both 1960 and 1965—a proportion bettered by nonwhite grade-school women in 1965—and all other groups were nearly unanimous in their approval. It is extremely difficult, in the face of these data, to conjure up the notion of great hostility to fertility control among the poor and near-poor (17a, 18).

Table 3. Number of children wanted by white and nonwhite wives under 30 years old, by income and farm residence of respondents, as shown by a 1965 study.*

Residence	Family income			
	>$8,000	$6,000-7,999	$4,000-6,999	< $4,000
Now living on farm	3.97	3.12	3.25	3.21
Once lived on farm	3.08	3.13	2.99	3.19
Never lived on farm	3.13	3.21	3.12	3.06

*Unpublished data from the 1965 National Fertility Study, made available by C. F. Westoff.

Table 4. Percentages (by income and farm residence of respondents) of white and nonwhite wives under 30 years old who had ever used, or expected to use, any form of contraception, as shown by a 1965 study.*

Residence	Family income			
	>$8,000	$6,000-7,999	$4,000-6,999	< $4,000
Now living on farm	84	100	85	89
Once lived on farm	91	97	95	88
Never lived on farm	95	96	93	92

*Unpublished data from the 1965 National Fertility Study, made available by C. F. Westoff.

For purposes of policy determination, the most salient questions relate, not to all poor and near-poor persons, but to those who are in their prime child-bearing years—that is, less than 30 years old. Presumably it is this group which would be most affected by public programs and whose attitudes policy makers would consider most significant. Data from the 1965 study, presented in Tables 3 and 4, permit direct comparison, for farm and nonfarm women below 30 in four income groups, of the number of children wanted and the proportion of women then using, or expecting to use, some form of contraception. The conclusion is clear: younger wives in the "poor" and "near-poor" categories want as few children as wives in higher income groups—or want fewer children than the higher-income wives—and have used or expect to use some form of contraception to a similar degree.

Despite the fact that 70 percent of poor and near-poor women regarded as in need of subsidized family planning services are white (19),

Blake frequently terms the recommended federal effort a "ghetto-oriented family planning program." She also describes the charge of "genocide" which has been leveled by some black militants as "difficult to refute." However, the desire of black couples for smaller families than are desired by whites—and for smaller families than they are now having—was clearly demonstrated in the 1960 study (12, pp. 41, 38) (see Table 5).

Table 5. Number of children wanted by white and nonwhite wives, as shown by a 1960 study.*

Couples	Number of children wanted		Percentages wanting two children or less	
	Minimum	Maximum	Minimum	Maximum
White	3.1	3.5	41	29
Nonwhite	2.7	3.0	55	46

*Data from 12, Tables 15 and 16.

Table 6. Desired family size, by race and by fertility planning status, as shown by a 1965 study.*

Desired number of children	Percentages of respondents who regard their fertility as completed			Percentages of respondents who desire more children		
	Total	White	Negro	Total	White	Negro
0-2	36.2	35.4	44.0	27.1	25.7	41.0
3	23.6	24.5	14.8	28.8	29.2	24.3
4	40.3	40.2	41.2	44.2	45.0	34.8

*Data from 13, Table 7.

Substantially the same pattern emerges from the 1965 study, as shown in Tables 6 and 7: significantly higher percentages of nonwhites continue to prefer a family of two children or less, and the proportion of nonwhites approving and using, or expecting to use, some method of fertility control is indistinguishable from that of whites, especially in the prime child-bearing ages.

Table 7. Percentages (by age and color of respondent) of women who approved of fertility control (including the rhythm method) and were using or expected to use some form of contraceptive, as shown by a 1965 study.*

Respondents	Percentages by age group			
	20-24 yr	25-29 yr	30-34 yr	35-39 yr
Approved of fertility control				
White	95	97	95	93
Nonwhite	92	93	90	87
Were using or expected to use contraceptives				
White	94	93	88	84
Nonwhite	96	90	84	71

*Data from 17a, Tables 8 and 14.

Excess Fertility

Serious d e m o g r a p h i c research has thus d o c u m e n t e d the disappearance of the traditional socioeconomic and ethnic differentials in fertility aspirations and in attitudes toward fertility control. "Clearly," as Westoff and Ryder have stated, "the norm of fertility control has become universal in contemporary America" (17a, p. 394). Yet within this general pattern the studies also reveal that many couples do not achieve the degree of control they wish. Some have more children than they want and can be classified in the "excess fertility" category; others fail to have their children when they want them and are described as "timing failures." More than half of U.S. couples reported one or another type of failure in 1965; 21 percent of all respondents acknowledged that at least one of their children was unwanted (15). (This must be regarded as an underestimate, since the questionnaire required that respondents characterize specific children already born as either wanted or unwanted.)

While excess fertility is found among all socioeconomic groups, it is more acute among the poor, among nonwhites (the majority of whom are poor or near-poor), and among those with higher parity and less education. In spite of the similarity of family-size preferences in all socioeconomic groups, the poor and near-poor had a fertility rate from 1960 to 1965 of 152.5 births per 1000 women aged 15 to 44, as compared to 98.1 for the non-poor (20). And in spite of the expressed preference of almost all low-income parents for less than four children, nearly half of the children growing up in poverty in 1966 were members of families with five or more children under 18; moreover, the risk of poverty increased rapidly from 9 percent for one-child families to 42 percent for families with six or more children (21). In terms of poverty, the most significant demarcation appears to be at the three-child level—the average family size wanted by low-income as well as other American couples: more than one-quarter of all families with four or more children were living in poverty, and four out of

Table 8. Relation of poverty to size of family, as shown by a 1966 study.*

Number of children	All U.S. families (in thousands)	The poor		The poor and near-poor	
		Number of families (in thousands)	Percentage of all U.S. families	Number of families (in thousands)	Percentage of all U.S. families
1	9,081	843	9.3	1,276	14.1
2	8,491	869	10.2	1,323	15.6
3	5,416	694	12.8	1,152	21.3
Total for parity 1-3	22,988	2,406	10.5	3,751	16.3
4	2,923	543	18.6	904	30.9
5	1,396	387	27.7	593	42.5
6 or more	1,286	541	42.1	747	58.1
Total for parity 4+	5,605	1,471	26.2	2,244	40.0

* Data from 21, Table 4.

ten were poor or near-poor. Their risk of poverty was two-and-a-half times that for families with three children or less (Table 8).

The 1965 National Fertility Study provides data on the percentage of unwanted births for each birth order, ranging from 5.7 percent of first births to 56.7 percent of sixth and higher-order births. Application of these percentages to actual births, by birth order, in the years 1960 to 1965 yields an estimated average of 850,000 unwanted births annually in all socioeconomic groups. Combination of these data with Campbell's calculation of differential fertility rates shows that approximately 40 percent of births to poor and near-poor couples were unwanted by one or both parents in the years 1960 to 1965, as compared to 14 percent of births to non-poor couples (22). [This result appears consistent with the 1960 finding of an inverse relation between education and excess fertility, with 32 percent of white, and 43 percent of nonwhite, grade-school-educated wives reporting more children than they wanted (12, p. 364).]

Equalizing Access to Effective Methods

It is precisely the reduction or elimination of this involuntary disparity between the poor and non-poor which has been the objective of publicly supported family planning service pro-

grams. Given the essentially similar preferences of the two groups concerning family size, programs which equalize access to modern methods of fertility control should also help to equalize the incidence of unwanted pregnancy for the two groups. Blake can regard this as a "fantastic . . . blanket decision" imposed by the family planners only if she ignores (i) the evidence on the type of birth control methods on which the poor rely, (ii) the evidence on the relative effectiveness of different contraceptive methods, and (iii) the response of poor persons to organized programs which offer them a complete range of methods.

The data on contraceptive practice cited above measure the combined use of all methods, including those methods known to be least effective in preventing conception. The cited studies also show that couples of higher socioeconomic status who can afford private medical care tend to use the more reliable medical methods, while low income couples depend more on less reliable, nonmedical methods. Among white Protestants in 1960, for example, half as many wives with a grade school education as college graduates used the diaphragm and twice as many relied on withdrawal (12, p. 281). Published and unpublished findings for 1965 on methods employed by whites and nonwhites reveal the same picture. Three times as many nonwhites as whites relied on the douche (16) and on suppositories (23, p. 2), and twice as many relied on foam (23). When the condom is classified among effective methods and rhythm is omitted from the analysis because of the different proportions of whites and nonwhites who are Catholic, we find that half of the nonwhite users of contraceptives rely on the least effective methods, as compared to about 30 percent of whites (16).

These findings are significant in two respects: (i) the methods on which the poor rely most heavily have considerably higher failure rates and thus would lead to a higher incidence of unwanted fertility; and (ii) the overwhelming majority of poor persons accept the best methods science has been able to develop when they are given the choice.

The relative rates of failure with the different methods range from 1 to 3 failures per 100 women-years of exposure for pills and IUD's to 35 to 38 failures for rhythm and douche, with the numbers for the condom, the diaphragm, and withdrawal clustering around 15 (24).

Response to Family Planning Programs

It is difficult to understand how the greater reliance of the poor on nonmedical methods can be attributed to their personal preferences in view of the considerable research demonstrating that the poor have little access to medical care for preventive services (25). When access to modern family planning services offered with energy and dignity has been provided, the response of poor and near-poor persons has been considerable. The number of low-income patients enrolled in organized family planning services under both public and private auspices has increased from about 175,000 in 1960 to 850,000 in 1968, as hospitals and public health departments have increasingly offered services which provide the new methods not associated with the act of coitus (22). In virtually all known programs offering a variety of methods, 85 to 90 percent of low-income patients voluntarily choose either pills or intrauterine devices (IUD's), the most effective methods currently known.

In 1965, a Chicago study found that three-fourths of patients continued to use the pills regularly 30 months after first coming to the clinic, an astonishingly high retention rate for any procedure requiring continuous self-medication (26).

A carefully planned program which introduced the first subsidized services in New Orleans, begun in 1967, has already enrolled nearly two-thirds of the target population, three-fourths of whom had not practiced birth control or had used nonprescription methods before attending the clinic. When given a genuine choice, 82 percent chose either pills or IUD's, while only 17 percent selected a nonprescription method (27). In the rural Louisiana parish where this program was first tested the birth rate among the indigent decreased by 32 percent in the first year after the clinic was opened, as compared to a decrease of only 6 percent in four surrounding control counties where no organized family planning services were available. The illegitimacy ratio in the county in question dropped from 172 per 1000 live births in 1966 to 121 in 1967, as compared to an increase in the control counties from 162 to 184 (28).

Five Million Women

Judith Blake challenges the estimate that there are 5 million poor and near-poor women who comprise the approximate population in need of subsidized family planning services. This estimate has been arrived at independently by Campbell (20) and the Planned Parenthood Federation Research Department (19), on the basis of Census Bureau tabulations of the characteristics of the poor and near-poor (17). Campbell estimated a total of 4.6 million, while Planned Parenthood estimated 5.3 million. The difference stems from the use of slightly different assumptions in analyzing the data available for obtaining a "need" figure which defines all women who are (i) poor or near-poor; (ii) not currently pregnant or wanting to become pregnant; (iii) fecund; and (iv) exposed to risk of pregnancy. The differences in the assumptions and results are not regarded as significant at this point, when fewer than 1 million low-income patients are reportedly receiving family planning services.

There exists, of course, no data base from which to define precisely women who have the characteristics listed above. Both estimates have been presented as approximations which reasonably interpret available information. It is important to note that 5 million represents a residual number of potential patients at any given time after subtraction, from the total of about 8 million poor and near-poor women aged 15 to 44, of an estimated number of those who are sterile, those who are pregnant or seeking to become pregnant (allowance being made for the fact that poor couples say they want three children, on the average), and those who are not exposed to the risk of pregnancy (20) (Table 3). The estimate does involve the policy assumption that all others should have available competent medical advice on regulating fertility—even if they choose to practice the rhythm method, or if they are less than normally fecund, or if they have sexual relations infrequently—since such advice will tend to make their family planning practice more effective. Whether or not all 5 million women would avail themselves of the opportunity remains to be seen. Until the poor are offered a genuine choice, there is no way to determine how many would actually prefer nonmedical methods. Nor is there any way to judge whether low-income Catholics will voluntarily choose methods officially proscribed by their Church to a degree equaling or possibly exceeding the 53 percent of all Catholics who reported in 1965 that they have already used methods other than the rhythm method (23, Table 3).

It is interesting to note that Judith Blake does *not* cite the one factor which might be a significant limitation on these estimates—namely, the proportion of low-income women who have been able to secure competent guidance in fertility control from private physicians. There exists no adequate information on this question, perhaps because most researchers have been singularly uninterested in the *processes* through which fertility control techniques are diffused. Fragmentary data from several state Medicaid programs suggest that, at most, the proportion of poor and near-poor persons receiving family planning services from private physicians is no higher than 10 percent of the population in need.

In sum, then, the 5-million estimate has been presented as a reasonable approximation, based on the inadequate data that are available, of those who need subsidized family planning services and for whom wise social policy would attempt to develop programs.

Population Policy

Judith Blake's article, hopefully, will stimulate responsible and dispassionate study and discussion of population policy in the United States. The scholarly community has thus far given little attention to this question, leaving the discussion largely to polemicists.

Her message is loud and clear: Our society should not waste its resources on family planning for the poor but should seek ways to restructure the family, reconsider male and female sexual roles (29), and develop satisfying nonfamilial roles for women, if it is to achieve population stability in the long run. We regard the first part of this proposition as erroneous and misleading. The second part, however, needs thoughtful examination as to its feasibility and the costs and benefits to society. The development of voluntary family planning in the immediate future is in no way antithetical to such realistic consideration of population policy for the long run.

It would be useful if Judith Blake were to develop proposals for specific programs to advance the objective of encouraging women to seek satisfaction in careers outside the home. It would be particularly interesting to see whether those programs do not subsume, as a necessary first step, the extension of effective fertility control measures to all women who want and need them—which we believe is the immediate objective of federal policy on family planning.

References and Notes

1. President's Committee on Population and Family Planning, *Population and Family Planning—The Transition from Concern to Action* (Government Printing Office, Washington, D.C., 1968).

2. J. Blake, *Science* **164**, 522 (1969).

3. L. B. Johnson, Message to Congress on Domestic Health and Education, 1 March 1966.

4. J. W. Gardner, Statement of Policy of the Department of Health, Education and Welfare on Family Planning and Population Programs, 24 January 1966.

5. ——. Memorandum to Heads of Operating Agencies on Family Planning Policy, 31 January 1968.

6. "The Growth of the U.S. Population." *Nat Acad. Sci. Nat. Res. Counc. Publ. 1279* (1965).

7. O. Harkavy, F. S. Jaffe, S. M. Wishik, "Implementing DHEW Policy on Family Planning and Population—A Consultant's Report," *Dept. Health Educ. Welfare Publ.* (1967) (available from the U.S. Department of Health, Education and Welfare).

8. Calculation of data on unwanted births from the 1965 National Fertility Study yields an estimate of an annual average of about 850,000 unwanted births among all classes in the period 1960-65 [see F. S. Jaffe and A. F. Guttmacher, *Demography* 5, 910 (1968)]. This figure must be regarded, for methodological reasons, as a minimum estimate of unwanted births. It amounts to about 40 percent of the excess of births over deaths in the 6-year period under study. Prevention of unwanted births among the poor and near-poor could have reduced the overall excess of births over deaths by slightly more than 20 percent, while prevention of unwanted births among the non-poor could have reduced it by slightly less than 20 percent. These approximations show the orders of magnitude of what might be expected from the extension of modern family planning to the poor and near-poor and from improved efficiency of fertility control for all Americans. They do not, of course, add up to a zero rate of growth, but they appear to offer the promise of more immediate progress toward reduced growth rates than any other proposed or currently feasible program of equivalent cost (or, for that matter, any cost).

9. See J. Rock, *The Time Has Come* (Knopf, New York, 1963), chap. 11; A. F. Guttmacher, *Babies by Choice or by Chance* (Doubleday, New York, 1959), chap. 8.

10. We are indebted to Dorothy Nortman of the Population Council for this observation.

11. R. Freedman, P. K. Whelpton, A. A. Campbell, *Family Planning, Sterility and Population Growth* (McGraw-Hill, New York, 1959).

12. P. K. Whelpton, A. A. Campbell, J. E. Patterson, *Fertility and Family Planning in the United States* (Princeton Univ. Press, Princeton, N.J., 1966).

13. N. B. Ryder and C. F. Westoff, "Relationships among intended, expected, desired and ideal family size: United States, 1965," *Population Res.* (March 1969) (available from the Center for Population Research, National Institute of Child Health and Human Development, Washington, D.C.). Their full statement of the limitations of the "ideal" question follows: "We asked the question to correspond exactly with the wording employed in many previous inquiries, *despite profound reservations about its usefulness.* The question can be interpreted as the respondent's opinion as to what she considers to be ideal for the average American family, or what the average American family considers ideal for themselves. In the second place, the wording prompts the further question, 'Ideal for whom?' That might be answered from the standpoint of the respondent, or of the average American family, or even of the total population—since it must face the consequences of the behavior of the 'average American family.' Thirdly, the question calls for a statistical judgment of the characteristics of the average American family, a judgment probably beyond the reach of most respondents and varying in relation to their own characteristics. In the fourth place, there is ambiguity about the scope of the term 'ideal': Does it mean the ideal parity considering the circumstances as well? Finally, there would seem to be a substantial risk with a question so worded that the respondent thinks she is being asked about the actual average number of children in an American family. In our opinion, the *sole justification for including this question in our inquiry is to explore statistically the validity of this very common but very dubious question* [emphasis added]."

14. Convergence is also demonstrated when actual behavior is examined, rather than attitudes, See C. F. Westoff and N. B. Ryder, in *Fertility and Family Planning: A World View*, S. J. Behrman, L. Corsa, Jr., R. Freedman, Eds. (Univ. of Michigan Press, Ann Arbor, 1969), Tables 13 and 15. In 1960 and 1965, by any measure of socioeconomic status, three-fourths to five-sixths of the lowest income groups had used or expected to use some form of fertility control (including relatively ineffective ones). As would be expected of a practice which has diffused down through the class structure, there is a lower level of practice in the lowest groups (which may also be a function of less availability of services).

15. N. B. Ryder and C. F. Westoff, "Fertility planning status of American women, 1965," paper presented before the Population Association of America, April 1968.

16. Unpublished data from the 1965 National Fertility Study, made available by C. F. Westoff.

17. Special tabulation by the Census Bureau of the characteristics of women living in poverty and near-poverty in March 1966.

17a. C. F. Westoff and N. B. Ryder, in *Fertility and Family Planning: A World View*, S. J. Behrman, L. Corsa, Jr., R. Freedman, Eds. (Univ. of Michigan Press, Ann Arbor, 1969).

18. Blake has much to say about the responses of white men and women of lower education and economic status to a poll question. "Do you think birth control pills should be made available free to all women on relief who are of childbearing age?" She ignores the ambiguity of the question, which would appear to require of the respondents judgment on at least four issues: (i) pills; (ii) the public assistance system ("welfare handouts"); (iii) the morals of women on public assistance; and (iv) the distribution of pills without medical supervision. If we were asked the question in this form, our answer would probably also be in the negative: "Not unless the distribution was under medical supervision and the assistance recipient wanted pills."

19. G. Varky, F. S. Jaffe, S. Polgar, R. Lincoln, *Five Million Women—Who's Who Among Americans in Need of Subsidized Family Planning Services* (Planned Parenthood-World Population, New York, 1967), a publication based on the Census Bureau tabulation cited in 17.

20. A. A. Campbell, *J. Marriage and the Family* 30, 236 (1968).

21. M. Orshansky, "The shape of poverty in 1966," *Soc. Security Bull.* (March 1968).

22. F. S. Jaffe and A. F. Guttmacher, *Demography* 5, 910 (1968).

23. C. F. Westoff and N. B. Ryder, "United States: Methods of Fertility Control, 1955, 1960 and 1965," *Studies in Family Planning No. 17* (1967).

24. C. Tietze, in *Manual of Contraceptive Practice*, M. S. Calderone, Ed. (Williams and Wilkins, Baltimore, 1964), Tables 3 and 4.

25. See, for example, A. F. Yerby, *Amer. J. Public Health Nat. Health* 56, 5 (1966).

26. R. Frank and C. Tietze, *Amer. J. Obstet. Gynecol.* 93, 122 (1 Sept. 1965). See also S. Polgar and W. B. Cowles, Eds., "Public Health Programs in Family Planning," supplement to *Amer. J. Public Health Nat. Health* 56 (Jan. 1966); S. Polgar, "U.S.: The PPFA Mobile Service Project in New York City," *Studies in Family Planning No. 15* (1966); D. J. Bogue, "U.S.: The Chicago Fertility Control Studies," *ibid.*, G. W. Perkin, "A family planning unit for your hospital?" *Hosp. Practice* 2, 64 (May 1967).

27. J. D. Beasley, *Family Planning Perspectives* 1, 2 (Spring 1969).

28. —— and V. W. Parrish, "Epidemiology and prevention of illegitimate births in the rural South," paper presented before the American Public Health Association, November 1968.

29. We confess that we do not comprehend how a society which has as much difficulty as Blake alleges ours does with regard to contraceptives for unmarried persons engaging in heterosexual activities can be expected to legitimate sexual deviancy as an antinatalist measure.

35

DEMOGRAPHIC FACTORS AND EARLY MODERN ECONOMIC DEVELOPMENT

Joseph J. Spengler

How slender an initial difference may come to be decisive of the outcome in case circumstances give this initial difference a cumulative effect.

—Thorsten Veblen

Sometime before the seventeenth century, perhaps as early as the fifteenth, a unique

Reprinted from *Daedalus* 97: 433-46, 1968.
Reprinted by permission from *Daedalus*, Journal of the American Academy of Arts and Sciences, Boston, Massachusetts.

marriage pattern began to develop in Western Europe. It apparently did not exist in the fourteenth century, but had become effective by the seventeenth, if not earlier. John Hajnal has described the genesis of this pattern, which seems to have been a product of both the rational elements in Western European culture and the prevailing institutional arrangements associated with that culture.

This pattern consisted of much later marriage than one found in Eastern Europe or outside Europe. It significantly intensified the birth-limiting influence of ecclesiastical and other forms of celibacy. It contributed greatly to the relatively low level of European birth rates which, "so far as we can tell, were rarely over 38 before the spread of birth control." Thus, it impeded the rate of population growth. This slowing down augmented, in turn, per-capita productivity as well as capital formation and cushioned the impact of numbers upon land and resources. It made average income higher than it otherwise would have been and thereby facilitated the emergence and successful launching of the Industrial Revolution, which finally freed Western man, especially the common man, from the trammels of static, catastrophe-prone, and poverty-ridden pain economies (1).

Population and Income Growth

The course of both population and income growth corresponded rather closely to that of a Malthusian model in Europe until around the sixteenth century, and in most of Asia and Africa almost to the present. Europe's population did not begin to grow continuously and without marked interruptions until the fifteenth century, but thereafter it proceeded at a slowly increasing rate. Europe's population, M. K. Bennett suggests, increased by about three quarters between the year 1000 and 1300, only to decline by perhaps three eighths during the next century, and then to return to the 1300 level by the early-sixteenth century. Thereafter it grew—about one quarter of 1 per cent per year in the sixteenth and seventeenth centuries and somewhat more rapidly in the eighteenth century, especially in the latter part. The long-term annual growth rate averaged about one half of 1 per cent in the eighteenth century and about three quarters of 1 per cent in the nineteenth: This increase in the growth rate seems to have been attributable mainly, if not entirely, to a decline in mortality. Before the nineteenth century, this decline is traceable chiefly to a marked diminution in the incidence of famine and pestilence and the catastrophic mortality associated therewith, especially in such periods as 1349-1470's, aptly described in Sylvia Thrupp as "the golden age of bacteria."

The movement of the per-capita output of goods and services in Europe was long dominated by the course of its population growth, itself often under the empire of unfavorable events and therefore very low over the long run according to modern standards. The countries of Europe were predominantly agricultural,

with three quarters or more of the population being rural. The mode of agricultural production was relatively traditional and unchanging. Supply was quite inelastic, and its increase depended principally upon the extension of cultivation. English and other data suggest that productivity was low and progressed slowly even when population pressure encouraged the abandonment of the three-field system. In Western Europe, as Phyllis Deane and W. A. Cole write: "The significant variable in the long preindustrial secular swings in productivity seems to have been the rate of population growth. When population rose, product per head fell: when population fell, product per head rose." The Malthusian tendency for numbers to keep abreast of agricultural output seems to have been characteristic also of Asia. Despite a generally higher birth rate, the population of Asia supposedly increased only about five sixths between 1650 and 1800, no more than that of Europe and Russia. Mortality regulated population growth in Asia much more than it did in Europe. As K. W. Taylor concluded: "Long periods of [population] stability are best explained by the Malthusian hypothesis, and the relatively short periods of rapid growth can be explained in terms of major technological or environmental changes." Even distribution of population, A. P. Usher found, was closely associated with the availability of food. This correlation remained constant until the Industrial Revolution converted mineral resources into a major determinant of population location. Density varied, of course, reflecting in part the fact that full maturity of settlement was not achieved in Northwestern Europe until around 1600— sixteen centuries later than in the Mediterranean world, but three centuries earlier than in India and China. In Northern and Western Europe, density varied greatly even before the Industrial Revolution, ranging from 137 inhabitants per square mile in Belgium and parts of Italy through 90 in England and 110 in France to about 5 in Norway (2).

So long as the numbers of people tended to press closely upon the food supply, average income and output could not increase greatly over the long run. The elasticity in the supply of produce was too low. Average output increased with the extension of settlement, the formation of capital, and the stimulus of the temporary economic upsurges manifest after 1100 and again after the late 1400's, but not much of this gain could be retained. Indeed, if it had been, average income in 1500 might have exceeded subsistence by 300 to 400 per cent, rather than the actual, much lower, margin. If average output in the Roman Empire around A.D. 200 had approximated 1.25 times a hypothetical subsistence level and thereafter had grown about one tenth of 1 per cent per year, by 1500 the level of output should have been about 3.5 times as high as it was thirteen centuries earlier, but it was not.

As English data suggest, in and long after the Middle Ages, population pressure tended to develop in the wake of a continuing growth in numbers. It became manifest, for example in the late-thirteenth and early-fourteenth centuries—after several centuries of growth, much of which was subsequently wiped out by the Black Death. Population pressure was again felt in the sixteenth and seventeenth centuries and resulted in complaints of unemployment as well as calls for the development of colonial outlets to absorb the excess numbers (3).

Even so, as Deane and Cole state, England and Wales had apparently achieved by the late-seventeenth century a higher level of material welfare than any other country with the exception of Holland, whose average income, according to Gregory King, was slightly above the English average and at least one fourth above the French average. Deane and Cole add, however, that the seventeenth-century English average did not greatly exceed that of the "rest of the world" or that of fifteenth-century England. They also observe that "change, outside the cataclysms produced by famines and epidemics, was generally small, slow, and easily reversed" in the seventeenth-century world in which King lived (4).

Three observations may now be made. Although our information in respect to Europe's rate of population growth before 1800 is incomplete, this rate appears to have been low, averaging perhaps one quarter of 1 per cent per year between 1500 and 1700 and about five twelfths of 1 per cent per year between 1700 and 1750. In France population increased somewhat between 1500 and 1600, though not steadily; in the seventeenth century, Pierre Goubert believes, it oscillated around an equilibrium of about nineteen million, standing nearer the minimum than the maximum in 1700. It grew about one third of 1 per cent per year in the eighteenth century, about .22 per cent per year in 1700-55, and about one half of 1 per cent in 1755-1801. In England and Wales, population grew about one third of 1 per cent per year between 1500 and 1700 and between 1700 and 1780. Even if English incomes and wages were not much greater in the late-seventeenth century than in the late-fifteenth, the slowness with which the population grew at least permitted the standards attained in the late-fifteenth century to be retained and perhaps even improved. Given the low rate of natural increase, overall real output per head could increase something like .3 per cent annually in England and Wales between 1700 and the 1770's, even though the aggregate real output grew slowly throughout the eighteenth century.

Despite the slowness with which average output advanced, it rose above the levels encountered in much of today's underdeveloped world. Phyllis Deane estimates that the average income in England and Wales in 1750 (at least one third above the 1700 level, but about two fifths below the 1800 level) would have been equivalent to £70 in the 1950's—a figure nearly treble that of India and two thirds that of Mexico in the 1950's. According to Simon Kuznets, "per worker income in the agricultural sector in today's most populous" underdeveloped countries (China, India, Pakistan, Burma, South Korea, and most of Africa) is only "one fourth or one third of per worker income in the currently developed countries in their preindustrialization phase" when six tenths or more of their labor force remained in agriculture. Accordingly, *total* income per worker in these countries was two to three times as high as it is in today's underdeveloped countries. "By comparison with many present-day preindustrial economies in Africa and Asia," Cole and Deane conclude, "the English economy of the late seventeenth and early eighteenth centuries had reached a relatively advanced stage of economic organization. So too, no doubt, had certain other countries" (5).

Theories of Population and Income Growth

A low rate of population growth may encourage the rate of growth of average income in three ways. These observations are especially true of predominantly agricultural economies that are equipped with an essentially traditional agricultural technique, are not yet subject to economies of scale, and are just beginning to assume a more commercial-industrial form.

If a population is growing slowly, the bulk of the savings which it generates can be devoted to increasing capital per head, thereby easing indirectly the pressure of population upon land and facilitating the growth of nonagricultural enterprises. Capital formation proceeded at a very slow pace in the seventeenth and early-eighteenth centuries. In England around 1700 the annual rate of saving fell within a range of something like 3 to 6 per cent of the national income. The French rate was probably lower, and the Dutch rate may have been higher. With such low saving rates, capital per head could increase significantly only if the rate of population growth were negligible and savings were not employed wastefully, as often happened in ancient and medieval times. Were population growth negligible and were only 4 per cent saved and invested annually to yield a 10 per cent rate of return, average income would rise about .4 of 1 per cent per year, enough to increase per-capita income by approximately one half in about ninety-five years. Were population growing as much as 1 per cent per year, this growth would absorb virtually all the savings, should they amount to only 4 or 5 per cent of the national income. Not even in Europe, however, was the former option always exercised. According to E. F. Heckscher, population growth in eighteenth-century Sweden absorbed the disposable resources available (6).

Slowing down population growth decreases the impact numbers and agriculturalists have

upon cultivatable land. Accordingly, the ratio of the agricultural labor force to cultivatable land was only 10 to 50 per cent as high in pre-industrial European countries as it is in today's underdeveloped countries. Even so, in and before David Ricardo's day, there was strong evidence of a classical diminishing of returns in England and possibly elsewhere. Nevertheless, because numbers had grown slowly, and limits to production had not been reached, time remained during which yields per acre could be increased or manufactures could be developed and exchanged for imports. This time was utilized, moreover, and yields were increased somewhat, certainly in greater measure than they have been today in those underdeveloped countries whose agricultural productivity has increased little over the centuries (7).

Potential productivity per capita in a population depends markedly upon the size of the fraction of the population that is of working age. Let this group be represented by those fifteen to fifty-nine or fifteen to sixty-four years of age. This fraction varies appreciably. In 1965, for example, the fraction aged fifteen to sixty-four approximated 54 per cent in Africa, Latin America, and Southeast Asia, much less than the 64 per cent found in Europe. Therefore, under *ceteris paribus* conditions, potential productivity was about 1.185 (64/54) times as high in Europe as in Africa, Latin America, and Southeast Asia. Northern and Western Europe enjoyed superiority in this respect as early as 1850, when the fraction aged fifteen to sixty-four years ranged between 60 and 66 per cent. Of course, the increase in potential productivity made possible would be actualized only if there were not offsetting increases in unemployment.

Before we attempt to estimate the magnitude of this fraction in the seventeenth and eighteenth centuries, we may examine a hypothetical stable population to observe how an age structure is generated by past mortality and fertility patterns. The relative number of persons of working age in a stable population rises as fertility (measured by the Gross Reproduction Rate [GRR]) and life expectancy at birth decrease; the relative number falls as fertility and life expectancy rise. If, for example, we hold expectation of life at birth constant at fifty years, the proportion aged fifteen to fifty-nine rises from 45.8 per cent with GRR at 4.0 to around 60 per cent with GRR at 1.25 to 1.50. If we hold GRR constant at 2.0, the proportion falls from 64 per cent with an expectation of life at birth of twenty years to 54.7 per cent with a life expectancy of over seventy years (70.2). Thus, declining mortality cancels out a portion of the improvement in age structure associated with a decline in the GRR. For example, combining a life expectancy of thirty years with a GRR of 3 results in a fraction of 0.545 aged fifteen to fifty-nine; a life expectancy of 70.2 with a GRR of 1.5, in a fraction of 0.577 aged fifteen to fifty-nine.

Information on the age composition of the pre-industrial countries of Northern and Western Europe may be found from two sources. The first source, hypothetical stable populations, furnishes only inferential information. In the body of Table 1, I give the percentages aged fifteen to sixty-four in stable populations resulting from combinations of GRR (see column 1) with expectations of life at birth (see line 2 in head of table). This fraction descends from 64 per cent when a GRR of 2.25 is combined with a life expectancy of twenty-five to fifty-five when a GRR of 3.0 is combined with a life expectancy of forty. The numbers in parentheses are rough indicators of the rates of natural increase per 1,000 inhabitants associated with designated combinations of GRR and life expectancy. We see at once how the proportion aged fifteen to sixty-four declines as GRR and life expectancy at birth increase (8).

The problem confronting us is that of selecting those combinations in the table which most closely approximate fertility and mortality conditions in pre-industrial Western Europe. The rate of population growth must be low. Life expectancy probably did not exceed

Table 1. Proportions Aged 15-64 Years: Rates of Growth.

GRR	*Expectation of Life at Birth*			
	25	30	35	40
2.25	64 (−3)	62 (3)	61 (7)	60 (11)
2.5	62 (1)	61 (7)	59 (11)	58 (15)
3.0	59 (7)	57 (13)	56 (18)	55 (22)

thirty-five years in whole populations before 1800. Let us suppose the most representative combinations to be those associated with a GRR of 2.25 to 2.5 and a life expectancy of thirty to thirty-five years. We would then expect the proportion aged fifteen to sixty-four to approach 59 to 62 per cent or, more likely, 61 to 62 per cent, since the rate of population growth was decidedly below 1 per cent per year. This proportion is at least 10 to 15 per cent greater than levels encountered in many of today's underdeveloped countries.

Extant data relating to fertility and mortality in pre-industrial Europe presumably support the suppositions made in the preceding paragraph. First, the birth rate was much lower in pre-industrial Europe than it is in present-day and pre-1900 Asia and Africa. During the 1700's the rate was around thirty-five, somewhat lower in England and Wales, France, and Scandinavia (exclusive of Finland, which had a rate sometimes just over forty). Between 1776 and 1800, when the Swedish birth rate averaged somewhat below thirty-five, the GRR averaged about 2.1. We find birth rates of roughly thirty-five to thirty-seven associated with a GRR of 2.25 and of roughly thirty-eight to forty-one associated with a GRR of 2.5. Although the birth rates reported for eighteenth-century Europe may be somewhat off the mark, they do suggest that the GRR was close to 2.25 or 2.5.

So far, information on mortality and life expectancy before 1800 is limited. Around 1800, expectation of life at birth may have been as high as thirty-five to forty years in some Western European countries; if so, it was higher than it was during the sixteenth and seventeenth centuries. Life expectancy at birth rose in Sweden between the period 1755-76 and the period 1816-40, increasing from 33.2 to 39.5 years for males and from 35.7 to 43.5 years for females. Female life expectancy at birth, usually somewhat higher than male life expectancy, was 44.7 years in Denmark in 1835-44; 42.18 in England and Wales in 1841; 40.83 in France in 1817-31; 37.91 in Iceland in 1850-60; and 35.12 in the Netherlands in 1816-25. K. F. Helleiner suggests that life expectancy rose during the eighteenth century because "the periodic erosion of growth by epidemic or harvest failure became less marked," especially after 1750. An alternative might be that other changes gave rise to a decline in mortality during this century. Mortality, however, appears to have been greater in the earlier parts of the eighteenth century and in the seventeenth century. Gregory King's data suggest a life expectancy of only thirty-two in England during 1690's, a figure which Peter Laslett finds fitting "in fairly well with what is known for the seventeenth century both in England and France." Studies of localized populations in the first half of the eighteenth century in France yield an estimate of about thirty-three years for expectancy of life at birth. According to S. Peller, life expectancy at birth among Europe's ruling families averaged only about thirty-one years in 1600-99, three years less than in the preceding century and six years less than in the eighteenth. Generation life tables of the British peerage suggest that expectation of life at birth was thirty-three years among males born between 1680 and 1729, but almost forty-five years (44.8) among those born between 1730 and 1779. If violent deaths are not included, male life expectancy at birth for those born between 1330 and 1679 remained in the range of thirty or thirty-one years. One may infer from these diverse data that life expectancy at birth probably did not exceed thirty-five years in any country before the late-eighteenth century.

Our second source of information is the statistics available for the age composition of pre-industrial Europe as well as Japan, a country whose people controlled their numbers. Persons aged fifteen to sixty-four constituted 60.5 and 62 per cent, respectively, of Sweden's population in 1750 and 1800; 62.2 and 61.4 per cent of France's population in 1775 and 1801; and 58.4 and 60.8 per cent of Japan's population in the eighth century and 1888. The proportion of the Danish population aged fifteen to sixty-four in 1787 was similar to that in Sweden in 1750. Iceland's population in 1703 included a larger proportion aged fifteen to sixty-four. Data on the age composition of eighteenth-century Europe suggest, when contrasted with those in Table 2 discussed below,

that this age composition was more favorable to economic production that that now found in much of the underdeveloped world with its high fertility and relatively low mortality. Although the conditions that made for high mortality and, hence, for a relatively low proportion of persons under fifteen years of age must have debilitated the population in some degree, they could hardly have offset the advantages derived from a low rate of population growth (9).

Thus, the age composition of populations in Western European countries was favorable to average productivity. It is difficult, of course, to assess the change in age composition that took place after the adoption of the unique Western European pattern of marriage. This may have increased the favorableness of the age composition by at least three units, or about 5 per cent. If per-capita productivity rose correspondingly, the rate of saving could have increased by a larger fraction. In any case, until late in the eighteenth century, the slow rate of population growth permitted savings to be devoted almost entirely to improving productive capital per head. This slowness also held down the rate of increase in population pressure, perhaps sufficiently to permit improvement in yields to offset small increases in population.

Yesterday's Europe Versus Today's Africa and Asia

Today the economic distance separating various parts of the underdeveloped world from various parts of the developed world is many times what it was two to three centuries ago. At one time, this distance might have been easily bridged. Had, as late as 1800, the index of performance in the most advanced lands been four times that in the least advanced, and had this index continued to improve at a rate of 1.5 per cent per year in the more advanced countries, the laggard countries might have caught up by the early-twentieth century. This did not happen. The index rose most rapidly in the advanced countries. Today real private consumption per head is between six and thirty-one times as high in Northern and Western

Europe as it is in various underdeveloped countries; it is even higher in the United States. This increase in spread is the result of what was done in the European sphere and not done in the underdeveloped world. In the latter category must be included failure to curtail fertility.

Agricultural population density increased faster in Asia than in Europe. By 1948, it was nearly double that in Africa and Europe, exclusive of the Soviet Union (147 per square kilometer of available land in Asia as contrasted with 83 and 86 in Africa and Europe) (10). Over three fifths of the labor force in Africa and Asia remained in agriculture, although output per agriculturalist and per acre remained low, often too low, to supply minimum nutritional requirements.

Population grew faster during the nineteenth century in Europe than it did in the underdeveloped countries, with their high levels of mortality. This relationship was eventually altered. Mortality declined in European countries, but so did the birth rates. Today the rate of population growth is much higher in the underdeveloped world than elsewhere and is a number of times what it was in pre-1800 Western Europe. Most Gross Reproduction Rates in Africa, mainland Asia, and Latin America fall within a range of 2.5 to 3.5; expectation of life at birth falls below forty years in Africa, between forty and fifty years in Asia, and between fifty and fifty-five in Latin America. The rate of natural increase per decade between 1970 and 2000 is expected to range from around 20 per cent in Asia to around 30 per cent in South America and, perhaps, Africa. These prospective rates, roughly double what they were in the period 1920-40, reflect declines in crude mortality uncompensated by declines in natality. These high rates of population growth will absorb much of the capital that is formed in the underdeveloped world and hence will greatly retard growth of output per head.

The age composition of the present-day underdeveloped countries is much less favorable to productivity than that encountered in the developed world or in European countries during their pre-industrial stage. As of 1965,

the fraction formed by the population fifteen to sixty-four years was as follows: East Asia (exclusive of Japan), 52.5 per cent; South Asia, 54.7 per cent; Africa, 54.2 per cent, ranging from 51.7 per cent in West Africa to 56.1 per cent in Eastern Africa; Central America, 50.8 per cent; Tropical South America, 53.4 per cent; Caribbean America, 56 per cent. The Philippines is exemplary, for the current fraction, 53 per cent, is much below the 57.2 per cent reported for 1903, but is consistent with an estimated birth rate in the upper-forties and a death rate in the low-twenties.

These percentages are compatible with current estimates of gross reproduction (2.5 to 3.0 in Africa and 2.5 to 3.5 in Asia and Latin America) and life expectancy at birth (around or below forty years in Africa; forty to fifty in Asia; fifty to fifty-five in Latin America). In Table 2, GRR and life expectancies are combined to yield stable populations and the percentages of the population aged fifteen to sixty-four. (In parentheses, we give the approximate rates of natural increase associated with these combinations.) The data suggest that in Africa the fraction aged fifteen to sixty-four will range between 55 and 58 per cent; in Asia, between 50 and 58 per cent; and in Latin America, between 49 and 56 per cent.

Table 2. Proportions Aged 15-64 Years: Rates of Growth.

GRR	Expectation of Life at Birth		
	40	*50*	*55*
2.5	58 (15)	56 (22)	56 (23)
3.0	55 (22)	53 (28)	52 (31)
3.5	52 (27)	50 (34)	49 (37)

The relatively low rates of fertility and natural increase—part the result of the unique fertility-regulating pattern of marriage that developed in Europe during the fifteenth or sixteenth centuries—must have contributed greatly to the growth of average income in the seventeenth and eighteenth centuries. The sustained increase in average income did not, of course, give rise to the Industrial Revolution, for this revolution, unlike the minor ones of the twelfth, fifteenth, and seventeenth centuries, was a *revolutionary* transformation of the British and Western European economies. It was the product of many cooperating factors (capital accumulation, inventions, innovations, favorable factor endowments, *laissez faire*, market expansion, earlier experience, and so forth). Among its causes was the relatively low level of fertility existing in Western Europe. Because fertility was low, the relative number of persons of productive age and, hence, the potential productivity per head were high. Natural increase also was low, so that the pressure of population upon agricultural land did not build up rapidly and nearly all savings could be devoted to improving the stock of capital instead of supporting population growth. Average income could rise, albeit slowly and somewhat intermittently, and pave the way for the coming of the Industrial Revolution.

References

1. On the marriage pattern, see John Hajnal, "European Marriage Patterns in Perspective," *Population in History*, eds. D. V. Glass and D. E. C. Eversley (Chicago, 1965), pp. 101-40; see also *Population in History*, pp. 46-51, 99, 298-99, 377, 448-85. On the fertility-controlling effectiveness of deferment of marriage, see J. W. Leasure, "Malthus, Marriage, and Multiplication," *Milbank Memorial Fund Quarterly*, Vol. 41, Part 2 (October 1963), pp. 419-35. For the impact of the Industrial Revolution on the standard of living, see discussion by E. J. Hobshawm and R. M. Hartwell, in *Economic History Review*, Vol. 16 (1963), pp. 120-46.
2. This paragraph and the one preceding are based on essays by K. F. Helleiner and the editors in *Population in History*; W. A. Cole and Phyllis Deane, "The Growth of National Incomes," *Cambridge Economic History of Europe*, eds. H. J. Habakkuk and M. M. Postan (Cambridge, 1966), Vol. 6, Chap. 1; D. V. Glass, "World Population, 1800-1950," *Cambridge Economic History*, Chap. 2; M. K. Bennett, *The World's Food* (New York, 1954), Chap. 1; Phyllis Deane and W. A. Cole, *British Economic Growth 1688-1959* (Cambridge, 1962), pp. 38, 65, 78-82; Phyllis Deane, *The First Industrial Revolution* (Cambridge, 1965), pp. 11-13; essays by K. W. Taylor, J. C. Russell, and A. P. Usher in *Demographic Analysis*, eds. J. J. Spengler and O. D. Duncan (Glencoe, 1965); W. Bowden, M. Karpovich, and A. P. Usher, *An Economic History of Europe Since 1750* (New York, 1937), pp. 3, 6–7; chapters by L. Genicot

and R. Kobner, *Cambridge Economic History of Europe*, eds. M. M. Postan (2nd ed.; Cambridge, 1966), Vol. 1; Roger J. Mols, S. J., *Introduction à la démographie historique des villes d'Europe du XIVe au XVIIIe siècle* (Louvain, 1955), Vol. 2, pp. 425-34, on mortality, and Vol. 3, pp. 284-87, on natality.
3. Manifestations of population pressure, especially in England, have been discussed frequently in the *Economic History Review*. See articles by M. M. Postan and E. E. Rich, in Vol. 2 (1950), pp. 221-46, 246-65; D. C. Coleman, Vol. 8 (1956), pp. 288-94; W. C. Robinson, with comments by M. M. Postan, Vol. 9 (1959), pp. 63-83; J. Z. Titow, Vol. 14 (1961), pp. 218-23; J. M. W. Bean, Vol. 15 (1963), pp. 423-37; G. S. L. Tucker, Vol. 16 (1964), pp. 205-18; P. E. Razzell, *ibid.*, pp. 312-32; E. A. Wrigley, Vol. 19 (1966), pp. 82-109. See also Genicot, *loc. cit.*, J. C Russell *British Medieval Population* (Albuquerque, 1948), pp. 156-59, 232, 312-14; *Population in History*, pp. 434-85 and 507-22 *passim*; J. W. Thompson, *An Economic and Social History of the Middle Ages (300-1300)* (New York, 1928), pp. 391-92; L. D. Stamp, *Man and Land* (London, 1955), pp. 92-94; also, essay by Charles Parain, *Cambridge Economic History of Europe*, Vol. 1, and essays by R. S. Lopez and M. M. Postan, *Cambridge Economic History*, Vol. 2; K. F. Helleiner's essay, *Cambridge Economic History*, Vol. 4.
4. Deane and Cole, *British Economic Growth 1688-1959*, pp. 38-39; E. H. Phelps Brown, *The Growth of British Industrial Relations* (London, 1959), p. 2.
5. In this and the preceding paragraph, I draw on S. Kuznets, *Economic Growth and Structure* (New York, 1965), pp. 176-93; Deane, *The First Industrial Revolution*, pp. 5-13; Cole and Deane, "The Growth of National Incomes," pp. 3-10; Deane and Cole, *British Economic Growth 1688-1959*, pp. 38, 65, 78-80; essays by Glass, G. Utterström, P. Goubert, L. Henry, and J. Meuvert in *Population in History*; J. C. Toutain, *Le produit de l'agriculture de 1700 à 1958* (Paris, 1961), Chap. 7, and *La Population de la France de 1700 à 1959* (Paris, 1963), pp. 24-29. See also W. W. Rostow, *The Economics of Take-Off into Sustained Growth* (London, 1963).
6. Deane and Cole, *British Economic Growth 1688-1959*, pp. 260-64; Cole and Deane, "The Growth of National Incomes," p. 5; E. F. Heckscher's essay in *Economic History Review*, Vol. 2 (1950), pp. 266-77.
7. On the course of yields, see C. Clark, *Conditions of Economic Progress* (2d ed.; London, 1951), pp. 224-27; Deane and Cole, *British Economic Growth 1688-1959*, pp. 64-67; M. M. Postan, in *Economic History Review*, Vol. 12 (1959), pp. 80-81; also M. J. R. Healy and E. L. Jones, "Wheat Yields in England, 1815-59," *Journal of Royal Statistical*

Society, Series A, Vol. 125 (1962), Part 4, pp. 574-579; C. Clark and M. R. Haswell, *The Economics of Subsistence Agriculture* (London, 1964), *passim*.

8. Tables 1 and 2 are based on Western-type stable populations, described in A. J. Coale and Paul Demeny, *Regional Model Life Tables and Stable Populations* (Princeton, 1966). See also on age composition and population prospects, United Nations, *The Aging of Populations and Its Economic and Social Implications*, Population Studies, No. 26 (New York, 1956) and *World Population Prospects*, Population Studies, No. 41 (New York, 1966).

9. Data on natality and mortality in this and the two preceding paragraphs are based upon United Nations, *Population Bulletin*, Nos. 6 and 7; Glass,

"World Population 1800-1950," *Population in History*, pp. 14, 52-57, 79-86, 98, 134, 215, 241, 274, 282, 304-07, 358-359, 446, 467, 469, 474-506, 506, 538, 555, 562-87; articles by H. Gille and H. Hyriennius, in *Population Studies*, Vol. 3 (1949), pp. 3-65, Vol. 4 (1951), pp. 421-31; R. R. Kuczynski, *The Balance of Births and Deaths*, Vol. 1 (Washington, 1928), pp. 6-7, 39, 94; L. I. Dublin, A. J. Lotka, and M. Spiegelman, *Length of Life* (2d ed.; New York, 1949), pp. 41-43, 348-51; Peter Laslett, *The World We Have Lost* (London, 1965), pp. 93-94; Irene Taeuber, *The Population of Japan* (Princeton, 1958), pp. 10, 46.

10. United Nations, *The Determinants and Consequences of Population Trends*, Population Studies, No. 17 (New York, 1953), p. 269.

PART FIVE

Pollution and Environment

We need not turn to the fate of passenger pigeons or dinosaurs to remind ourselves that sheer numbers or size do not alone guarantee survival. In the hundred thousand years or so of our own existence, lacking even one of these two advantages, our species must at times have come very close to disaster. What we mostly risked before, however, was *local* extinction. The possibilities that begin to loom ahead now involve the potential destruction of our *total* global population.

Because their effects are relatively long term, the demographic issues surveyed in Part Four may appear, albeit quite erroneously, to have little immediate urgency in this context. As Garret Hardin remarks, no one ever died of overpopulation. By contrast, many aspects of pollution have patently become extremely critical, especially on a local basis. We can all see the smog that envelops our cities on any working day and the garbage that accumulates in our streets during a strike. The pollution of our natural waters is something many of us have experienced firsthand. Some at least can comprehend the consequences of contamination of our environment with pesticides and other deadly poisons. To put it in colloquial terms, it is apparent to all of us that the global plumbing system is out of order, and we have to fix it, and to fix it quickly, if we are to avert total and immediate disaster.

There may still be a few who believe that for their own lifetime, and perhaps for that of their children, it will be possible to flee from the problems of urban blight, just as there is a present escape from the population pressures of our more crowded metropolitan regions, by retreating to remote parts of the earth. The demonstration of a global umbrella of pesticides, the universal fallout of radioactive materials, and the presence of pollutants and other aerosols in all the airsheds of our globe, now emphasize that any belief of permanent escape is an illusion. There is no doubt left that ecocatastrophe threatens our survival.

All forms of pollution, as the papers in this part explain, are created directly or indirectly by our urban ecosystems and their burgeoning technologies. This is well illustrated by the survey paper on air pollution (36), written by the discoverer of photochemical smog, A. J. Haagen-Smit. He describes the consequence of the auto exhaust gas release into city airsheds. Other aspects of auto exhaust fume interactions are considered by Vincent J. Schaefer in a paper dealing with ice nuclei formation (37). Certain other influences of air pollution on weather are examined in a general presentation by Eric Aynsley (38). We are reminded, in a paper (39) by Theodore T. Frankenberg, that industry as well as autos contributes to this air pollution.

Besides such specific and general effects, many other kinds of damage have been attributed to these and other forms of air pollutants. To emphasize potential effects on human health, an alarming and still controversial series of deductions by Ernest J. Sternglass (40), regarding the effects of radioactive fallout from atomic weapons testing, is included. The reaction to this paper as stated by one of many researchers in this field, Alice Stewart (41), illustrates the extent to which the ideas presented by Sternglass remain unaccepted. That some health hazards may however be attributable to physical rather than to chemical features of the environment is stressed in a presentation by Ian W. Monie (42). G. Melvyn Howe describes the regional correlations that exist between these hazards and pollution levels (43). The possibilities of monitoring the regional amounts of chemical pollution are discussed in a paper (44) by George B. Morgan et al.

One result of water pollution may be eutrophication. The general problem of eutrophication is surveyed by Clair N. Sawyer (45). The most extensive illustration of this is provided by the Great Lakes, which are the subject of a classic paper (46) by Alfred M. Beeton. One recent implementation of a solution to water pollution on a local scale is described by Russell Culp (47). The resolution of the problem on a more general basis is outlined by Rolf Eliassen and George Tchobanoglous (48).

The various air or water pollutants discussed in the papers of this part are by-products of industrial activity. There is yet another group of pollutants that are released into the atmosphere by agricultural activity—as Göran Löfroth (49) relates—the persistent pesticides. Six papers were chosen to describe one aspect or another of this pesticide problem. Early work in this field, which focused on birds, is illustrated in the paper (50) by D. A. Ratcliffe on eggshell thickness. Robert W. Risebrough et al. discuss the occurrence of DDT residues in marine food chains (51). In another paper (53) by Risebrough and some of his colleagues, it is demonstrated how such persistent pesticides can be transported great distances in air currents. J. O. G. Tatton and J. H. A. Ruzicka report detection of DDT residues in Antarctica (52), far from any possible use area, Vera Fiserova-Bergerova et al. report on levels of pesticides encountered in human tissues (54), and August Curley and Renate Kimbrough report on the amounts of pesticides found in human milk (55). In the last paper (56) on this subject, A. W. Brown reviews the ever-increasing problem that is presented by the development of resistant races of pests as a result of continuing exposure to various pesticides. A very similar difficulty, arising from the indiscriminate use of biotics, is described by Bernard Dixon (57). If the use of persistent and dangerous biocides is to be prohibited, then pest control must be achieved through *biological* means. Integrated control is an immediate step toward the realization of this goal. Such further aspects of environmental pollution, together with new threats such as those arising from the release into the atmosphere of PCB, are discussed in papers listed in the Additional Readings for this section.

One form of air pollution of a somewhat different sort has to be included here, *noise pollution.* David H. Boggs and J. Richard Simon discuss the more general effects of noise on our performance abilities (58). Airplanes, like the much-discussed SST, can bring about major environmental changes, and they can also contribute to the general cacophony of sound that urban inhabitants struggle to endure. Ron Brown examines the effect of the sonic booms that are produced by the new generation of faster-than-sound aircraft (59).

A more tangible urban pollution problem, the accumulation of waste, is described by Edward Gross (60). Accidental oil spill may account for some water pollution, but the more general effects of oil in ecosystems are discussed by Robert W. Holcomb (61). Another type of water pollution, thermal pollution, is incidental rather than accidental. As with other problems of water pollution, the difficulties presented by thermal pollution are not insuperable, which is the conclusion of the article (62) by Luther J. Carter, dealing with warm water irrigation. In this general area of accidental or incidental environmental poisoning, space permits the inclusion of only these few selections. It is not possible to cover the effects of various heavy metals, now receiving increasing attention, or of biological pollution.

Technological problems like those described in this part can be supplied with technological solutions. There is no mystery as to how we expect to solve most of these occurrences of environmental pollution. It is largely a question of exploring their extent and gravity and weighing these factors against other factors, which in the short or long run are usually *economic*. For most human societies, there will have to be a compromise between technological growth, affluence, and the "quality of life." Where we strike a particular balance, and at what level we decide to maintain a steady state, will be a matter of our own choice. Other regions may decide quite differently. Some decisions, however, cannot be made on a regional basis, for they affect our global ecosystems. They will require the much more difficult international realization of the necessity for compromise and agreement.

Because they are tangible issues, the pollution problems discussed in this part will no doubt be the problems that we will seek to solve first in this decade. This does not mean either that they are the *only* ecological problems that confront us, or that they are indeed the most urgent and important ones. Why this is so, and the basis for reaching any agreement on the solution of these technological issues and other environmental matters, is discussed in Part Six.

Additional Readings

Aaronson, T. "Mercury in the environment," *Environment* 13(4):16-23, 1971.

Abelson, P. H. "Methyl mercury," *Science* 169: 237, 1970.

Alexander, W. "Some harmful effects of noise," *Can. Med. Ass'n. J.* 99(1): 27-31, 1968.

Ames, P. L. "DDT residues in the eggs of the osprey in the northeastern United States and their relation to nesting success," *J. Appl. Ecol.* 3 (Suppl.): 87-97, 1966.

Anderson, J. M., and Peterson, M. R. "DDT: Sublethal effects on brook trout nervous system," *Science* 104: 440-41, 1969.

Anon. "Air pollution control in California," 1968 Annual Report, *Air Resources Board,* State of California, 1969.

Anon. "Mercury in the air," (Staff Report) *Environment* 13(4): 24, 29-33, 1971.

Anthrop, D. F. "Environment noise pollution: A new threat to sanity," *Bull. Atomic Scientists* 25(5): 11-16, 1969.

Atkinson, B. W. "A preliminary examination of the possible effect of London's urban area on the distribution of thunder rainfall 1951-1960," *Trans. Inst. Brit. Geograph.* 44: 97-118, 1968.

Barrons, K. C. "Some ecological benefits of woody plant control with herbicides," *Science* 165: 465-68, 1969.

Berger, R., and Libby, W. F. "Equilibration of atmospheric carbon dioxide with sea water: Possible enzymatic control of rate," *Science* 164: 1395-97, 1969.

Biros, F. J., Walker, A. C., and Medbery, A. "Polychlorinated biphenyls in human adipose tissue," *Bull. Environ. Contam. Toxicol.* 5: 317-23, 1970.

Bitman, J., Cecil, H. C., Harris, S. J., and Fries, G. F. "DDT induces a decrease in eggshell calcium," *Nature* 224: 44-46, 1969.

———. "DDT-induced inhibition of avian shell gland carbonic anhydrase: a mechanism for thin eggshells," *Science* 168: 594-96, 1970.

Boffey, P. M. "Ernest J. Sternglass, Controversial prophet of doom," *Science* 166: 195-200, 1969.

———. "Energy crisis: Environmental issue exacerbates power supply problems," *Science* 168: 1554-59, 1970.

Boughey, A. S. "The explosive development of a floating weed vegetation on Lake Kariba," *Andansonia* 3(1): 49-61, 1963.

Bowen, D. H. M. "The great phosphorus controversy," *Environ. Sci. Technol.* 4(9): 725-26, 1970.

Bowen, V. T., Noshkin, V. E., Volchok, H. L., and Sugihara, T. T. "Strontium-90: Concentration in surface waters of the Atlantic Ocean," *Science* 164: 825-27, 1969.

Breidenbach, A. W., and Eldredge, R. W. "Research and development for better solid waste management," *Bioscience* 19: 984-88, 1969.

Briggs, J. C. "The sea-level Panama Canal: Potential biological catastrophe," *Bioscience* 19: 44-47, 1969.

Brodine, V. "Episode 104," *Environment* 13(1): 2-27, 1971.

Broecker, W. S. "Man's oxygen reserves," *Science* 168: 1537-38, 1970.

Bryson, R. A., and Kutzbach, J. E. "Air Pollution" *Ass'n. Amer. Geographers Commission on College Geog. Resources Paper No. 2* Washington D.C., 1968.

———, and Peterson, J. T. "Atmospheric aerosols: Increased concentrations during the past decades," *Science* 162: 120-21, 1968.

Butler, P. A. "Monitoring pesticides pollution," *Bioscience* 19: 889-91, 1969.

Cable, A., Langan, L., and McCaull, J. "New eye on the air," *Environment* 13(4): 34-41, 1971.

Cadle, R. D., and Allen, E. R. "Atmospheric photochemistry," *Science* 167: 243-49, 1970.

Cain, S. A. "Ecology: Its place in water management," *Water Spectrum,* 1(1): 10-14, 1969.

Cairns, J. "Coping with heated waste water discharges from steam-electric power plants," *Bioscience* 22: 411-19, 423, 1972.

Carter, L. J. "SST: Commercial race or technology experiment?" *Science* 169: 352-55, 1970.

Caswell, C. A. "Underground waste disposal: Concepts and misconceptions," *Environ. Sci. Technol.* 4(8): 642-47, 1970.

Changon, S. A. "Recent studies of urban effects on precipitation in the United States," *Bull. Amer. Meteor. Soc.* 50: 411-21, 1969.

Charlson, R. J., and Pilat, M. J. "Climate: The influence of aerosols," *J. Appl. Meteorol.* 8: 1001-1002, 1969.

Charnell, R. L., Zorich, T. M., and Holly, D. E. "Hydrologic redistribution of radionuclides around a nuclear-excavated sea-level canal," *Bioscience* 19: 799-803, 1969.

Chesher, R. H. "Destruction of Pacific corals by the sea star *Acanthaster planci*," *Science* 165: 280-83, 1969.

Chisolm, J. J. "Lead poisoning," *Scientific American* 224(2): 15-23, 1971.

Clark, J. R. "Thermal pollution and aquatic life," *Scientific American* 220(3): 18-27, 1969.

Cohen, A. "Effect of noise on psychological state," *Amer. Soc. Safety Eng. J.* 14: 11-15, 1969.

Cole, LaMont C. "Thermal pollution," *Bioscience* 19: 989-92, 1969.

Commoner, B. "Nature unbalanced: How man interferes with the nitrogen cycle," *Scientist and Citizen* 10(1): 9-13, 28, 1968.

———. "Evaluating the biosphere," *Science J.* 5A(4): 67-72, 1969.

———. "Review: The closing circle," *Environment* 14(3): 25, 40-52, 1972.

Cox, J. L. "DDT residues in marine phytoplankton: Increase from 1955-1969," *Science* 170: 71-72, 1970.

Curley, A., Sedlak, V. A., Girling, E. F., Hawk, R. E., Barthel, W. F., Pierce, P. E., and Likosky, W. H. "Organic mercury identified as the cause of poisoning in humans and hogs," *Science* 172: 65-67, 1971.

Davidson, B., and Bradshaw, R. W. "Thermal pollution of water systems," *Environ. Sci. Technol.* 1(8): 618-30, 1967.

Davies, J. C. *The Politics of Pollution,* New York, Pegasus, 1970.

Dimond, J. B., and Sherburne, J. A. "Persistence of DDT in wild populations of small mammals," *Nature* 221: 486-87, 1969.

Edwards, C. A. "Soil pollutants and soil animals," *Scientific American* 220(4): 88-89, 1969.

Egan, H., Goulding, R., Roburn, J., and Tatton, J. O'G. "Organo-chlorine pesticide residues in human fat and human milk," *Brit. Med. J.* 3: 66-69, 1965.

Egler, F. E. "Pesticides in our ecosystem," *Amer. Scientist* 52: 110-36, 1964.

Ehrlich, P. R., and Holdren, J. P. "Review: The closing circle," *Environment* 14(3): 24, 26, 31-39, 1972.

Enderson, J. H., and Berger, D. D. "Pesticides: Eggshell thinning and lowered production of young in prairie falcons," *Bioscience* 26: 355-36, 1970.

Epstein, S. S. "A family likeness," *Environment* 12(6): 16-25, 1970.

Fletcher, J. E. "Weather modification," *Science* 158: 276-77, 1967.

Fogg, G. E. "The physiology of an algal nuisance," *Proc. Roy. Soc. Ser. B.* 173(1013): 175-89, 1969.

Fonselius, S. H. "Stagnant sea," *Environment* 12(6): 2-11, 40-48, 1970.

Frost, J. "Earth, air, water," *Environment* 11(6): 15-25, 1969.

Gofman, J. W., and Tamplin, A. R. "Radiation: The invisible casualties," *Environment* 12(3): 12-19, 1970.

Golden, J., and Mongan, T. R. "Sulfur dioxide emissions from power plants: Their effect on air quality," *Science* 171: 381-83, 1971.

Goldman, M. I. *Controlling Pollution: The Economics of a Cleaner America*, Englewood Cliffs, N.J.: Prentice-Hall, 1967.

Goldsmith, J. R., and Landaw, S. A. "Carbon monoxide and human health," *Science* 162: 1352-58, 1968.

Gram, A. L., and Isenberg, D. L. "Waste water treatment," *Science J.* 5(3): 77-81, 1969.

Grant, N. "Mercury in man," *Environment* 13(4): 3-15, 1971.

Gustafson, C. G. "PCB's—prevalent and persistent," *Environ. Sci. Technol.* 4(10): 814-19, 1970.

Hamilton, D. H., Flemer, D. A., Keefe, C. W., and Mihursky, J. A. "Power plants: Effects of chlorination on estuarine primary production," *Science* 169: 197-98, 1970.

Hammond, A. L. "Mercury in the environment: Natural and human factors," *Science* 171: 788-89, 1971.

Hasler, A. D. "Cultural eutrophication is reversible," *Bioscience* 19: 425-31, 1970.

———, and Ingersoll, B. "Dwindling lakes," *Natural History* 77(9): 8-19, 1968.

Hedgepeth, J. W. "The oceans: World sump," *Environment* 12(3): 40-47, 1970.

Heimann, H. "Status of air pollution health research," *Arch. Environ. Health* 14: 488-503, 1967.

Hennigan, R. D. "Water pollution," *Bioscience,* 19: 976-78, 1969.

Hewlett, P. S. "Synergism and potentiation in insecticides," *Chem. Ind.,* June 1, 1968, pp. 701-06.

Hickey, J. J., ed. *Peregrine Falcon Populations—Their Biology and Decline,* Madison, Wisc.: University of Wisconsin Press, 1969.

———, and Anderson, D. W. "Chlorinated hydrocarbons and eggshell changes in raptorial and fish-eating birds," *Science* 152: 271-72, 1968.

Hinkley, E. D., and Kelley, P. L. "Detection of air pollutants with tunable diode lasers," *Science* 171: 635-39, 1971.

Holcomb, R. W. "Insect control: Alternatives to the use of conventional pesticides," *Science* 168: 456-68, 1970.

———. "Waste-water treatment: The tide is turning," *Science* 169: 457-59, 1970.

Holm, L. G., Weldon, L. W., and Blackburn, R. D. "Aquatic weeds," *Science* 166: 699-709, 1969.

Holzworth, G. C. "Mixing depths, wind speeds and air pollution potential for selected locations in the United States," *J. Appl. Meteorol.* 6: 1039-44, 1967.

Hoult, D. P., ed. *Oil on the Sea,* New York and London: Plenum Press, 1969.

Howells, G. P., Kneipe, T. J., and Eisenbud, M. "Water quality in industrial areas: Profile of a river," *Environ. Sci. Technol.* 4(1): 26-35, 1970.

Idyll, C. P. "The Everglades: A threatened ecology," *Science J.* 5A (2): 66-71, 1969.

Ingersoll, J. M. "The Australian rabbit," *Amer. Scientist* 52: 265-73, 1964.

Irving, G. W. "Agricultural pest control and the environment," *Science* 168: 1419-24, 1970.

Joensuu, O. I. "Fossil fuels as a source of mercury pollution," *Science* 172: 1027-28, 1971.

Jones, F. J. S., and Summers, D. D. B. "Relation between DDT in diets of laying birds and viability of their eggs," *Nature* 217: 1162-63, 1968.

Jukes, T. H. "Antibiotics in animal feeds and animal production," *Bioscience* 22: 526-34, 1972.

Kardos, L. T. "A new prospect," *Environment* 12(2): 10-21, 1970.

Kasymov, A. G. "Industry and the productivity of the Caspian Sea," *Marine Poll. Bull.* 1: 100-103, 1970.

Kermode, G. O. "Food additives," *Scientific American* 226(3): 15-21, 1972.

Klein, D. H., and Goldberg, E. D. "Mercury in the marine environment," *Environ. Sci. Technol.* 4: 765-68, 1970.

Korringa, P. "Biological consequences of marine pollution with special reference to the North Sea fisheries," *Helgolander Wiss. Meeresunters* 17: 126-40, 1968.

Kryter, K. D. "Sonic booms from supersonic transport," *Science* 163: 359-67, 1969.

Lagerwerff, J. V., and Specht, A. W. "Contamination of roadside soil and vegetation with cadmium, nickel, lead, and zinc," *Environ. Sci. Technol.* 4(7): 583-86, 1970.

Lave, L. B., and Seskin, E. P. "Air pollution and human health," *Science* 169: 723-33, 1970.

Laws, E. R., Curley, A., and Biros, F. J. "Men with intensive occupational exposure to DDT," *Arch. Environ. Health* 15: 766-75, 1967.

Leinwand, G., ed. *Air and Water Pollution,* New York: Washington Square Press, 1969.

Likens, G. E., Bormann, F. H., and Johnson, N. M. "Acid rain," *Environment* 14(2): 33-40, 1972.

Litspeich, F. B. "Water pollution in Alaska: Present and future," *Science* 166: 1239-45, 1969.

Lofröth, G., and Duffy, M. E. "Birds give warning," *Environment* 11(4): 10-17, 1969.

Lowman, F. G. "Radionuclides of interest in the specific activity approach," *Bioscience* 19: 993-99, 1969.

Lowry, W. P. "The climate of cities," *Scientific American* 217(2): 15-23, 1967.

McCaull, J. "The black tide," *Environment* 11(9): 2-16, 1969.

——. "Mix with care," *Environment* 13(1): 39-42, 1971.

McCuna, D. C., and Daines, R. H. "Fluoride criteria for vegetation reflect the diversity of plant kingdom," *Environ. Sci. Technol.* 3:720-32, 1969.

Machta, L., and Hughes, E. "Atmospheric oxygen in 1967 to 1970," *Science* 168: 1582-84, 1970.

Marwick, C. "Death in Skull Valley," *New Scientist* 38: 166-67, 1969.

Marx, Wesley. "How not to kill the ocean," *Audubon* 71: 27-35, 1969.

Meeks, R. L. "The accumulation of C1-36 ring-labelled DDT in a freshwater marsh," *J. Wildlife Management* 32: 376-98, 1968.

Menzel, D. W., Anderson, J., and Randtke, A. "Marine phytoplankton vary in their response to chlorinated hydrocarbons," *Science* 167: 1724-26, 1970.

Messenger, P. S. "Utilization of native natural enemies in integrated control," *Ann. Appl. Biol.* 65: 328-30, 1965.

Mihursky, J. A. "On possible constructive uses of thermal additions to estuaries," *Bioscience* 17: 698-702, 1967.

Miller, M. E., and Holzworth, G. C. "An atmospheric diffusion model for metropolitan areas," *J. Air Pollut. Control. Ass'n. Amer.* 17: 46-50, 1967.

Moore, N. W. "A synopsis of the pesticide problem," *Advan. Ecol. Res.* 4: 75-129, 1967.

Morgan, K. Z. "Never do harm," *Environment* 13(1): 28-38, 1971.

Motto, H. L., et al. "Lead in soils and plants: Its relationship to traffic volume and proximity to highways," *Environ. Sci. Technol.* 4(3): 231-37, 1970.

Mrak, G. M., ed. "Report of the secretary's commission on pesticides and their relationship to environment and health," Washington, D.C.: USDHEW, APO, 1969.

Nace, R. L. "Arrogance toward the landscape: A problem in water planning," *Bull. Atomic Scientists* 25(10): 11-14, 1969.

Nash, R. G., and Beal, M. L. "Chlorinated hydrocarbon insecticides: Root uptake versus vapor contamination of soybean foliage," *Science* 168: 1109-1111, 1970.

Nash, R. G., and Woolson, E. A. "Persistence of chlorinated hydrocarbon insecticides in soils," *Science* 157: 924-27, 1967.

Navonne, R., Harmon, J. A., and Voyles, C. F. "Nitrogen content of groundwater in Southern California," *J. Amer. Water Works Ass'n.* 55: 615-18, 1963.

Nelson, N., et al. "Hazards of mercury," *Environmental Research*, 4: 3-69, 1971.

Newell, R. E. "Stratospheric temperature change from the Mount Agung volcanic eruption of 1963," *J. Atmospheric Sci.*

——. "Modification of stratospheric properties by trace constituent changes," *Nature* 227: 697-699, 1970.

Newman, W. A. "Acanthaster: A disaster?" *Science* 167: 1274-75, 1970.

Nielson, E. S., and Wium-Andersen, S. "Copper ions as poison in the sea and in fresh water," *Marine Biol.* 6: 93-97, 1970.

Nisbet, I. C. T., and Miner D. "DDT substitute," *Environment* 13: 10-17, 1971.

North, W. J., and Pearse, J. S. "Sea urchin population explosion in Southern California Coastal waters," *Science*, 167: 209, 1970.

Novick, S. "A new pollution problem," *Environment* 11(4): 2-9, 1969.

Nuessler, V. D., and Holcomb, R. W. "Will the SST pollute the stratosphere?" *Science* 168: 1562, 1970.

Oberle, M. W. "Lead poisoning: A preventable childhood disease of the slums," *Science* 165: 991-92, 1969.

Odum, W. E. "Insidious alteration of the estuarine environment," *Amer. Fish Soc. Trans.* 99: 836-47, 1970.

Orians, G. H., and Pfeiffer, E. W. "Ecological effects of the war in Vietnam," *Science* 168: 544-54, 1970.

Panofsky, H. A. "Air pollution meteorology," *Amer. Scientist* 57(2): 269-85, 1969.

Parker, F. L. "Disposal of low-level radiactive wastes into the ocean," *Nucl. Safety* 8(4): 376-82, 1967.

Patterson, C. C., and Salvia, J. D. "Lead in natural environment: How much is natural?" *Environment* 10: 66-79, 1968.

Peakall, D. B. "Pesticides and the reproduction of birds," *Scientific American* 222(4): 73-78, 1970.

——, and Lincer, J. L. "Polychlorinated biphenyls," *Bioscience* 20: 958-64, 1970.

——, and Lovett, R. J. "Mercury: Its occurrence and effects in the ecosystem," *Bioscience* 22: 20-25, 1972.

Peterle, T. J. "Pyramiding damage," *Environment* 11(6): 34-40, 1969.

Peterson, J. T. *The climate of cities, A survey of recent literature,* Nat. Air. Pollut. Control Admin. Publ. No, AP-59, 1969.

Pilat, M. J. "Application of gas-aerosol absorption data to the selection of air quality standards," *J. Air Pollut. Control Ass'n. Amer.* 18: 751-53, 1968.

Porter, R. D., and Weimeyer, S. N. "Dieldrin and DDT: Effects on sparrow hawk egg-shells, and reproduction," *Science* 165: 199-200, 1969.

Pramer, D. "The soil transforms," *Environment* 13(4): 42-46, 1971.

Presst, I., Jefferies, D. I., and Moore, N. W. "Polychlorinated biphenyls in wild birds of Britain and their avian toxicity," *Environ. Pollut.* 1:3-26, 1970.

Purves, D., and MacKenzie, E. J. "Trace element contamination of parklands in urban areas," *J. Soil Sci.* 20(2): 288-90, 1969.

Radford, E. P., et al. "Statement of concern," *Environment* 11(7): 18-27, 1969.

Rantz, S. E. "Urban sprawl and flooding in Southern California," *U.S. Geol. Survey Circ.* 601-B, 1970.

Rehoe, R. A. "Lead intake from food and water," *Science* 159: 1000, 1968.

Risebrough, R. W., Rieche, P., Peakall, D. B. Herman, S. G., and Kirven, M. N. "Polychlorinated biphenyls in the global ecosystem," *Nature* 220: 1098-1102, 1968.

Rivera-Cordova, A. "The nuclear industry and air pollution," *Environ. Sci. Technol.* 4: 302-397, 1970.

Rohrman, F. A., Steigerwald, B. J., and Ludwig, J. J. "Industrial emissions of carbon dioxide in the United States: A protection," *Science* 156: 931-32, 1967.

Rubinoff, L. "Central American sea-level canal: Possible biological effects," *Science* 161: 857-61, 1968.

Rühling, A., and Tyler, G. "Ecology of heavy metals—a regional and historical study," *Botan. Notiser* 122: 248-59, 1969.

Rutzler, K., and Sterrer, W. "Oil pollution," *Bioscience* 20: 222-24, 226, 1970.

Ryther, J. H. "Is the world's oxygen supply threatened?" *Nature* 227, 374-75, 1970.

——, and Dunstan, W. M. "Nitrogen, phosphorus and eutrophication in the coastal marine environment," *Science* 171: 1008-13, 1971.

——, Dunstan, W. M., Tenore, K. R., and Huguenin, J. E. "Controlled eutrophication—increasing food production from the sea by recycling human wastes," *Bioscience* 22: 144-52, 1972.

Sanders, J. H. "Chemical mutagens. (I) The road to genetic disaster. (II) An expanding roster of suspects," *Chem. Eng. News* 47(21): 53-71; 47(23): 54-68, 1969.

Sax, K., and Sax, H. J. "Possible mutagenic hazards of some food additives, beverages, and insecticides," *Japan J. Genetics* 43(2): 89-94, 1968.

Schaefer, V. J. "Some effects of air pollution on our environment," *Bioscience* 19: 896-97, 1969.

Selikoff, I. J. "Asbestos," *Environment* 11(2): 2-7, 1969.

Skye, E. "Lichens and air pollution," *Acta Phytogeographica Suecica*, 52: 123, 1968.

Slade, D. "Modelling air pollution in the Washington D.C. to Boston megalopolis," *Science* 157: 1304-07, 1967.

Stern, A. C. "The changing pattern of air pollution in the United States," *Amer. Indust. Hyg. Ass'n. J.* 28: 161-65, 1967.

Sternglass, E. J. "Infant mortality," *Environment* 11(10): 9-13, 1969.

Stewart, B. A., Viets, F. G., and Hutchinson, G. L. "Agriculture's effect on nitrate pollution of groundwater," *J. Soil and Water Conservation* 23(1): 13-15, 1968.

Storch, W. V., and Taylor, R. L. "Some environmental effects of drainage in Florida," *Amer. Soc. Civil Eng. Proc.* 95: 43-59, 1969.

Tarrant, K. B., and Tatton, J. O'G. "Organo-pesticides in rainwater in the British Isles," *Nature* 219: 725-727, 1968.

Task Group Report 261 OP. "Sources of nitrogen and phosphorus in water supplies," *J. Amer. Water Works Ass'n.* 59: 344-66, 1967.

Thomas, H. E., and Schneider, W. J. "Water as an urban resource and nuisance," *U.S. Geol. Survey Circ. 601-D*, 1970.

Thomas, M. D. "Reactivities of smog components are central issue in setting control standards," *Environ. Sci. Technol.* 3: 629-33, 1969.

Topp, R. W. "Interoceanic sea-level canal: Effects on the fish faunas," *Science* 165: 1324-27, 1969.

Van Valen, L. "The history and stability of atmospheric oxygen," *Science* 171: 439-43, 1971.

Westberg, K., Cohen, N., and Wilson, K. W. "Carbon monoxide: Its role in photochemical smog formation," *Science* 171: 1013-15, 1971.

Wheeler, A. "Fish return to the Thames," *Science J.*, 28-32, Nov. 1970.

Wilson, B. R., ed., *Environmental Problems—Pesticides, Thermal Pollution, and Environmental Synergisms,* Philadelphia: Lippincott, 1968.

Wolfe, M. "Using systemic fungicides," *New Scientist* 44: 551-53, 1969.

Wolman, A. "Air pollution: Time for appraisal," *Science* 159: 1437-40, 1968.

Woodlief, C. B. "Effect of random noise on plant growth," *Accoust. Soc. Amer. J.* 46: 481-82, 1969.

Woodwell, G. M. "Radioactivity and fallout: The model pollution," *Bioscience* 19: 884-87, 1969.

——. "Effects of pollution on the structure and physiology of ecosystems," *Science* 168: 429-33, 1970.

——, Craig, P. P., and Johnson, H. A. "DDT in the biosphere: Where does it go?" *Science* 174: 1101-07, 1971.

World Meteorological Organization. "Urban climates," *Tech. Note No. 108*, 1970.

Wurster, C. F. "Chlorinated hydrocarbon insecticides and the world ecosystem," *Biological Conservation* 1(2): 123-29, 1969.

Yarwood, C. E. "Man-made plant diseases," *Science* 168: 218-20, 1970.

Young, H. A. "Legal aspects of noise pollution," *Plant Eng.* 23: 66-67, 1969.

36

AIR CONSERVATION

A. J. Haagen-Smit

Today the majority of people in all parts of the world are breathing polluted air. Incomplete combustion of fuels, industrial activities and miscellaneous operations such as burning of wastes spreads yearly hundreds of millions of tons of pollutants into the air (1). Irritation of throat and eyes and offensive odors have become a frequent if not continuous aspect of city living. Some of the pollutants pass deep into our respiratory system, affecting the delicate mechanism which supplies us with oxygen and carries away carbon monoxide. Progressive destruction of this system leading to emphysema and chronic bronchitis is caused by air pollution, smoking included. Today emphysema is the fastest growing cause of death in this country. In the ten year period between 1950 and 1959 deaths among males from emphysema rose from 1.5 per hundred thousand to 8 per hundred thousand. Bronchial asthma is a condition often aggravated by air pollution. A special form of asthma appeared in 1946 among American troops and their dependents living in Yokohama and Tokyo in Japan. This asthma is correlated with the intense pollution in the heavily industrialized area in the Kanto plain adjacent to these cities. In New Orleans epidemic outbreaks of asthma attacks have been associated with city dumps burning underground as well as with other air pollution-causing activities. Epidemiological studies have shown that air pollution correlates with increased frequency of acute infections of the upper respiratory tract leading to common colds.

Dramatic evidence of the effects of air pollution is recorded in fatal incidents in the Meuse Valley in Belgium and the London black fogs of 1952 and 1962 when thousands of excess deaths were reported. In this country air pollution took its toll in the 1948 disaster in Donora, Pennsylvania, and New York in 1952 and 1962 as hospital and death records witness.

Air pollution interferes in many other ways with life on earth. Fluorides are still seriously affecting cattle and cause extensive damage to crops. Smelters in British Columbia emitted at one time an average of 600 tons of sulfur per day resulting in a nearly complete eradication of fir and pine trees for dozens of miles. From Florida we hear about damage to orange trees; in southern California growing of spinach has been drastically curtailed. In metropolitan areas exhaust from automobiles has made it impossible to raise orchids commercially and growers have been driven to remote rural areas. In Maryland damage to the tobacco leaves caused by automobile pollution originating in Washington, D.C., caused heavy financial loss to the farmers. The damage to vegetation has become so widespread that the visible markings of pollution are often used as an indicator of pollution and experts can tell with a great degree of certainty what type of agent must have caused the damage.

Agricultural losses in the U.S.A. alone are estimated to be around 500 million dollars per year. This is only a few percent of the total cost of air pollution. We have to add the deterioration of materials which increase maintenance and replacement costs. Metals, fabric, paper, rubber, plastics, and building materials suffer directly, but in addition their life is shortened in costly cleaning processes. The complex and expensive control systems in factories, in business offices, in various electronic systems, can be ruined and malfunction through corrosive and soiling action of various pollutants. Wherever cleanliness is desired in the manufacture of electronic equipment, foods, beverages, in research laboratories, incoming air has to be thoroughly cleaned at considerable expense.

Pollution from the oxides of sulfur causes destruction of paint pigments and at slightly higher levels it may attack fresh paint films delaying drying and producing sensitivity to water.

Erosion of building stone statuary is common all over the world and in many cities

Reprinted from *Scientia* 163: 359-67, 1969, with the permission of the publishers.

conservationists are moving works of art indoors to protect them from the action of acidic pollutants. It is reported that Cleopatra's needle has deteriorated more since its arrival in New York in 1881 than it did during the more than three thousand years spent in Egypt. Particulate matter leaves a grimy deposit on and in the houses, soils curtains and clothes and raises our cleaning and painting bills.

An interesting survey was made by the U.S. Public Health Service on the cost of cleaning in two towns of similar economic and social status but which differed in one being highly industrial, the other predominantly residential. The results in Table 1 clearly show that dirty air is costly; it means more frequent painting of inside and outside of the house, higher laundry bills and cost of personal care.

Table 1. Survey on cleaning in a residential and in an industrial town. Difference per year per person.

Outside maintenance of house	$17.00
Inside maintenance of house	32.00
Laundry	25.00
Hair, facial care, etc.	10.00
	$84.00

Exact data are not available on the total cost of air pollution to the community, but estimates for the U.S.A. have placed this figure at about 12 billion dollars (12×10^9). This figure does not include any estimate on the values to be placed on the health and the enjoyment of life of the community.

Government and industry has, up to date, spent only a fraction of this yearly recurring cost on attempts to control objectionable emissions and a far greater effort seems like a fair price to pay for all the benefits we derive from breathing clean air. A greatly accelerated and intensified program is needed to reduce materially the huge quantities of air contaminants released from industrial operations, house heating, driving cars, and numerous other miscellaneous activities of people.

An estimate of the magnitude of the foreign materials added to the air is shown in Table 2. For comparison the estimated contribution from natural sources, fog, pollen and dust, is listed (2).

Table 2. Major air contaminants over U.S.A. in millions of tons per year.

Natural fog (25 feet high)	15
Pollen	1
Natural dust	30
Smoke (carbon)	5
Industrial dust and ash	10
Sulfur oxides	20
Nitrogen oxides	5
Miscellaneous vapors (mostly organics)	40
Carbon monoxide	50
Carbon dioxide	10,000

The magnitude of these emissions is more readily understood when one considers that a million twenty-ton tank trucks would be necessary to transport all the sulfur dioxide released next year by smelters, refineries and fuel burners. Such a procession would reach around the earth.

The carbon dioxide released by burning our fossil fuels raises the carbon dioxide content of the air by 0.23% per year. This by-product of our industrial era may eventually have some disturbing consequences. Geochemists have predicted that a general warming of our atmosphere, melting of polar caps, and rise of the levels of the oceans may be the result (3, 4).

To answer the question as to why we pollute the air in this irresponsible manner, we can go back to an English scientist of a few centuries ago, Robert Boyle, well known for his formulation of the gas laws, who said: "The generality of men are so accustomed to judge of things by their senses that because the air is invisible they ascribe but little to it and think it but one removed from nothing."

To most people air and space are about synonymous; both seem to be available in unlimited amounts to please mankind. Our generation has discovered that unfortunately nothing on earth is unlimited, and we have begun to worry about the limitation of our soil, water, and, lately, of our air. It is clear to many that our generation has a responsibility to future ones in using these resources wisely. We cannot any longer use the air indiscriminately as a dumping ground of all our by-products, especially not when the natural ventilation is inadequate.

The total amount of air available to a world population of nearly four billion people is 4 x 10^{18} cubic meters. Each person can therefore claim about a billion cubic meters of air. This is quite a large quantity, but such a figure acquires meaning only when we determine how much air a person uses for his daily existence. In the first place he needs air to breathe; this amounts to 12 m^3 per day. In addition he uses air in various operations such as fuel burning for house heating, automobile driving, power production. And finally in the manufacture of goods considerable quantities of air have been consumed. The total varies greatly with the standard of living however; for most industrial countries one calculates that about 150 m^3 of air per day is made unfit to breathe.

This calculation shows that our world citizen does not have to worry much. Even if we apply a factor of a thousand for dilution of the used air, as air conditioning engineers recommend, he would have enough air to last him for many thousands of years. There is, however, the assumption that everyone has free access to the world air supply and here is where the difficulty begins.

When the natural ventilation is inadequate, when mountain ranges prevent unobstructed flow of the air, and when temperature inversion conditions limit the vertical movement, the available air is greatly restricted. Temperature conditions are quite frequent along the Pacific coast where a cold layer of air at ground level effectively prevents the free exchange of air with higher ones. These temperature inversions occur in many parts of the world and occur far more often than is generally thought. They extend to greatly varying height, from only a few feet from the ground to several thousand feet.

The lack of ventilation through both geographic and meteorological conditions is a prime factor in the formation of the Los Angeles smog. It is of interest to see how the air supply of the inhabitant of such a valley compares with that of the world citizen. During heavy smog the cold layer may extend to about 300 m height over an area of 2000 square kilometers. The air in this flat box is shared by 7½ million people, which means that during adverse meteorological conditions only 80,000 cubic meters per person are available. This is about two times less than sound air conditioning prescribes and it is not surprising that Los Angeles has become famous in air pollution circles.

The 10,000 tons of carbon monoxide coming from the exhaust of 3½ million cars establishes, readily, concentrations of 15 and more parts per million and surpasses frequently the adverse standards for community health adopted by California's health authorities. In heavily travelled streets with little ventilation concentrations of a hundred parts per million have been registered. Figure 36-1 illustrates graphically the exposure to high concentrations of carbon monoxide from automobile exhaust during city driving (5). The driver going toward Los Angeles at the evening hour does not meet with much traffic; however, coming back the daily recurring traffic jam is indicated by the high levels of carbon monoxide and a longer duration of the trip.

Fig. 36-1. Carbon monoxide concentration in city and freeway driving routes.

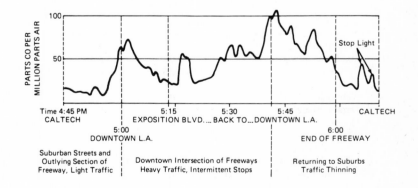

Air Pollution Control

One of the most common forms of air pollution is that caused by smoke. A cross-country trip by airplane should convince anyone that smoke is a problem in every great city in the U.S.A. as well as in the rest of the world. Large streamers, extending for scores of miles, have their origin in open burning dumps, lumber yards, steel mills, foundries, and power plants, to name only a few of the multitude of sources. This is an old problem; some 200 years ago laws were passed in England to regulate the burning of certain types of coal. Even today combustion is still a major source of air pollution.

At first sight controlling the emission of smoke appears quite simple—just wash it out! But we have only to think how tobacco smoke from a Turkish pipe bubbles, seemingly undisturbed, through water to realize that perhaps this problem is not so easily solved after all.

There is a large variety of particles, very large ones, in fly ash and coal dust; and on the other side of the spectrum there are particles close to the size of large molecules. Large particles of soot and dust can readily be removed in settling chambers or in cyclones, where gravitational or centrifugal forces are used to separate the particles by weight. Other methods consist in filtering out the dust through cloth made of cotton, woven plastics, or glass fibers. For very fine dust of the order from 0.5 to 1.0 micron we have to apply processes whereby the electrically charged particle is removed by electrodes kept at a potential difference of 15,000 to 40,000 volts (6, 7). By catching the particles of a size close to the wavelength of light an important fraction of the dust responsible for the scattering of light is removed and therefore the probability of visible plume formation is substantially decreased. Each one of these dust-collection processes has found wide application in industry, but even today systematic studies to increase their efficiency would be most welcome (8).

The dust present in fuel is not the only agent responsible for objectionable emissions from smokestacks. Virtually all other constituents of flue gas—water, carbon monoxide, and oxides of sulfur and nitrogen—play some role.

A great deal of attention has been given to the fate of the oxides of sulfur after they have left the stack. The small amount of sulfuric acid combines with water and some of the ash constituents to form the visible, bluish plumes often seen coming from industrial smokestacks. The sulfur dioxide reacts slowly with oxygen to form sulfuric acid and the corresponding sulfates and contributes in this way to the haziness often noticeable at considerable distance from industrial establishments.

Evidence that such oxidations do take place when the gases have left the stack is found in an interesting pollution balance prepared for the Los Angeles Basin and shown in Table 3. The amount of emission of sulfur dioxide from all sources—refinery operations, oil burning and

Table 3. Comparisons of measured and calculated concentrations of pollutants in downtown Los Angeles.

Pollutant	Clear day[1] (parts per million by vol.)		Day of intense smog[2] (parts per million by vol.)	
	Measured	Calculated	Measured	Calculated
Carbon monoxide	3.5	3.5[3]	23.0	23.0[3]
Oxides of nitrogen	0.08	0.10	0.4	0.6
Sulfur dioxide	0.05	0.08	0.3	0.5
Total hydrocarbons	0.2	0.40	1.1	2.6
Aldehydes	0.07	0.02	0.4	0.2
Organic acids	0.07	0.03	0.4	0.2
Ozone	0.02	0.02	0.50	0.02

[1] Visibility 7 miles.
[2] Visibility less than 1 mile.
[3] The method defines the calculated value as the same as the measured value for CO.

gasoline consumption—is well known. We also know the area in which this emission is dispersed, as well as the height of the inversion layer which limits its upward movement. From these data we are able to calculate the expected sulfur dioxide concentration. We find, in making up this balance, that about one-third of the sulfur dioxide is lacking. This missing sulfur dioxide is found mostly as calcium and ammonium sulfates in dust settling over the country. Free sulfuric acid, except in close proximity to the stack, is mostly absent.

The table shows some other interesting discrepancies in the values of oxides of nitrogen and hydrocarbons. Their concentration in the air is considerably less than one would expect from the known emissions established with great accuracy in source testing. On the other hand, we notice that concentration of organic acids, aldehydes, and ozone are much higher than we would expect. Apparently, as in the case of the sulfur oxides, an oxidation has taken place whereby the hydrocarbons, mostly gasoline, have been converted to oxygen derivatives. Especially intriguing is the appearance of ozone in a polluted atmosphere, which, from past experience in other areas, is usually absent in cities.

The Los Angeles air is different in some other respects. There is no resemblance at all to the problems of cities in the eastern part of the United States where coal is the major source of energy and where, consequently, soot blackens all buildings and the oxides of sulfur corrode materials. Los Angeles is a very clean city in this respect, with a dust fall of only 20 to 30 tons per month per square mile, as compared with several times this quantity in other industrial cities. The eye-irritating clouds in Los Angeles are accompanied by complaints from farmers about crop damage and, strangely enough, from rubber manufacturers, who observed that their products cracked more heavily in this area than in other sections of the country. Control of dusts and sulfur dioxide did not help, for the phenomena are due to an effect quite different from the more old-fashioned, reducing type of air pollution. Los Angeles smog, contrary to this type of pollution, is typified by its strong oxidizing action (9).

For practical measurement of the typical oxidizing effect of Los Angeles smog, liberation of iodine from potassium iodide is used. Because the concentration of sulfur dioxide, a reducing substance, is low in Los Angeles smog, interference in the oxidant measurements is usually negligible. This is not true for other areas where the presence of the oxidizing pollutants has often escaped attention because of the masking effect of reducing substances. It is now well recognized that similar oxidizing smog producing pollution is present in most of our metropolitan areas and the only difference is in the frequency and severity of the pollution.

The concentration of the oxidant varies during the day, increasing toward noon and decreasing to virtual absence during the evening and night hours. The time of increased concentration of the oxidant is invariably correlated with eye irritation and haze. The type of damage to plants from oxidizing pollutants is readily distinguishable from damage from other types of pollutants, such as sulfur dioxide or fluoride. Sensitive plants—spinach, sugar beet, alfalfa, endive, oats, and pinto beans—are used extensively to gauge the spread of the pollution (10). A major part of the oxidant consists of ozone, which is directly responsible for the excessive rubber cracking observed in the Los Angeles area. Spectrographic, as well as chemical, methods have definitely established the presence of ozone concentrations 20 to 30 times higher than those found in unpolluted air where the normal concentration amounts to 1 to 3 parts per hundred million.

A simple and inexpensive method of measuring ozone involves the use of bent pieces of antioxidant-free rubber as indicators. The time necessary for the appearance of the cracks is directly related to the ozone content of the air. At night, and on smog-free days, it may take as long as an hour for the first cracks to appear; on a smoggy day cracks are often evident in a few minutes (11). In the atmosphere over a city it is to be expected that the reactive ozone will enter into reactions with a number of other pollutants. Among the most prevalent of these groups are olefins, present in gasoline; fumigation experiments with gasoline fractions and also

*Fig. 36-2. Schematic
summary of the main
mechanism leading to
photochemical smog
symptoms.*

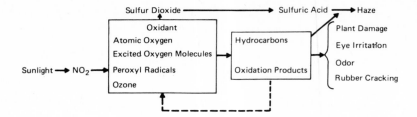

with pure olefins which have been allowed to
react with ozone led to a reproduction of the
typical plant-damage symptoms and to eye
irritation, haze formation, and typical smog
odor, as well. These experiments strongly indicate that the irritating materials were intermediate oxidation products of hydrocarbon
oxidation and are of peroxidic nature since the
usual end products—aldehydes, ketones, and
organic acids—are inactive in the concentration
range used.

Most organic compounds are relatively stable
against oxidation when completely pure, but
the presence of peroxides speeds the auto-oxi-
dation considerably through a chain reaction
initiated by hydrogen removal from the carbon
chain. This effect can be accomplished also
through the action of light either on the
hydrocarbon or on the oxygen molecule. In the
latter case the excited oxygen may remove
hydrogen. Most hydrocarbons do not have
absorption bands in the wavelength region of
sunlight for a direct photochemical reaction,
but similar reactions take place in a roundabout
way by having a substance present which
accepts the light energy and subsequently transfers it to the compound to be oxidized. In
nature we find such substances in chlorophyll
and other photochemically active pigments. In
polluted atmospheres nitrogen dioxide functions as an oxidation catalyst. Strong absorption
of light by nitrogen dioxide occurs from the
near ultraviolet through the blue part of the
spectrum, and, upon irradiation, nitrogen dioxide splits into atomic oxygen and nitric
oxide. Fumigation experiments in sunlight with
gasoline or olefin in the presence of oxides of
nitrogen resulted in eye irritation and the same
type of plant damage that was previously
obtained with ozone acting on the olefins
directly. Sulfur dioxide is oxidized by the same

photochemical system and contributes to the
visibility reduction.

Figure 36-2 gives a schematic view of the
main mechanism leading to the smog symptoms.

Theoretical Investigations

When all the typical symptoms of smog had
been reproduced, the problem remained of
accounting for the relatively high ozone content in the polluted atmosphere. It is now well
established that the generation of ozone is
intimately connected with the same photochemical reaction of organic material in the
presence of oxides of nitrogen which causes eye
irritation and plant damage. The formation of
ozone is apparently a general phenomenon and
is observed with many types of organic compounds. The production of ozone has been
attributed to the intermediate formation of
peroxide radicals as shown in equations a to f.

(a) $NO_2 + Light \rightarrow NO + O$ photo dissociation of nitrogen dioxide

(b) $O + RH \rightarrow HO. + R.$ alkyl radical formation

(c) $R. + O_2 \rightarrow ROO.$ peroxyl radical formation

(d) $ROO. + O_2 \rightarrow RO. + O_3$ ozone formation

(e) $ROO. + NO_2 \rightarrow ROONO_2$ peracyl nitrate formation

(f) $O + O_2 \rightarrow O_3$ ozone formation

We may visualize, first, a light-activated
dissociation of nitrogen dioxide to nitric oxide
and atomic oxygen (eq. a) followed by the
formation of free radicals through the action of
the atomic oxygen on organic compounds (eq.
b). Subsequent formation of peroxyl radicals

leads to eye irritating and plant damaging peracyl nitrates and to ozone (eq. d, e, and f).

A systematic study of the concentrations of hydrocarbons and oxides of nitrogen where ozone formation takes place showed that the reaction is limited to quite low concentrations of the reactants. Experiments of this type have focused attention on the circumstances peculiar to the problem of air pollution—that is, the extreme dilution. A chemist referring loosely to slow and fast reactions has in mind laboratory conditions where concentrations in the order of 10 percent are most commonly used. In atmospheric reactions the concentrations are in the order of 0.00001 percent—about one millionth as much. As a result, reactions which under the usual laboratory conditions are considered fast become very slow. For example, when a bimolecular reaction with participants in the concentration range of 10 percent (100,000 parts per million) requires 0.0036 second to go halfway to completion, it takes 10^6 times as long, or a whole hour, to reach the same point with a concentration of 0.1 part per million. Under the latter circumstances not only can ozone exist in the presence of reducing agents but even free radicals have a far better chance of survival. It took many years to unravel relatively simple reactions such as the photodecomposition of acetone, diacetyl, and other compounds. In the air these reactions are complicated by the presence of oxygen, water, carbon dioxide, and an almost infinite variety of organic compounds from the evaporation and combustion of gasoline and from the burning of trash in its many forms.

The field of atmospheric reactions is now being actively studied by a number of physical chemists and provides an interesting example of the way in which a practical problem has stimulated a number of theoretical investigations. Such study has familiarized a large group of physical chemists with the exciting field of extreme dilution in which research should prove to be far less disturbed and complicated than research at higher concentrations where molecules collide all too frequently. In addition, the practical aspects of air-pollution photochemistry have made available the instrumentation necessary to study these phenomena

from a theoretical point of view. The purely theoretical physicist and chemist would have difficulty in obtaining the millions of dollars which have gone into the development of these instruments. It is gratifying to find that as a by-product of the study of an unpleasant problem such as air pollution a significant contribution to fundamental problems in chemistry could be made (12, 13).

Automobile Exhaust Fumes

These remarkable reactions confirmed in several laboratories provide a firm basis for control measures. To prevent the occurrence of the unpleasant symptoms we must control the emissions of the primary pollutants, hydrocarbons and oxides of nitrogen. The loss of hydrocarbons at refineries has long been corrected in Los Angeles and presently the major remaining source of hydrocarbons is the exhaust of automobiles. These emissions are due to incomplete fuel combustion and escape of the unburned gasoline through the exhaust. The crankcase, carburetor, and tank contribute to the emission of hydrocarbon through evaporation of the fuel. The relative importance of these emissions is shown in Table 4.

Table 4. Emission of pollutants from the average automobile in grams per liter of gasoline used.

	Hydro-carbons	Carbon mon-oxide	Oxides of nitrogen
Exhaust	50 gr.	330 gr.	18 gr.
Crankcase vent	17 gr.	0.8 gr.	—
Evaporation (carburetor + tank)	12 gr.	—	

The total loss of fuel for the average driver using 8 liters of gasoline per day is 0.6 liter or about 8%. The actual loss in *fuel value* is even greater and amounts to 15% when the large emission of carbon monoxide is included. The tremendous waste of fuel by the 90 million automobiles in the United States alone because of inefficiency of combustion is 100 million liters per day.

Devices have been developed which burn the hydrocarbons in specially constructed exhaust mufflers. While these were successful, their relatively high cost and maintenance remained an objection (14). Since 1966 General Motors and Ford cars have been equipped with an air injection system which allows the burning of the excess fuel to take place in the exhaust manifold. Chrysler has adopted a system which gives a more complete combustion in the engine itself by using a leaner fuel-air mixture coupled with carburetor adjustments and retarding of the spark timing. The emission from the crankcase is now recirculated through the air filter and burned together with the normal flow of gasoline.

Control of Oxides of Nitrogen

The oxides of nitrogen are formed in high temperature combustions from nitrogen and oxygen of the atmosphere. Power plants and automobiles in Los Angeles produce, respectively, 300 and 600 tons of oxides of nitrogen per day while burning 100,000 barrels of fuel oil. Several engineering laboratories are now searching for ways to reduce the nitrogen dioxide content of exhaust gases from gas, oil, and gasoline combustion through studies of the variable combustion conditions which can be obtained by boiler modifications or changes in engine design. In power plants a 50% reduction in oxides of nitrogen has been accomplished by the introduction of secondary combustion. The main body of the fuel is burned with a deficiency in oxygen; additional air is subsequently introduced completing the combustion of the fuel.

In automobile engines a promising method returns a fraction of the exhaust air back to the air intake. In this way the flame temperature is lowered and fewer oxides of nitrogen are formed. The reduction is as high as 80% without noticeably affecting drivability (15, 16).

Often the question has come up, "Can't we do one or the other—hydrocarbon control or nitrogen dioxide control?" The answer, I believe, is "No." Most of the smog reactions are directly dependent on the product of the concentration of both hydrocarbons and oxides of nitrogen.

The private automobile is a major offender in both respects, and there is no reasonable basis for hope that control devices in the hands of the average car owner will give anywhere near the performance they give in an automobile testing laboratory. Also, changes in gasoline composition could not be expected to have a drastic effect on smog-producing hydrocarbons in the exhaust. The steady increase in population tends to neutralize any control effort, and it is therefore evident that emissions must be controlled wherever possible. Besides being an objectionable factor in the photochemical reactions, the nitrogen oxides are objectionable in their own right and are quite toxic even in low concentrations. Fortunately we have not yet reached anywhere near the adverse health level of 3.0 parts per million, but the concentration of this pollutant is steadily increasing; and since it appears in all combustions, the increase is practically proportional to the increase in population. Especially in areas of heavy traffic the concentration might at times surpass the safe limits, or, rather, what we now believe are safe limits. Oxides of nitrogen are yellow and at low concentration would color the sky. On this basis California's State Health Department has set community health standards which require a 75% reduction of the oxides of nitrogen in automobile exhaust as soon as a practical device becomes available.

Engine Modification

Because of the difficulties inherent in accomplishing a complete combustion in conventional engines, considerable effort is being put into the development of electric cars. Some of these operate on light weight batteries such as zinc-sulfur, sodium-sulfur, or lithium-sulfur combinations. Others use a fuel cell with hydrogen and oxygen as fuel. A third type and perhaps the most promising is a hybrid gasoline electric car. Because its gasoline engine runs at a fixed speed to keep the batteries charged, it can be set at a minimum emission. The future of any one of these cars, which are still in the early stages of development, is uncertain. Some predict that in 15-20 years most cars in urban areas will be powered by electricity. A more sober and more likely forecast is that the internal combustion, piston engined automobile will continue to dominate our roads for the next 30 years at least.

Community Health Standards

Air pollution control administrations have a difficult task in surviving the years of waiting for engineering to catch up with the demands of the community. Programs for meeting emergency conditions have somewhat contributed to better feelings on the part of the public. It is understandable that most people not accustomed to smelling or inhaling a concoction of ozone, oxides of nitrogen, ozonides, and substances x, y, and z begin to be a little worried. In recent years the medical profession in Los Angeles has set certain levels below which a catastrophe would be unlikely to occur. This is admittedly a very difficult decision to make and it has pointed to a serious deficiency in our knowledge of environmental hygiene.

In studies of the health effects of air contaminants it becomes evident that there is a great difference between the industrial and general population levels. The industrial group are healthy individuals from whom the extra sensitive have been removed because the working conditions did not agree with them. For the whole population such a selection does not take place to any large degree, and we are dealing with the oversensitives—the sick, the young, and the very old. Public health officers have a most difficult task in establishing pollution levels for such a heterogeneous group, and it is a foregone conclusion that when levels are finally adopted there will be those who will maintain that they are too high, while others will charge persecution of industry because the levels are set too low. Animal experiments, and even experiments with human beings, while indicating some level of toxicity or annoyance, cannot give the answer for a general population. In

urban areas we are dealing with several million people, and many would call the death of one or two persons per million, or some 20 for a town the size of Los Angeles, a disaster. The impossibility of approaching this accuracy of prediction in an experimental human, or even animal, colony is evident, for we would have to experiment with a few million individuals to get a statistically valid answer.

We therefore come to the conclusion that the only person able to give answers with any certainty about the result of some large-scale fumigation is the epidemiologist gathering data on death rates and general health status. It is, of course, unfortunate that this kind of study comes too late to prevent the disaster; on the other hand, these studies furnish extremely valuable data on ways to prevent recurrence of the same series of events. The study of pretoxic effects consisting in physiological responses warning of the danger ahead is one of the most promising approaches to the study of pollution levels. One of the physiological changes intensively studied is greater flow resistance in the respiratory system (1). The effects found at lower concentration do not necessarily represent toxic symptoms but may be regarded in the same class as sneezing, coughing, or blinking of the eye—therefore as warning signs and pretoxic symptoms. Such experiments will eventually form the basis for community health standards.

Preventive Control

Air pollution disasters can be prevented and nuisance effects can be minimized by planning at the right time. Such planning requires some basic information about the progress of a package of air loaded with pollutants over the area. Also needed are data on changes taking place in the pollution cloud when, as in Los Angeles, relatively harmless gases react to form irritants.

When all these facts, plus the size and nature of the emission, are known, we can begin to think of plotting the trajectories and the isopollution lines for different substances. This kind of calculation has been made by Frenkiel (17) for a hypothetical case in the Los Angeles area but is generally applicable to other areas. Its use will become more widely accepted when population density rises. In acute air pollution incidents, explosions, or release of toxic chemicals which require an immediate assessment of the area to be evacuated, modern computing facilities could give the answer in seconds.

The environmental engineer has another important function in advising about the location of industry. A mistake in judgment in this respect may result in years of costly legal procedures with no victory for either side. Numerous examples could be given of the thoughtless establishment of industries in poorly ventilated areas resulting in heavy pollution, high control expenses, and poor public relations. A detailed knowledge of meteorological and geographic characteristics of an area allows the applied mathematician to assess the impact of emissions from individual sources on other areas. Modern computing science can solve problems dealing with a diffuse source such as the automobile by calculating and integrating the individual contribution of this multiple source.

Knowing the rates of increase or control of every source, accurate predictions can be made on future pollution levels, and these predictions can guide the control officials in their task (18, 19). The mathematical treatment of the expansion and movement of pollution clouds aids in settling the question of the relative contributions of various sources on a given location. It is quite common to refer loosely to minor and major sources, completely losing sight of the fact that in certain neighborhoods a local source may have a greater nuisance effect than larger sources located far away. A great deal of friction could be avoided by recognizing this simple fact, and relative contribution charts for different locations could be of great help in objectively settling some of the hot arguments.

Manpower

Air pollution problems are as varied as the activities of people themselves. Problems met in air conservation are extremely complex and need the cooperative assistance of many scientific and technical disciplines. There is hardly any field of human endeavor that is not touched. The student of environmental hygiene has hundreds of square miles as his laboratory and about everything a population emits to the air as his chemicals—in other words, a mixture representing a sizable portion of the inorganic and organic chemicals. His accomplishments have to be attuned to a population so varied in reactions and responses that an "average" person has no meaning in his problem. Entering into and often interfering with the normal occupations of the community, he has to be endowed with diplomatic and legal talents.

The smoke inspector of the past still performs a useful function, but the control of emissions from modern industry, motor vehicles, insecticides, weed killers, and miscellaneous solvents need skills which involve the use of the whole array of modern laboratory equipment, optical instruments, spectrographs, and gas chromatography. The increased importance of the task of the environmental engineer and scientist in protecting the cleanliness of the air is felt in many quarters, and several universities and federal agencies have started courses in practical and theoretical aspects of air pollution control (ref. 3, page 33).

Future of Control

Our confidence in the abundance of the four principal elements of our forefathers has been severely shaken in recent times. We have learned that the increasing population will have less and less room in which to grow its crops and keep its cattle. Coal, oil, and gas reserves have definite time limits and the water of our rivers and lakes has become more and more polluted. Finally, our supposedly infinite supply of air has turned out to be limited too. With the advent of atomic energy, many of these problems can be solved, but the universal use of atomic energy will make the problem of keeping our air fit to breathe even more difficult. Now we are concerned with constituents present in concentrations of a few parts per million. The future, and part of the present, generation must worry about the removal of pollutants in quantities smaller by a factor of many powers of ten. In this more efficient cleaning process, the theoretical knowledge and technical skill required will be far greater than the knowledge and skill available today.

The tremendous cost to the community of air pollution justifies that we apply a major effort in controlling this problem and enlist top scientists and engineers to cope with the ever-increasing problems. We can afford to pay for clean air.

In the Los Angeles area alone it is estimated that several hundred million dollars have been spent already to curtail some emissions, and many more will have to be spent before the smog will again be unnoticeable. At the present time the air pollution control authorities, working against a 4 percent increase in population, are doing somewhat better than holding the line. Over the whole nation the expense will be staggering and will run into billions of dollars. Controlling the 90 million automobiles in the U.S.A. alone will cost in the order of 9000 million dollars. This doesn't include the cost of

renewal and maintenance which is estimated to be at least a billion dollars per year.

It is understandable that there has been a great deal of resistance to the installation of costly control equipment which often does not contribute in a direct manner to profits. Some of the objections have been removed in recent years, and it is now generally conceded that damage from air pollution is large and that recovery measures often pay for themselves and in some cases may even make profits. Corrosion due to the emission of various chemicals is a source of tremendous expense to the public. (See Fig. 36-3.) Recovery methods will reduce this corrosion and will also lower the cleaning bills for the outside, as well as the inside, of our houses, as mentioned earlier.

But even if no direct profit is made, the many intangibles make it worthwhile to improve living conditions. The standard of living of the workers is raised and possible adverse effects on their health are eliminated. This contributes to an increased efficiency on the part of the worker. It also raises the value of

Fig. 36-3. More than 1 million cars converge upon the center of town, establishing high levels of air pollution.

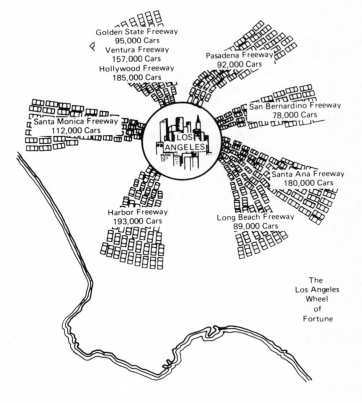

Golden State Freeway
95,000 Cars
Ventura Freeway
157,000 Cars
Hollywood Freeway
185,000 Cars

Pasadena Freeway
92,000 Cars

San Bernardino Freeway
78,000 Cars

Santa Monica Freeway
112,000 Cars

LOS ANGELES

Santa Ana Freeway
180,000 Cars

Harbor Freeway
193,000 Cars

Long Beach Freeway
89,000 Cars

The
Los Angeles
Wheel
of
Fortune

the industrial property and of the surrounding real estate. In many cases management has gone much further than merely curing existing air pollution problems. At the present time climatological and topographical conditions are examined carefully in selecting the site for new industry, and in the construction of new buildings the installation of air pollution control equipment is considered beforehand rather than at a time when public relations have already suffered a severe setback.

The old slogan, "Prosperity is measured by the number of smoking stacks," is no longer true. Today prosperity can be gauged by the number of strange looking bulges protruding from the roofs of the factories. These bulges are dust and fume collectors and indicate that the community and its industry have progressed to a standard of living and social consciousness that does not permit objectionable emissions to spread over other peoples' property. Many modern factories and offices have installed extensive air purification systems since experience has shown that clean air is healthier and leads to less absenteeism and, in addition, keeps cleaning and redecorating costs at a minimum. Scientific laboratories, too, have found that air purification is worthwhile for the protection from plant damage, from interference in sensitive enzyme systems, and from destruction of oxidant-sensitive organic compounds.

Less satisfactory, from a hygienic point of view, is the way many of us spend our day undergoing fumigations of tobacco smoke and engine exhaust—a combination which for many years has been under suspicion where its effects on health are concerned.

The determined effort of the Federal Government to return clean air to this country is seen in the rise in appropriations for its air pollution activities. Funding started in 1955 with $186,000, reached 4 million in 1960, and is expected to be 64 million this year. The Clean Air Act has made provisions to act in disputes between states and has, through the establishment of federal community health standards, the means to correct violations within the states when local efforts are unwilling or powerless to do so.

Urban Government Reorganization

Air doesn't respect legal boundaries. It moves freely from city to city within a natural basin, "an airshed," a geographical and meteorological entity. This might be a narrow valley or broad area covering thousands of square kilometers. The air carries with it the pollution from one jurisdiction to another and in combating air pollution in modern urban areas we need governmental structures which can cope with this evil.

Federal laws are now available which can cope with interstate pollution problems when pollution crosses state boundaries. A concerted attack on the urban areas is still in its infancy.

American cities are a conglomeration of separate legal entities. Los Angeles County contains 76 separate cities, each defending its independence and private interests at all costs. Most students of air pollution and urban areas have come to the conclusion that a reorganization and a new thinking in city government is essential. This holds not only for air pollution, but holds with equal force for other aspects of urban life—transportation, education, taxation, etc. All these facets of urban life are closely interrelated and interdependent. The provisions we make for the transport of people, the location of our industries, the way we fuel our industries and how we dispose of our mountains of waste products—all these aspects of community design determine the future quality of our community air supplies. With an intelligent and aggressive approach to our community problems, with a willingness of a majority of the people to forego short term profits for the far greater advantage of breathing clean air, we can prevent smog anywhere at all times.

Literature

1. Extensive reviews of the effects of air pollution on humans, animals, plants, and materials are found in publications of the United States Department of Health, Education and Welfare in Washington, D.C.; in the World Health Organization's Monograph No. 46 entitled Air Pollution (1961) and in volume 1 of *Air Pollution* edited by A. C. Stern

(1962). The chapter by M. D. Thomas in the World Health Organization volume, *Effects of air pollution on plants,* contains many colored pictures of smog damage.

2. *The Air Pollution Handbook.* P. L. Magill, F. R. Holden, C. Ackley, McGraw-Hill, New York (1956).

3. *Atmospheric carbon dioxide.* Chapter on Restoring the Quality of Our Environment, pp. 112-133. Report of the Environmental Pollution Panel, President's Science Advisory Committee (Nov. 1965). Government Printing Office, Washington, D.C., U.S.A.

4. *Air Conservation.* Report of Air Conservation Commission of the American Association for the Advancement of Science, Publication no. 80. Am. Assn. Adv. of Science, Washington D.C. (1965).

5. Haagen-Smit A. J., *Carbon monoxide levels in city driving. Arch. Environ. Health 12, 548-551, (1966).*

6. Munger H. P., *The spectrum of particle size and its relation to air pollution*, I. C. McCabe, *Air Pollution.* McGraw-Hill, New York (1952). Chapter 2, p. 2.

7. Green H. L., and W. R. Lane, *Particulate Clouds, Dusts, Smokes and Mists.* Van Nostrand Co., Princeton, New Jersey, U.S.A. (1964).

8. *Air Pollution,* edited by A. C. Stern. Control methods are discussed in volume 2 (1962).

9. Haagen-Smit A. J. *Chemistry and physiology of Los Angeles smog.* Industrial and Engineering Chemistry, *414*, 1342-1346 (1952).

10. Middleton J. T., and A. J. Haagen-Smit, *The occurrence, distribution, and significance of photochemical air pollution in the United States, Canada and Mexico.* J. Air Pollution Control Association 11, 129-134 (1961).

11. Haagen-Smit A. J., and C. E. Bradley, *The application of rubber in the quantitative determination of ozone.* Rubber Chemistry and Technology 24, 750 (1951).

12. Haagen-Smit A. J., *Reactions in the atmosphere. Air Pollution,* edited A. C. Stern, volume 1, pp. 41-62. Academic Press, 1962. Revised edition in press (1968).

13. Leighton, P. A., *Photochemistry of Air Pollution.* Academic Press, New York (1961).

14. Vehicle emissions. Technical Progress Series. Volume 6. Society of Automotive Engineers, Inc., 485 Lexington Ave., New York 10017. Distribution Pergamon Press Ltd., Oxford, England (1964).

15. Kopa R. D., and H. Kimura, *Exhaust gas recirculation as a method of nitrogen oxides control in an internal combustion engine.* 53 Ann. Meeting APCA, Cincinnati, Ohio (May 1960).

16. Daigh H. D., and W. F. Deeter, *Control of nitrogen oxides in automotive exhaust.* Am. Petrol Inst. 27th Meeting, San Francisco, Calif., (May 17, 1962).

17. Frenkiel F. N., *Atmospheric pollution and zoning in an urban area.* Sci. Mon. *82*, 194-203 (1956).

18. Turner D. B., *A diffusion model for an urban area.* J. Appl. Meteor. *3*, 83-91 (1964).

19. Miller M. E., and G. C. Holzworth, *An atmospheric diffusion model for metropolitan areas.* J. Air Pollution Control Assn. of America *17*, 45-50 (1967).

37

THE INADVERTENT MODIFICATION OF THE ATMOSPHERE BY AIR POLLUTION

Vincent J. Schaefer

Abstract

There has been a very noticeable increase in air pollution during the past ten years over and downwind of the several large metropolitan areas of the United States such as the Northwest—Vancouver-Seattle-Tacoma-Portland; the West Coast from San Francisco-Sacramento-Fresno-Los Angeles; the Front Range of the Rockies from Boulder-Denver-Colorado Springs-Pueblo; the Midwest—Omaha-Kansas City-St. Louis-Memphis; the Great Lakes area of Chicago-Detroit-Cleveland-Buffalo; and the Northeast—Washington-Philadelphia-New York-Boston. The worst accumulation of particulate matter occurs at the top of the inversion which commonly intensifies at night at levels ranging from 1000 to 4000 ft or so above the ground. This dense concentration of air-suspended particles is the most apparent to air travelers. Thus, it has not as yet disturbed the general public except during periods of stagnant weather systems when the concentration of heavily polluted air extends downwards and engulfs them on the highways, at their homes and in their working areas.

Recent Modification of Our Air Environment

Until recently there is little question that except in very exceptional cases, natural processes dominated the mesoscale weather systems by initiating the precipitation mechanism.

Reprinted from the *Bulletin of the American Meteorological Society*, vol. 50, 1969, pp. 199-206, with the permission of the publishers.

The effluent from the larger cities was quickly diluted by the surrounding "country air" so that at a distance of a few miles downwind of a city, little evidence of air pollution could be detected.

The recent spread of urban developments due to better roads and the massive proliferation of people and automobiles has led to a nationwide network of country, state, and interstate highways. This interconnection of thousands of smaller towns with larger cities and the phenomenal increase in auto, truck and air traffic has caused a massive reduction in the regions which have "country" type air. This increase in massive air contamination is of fairly recent origin. It is not easy to document this fact in the detail I would prefer since we have not had reliable automatic recording equipment for measuring Aitken, cloud and ice nuclei until the last few years. However, using simpler devices with which we made measurements at a number of scattered locations during the past ten years, we have in the past year used the same techniques to make comparative observations. The measurements indicate an increase in airborne particulates at these sites of at least an order of magnitude during this ten year period. At Yellowstone Park in the winter-time, which has the cleanest air we have found in the continental United States, the background levels of Aitken nuclei have increased from less than 100 to the 800-1000 ml^{-1} range within a five-year span. At Flagstaff, Ariz., where in 1962 the background levels ranged from 100-300 the concentration now lies between 800-3000. At Schenectady, N.Y., the average concentration of these nuclei has risen from less than 1000 to more than 5000 with values occasionally exceeding 50,000 ml^{-1}.

While it is difficult to ascribe these increases to any one cause, it is obvious that the increased demand for electric power, the large increase in garbage and trash incineration and the automobile, are likely to represent the major sources of increased pollution, especially since many industrial plants have been forced to reduce their pollution due to more rigorous regulations.

Just as it is not easy to place the blame for increased air pollution specifically on the power plants, incinerators and automobiles, it is equally difficult to demonstrate clean cut or unequivocal atmospheric modification to these sources. I am confident that in time there will be ample proof of these effects which are now inadvertently modifying the atmosphere.

The presence of high concentrations of visible as well as invisible particulates above and downwind of our cities produces a heat island effect as real as a sun-drenched Arizona desert or a semitropical island in the Caribbean.

Those cities like Boston, New York, and Philadelphia which are not affected by geographic barriers as are Los Angeles, Salt Lake City, or Denver are able to get rid of much of their effluent whenever the wind blows. Their plumes of airborne dirt extend as visible streamers for many miles downwind of the source areas. In the case of the metropolitan New York City—northeastern New Jersey complex, these plumes will be found in the upper Hudson Valley, in southeastern New England or over the Atlantic Ocean.

Commercial airline pilots flying the Atlantic are often able to pick up these pollution plumes hundreds of miles at sea. Hogan recently obtained data which provides a quantitative measurement of the New York effluents near the surface of the Atlantic between the United States and Europe. This same paper (1) amply demonstrates a similar zone of air pollutants being exuded over the seas surrounding Europe, the British Isles and the east and west coast of the United States.

Properties of Maritime and "Country" Air

We have known for twenty years that maritime air is characterized by low levels of both cloud droplet and Aitken nuclei. Vonnegut (2) showed by a very simple experimental device that about 50 effective nuclei at low water saturation droplet formation existed on the upwind coast of Puerto Rico where the trade wind clouds are seen. We were all much surprised when we established the nature of trade wind clouds during our research flights near Puerto Rico in 1948 (3). Following these activities, I pointed out (4)

the large difference noticeable even then between the "raininess" of the clouds upwind of the island and those which formed over the land after entraining the polluted air from San Juan, the sugar fields and refineries, the cement mills and the myriads of charcoal pits which dotted the island, each sending out its plume of bluish smoke. In our studies in the vicinity of Puerto Rico we observed that in many instances trade wind clouds would start raining by the time the clouds had a vertical thickness of not more than a mile while those over or immediately downwind of the island often reached three times that thickness without raining.

During a continent-wide flight over a large area of Africa, I found (5) an even more spectacular effect of inadvertent cloud seeding. As a result of the massive bush and forest burning initiated by the inhabitants preceding the onset of the rainy season, huge cumulus clouds, some of them reaching a height of more than 35,000 ft. (vertical thickness 4-5 miles) were observed which were not producing any rain. Instead the clouds grew so high that very extensive ice crystal plumes hundreds of miles long extended downwind of the convective clouds. No evidence of glaciation was observed in the side turrets of the clouds indicating a deficiency of ice nuclei at temperatures warmer than the homogeneous nucleation temperature of −40C. Thus it appeared that the precipitation process was being controlled almost entirely by coalescence and that so many cloud droplet nuclei were being entrained into the clouds from the fires below, that the coalescence process was impaired so that no rain developed. If ice nuclei were present, they were probably deactivated by the high concentration of smoke particles and gases flowing into the base of the clouds. Similar effects have been observed on a smaller scale in the Hawaiian Islands. During the trade winds cloud regime, clouds which form over sugar cane fields when they are burned prior to harvest are actually larger than the surrounding clouds but they have never been observed to rain even though smaller ones nearby produce showers. Warner more recently has documented such observations (6).

A further observation of secular change in the microphysics of clouds has been observed in the vicinity of large cities during airplane flights through convective clouds. The observations I have noted in particular were made in commercial twin engine planes over the past ten years. Of recent years it has been noticed that such clouds often have so many cloud droplets in them that visibility is restricted so much that the engine is hardly visible. In my earlier observations I can never recall being in clouds so opaque that the wing tips could not be seen. Several of my colleagues have reported similar experiences.

Perhaps the most impressive field evidence of inadvertent weather modification is the overseeding of supercooled clouds which is readily observed over the downwind of our northern cities in the wintertime.

Ice Crystals from Polluted Air

Although I have been observing such phenomena for more than ten years, the effect was brought to my attention in a vivid way during a flight from Albany to Buffalo on 20 December 1965. After flying above a fairly thin deck of supercooled stratus clouds downwind of the Adirondack Mountains, I noted a massive area of ice crystals above and downwind of Rochester, N.Y. The crystals were so dense that the reflection from the undersun* was dazzling as illustrated in Fig. 37-1. Since that time I have observed similar high concentrations of crystals at low level above and downwind of most of the large northeastern cities such as New York, Albany, Utica, Syracuse, and Buffalo as well as Detroit, Chicago, Sacramento and Los Angeles. In all instances the ice crystals were observed at low level (below 5000 ft. above the ground in

---

* Note: The undersun is an optical phenomenon caused by the specular reflection of the Sun from the surfaces of myriads of hexagonal plate ice crystals. In order to produce an undersun, it is necessary for the crystals to consist of smooth-surfaced plates which float with their long axes horizontal to the ground. They thus act as many tiny mirrors. If the crystals were not hexagonal plates but rather prisms, the optical effects would include under parhelia and other reflections which are well known and have been related to crystal types during our winter studies at Yellowstone Park.

most instances), and extending for at least 50 miles downwind of the city sources and without cirrus clouds above the areas affected. In a few instances when the plane passed through the crystal area, I observed the particles to be like snow dust, though in a number of instances after landing I observed very symmetrical though tiny hexagonal crystals drifting down from the sky.

Misty Rain and Dust-like Snow

For the past several years I have also been observing a number of strange snow and rain storms in the Capital District area in the east central part of New York State. These storms consist of extremely small precipitation particles. When in the form of snow, the particles are like dust having cross sections ranging from 0.02 cm (200 μ) to 0.06 cm (600 μ). When in the form of droplets, they often are even smaller in diameter, at times so tiny that they drift rather than fall toward the Earth. When collected on clean plastic sheets, the precipitation is found to consist of badly polluted water. It is a well-known fact that precipitation "cleanses the air." In the past much of this cleansing action has been ascribed to the sweeping up of suspended aerosols by rain and snow. Little attention has been given to the possibility that submicroscopic particulates from manmade pollution may in fact be initiating and controlling precipitation in a *primary manner* rather than being involved in the secondary process wherein precipitation elements coming from "natural" mechanisms serve to remove the particles by diffusion, collision and similar scavenging processes.

My first evidence that there might be substances in urban air which would react with other chemicals was encountered while studying ice nucleation effects at the General Electric Research Laboratory in 1946 (7). At that time I found that laboratory air contained aerosols which would react with iodine vapor to form very effective ice nuclei but that when the air was free of particulate matter, no further ice particles would form.

Fig. 37-1. Undersun photographed downwind of Rochester, N.Y. 20 December 1965.

Potential Ice Nuclei from Auto Exhaust

In 1966 I published a paper (8) which suggested that air pollution in the form of automobile exhaust could account for the high concentration of ice crystals which I have observed downwind of the larger cities in the United States and in any area where a considerable number of automobiles are used. My laboratory studies have shown that submicroscopic particles of lead compounds produced from the combustion of leaded gasoline can be found at concentrations exceeding 1000 cm^{-3} in auto exhaust. These were measured by exposing auto exhaust samples to a trace of iodine vapor before or after putting the samples into a cold chamber operating at $-20C$. Presumably this reaction with iodine formed lead iodide which is an effective sublimation nucleus for ice crystal formation. Evidence that the active ingredient in auto exhaust consists of submicroscopic particles of lead was determined by comparing its temperature ice nucleation activity pattern with that of lead oxide smoke produced by electrically sparking lead electrodes which was also reacted with a trace of iodine vapor. Figure 37-2 is a photomicrograph of replicated ice crystals formed on submicroscopic lead compounds from auto exhaust reacted with iodine vapor. One of the problems related to the evidence that leaded gasoline is responsible for the ice crystals observed in laboratory and field experiments concerned with auto exhaust is the source of the iodine needed to produce the lead iodide reaction. All evidence thus far encountered shows that only a few hundred molecules of iodine are required to produce a nucleating

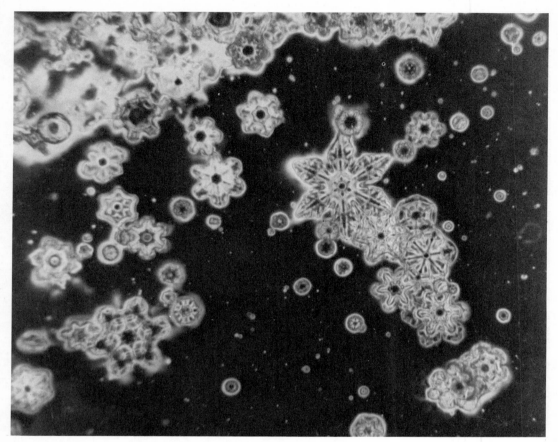

Fig. 37-2. Photomicrograph of replicated ice crystals formed at −16C in a supercooled cloud on nuclei from auto exhaust exposed to trace of iodine vapour.

zone for ice crystal formation. The amount of iodine reported in oceanic (9) air (the order of 0.5 U G. m⁻³) is orders of magnitude greater than would be required to activate such particles.

I have recently completed further studies in Arizona, New York and France (10, 11) and have found that wood smoke and other organic sources add iodine to the air which could react with the auto exhaust submicroscopic lead compounds which are always present in urban pollution. Hogan has recently showed (12) that similar reactions will proceed from the vapor phase.

Admittedly we are dealing with chemical reactions in the realm of surface and even "point" chemistry as Langmuir termed such molecule by molecule reactions. This is an area of particulate research for which there is very

little experimental data or practical experience. The size of the primary lead particles from auto exhaust which are 0.008-0.010 diameter are far too small for analysis by any currently available chemical reaction techniques. All of my laboratory experiments indicate that the submicroscopic particles in auto exhaust which react with iodine vapor act only as nuclei for ice formation from the vapor phase. No evidence has been found that they act as freezing nuclei.

The Effect of Large Concentrations of Ice Crystals

The presence of high concentrations of tiny ice crystals in air colder than 0C over thousands of cubic miles raises interesting aspects of the dynamics of weather systems. Such crystals continually modify small supercooled clouds soon after they form. The net result is a reduction in the number of local rain or snow showers and the production of extensive sheets of "false" cirrus. Bryson has pointed out (13) that cirrus sheets and even the presence on a large scale of airborne dust exerts a measurable decrease of insolation. If a much larger supply of moist air moves into such a region, the entrainment of high concentrations of crystals by more vigorous supercooled clouds may trigger the formation of a massive storm through the release of the latent heat of sublimation. Langmuir described (14) such a storm system which he believed was initiated and then intensified when dry ice in successive seeding operations was put into the lower level of a rapidly developing storm.

Findings of Project Air Sample

In order to determine whether or not polluted air above cities contained particles which would react with free iodine molecules, eight transcontinental flights have been made by Atmospherics, Inc., under our auspices during the Fall of 1966 and 1967 and the Spring and Fall of 1968. The flight routes are shown in Fig. 37-3. A Piper Aztec aircraft was fitted with instruments which could measure in a semi-quantitative manner the concentration of atmospheric particulates which would become ice nuclei by the reaction with iodine, and which would also measure natural nuclei for ice crystal formation. The iodine reactions were conducted in a cold chamber at $-20C$. The determination of naturally occurring nuclei was done at $-22C$. In addition, measurements were also made of Aitken nuclei (a measure of polluted air) and cloud nuclei. This last measurement which is made at very low water saturation is also a measure of the degree of air pollution since values above 50 cloud nuclei and 500 Aitken nuclei per cubic centimeter is indicative of some degree of air pollution. The flight samples were made mostly just below the top of the haze layer which ranged from 1500 to 5000 ft. above the ground throughout the flights. Figure 37-4 illustrates the aircraft used

in Project Air Sample flights and the A.S.R.C. Experimental Laboratory. Of the 266 measurements in November 1966, 31 were made on the ground. All of these showed excessive pollution levels. Great care was exercised in making these observations to avoid contamination from the engine exhaust of the aircraft being used for the measurements.

At several locations observations were made above as well as within the upper part of the haze layer. In every instance the air above the visible top of the haze layer was low in lead particles while that just below the top or farther down showed very high concentrations.

All other locations where counts of the ice nuclei were low involved regions free of pollution sources. Of 266 observations 108 or 40% of the measurements were in areas such as upwind of cities (9); above large lakes (8); above haze layers (22); and above woods and farms (33). The 60% remaining had values of potential ice nuclei of 100 per liter or more. Some 115, all of them above or downwind of cities had values in excess of 200 per liter which I consider would lead to definite overseeding of the atmosphere with ice particles if suitable moisture was available. Values of 1000 per liter or more occurred at 101 of the stations. If concentrations of ice crystals that high occurred, the cloud would resemble a stable ice fog such as occurs at Fairbanks, Alaska, or the Old Faithful area of Yellowstone Park (15) when the temperatures are colder than $-40C$. With crystal concentrations of this magnitude, the particles grow very slowly if at all and thus remain floating in the air for extended periods. This then reduces the incoming solar radiation to a noticeable degree. If such areas are extensive, they cannot help but cause changes in the weather patterns of the affected areas.

Similar findings characterized our second, third and fourth round-trip transcontinental flights covering more than 25,000 additional miles and consisting of over 1500 more observations. In practically every instance where polluted air was present, high values in potential ice nuclei (using the iodine reaction) were found. The only exceptions were instances where the plumes of steel mills, forest fires and other highly concentrated effluents were

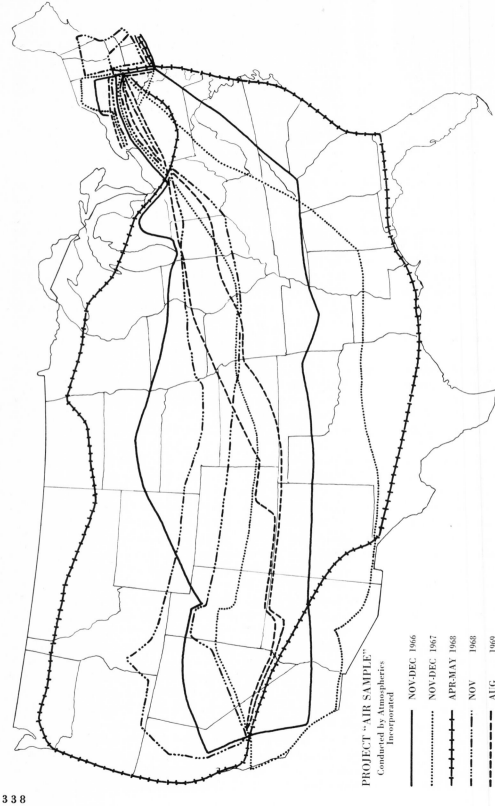

PROJECT "AIR SAMPLE"
Conducted by Atmospherics
Incorporated

————	NOV-DEC 1966
··········	NOV-DEC 1967
++++++	APR-MAY 1968
—·—·—	NOV 1968
— — —	AUG 1969

Fig. 37-3. Flight routes of Project Air Sample 1–4, 1966-1968.

Fig. 37-4. Experimental Laboratory for Cloud Physics and aircraft used for air pollution studies.

measured in areas where auto exhausts could contribute very little if anything to the sampled air.

Figure 37-5 illustrates the type of pollution which still occurs along Lake Erie at Buffalo and Fig. 37-6 a zone of snow falling from low clouds about eighty miles downwind of Buffalo at a location where the iodine-activated nuclei had dropped from 5000 per liter measured at Buffalo to 500 near Cayuga Lake and the Aitken count from 25,000 ml^{-1} to 4500 as measured at 3000 ft above the terrain.

Figure 37-7 illustrates the fantastic amount of smoke which shrouded the metropolitan New York area of 23 November 1966, when one of the first dangerous smog alerts was sounded by New York City health officials. Just prior to obtaining this picture the airplane was flown up through the smog. At 600 ft. the cloud nucleus count was 2000 ml^{-1}, the Aitken

count 25,000 and the ice nuclei measured were 0 for the natural background and 50,000 to 100,000 per liter for ice nuclei activated with iodine vapor.

Figure 37-8 shows the conditions at Albany, N.Y., on the previous day. At 1200 ft. the cloud droplet nuclei numbered 900 ml^{-1}, the Aitken count was 4000, the natural ice nucleus background was 0 but the concentration of ice nuclei activated with iodine was 50,000 per liter. These are concentrations which are commonly observed in the air below the top of the inversion over and downwind of all large cities. In many instances the smoke concentrations in such areas is not as spectacular as shown in Figs. 37-6 and 37-7 since a considerable portion of the pollution is submicroscopic. These aerial photos were taken by Thomas Henderson who also made the air measurements.

Fig. 37-5. Example of pollution which occurs along Lake Erie at Buffalo, N.Y.,
20 November 1967.

Flight Observations of Inadvertent Seeding

It is quite feasible to detect and observe the massive systems of ice crystal nuclei which produce inadvertent effects on cloud and weather systems due to man's activities. This is accomplished most easily by riding on the sunny side of a jet aircraft.

I observed and photographed three such systems in 1967 during a flight from Buffalo, N.Y., to Denver, Colo., by way of Chicago, returning directly from Denver to New York City.

Ice Crystals Related to Polluted Air

On Wednesday, 6 November 1967, I left Buffalo at 1035 by Boeing 727 landing at Detroit and Chicago. Upon take-off I noted a heavy pollution pall over Buffalo extending westward to the horizon. Just west of Buffalo we climbed above stratiform clouds estimated to be at 15,000 ft. or lower which consisted of very high concentrations of ice crystals as established by an undersun. This extensive zone of ice crystals was observed all the way to Detroit and was associated with visibly polluted air. We flew at 20,000 ft. where the temperature was −20C. Enroute from Detroit to Chicago I found the same condition to exist from the 1108 take-off until 1132 at which time only supercooled clouds were visible. At the same time all evidence of polluted air disappeared, visibility between cloud decks was unlimited and no further trace of ice crystals could be seen as we landed at Chicago. The air pollution from Chicago was being carried to the southeast over Indiana about 30 miles south of our jet route.

Ice Crystals Produced by Dust from Plowed Land

Upon take-off at Chicago in a Boeing 707 at 1320 CST, the air was clear, several decks of

Fig. 37-6. Snow showers falling from thin clouds about 80 miles downwind of Buffalo, N.Y., 20 November 1967.

stratiform clouds were visible with no evidence of ice crystals. Heading west I saw no ice crystals until 1424. Just previous to that time a peculiar zone of dusty air could be seen ahead of us extending toward the southwest. Within a few minutes a brilliant undersun could be seen which persisted for the next half hour. When we finally emerged from the affected zone over northeastern Colorado it was quite obvious that the 300 miles long zone of ice crystals was due to very extensive dust storms caused by 50-100 mph katabatic ground winds pouring down out of the Front Range of the Rockies and blowing top soil from the extensive wheat fields extending from northeastern Colorado to the region about 50 miles east of Pikes Peak. The low level dust was rising only from tilled land, the grassy areas such as the Pawnee Grass Lands were unaffected.

A similar massive dust storm which produced very extensive cloud seeding was observed by me on the afternoon of 12 April 1967, between Amarillo, Tex., and Denver, Colo. This affected region was so extensive and had such a profound effect on the Great Plains and midwest weather systems that I was able to identify it and see its effects over western Illinois two days later.

On the return flight from Denver on 8 December, a third source of inadvertent weather modification was observed. Take-off in a DC9 occurred at 1206 MST on a non-stop jet flight to New York City. Very fine snow was falling at the ground upon take-off. Four minutes afterward we climbed above an extensive area of ice crystals. A bright undersun became visible and was seen continuously all the way from the Denver area to the Atlantic

Fig. 37-7. Example of severe pollution over New York City, 23 November 1966.

Ocean east of New Jersey. Jet contrails appeared to be the source of these crystals throughout the entire flight which was conducted at 37,000 ft. More than a dozen different planes were seen coming from the east within the flight corridor we were using, most of them several thousand feet below us. From time to time we were close to contrails being made by planes at our level but ahead of us.

The most striking effect observed was the sharp line of demarcation between the area affected by contrail seeding along our flight corridor and an extensive area of high alto-cumulus cloud (or cirrocumulus) which paralleled our zone at its southern extremity. This region of non-modified clouds was estimated to be about 10 to 20 miles away and extended over large regions of the country. I expect that an effect such as was observed could be seen on satellite cloud photographs.

Perhaps the most disturbing feature about inadvertent weather modification is that in a subtle manner it seems to be changing the nature of clouds over increasingly large areas of the globe. Much of our current consideration of cloud seeding assumes the ubiquity of super-cooled clouds and the effectiveness of a seeding material for triggering the instability of such systems.

If pollution sources lead to increased dustiness from ill-used land, more cloud nuclei from burning trash and many more ice nuclei from the lead-permeated exhaust of internal combustion engines, not only will we lose the possible advantage we now have of extracting some additional water from our sky rivers, but we might even be confronted with a drastic change in our climatological patterns.

Interesting climatological evidence of inadvertent weather modification has been found

Fig. 37-8. Example of heavy air pollution at Albany, N.Y., 22 November 1966.

by Changnon [16] to exist in the area downwind of the Chicago, Ill.-Gary, Ind., complex of extensive urban, highway and steel mill concentrations.

A very noticeable increase in precipitation and storminess is evident in the records of the past three decades. The LaPorte, Ind., region whose record is cited as evidence of this effect is downwind of the heavy pollution source mentioned above as well the close proximity to a very moist air source in the form of Lake Michigan. It is a common observation to see a lake effect street of cumulus clouds extending in the convergence zone south and southeast of Lake Michigan. The combination of very moist air and an abundance of ice nuclei are apparently in a very favorable juxtaposition for an optimum reaction to occur. The LaPorte anomaly was first observed by a local weather observer which was then evaluated by Changnon. He found that there has been a

notable increase in precipitation starting about 1925 with definite increases since that time also of the number of rainy days, thunderstorms and hail storms. There has been a 31% increase in precipitation, 38% of thunderstorms and 240% increase of hail incidences. The increases show a marked correlation with the production of steel.

Since this data was obtained entirely from an evaluation of the climatological records, it is of great importance that careful "on-the-spot" field observations should be made in the LaPorte area to establish the atmospheric dynamics which are responsible for the apparent change in the precipitation pattern of the area. It is particularly important that the concentration of particulate matter be correlated with storm patterns. The weather systems at the mesoscale level should especially be studied to determine whether the area receiving increased precipitation is in the centre or edge of the city-industrial plume effluent and the properties of the moist air moving in from Lake Michigan.

Experimental Production of Large Areas of Ice Crystals

During the past ten winters field operations have been developed by our Yellowstone Expeditions in which we have established certain relationships of ice crystal concentrations in the free atmosphere. The early morning inversions of the Old Faithful Geyser Basin in the wintertime often have liquid water contents ranging from 0.5 to 1 gm m^{-3}. This rich supply of moisture is contained within a strong ground-based inversion having a vertical thickness of about 100 m. At a distance of 2000 m from a point source of seeding, ice crystal concentrations up to 10,000 per liter have been measured. Such crystals at −12C are hexagonal plates with cross sections of from ten to a thousand microns, the size depending on concentration and moisture supply. Those of 200 μ occur typically at a concentration of 200 per liter with a fall velocity of 10 cm sec^{-1}. The brilliance of the undersun and related optical phenomena indicates that the number of crystals observed in areas caused by air pollution, jet contrails or dust storms often have concentrations as high or higher than observed in our experiments. Thus at Yellowstone we have an ideal outdoor laboratory to study some of the factors which must be better understood if we are to work out the physical interactions resulting from the inadvertent modification of the atmosphere.

The Need and Opportunity to Study These Phenomena

The effects cited are but a few examples of many which I have observed and photographed during the past few years. It is the rule rather than the exception that such massive zones of ice crystals can be observed over large areas of the country which can be related to man-caused modification.

Such occurrences must be exercising a detectable effect on the weather systems of the Northern Hemisphere. I feel that nowhere near enough effort has been directed toward the establishment of an organized and continuing study to determine the effect of such inadvertent seeding mechanisms on the synoptic weather patterns of our country. Such studies should have a major place in the World Weather Watch and the Global Atmospheric Research Project. I strongly recommend that the part played by atmospheric particulates should become an important research feature of this program.

There is a critical need for knowledgeable field scientists having an extremely broad scientific background who can work effectively in the real atmosphere under all types of conditions and extract quantitative and meaningful data from such systems.

Our Universities must place far more emphasis on this type of training than is being done at present. The eventual understanding of these complex interrelationships do depend on computers, electron microscopes, mass spectrometers and other costly instruments and equipment. However, the real atmosphere is the thing that must be understood and it is not enough to rely on data obtained by automatic instruments and uninformed field men as is too often the case. It is not easy to conduct efficient field operations. We must approach nature to an ever increasing degree but this confrontation must involve "intelligent eyes," an understanding of the physics, chemistry and electricity of the reactions which can occur and a zeal to understand the things which combine to produce atmospheric phenomena.

References

1. Hogan, A., 1968: Experiments with Aitken counters in maritime atmospheres. *J. de Recherches Atmosphériques*, 3, 53.
2. Vonnegut, B., 1950: Continuous recording condensation nuclei meter. Proc. First Natl. Air Pollution Symposium, Pasadena, Calif., 1, 36.
3. Schaefer, V. J., 1953: Final Report Project Cirrus Part 1 Laboratory, Field and Flight Experiments. Report No. RL-785 General Electric Research Laboratory, March 1953, Schenectady, New York.

4. Schaefer, V. J., 1956: Artificially induced precipitation and its potentialities. *Man's Role in Changing the Face of the Earth*, W. L. Thomas, Editor, University of Chicago Press.

5. ——. 1958: Cloud explorations over Africa. *Trans. N. Y. Acad. Sciences*, 20, 535.

6. Warner, J., 1968: A reduction in rainfall associated with smoke from sugar cane fires—an inadvertent weather modification. *J. Appl. Meteor.*, 7, 247-251.

7. Schaefer, V. J., 1948: The production of clouds containing supercooled water droplets or ice crystals under laboratory conditions. *Bull. Amer. Meteor. Soc.*, 29, 175.

8. ——, 1966: Ice nuclei from automobile exhaust and iodine vapor. *Science*, 154, 155.

9. Junge, C. E., 1963: *Air Chemistry and Radioactivity*. Academic Press, New York.

10. Schaefer, V. J., 1968: Ice nuclei from auto exhaust and organic vapors. *J. Appl. Meteor.*, 7, 113.

11. ——, 1968: The effect of a trace of iodine on ice nucleation measurements. *J. de Recherches Atmosphériques*, 3, 181.

12. Hogan, A., 1967: Ice nuclei from direct reaction of iodine vapor with vapors from leaded gasoline. *Science*, 158, 800.

13. Bryson, R. A., 1967: Is man changing the climate of the Earth? *Saturday Review*, p. 52, April 1.

14. Langmuir, I., 1962: Results of the seeding of cumulus clouds in New Mexico. *The Collected Works of Irving Langmuir*, Pergamon Press, Vol. II, pp. 145-162, New York.

15. Schaefer, V. J., 1962: Condensed water in the free atmosphere in air colder than −40°C. *J. Appl. Meteor.*, 1, 481.

16. Changnon, Stanley A., 1968: LaPorte weather anomaly, fact or fiction. *Bull. Amer. Meteor. Soc.*, 49, 4.

38

HOW AIR POLLUTION ALTERS WEATHER

Eric Aynsley

For some years now, carbon dioxide has been under suspicion as a potential cause of major climatic alteration on a global scale. Carbon dioxide results from burning of all carbonaceous fuels, and since the turn of the century background levels of carbon dioxide have increased from 290 to 330 parts per million of air (ppm). The Earth's energy input is derived mainly from absorption of solar radiation, the Earth maintaining its temperature balance by re-radiating long wave energy back to space. The absorption of incoming radiation by carbon dioxide is small and changes in carbon dioxide concentration have no appreciable effect upon the transmission of energy from the Sun to the Earth. Nevertheless, carbon dioxide does absorb a major fraction of the long wavelength energy that is re-radiated by the Earth. Consequently, increases in atmospheric carbon dioxide concentrations tend to reduce the heat loss from the Earth by diminishing the radiation loss from the Earth's surface. This causes increased ambient temperatures. Similar effects are observed in greenhouses, where the result of this diminished re-radiation through glass manifests itself in the form of increased temperature.

Many scientists have tried to assess the increase of world temperature which could result from increases in atmospheric carbon dioxide levels. The problem is complicated due to the interaction of cloud coverage, atmospheric circulation and humidity with the Earth's radiation budget. Nevertheless, whilst making due allowance for the modifying effect on the Earth's cloud cover, it is estimated that with carbon dioxide levels at 600 ppm the Earth's temperature would rise by 1.5°C, although again the interaction of global circulation and humidity could radically alter the conclusions. A change of 1.5°C in the Earth's temperature sounds insignificant until it is realized that the last ice age resulted from an average temperature drop of between 7° and 9°C.

Although the build-up of atmospheric carbon-dioxide levels is not to be overlooked,

Reprinted from the *New Scientist* 44: 66-67, 1969, with the permission of the publishers.

recent observations have indicated a far more important aspect is the continual accumulation of atmospheric aerosols. This increase of atmospheric dustiness or turbidity has only recently been substantiated and if it continues unchecked can have devastating consequences. Measurements at the Moana Loa Observatory in Hawaii, which is remote from any local sources of air pollution, indicate a long-term increase in turbidity or atmospheric dustiness. Mr. R. A. McCormick and Mr. J. H. Ludwig at NAPCA in Cincinnati have shown increases in recent years of turbidity over Washington, D.C. of 57 per cent and over Switzerland the increase was 88 per cent and Dr. V. J. Schaefer and his co-workers at the State University of New York have documented many examples of large increases in atmospheric particulates of the order of tenfold during the last five years.

It is evident that Man's pollution of his own environment is increasing with world population, increased industrialization, urbanization and bad farming practices. Plumes of pollution emanating from the eastern United States can often be observed hundreds of miles out over the Atlantic. Similar air pollution zones are associated with Britain, Europe and the western coast of the United States. This atmospheric dustiness acts like an umbrella and shields the Earth from the Sun's radiation. Excessive dustiness can also initiate cloud formation, which both alters precipitation patterns and further reduces solar radiation.

Little is known of the Earth's total radiation budget although this is the prime function responsible for both global wind and oceanic circulations. Evidence is beginning to accumulate that build-up of atmospheric dustiness is having a distinctly more profound effect than carbon dioxide accumulation. A slight reduction in the Earth's temperature has already been recorded in the last decade, and the Northern Atlantic ice coverage last year was the most extensive for 60 years. On the global scale Dr. R. A. Bryson, a climatologist at the University of Wisconsin, suggests that pollution may even be responsible for the observed weakening of the trade winds and westerlies over the last decade. New comprehensive data on solar radiation is now becoming available from meteorological satellite observations and this will enable a more precise determination of the magnitude and variation of solar fluxes.

Atmospheric dusts provide excellent centres or nuclei for cloud condensation, and very small particles are a necessary prerequisite for initial condensation of water vapour. Once condensation has been initiated the water drops grow from further condensation and coalescence. Depending on the prevailing meteorological conditions, either fogs or clouds are formed, the concentration of dust and atmospheric conditions dictating the extent and type of fog or cloud formation. An excess of dust produces small droplets under condensing conditions which grow from further condensation and coalescence and ultimately fall as precipitation. Information gained from intentional cloud seeding experiments indicates that precipitation can be either increased, decreased, or not even affected. The final outcome of cloud seeding depends on the cloud type and prevailing meteorological conditions.

An example of increased precipitation from air pollution appears to exist at La Porte, Indiana, some 30 miles downwind from the smoky steel works of Gary and South Chicago. During the 14 years up to 1965 La Porte had 31 per cent more rain, 38 per cent more thunderstorms and 245 per cent more days with hail than nearby communities. In fact, rainfall at La Porte increases in harmony with steel production rates at Gary!

Excessive dustiness in the atmosphere can also reduce rainfall under certain conditions when overseeding occurs. This happens when many small droplets, formed by condensation, do not fall to earth if there is insufficient moisture available to continue the droplet growth by condensation. Consequently what would have fallen as rainfall now stays in the form of clouds. A case in point of this reduction in rainfall has occurred in the sugar producing area in Queensland, Australia. During the cane-harvesting season the common practice is to burn off the cane leaf before cutting and harvesting. This results in fires over extensive areas and large palls of smoke. The fine smoke particles have modified the cloud formation and hindered the rainfall process. A reduction of up to 25 per cent in the rainfall has occurred downwind of these areas, but there is no such effect in neighbouring areas unaffected by the smoke plume. Similarly such effects have been reported by Dr. Schaefer to occur downwind of Puerto Rico.

The ubiquitous automobile has a great potential to cause inadvertent weather modifications. The major offenders are components of the exhaust, which become highly reactive under intense sunlight, producing the well known brown smog. The lead additives in petrol combine in the car exhaust and atmosphere with the small numbers of iodine molecules present and provide excellent particles for ice crystal formation. Dr. Schaefer has observed extensive ice crystal plumes in the winter around a number of large American cities.

Even steam and water vapour can alter the climate. The very large hyperbolic water-cooling towers that are becoming more popular throughout the United States, evaporate large quantities of water. These cooling tower plumes can, if trapped under an inversion layer under stable weather conditions, generate and maintain a dense and persistent fog over wide areas. Already, flying at the Morgantown Airport in West Virginia has been disrupted by fogs which are believed to result from a cooling tower a few miles away. Ironically, it is planned to construct the world's largest cooling tower at a nearby power station! A further example of local climate modification by water vapour is Edmonton in Canada, which has more low-temperature fogs than neighbouring areas. During cold winter spells the air cannot absorb all the moisture produced from the additional natural gas burnt for space heating. Thus extended periods of fog or ice crystal fogs are experienced.

The vapour trails associated with high-flying aircraft are well known. What is not generally known is that aircraft inject carbon dioxide, water vapour and considerable quantities of fine particles into the rarified upper atmosphere. It is estimated that the high wispy cirrus clouds formed from jet contrails have already increased cloud coverage between North America and Europe by five to ten per cent. These hazards of artificial clouds will be greatly increased as supersonic transport aircraft become a commercial reality. Dr. Bryson estimates that cirrus clouds could well attain 100 per cent coverage in these operational regions.

Cloud coverage, especially at lower altitudes, is the most effective method of cutting off the Sun's rays and reducing the Earth's surface temperature. Global average cloud cover averages around 31 per cent. It is estimated that an increase of only five per cent in coverage of lower clouds would reduce surface temperatures sufficiently that a return to ice-age conditions could become a reality.

It is strongly suspected that particulate air pollutants are responsible for the many examples of inadvertent weather modifications I have discussed, though very few investigations of this problem have been conducted to date. Fortunately for mankind, the natural atmospheric cleaning processes are very efficient. Rain and snow are both effective scavengers of dust and certain gases, and only a few turnovers of the atmospheric water content are necessary to remove almost all air pollutants. But it seems that atmospheric particulates are associated with the major process of cloud initiation and related control of precipitation and reduction of sunlight, as well as the minor role involved in precipitation scavenging.

Man's knowledge of his ability to inadvertently modify his climate is still at best fragmentary. Insufficient is known about the long-term build-up of air pollutants, the effects and their interrelationships. A point of no return may be reached when air pollutant levels cause the climate to be modified to such a degree that a major irreversible global weather modification may follow. It is essential that mankind faces up to this problem to save his own atmospheric environment. Although detailed studies of air pollution and interrelated weather effects are necessary, the primary solution requires a continuing effort aimed at control and ultimate abatement of air pollution sources. Only then will a future of clear blue skies be assured.

39

AIR POLLUTION FROM POWER PLANTS AND ITS CONTROL

Theodore T. Frankenberg

At the first National Conference on Air Pollution held four years ago, G. V. Williamson of the Union Electric Company made an able report on the status of thermal power plants as they affect the atmosphere. At that time engineering progress had given the industry fairly trouble-free designs, or the information on which to base such designs, in at least three areas:

1. Elimination of smoke, i.e. unburned hydrocarbons from coal and oil.
2. Flyash. That is the particulate matter associated with the combustion of pulverized coal.
3. Stack design. That is the prevention of problems associated with turbulence caused by the plant or the nearby terrain, and the safe diffusion of SO_2 for the size of the plants then being built.

Today, it is possible to say that there have been no adverse developments in these three problems which were then regarded as solved. There has been continued effort to tighten the limits so far as the discharge of particulate matter is concerned. In stack design a new problem has developed, but will be discussed later.

In 1958 two areas were listed as problems under observation, with solutions still to be developed:

(a) Sulfur. This included the problems associated with removing a relatively large fraction of the sulfur from the coal before burning it, or the elimination of the resulting sulfur oxides from the stack gas after combustion.

Reprinted from *Combustion* 34: 28-31, 1963, with the permission of the publishers.

(b) Nitrogen Oxides. These materials had then just been identified as possibly contributing to the air pollution problem in certain west coast situations.

While a great deal of work has been done in direct attack on each of these areas the existing solutions are mainly means of making an oblique adjustment to the situation. The results of direct attack and the current adjustments to the two problems are:

(a) Sulfur. The elimination of sulfur from the coal before burning continues to be a difficult technical problem, and a matter for joint research effort by the utility and coal industries. Some very useful work has been accomplished in this period, but it appears that an economically satisfactory solution is still some distance in the future.

Removal of sulfur oxides from the combustion gas has also received continuous research attention. Problems here are of both a technical nature and a matter of economics. A number of methods have been investigated, and work is continuing on the most promising one.

The method of adjusting to this problem has been to exercise a great deal more care and foresight in the selection of stack heights, giving due consideration to the expected local meteorological conditions. All of this to the end that sulfur oxides will be fully and effectively diffused in the atmosphere; and thus never become a problem at ground level.

(b) Nitrogen Oxides. Further development in the study of the oxides of nitrogen seem to indicate that, under most normal conditions, and in the low concentrations produced by power plants, they produce no adverse effect on the atmosphere. In special situations where particular hydrocarbons are available from sources other than power plants, there is some evidence of the formation of irritating compounds; and, again under special conditions, these may become concentrated to the degree that real problems exist.

Some work has been done towards the direct elimination of nitrogen oxides by changes in the methods of combustion. Two methods of adjustment to the problem, however, seem more effective in producing the desired final

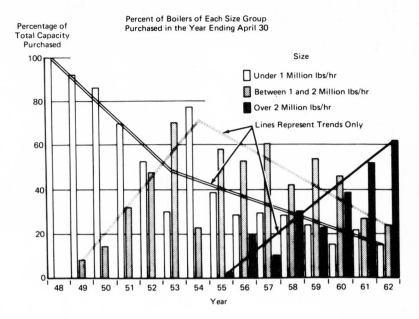

Fig. 39-1. Percent of boilers of each size group purchased in the year ending April 30.

Fig. 39-1. Percent of boilers of each size group purchased in the year ending April 30.

improvement. It appears likely that the control of the volatile hydrocarbons, which is a desirable end in itself so far as air pollution is concerned, will solve any problem associated with oxides of nitrogen emitted from power plants. Under nearly all meteorological conditions high stacks are of considerable help in diffusion of these gases and preventing their interaction with the hydrocarbons.

New Developments

Beginning about the middle 1950's the utility industry has shifted very rapidly to generating units of a size that were not seriously contemplated a decade ago. Figure 39-1 shows the amount of steam-generator capacity in each of the three size categories purchased since 1948. At the beginning of this time, steam-generators rated less than one million pounds of steam per hour constituted 100 per cent of the market. This size of unit has suffered an almost steady decline until in 1962 it represented only about 15 per cent of the capacity sold. For the size between one and two million pounds of steam per hour, the chart shows that they rose from nothing at the start of the period until they achieved 70 per

cent of the market in 1953, and have since been in a steady decline. Steam-generators in the over two million pound per hour size began to appear in 1955 and by 1962 they came to represent slightly over 60 per cent of the capacity sold. It should be remembered that units sold in 1960 are just now coming into service, and therefore the full effects of this trend to larger units are still to be felt. Similar trends could be shown for the size of turbine-generator units purchased in this period, since nearly all were constructed on the unit system, that is, a single boiler serving a single turbine without cross-connections to other units in the plant.

Along with the tendency to install larger units, the industry has also witnessed a rather sharp increase in the total amount of power on one site. Figure 39-2 indicates the relative sizes of the 15 largest thermal plants in the U.S. in 1952 and above them are plotted the 15 largest plants in operation at the close of 1961 as reported by the Federal Power Commission. While in 1952 the largest thermal plant did not quite reach 1000 Mw in size, there are today 15 plants which exceed that mark, one by as much as 40 per cent.

The advent of plants well above 1000 Mw has brought a new problem or new dimension

Fig. 39-2. The 15 largest thermal power plants in 1952 and 1962.

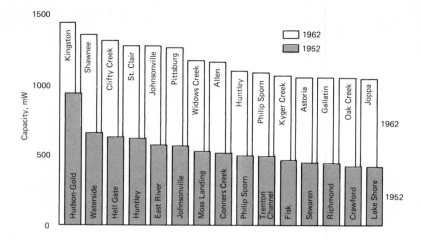

to the problem of proper disposal of the stack gases. Heretofore, the air pollution problem confined itself principally to the area immediately surrounding the plant. Assuming that adequate elimination of particulate matter was accomplished, and that by wind tunnel studies the stacks were chosen of a height that prevented aerodynamic downwash due either to the plant structure or to terrain features, there was little reason to fear that a plant of 400 to 500 megawatts would become a community problem.

These simple precautions are no longer sufficient for the new group of very large plants, although they must of course be even more carefully followed. Beginning with the design of Clifty Creek Plant of roughly 1200 Mw output, the selection of stack heights has become a matter of a great deal of study and one requiring contemplation of many variables. These would include:

(a) Study of the adjoining terrain.
(b) Land use in the area.
(c) Population density.
(d) General and particular meteorological features.
(e) Aeronautical factors.
(f) Fuel, or fuels to be burned.
(g) Stack gas exit velocity and temperature.
(h) Gas diffusion for volumes involved.

Some of these can be considered together by the use of the Bosanquet, Carey and Halton formulae for gas rise, and those of Sutton for

its diffusion. Such calculations bring together the effects of sulfur content of the fuel, gas exit velocity, gas exit temperature and the mass flow involved, and relate them to a stack height and to some resulting sulfur dioxide concentrations at varying distances from the stack under various meteorological conditions. These processes are iterative, and, in the absence of modern computers, were extremely tedious. By necessity the Clifty Creek stacks had to be based on a minimum number of such calculations. The stack height selected for Clifty—683 ft. above grade—represents a combination of:

(a) The diffusion approach for the more distant areas.
(b) A wind tunnel study of a difficult terrain feature only 2500 feet from the plant.
(c) Finally a slight compromise to satisfy the Federal Aviation authority although the plant was over 40 miles from the Louisville airport.

Thus, on one site there was an illustration of all of the factors which enter into determining the stack height for the larger plants now coming into being. Construction of these stacks was followed by the installation of a number of SO_2 analyzers and dust fall stations which proved that the actual results were appreciably better than predicted by the design calculations. Even more gratifying from a community relations standpoint, has been the fact that in the nearly seven years of operation not a single air pollution complaint related to these stacks has been received. The Clifty stacks and those of the sister units at Kyger Creek plant, were instrumental in setting a trend toward effective high level dispersion of stack gases.

In addition to the checking of results at Clifty Creek and Kyger Creek Plants, the diffusion equations have been verified at several other locations. The area around two of the large TVA plants has been extensively studied by special techniques, such as: gas sampling along the stack plume by means of helicopters, installing a network of ground level SO_2 recorders, and carefully recording the meteorological data from the region. This work has shown a high degree of correlation between the predicted and the actual results. Since 1958 the diffusion studies have been arranged for solution by digital computers, and the way has been opened to make extensive studies before building any plant. As a result of such studies there is a growing appreciation of the part that gas temperature plays in producing adequate plume rise from very large plants. At the same time there has been some lessening of dependence on high exit gas velocity to solve problems.

In engineering, as in other phases of life, the solution of one problem may only serve to bring another into being. While the high concrete stack accomplished its air pollution function in a highly satisfactory manner, the utility industry is now faced with the problem of sulfate attack on some of the concrete stacks built since 1954. The best available study of the problem does not bring out any clear pattern or suggest definite methods by which those stacks which might be affected could be predicted in advance. In the absence of such information, many companies in their new designs are resorting to either an independently supported brick lining with a ventilated space between it and the shell or providing a free-standing, insulated, steel lining within the concrete stack. Either of these steps involve a considerable extra cost for disposing of the flue gas. Particularly heavy expense has been incurred in those cases where existing stacks had to have liners added after several years of service. Some believe that as exit gas velocities were increased,

a situation of positive pressure in the stack was created, and this change to positive pressure from what had heretofore been a suction condition resulted in accelerating the action of the sulfur oxides on the concrete. This general supposition is not borne out completely by the study of the available data, since a number of positive pressure stacks have not been seriously involved. Further study and possibly design changes will indubitably dispose of this problem which has come about as a corollary to improvements in the air pollution situation.

The trend toward ever tighter control of particulate matter has been mentioned. While we are fully in accord with the central portion of this trend, there are some points which the author feels can react unfavourably on the public which we serve without providing them with any significant improvement in air pollution. These points are:

(a) Imposing limits that may be beyond any economic justification for large units, while setting much less drastic limits for numerous small units that may actually be creating much more of a problem.

(b) Over-stressing of the appearance of the stack effluent, which as stacks increase in diameter may become almost impossible to meet.

(c) No credit is given for the use of high stacks as a valued aid in reducing the effect of particulate matter emitted.

(d) Apparent disregard of the mounting cost and size of equipment as absolute perfection is approached. Figure 39-3 shows this effect for electrostatic dust collecting equipment.

Items (c) and (d) combine to have a particularly adverse effect on the power plant designer since he is barred from balancing dollars spent in two different ways to produce the best overall result. It should be evident that the utility industry can do many things to satisfy public requirements. The public should, however, at the same time be aware that increased costs from nonproductive facilities will ultimately be borne by them in the form of higher rates. In simple justice to the public, those who seek to establish limits should leave the door open to producing the overall result in the most economic manner.

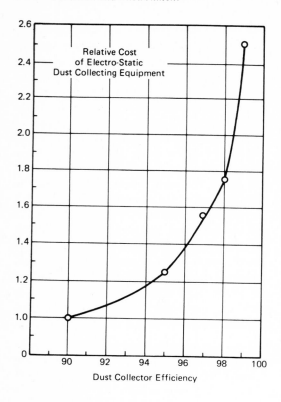

Fig. 39-3. Dust collector efficiency.

Conclusion

The principal new factor affecting air pollution from power plants and its control that has appeared in the past decade is the shift to larger individual units and to larger total plants. Figure 39-4 shows stack heights capacity of coal-fired units which they serve for a number of plants built or modified during the past six years. Contrasting symbols show the same data for some plants now in the design stage and which will be placed in service prior to 1966. The general upward trend in stack height is unmistakeable, although differences in plant sites, fuel burned, population density, proximity to airports, and possibly other variables create wide individual differences among the plants.

It can be seen that the power industry observed this new factor and promptly moved to maintain optimum community relations by disposing of the vast quantities of gases from these new plants in a highly satisfactory manner. This has involved stacks which were larger than any previously built in the United States such as the 683 ft. structures at Clifty

Fig. 39-4. Stack height vs. milliwatts for units completed or to be completed in the years indicated.

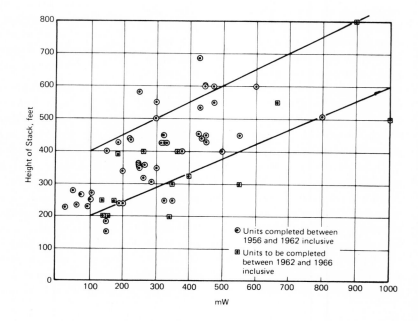

Creek. Structures of this magnitude introduce new problems in both their construction and maintenance, as well as adding significantly to the original cost of the plant. The forward-looking utility accepts these costs and design problems in full knowledge of its community responsibility.

It is our feeling that the freedom to ap-proach these problems openly and honestly seeking for an optimum solution which includes due consideration of the community, the rate-payers, and the stockholders, is a valuable one. This freedom should not be lost to those who would promote arbitrary regulation in a field which has, and apparently will continue to develop as rapidly as this one.

40

HAS NUCLEAR TESTING CAUSED INFANT DEATHS?

Ernest J. Sternglass

Strontium-90 from nuclear explosions has long been recognized as a hazard to Man. On ingestion, it goes straight to the bone, along with calcium, and the fear is that it might, many years later, give rise to leukaemia and bone-marrow cancer. But no one believed that the low doses of fallout to which mankind as a whole has been exposed since the explosion of the first atomic weapons could be sufficient to cause any *genetic* damage. After all, studies on the children of the survivors of Hiroshima and Nagasaki revealed that they had suffered no genetic defects as a result of their parents' exposure to very high and, supposedly, much more damaging radiation doses. In recent years, however, evidence has been accumulating that even very small doses of strontium-90 injected into animals *can* cause genetic damage, and gives rise to an increased incidence of foetal deaths. I believe that I have accumulated con-vincing statistical evidence that the same thing has happened to the human population as a result of its exposure to low doses of strontium-90 from nuclear weapons testing, and that an unknown number of children have died either

Reprinted from the *New Scientist* 43: 178-81, 1969, with the permission of the publishers.

while still in the womb or shortly after birth as a result of such tests.

The first evidence that strontium-90 can cause genetic damage in animals came in 1963 as a result of the work of Dr. K. G. Laning and his co-workers in Sweden. They showed that small doses of strontium-90 injected into male mice three to four weeks before they were mated produced an increase in foetal deaths among their offspring which was not observed when corresponding amounts of caesium-137 were injected. More recent evidence has ex-tended these results to the demonstrations of severe chromosome damage, foetal deaths and congenital malformation in the offspring of female mice injected with strontium-90 before and during pregnancy. Furthermore, similar effects have now been seen for very small quantities of tritium, produced by both atomic and relatively "clean" hydrogen weapons.

In the light of these results obtained with animals, the absence of significant genetic effects in Hiroshima and Nagasaki can now be understood. Unlike the first test of an atomic device in Almogordo, New Mexico, the bombs dropped on Japan were detonated not on the ground but at such an altitude that there was essentially *no* fallout in these two cities. The radiation to which the bombs' survivors were exposed came almost exclusively from the brief flash of X-rays, neutrons and gamma rays at the instant of detonation, and not from internally deposited strontium-90. It was therefore rea-sonable to expect that even though the popu-lation exposure from peacetime fallout was relatively small (especially when averaged over the 70-year life-span of the adult), there might nevertheless be effects of a more subtle genetic type similar to the increase in foetal deaths observed for strontium-90 in mice. But to detect such effects one would have to examine large human populations exposed to the fallout from specific nuclear tests over long enough periods of time.

That such effects on the developing human embryo may in fact be detectable was initially suggested by the data on foetal death rates in the area around the towns of Albany and Troy, in New York State, following the rain-out of radioactive debris from a 43-kiloton test in Nevada in April, 1953. Examination of these data showed that the foetal death rate, which had previously been declining steadily for a number of years, changed to a much lower rate of decline within a period of a year or two of the test. It remained at this lower value until 1966, even though the measured external gamma radiation dose to the population was only 0.1 rad over a period of some ten weeks following the rain-out from the passing radio-active dust-cloud. This dose represents what is normally received from natural background radiation in the course of a year. The rain-out of radioactive debris was also followed by an increase in childhood leukaemia beginning some five years later, accompanied by a shift in age distribution towards older age at death. Dr. Alice Stewart of Oxford University has pointed out that such age shifts are characteristic of leukaemia caused by radiation, as a result of her work on children exposed to diagnostic X-rays *in utero*. It appeared, therefore, that there might be a causal connection between the rate of change of the foetal death rate and the arrival of the fallout.

The next step was to see whether changes in foetal death rate appeared not only in the Albany-Troy area, but also in New York State as a whole, and whether subsequent tests were also reflected in changes in the foetal mortality. The figures are again certainly highly suggestive. In New York State, the foetal death rate began to deviate from the 1935-50 rate of decline in 1951, the year that atmospheric weapons tests began at the Nevada test-site. The rate of decline slowed from 1935-50 value, after which the death rate started to change sharply, level-

ling off at about 23 per 1000 live births between 1957 and 1963. In 1964, it increased sharply to 27.3 per 1000 live births declining somewhat in 1965 and 1966.

In contrast to this anomalous behaviour, the foetal death rate for California—which received less fallout from the Nevada test due to its location "upwind" from the test-site and the lower annual rainfall—maintained its steady decline. However, even in California a decrease in the rate of decline became evident, beginning within two or three years after the onset of hydrogen bomb tests in the Pacific in 1954 to the west of that state.

In order to see whether the sharp rise in the foetal death rate in New York State might be connected with the accumulated fallout from weapons testings, I plotted the excess of the foetal mortality over the value expected if the 1935-50 rate of decline had persisted, against the cumulative strontium-90 deposited in the New York area. Except for the first few years of testing in Nevada, when short-lived isotopes rather than the long-lived strontium-90 were dominant, the foetal death rate followed the same general pattern as the accumulated strontium-90 on the ground. The two curves show the same decrease in rate of climb coincident with the temporary stoppage of nuclear testing in 1958 to 1961, and the sharp rise beginning with the large USSR test series in 1961. Two years after the test-ban in 1963, both the foetal death rate and the radioactivity in the environment once again began to decline.

A similar pattern in the registered foetal death rate (or rate of still-births) exists in the data for the United States as a whole for all periods of gestation up to nine months. Again, there is a steady rate of decline, which levels off in 1951-52, coincident with the onset of nuclear weapons testing at the Nevada test-site in 1951. An actual rise in the foetal death rate occurred in 1954, when the first large hydrogen weapons were tested in the Pacific. A second rise took place in 1961, at the same time as the onset of large megaton weapons by the USSR in that year.

More direct evidence for genetic effects in Man comes from a comparison of foetal mortality with the long-lived strontium-90 concen-

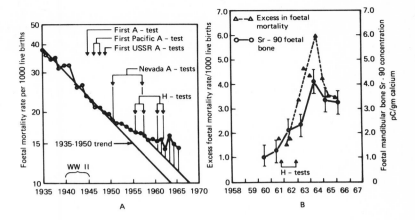

Fig. 40-1. (a) Foetal mortality in Missouri for the period 1935 to 1966. (b) Excess foetal mortality in St Louis (for derivation see text) plotted with strontium-90 concentrations in foetal mandibular bones.

tration in foetal mandibular bone as measured by Dr. H. L. Rosenthal and his co-workers at the School of Dentistry of Washington University in St. Louis, Missouri. Figure 40-1(a) is a semi-log plot of the foetal mortality in Missouri for the period 1935 to 1966, as reported in the U.S. Vital Statistics. Figure 40-1(b) shows a plot of the excess mortality above that which would be expected if the number of foetal deaths had continued to decline from its 1959 level at the same rate that it had been declining in the period 1935-50, prior to the onset of large-scale nuclear testing in Nevada and at the Pacific test-sites. Also plotted in Figure 40-1(b) are the strontium-90 concentrations measured in a series of 62 aborted foetuses, showing a closely parallel rise and decline before and after the test-ban of 1963.

But even though the evidence based on foetal deaths parallels that in the case of the mice, foetal death statistics are not nearly as reliable as infant mortality rates. The latter are reported with better than 95 per cent efficiency in most advanced countries, while only about 15 per cent of all foetal deaths are typically registered in the US. It was therefore important to examine figures on infant mortality, and to correlate changes in these rates with measured quantities of strontium-90 in the body. For the case of infants, Dr. Rosenthal and his co-workers reported concentrations of strontium-90 in various deciduous teeth such as the crowns of second molars. His results are plotted in Figure 40-2 for the period 1947 to 1958. These data may be compared with the excess infant mortality (age 0-1 year) above the normally

Fig. 40-2. Excess infant mortality (0 to 1 year) in Missouri (calculated with respect to the 1935-1950 trend); and the strontium-90 concentration in teeth—specifically in the crowns of deciduous second molars.

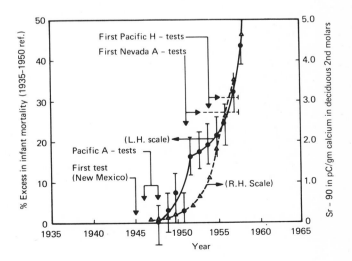

expected rates determined from a fit to the 1935-50 infant mortality rates for Missouri.

Again, a close correspondence can be seen. The two quantities begin to rise shortly after the onset of testing in Nevada directly upwind from St. Louis, and maintain a closely parallel course of increasing steepness from 1954 to 1958. This represents the first period of large hydrogen weapons testing in the Pacific, when the amounts of long-lived strontium-90 released high into the stratosphere were many times greater than during the testing of the much smaller kiloton weapons.

The close correlation between changes in strontium-90 levels and infant mortality after the onset of megaton-weapons testing in 1954 further substantiated by a similar state-by-state comparison of infant mortality excesses in the U.S. with the levels of strontium-90 in the milk. This correspondence may be seen for the cases of six typical states of widely different strontium-90 levels and socio-economic patterns for which strontium-90 data in the milk are available prior to 1960—Georgia, Illinois, Missouri, New York State, Utah and Texas. In each case the 1935-50 trend was determined by a least-square fit, calculated by computer, and the rate for 1955 was taken as the reference value. The milk data after 1959 are four-year averages of the Public Health Service's Pasteurized Milk Network measurements, four-year averages having been found to reflect best the three to five-year integration and delay in onset of infant mortality.

The trend for the U.S. as a whole is shown in Figure 40-3, where the computer-fitted period is again the pre-testing period of 1935 to 1950. Also shown in this figure are the total amount of strontium-90 produced by weapons testing, the strontium-90 deposited on the ground in the Northern Hemisphere, and the four-year moving average of the milk concentration of strontium-90 for the U.S. as a whole. The pattern of infant mortality and strontium-90 produced, deposited on the ground, and reaching the milk, are closely parallel except for the initial period from 1951 to 1954, when only small atomic weapons were tested. During this period the short-lived strontium-89 (50-day half-life) added significantly to the total biological effect.

All the data I have described do not, of course, exclude the possibility of a merely accidental association between excess infant mortality and strontium-90 levels. Thus, it is at least conceivable that other factors—such as for instance, the growing use of DDT beginning after World War II and reaching a maximum close to 1963-65—might be the principal reason that led to the observed excess infant mortality above the expected rates during this period. That the association with fallout from nuclear testing is not likely to be accidental may be seen from the maps in Figure 40-4. In these, the state-by-state infant mortality excesses or decrements relative to the computer-calculated 1940-45 trend have been plotted for the first and fifth year following the detonation

Fig. 40-3. Percentage excess infant mortality for the United States relative to the 1935-50 period. Also plotted is the total amount of strontium-90 produced; the strontium-90 deposited in the northern hemispheres; and the four-year average strontium-90 content in U.S. milk.

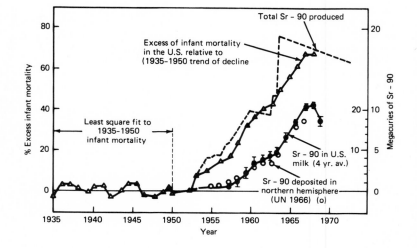

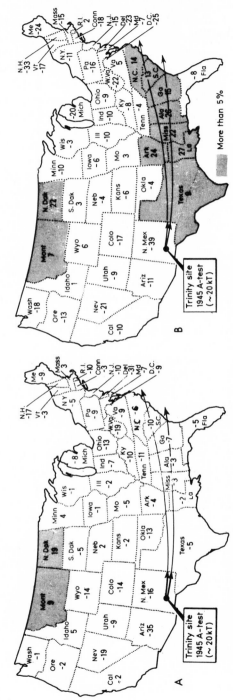

Fig. 40-4. Geographical distribution of excess infant mortality in the United States, relative to the values expected on the 1940-45 rate of decline. Map A shows the situation in 1946, one year after the test in New Mexico; Map B represents 1950. The excess mortality in North Dakota may be correlated with the very high level of strontium-90 recorded in the milk of this state for the 1950s.

of the first atomic bomb in Almogordo, New Mexico, on 16 July, 1945.

The main fallout cloud of this explosion drifted generally eastward across the United States, carried along by the prevailing westerly winds at high altitudes. In 1946, one year after the detonation, there was no sign of any excess infant mortality in the states downwind from New Mexico. However, the map for 1950 shows that by the time five years had elapsed, a clear change towards excess infant mortality appeared in the states, over which the fallout cloud had drifted.

The excess mortalities are distributed in a manner that would be expected from nuclear fallout originating in New Mexico. The effects are lowest in the dry area of western Texas, and largest in the areas of heavy annual rainfall first encountered by the cloud—namely Arkansas, Louisiana, Mississippi and Alabama. East of these states the mortality excesses become progressively less severe with increasing distance, in a manner now known to be characteristic of the activity along the axis of the path of a tropospheric fallout cloud. By contrast, no significant increases in mortality rates relative to 1946 are seen to have occurred in Florida to the south of the path of the cloud, or in the states to the north and west of the test-sites.

Since no excesses of infant mortality rates were registered along the path of the Almogordo fallout cloud within a year after the detonation, it could not have been the direct effect of radiation on the developing embryo or the young infant that was dominant. If it were, the effect would have appeared in the figures for infants 0 to 1 year old that died in 1946.

The only area that showed significant excess infant mortality over the 1940-45 period is North Dakota, where subsequent measurements of strontium-90 in the milk carried out by the Health and Safety Laboratories of the Atomic Energy Commission revealed the highest concentrations of any state in the U.S. on which data are available prior to 1960. The reasons for these abnormally high strontium-90 levels are not yet fully understood, but may be related to the known accidental discharges of radioactivity from the Hanford plutonium production plants located directly to the west in the state of Washington, where nearly all the U.S. weapons material has been produced beginning in 1944.

I believe that the evidence I have presented indicates that a genetic effect of strontium-90 from nuclear weapons testing exists, and that it expresses itself most strongly in a close correlation of foetal and infant mortality with strontium-90 concentrations in the milk and bone. All the evidence, both from animal studies and large human populations, suggests therefore, that radioactive strontium appears to be a more serious hazard to Man through its action on the genetic material of the mammalian cell than had been expected on the basis of its tendency to produce bone-cancer and leukaemia.

The excess mortality probably results from such factors as lowered birth-weight or immaturity, and lower resistance to infectious diseases among the newborn. These two causes of death have been observed to show the greatest change in the United States relative to other advanced countries of western Europe since the early 1950s. Although the present evidence appears to implicate strontium as the most important single element from a genetic standpoint, there is a possibility that the long-lived carbon-14 produced even by "clean" hydrogen bombs may also be involved. The measured activity of carbon-14 in the world's atmosphere closely parallels that of strontium-90 in the milk. A major effort to investigate experimentally the genetic effect of these biologically important isotopes in mammalian reproductive cells will clearly be required before the detailed mechanisms of action are fully understood.

After steadily declining since the beginning of the century, infant mortality in the United States suddenly levelled off drastically in the early 1950s, while the downward trend continued in Europe until the late 1950s. The result was that the United States dropped down to eighteenth place among all medically advanced nations of the world. The primary blame for this disturbing situation has generally been placed on the medical profession in the U.S. and the supposed failure to deliver adequate health care to the poor in the rural and urban slums. But it now appears that what we may have witnessed was a totally unanticipated genetic action of strontium-90 on the human reproductive cells of such a magnitude that it may well have turned the world's existing stockpiles of nuclear weapons into a biological doomsday machine for all mankind.

To appreciate the full significance of this threat, it must be remembered that the first nuclear weapon detonated in New Mexico, a detonation that appears to have led to infant mortality increases above the normally expected values of 20 to 30 per cent, was what is now referred to as a small "tactical" nuclear weapon. Of these weapons, the U.S. has presently stockpiled some 8000 in Europe, to

be used for the protection of the NATO countries in the event of a Russian attack. Thus, although by the use of shelters—and possibly even successful anti-ballistic-missile systems using large numbers of multi-megaton bombs detonated high above the atmosphere—it may indeed be possible to save significant numbers of adult population in the event of a nuclear war, it now appears likely that the survivors on either side and in neutral nations all over the world will be saved only to watch the newborn die from the long-term effect of strontium-90 before they could give rise to another generation of Man on this planet.

41

THE PITFALLS OF EXTRAPOLATION

Alice Stewart

A glance at Figure 40-1 of Dr. Sternglass's article will show that he has postulated a foetal mortality trend which would eventually produce rates well below the level which—according to his own theory—would result from background radiation alone. If anyone doubts the misleading effects which this has had on Dr. Sternglass's interpretation of an undoubted fact (namely, a slower decline in foetal death rates between 1950 and 1965 than between 1935 and 1955), he should consult pages 30 and 31 of *Facts and Figures* (Moroney, Penguin, 1960), where he will learn that this is not the first time that a reputable scientist has fallen into the trap of overconfident extrapolation, or asked his readers to believe in an implausible situation (see Figure 41-1).

Reprinted from the *New Scientist* 43: 181, 1969, with the permission of the publishers.

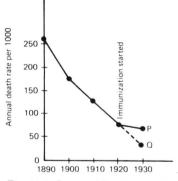

Fig. 41-1. Overconfident extrapolation. The anonymous author of this graph claimed that, in the absence of immunization, the death rate would have continued to fall to Q. In fact, it only reached P.

The most likely explanation of the observed change in trend is that it is a reversion towards normality of a death rate which had, for 20 years, been experiencing booster effects—first from the introduction and dissemination of sulphonamides, and then from the introduction and dissemination of antibiotics.

Dr. Sternglass is also mistaken in thinking that a shift towards older age at death is characteristic of radiogenic leukaemias. The age of maximum incidence of the leukaemias caused by obstetric X-rays is slightly older than the age of maximum incidence of all childhood leukaemias. But this is only because the first half of pregnancy is a relatively common starting date for a juvenile cancer, whereas the risk of being X-rayed *in utero* is virtually confined to the second half of pregnancy.

For many years we have insisted that the carcinogenic effects of small doses of radiation are felt with equal force by all foetal tissues, and that it is futile to ascribe a temporary increase in the prevalence of childhood leukaemias to "extra" radiation effects unless it is accompanied by an equally marked rise in the death rate of juvenile cancers other than leukaemia (Stewart and Kneale, *Lancet*, 1968, vol. 1, p. 104). More recently we have had occasion to draw attention to the risk of an infection death between the start of a leukaemic process and the onset of symptoms

(Stewart and Kneale, *Nature*, in press). We have also pointed to misleading effects which this pre-leukaemic hazard has had on official and unofficial estimates of leukaemia and lympho-sarcoma prevalence in Europe, America and Africa.

In practice, infection deaths are so strongly correlated with sex, age, wealth, climate, density of population, chemotherapy, and so on, that any deviation from normality of related death rates and prevalence rates (for example infant mortality, leukaemia mortality and leukaemic clusters) can only be regarded as significant *after* these effects have been eliminated.

42

INFLUENCE OF THE ENVIRONMENT ON THE UNBORN

Ian W. Monie

Throughout our lives we are constantly reacting to the environment in which we live. Heat, light, atmospheric pressure, terrestrial and extraterrestrial radiation, gravity, microorganisms and the multitude of chemicals contained in food, water and air are continually acting upon us, determining our constitutions and our densities. At one time it was felt that the mammalian fetus was relatively sheltered from the effects of such environmental factors but careful clinical and experimental studies have now shown this belief to be untenable.

While the mother does afford protection to the unborn in many ways—for example, by detoxifying noxious substances and by destroying microorganisms which would be harmful were they to reach the young—this is secondary

Reprinted from *California Medicine* 99: 323-27, 1963, with the permission of the publishers.

to the preservation of her own organism. Where the agent is not harmful to the mother and protective reactions are absent, the effect on the embryo can be disastrous. Indeed, the majority of teratogenic (malformation-producing) agents or procedures belong to this category and are especially destructive in the early stages of gestation. Thus, rubella, if contracted by the mother during the first trimester, causes little maternal upset but may result in serious eye, ear and cardiovascular malformations in the embryo (11). Again, maternal ingestion of thalidomide, a glutamic acid imide that once was supposed to be a harmless sedative, has recently been linked with a syndrome of phocomelia, cavernous angioma and duodenal stenosis in the offspring (17).

The Maternal and Embryonic Environments

The unborn has to contend with three environments. The one with which it is in immediate contact, consisting of the amniotic fluid, the placenta and membranes, has been designated the *microenvironment* by Warkany (7). The maternal body may be called the *macroenvironment*, and the surroundings of the mother, the *matroenvironment* (Fig. 42-1).

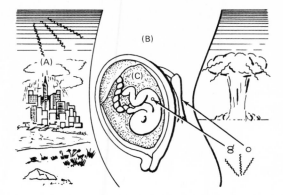

Fig. 42-1 The maternal and embryonic environments. (A) the matroenvironment *consisting of the physical and chemical components, and the animal and plant life, in the surroundings of the mother. Radiation from outer space, the earth, and man-made sources is indicated by wavy lines; (B) the* macroenvironment *or maternal body; (C) The* microenvironment *composed of the placenta, membranes, and amniotic fluid. (B) and (C) constitute the embryonic environment.*

Substances inhaled or ingested by the mother from the matroenvironment may reach the embryo unchanged, or may produce changes in the macroenvironment or microenvironment which are ultimately experienced by the embryo. It is also possible for substances to pass from the macroenvironment and accumulate in the microenvironment in large enough amounts to cause embryonic damage. In the case of radiation the embryo may be directly affected, or it may be affected by the products of reaction with the macroenvironment.

Environment and Genetic Factors

Nineteenth century experimental embryologists clearly showed that environmental change could disturb development both in invertebrates and in lower vertebrates, and by the beginning of the present century considerable attention was being directed to abnormal intrauterine conditions as causes of malformation and abortion in man (2, 18). However, the importance of inherited factors in the normal and abnormal development of mammals was now appreciated and the significance of the

environment gradually became subordinated to that of the germ-plasm; this concept generally prevailed until the early forties.

Nevertheless, during the period when genetic factors were considered of primary importance in the causation of congenital abnormalities, reports continued to appear on the influence of the environment on the unborn. It became evident, for example, that x-irradiation (13, 14) or radium treatment of the mother during pregnancy could result in fetal death or deformity, and that lack of iodine in pregnant sows resulted in reduced litter-size (27). Cleft palate (3) was frequently seen in whelps of captive lions unless the mothers were fed goat flesh and soft bone during pregnancy, while sows receiving a vitamin A-deficient diet producted piglets with eye defects (12) and other malformations. However, it was not until 1940 and the publication of a study by Warkany and Nelson (28) showing that pregnant rats fed a deficient diet (later shown to be riboflavin deficiency) produced young with skeletal and other abnormalities, that attention was again seriously directed to the influence of the environment on mammalian development. The teratogenic effect of rubella on the human fetus observed soon after this gave further impetus to the renewed interest in environmental factors; since then a host of teratogenic agents or procedures have been discovered (Table 1).

Today, however, it is generally agreed that the majority of congenital abnormalities result from the interplay of *both* genetic environmental factors (9) although in certain instances one may play a much more important role than the other. Since there is no apparent structural difference between congenital abnormalities produced by genetic and by environmental factors, in many cases it is difficult to determine which is of primary or sole importance.

In addition to malformations resulting from environmental or genetic factors, or to a combination of these, it is now known that abnormality of chromosomal number is responsible for such conditions as Turner's and Klinefelter's syndromes, and for mongolism. What role, if any, environmental or genetic factors play in the determination of such chromosomal disturbance has not yet been determined.

Table 1. Some factors which produce malformations.

	In animals	In man
Physical	Radiation, hypothermia	Radiation
Chemical		
Hormones	Insulin, cortisone, androgen, estrogen, epinephrine	Sex hormones
Antigrowth factors	Nitrogen mustard, chlorambucil, azaserine, 6-mercaptopurine	?
Other	Trypan blue, quinine, hypoxia, salicylate, colchicine, iodine deficiency, antibiotics	Thalidomide
Nutritional		
Deficiency	Vitamins A, $B_{1\,2}$, D, E,* folic acid (PGA*), pantothenic acid,* nicotinic acid,* riboflavin*	Aminopterin†
Excess	Vitamin A	–
Other	Starvation	–
Micro-organismal	Hog cholera, influenza A, Newcastle virus	Rubella, syphilis, toxoplasmosis

* Vitamin antagonist employed alone or with deficient diet.
† A folic acid antagonist.

Teratogenic Agents—Timing and Specificity

It would appear that either an excess or an insufficiency of almost any chemical or physical agent can, in certain circumstances, result in defective embryonic development; thus, either maternal insufficiency (31) or excess (5) of vitamin A produces abnormal rat young when occurring at a particular stage of pregnancy.

The time of introduction of a teratogenic agent is especially important, the embryo usually being most sensitive when the principal body systems are being established; in man, this is between the third and eighth week, and in rats during the second week of gestation (parturition occurs on the 22nd or 23rd day). In the later stages of pregnancy the fetus is much less sensitive but by no means immune to environmental influence; thus, in man, toxoplasmosis can produce hydrocephaly, and syphilis a variety of malformations in the later stages of gestation. Also, in rats the giving of 6-aminonicotinamide (6-AN), a nicotinic acid antimetabolite, as late as the 19th day of gestation can produce hydrocephaly in the young (4).

Generally, when a teratogenic agent is given very early in gestation it either does not disturb the conceptus or it destroys it entirely, while, if given late in pregnancy its effects may be greatly reduced or absent; there is consequently a critical time for each agent during which maximum damage to the conceptus will result, and this varies with the species involved. In the case of thalidomide, for example, it has been observed that the human embryo is most sensitive between the 27th and 43rd days after conception (17).

While the time of introduction of the agent is undoubtedly of importance, there is generally mounting evidence that certain agents have a predilection for one or more systems or regions of the embryo (30). This is suggested, for example, by the preponderance of limb damage in human fetuses by thalidomide, and by the frequent absence of the kidney in rat young from chlorambucil (23). On the other hand, certain teratogenic factors, such as maternal folic or pteroylglutamic acid (PGA) deficiency (10, 25, 26), are associated with a broad spectrum of malformations and are considered "universal" teratogens.

The employment of teratogens in experimental animals is exceedingly valuable for studying the pathogenesis of many congenital abnormalities, and different defects can be produced by varying the time of action of the same agent, or by using different agents (Figs. 42-2 to 42-7). Thus, a transitory PAG-deficiency in rats from the 7th to 9th day of gestation produces many abnormalities of the brain and

Fig. 42-2 to 42-7. Congenital abnormalities resembling those occurring in man produced in rat young as a result of trypan blue (Fig. 2), and folic acid (PGA) deficiency. (Fig. 3-7) during pregnancy; (2) transposition of the great vessels and double aorta; (3) facial defects and cleft palate; (4) control and hydrocephalic brains from three-week-old rats; (5) exencephaly, micrognathia, and glossoptis; (6) pelvic and supernumerary kidneys; and (7) bilateral hydronephrosis.

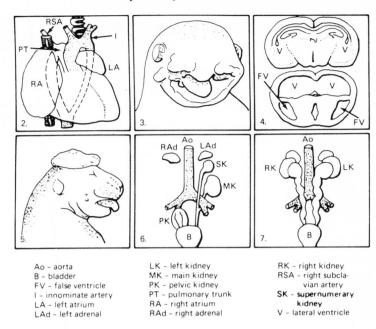

Ao – aorta	LK – left kidney	RK – right kidney
B – bladder	MK – main kidney	RSA – right subcla-
FV – false ventricle	PK – pelvic kidney	vian artery
I – innominate artery	PT – pulmonary trunk	**SK – supernumerary**
LA – left atrium	RA – right atrium	**kidney**
LAd – left adrenal	RAd – right adrenal	V – lateral ventricle

eye; from the 9th to 11th day, mainly cardio-vascular abnormalities (1, 21); and from the 10th to 13th days, principally urogenital malformations (22). However, if it is desired to study dextrocardia or transposition of the great vessels, trypan blue (8) is the agent of choice, as it provides a much higher incidence of these anomalies than maternal PGA-deficiency.

Human Teratogens

Of the great number of agents or procedures recognized as teratogenic in mammals, only a few are definitely known to affect humans. Proven teratogenic agents in man are: rubella, sex hormones, aminopterin (4-amino PGA), toxoplasmosis, radiation and thalidomide (Table 1). Many other chemical substances, physical factors and microorganisms are suspect but absolute proof is lacking.

It is sometimes stated that experimentally produced congenital malformations are caused by dosages of teratogenic agents at levels much greater than ever experienced by man. In many instances this is probably true but the effects of combinations of small amounts of teratogens cannot be overlooked and work on this important aspect is now proceeding (6). Prelim-

inary results indicate that certain combinations of low dosages of teratogenic agents have an adjuvant effect on the production of malformations while others seem to show a protective effect. The problem, however, is complex and requires more detailed study.

Pathogenesis of Malformations

The ability to produce abnormal embryos in animals by means of teratogenic agents has made it possible to obtain more accurate information on the genesis of many malformations. Thus, absence of a kidney is not always the result of primary renal agenesis but may be due to degeneration of the metanephros secondary to maldevelopment of the ureter or the Wolffian duct (23); again, renal ectopia can result from retarded growth of the vertebral column (22). Further, hydrocephaly may follow from retarded development of the cerebral cortex, and closure of the aqueduct result from secondary compression of the midbrain by the distended cerebral hemispheres (24).

Any congenital abnormality must spring initially from disturbance of intracellular chemistry. Actively dividing cells are the most sensitive to teratogenic agents, although the phase when such sensitivity is maximal varies. Thus, radiation and radiomimetic substances such as chlorambucil cause fragmentation of chromosomes, the cell being most sensitive during the resting phase; colchicine, on the other hand, interferes with anaphase, so that mitosis is incomplete.

The mode of action of many teratogenic agents is uncertain although seemingly relevant facts are known in some instances. Thus, trypan blue, at one time used to treat mange in animals, is highly teratogenic and when injected into pregnant animals rapidly stains the maternal tissues; no similar coloration occurs in the embryo and it has been suggested that it may cross the placenta in a colorless form. However, when injected into pregnant rabbits, trypan blue alters the serum protein content of the maternal blood (16) and it is possible that this may lead, in turn, to abnormal placental transfer and subsequent fetal abnormality. In the case of PGA-deficiency the formation of nucleoproteins essential for growth and cell-division is probably disturbed; riboflavin deficiency, on the other hand, possibly interferes with oxidative processes in both the mother and the embryo.

The site of primary damage by a teratogenic agent conceivably many be either the placenta or the embryo; studies on the effect of maternal PGA deficiency, however, have shown that embryonic death precedes placental change, and it is probable that this sequence is common to many teratogenic procedures (15).

The teratogenic effects of antimetabolites generally can be counteracted by simultaneously supplying an adequate amount of the corresponding vitamin, yet in some instances an entirely different substance may also have an alleviating effect. Thus, in maternal vitamin A-deficiency in rats it has been observed that fetal damage can be reduced by thyroxine (20). Also, recent studies, again in rats, have shown that thalidomide increases the sensitivity of hemoglobin to oxidation by nitrites and that this can be prevented by simultaneously giving pyridoxine and riboflavin (19). In the future, it is possible that teratogenic side-effects of other-wise useful drugs may be prevented by prescribing with them antidotes to their undesired effects.

Testing for Teratogenicity

The fact that thalidomide has produced severe malformations in man when no such effects were found in test animals has drawn attention to the difficulties of screening substances for possible teratogenicity in man. Species, and even strain, differences often result in decidedly different responses to the same agent and this undoubtedly is related to genetic make-up.

Even where a drug is non-teratogenic for the majority of humans, there is always the possibility of teratogenic effect in a few individuals on account of their genetic constitution. This, however, is no different from drug sensitivity or post-vaccinal conditions which we are accustomed to anticipate in a small number of cases. New drugs, of course, must be intensively screened in a greater variety and number of test animals than before. This will help to reduce the chance of disaster in man. Also, we should not fail to check the old established drugs, the long-trusted components of the physician's armamentarium. In this regard, the demonstration of teratogenic action by salicylates (29) in rats should be kept in mind. In view of our present knowledge, avoiding drugs of all kinds in the early stages of pregnancy unless deemed absolutely necessary by the physician is obvious.

The quest for information on the causation of malformations also requires the detailed study of aborted human embryos. Too often normality or abnormality is determined by external inspection alone and, since a normal-looking embryo can have severe visceral abnormalities within, a diagnosis is of little value unless based on dissection, and possibly on histological and biochemical studies as well. Detailed examination of such material is time-consuming and requires special skills, but it must be undertaken and, wherever possible, the findings related to the maternal history. The establishment of centers to which human abortion material could be sent for special study would doubtless facilitate such an undertaking.

Lastly, while laboratory studies have an important part in the detection of teratogenic agents, an equally significant role is played by the practicing physician, for by astute observation and careful recording he can, as he has so often in the past, draw attention to actual or potential dangers and open the way to appropriate safeguards.

References

1. Baird, C. D. C., Nelson, M. M., Monie, I. W., and Evans, H. M.: Congenital cardiovascular anomalies induced by PGA-deficiency in the rat, Circulation Res. 2:544-554, 1954.
2. Ballantyne, J. W.: Manual of Antenatal Pathology, Vol. II, William Wood & Co., New York, 1902.
3. Bland-Sutton, J.: The Story of a Surgeon, Methuen, London, 1930.
4. Chamberlain, J.: Effects of 6-Aminonicotinamide on rat embryogenesis, Ph.D. Thesis, University of California, 1962.
5. Cohlan, S. Q.: Congenital anomalies in the rat produced by excessive intake of vitamin A during pregnancy, Pediatrics, 13:556-567, 1954.
6. Chin, E.: Combinations of teratogenic procedures in rat embryogenesis, Ph.D. Thesis, University of California, 1963.
7. Ebert, J. D.: First International Conference on Congenital Malformations, J. Chron. Dis., 13:91-132. 1961.
8. Fox, M. H., and Goss, C. M.: Experimental production of a syndrome of congenital cardiovascular defects in rats, Anat. Rec., 124:189-207, 1956.
9. Fraser, F. C.: Causes of congenital malformations in human beings, J. Chron. Dis., 10:97-110, 1959.
10. Giroud, A. J., and Lefebvres, J.: Anomalies provoquées chez le foetus en l'absence d'acide folique, Arch. franç. pediat., 8:648-656, 1951.
11. Gregg, N. M.: Congenital cataract following German measles in mother, Tr. Ophth. Soc. Australia, 3:35-46, 1942.
12. Hale, F.: Pigs born without eyeballs, J. Hered., 24:105-106, 1933.
13. Hanson, F. B.: Effects of x-rays on the albino rat, Anat. Rec., 24:415, 1923.
14. Job, T. T., Leibold, G. J., and Fitzmaurice, H. A.: Biological effects of roentgen rays, Amer. J. Anat., 56:97-117, 1935.

15. Johnson, E. M., and Nelson, M. M.: Morphological changes in embryonic development resulting from transitory PGA-deficiency in early pregnancy, Anat. Rec., 133:294, 1959.
16. Langman, J., and van Drunen, H.: The effect of trypan blue upon maternal protein metabolism and embryonic development, Anat. Rec., 133:513-526, 1959.
17. Lenz, W., and Knapp, K.: Thalidomide embryopathy, Arch. Envir. Health, 5:100-105, 1962.
18. Mall, F. P.: In Keibel and Mall's Human Embryology, Vol. 1, J. B. Lippincott Co., Philadelphia, 1910.
19. Metcalf, W. K.: Thalidomide, the nitrite sensitivity reaction and the vitamin B complex, Proc. Anat. Soc. Gt. Brit. and Ire., February 1963.
20. Millen, J. W., and Woollam, D. H. M.: Thyroxine and hypervitaminosis, A. J. Anat., 93:566, 1959.
21. Monie, I. W., Nelson, M. M., and Evans, H. M.: Persistent right umbilical vein as a result of vitamin deficiency during gestation, Circulation Res., 2:187-190, 1957.
22. Monie, I. W., Nelson M. M., and Evans, H. M.: Abnormalities of the urinary system of rat embryos resulting from transitory PGA-deficiency during gestation, Anat. Rec., 127:711-724, 1957.
23. Monie, I. W.: Chlorambucil-induced abnormalities of the urogenital system of rat fetuses, Anat. Rec., 139:145-152, 1961.
24. Monie, I. W., Armstrong, R. M., and Nelson, M. M.: Hydrocephaly in rat young as a result of PGA-deficiency from the 8th to 10th day of gestation, Anat. Rec., 139:315, 1961.
25. Nelson, M. M., Asling, C. W., and Evans H. M.: Production of multiple congenital abnormalities in young by maternal PGA-deficiency during gestation, J. Nutrition, 48:61-80, 1952.
26. Nelson, M. M., Wright, H. V., Asling, C. W., Evans, H. M.: Multiple congenital abnormalities resulting from transitory PGA-deficiency during gestation in the rat, J. Nutrition, 56:349-370, 1955.
27. Smith, G. E.: Fetal athyrosis. A study of the iodine requirements of the pregnant sow, J. Biol. Chem., 29:215-225, 1917.
28. Warkany, J., and Nelson, R. C.: Appearance of skeletal abnormalities in the offspring of rats reared on a deficient diet, Science, 92:383-384, 1940.
29. Warkany, J., and Takacs, E.: Experimental production of congenital malformations in rats by salicylate poisoning, Am. J. Path., 35:315-331, 1959.
30. Wilson, J. G.: Experimental studies on congenital malformations, J. Chron. Dis., 10:111-130, 1959.
31. Wilson, J. G., and Barch, S.: Fetal death and maldevelopment resulting from maternal vitamin A deficiency in the rat, Proc. Soc. Exp. Biol. & Med., 72:687-693, 1949.

43

THE GEOGRAPHY OF DEATH

G. Melvyn-Howe

Britain's comprehensive National Health Service ensures that medical care and attention is available to all classes of society with a comparatively high degree of equality. It also means that relatively uniform statistics are available about the nation's health. Causes of death, for instance, are classified according to an internationally agreed system, and all deaths are listed according to the place of usual residence of the deceased. Using such data, and making due allowances for differences in sex, local age structure and degree of urbanization, we can compute "standardized mortality ratios" for different administrative units of the country—counties, towns, and so on. The standardized mortality ratio (SMR) expresses the mortality for the inhabitants of a particular local area as a percentage of that for the country as a whole, which is taken as 100.

When we plot such ratios on a map, some interesting variations emerge. Figure 43-1 shows the distribution of deaths (SMR's) in England and Wales from all causes for men for the period 1959-63. Broadly speaking, mortality is above the national average north and west of a line from the Severn estuary to the estuary of the Humber, and it is below the national average to the east and south. There are some exceptions to this generalization in the London area, as shown in the inset map.

Of course, such geographical maps could be misleading. The map of England and Wales used as the base for Fig. 43-1, for example, represents the *areas* in which people die—i.e. the metropolitan boroughs, county boroughs and urban and rural districts of administrative counties. It thus tends to give undue prominence to the

mortality data of extensive, sparsely and unevenly populated areas such as parts of Cumberland, Westmorland, Northumberland, Montgomeryshire, Radnorshire, Merioneth and Devon. Conversely, it gives insufficient weight to the limited and localized areas of dense population associated with the industrial and manufacturing complexes of Greater London, Birmingham—Black Country, Manchester—Salford, Liverpool, Leeds and Bradford. The map creates incorrect visual impressions of regional intensities of mortality incidence.

We can overcome this distortion by relating deaths to numbers of people, rather than areas of the country. Figure 43-2 shows a map of this sort, which illustrates the same mortality data as that in Fig. 43-1 (male deaths from all causes 1959-63), but in this instance it is related to local *populations* "at risk" to disease. The squares represent urban populations and the diamonds rural populations. When we use such a demographic base map, main centres of population assume increased proportions, while large counties with numerically small populations are reduced in area relative to the country as a whole.

On this map it can be seen that the Merseyside-South Lancashire area has extremely high mortality ratios—24 and 22 per cent above the national average in Manchester and Salford respectively. The peak occurs in Salford, where the SMR is 133. Across the Pennines, the high ratios in Leeds, Sheffield and the municipal boroughs and urban districts of the West Riding culminate in exceptionally high ratios in Bradford, Halifax and Dewsbury.

In the Midlands, Stoke-upon-Trent, West Bromwich and Burton-upon-Trent stand out as concentrations of particularly unfavourable mortality in an area characterized otherwise by only moderately high ratios. In the North East, the figures are particularly unfavourable in Middlesbrough, Newcastle-upon-Tyne, Gateshead and South Shields and in South Wales the mining towns of Glamorgan record extremely high ratios.

Four of the metropolitan boroughs—Southwark, Stepney, Shoreditch and St. Marylebone have extremely high mortality ratios, and several others come into the moderately high

Reprinted from the *New Scientist* 40: 612-14, 1968, with the permission of the publishers.

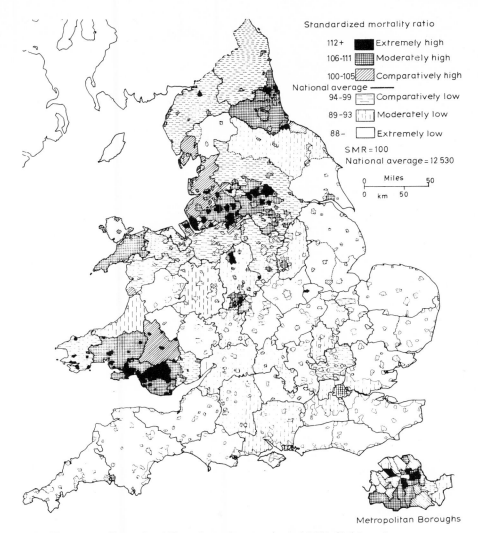

Standardized mortality ratio

112+	■	Extremely high
106-111	▦	Moderately high
100-105	▨	Comparatively high
National average	——	
94-99	▤	Comparatively low
89-93	▥	Moderately low
88-	☐	Extremely low

S M R = 100
National average = 12 530

Miles
0   50
0   km   50

Metropolitan Boroughs

43-1. Mortality in England and Wales from all causes (males) 1959-63 (plotted on a geographical base map).

category. In contrast, the large urban populations of Middlesex, Surrey, Kent, Essex and Herefordshire have mortality ratios that are 10 per cent below the national average.

Geographical patterns of mortality are also evident when individual diseases are examined on a more local scale. Thus the SMR for chronic bronchitis in London is 35 per cent above the national rate, according to the figures for the period 1959-63. Yet there are remarkable variations of mortality in different parts of London. Shoreditch is exceptional, with a SMR two and a half times the national average. Stepney, Bethnal Green and Southwark have

ratios which are twice the national figure. Chelsea, Hampstead, Holborn, Kensington and Westminster, on the other hand, have ratios which are *below* the national average, by as much as 17 per cent in the case of Hampstead.

The origins of chronic bronchitis are not fully understood but there is strong evidence that cigarette smoking, air pollution and episodes of infection are important causal factors. Are variations in smoking habits or in the distribution of atmospheric pollution within the London area such as to account for such pronounced local variations in mortality from chronic bronchitis? Or do the variations hint at

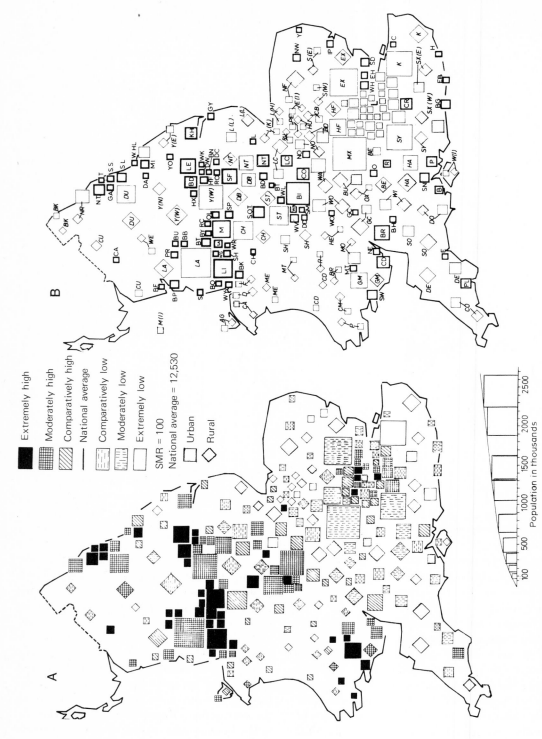

Fig. 43.2. (A) Mortality in England and Wales from all causes (males) 1959-63 (plotted on a demographic base map). (B) Key.

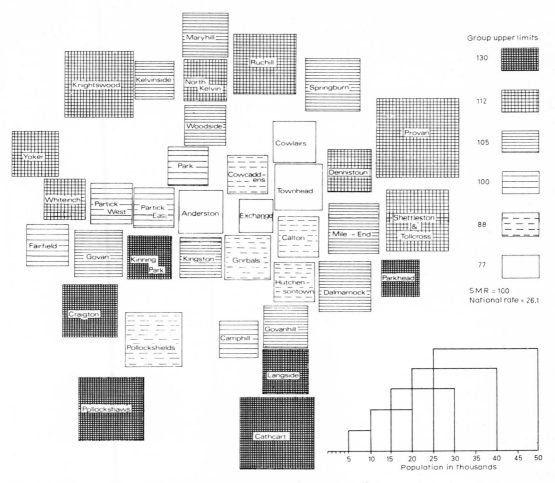

Fig. 43-3. *Mortality from arteriosclerotic heart disease, including coronary disease (males) in Glasgow, 1959-63.*

a social or occupational gradient, or a constitutional element in susceptibility to the condition? Presumably atmospheric pollution is one of the major factors at work, but we still do not understand the relative importance of the other possible factors.

Disease patterns are discernible even on the scale of individual wards or parishes. Figure 43-3 shows the distribution of standardized mortality ratios for coronary heart disease in men for the period 1959-63 in the 37 wards of Glasgow. The city as a whole has a mortality rate for coronary disease that is 25 per cent above the national average. Some wards on the south side of the city (Kinning Park, Craigton, Pollokshaws, Cathcart and Langside) have a

concentration of high ratios, ranging from 13 to 30 per cent above the United Kingdom rate. Yet other wards near the centre of the city (Anderston, Exchange, Townhead, Cowlairs) have quite favourable mortality figures. Here the ratios are 20 per cent or more *below* the national average.

Coronary heart disease is a disease of old age, although there are indications that the cause may be found in diet and in the neuroendocrine stress of modern life. A relationship with water supply has been hinted at. In this context the mortality figures for Glasgow and London are interesting. Glasgow is a soft water supply and a high rate of cardiovascular disease, London has a hard water supply and a much lower rate from the disease. But there are appreciable variations in the character of the London water supply in different areas and also areal variations in mortality from cardiovascular disease. Between 1959 and 1963, the London administrative county had an overall SMR of 102, but for Hampstead the figure was 117. St. Marylebone had a SMR of 115, Stoke Newington 112, Poplar 95, Greenwich 92 and Holborn 85.

The mortality variations within Glasgow, shown on Fig. 43-3, may occur because this city also has different water sources (Loch Katrine, Gorbals, etc.) and different characters to its water supply. It seems unlikely that the stress and responsibilities of modern life are any greater in Glasgow than they are in London, or that the diets are very different.

The demonstration of mortality patterns for various causes of death, whether on a national or more local scale, provide planners with valuable information on social malaise and at the same time contribute to epidemiological research. When a mortality index is used, a direct measure of incidence is provided for those diseases which have a high fatality rate. But for disease in which the fatality rate is low—as for example, rheumatoid arthritis—the mortality index is at best a poor index of incidence. Even so, it is possible that additional knowledge of geographical incidence of specific disease in population groups will provide clues to the causation of diseases for which the aetiology is as yet unknown.

Certainly, the information obtained provides pointers to local areas for research in depth. If the economic, social, genetic and other factors involved can be reduced to manageable parameters, statistical techniques and appropriate computer programmes might be used to evaluate the measure of correlation of possible cause-effect relationships.

44

AIR POLLUTION SURVEILLANCE SYSTEMS

George B. Morgan, Guntis Ozolins, and Elbert C. Tabor

The activities of man, the intellectual species, must be in harmony with the natural environment. Such harmony, however, will be achieved only when precepts for managing the renewable resources are as firmly entrenched in our individual lore of survival as the tutored reflex to "look both ways before crossing the street." Until that day arrives, organized society will have to compensate collectively for indifferent, careless, or deliberately negligent in-

Reprinted from *Science* 170: 289-96, 1970, with the permission of the publishers. Copyright 1970 by the American Association for the Advancement of Science.

dividuals. Policing the potability of drinking water is representative of such community action on behalf of the individual. Likewise, management of our air resources is increasingly being reorganized as a new community responsibility.

Surveillance of air pollution is an integral and very important part of the total effort to control air pollution. The data derived from atmospheric monitoring and emission measurements are required throughout the various stages of the abatement effort. Atmospheric surveillance efforts serve to identify the pollutants emitted to the air, to establish their concentrations, and to record their trends and patterns. Subsequently, after air quality and emission standards have been legislated, surveillance systems may be used to evaluate the progress being made in meeting standards, and to facilitate direct enforcement activities including the activation of emergency control procedures during episodes of high air pollution.

In the following discussion of surveillance we shall briefly summarize the types of pollutants and their sources, describe the current instrumentation and anticipated developments of more specific and sensitive sensors, and discuss the contrast between the air quality in our nation's urban environment and that of the rural environment or so-called background air quality.

Nature and Origins of Pollutants

Air pollutants can occur in the form of gases, solid particles, or liquid aerosols. These forms can exist either separately or in combinations; for example, gases may be sorbed on particulates or in liquid droplets (1). Gaseous pollutants constitute about 90 percent of the total mass emitted to the atmosphere, and particulates and liquid aerosols make up the other 10 percent.

Gaseous pollutants are evolved primarily from combustion of fuels and refuse. In the case of sulfur oxides, the burning of high-sulfur fuels in stationary sources is the primary source. Motor vehicles account for most of the carbon monoxide and hydrocarbon emissions which result from the incomplete combustion of the fuel used. Estimated emissions of particulates and the principal gaseous pollutants for the United States for 1968 are shown in Table 1 (2).

Particulates are emitted by a diverse group of sources and vary over a wide range of sizes, shapes, densities, and chemical compositions. Combustion of fuels, incineration of waste materials, and industrial process losses are responsible for the major share of particulate pollutants. Abrasion and wear of materials plus reentrainment resulting from vehicular traffic and wind action make a small contribution to the total burden. Even though particulates make up only 10 percent of the total quantity of pollutants released to the atmosphere, they are a significant problem because of their widely varying economic and biological effects (3).

Particulate pollutants are readily transported and dispersed by the wind (4). Small particles essentially become permanent residents in the atmosphere until removed by some process such as rainout, or by agglomeration into larger particles. Included in this size range are the respirable particulates, that is, those particles smaller than about 10 micrometers (5). This range also includes the particles that increase atmospheric turbidity, which attenuates both solar and terrestrial infrared radiation, and thereby is capable of affecting climate on a global basis (6).

Given suitable conditions, many of the primary pollutants (those gases and particulates that are emitted directly from sources) will participate in reactions in the atmosphere that produce secondary pollutants such as those found in photochemical smog. One example of the production of secondary pollutants is the combination of water vapor with acid anhydrides to produce an acid aerosol that is corrosive. Particulates may provide a substrate for such atmospheric reactions or may contain metallic catalysts. Solar energy, primarily the ultraviolet portion of the spectrum, accelerates these reactions.

Concentrations of pollutants are extremely

Table 1. Estimated emissions of principal pollutants in the United States during 1968 (in metric tons per year × 10⁶).

Source	Particu- lates	Sulfur oxides (SO_x)	Nitrogen oxides (NO_x)	Carbon monoxide	Hydro- carbons (HC)
Stationary fuel combustion	8.1	22.1	9.1	1.7	0.6
Mobile fuel combustion	1.1	0.7	7.3	57.9	15.1
Combustion of refuse	0.9	0.1	0.5	7.1	1.5
Industrial processes	6.8	6.6	0.2	8.8	4.2
Solvent evaporation					3.9
Total	16.9	29.5	17.1	75.5	25.3

variable from one city to another and also within a given urban area. The relative intensity and spatial configuration of sources, the topography, and the meteorology of an area affect pollutant concentrations. Zones of heavier pollution in each city are caused by the clustering of major sources of air pollution, that is, traffic-congested central business districts and industrial sectors. In cities characterized by good ventilation, emissions are dispersed more rapidly than in cities that are surrounded by hills or where the winds are low and temperature inversions are frequent.

Even areas with typically good dispersion can occasionally suffer pollution episodes when a stagnant high-pressure air mass persists. The Environmental Science Services Administration (ESSA), in cooperation with the National Air Pollution Control Administration (NAPCA), provides forecasts of stagnant conditions through the issuance of High Air Pollution Potential Advisories. An example of the forecast map which can be produced from these data is shown in Fig. 44-1 (7). The extensive area covered by the advisory report indicates the need for nationwide forecasting and coordinated control strategies.

Fig. 44-1. Advisory No. 122 (National Meteorological Center Advisory of High Air Pollution Potential, 28 July to 1 August 1970, 1300 E.S.T.)

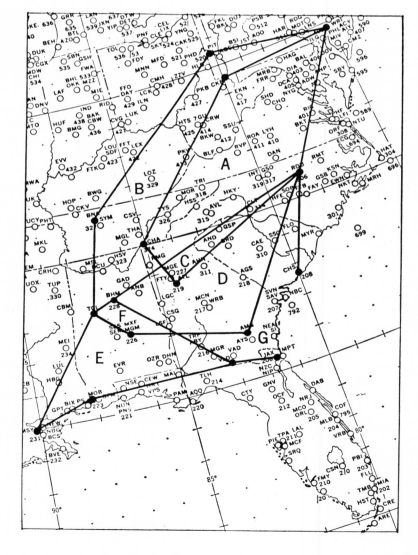

Surveillance

The first national air surveillance system was implemented in 1953 when the Public Health Service, in cooperation with state and local health departments, set up air sampling stations in 17 communities. Samples were collected primarily to permit the determination of total airborne protein. In addition, they were analyzed for total suspended particulates, organic matter soluble in benzene and acetone, and several inorganic pollutants. At present NAPCA is collecting air quality data for the pollutants listed in Table 2. Table 3 presents some typical average concentrations of some of these pollutants for the period from 1964 to 1965.

The present-day surveillance of the nation's air quality is a cooperative effort involving local, state, and federal air pollution control agencies. There are over 7,000 sampling stations, with some 14,000 samplers, located throughout the United States (Table 4). They range in complexity from simple static sampling

Table 2. Atmospheric pollutants currently being measured by NAPCA.

Elements	Radicals
Antimony	Ammonium
Arsenic	Fluoride
Barium	Nitrate
Beryllium	Sulfate
Bismuth	
Boron	Others
Cadmium	Aeroallergens
Chromium	Asbestos
Cobalt	β-Radioactivity
Copper	Benzene-soluble organic
Iron	compounds
Lead	Benzol[a]pyrene
Manganese	Pesticides
Mercury	Respirable particulates
Molybdenum	Total suspended particulates
Nickel	
Selenium	Gases
Tin	Carbon monoxide
Titanium	Methane
Vanadium	Nitric oxide
Zinc	Nitrogen dioxide
	Pesticides
	Reactive hydrocarbons
	Sulfur dioxide
	Total hydrocarbons
	Total oxidants

devices to continuous sampler-analyzers that record the concentrations of numerous gaseous air pollutants. Most of these sampling stations are located in the major metropolitan areas of the country. Table 4 provides an analysis of current sampling activities in the United States by type of sampler and pollutant.

The surveillance conducted by state and local air pollution control agencies is directed toward enforcement activities. Aerometric data are used to appraise concentrations of specific pollutants to determine if they exceed the standards, to provide direct control actions, to determine ambient air quality in nonurban areas of a region, and to provide air quality data during air pollution episodes. These surveillance systems are primarily designed to sample for pollutants for which criteria documents have been issued, that is, total suspended particulates, sulfur dioxide, carbon monoxide, total oxidants, and total hydrocarbons. The placement or location of sampling stations within the surveillance network must be such that ensuing data can be gainfully employed to meet the following objectives: (i) Stations must be oriented to define air quality in heavily polluted areas; (ii) stations must be oriented to define air quality in heavily populated areas; (iii) stations must be located to provide area-wide representation of ambient air quality; (iv) stations must be oriented with respect to the source category or source, or both, to provide feedback relative to the effectiveness of adopted control strategies.

The federal monitoring system provides a uniform data base throughout the country against which all other air quality data can be verified; this system measures pollutants that are expensive or unusually difficult to analyze, identifies and quantifies new or newly recognized pollutants, conducts research in measurement techniques, and demonstrates the impact of pollutant emissions of the air quality of both urban and nonurban areas.

Instrumentation

Solid-state or advanced sensors that have sensitivity, specificity, and reliability are

Table 3. Arithmetic mean and maximum urban particulate concentrations in the United States, biweekly sampling, 1964 to 1965 (16, p. 16).

Pollutant	Number of stations	Concentration ($\mu g/m^3$)	
		Arithmetic average*	Maximum
Suspended particulates	291	105	1254
Fractions:			
Benzene-soluble organic compounds	218	6.8	†
Nitrates	96	2.6	39.7
Sulfates	96	10.6	101.2
Ammonium	56	1.3	75.5
Antimony	35	0.001	0.160
Arsenic	133	0.02	†
Beryllium	100	<0.0005	0.010
Bismuth	35	<0.0005	0.064
Cadmium	35	0.002	0.420
Chromium	103	0.015	0.330
Cobalt	35	<0.0005	0.060
Copper	103	0.09	10.00
Iron	104	1.58	22.00
Lead	104	0.79	8.60
Manganese	103	0.10	9.98
Molybdenum	35	<0.005	0.78
Nickel	103	0.034	0.460
Tin	85	0.02	0.50
Titanium	104	0.04	1.10
Vanadium	99	0.050	2.200
Zinc	99	0.67	58.00
Gross β-radioactivity	323	0.8 pc/m^3	12.4 pc/m^3

* Arithmetic averages are presented to permit comparable expression of averages derived from quarterly composite samples.
† No individual sample analyses performed.

urgently needed and would overcome the problems that now exist with present wet chemical methods. In addition, new techniques will be needed as the air pollution control effort is expanded to encompass the less abundant and newly recognized air pollutants. Examples of some of the pollutants for which adequate or economical instrumentation and analytical techniques are not yet available include asbestos, pesticides, mercury, odors, and selenium. It is important that measurement methods be capable of providing information for averaging times (8) consistent with established air quality standards.

A variety of sampling devices are currently being used to evaluate ambient air quality. Table 5 illustrates the general classes and their applicability. Mechanized samplers are the most generally used in surveillance systems to collect integrated samples in the field. The most common of these devices is NAPCA's high volume (Hi-Vol) sampler which collects particulates on glass-fiber filters. Analysis of these samples provides information on concentrations of total suspended particulates, trace metals, and other organic and inorganic pollutants. In addition to the glass-fiber filter, the membrane filter is used to collect for subsequent analysis pollutants such as zinc, asbestos, boron, and silicates. Impactors of different designs are used to measure fractions of suspended particulates of various particle sizes in the respirable range.

Mechanized bubbler devices may be employed to collect sulfur dioxide, nitrogen

Table 4. Estimated number of air surveillance devices in routine operation in the United States, June 1970. Static equipment passively depends upon the natural movement of air currents to bring pollutants to the collector. Mechanized collection devices accumulate samples continuously or intermittently for subsequent laboratory analysis. Automatic devices are continuously operating sampler-analyzers that produce results directly in numerical or visual form, or both.

Pollutant and method	Nonfederal agencies	NAPCA	Total
	Static		
Gases: sulfation rate	2,933	214	3,147
Particulates:			
Settleable (dustfall)	3,220		3,220
Windblown (sticky paper)	897		897
	Mechanized		
Gases:			
Aldehydes	271		271
Ammonia	262		262
Nitrogen dioxide	362	200	562
Oxidants	395		395
Mercury		50	50
Sulfur dioxide	515	200	715
Hydrogen sulfide	153		153
Particulates:			
Suspended (Hi-Vol)	2,074	293	2,367
Membrane filter		55	55
Cascade-fractional		15	15
Soiling (spot tape)	461	10	471
	Automatic		
Gases:			
Aldehyde	16		16
Carbon monoxide	218	10	228
Carbon dioxide	10		10
Hydrogen sulfide	83		83
Nitric oxide	117	17	134
Nitrogen dioxide	189	17	206
Oxidants	122	14	136
Sulfur dioxide	235	44	279
Particulates:			
Soiling (automatic tape)	367	7	374
Total	12,900	1,146	14,046

dioxide, oxidants, hydrogen sulfide, aldehydes, carbon dioxide, and ammonia. These samplers, although typically designed for the collection of 24-hour integrated samples, can be modified to collect 1- or 2-hour samples in sequence for the definition of diurnal variations. In the automatic sampler-analyzer the collection and analytical processes are combined in a single device. This type of instrument produces a continuous analysis with the output in a machine-readable format or in a form suitable for telemetry to a central data-acquisition facility. Continuous analyzers of this type are now available for carbon monoxide, carbon

dioxide, nitric oxide, nitrogen dioxide, sulfur dioxide, total hydrocarbons, methane, oxidants, ozone, and hydrogen sulfide. Although a large number and variety of these analyzers are on the market, only a few have been properly field-tested to determine their limitations, reliability, and durability and to provide necessary information on interferences.

The National Air Pollution Control Administration, in cooperation with the Intersociety Committee (9), is actively engaged in the development of standard methods. In the interim, the criteria documents published by NAPCA under the provisions of the Clean Air

Table 5. Classification of air pollution sampling techniques. Cost basis: low, 0 to $500; moderate, $500 to $2000; high, above $2000. Personnel training: low, maintenance level; moderate, technician; high, experienced technician or professional with professional support staff.

Type	Use	Specificity	Common averaging time	Relative cost	Required training of personnel	Remarks
Static						
Settleable particulates (dustfall)	Mapping and definition of special problem areas	Total settled particulates and general classes of pollutants	1 month	Collection, low; analysis, high	Collection, low; analysis, moderate	Well-equipped laboratory required for analysis only for definition of problem areas where a chemical analysis will pinpoint a particular source. Sensitive to temperature, wind, and humidity.
Sulfation devices	Mapping and general survey for sulfur dioxide	Responds to oxides of sulfur, hydrogen sulfide, and sulfuric acid	1 month	Collection, low; analysis, high	Collection, low; analysis moderate to high	
Mechanized						
Hi-Vol	Integrated quantification of suspended particulate	Total suspended particulate and multiple specific pollutants	24 hours	Moderate	Moderate	Detailed chemical analysis of Hi-Vol and gas samples requires sophisticated laboratory, trained chemists; cost is high.
Gas sampler	Integrated quantification of gases	Sulfur dioxide, nitrogen dioxide, ammonia, total oxidants, aldehydes, and other gases	24 hours	Moderate	High	
Automatic						
Spot tape sampler	Relative soiling index	Unknown	2 hours	Low	Low	Provides only a rough, relative index of particulate soiling.
Gas	Continuous analysis of gaseous pollutants	Single gas or group of related gases	Continuous; sample integration usually 1 to 15 minutes	Moderate to high	Moderate to high	Continuous measurements allow use of any desired averaging time by computation. Accuracy is generally much better than other methods. Calibration is simplified. Data are available instantaneously.
Particulate: soiling (automatic tape)	Continuous analysis of soiling rate	Unknown	Continuous; sample integration usually 1 to 15 minutes	Moderate	Moderate	

Act of 1967 include recommendations that reference methods be used for the intercomparison of analysis schemes.

For the production of valid data, by whatever method, it is vital that calibration of the sensors be maintained by use of a dynamic system. Pollutants are commonly found in the atmosphere in such low concentrations that the production of calibration standards is a problem. The National Air Pollution Control Administration has developed permeation devices for a few gases (10) which, when properly employed in a dynamic calibration system, can be used to deliver known quantities of certain gases for spiking ambient air. Techniques for the dynamic calibration of particulate samplers, especially with regard to size fractionation, are poorly developed at this time.

Future Instrument Development

In the past, the operation of most mechanized and automatic analyzers has been based on wet chemical methods. These methods have inherent problems and are not entirely satisfactory for typical field applications because they must be attended frequently, reagents are unstable, and the instrumentation requires complex plumbing and accurate solution pumps with the result that the instruments are heavy and bulky. Future instruments hopefully will utilize the physical or physicochemical properties of pollutants for identification and quantification.

The following new instruments are now in the final stages of development and field-testing by NAPCA:

1. A chemiluminescent method for determining ozone.
2. A flame-luminescent method for measuring sulfur.
3. A triple system for continuously measuring carbon monoxide, sulfur dioxide, and nitrogen dioxide. The sensors in this system are based upon the fuel-cell principle and time-share the circuitry.
4. An automated gas chromatograph for the simultaneous determination of carbon monoxide, methane, and total hydrocarbons.
5. An automated gas chromatograph for measuring hydrogen sulfide and certain organic sulfides.
6. A special adaptation of lidar (light detection and ranging) instruments for estimating concentrations of atmospheric particulates.
7. An atomic absorption method for continuously measuring lead.
8. A piezoelectric instrument for the continuous measurement of particulate concentrations.
9. A specific-ion electrode method for the continuous measurement of fluorides.
10. A method for determining oxides of nitrogen in which ozone is titrated in the gas phase with a reactive gas and the reaction produces light by chemi-luminescence.

Extensive research is in progress to develop remote sensing devices to be used at ground level, in aircraft, and in earth satellites for area-scanning and profiling. The application of newer laboratory techniques such as microwave absorption spectrometry (11), electron or ion microprobe analysis (12), and neutron activation analysis (13) have recently been reported. In NAPCA's laboratories emission spectrometry, atomic absorption spectrometry, chromatography, and several other techniques are now computer-interfaced and in routine use.

Data Handling and Analysis

A vital part of any successful surveillance system is the processing and reporting of the data in a format that can be used conveniently by the control official or researcher. The National Air Pollution Control Administration is developing a National Aerometric Data Information Service (NADIS) which will incorporate the present National Aerometric Data Bank (NADB) and a software system for the Storage and Retrieval of Aerometric Data (SAROAD), which provides a system for reporting, storing, and analyzing aerometric data from a wide variety of sources. All agencies collecting air quality and emission data are urged by NAPCA to use this format. These efforts will put all aerometric data on a comparable basis and will permit data from various regions of the United States to be compared.

Current Air Quality and Trends

A recent summary of data on suspended particulates from 60 urban stations (14) for the period 1957 to 1966 shows a slight downward trend at most center-city sites. This trend results primarily from urban renewal, replacement of coal by fuel oil and gas for space heating, and more effective control of particulate emission. In comparison, an analysis over a period of 10 years of data on suspended particulates from 20 nonurban locations shows an upward trend at stations that are considered rural.

A comparison of Tables 6 and 7 indicates two distinct patterns of pollution. The incidence of suspended particulates is not directly related to city size; in fact, stations with the highest levels are found in medium-sized, heavily industrialized cities. In large urban areas, the sources of particulate pollution are dispersed,

whereas in heavily industrialized, medium-sized cities sources generally are clustered in areas proximate to the urban core. In contrast, sulfur dioxide concentrations are usually higher in large cities because of the combustion of fossil fuels for space heating and power. These sulfur dioxide sources are also more evenly distributed than particulate sources. A linear relationship exists between population and sulfur dioxide pollution. This relationship is quite evident for areas where high-sulfur fuels are in general use.

The numbers in boldface type in Tables 6 and 7 indicate the approximate range for yearly averages of total suspended particulates and sulfur dioxide at which ambient air quality standards are being set (15, 16). The data in Tables 6 and 7 represent center-city sites, and in many cases the concentrations are not necessarily the highest concentrations existing within the community.

Table 8 shows average concentrations of carbon monoxide, nitric oxide, nitrogen dioxide, sulfur dioxide, hydrocarbons, and oxidants at NAPCA's six continuous-monitoring stations. No clear trends have been identified in the concentration of these gaseous pollutants at these six center-city sites, an indication that for some time emissions have

Table 6. Distribution of National Air Surveillance Network data from stations that monitor suspended particulates for 1968. Entry in body of table shows number of center-city stations, grouped by city population, whose annual geometric means fall in each concentration range. Boldface values indicate concentration range in which urban U.S. standards were being set as of July 1970 (17).

Population	Suspended particulates ($\mu g/m^3$)											
	0–19	20–39	40–59	60–79	80–99	100–119	120–139	140–159	160–179	180–199	200	Total
					Urban							
>3,000,000						**2**						2
1,000,000 to 3,000,000						**1**	2					3
700,000 to 1,000,000			1	2	3		3					9
400,000 to 700,000			1	4	9	**1**	1	1	1			18
100,000 to 400,000			6	25	16	**17**	5	1	2	1	1	74
50,000 to 100,000			5	18	19	**12**	4	3				62
25,000 to 50,000		4	13	16		**2**	2				2	46
10,000 to 25,000		3	12	15	7	**5**		1				43
<10,000		7	8	18	11	**1**	1		1			47
Total		14	46	98	72	**41**	18	6	4	1	4	304
					Nonurban							
	10	16	4									

Table 7. Distribution of National Air Surveillance Network data from stations monitoring sulfur dioxide for 1968. Entry in body of table shows number of center-city stations, grouped by city population, whose annual arithmetic means fall in each concentration range. Boldface values indicate concentration range in which urban U.S. standards were being set as of July 1970 (17).

Population	Sulfur dioxide (µg/m³)											
	0–9	10–19	20–29	30–39	40–49	50–59	60–69	70–79	80–89	90–99	>100	Total
>3 million					Urban						2	2
1,000,000 to 3,000,000							1			1		2
700,000 to 1,000,000	1	3		1			1		3	1		10
400,000 to 700,000	2	5	5	3		1		1			1	18
100,000 to 400,000	7	5	11	2	5	4	2	2	2		2	42
50,000 to 100,000	1	4	2	2			2	1	1			13
25,000 to 50,000	1	1			1							3
10,000 to 25,000	1	2	1									3
<10,000	13	1	2			1						5
Total		21	21	8	6	6	6	4	6	2	5	98
					Nonurban							
	2	3										

Table 8. Average 1968 concentrations of carbon monoxide, nitric oxide, nitrogen dioxide, sulfur dioxide, hydrocarbons, and total oxidants at NAPCA's continuous monitoring stations.

Concentration	CO (mg/m³)	NO (µg/m³)	NO₂ (µg/m³)	SO₂ (µg/m³)	HC (mg/m³)	Oₓ (µg/m³)
	CO (mg/m³)	NO (µg/m³)	NO_2 (µg/m³)	SO_2 (µg/m³)	HC (mg/m³)	O_x (µg/m³)
			Chicago			
Annual av.	7.1	89	90	310	1.9	47
Max. monthly av.	8.2	130	110	700	2.2	86
Max. 24-hr. av.	18.0	280	190	1340	3.5	220
Max. 1-hr. av.	46.0	750	340	2300	8.1	350
			Cincinnati			
Annual av.	6.4	*	60	45	1.7	*
Max. monthly av.	8.9	95	90	89	2.1	*
Max. 24-hr. av.	37	420	190	210	3.7	98
Max. 1-hr. av.	48	1250	1100	1000	9.5	270
			Denver			
Annual av.	6.2	46	68	34	1.9	58
Max. monthly av.	8.4	89	98	71	2.7	78
Max. 24-hr. av.	24	260	230	130	4.2	160
Max. 1-hr. av.	91	750	510	630	11.3	510
			Philadelphia			
Annual av.	9.9	66	73	210	1.4	45
Max. monthly av.	13.2	120	100	430	1.6	60
Max. 24-hr. av.	27	460	170	940	3.1	160
Max. 1-hr. av.	40	1750	380	2300	6.4	410
			St. Louis			
Annual av.	5.3	39	43	73	2.2	43
Max. monthly av.	6.4	60	70	140	3.1	57
Max. 24-hr. av.	10	160	94	420	6.4	98
Max. 1-hr. av.	30	500	340	1800	10.8	450
			Washington, D.C.			
Annual av.	3.9	43	88	97	1.5	53
Max. monthly av.	7.6	94	100	250	2.0	84
Max. 24-hr. av.	16	380	150	470	3.7	200
Max. 1-hr. av.	31	850	450	1100	8.8	490

* Insufficient data for a representative value.

essentially reached a plateau, probably because of source saturation of the centers of most cities.

Summary

Atmospheric surveillance is necessary in order to identify airborne pollutants, to establish ambient concentrations of these pollutants, and to record their trends and patterns. Air pollutants may occur in the form of gases, liquids, and solids, both singly and in combination. Gaseous pollutants make up about 90 percent of the total mass emitted to the atmosphere with particulates and aerosols accounting for the remaining 10 percent. Small particulates are of particular importance because they may be in the respirable size range. These small particles may contain biologically active elements and compounds. Furthermore, they tend to remain in the atmosphere where they interfere with both solar and terrestrial infrared radiation, which may affect climate on a global basis.

Gases and particulates may undergo a variety of reactions to produce secondary pollutants that in some cases are more toxic than the parent pollutants. This is particularly true in the case of photochemical smog. Pollutant concentrations are directly related to the density of industry and the use of fossil fuels for power and space heating. Cities that have poor ventilation or frequent temperature inversions are plagued with air pollution episodes.

States have the primary responsibility for atmospheric surveillance. Surveillance systems are usually established on a city or regional basis. The federal monitoring system is to provide a base of uniform data for verification of data from the various agencies and to quantify pollutants that are difficult or expensive to measure.

Presently, the operation of most of the devices and analyzers used for measuring air pollutants is based on wet chemical methods. New techniques are needed in which solid-state or advanced sensing techniques that are based upon the physical or physicochemical properties of pollutants are used. A number of new instruments are presently being developed by NAPCA. In addition, NAPCA has automated and computer-interfaced some of its more sophisticated laboratory and field instrumentation.

Data presented indicate that concentrations of small particulates in the rural or nonurban parts of the country are increasing. Gaseous pollutant concentrations in center-city sites show no particular trend, an indication that downtown areas probably are, and have been for some time, source-saturated.

References and Notes

1. M. O. Amdur, *J. Air Pollut. Contr. Assn.* **19**, 638 (1969).
2. "National Emission Reference File," 1970 edition, compiled by A. Hoffman, National Air Pollution Control Administration, Durham, North Carolina.
3. P. M. Wolkonsky, *Arch. Environ. Health* **19**, 586 (1969).
4. A. C. Stern, Ed., *Air Pollution* (Academic Press, New York, ed. 2, 1968), vol. 1, p. 30. This work consists of three volumes containing basic resource information on air pollution.
5. T. F. Hatch, in *The Air We Breathe*, S. M. Farber and R. H. C. Wilson, Eds. (Thomas, Springfield, Ill., 1961), p. 115.
6. P. A. Sheppard, *Int. J. Air Pollut.* **1**, 31 (1968).
7. "The National Air Pollution Potential Forecast Program" [*Environ. Sci. Serv. Admin. Tech. Mem. WBTM NMC* 47 (May 1970)].
8. Averaging times are selected on the basis of data on pollutant effects. Common pollutant averaging times are 1 hour, 2 hours, 8 hours, 24 hours, 1 month, 3 months, and 1 year.
9. Member societies are: Air Pollution Control Association (APCA), American Council of Governmental Industrial Hygienists (ACGIH), American Industrial Hygiene Association (AIHA), American Public Health Association (APHA), American Society of Mechanical Engineers (ASME), American Society for Testing and Materials (ASTM), and Association of Official Analytical Chemists (AOCA).
10. A. E. O'Keefe and G. C. Ortman, *Anal. Chem.* **38**, 760 (1966).
11. A. P. Altshuller, personal communication.
12. O. U. Auden, *Anal. Chem.* **41**, 428 (1969).
13. B. Henry, personal communication.
14. R. Spirtas and H. J. Levin, "Characteristics of Particulate Patterns, 1957-1966" [*Nat. Air Pollut. Contr. Admin. Publ. No. Ap-61* (March, 1970)].
15. "Air Quality Criteria for Sulfur Oxides" [*Nat. Air Pollut. Contr. Admin. Publ. No. AP-50* (Jan. 1970)].

16. "Air Quality Criteria for Particulate Matter" [*Nat. Air Pollut. Contr. Admin. Publ. No. AP-49* (Jan. 1969)].

17. "1968 Data Tabulations and Summaries, Continuous Air Monitoring Project, Chicago" [*Air Pollut. Tech. Doc. 69-15* (1969)]; "Continuous Air Monitoring Project Cincinnati" [*Air Pollut. Tech. Doc. 69-16* (1969)]; "Continuous Air Monitoring Project, Denver" [*Air Pollut. Tech. Doc. 69-17* (1969)]; "Continuous Air Monitoring Project, Philadelphia" [*Air Pollut. Tech. Doc. 69-18* (1969)]; "Continuous Air Monitoring Project, St. Louis" [*Air Pollut. Tech. Doc. 69-19* (1969)]; "Continuous Air Monitoring Project, Washington, D.C." [*Air Pollut. Tech. Doc. 69-20* (1969)].

45

BASIC CONCEPTS OF EUTROPHICATION

Clair N. Sawyer

Eutrophication is a new word in the vocabulary of many sanitary engineers and scientists and is destined to become a part of the normal complement of words used by everyone concerned with the broad concept of water resources. The term is not a new one. It has been used by limnologists for nearly 50 years to describe the change in biological productivity which all lakes and reservoirs undergo during their life history.

Life History of Lakes and Reservoirs

Lakes and reservoirs are not permanent features of the landscape. Geologically speaking, they are only water-filled natural or man-made depressions in the earth's crust that are destined to become filled with soil and organic deposits as time passes. Fundamentally, they are giant sedimentation basins which not only serve to remove suspended matter from tributary waters but also act as giant reaction vessels for biological phenomena involving production of both plants and animals. From a strict conservationist viewpoint, the function of lakes is to retain on the land areas of the world those

Reprinted with permission from *Journal Water Pollution Control Federation* Vol. 38, pp. 737-744, 1966, Washington, D.C. 20016.

matters of value to the land and to prevent their being carried to the oceans.

The life span of lakes is normally reckoned in millenniums or even eons of time; however, there are exceptions. Lake Mead, the impoundment above Boulder Dam, is predicted to have a life of less than 150 years because of the tremendous silt load carried by the Colorado River (1). Lake Constance in the Rhine is expected to have a life of only 12,000 years, one-half already spent (2).

Historically, young lakes are relatively barren bodies of water in terms of the amount of biological life which they support. In this phase they are referred to as being oligotrophic. As aging progresses the materials retained by the lake gradually increase in the bottom sediments and, through bacterial and other decomposition of the sediments, the lake waters become richer and richer in nutrient materials on which phytoplankton thrive. Concurrent with the increase in phytoplankton, the population of zooplankton and higher animal forms responds accordingly, as the food supply gains in amount.

With the increase in biological productivity of a lake, major changes occur in both the surface and deeper waters. The lake passes from the oligotrophic phase through the mesotrophic and finally into the eutrophic phase. It continues in this until deposits from biological activity, both organic and inorganic, plus materials settled from tributary waters, fill the basin to the extent that rooted aquatic plants take command of the situation and gradually convert the area to marsh land. These changes are illustrated in Fig. 45-1.

The aging process of lakes and the effect of fertilization have been described admirably by

Fig. 45-1. Natural transition of a lake through various stages of productivity eventually resulting in extinction.

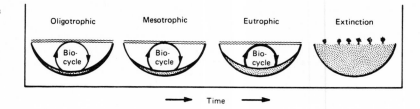

Hasler (3) as shown in Fig. 45-2. It also shows the effect of artificial fertilization on hastening the onset of eutrophication and shortening the life span of lakes. In a nutshell, it explains why we must consider the subject of eutrophication and what we can do about it.

Eutrophication

Is eutrophication good or bad? That is a question to which there is no "pat" answer, since so much depends on the purposes for which the lake or reservoir is used and the degree of eutrophication. Many oligotrophic lakes are "gems of beauty" which reflect the azure blue of the sky beyond description, serve as admirable water supplies, but provide little recreational opportunity beyond swimming and boating. In some instances (4) oligotrophic lakes have been fertilized purposely to increase the production of phytoplankton and indirectly the population of fish life, the desired product.

Some of our eutrophic lakes are extremely valuable because of their ability to provide excellent fishing and serve as general purpose recreational areas. Others are notorious because of their ability to produce highly obnoxious blooms of nuisance algae which are aesthetically objectionable to recreationists and to residents on the shore.

Although there are many factors such as depth, size, shape, and geographical location which determine the degree of eutrophication which would be classed as beneficial or detrimental, in general the basic factor involved is the algae nutrient budget of the lake as shown in Fig. 45-3. It is conceded generally that the biological productivity of a lake, in terms of phytoplankton, is related directly to the nutrients available per unit volume of water in the trophic zone. Of the nutrients entering a lake only a fraction escape in the effluent. The fraction depends on a great many factors of which retention time, location of outlet with respect to prevailing winds, and nature of dominant blooms are perhaps most significant.

Of the nutrients which enter the lake, a major part becomes incorporated into algae and other forms of life which eventually die and settle to the lake bottom. There they are digested by bacteria, protozoa, worms, etc.,

Fig. 45-2. Natural and induced eutrophication. [From Hasler (3).]

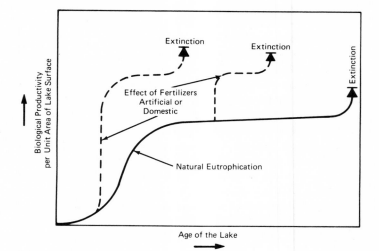

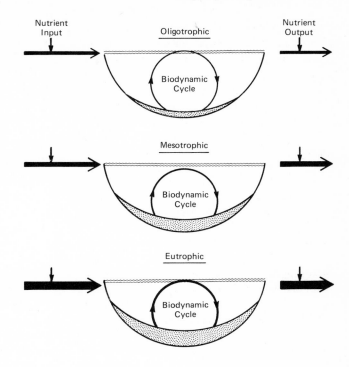

Fig. 45-3. Relationship between nutrient budget and the magnitude of the biodynamic cycle in various types of lakes.

with much of the nutrient materials solubilized. They then are free to leach back into the waters above and eventually become available to support further phytoplankton growths. The amount of nutrients which recycle from the bottom muds, of course, is proportional to the amount of material which drops to the mud from above.

There are many points of view on the question of eutrophication. Considering extreme positions, one might argue that the natural order of things is to let lakes convert to dry land and do nothing to stay the transition. Such a person has never had the experience of residing near a highly eutrophic lake or lived in an area devoid of lakes. On the other extreme, there are some who take the position of Hasler, who is reported to have said "it is clear that any increase in the rate of eutrophy, even if this involves only the acceleration of a natural and inevitable process is, from a human point of view, thoroughly undesirable." The latter seems somewhat idealistic. Somewhere between the two extremes should lie the "Happy Fishing Lake."

Parameters of Eutrophication

There are many parameters of eutrophication. In its advanced stages it can be detected by visual observation and often by the sense of smell. When conditions become repulsive and drastic steps are required to control obnoxious growths of algae, then there is no longer need to marshall experts or scientific equipment to explain what has happened.

It is the responsibility of the scientist and the engineer to devise ways and means of measuring the degree of eutrophication and of developing methods of arresting its onslaught. We no longer must be satisfied with methods which simply measure trends toward eutrophication and regard them as irresistible changes over which man has no control. We must recognize as did Strom (2) over 40 years ago as he wrote "When a lake has reached the real eutroph stage, the changes toward a greater degree of eutrophy are very speedily effected, indeed; the character of a lake can be materially changed within a generation" and we must be prepared to act.

The parameters of eutrophication may be placed into two broad classifications. One group may be classed as indirect indicators as they in themselves play no part in increasing the biological productivity on which eutrophication depends. Most of these are chemical in nature and have been called on for lack of more definitive data in many cases. Beeton (5) in his paper discussing eutrophication of the Great Lakes, resorts to the increases of total solids, calcium, sodium, potassium, sulfate, and chloride as supporting evidence of the growing eutrophication of all the lakes except Superior. None of these elements are prime factors in biological productivity. If they were, the oceans of the world would know no limit. The mounting amounts of these materials are concrete evidence of increasing amounts of human, industrial, and agricultural wastewaters, all of which carry prime nutrients and possibly stimulants for biological growths. Beeton made no mention of the nitrogen and phosphorus associated with these cations and anions, an oversight that has been perpetuated time and time again by limnological investigators in spite of the fact that it has been known for over 40 years (6) that the principal components of all aquatic life are carbon, hydrogen, oxygen, nitrogen, and phosphorus.

The direct methods of evaluating eutrophication may be subdivided into qualitative and quantitative types.

Qualitative

The qualitative type is well illustrated by the information presented in Table 1 which shows the nature of plankton in oligotrophic and eutrophic lakes according to Rawson (7). Use of the parameters listed to eutrophic lakes and recognition of their presence come much too late on the time scale and drastic action is required to overcome the damage done.

Certain organisms also have been proposed as indicators of the onset of eutrophication. A favorite one has been *Oscillatoria rubescens*. Others have been *Anabaena* of several species, *Aphanizomenon flos-aquae*, and *Microcystis aeruginosa*. All of these indicators signal that eutrophic conditions have arrived and that great damage may have occurred already.

Table 1. Plankton of oligotrophic and eutrophic lakes.

Parameter	Oligotrophic	Eutrophic
Quantity	Poor	Rich
Variety	Many species	Few species
Distribution	To great depths	Trophogenic layer
Diurnal migration	Extensive	Limited
Water-blooms	Very rare	Frequent
Characteristic algal groups or genera	Chlorophyceae	Cyanophyceae
	Desmids	*Anabaena*
	Staurastrum	*Aphanizomenon*
	Diatomaceae	*Microystis*
	Tabellaria	Diatomaceae
	Cyclotella	*Melosira*
	Chrysophyceae	*Fragilaria*
	Dinobryon	*Stephanodiscus*
		Asterionella

In the case of deep lakes which stratify, salmonid fishes have served as indicators. Their presence is used as evidence that the lake is oligotrophic; their absence and the presence of other coarser forms is considered evidence of eutrophic conditions.

Quantitative

A considerable variety of methods exists for the evaluation of the degree of biological productivity of a lake or reservoir. Fundamentally, we are concerned with all gradations of conditions between oligotrophic and eutrophic waters. Since the transition from one form to the other is gradual, the intermediate phase commonly is referred to as mesotrophic and is of great interest to those concerned with multiple uses of water resources.

The methods of quantitative assessment of the degree of eutrophication are listed in Table 2. Of these methods of measurement, oxygen determinations were the first to be used. Observations in the least productive lakes showed little change with depth while the more productive lakes showed a marked decrease in the hypolimnion, during the summer stagnation period, as illustrated in Figure 45-4. The changes in oxygen concentration were associated with the amount of organic matter in the form of dead algae and other life which entered the hypolimnion and exerted an oxygen de-

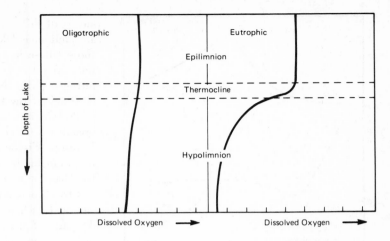

Fig. 45-4. Typical DO curves in oligotrophic and eutrophic lakes during summer stagnation.

Table 2. Methods of quantitative assessment of eutrophication.

Hypolimnetic oxygen
   Dissolved
   Rate of consumption
Biological productivity
   Standing crop
   Volume of algae
   Transparency
   Chlorophyll in epilimnion
   Oxygen production
   Carbon dioxide utilization
Nutrient levels
   Nitrogen
   Phosphorus
   Nitrogen-phosphorus ratios

mand in proportion to their quantity due to bacterial decomposition. From these observations, oligotrophic lakes were identified as those in which DO was not depleted seriously during the summer stagnation period and eutrophic lakes vice versa.

The use of DO as a parameter of eutrophication was refined further by Hutchinson (8) when, through observations of the rate of oxygen depletion, he concluded that the rate of loss of hypolimnetic oxygen in oligotrophic lakes ranged from 0.004 to 0.033 mg/day/sq cm and the rate of loss in eutrophic lakes ranged from 0.05 to 0.14 mg/day/sq cm as the upper limit for oligotrophy and 0.055 mg/day/sq cm as the lower limit for eutrophy. The range between 0.025 and 0.055 is reserved for mesotrophic lakes.

Measurements of biological productivity are, of course, the most direct way of evaluating eutrophication. Seven different methods have been used.

1. *Standing Crop.* Perhaps the oldest method of determining the extent of biological productivity of a body of water was to make observations on the concentrations of individual organisms of the various types at periodic intervals over a growing season. Under normal circumstances the results obtained produced a reasonable picture of the biological productivity which could be related to lake type but it entailed a great deal of time and effort.

2. *Volume of Algae.* Because of the great amount of labor involved in evaluating the standing crop many investigators have turned to a gross measurement of algae in terms of volume of algae. The results reported by Anderson (9) to show the increasing eutrophication of Lake Washington as shown in Figure 45-5 are typical.

3. *Transparency.* A favorite and very simple way of measuring eutrophication is by measuring transparency with the Secchi disc. This method also measures gross biological productivity.

4. *Chlorophyll in Epilimnion.* Perhaps the easiest method of all of measuring biological productivity and thereby the state of eutrophication is to determine the chlorophyll *a* content of near surface waters at periodic intervals over a growing season. Since the chlorophyll *a* content of lake waters is related directly to the

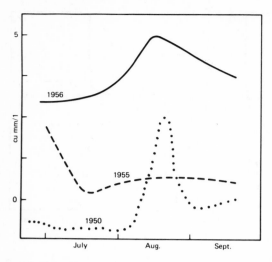

Fig. 45-5. Volume of algae as a measure of progressive eutrophication of Lake Washington (9).

amount of phytoplankton present, it furnishes indisputable evidence.

5. *Oxygen Production.* The measurement of photosynthetic oxygen by the light- and dark-bottle technique has been used quite extensively to measure primary biological productivity but interpretation of data is a much disputed matter. Considerable doubt exists as to the reliability of this method but, in general, it yields quite valuable information.

6. *Carbon Dioxide Utilization.* One of the newer methods of measuring primary biological productivity is by determining carbon dioxide utilization. The technique is simplified somewhat by using $C^{14}O_2$ as a tracer.

7. *Nutrient Levels.* As our Knowledge of the primary biological productivity of surface waters has increased there has been a growing awareness of the role of the major nutrients, carbon dioxide, nitrogen, and phosphorus. Since there is little possibility of controlling carbon dioxide levels in natural waters, attention has been focused on the fertilizing elements, nitrogen and phosphorus, which are such significant components of human wastes, certain industrial wastes, and drainage waters from agricultural lands.

The author (10), after studying 17 lakes in southeastern Wisconsin, was so brash as to suggest limits of inorganic phosphorus as a

means of differentiating between well-behaved and nuisance lakes. Well-behaved lakes were those whose inorganic phosphorus content did not exceed 0.015 mg/ and whose inorganic nitrogen (NH_3, NO_2^-, NO_3^-) did not exceed 0.30 mg/ at the time of the spring overturn.

Protein is a major component of plankton organisms. Catches of net plankton from the Madison, Wisconsin, lakes showed protein contents ranging from 42 to 58 percent on an ash free basis and nitrogen content ranging from 6.8 to 10 percent (6). It might be reasonable to say that each part of nitrogen will give rise to 12 parts of plankton organisms. Thus, it seems logical to include nitrogen determinations as a means of evaluating biological productivity and, thereby, eutrophication. There are two precautions, however, to keep in mind in using nitrogen as a parameter. In the first place, the evaluations of inorganic nitrogen should be performed at the time the spring turnover is complete but before any significant growth or conversion of inorganic nitrogen to organic forms has occurred. The second relates to the fact that certain blue-green algae are capable of fixing nitrogen from the dissolved nitrogen in the water, provided other necessary nutrients are available. Evaluations of biological productivity on the basis of nitrogen alone are not necessarily reliable, unless phosphorus is included in the considerations.

Phosphorus is also one of the major nutrients required by phytoplankton. It appears to be much more labile or less firmly fixed within the cell tissue than nitrogen and the amounts required do not appear to be established very firmly. However, restrictions on phosphorus can be shown to limit and alter the nature of plankton growths. On the other hand, it has been demonstrated (11) (12) that adequate supplies of phosphorus are stimulatory to nitrogen fixing blue-green algae. For this reason phosphorus has been considered by many investigators as a key element in the control of biological productivity. There is ample reason to believe that it will be used more and more as one of the parameters of eutrophication.

Some investigators believe that nitrogen to phosphorus ratios are significant in predicting biological productivity. It is based on the premise that nutrients should be abstracted from water in the same ratio as that in which they occur in the living organisms. Although the nitrogen to phosphorus ratio varies in individual plankton forms from about 6 to 1 to about 25 to 1, a normal or average ratio for gross plankton is considered to be about 15 to 1. On this basis, it is argued that waters which contain nitrogen and phosphorus in ratios greater than 15 to 1 will show productivities which are nitrogen dependent and waters which have ratios less than 15 to 1 will have productivities that are phosphorus dependent. The latter, because of the possibility of containing excess phosphorus, would be stimulatory toward the development and growth of blue-green algae.

Summary

Lakes and reservoirs are classified normally as oligotrophic, mesotrophic, or eutrophic based on biological productivity or parameters related to it. In the normal aging process natural lakes pass from oligotrophic to eutrophic bodies of water and eventually revert to marshes or moors and then dry land.

The parameters for measuring eutrophication are many. The basic problem concerning sanitary scientists and engineers, however, is how to arrest or control eutrophication.

The natural conversion of oligotrophic lakes to eutrophic lakes has been accelerated greatly by agricultural, human, and industrial wastes carrying fertilizing matters, principally nitrogen and phosphorus, stimulatory to phytoplankton.

It is axiomatic, therefore, that a major factor in the control of eutrophication depends on limiting the amount of nutrients entering a lake.

References

1. Stevens, J. C. 1946. "Future of Lake Mead and Elephant Butte Reservoir." *Trans. Amer. Soc. Civil Engr.*, 111:1231.
2. Welch, P. S. 1952. "Limnology." 2nd Ed., McGraw-Hill Book Co., New York, N.Y., 353.
3. Hasler, A. D. 1947. "Eutrophication of Lakes by Domestic Drainage." *Ecology*, 28:383.
4. Hasler, A. D., and W. G. Einsele. 1948. "Fertilization for Increasing Productivity of Natural Inland Waters." *Trans. 13th N. Amer. Wildlife Conf.*, 527.
5. Beeton, A. M. 1965. "Eutrophication of the St. Lawrence Great Lakes." *Limnol. and Oceanog.*, 10:240.
6. Birge, E. A., and C. Juday. 1922. "The Inland Lakes of Wisconsin. The Plankton. I. Its Quality and Chemical Composition." *Wis. Geol. Nat. History Survey Bull.*, 64.
7. Rawson, D. S. 1956. "Algal Indicators of Trophic Lake Types." *Limnol. and Oceanog.*, 1:18.
8. Hutchinson, G. E. 1957. "A Treatise on Limnology." John Wiley & Sons, New York, N.Y., Vol. 1:64.
9. Anderson, G. C. 1961. "Recent Changes in the Trophic Nature of Lake Washington, Algae and Metropolitan Wastes." *Trans. 1960 Seminar*, Robert A. Taft San. Eng. Center, U.S.P.H.S., Cincinnati, Ohio.
10. Sawyer, C. N. 1947. "Fertilization of Lakes by Agricultural and Urban Drainage." *Jour. N. E. Water Works Assn.*, 61:109.
11. Sawyer, C. N., and A. F. Ferullo. 1961. "Nitrogen Fixation in Natural Waters under Controlled Laboratory Conditions." *In:* "Algae and Metropolitan Wastes," Robert A. Taft San. Eng. Center, Cincinnati, Ohio.
12. Dugdale, R. C., and J. C. Nees. 1961. "Recent Observations on Nitrogen Fixation in Blue-Green Algae." *In:* "Algae and Metropolitan Wastes." *Trans. 1960 Seminar*, Robert A. Taft San. Eng. Center, Cincinnati, Ohio.

46

EUTROPHICATION OF THE ST. LAWRENCE GREAT LAKES

Alfred M. Beeton

Introduction

Evidence of appreciable change in the biota and physicochemical conditions in Lake Erie (Beeton 1961) and speculation on possible changes in the other lakes, stemming from increases in total dissolved solids (Ayers 1962; Rawson 1951), have directed attention to eutrophication of the Great Lakes. The question does not concern the existence of eutrophication, because all lakes are aging and there is no reason to believe that the Great Lakes are exceptional. Of greatest consequence is the possibility of detection and perhaps even measurement of the rate of eutrophication of these large lakes. Important also is the effect of mankind on the normal rate of eutrophication.

Accelerated rates of aging due to man's activity have been detected in a number of lakes (Hasler 1947). The classic example is the Untersee of Lake Zürich, which urban effluents have changed from an oligotrophic to an eutrophic lake in a relatively short time. Recently, studies of Lake Washington at Seattle (Edmondson, Anderson, and Peterson 1956), and Fure Lake, Denmark (Berg et al. 1958) have demonstrated that these relatively large lakes are undergoing accelerated eutrophication due to man's influence. None of these lakes, however, is large in comparison with any of the St. Lawrence Great Lakes.

Present Trophic Nature of the Great Lakes

The meaning of eutrophication seems to vary according to the special interests of the

Reprinted from *Limnology and Oceanography* 10: 240-54, 1965, with the permission of the publisher.

individual. Limnologists agree that eutrophication is part of the aging of a body of water and implies an increase in the nutrient content of the waters. Most lakes change gradually from a nutrient-poor, oligotrophic, to a nutrient-rich, eutrophic, condition. At this point agreement ends in arguments on lake classification. Although the terms eutrophic, mesotrophic, and oligotrophic are used freely by limnologists and are well established in the literature, it is difficult to determine precisely what is meant by them. Various investigators have attached considerable significance to one or more of the following criteria in classifying lakes: abundance or species of plankton or both; benthic organisms; chemical characteristics; sediment types; distribution of dissolved oxygen; productivity; fish populations; and morphometry and morphology of the lake basin. Lake classification has been closely related to regional limnology and has been developed primarily for observations on small lakes. It is not surprising, then, to find that the Great Lakes do not fit readily into the various classification schemes that have been proposed. Rawson (1955, 1956) reviewed the problem of classifying large lakes and considered certain characteristics of the St. Lawrence Great Lakes.

Despite the troublesome problems of lake classification, an attempt should be made to classify the Great Lakes for discussion of their eutrophication, and to facilitate comparison with other lakes. A better classification surely is needed since Lake Erie, for example, has been called oligotrophic, mesotrophic, and eutrophic by various investigators over the past 30 years.

Physicochemical Conditions

Morphometry, transparency, total dissolved solids, conductivity, and dissolved oxygen content of the water appear to be useful in lake classification. On the basis of these five physical and chemical factors, two of the lakes would be classified as oligotrophic, one as tending toward the mesotrophic, and two as eutrophic. The low specific conductance and total dissolved solids, and the high transparency and dissolved oxygen of Lakes Huron and Superior agree with the commonly accepted characteristics of oligo-

Table 1. **Physical and chemical characteristics of the Great Lakes.***

Lake	Mean depth (m)	Transparency (average Secchi disc depth, m)	Total dissolved solids (ppm)	Specific conductance (µmhos at 18C)	Dissolved oxygen
Oligotrophic	>20	High	Low: around 100 ppm or less	<200	High, all depths all year
Superior	148.4	10	60	78.7	Saturated, all depths
Huron	59.4	9.5	110	168.3	Saturated, all depths
Michigan	84.1	6	150	225.8	Near saturation, all depths
Eutrophic	<20	Low	High: > 100	>200	Depletion in hypolimnion: <70% saturation
Ontario	86.3	5.5	185	272.3	50 to 60% saturation in deep water in winter
Erie average for lake	17.7	4.5	180	241.8	
Central basin	18.5	5.0	—	—	<10% saturation, hypolimnion
Eastern basin	24.4	5.7	—	—	40 to 50% saturation, hypolimnion

* Criteria designating lake types are based primarily on factors considered important by Rawson (1960); specific conductance limits from Dunn (1954); dissolved oxygen criteria, Thienemann (1928). Data from Bureau of Commercial Fisheries except transparency and dissolved oxygen for Lake Ontario (Rodgers 1962).

trophy (Table 1). Lakes Erie and Ontario have the high specific conductance and total dissolved solids and, of special significance, the low concentration of dissolved oxygen in the hypolimnion characteristic of eutrophic lakes. Data were not available on the oxygen content of the hypolimnetic waters of Lake Ontario, but it is even more significant that the deep waters had a low percentage saturation of dissolved oxygen under essentially isothermal conditions. The transparencies of Lakes Erie and Ontario are not especially low in comparison with many small lakes, but in comparison to Lakes Huron and Superior, their average transparencies are indeed low. Lake Michigan falls between the other lakes from the standpoint of specific conductance, total dissolved solids, and transparency. The dissolved oxygen content of Lake Michigan water is near saturation, however, at all depths. On occasion, water in the deeper areas has a saturation between 70 and 80%, but these low values are infrequent.

Biological Characteristics

The biological characteristics of all the Great Lakes, except Lake Erie, may place them in the oligotrophic category (Table 2). This classification surely holds for Lakes Huron, Michigan, and Superior, but is uncertain for Lake Ontario, where recent and detailed information is lacking on benthos and plankton. The types of bottom fauna, especially the dominant midge larvae, have been recognized for many years as good criteria for classifying lakes (Elster 1958); Brundin (1958) held this basis had world-wide application. Lakes Huron, Michigan, and Superior are all of the *Orthocladius-Tanytarsus (Hydrobaenus-Calopsectra)* type. *Hydrobaenus* and related genera are the only midges in the deeper parts of these lakes. *Calopsectra* occurs in shallower areas with a variety of other midges. In Lake Erie, *Procladius* and *Tendipes* spp. (*T. plumosus* group) are the dominant midges. *Cryptochironomus* and *Coelotanypus* also are abundant in the western basin. *Calopsectra* and a variety of midge larvae become progressively more abundant toward the eastern end of the lake and only a few *Tendipes* appear in samples from the deep (maximum, 64 m) eastern basin.

The crustaceans, *Mysis relicta* and *Pontoporeia affinis*, are characteristic of oligotrophic lakes, although they occur in lakes classed as mesotrophic. Both organisms require fairly high

Table 2.   Biological characteristics of the Great Lakes.*

Lake	Bottom fauna and dominant midges	Dominant fishes	Plankton abundance	Dominant phytoplankton†
Oligotrophic	*Orthocladius-Tanytarsus* type (*Hydrobaenus-Calopsectra*)	Salmonids	Low	*Asterionella formosa* *Melosira islandica* *Tabellaria fenestrata* *Tabellaria flocculosa* *Dinobryon divergens* *Fragilaria capucina*
Superior	*Pontoporeia affinis* *Mysis relicta* *Hydrobaenus*	Salmonids	Very low	*Asterionella formosa* *Dinobryon* *Synedra acus* *Cyclotella* *Tabellaria fenestrata* *Melosira granulata*
Huron	*Pontoporeia affinis*‡ *Mysis relicta* *Hydrobaenus* *Calopsectra*	Salmonids	Low	*Fragilaria crotonensis* *Tabellaria fenestrata* *Fragilaria construens* *Fragilaria pinnata* *Cyclotella kutzingiana* *Fragilaria capucina*
Michigan	*Pontoporeia affinis*§ *Mysis relicta* *Hydrobaenus*	Salmonids	Low	*Fragilaria crotonensis* *Melosira islandica*‖ *Tabellaria fenestrata* *Asterionella formosa* *Fragilaria capucina*
Ontario	*Pontoporeia affinis* *Mysis relicta*	Salmonids, ictalurids, percids	—	—
Eutrophic	*Tendipes plumosus* type	Yellow perch, pike, black bass	High	*Microcystis aeruginosa* *Aphanizomenon* *Anabaena*
Erie Central basin	*Tendipes plumosus*	Yellow perch, smelt, freshwater drum	High	*Melosira binderana* *Stephanodiscus* *Cyclotella* *Fragilaria crotonensis*
Eastern basin	*Pontoporeia affinis* few *Calopsectra*	Yellow perch, smelt, few salmonids	High	*Microcystis* *Aphanizomenon*

* Criteria for lake types as follows: tendipedid larvae, Brundin (1958); fish and plankton abundance, Welch (1952); dominant phytoplankton, Rawson (1956).
† Data for Lake Michigan from Bureau of Commercial Fisheries; Lake Superior from Putnam and Olson (1961); Lake Erie from Davis (1962); Lake Huron from Williams (1962).
‡ Data from Teter (1960).
§ Data from Merna (1960).
‖ Refers to *Melosira islandica-ambigua* type.

dissolved oxygen concentrations and cold water. Consequently, they are absent from highly eutrophic lakes. Both crustaceans are found in all of the Great Lakes, but in Lake Erie the major population is restricted to the eastern basin.

Oligotrophic lakes of the north have been considered salmonid lakes. It is not implied that salmonids do not occur in eutrophic lakes, but, when present, they are not the dominant fishes and usually they have a restricted bathymetric distribution. Salmonids dominate the fish populations in all of the lakes except Lake Erie, although in Lake Ontario ictalurids and percids are almost as important in the commercial fishery as salmonids (Table 2). Three native species (formerly four) of salmonids occur in Lake Erie, but during most of the year they are restricted to the eastern basin. Warmwater fishes dominate the fish fauna of Lake Erie now, including the eastern basin.

Considerable controversy exists over the value of plankton in lake classification. Rawson (1956) pointed out that the number of species present, as well as the ecological dominants, should be considered in characterizing plankton. He stresses that the dominant species of plankters in the oligotrophic lakes of Canada, as well as the Great Lakes, were not the species usually associated with oligotrophic lakes. Furthermore, a number of plankters commonly accepted as indicative of eutrophy are dominant species in these lakes. These observations are supported by the more recent plankton data from the Great Lakes. *Fragilaria crotonensis* is a dominant diatom species in Lakes Huron and Michigan as well as Lake Erie, and *Melosira granulata* is a dominant plankter in Lake Superior. Both species are considered to be indicators of eutrophy by Teiling (1955). On the other hand, plankters that are accepted as indicators of oligotrophy (*Dinobryon, Tabellaria, Cyclotella*) are also dominant in the Great Lakes (Table 2). It is agreed, nevertheless, that the Cyanophyceae, *Aphanizomenon, Anabaena*, and *Microcystis*, which are among the dominant plankters in Lake Erie, are good indicators of eutrophy. Little purpose could be served here, however, by further discussion of the problem of plankton indicators of lake types. Consequently, Rawson's (1956) ranking of algae in order of their occurrence from oligotrophy to eutrophy has been used, in part, in Table 2, since he worked on lakes similar in many ways to the St. Lawrence Great Lakes. On the basis of plankton abundance and the dominant species of phytoplankton, Lakes Huron, Michigan, and Superior would be considered oligotrophic and Lake Erie eutrophic.

The combined biological, chemical, and physical characteristics of Lakes Huron and Superior clearly are those of oligotrophy. The biota and the high dissolved oxygen content of the deep hypolimnetic waters characterize Lake Michigan as oligotrophic but contrariwise, the high content of total dissolved solids indicates a trend toward mesotrophy. Lake Ontario, as a mesotrophic lake, retains the biota of an oligotrophic lake, but the physicochemical characteristics are those of eutrophy. The chemical content of the waters of Lake Ontario is closely similar to that of Lake Erie, since the main inflow to Lake Ontario is from Lake Erie via the Niagara River. The trophic nature of Ontario has been determined to a large extent by the chemical history of Lake Erie waters. Lake Ontario, and perhaps Lake Michigan, would be eutrophic except for the large volumes of deep waters. Even in Lake Erie, the eastern basin has components of a fauna associated with oligotrophy and sufficient deep, cold, oxygenated water to maintain this fauna. These conditions exist despite the highly eutrophic nature of the central basin (flow through the lake is from west to east). The evident ability of the total dissolved oxygen content of the deep hypolimnetic waters to meet the oxygen demand of the organic production of the epilimnetic waters, as well as the oxygen demand of allochthonous materials, makes Lakes Michigan, Ontario, and eastern Lake Erie in some measure oligotrophic (or mesotrophic) because of their morphometry.

Evidence of Eutrophication

The present trophic nature of the Great Lakes is to a considerable degree the result of their gradual aging since formation. Evidence is accumulating, however, which indicates that human activity is greatly accelerating the eutrophication of all of the lakes but Lake Superior. This evidence is most spectacular for Lake Erie. A difficult problem is one of finding acceptable indices of change.

Various criteria have been used by different investigators to demonstrate eutrophication. Hasler (1947) compiled information on 37 lakes affected by enrichment from domestic and agricultural drainage. Among the changes in many of these lakes were: the dramatic decline and disappearance of salmonid fishes and increases in populations of coarse fish; changes in the species composition of plankton; and blooms of blue-green algae. Special significance has been attached to blooms of *Oscillatoria rubescens*. As the Untersee of Lake Zürich changed from a salmonid to a coarse-fish lake, plankton abundance increased, different species became dominant in the plankton, transparency decreased, and the dissolved oxygen content of the deep waters decreased. At the same time, the concentrations of chlorides and organic matter increased (Minder 1918, 1938, 1943). Minder (1938) attributed the increase and changes in the plankton to the growing amount of phosphorus and nitrogen from domestic sources. *Oscillatoria rubescens* appeared explosively in 1898 and replaced the formerly dominant *Fragilaria capucina*. The cladoceran *Bosmina longirostris* replaced *B. coregoni* after 1911. Blooms of *Oscillatoria rubescens*, declines in the hypolimnetic oxygen, decrease in transparency, and increases in the abundance of plankton were cited by Edmondson, Anderson, and Peterson (1956) as evidence of eutrophication of Lake Washington. They held this increased productivity to be the result of growing discharges of treated sewage into the lake. Similar changes were observed in Fure Lake by Berg et al. (1958). Species composition of the phytoplankton changed, transparency decreased, dissolved oxygen concentrations became low in the hypolimnion, and conductivity rose. These changes have occurred during the last 40 to 50 years. Berg (Berg et al. 1958, p. 176) stated, "The cause is an increased introduction of material with the sewage."

Our knowledge of the limnology of the Great Lakes in earlier years is seriously deficient. Observations useful for tracing changes in the Great Lakes are mostly limited to water-quality data, commercial fishing records, and a few observations on plankton. The fishing records and chemical data have the longest history and are the most reliable.

Chemical Characteristics

Chemical data representative of the lakes proper were compiled from many sources (Table 3) ranging from isolated samplings and water-intake data to extensive lake-wide sampling. Consequently, records for a particular year may represent an average of hundreds, thousands, or only a few determinations. Data on magnesium were available from most of the sources plotted in Figures 46-2 and 46-3, but they are not included because no significant change in concentration could be detected in any of the lakes. For example, magnesium concentrations in Lake Erie averaged 7.6 ppm in 1907 (Dole 1909), 8.0 ppm in 1934 (Mangan, Van Tuyl, and White 1952), and 8.0 ppm in recent years (Bureau of Commercial Fisheries data). Broadly speaking, there has been no significant change in Lake Superior. Other lakes in order of increasing chemical change are Huron, Michigan, Erie, and Ontario.

*Lake Superior—*The indicated slight downward trend in total dissolved solids in Lake Superior is not significant and concentrations

Table 3. Sources of data used in preparing Figs. 46-1, 46-2, and 46-3.

Source and date	Data
Allen (1964)	Major ions, south-central Lake Huron, 1956.
Bading (1909)	Chlorides, Lake Michigan, 1909.
Barnard and Brewster (1909)	Chlorides, Lake Michigan, 16 Sept 1908, table 29.
Bartow and Birdsall (1911)	Major ions, average concentrations in 10 open Lake Michigan samples collected about 1910.
Beeton, Johnson, and Smith (1959)	Major ions, Lake Superior, 1953.
Birge and Juday (no date)	Total dissolved solids, Lake Erie, 1928-1930; data on analyses for total dissolved solids by L. A. Youtz for Lakes Erie, Huron, and Superior, 1928.
Bowles (1909)	Total dissolved solids, Lake Michigan, April 1908.
Collins (1910)	Major ions, Lake Michigan, 1885, from J. H. Long; total dissolved solids and chlorides, Chicago, average of weekly values 1897-1900.
Clarke (1924)	Major ions, Lake Michigan, Milwaukee, 1877; Kenosha and Racine, Wis., 1911.

Table 3. (*continued*)

Source and date	Data
Dole (1909)	Major ions and total dissolved solids, Lakes Erie, Huron, Michigan, Ontario, and Superior, averages of monthly determinations 1906-07.
Eddy (1943)	Major ions and total dissolved solids, Lake Superior, 1934.
Erie, Pa., Bur. Water (1956, 1957, 1959)	Major ions and total dissolved solids, Lake Erie, 1956, 1957, 1959.
Fish (1960)	Chlorides, Lake Erie, 1929.
Hunt (1857)	Major ions in water collected at Pointe des Cascades, Vandreuil, Que., Lake Ontario, 1854.
International Joint Commission (1951)	Chlorides and total dissolved solids, open Lake Erie near Detroit River mouth, sampling ranges P-1-W. and LC, table N-17; open Lake Huron above Port Huron; open Lake Ontario, sampling locations 4 miles (6.4 km) or more from Niagara River, 1946-48.
Jackson (1912)	Chlorides and total dissolved solids, Lake Erie, 1910, tables 69, 70; 1911, tables 71, 72; 1912, table 68.
Kramer (1961)	Major ions, except potassium, Lake Erie, 1961.
Kramer (1962)	Major cations, western Lake Ontario, 1959.
Lake Michigan Water Commission (1909)	Chlorides and total dissolves solids, Lake Michigan, October 1908.
Lane (1899)	Sodium chloride, Lake Huron, 12 miles (19.3 km) above Port Huron and Alpena, Mich., 1895; Lake Michigan, 5 miles (8 km) off Milwaukee, Wis., 1895-99; total solids, Chicago, Ill., 1895; major ions and total dissolved solids, open Lake Superior 50 miles (80 km) from Keweenaw Pt., 1886.
Lenhardt (1955)	Major ions and total dissolved solids, Lake Michigan, 1954.
Leverin (1942)	Major ions and total dissolved solids, Lake Huron, Pt. Edward, Ont., 1934-37; Lake Ontario, average of 6 analyses, Kingston, Ont., 1934-38 and 1940.
Leverin (1947)	Major ions and total dissolved solids, Lake Erie, average of 6 determinations, Fort Erie, Ont., 1934-38; Lake Ontario, average of 7 determinations, Toronto, Ont., 1934-38; Lake Superior, average of 5 determinations, Sault Ste. Marie, Ont., 1936-38, one sample taken in open lake midway between Fort William and Sault Ste. Marie, 1942.
Lewis (1906)	Chlorides and total dissolved solids, Lake Erie, average of 6 analyses, Erie, Pa., 1901-1903.
Mangan, Van Tuyl, and White (1952)	Major ions and total dissolved solids, Lake Erie, 1934, 1945, and 1951.
Michigan Water Resources Commission	Major ions and total dissolved solids, Lake Huron at Alpena, East Tawas, and Harbor Beach, Mich.; Lake Michigan at Muskegon, St. Joseph, and Traverse City, Mich.; Lake Superior at Calumet, Mich.
Ohio, State of (1953)	Major ions, Lake Erie, Lorain, O., average values, 1950-52.
Reade (1903)	Major ions, Lake Ontario, water sample collected in the St. Lawrence River opposite Montreal, Que., 1884.
Thomas (1954)	Major ions and total dissolved solids, Lake Erie, at Chippawa, Ont; Lake Huron at Goderich and Sarnia, Ont.; Lake Ontario at Gananoque and Port Hope, Ont.; Lake Superior at Sault Ste. Marie, Ont., averages of monthly analysis, 1948-49.
U.S. Geological Survey (1960)	Major ions and total dissolved solids, Lake Erie, Niagara River at Buffalo, N.Y.; Lake Ontario, St. Lawrence River at Cape Vincent, N.Y., analyses for August 1957.
U.S. Public Health Service (1961)	Chlorides, sulfates, and total dissolved solids, Lake Erie at Buffalo N.Y.; Lake Huron at Port Huron, Mich.; Lake Michigan at Milwaukee, Wis.; Lake Ontario at Massena, N.Y.; Lake Superior at Duluth, Minn,; average values for Oct 1960-30 Sept 1961.
Wright (1955)	Chlorides, western Lake Erie, 1930.

Fig. 46-1. Concentrations of total dissolved solids in the Great Lakes. Circled points are averages of 12 or more determinations. Data are from sources presented in the bibliography and Table 3.

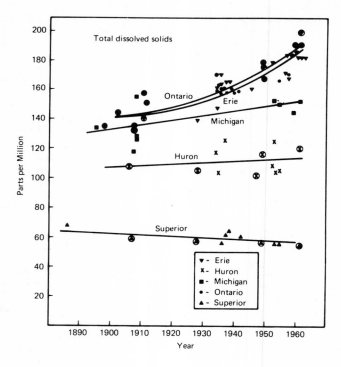

have remained at approximately 60 ppm throughout the years (Fig. 46-1). Calcium, chloride, and sulfate concentrations also have remained the same since 1886 (Fig. 46-2). The close agreement among analysis of Lake Superior water by various individuals using different methods and techniques is unusual. The slight decrease in the sodium-plus-potassium content of the water probably is not real, because present analytical methods differ substantially from former ones. The uniformity in the chemical analyses here lends confidence to the reliability of the chemical data for the other lakes.

Lake Huron—The slight increase in total dissolved solids in this lake is probably real, since about 30% of the inflow to Lake Huron is from Lake Michigan, where dissolved solids have risen significantly (Fig. 46-1). The sodium-plus-potassium content has remained about the same over the years of record. Some rather low values were reported for these ions during the 1930's, but the 1890-1910 data agree with recent determinations (Fig. 46-2). An increase of 3 ppm in chloride appears to have occurred during the past 30 years. The major source of chlorides within the Lake Huron watershed is in the Saginaw Valley,

where considerable quantities of brine are pumped to the surface in the oil fields and for use in the chemical industry. The increased influx of brine during the past 30 years may account for most of the increase in chloride in the lake. Sulfate concentrations have increased 7.5 ppm in the past 54 years.

Lake Michigan—Total dissolved solids have increased about 20 ppm since 1895 (Fig. 46-1). Calcium has remained constant (Fig. 46-2). The greatest increase in any ion in Lake Michigan has been that of sulfate, which has risen 12 ppm since 1877. The chloride concentrations have risen slowly but steadily by 4 ppm. The sodium-plus-potassium content has not changed since 1907 but it exceeds that extant in 1877-1900. The determinations before 1907 may be too low, since they are below those reported for Lakes Huron and Superior. If, however, these early determinations are reasonably accurate, the increase that occurred between 1877 to 1907 may be attributed to population growth in the Chicago area. The population of Chicago exceeded 1 million in 1890 and the Chicago Sanitary Canal, to divert sewage away from the lake, was not completed until 1900. Consequently, during these early

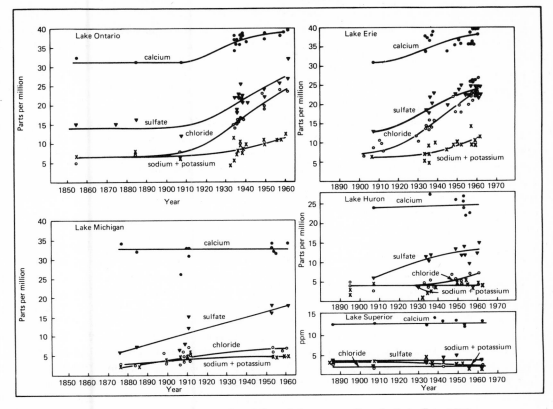

Fig. 46-2. *Changes in the chemical characteristics of Great Lakes waters. Data for Lake Erie, 1958;
Lake Huron, 1956; Lake Michigan, 1954, 1955, 1961; Lake Ontario, 1961; Lake Superior, 1952,
1953, 1961, 1962 are from the Ann Arbor Biological Laboratory, U.S. Bureau of Commercial
Fisheries. Other data are from sources presented in the bibliography and Table 3.*

years considerable amounts of raw sewage
entered the lake at Chicago.

Lake Erie—Total dissolved solids, calcium,
chloride, sodium-plus-potassium, and sulfate all
increased significantly in Lake Erie during the
past 50 years. Total dissolved solids have risen
by almost 50 ppm (Fig. 46-1). Increases of
approximately 8, 16, 5, and 11 ppm have taken
place in the concentrations of calcium, chloride, sodium-plus-potassium, and sulfate, respectively (Fig. 46-2).

Lake Ontario—The rate of increase in total
dissolved solids in Lake Ontario has been the
same as in Lake Erie. This rate was similar to
that occurring in Lake Michigan prior to the
late 1920's but has been higher than in Lake
Michigan since about 1930 (Fig. 46-1). Close
agreement of chemical data for Lake Ontario
for 1854 and 1884 with those for 1907

indicates that the chemical characteristics of
the water were altered little during this period
(Fig. 46-2). Calcium chloride, and sodium-plus-
potassium increased to the same extent as
noted in Lake Erie since 1910. Sulfate concentrations increased by 13 ppm, which is somewhat higher than in Lake Erie.

Summary of chemical changes—The extent
of change in total dissolved solids in Lakes Erie,
Michigan and Ontario has not been as great as
that indicated by Ayers (1962) for Lake Michigan or by Rawson (1951) for Lakes Erie and
Ontario; both used the observations of Dole
(1909) in 1906-1907 as their base. Dole's
estimates of total dissolved solids (and of
various ions as well) for these lakes were 9 to
18 ppm lower than those of several other
investigations during this period. The 1907 data
for Lake Michigan on sulfate, chloride and

especially calcium probably were all low because Dole collected his samples in the Straits
of Mackinac where Lake Michigan water enters
Lake Huron and the mixing of the water from
these two lakes, as well as the occasional inflow
of Lake Superior water into this area, could
produce low concentrations of ions.

Changes in the chemical characteristics of
Lake Ontario have closely paralleled those in
Lake Erie (Fig. 46-3). Prior to 1910 the chemical characteristics of the two lakes were similar
and conditions in Lake Erie were probably the
same as indicated by the 1854 and 1884
analyses of Lake Ontario water. Concentrations
of calcium chloride, sodium-plus-potassium,
and sulfate have been somewhat higher in Lake
Ontario than in Lake Erie during the past 50
years. The greater concentrations of salts in
Lake Ontario probably can be attributed to
growth of the Toronto, Hamilton, and Rochester metropolitan areas and the industrial expansion along the upper Niagara River.

Lakes Erie and Ontario are the only lakes in
which calcium increased materially (Fig. 46-3).
Increases in sulfate have been significant in all

of the lakes except Superior. The 11 ppm and
13 ppm increases in Lakes Erie and Ontario
have taken place in 30 years, whereas the rise of
12 ppm in Lake Michigan has been more
gradual over a period of 84 years. The sulfate
change in Lake Huron parallels that in Lake
Michigan and may have resulted largely from
the inflow of Lake Michigan waters. The degree
of change in the chloride content of Lakes Erie
and Ontario is similar to that for sulfate, but
chloride has not increased as much as sulfate in
Lakes Huron and Michigan.

Plankton

Few plankton data are available for Lakes
Huron, Ontario, and Superior, especially for
earlier years. Some rather extensive plankton
data do exist, however, for Lakes Erie and
Michigan.

Lake Michigan–Studies of Lake Michigan
phytoplankton by Briggs (1872), Thomas and
Chase (1886), Eddy (1927), Ahlstrom (1936),
Damann (1945), and Williams (1962) show that
the diatom species dominant 90 years ago have

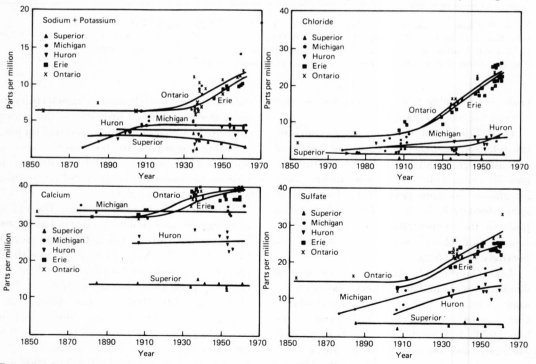

Fig. 46-3. *Changes in the concentrations of calcium, chloride, sodium-plus-potassium, and sulfate in
each of the Great Lakes. (Sources of data same as for Fig. 46-2.)*

maintained their importance. The relative abundance and occurrence of individual species give no evidence of change in the phytoplankton. (Some confusion exists over the identification of certain species and some species are listed by one investigator and not by another.)

The best information of change of plankton abundance probably comes from Damann's (1960) publication on 33 years of plankton data from the Chicago water intake which showed an average increase of 13 organisms per ml per year in the standing crop of the total plankton. Damann's work, and indeed most of the past work on plankton, has been in the extreme southern end of the lake except for the open-lake data of Ahlstrom (1936). Damann (1945, p. 771) pointed out that the data he published ". . . are an expression of the plankton activity in only a small portion of the southwestern corner of Lake Michigan."

Recent plankton collections during July 1960 to July 1961 from Gary, Indiana, at the southern end of the lake, and Milwaukee, Wisconsin, near the middle of the lake (Williams 1962), show considerable differences between these two localities. The average phytoplankton count at Milwaukee was 975 plankters/ml. This figure is close to the annual average of 952/ml for the Chicago water intake 1926-1942 (Damann 1960). The average phytoplankton count at Gary was 1,914 plankters/ml, well above the annual average of 1,222/ml reported at Chicago for 1943-58 (Damann 1960). Local differences in the relative importance of the major diatom species at Gary and Milwaukee also are apparent. Sampling by the Bureau of Commercial Fisheries, in 1960, yielded further evidence of wide variability. The relative abundance of the plankton species was different from that at the Gary and Milwaukee water intakes, and a much higher abundance of plankton was obtained with nets towed vertically. Plankton counts in the open-lake samples ranged from about 450 to 12,000 plankters/ml and averaged around 4500/ml.

Two changes in the species composition of the zooplankton of Lake Michigan may be of some consequence. Apparently the cladoceran, *Bosmina longirostris*, has replaced *B. coregoni*. A similar change was noted as evidence of eutrophication in Lake Zurich (Minder 1938). Wells (1960) did not find *B. coregoni*, although *B. longirostris* was present in all of his 1954 and 1955 samples. *Bosmina coresgoni (B. longispina)* was the most abundant cladoceran in samples collected in 1887-1888 and 1926-1927, and *B. longirostris* was listed as rare (Eddy 1927). *Bosmina coregoni* is an important component of the Lake Superior plankton (Putnam and Olson 1961), whereas *B. longirostris* has been important in Lake Erie plankton for many years (Fish 1960; Davis 1962).

The other possible change in the Lake Michigan plankton is the increased prominence of *Diaptomus oregonensis*. This species was not found by Eddy (1927), but Wells (1960) reported it to be present on all collection dates and it was a dominant diaptomid in the fall of 1955.

Lake Erie—Some significant changes have been observed in the plankton of Lake Erie. Evidently copepods and especially cladocerans have shown a marked increase in abundance since 1939 (Bradshaw 1964). Bradshaw attached some importance to the "recent" occurrence of the cladocerans *Eurycerus lamellatus*, *Chydorus sphaericus*, and *Ilyocryptus* sp., since they had not been found by Chandler (1940) in 1938-1939. *Eurycerus lamellatus*, *Chydorus sphaericus*, and two species of *Ilyocryptus* were present, however, in 1929 (Fish 1960). A copepod, *Diaptomus siciloides*, which was reported as "incidental" in Lake Erie plankton in 1929 and 1930 (Wright 1955), is now one of the two most abundant diaptomids (Davis 1962). Marsh's (unpublished manuscript) account of plankton in 1929 and 1930 included the statement, "The occurrence of *Diaptomus siciloides* in Lake Erie is a matter of decided interest, as it has never before been found in any of the Great Lakes." Later he continued, "*D. siciloides* may be considered an accidental intruder in the lake plankton . . ."

Changes in Lake Erie

Several important changes in Lake Erie have not been detected in the other lakes; all indicate an accelerated rate of eutrophication.

Fish Populations

The abundance of several commercially important fishes in Lake Erie has changed markedly during the past 40 years. The fish populations of all of the lakes have changed but most changes, except in Lake Erie, have been the direct or indirect consequence of the buildup in sea lamprey populations (Smith 1964). The sea lamprey has not been important in Lake Erie, where few of the tributaries offer suitable spawning conditions.

The lake herring or cisco contributed around 20 million pounds (9 million kg) annually and as much as 48.8 million pounds (22.1 million kg) to the commercial catch (U.S. and Canada) prior to 1925. In 1925, the production declined to 5.8 million pounds (2.6 million kg) and continued to decrease. The take has amounted to a fraction of that since the early 1930's, except for landings of more than 2 million pounds (about 1 million kg) in 1936 and 1937 and a production of 16.2 million pounds (7.4 million kg) in 1946. The total production was only 7,000 pounds (3,200 kg) in 1962.

The whitefish fishery has been at an all-time low since 1948. The 1962 catch was 13,000 pounds (6,000 kg) whereas production had been 2 millions pounds (1 million kg) or more for many years.

The sauger was contributing 1 million pounds (500,000 kg) or more to the commercial production prior to 1946. The catch has not reached 0.5 million pounds (0.22 million kg) since 1945 and has declined progressively since 1953. Production has been only 1 to 4 thousand pounds (450-1,800 kg) in recent years.

The walleye production increased during the 1940's and 1950's to reach 15.4 million pounds (7 million kg) in 1956. Production has decreased since 1958 and recently it has amounted to less than 1 million pounds (450,000 kg).

The commercial catch of blue pike has dropped disastrously. The production fluctuated around an average of about 15 million pounds (6.8 million kg) for many years. The landings dropped to 1.4 millions pounds (640,000 kg) in 1958, to 79,000 pounds (36,000 kg) in 1959, and to only 1,000 pounds (450 kg) in 1962. Of the few blue pike caught in 1963 most were more than ten years old.

The total production of all species in Lake Erie continues to be around 50 million pounds (22.7 million kg), but only because more freshwater drum (sheepshead), carp, yellow perch, and smelt are being caught than in the past. The major factor in the decline in the commercial catch of the more desirable species has been their failure to reproduce.

Bottom Fauna

The changes in the species composition of the bottom fauna of the area west of the islands in Lake Erie have been sweeping. Carr and Hiltunen (unpublished manuscript) have show that few of the formerly abundant mayfly nymphs (*Hexagenia*) now inhabit this area and that tubificids are far more abundant now than 30 years ago (Fig. 46-4). Midge larvae and tubificids have increased and mayflies have decreased also among the islands and in the western part of the central basin (Beeton 1961).

Dissolved Oxygen

Synoptic surveys of Lake Erie in 1959 and 1960 have demonstrated that low dissolved oxygen concentrations (3 ppm or less) appear in about 70% of the hypolimnetic waters of the central basin during late summer (Beeton 1963). Scattered observation of some relatively low dissolved oxygen concentrations have been made during the past 33 years. The information we have indicates that the severity of depletion is more frequent and greater now than in the past and probably affects a more extensive area (Carr 1962).

Conclusion

The chemical content of the water in all of the Great Lakes except Lake Superior has changed in some measure. The biota also has changed in Lake Michigan and especially Lake Erie. These changes, remarkable for such large lakes, are those characteristic of eutrophication in smaller lakes and have come about over the relatively short time of 50 to 60 years. Man's

Fig. 46-4. Distribution and abundance of Hexagenia *nymphs and oligochaetes in western Lake Erie, 1930 and 1961.*

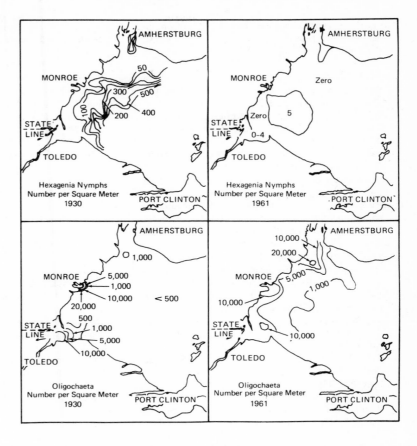

activities clearly have accelerated the rate of eutrophication. This rate has been greatest in Lakes Erie, Ontario, and Michigan and these lakes have had the largest population growth within their drainage areas. An indication of the growth of population comes from census data for the northeast central states; the population there increased from 4.5 million to 16 million between 1850 and 1900, and by 1960 the population was 36.3 million. The rate of population growth increased sharply after 1910. The substantial increases in the chemical content of the waters of Lakes Erie and Ontario also have appeared since 1910. The increases have been greatest for chloride and sulfate, both of which are conspicuous in domestic and industrial wastes, whereas magnesium concentrations have not changed measurably. Most of the magnesium comes from the limestones in the Lake Michigan basin; the stability of magnesium concentrations, therefore, indicates no appreciable change in the erosion of these

deposits. The population along Lake Superior always has been sparse. The population along Lake Huron has been far less than on Lakes Michigan, Erie, and Ontario. Most changes in the open-lake waters of Lake Huron have resulted from the inflow of Lake Michigan water. Undoubtedly, Saginaw Bay, Lake Huron, has been changed appreciably by the extensive growth of industry and agriculture within the Saginaw River valley during the past 50 years. High chloride concentrations have been measured in the bay (Adams 1937); no attempt has been made, however, to assess the extent of change.

References

Adams, M. P. 1937. Saginaw Valley report. Mich. Stream Control Commission. 156 pp.

Ahlstrom, E. H. 1936. The deep-water plankton of Lake Michigan, exclusive of the Crustacea. Trans. Am. Microscop. Soc., 55: 286-299.

Allen, H. E. 1964. Chemical characteristic of south-central Lake Huron. Great Lakes Res. Div., Inst. Sci. and Tech., Univ. Mich., Publ. No. 11, pp. 45-53.

Ayers, J. C. 1962. Great Lakes waters, their circulation and physical and chemical characteristics. Am. Assoc. Advan. Sci., Publ. No. 71, pp. 71-89.

Bading, G. A. 1909. Water conditions at Milwaukee. Lake Michigan Water Comm., Rept. No. 1, pp. 36-39.

Baldwin, N. S., and R. W. Saalfeld, 1962. Commercial fish production in the Great Lakes 1867-1960. Great Lakes Fish. Comm., Tech. Rept. No. 3. 166 pp.

Barnard, H. E., and J. H. Brewster. 1909. The sanitary condition of the southern end of Lake Michigan, bordering Lake County, Indiana. Lake Michigan Water Comm., Rept. No. 1, 193-266. 6.

Bartlow, E., and L. I. Birdsall. 1911. Composition and treatment of Lake Michigan water. Lake Michigan Water Comm., Rept. No. 2, pp. 69-86.

Beeton, A. M. 1961. Environmental changes in Lake Erie. Trans. Am. Fisheries Soc., **90**: 153-159.

———. 1963. Limnological survey of Lake Erie 1959 and 1960. Great Lakes Fish. Comm., Tech Rept. No. 6. 32 pp.

———, J. H. Johnson, and S. H. Smith. 1959. Lake Superior limnological data. U.S. Fish Wildlife Serv., Spec. Sci. Rept. Fisheries No. 297. 177 pp.

Berg, K., K. Andersen, T. Christensen, F. Ebert, E. Fjerdingstad, C. Holmquist, K. Korsgaard, G. Lange, J. M. Lyshede, H. Mathiesen, G. Nygaard, S. Olsen, C. V. Otterstrom, U. Roen, A. Skadhauge, E. Steedmann Nielsen. 1958. Investigations on Fure Lake 1950-54. Limnological studies on cultural influences. Folia Limnol. Scandinavica, 10 (1958). 189 pp.

Birge, E. A., and C. Juday. No date. The organic content of the water of Lake Erie. Supplemental data to "A limnological survey of western Lake Erie with special reference to pollution," by Stillman Wright. Ohio Div. Wildlife. Unpublished manuscript. 281 pp.

Bowles, J. T-B. 1909. Investigation of typhoid fever epidemic at Sheboygan, Wisconsin. Lake Michigan Water Comm., Rept. No. 1, pp. 90-95.

Bradshaw, A. S. 1964. The crustacean zooplankton picture: Lake Erie 1939-49-59; Cayuga 1910-51-61. Verhandl. Intern. Ver. Limnol., **15**: 700-708.

Briggs, S. A. 1872. The Diatomaceae of Lake Michigan. The Lens, **1**: 41-44.

Brundin, L. 1958. The bottom faunistical lake type system. Verhandl. Intern. Ver. Limnol., **13**: 288-297.

Carr, J. F. 1962. Dissolved oxygen in Lake Erie, past and present. Great Lakes Res. Div., Inst. Sci. and Tech., Univ. Mich., Publ. No. 9, pp. 1-14.

Chandler, D. C. 1940. Limnological studies of western Lake Erie. I. Plankton and certain physical-chemical data of the Bass Islands Region, from September, 1938, to November, 1939. Ohio J. Sci., **40**: 291-336.

Clarke, F. W. 1924. The composition of the river and lake waters of the United States. U.S. Geol. Surv., Profess. Papers, No. 135. 199 pp.

Collins, W. D. 1910. The quality of the surface waters of Illinois. U.S. Geol. Surv., Water Supply Papers, 239. 94 pp.

Damann, K. E. 1945. Plankton studies of Lake Michigan. I. Seventeen years of plankton data collected at Chicago, Illinois. Am. Midland Naturalist, **34**: 769-796.

———. 1960. Plankton studies of Lake Michigan. II. Thirty-three years of continuous plankton and coliform bacteria data collected from Lake Michigan at Chicago, Illinois. Trans. Am. Microscop. Soc., **79**: 397-404.

Davis, C. C. 1962. The plankton of the Cleveland Harbor area of Lake Erie in 1956-1957. Ecol. Monographs, **32**: 209-247.

Dole, R. B. 1909. The quality of surface waters in the United States. Part I. Analyses of waters east of the one hundredth meridian. U.S. Geol. Surv., Water Supply Papers, 236. 123.

Dunn, D. R. 1954. Notes on the bottom fauna of twelve Danish lakes. Vidensk. Medd. Dansk Naturhist. Foren., **116**: 251-268.

Eddy, S. 1927. The plankton of Lake Michigan. Illinois Nat. Hist. Surv., Bull., **17**: 203-232.

———. 1943. Limnological notes on Lake Superior. Proc. Minn. Acad. Sci., **11**: 34-39.

Edmondson, W. T., G. C. Anderson, and D. R. Peterson. 1956. Artificial eutrophication of Lake Washington. Limnol. Oceanog., **1**: 47-53.

Elster, H.-J. 1958. Das Limnologische Seetypensystem, Rückblick und Ausblick. Verhandl. Intern. Ver. Limnol., **13**: 101-120.

Erie, Pennsylvania Bureau of Water. 1956. Ninetieth annual report, 1956. 63 pp.

———. 1957. Ninety-first annual report, 1957. 63 pp.

———. 1959. Ninety-third annual report, 1959. 56 pp.

Fish, C. J. 1960. Limnological survey of eastern and central Lake Erie, 1928-1929. U.S. Fish Wildlife Serv. Spec. Sci. Rept. Fisheries, No. 334. 198 pp.

Hasler, A. D. 1947. Eutrophication of lakes by domestic drainage. Ecology, **28**: 383-395.

Hunt, T. S. 1857. The chemical composition of the waters of the St. Lawrence and Ottawa Rivers. Phil. Mag., Ser. 4, **13**: 239-245.

International Joint Commission. 1951. Report of the International Joint Commission United States and Canada on pollution of boundary waters. Washington and Ottowa. 312 pp.

Jackson, D. D. 1912. Report on the sanitary conditions of the Cleveland water supply. Cleveland. 148 pp.

Kramer, J. R. 1961. Chemistry of Lake Erie. Great Lakes Res. Div., Inst. Sci. and Tech., Univ. Mich., Publ. No. 7, pp. 27-56.

Kramer, J. R. 1962. Chemistry of western Lake Ontario. Great Lakes Res. Div., Inst. Sci. and Tech., Univ. Mich., Publ. No. 9, pp. 21-28.

Lake Michigan Water Commission. 1909. Comparative analysis of samples of water from Lake Michigan. Rept. No. 1, pp. 103-105.

Lane, A. C. 1899. Lower Michigan waters: a study into the connection between their chemical composition and mode of occurrence. U.S. Geol. Surv. Water-supply Irrigation Papers, 31. 97 pp.

Lenhardt, L. G. 1955. Water quality and water usage of the Great Lakes public water supplies. The Great Lakes and Michigan. Great Lakes Res. Inst., Univ. Mich., pp. 13-15.

Leverin, H. A. 1942. Industrial waters of Canada. Can. Dept. Mines Resources, Mines Geol. Branch, Rept., 807. 112 pp.

———. 1947. Industrial waters of Canada. Can. Dept. Mines Resources, Mines Geol. Branch, Rept. 819. 109 pp.

Lewis, S. J. 1906. Quality of water in the upper Ohio River basin and at Erie, Pa. U.S. Geol. Surv. Water-supply Irrigation Papers, 161. 114 pp.

Mangan, J. W., D. W. Van Tuyl, and W. F. White, Jr. 1952. Water resources of the Lake Erie shore region in Pennsylvania. U.S. Geol. Surv. Circ., 174. 36 pp.

Marsh, C. D. No date. The Crustacea of the plankton of western Lake Erie. Supplemental data to "A limnological survey of western Lake Erie with special reference to pollution," by Stillman Wright. Ohio Div. Wildlife. Unpublished manuscript. 31 pp.

Merna, J. 1960. A benthological investigation of Lake Michigan. M.S. Thesis, Michigan State Univ. 74 pp.

Michigan Water Resources Commission. 1954. Great Lakes water temperatures. Unpublished manuscript. 50 pp.

Minder, Leo. 1918. Zur Hydrophysik des Zürich u. Walensees, nebst Beitrag zur Hydrochemie u. Hydrobakteriologie des Zürichsees. Arch. Hydrobiol., 12: 122-194.

———. 1938. Der Zürichsee als Eutrophierungs-phänomen. Summerische Ergebnisse aus fünfzig Jahren Zürichseeforschung. Geol. Meere Binnengewasser, 2: 284-299.

———. 1943. Neuere Untersuchungen über den Sauerstoffgehalt und die Eutrophie des Zürichsees. Arch. Hydrobiol., 40: 279-301.

Ohio, State of. 1953. Lake Erie pollution survey, supplement. Ohio Div. Water, Final Rept., Columbus, Ohio. 39 tables, 125 pp.

Putnam, H. E., and T. A. Olson. 1961. Studies on the productivity and plankton of Lake Superior. School Public Health, Univ. Minn., Rept. No. 5. 58 pp.

Rawson, D. S. 1951. The total mineral content of lake waters. Ecology, 32: 669-672.

———. 1955. Morphometry as a dominant factor in the productivity of large lakes. Verhandl. Intern. Ver. Limnol., 12: 164-174.

———. 1956. Algal indicators of trophic lake types. Limnol. Oceanog., 1: 18-25.

———. 1960. A limnological comparison of twelve large lakes in northern Saskatchewan. Limnol. Oceanog., 5: 195-211.

Reade, T. M. 1903. The evolution of earth structure. Longmans, Green, New York. 342 pp.

Rodgers, G. K. 1962. Lake Ontario data report. Great Lakes Inst., Univ. Toronto, Prelim. Rept., No. 7. 102 pp.

Smith, S. H. 1964. Status of the deepwater cisco population of Lake Michigan. Trans. Am. Fisheries Soc., 93: 209-230.

Teiling, E. 1955. Some mesotrophic phytoplankton indicators. Verhandl. Intern. Ver. Limnol., 12: 212-215.

Teter, H. E. 1960. The bottom fauna of Lake Huron. Trans. Am. Fisheries Soc., 89: 193-197.

Thienemann, A. 1928. Der Sauerstoff im eutrophen und oligotrophen See. Die Binnengewässer, Band 4, Schweizerbart, Stuttgart. 75 pp.

Thomas, F. J. F. 1954. Industrial water resources of Canada. Upper St. Lawrence River-central Great Lakes drainage basin in Canada. Can. Dept. Mines Tech. Surv., Water Surv. Rept. No. 3, Mines Branch Rept. 837. 212 pp.

Thomas, B. W., and H. H. Chase. 1887. Diatomaceae of Lake Michigan as collected during the last sixteen years from the water supply of the city of Chicago. Notarisia, Commetarium Phycologium, 2: 328-330.

U.S. Geological Survey. 1960. Quality of the surface waters of the United States. U.S. Geol. Surv., Water Supply Papers, 1520. 641 pp.

U.S. Public Health Service. 1961. National water quality network. Annual compilation of data October 1, 1960—September 30, 1961. U.S. Public Health Surv. Publ. 663. 545 pp.

Welch, P. S. 1952. Limnology. McGraw-Hill, New York. 538 pp.

Wells, LaRue. 1960. Seasonal abundance and vertical movements of planktonic Crustacea in Lake Michigan. U.S. Fish Wildlife Serv., Fishery Bull., 60 (172): 343-369.

Williams, L. G. 1962. Plankton population dynamics. U.S. Public Health Serv. Publ., 663. 90 pp.

Wright, Stillman. 1955. Limnological survey of western Lake Erie. U.S. Fish Wildlife Serv., Spec. Sci. Rept. Fisheries, 139. 341 pp.

47

WATER RECLAMATION
AT SOUTH TAHOE

Russell Culp

Within the context of this series of articles on water reuse, the South Tahoe project probably fits best into the category of the direct cycle of water reuse. All the reclaimed water from the South Tahoe Public Utility District plant is exported out of the Lake Tahoe Basin to Indian Creek Reservoir in Alpine County.

Last summer, all water was withdrawn from the reservoir for irrigation of alfalfa, hay, and pasture land. Because the water quality is suitable also for water contact sports, there are plans to develop a conservation pool and adjoining lands for recreation. A trail planting of rainbow trout fingerlings is thriving, and the lake will probably be fully stocked this spring.

In addition, the plant is being used by the District and the Federal Water Pollution Control Administration to demonstrate phosphorus and nitrogen removal, regeneration and reuse of granular activated carbon, lime recalcination, sludge incineration, and other advanced waste treatment processes. Reclaimed water of exceptionally high quality has been produced so far without interruption. Not only the quality but also the cost of finished water can be tailored to any intended water use (even higher than present uses) merely by the appropriate adjustment of chemical dosages and other minor operational changes.

Treatment Process

Because the Tahoe process has already been described elsewhere, it will be only summarized here. Basically, wastewater treatment is divided into liquid processing and the more difficult

process of solids handling (Fig. 47-1). The design as well as the ease and economy of operation of any tertiary treatment plant must therefore revolve around the requirements for dewatering and disposal of sludge. Table 1 summarizes the basic steps in liquid processing and solids handling at South Tahoe.

Table 1. Treatment processes used at South Tahoe.

Liquid Processing
Conventional treatment ("complete" treatment)
Primary treatment (solids separation)
Secondary treatment (biological oxidation)
Advanced waste treatment ("tertiary" treatment)
Chemical treatment and phosphate removal
Nitrogen removal
Mixed-media filtration
Activated carbon adsorption
Disinfection (chlorination)

Solids Handling
Primary and secondary sludge
Incineration and disposal
Spent granular carbon
Thermal regeneration and reuse
Lime sludge
Recalcination and reuse

Water Reclamation

The water reclamation plant has a capacity of 7.5 mgd. Liquid processing begins with prechlorination for odor control, followed by coarse screening and flow measurement. The two primary settling tanks are of conventional design, with continuous mechanical sludge removal. Inflow to the primary tanks includes raw domestic sewage, overflow water from the lime mud thickener, concentrates from the lime and sludge centrifuges, and waste spent lime mud.

At times, fresh lime or recalcined (active) lime was added to the primary settling tanks. The advantage is that the phosphorus is exited immediately from the system along with the primary sludge and then incinerated. There is, however, a very serious disadvantage; satisfactory dewatering of the sludge produced becomes much more difficult because the lime floc carries more fine colloidal particles than

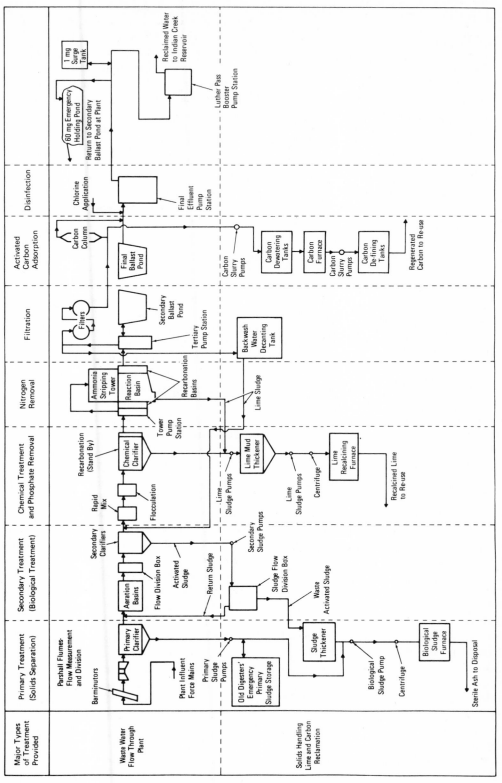

Fig. 47-1. Schematic flow and process diagram.

does plain sedimentation. Because of this difficulty and the added cost of sludge incineration, the addition of active lime has been discontinued. Instead, about 25 percent of the spent (inactive) lime mud from the chemical clarifier is wasted to the primary tanks, and the phosphorus is thus removed from the system without interference in dewatering of the primary sludge.

Parallel biological treatments are accomplished in conventional plug-flow diffused air tanks and in complete mix basins using mechanical aeration plus diffused air. Conventional circular secondary settling basins are used with mechanisms for continuous rapid pickup and recirculation of the settled activated sludge.

Tertiary Treatment

Conventional secondary treatment would end at this point. The additional five steps of treatment provided in this plant are collectively referred to as "tertiary" or advanced waste treatment.

The secondary effluent and waste filter backwash water are treated with about 400 mg per L of lime, as CaO, to a pH of 11, introduced to a mechanical rapid mix basin, and then slowly mixed by means of air agitation. As the flocculated water flows to the chemical clarifier, a polymer (about 0.2 mg per L) is added. This addition ahead of the rapid mix and flocculation basins results in formation of a large instantaneous floc that settles very well in the chemical clarifier. The prolonged mixing of the fine floc particles affords more opportunities for contact with the phosphorus and greatly improves phosphorus removal. (Delayed application of the polymer, on the other hand, permits the formation of some coarse settleable floc and the reduction of the residual phosphorus from only about 0.7 to 0.15 mg per L with no increase in the amount of chemicals used.)

The clear high-pH water overflow from the chemical clarifier is pumped to the nitrogen removal tower (Fig. 47-2). With almost all the ammonia present as dissolved gas and the amount of ammonium ion in solution very small, virtually all the ammonia may be stripped from the water in a properly designed tower. The rate of transfer of the dissolved ammonia gas out of the water is influenced by two techniques that relate to surface tension at the air-water interface, to ammonia concentration in the surrounding air, and to air and water temperatures. One technique involves forming, coalescing, and reforming droplets to provide minimum surface tension for the longest period; for example, in one pass through the tower, 240 droplet formations occur. The other technique minimizes ammonia concentrations in the ambient air by providing for adequate air circulation.

Tremendous quantities of air (390 cfm per gal of water) are required in the tower. To minimize power costs, an open-type tower packing is used to reduce head losses. It is not economically possible, however, to control air or water temperatures, and thus ammonia removals increase in warm weather and decrease in cold weather. The nitrogen removal efficiency varies with temperature from 50 to 98 percent.

The stripping tower effluent is collected in a catch basin beneath the tower and conducted to a two-stage recarbonation basin with an intermediate reaction and settling basin mechanically equipped for continuous removal of calcium carbonate sludge. The pH is reduced from 11 to 9.3 in the primary stage and from 9.3 to 7.5 in the second stage of recarbonation. Stack gases from the lime recalcining and sludge incineration furnaces are compressed and used as the source of the carbon dioxide gas for recarbonation.

The stabilized water then flows to two ballast ponds that provide storage for filter backwash water and equalize flows to the filters and carbon columns in the "tertiary" building (Fig. 47-3). As the water flows to the pressure filters, it is treated with about 5 mg per L of filter aid (alum). The filters consist of three pairs of mixed-media, coarse-to-fine (Micro-Floc*) beds. Each pair of beds operates in series, giving a 6-ft. depth of fine filter media.

The filters are equipped with rotary surface

*Manufactured by Neptune Micro-Floc, Inc.

Fig. 47-2. Nitrogen stripping tower.

wash and rotation indicator lights and can obtain runs of 20 to 40 hr. When a pair of filters no longer produces a satisfactory effluent turbidity, it is automatically removed, backwashed, filtered to waste, and then restored to service. The waste backwash water is stored in a decant tank for flow equalization and slowly returned to the rapid mix basin for reprocessing.

The filtered water flows under pressure to eight carbon columns (Fig. 47-4), each of which contains 22 tons of granular activated carbon. The columns are of the moving-bed, countercurrent-flow type. The water flow is up from bottom to top, and the carbon movement is down from top to bottom. This arrangement permits peak efficiency, as only completely spent carbon is withdrawn for regeneration. For 15 to 45 min. the water is in contact with the carbon, which absorbs the dissolved organics.

The effluent, low in dissolved organics, is colorless, odorless, and sparkling clear. Chlorine demand is low, which permits the effective use of chlorine for disinfection of the reclaimed water.

Solids Handling System

Three solid wastes are processed in multiple-hearth furnaces: primary and secondary sludges, spent lime mud, and spent granular carbon. The waste sludges are incinerated to sterile insoluble ash; the granular carbon is thermally regenerated and reused in the process; and the spent lime mud is recalcined and reused.

The waste sludge mixture is centrifuged to about 19 percent solids and burned at 1600°F. The stack gas scrubbers cool the off-gas to

110°F, and there is no smoke, steam plume, odor, or air pollution.

The spent lime mud is stirred to a thick solids content of about 20 percent, centrifuged to 50 percent solids, and recalcined at 1850°F to 50 to 80 percent calcium oxide.

Spent granular carbon is partially dewatered to 40 percent moisture, regenerated at 1680°F in an atmosphere of steam and limited oxygen, quenched, and de-fined. The carbon is then restored to its original activity and apparent density levels, with losses about 5 percent per cycle.

Plant Operation

Except for the nitrogen removal tower, which was completed in November 1968, the expanded 7.5 mgd water reclamation plant has operated continuously for nine months. Various treatment units have sometimes been taken out of service, but the plant's built-in flexibility permits uninterrupted operation with no loss in reclaimed water quality.

From April through December, a total of 546 mil gal of reclaimed water was exported to Indian Creek Reservoir. From July 15 to Sept. 18, a total of 326 mil gal of water was withdrawn from the reservoir for pasture irrigation, and 7.2 mil gal was drawn off to sprinkle road fill. Since Sept. 18, the end of the irrigation season when the reservoir level was down to near the top of the outlet pipe, all inflows have been stored in the reservoir.

The quality of the reclaimed water is excellent and has always exceeded the high standards set by the Lahontan Regional Water Quality Control Board and the Alpine County Water Agency. Average removals and details of water quality are shown in Table 2.

During the nine months, 26 tons of phosphorus were removed from the wastewater by treatment with about 400 mg per L of lime and

Fig. 47-3. Tertiary process building, pressure filters, and backwash decant tank (left rear).

Fig. 47-4. Carbon columns as viewed from upper catwalk at tertiary building ceiling.

Table 2. Quality of reclaimed water.

Parameter	Ave, removal (%)	Ave. final content (mg/L unless shown)
BOD	99.8	0.7
COD	96.0	12
MBAS	98.0	0.15
Suspended solids	100.0	0
Color	100.0	≤5 units
Odor	100.0	None
Coliforms	≤100.0	...
Phosphorus	94.0	0.7
Turbidity	99.9	0.5 Ju
MPN	...	2.2/100 ml

0.2 mg per L of a polymer at pH 11.0, followed by recarbonation to pH 7.5±. A combination lime-alum treatment was tried briefly at pH 9.3 with 50 mg per L of alum and 0.2 mg per L of a polymer, but with no recarbonation. Also in the treatment process, a total of 550 tons of lime was recalcined and reused, its CaO content varying from 44 to 85 percent.

Granular activated carbon, regenerated thermally, is also reused in the process, some in the third cycle of use and some in the first. Since February 1966, 114 tons of carbon have been regenerated.

All primary sludge, waste activated sludge,

Table 3. Water quality at various stages of treatment

	BOD		COD		Suspended solids		Turbidity		MBAS (detergents)		Phosphorus		Coliforms	
	Removal (%)	Content (mg/L)	Removal (%)	Content (mg/L)	Removal (%)	Content (mg/L)	Removal (%)	Content (Ju)	Removal (%)	Content (mg/L)	Removal (%)	Content (mg/L)	Removal (%)	Content (mpn/100 ml)
Raw wastewater	0	300	0	280	0	233	0	250	0	7	0	12	0	50,000,000
Primary effluent	66	100	21	220	57	100	...	...	...	...	22	9.3	...	2,400,000
Secondary effluent	90	30	86	40	89	26	80	50	93	0.5	52	5.7	95	2,400,000
Chemical clarifier	—	...	...	...	...	...	96	10	...	...	87	1.6	...	...
Carbon column effluent	...	...	...	...	...	...	...	...	...	...	...	...	...	...
Reclaimed water	99.8	0.7	96	12	100	0	99.8	0.3	98	0.15	94	0.7	99.99+	240
Separation bed effluent	...	...	93	20	100	0	...	...	94	0.4	...	...	99.99+	<2.2*

*In chlorinated reclaimed water.

and waste lime sludge have been incinerated to sterile ash and the ash disposed of on the plant grounds. Details of water quality at various stages of treatment are shown in Table 3. The

Table 4. Secondary treatment vs. Tahoe process.

| | Removal (%) | |
Parameter	Secondary treatment	Tahoe process
Suspended solids	89	100
Turbidity	96	99.9
BOD	90	99.8
COD	86	96
MBAS (detergents)	93	98
Coliforms	95	99.99+
Phosphorus	52	94
Nitrogen	0	50–98
Color	Incomplete	100
Odor	Incomplete	100

quality of water produced by secondary treatment is compared with that produced by the Tahoe process in Table 4.

At the plant, a pump station is equipped with three variable speed pump units, which deliver water against a head of 270 ft. through 10 miles of pipeline to a 1 mil gal storage tank at Luther Pass. Here a second set of pumps lifts the water to a static level 1500 ft above and through 17 additional miles of pipeline to Indian Creek Reservoir. The total storage capacity of the reservoir is 1 bil gal, of which 700 mil gal is irrigation water storage and 300 mil gal is conservation storage, or minimum recreational pool (90 surface acres).

The plant has successfully operated to show the effectiveness of its designed purpose. It will continue to serve as a large-scale demonstration of what can be done to reclaim wastewater for further use.

48

REMOVAL OF NITROGEN AND PHOSPHORUS FROM WASTE WATER

Rolf Eliassen and George Tchobanoglous

The removal of nitrogen and phosphorus compounds from waste waters is receiving worldwide attention because these contaminants promote unwanted growth of algae and aquatic plants. Unless steps are taken to control the discharge of these contaminants, overfertilization will continue to increase with the trend to multiple reuse of water.

The presence in the environment of compounds containing available nitrogen and phos-

Reprinted from *Environmental Science and Technology* 3: 536-41, 1969, © 1969 by the American Chemical Society. Reprinted by permission of the copyright owner.

phorus results from both natural and man-made sources. Significant natural sources of these compounds include runoff and rainfall; man-made sources include both domestic and industrial wastes, runoff from agricultural land, farm animal wastes, and urban runoff.

Ammonia, nitrites, and nitrates are the nitrogen compounds of major importance in water and treated waste water. These compounds are water soluble; thus, their nitrogen is readily available for plant growth. Stable forms of nitrogen, such as atmospheric nitrogen gas (N_2) and organic or complexed compounds, are of secondary importance as aquatic plant nutrients. Phosphorus compounds of importance in waste water may occur in a variety of forms, including organic phosphorus, complex inorganic phosphates—such as the polyphosphates used in detergents—and the soluble inorganic orthophosphates and metaphosphates.

Removal Processes

Since most of the nitrogen and phosphorus compounds found in waste water are not removed by conventional treatment processes, advanced waste water renovation methods and modifications of existing processes have been applied to the problem of removal of these nutrients. These treatment processes may be classified as biological, chemical, or physical. There is considerable overlap within the classifications, for example, the removal of nitrogen in the form of ammonia by stripping may be considered to be a physico-chemical process. In addition, many of the processes can be used both for nitrogen and phosphorus removal.

Selection of a given process or combination of processes will depend on:

1. Whether nitrogen, phosphorus, or both are to be removed.
2. The use to be made of the treated waste water, which normally governs the required removal efficiency.
3. The available means for ultimate disposal of the contaminants.
4. The economic feasibility of the various processes.

At present, a major difficulty in designing or planning for removal of nitrogen and phosphorus is the lack of reliable information on the levels which minimize or eliminate their adverse effects. Much investigative work remains to be done to establish critical concentration levels for specific locations and to evaluate the effects of trace elements on biostimulation.

Another important aspect in the design of nutrient removal processes is the ultimate disposal of the extracted waste materials. Concentrated contaminants resulting from various removal processes cannot be returned to water bodies, if pollution problems are to be diminished. From a systems analysis standpoint, nitrogen and phosphorus removal may be considered a two-phase operation: the separation of nutrients, and the disposal of concentrated contaminants. Therefore, for technically feasible processes, cost data must be developed for both the separation and disposal phases. Taken together, these costs and the value of the reclaimed water will determine the cost effectiveness of the particular nutrient removal plan.

Nitrogen Removal

The following is a discussion of the processes used for the removal of nitrogen and its compounds and an overall comparison of the different methods, including efficiencies and costs (see Table 1). Data on the ultimate disposal of the removed contaminants will be presented and discussed after dealing with phosphorus removal.

Biological Treatment

The removal of nitrogen compounds by biological treatment depends on the fact that the continued and normal growth of biological matter requires that certain elements and nutrients be available, as well as a source of energy. In secondary methods of sewage treatment employing biological processes, bacteria transform soluble and colloidal carbohydrates, fats, and proteins, and other organic matter into bacterial growth and stable end products through the utilization of such materials for food and energy. In this transformation, a certain quantity of nitrogen and phosphorus is utilized in the production of cell material and is stored in organically bound forms in the cell tissue. The amount of nitrogen and phosphorus removed is dependent on the amount of growth, which in turn is dependent on the amount of food available.

The gross composition of the biological growth is $C_5H_7NO_2$, which indicates that about 0.13 pound of nitrogen will be required for each pound of growth produced. The amount of phosphorus required is about one fifth of the nitrogen. If the food source were properly selected and adjusted, it should be possible to convert all soluble forms of nitrogen and phosphorus into organic forms contained in bacterial cells. Although the complete removal of these elements has been demonstrated in the laboratory, the conversion of the compounds of nitrogen and phosphorus in sewage to bacterial protoplasm usually will require the addition of carbohydrates or similar materials as a source of food and energy. Without fortification, only about 30-40% of the nitrogen found in do-

Table 1. Comparison of nutrient removal processes.

Process	Class	Removal efficiency, %	Estimated cost, $/mg	Wastes to be disposed of	Remarks
Nitrogen					
Ammonia stripping	Chemical	80-98	9-25	—	Efficiency based on ammonia nitrogen only
Anaerobic denitrification	Biological	60-95	25-30	None	
Algae harvesting	Biological	50-90	20-35	Liquid and sludge	Large land area needed
Conventional biological treatment	Biological	30-50 nitrogen 10-30 phosphorus	30-100	Sludge	
Nitrogen, Phosphorus					
Ion exchange	Chemical	80-92 nitrogen 86-98 phosphorus	170-300	Liquid	Efficiency and cost depend on degree of pretreatment
Electrochemical treatment	Chemical	80-85	4-8[a]	Liquid and sludge	
Electrodialysis	Chemical	30-50[b]	100-250	Liquid	Cost based on 1-10 mgd capacity, 1000 p.p.m. solids
Reverse osmosis	Physical	65-95	250-400	Liquid	
Distillation	Physical	90-98	400-1000	Liquid	
Land application	Physical	60-90 phosphorus[c]	75-150	None	Large land area needed
Phosphorus					
Modified activated sludge	Biological	60-80	30-100	Sludge	
Chemical precipitation	Chemical	88-95	10-70	Sludge	
Chemical precipitation with filtration	Chemical	95-98	70-90	Liquid and sludge	
Sorption	Chemical	90-98	40-70	Liquid and solids	Cost based on water treatment costs

[a] Power cost only; installation costs unavailable
[b] Efficiency per single stage
[c] Nitrogen efficiency depends on form of nitrogen

411

mestic sewage will be transformed to organic nitrogen in cell tissue by conventional secondary biological treatment processes. A recent study by Metcalf and Eddy showed that it was possible to tie up all of the nitrogen, but a considerable amount of the phosphorus remained in soluble form. This is reasonable in view of the high ratio of phosphorus to nitrogen in normal domestic sewage attributable to the extensive use of synthetic detergents containing phosphate additives.

Anaerobic Denitrification

As early as 1860 it was observed that in fermentations taking place in the presence of nitrates, it was common for nitrite, nitrous oxide, and nitrogen gas to be produced. In 1909, Beijerinck and Minkman recognized that the reduction of nitrate involved the use of the oxygen of the nitrate radical as a hydrogen acceptor. Furthermore, the requirements for this reaction include a source of combined hydrogen and the lack of free oxygen. Using these conditions, Beijerinck and Minkman studied the reduction of nitrate under anaerobic conditions using a variety of organic compounds as hydrogen donors. From their experiments they found that the composition of the gas produced varied with the nitrate concentration and carbon source. Since that time, the denitrification process has been studied extensively and is well documented.

This process has recently received considerable attention as a means of removing nitrates from waste waters, especially irrigation return water which may be high in nitrates and low in organic materials. The treatment of dilute waste waters containing nitrate involves the addition of an organic material—such as methanol, ethanol, acetone, acetic acid, or other source of carbon—in an anaerobic environment. Under these conditions, the nitrate is reduced by denitrifying bacteria to nitrogen gas and some nitrous oxide, both of which escape to the atmosphere. With methanol as a carbon source, the chemistry of the process may be represented as shown by the following equation:

$$6H^+ + 6NO_3- + 5CH_3OH \rightarrow$$
$$5CO_2 + 3N_2 + 13H_2O$$

In practice, an excess of 25-35% methanol is required to satisfy the organism's growth and energy requirements.

In treating irrigation return water, a carbon source is added to the incoming flow which then is routed to a deep pond or holding basin where anaerobic conditions prevail. After a detention time of about 10 days, the treated effluent is withdrawn and aerated prior to discharge. The major advantage of this process over other available methods for nitrate removal is that there are no waste products requiring disposal.

Algae Harvesting

Nitrogen in waste water may be removed by algae which are grown at the maximum sustainable rates in specially designed shallow ponds. The concept involved is the same as that previously described for the biological removal of nitrogen by conventional treatment processes through the transformation of soluble and colloidal nitrogen to algal cell tissue. The growth of cell tissue in such a system may be represented by an equation:

$$aCO_2 + cNO_3 - + ePO_4^{-3} +$$
$$(c + 3e)\,H^+ + \frac{1}{2}\,(b - c - 3e)\,H_2O \leftrightarrows$$
$$C_aH_bN_cO_dP_e + \left(a + \frac{b}{4} + \frac{5c}{4} - \frac{d}{2} + \frac{5c}{4}\right)\,O_2$$

Although this process is theoretically feasible, preliminary studies indicate that it may be necessary to supplement the untreated waste with carbon dioxide and a carbon source such as methanol in order to achieve complete nitrogen removal. Depending on the characteristics of the feed, the design of the ponds, climatic conditions, and the harvesting method, an estimated 40-90% of the nitrogen could be removed by this process.

At the present time, the major disadvantages of this process are the large land area requirements and the problems and costs associated with harvesting and disposal of the algae. The latter problem could be overcome if the harvested algae could, for example, be incorporated into some type of solid pelletized animal feed.

Ammonia Stripping

Ammonia stripping is a modification of the aeration process used for the removal of gases from water. Ammonium ions in waste water exist in equilibrium with ammonia and hydrogen ions as shown by:

$$NH_4 + \leftrightarrows NH_3 + H^+$$

As the pH of the waste water is increased above 7, the equilibrium is displaced to the right. At a pH above 10, more than 85% of the ammonia present may be liberated as a gas by agitating the waste water in the presence of air. This generally is done in a packed tray tower equipped with an air blower.

In raw sewage, about 90% of the nitrogen is present as ammonia or compounds from which ammonia is readily formed. In secondary waste water treatment processes, ammonia is converted to nitrate if proper environmental conditions are provided. However, nitrification can be retarded by maintaining a relatively high organic loading on the secondary process. Where applicable, the removal of nitrogen in the form of ammonia may offer economic and operational advantages over nitrate nitrogen removal.

Results of a recent study by Culp and Slechta on the ammonia stripping process indicate that it is possible to achieve 95% removal of ammonia nitrogen at a pH of about 11.5 using 400 cubic feet of air per gallon of sewage. Other work indicates that the quantity of air can be reduced if optimum air-water contact is provided.

Ion Exchange

Ion exchange is a unit process in which ions of a given species are displaced from an insoluble exchange material by ions of different species from solution. In practice, an ion exchange resin is placed in a bed and the waste to be treated is passed through it. When the exchange capacity of the bed has been depleted, the feed is stopped and a regenerating solution passed through the bed. The chemistry of the ion exchange process may be represented as:

$$NO_3^- + RCl \underset{\text{Regeneration}}{\overset{\text{Recreation}}{\rightleftharpoons}} Cl^- + RNO_3$$

Using an anion exchanger, anionic phosphorus and nitrogen compounds can be removed with efficiencies in the range of 80-90%. One problem with an anion exchanger is that organic material tends to foul the resin by selective adsorption on the resin particles. This action may be used to advantage as a mechanism for the removal of organics.

To make ion exchange economical for tertiary treatment, it would be desirable to use regenerants and restorants that would remove both the inorganic anions and the organic material from the spent resin. An economical regenerant for anionic resins is the chloride ion (Cl^-) in common salt, available in large quantities at low cost. Chemical and physical restorants found to be successful in the removal of organic material from resins include sodium hydroxide, hydrochloric acid, methanol, and bentonite.

Application of the anion exchange process to nitrogen and phosphorus removal depends on two factors that will be different for each locality and will affect the economy of the operation. These are the chemical composition of the waste water to be treated, and the ultimate disposal of the contaminants. Sulfates and other anions in the waste water may use up the resin capacity before adequate removal of nitrogen and phosphorus compounds can take place. Wastes from the exchange process will consist of backwash water, rinse water, and spent brine containing small amounts of exchanged ions. Most of the backwash water can be salvaged by recycling it. However, means for disposing of the spent brine must be available.

Electrochemical Treatment

An electrochemical, method for the precipitation of phosphorus and ammonia nitrogen from raw sewage was developed in Norway by Föyn. In this process, sewage is mixed with seawater and passed into a single cell containing carbon electrodes. Because of the relative densities of the seawater and the seawater-sewage mixture, the seawater accumulates in the anode area at the bottom of the cell, and the mixture at the cathode area near the top of the cell. The applied current raises the pH at the cathode, thus precipitating the phosphorus and ammonia as $Ca_3(PO_4)_2$ and $MgNH_4PO_4$, along with $MG(OH)_2$. Hydrogen bubbles, generated at the cathode, lift the sludge to the surface where it is skimmed off and disposed of by normal sludge handling means. Chlorine developed at the anode of the cell provides for disinfection of the effluent. The remaining seawater-sewage mixture then is discharged to the ocean. This method reduces ortho-phosphate concentration in sewage by an average of 83% and ammonia nitrogen by 82%, according to Föyn.

Demineralization Processes

Processes used for the separation of salts from brackish and saline waters include electro-dialysis, reverse osmosis, and distillation. Although ion exchange can be regarded as a demineralization process, usually, it is consider-ed separately because of the availability of selective ion exchange resins. In demineraliza-tion processes, compounds of nitrogen and phos-phorus will not be removed selectively, but will be removed along with the other salts in solution.

Electrodialysis uses an induced electric cur-rent to separate the cationic and anionic com-ponents of a solution by means of selective membranes. These membranes permit ions to pass from the dilute solution on one side to the concentrated solution on the other. The mem-branes are placed at right angles to the line of flow of the electric current. A single pass through an electrodialysis unit will remove about 40% of the ions, and most species of ions are removed in direct proportion to their concentrations.

Problems associated with the electrodialysis process for waste water renovation include chemical precipitation and membrane clogging. Salts with low solubility levels such as calcium carbonate are capable of depositing precipitates on the membrane surface. Acidification of the concentrate or the entire feed stream is one means of overcoming this problem. In addition, colloidal organic matter in secondary plant effluents tends to collect near or on the membranes, causing physical damage to the membranes and increasing operating costs. In order to reduce membrane fouling, activated carbon pretreatment, possibly preceded by chemical precipitation and some form of polish-ing filter, may be necessary to remove organic ions and colloids.

Reverse osmosis involves the enforced pas-sage of water through cellulose acetate mem-branes against the natural osmotic pressure. The waste water must be subjected to pressures up to 750 p.s.i. to accomplish separation of water and ions.

Proposed mechanisms for the action of the cellulose acetate membranes used in reverse osmosis cells include sieving, surface tension, and hydrogen bonding. Although plausible, the sieving theory does not explain the action of the membrane in removing small ions. For example, sodium and chloride ions, which are approximately the same size as water molecules easily pass through the membrane.

Problems associated with the application of the reverse osmosis process for desalination include concentration polarization, membrane fouling, and the passage of certain ions through the membrane. Concentration polarization usu-ally is counteracted by designing the reverse osmosis equipment to operate with high tan-gential velocities at membrane surfaces. Mem-brane fouling usually necessitates the use of pretreatment facilities such as sand and carbon filters when the reverse osmosis process is used for the treatment of waste water. In a recent study of the use of this process for the removal of nitrates from irrigation return water, it was found that a portion of the nitrate ions passes through the membrane, thereby limiting its use-fulness in this application.

Distillation is classified as a vapor-liquid transfer operation and involves the driving off of water vapor from waste water by heating in a retort or still, followed by condensation of the water vapor. In practice, a variety of different processes exist, such as flash distillation, differ-ential distillation, and steam distillation. Be-cause of high costs, they probably will not find wide application for the removal of nitrogen and phosphorus.

Land Application (Soil Mantle Treatment)

As water percolates through soil, various constituents are removed, indicating that the soil system may be used as a treatment process for the removal of certain impurities. The two most important factors which control the movement of nitrogen through soils are physical adsorption and biological action. Physical adsorption seems to be the principal mechanism in the removal of nitrogen in the form of ammonium ion. It appears that nitrates travel unimpeded through the soil system (see Table 2).

The efficiency, operational characteristics, and costs of the various processes for nitrogen removal are extremely variable. Referring to the data summarized in Table 1, the information on removal efficiencies is probably the most reliable, since a number of experimental and demonstration studies have been conducted on these processes. The wide spread in the cost data reflects the fact that little reliable information has been published.

Phosphorus Removal

Many of the processes applicable to the removal of phosphorus compounds have been discussed in the section dealing with nitrogen compounds. Therefore, the following discussion deals only with processes related specifically to the removal of phosphorus.

Biological Treatment

Biological treatment processes which have been used to remove phosphorus include conventional biological treatment such as activated sludge and trickling filters, modified activated sludge, and algae harvesting.

Here again, the principle is the same as in the removal of nitrogen from solution, namely, the conversion of soluble phosphorus compounds to organically bound forms in biological cell tissue. In the case of phosphorus, however, due to the unbalanced relationship between the quantity of phosphorus and nitrogen found in sewage, it appears that not more than 20-40% of the phosphorus normally present in domestic sewage can be removed by conventional biological treatment methods.

However, removal of phosphorus by adsorption on activated sludge floc rather than by conversion overcomes this problem. In this method, the activated sludge process is operated in the dispersed growth phase with a detention time of about one-half to one hour. The biological floc containing the adsorbed phosphorus is removed from the effluent and disposed of separately. A variety of removal methods are currently under investigation.

Table 2. Nutrients in waste water stem from natural and man-made sources.

Source	Nitrogen		Phosphorus	
	Millions of pounds per year	Concentration as discharged (mg/l as N)	Millions of pounds per year	Concentration as in discharged (mg/l as P)
Domestic waste	1,100-1,600	18-20	200-500	3.5-9
Industrial waste	>1000	0-10,000	n.a.	n.a.
Rural runoff:				
Agricultural land	1,500-15,000	1-70	120-1,200	0.05-1.1
Non-agricultural land	400-1,900	0.1-0.5	150-750	0.04-0.2
Farm animal waste	>1000	n.a.	n.a.	n.a.
Urban runoff	110-1,000	1-10	11-170	0.1-1.5
Rainfall direct to water surface	30-590	0.1-2.0	3-9	0.01-0.03

n.a.—not available

Chemical Precipitation

Precipitation of phosphorus in waste water usually is accomplished by the addition of coagulants such as alum, lime or iron salts, and polyelectrolytes. Commercial processes involving the use of metal ions and polyelectrolytes are available. Chemical precipitation may be carried out in the primary or secondary treatment or as a separate operation.

In the primary stage, most of the phosphorus is removed in the primary sedimentation tank. The remaining phosphorus normally will be removed, by conversion, in the biological treatment phase. When precipitation is to be accomplished in the secondary or biological state of treatment, chemicals usually are added to the aeration tank. The precipitates formed in the biological reactor are removed in the secondary settling tank. Using a combination of chemical and biological treatment, phosphorus removal efficiencies are in the range of 80-95%. Depending on the chemical dosage, incremental removal of biological oxygen demand (BOD), chemical oxygen demand (COD) and surfactant also can be achieved.

In some tertiary treatment installations, phosphorus is precipitated as a separate operation, following conventional biological treatment. Using alum or lime as a coagulant and precipitant, the coagulation-sedimentation process will remove phosphates to a level of 0.5 mg/1, or less, provided sufficiently large dosages (200-400 mg./l.) are used. The fact that coagulation-sedimentation treatment will not remove nitrate may not preclude its application to the solution of eutrophication problems caused by phosphorus.

One promising modification of the chemical coagulation process is precipitation of phosphorus with a coagulant such as alum on filter or separation beds. Coagulants, coagulant aids such as polyelectrolytes, and pH adjusters are added to the activated sludge treatment plant effluent just before the filter. Culp reported that the process can reduce ortho-phosphates to less than 1 mg./l. using alum doses of about 100-200 mg./l. In addition, BOD is consistently reduced to less than 1 mg./l., and the COD is reduced by about 50%.

Sorption

Conventional alum treatment for phosphate removal will increase the concentration of sulfate ion in solution. Sorption is a process developed to remove various forms of phosphate without increasing the sulfate concentration. Activated alumina is used to sorb phosphates by passing a stream of water through the sorption column. Regeneration of the activated alumina for reuse is accomplished using small amounts of caustic and nitric acid. Yee reported that phosphate removal efficiencies up to 90% can be accomplished without adding any salts to the water or changing its pH.

Ultimate Disposal of Contaminants

The quantities of contaminants, both liquid and solid, which will require ultimate disposal vary with the removal method. For small plants, these contaminants can be handled quite readily in lagoons, sludge drying beds, or sanitary landfills. However, as the treatment plant capacity increases, waste tonnages requiring ultimate disposal by other means may become significant.

Various ultimate disposal methods have been studied. There are four general possibilities: dumping; subsurface injection; conversion and dumping; and conversion, product recovery, and dumping. Of these four methods, the last, although the most desirable, is at present, the least practical.

The costs of these ultimate disposal methods vary over an extremely wide range. Due to this wide variation in cost, ultimate disposal methods must be considered carefully since this cost component may be the controlling factor governing the overall feasibility of nutrient removal.

Additional Reading

Bennett, G. E., Eliassen, R., and McCarty, P. L., "Water Reclamation Study Program." Progress Report Demonstration Project Grant No. WPD 21-04, Water Quality Control Laboratory, Stanford University (Aug. 1966).

Bureau of Sanitary Engineering, Waste Water Reclamation, California State Department of Public Health, Berkeley, Calif. (Nov. 1967).

Culp, G., and Slechta, A., "Nitrogen Removal from Sewage." Final Progress Report, USPHS Demonstration Plant Grant 86-01 (Feb. 1966).

Culp, R. L., "Wastewater Reclamation by Tertiary Treatment," *J. Water Pollution Control Federation*, 35, 6 (June 1963).

Eliassen, R., and Tchobanoglous, G., "Chemical Processing of Wastewater for Nutrient Removal." Presented at the 40th Annual Conference of the Water Pollution Control Federation, New York. N.Y. (Oct. 1967).

Föyn, E., "Removal of Sewage Nutrients by Electrolytic Treatment," *Inter. Ver Theoret. Angew, Limnol., Verhand.*, 15 (1962). Published in English (1964).

Herbert, C. P., and Schroepfer, G. S., "The Travel of Nitrogen in Soils." *J. Water Pollution Control Federation*, 39, 1 (Jan. 1967).

McCarty, P. L., "Feasibility of the Denitrification Process for Removal of Nitrate Nitrogen from Agricultural Drainage Waters." Report to the San Joaquin District, California State Department of Water Resources (1966).

Metcalf and Eddy Engineers, "Report to the Spring Creek Committee upon Disposal of Sewage and Industrial Wastes on the Spring Creek Watershed, Centre County, Pennsylvania," Boston, Mass. (Mar. 1961).

Nesbitt, J. B., "Removal of Phosphorus from Municipal Sewage Plant Effluents," Engineering Research Bulletin B-93, College of Engineering, Pennsylvania State University (Feb. 1966).

Oswald, W. J., Crosby, D. G., and Goulucke, C. G., "Removal of Pesticides and Algal Growth Potential from San Joaquin Valley Drainage Waters (A Feasibility Study)." Report to the San Joaquin District, California State Department of Water Resources (1964).

Sawyer, C. N., "Biological Engineering in Sewage Treatment," *Sewage Works J.*, 16, 9 (Sept. 1944).

Task Group Report, "Sources of Nitrogen and Phosphorus in Water Supplies," *J. Am. Water Works Assoc.*, 59, 3 (Mar. 1967).

Thimann, K. V., "The Life of Bacteria" (2nd Edition), Macmillan Co., New York (July 1963).

Yee, W. C., "The Selective Removal of Mixed Phosphates from Water Streams by Activated Alumina," Oak Ridge National Laboratory, TM-1135 (Nov. 1965).

49

PESTICIDES AND CATASTROPHE

Göran Löfroth

At last, people are beginning to realize that a healthy environment is as essential for human survival as the five basic necessities—food, water, housing, education, and medical care— and that the cost of protecting the environment ought to be paid before we are allowed the luxury of consuming other relatively unnecessary goods. One might expect the environmental conditions in Sweden to be much better than those in many other countries, but if the facts of the situation were fully disclosed the

Reprinted from the *New Scientist* 40: 567-68, 1968, with the permission of the publishers.

citizens might lose confidence in their authorities. I have written this article because I am convinced that stating hard, scientific facts is the only way to create changes that will lead to a better environment.

Since the mid-forties, when the large-scale distribution of organochlorine compounds began, something of the order of a million metric tons of DDT have been distributed on the Earth in various ways. DDT and its metabolic products DDE and DDD are persistent— meaning that they are degraded only very slowly or not at all to non-toxic compounds. These DDT-compounds can now be found in any randomly selected biological area at a considerable distance from where they were originally distributed.

It must be remembered, that the levels found in Man and food reflect only the past and present exposure; they do not take into account the background level of organochlorine compounds which is being built up all over the world. The total level is, in fact, higher than most people imagine, because experimental studies rarely take into account run-off and evaporation.

Baltic 'Grossly Polluted'

Data gathered in Sweden by S. Oden of Uppsala and his collaborators show that a total of about 1250 metric tons of DDT-compounds are distributed in Swedish soils. In addition, 500 recent analyses of soils which *have not* been treated with DDT show that the DDT-content progressively increases from South Sweden to North Sweden; the average concentration is about 0.1 ppm—and the same pattern is observed with lindane. It is also a fact that, due to the aerial transportation of organochlorine pesticides and their fall-out in rain and snow, these compounds are being widely distributed in regions where more food is grown than anywhere else.

Only scattered information on the organochlorine intake of the Swedish fauna is available. But DDT-analyses of pike suggest that if the contamination was controlled by law—as it ought to be but is not, the fish would be regarded as unfit for human consumption.

Johnels, Jensen and their co-workers are at the moment studying the conditions in the Baltic, and their studies, although incomplete, give the impression that the Baltic is grossly polluted. The eggs of resident gulls (guillemots) contain 1-5 ppm DDT, 17-54 ppm DDE, and 0.1-0.3 ppm dieldrin. These levels threaten to impair the reproductive capacity of the birds. Baltic herring also contains appreciable amounts of chlorinated hydrocarbons and some should be considered unfit for human consumption.

Recently, very high dieldrin concentrations were found in the sludge emitted from a textile town in Middle Sweden (Borås). It was found that fish caught downstream contained up to 3 ppm dieldrin. After these facts were published, the industry stopped using dieldrin and the local authorities declared that fish from the polluted waters were unfit for human consumption. The use of dieldrin in general is not, however, forbidden as it has yet to be proved that anyone has died of dieldrin poisoning.

Unjustifiable Uses

Another cause for concern is the fact that textiles are being treated with organochlorine compounds to a level of 200-500 ppm to yield moth-proof materials. They are also being added to dry-cleaning liquids. Other less toxic compounds, such as eulan and mittin, are also available to the textile industry. In 1961, Maier-Bode disclosed that human sweat dissolves appreciable quantities of dieldrin from treated textiles whereupon the solute then enters the body by absorption through the skin.

Our past and present exposure to organochlorine pesticides can be measured by analysing the concentrations of these compounds in the human body, as they are stored mostly in the fat. About 5-27 ppm of DDT-compounds are now found in the adipose tissue of persons living in countries with widespread use of DDT, and according to Widmark and Jensen most members of the Swedish adult population carry about 7 ppm of these pollutants in their tissue.

From the known relationship between oral intake and storage in adipose tissue, it can be calculated that affected populations have a daily intake which is less than 0.001 mg/DDT-compounds per kg bodyweight. This is 10 or more times less than the maximum acceptable daily intake of 0.01 mg per kg bodyweight which has been recommended by the agencies of the United Nations.

The recommendations of the UN agencies came after evaluations of a considerable amount of toxicological work, including studies on healthy adult men exposed to DDT for 6.5 years or less. Nevertheless, on the basis of animal studies, it looks as if the maximum acceptable intake for Man should be 20 times less than what is currently recommended as a danger line. These studies, by Kemény and Taján show that a relatively low oral intake of DDT gives a significant increase in tumour frequency and those by Kinoshita and others suggest that still lower intakes produce hepatic enzyme induction and that this induction causes steroid hydroxylation.

Although the adult population of the world appears to consume at least 10 times less DDT-compounds than the amount reckoned dangerous, an appreciable fraction of the population takes in, with its food, much more than the most it should consume. As Woodward and his colleagues reported more than 20 years ago in *Science,* this is largely because ingested DDT is excreted with the milk.

According to the National Institute of Public Health, human milk in Sweden contains an average of 0.117 ppm DDT-compounds. This means that breast-fed babies consume 0.017 mg DDT-compounds per day per kg body weight or, to put it more simply, 70 per cent above the present maximally acceptable amount. British breast-fed babies have a similar intake and, to judge from Egan and Quinby's results, American ones have a still higher intake.

The situation in respect of dieldrin is equally disturbing, as 40 per cent of the breast-fed babies in Sweden ingest at least twice the amount maximally acceptable, and Egan has shown that British and American breast-fed babies consume about ten times the recommended limit.

The adult population of Western Australia has an average concentration of 0.67 ppm dieldrin in the adipose tissue. This is about three times the concentration found in the British population, and consequently their breast-fed babies might have an intake as high as 30 times the maximally acceptable one. Summing up, we see that we are exposing coming generations to amounts of organochlorine pesticides which are greatly in excess of those to which we are exposing ourselves.

Many parents are faced by a difficult choice. Should they expose their child, during an important and sensitive phase of development, to an unknown and high amount of organochlorine pesticides, or should they deprive the child of nutritious milk and warm contact with its mother? The danger notwithstanding, it looks as if the positive advantages of breast-feeding outweigh the organochlorine hazard. But the outlook for the future is, to say the least, distinctly disturbing.

Individual citizens have few ways of protecting themselves against a multitude of contemporary social hazards, but anyone can decrease their exposure considerably by avoiding *all* household formulations that contain these compounds. The use of organochlorine pesticides in agriculture, and in eradicating disease-carrying insects in the tropic and sub-tropic parts of the world, cannot be abolished abruptly. But, during the course of the next few years, we must switch over to the less toxic and non-persistent pesticides which are available, while we await the development of selective compounds. This switch will be accelerated by the fact that an increasing number of insect populations is becoming resistant to organochlorine pesticides. One wholly effective method of decreasing the pesticide danger is by demanding stricter control over their use.

Deichmann and Radomski have recently shown that the mean concentration of DDT, DDE, DDD, and dieldrin found in autopsy adipose tissues of non-occupationally exposed individuals who died from portal cirrhosis, carcinoma, and hypertension, were two to three times higher than concentrations found in the tissues of those who died from accidental deaths.

The case for regarding the organochlorines as unacceptably dangerous poisons is building up fast, and Man himself is the potential victim— not just those birds and beasts for whom these chemicals have already proved disastrous. There is at least the possibility of a human tragedy of global proportions occurring if our present practices continue unrestrained. Must we demand the evidence of catastrophe before we act?

50

DECREASE IN EGGSHELL WEIGHT IN CERTAIN BIRDS OF PREY

D. A. Ratcliffe

The incidence of broken eggs in nests of peregrine falcon *Falco peregrinus*, sparrowhawk *Accipiter nisus* and golden eagle *Aquila chrysaetos* in Britain has increased considerably since 1950. In 109 peregrine eyries examined in 1904-50, there were only three instances of egg breakage, compared with forty-seven in 168 eyries examined in 1951-66. Two of thirty-five golden eagle eyries examined in 1936-50 contained broken eggs, compared with twelve out of forty-eight examined in 1951-63. One breakage was found in twenty-four sparrowhawk nests in 1943-50, but eight in twenty-seven nests in 1951-60. Peregrines have been witnessed eating their own eggs (1), and most recent egg breakages in all three species appeared to involve parental destruction.

Eggshell thickness was investigated by measuring weight and size of blown eggs of varying age (see Table 1), using specimens cleanly emptied through a hole not exceeding 7 mm in diameter, thus rejecting heavily incubated eggs. In peregrine and sparrowhawk, eggshell weight/size ratio decreased significantly and suddenly in 1946-50, and has not recovered. Since 1947, the only "normal" peregrine eggshells were four of the seven available from the East Highlands. After 1946, sparrowhawk eggshells from Surrey were significantly lighter than those from Cumberland, Dorset and Hampshire. Golden eagle eggshells from West Scotland were slightly yet very significantly lighter but East Highland eggshells remain unchanged. Fewer golden eagle eggs were available, but change during 1945-50 is again indicated.

The eggshells as measured consisted largely of calcium carbonate (about 90 per cent in

Reprinted from *Nature* 215: 208-10, 1967, with the permission of the publishers.

"normal" eggs), the remaining fraction being shell protein (2), adherent shell membranes, and residual film of contents. The decrease in eggshell weight has involved mainly the calcium carbonate fraction. Decrease in shell thickness rather than density is implied, but this has not been measured directly.

Thickness of eggshells and production of eggs vary according to diet (especially calcium) and condition in poultry; eggshell thickness is also genetically influenced, and diminished by disease and increasing age (3). Certain chemicals, for example sulphanilamide (4), cause decrease in eggshell thickness, as can stress; severe fright can stop poultry laying for a time. Occasional thin-shelled eggs may be laid by any wild bird species, but before 1946, mean eggshell weight and size for clutches from the same female raptor, year by year, were fairly constant, though weight size of eggshells within one clutch was less consistent.

Decrease in eggshell weight in peregrine and sparrowhawk was synchronous, rapid and widespread. (See Figs. 50-1 and 50-2). It occurred in successive clutches of the same female peregrines at four different eyries, but three other females laid at least one clutch of normal weight after they had produced light eggs. General ageing or genetic shift in the population are thus not likely to be involved, while the synchronous effect on three raptors with different ecology and distributions, and the varying geographical response, make disease an unlikely explanation.

Decrease of calcium carbonate for eggshell formation could result from reduced food consumption, but no decline in available food supply for these raptors was known in 1940-50. Loss of hunting efficiency could cause an effective food shortage, or change in metabolic regulation could induce internal shortage of calcium, without less food being consumed. A different possibility is premature extrusion of eggs, known in poultry (personal communication from C. Tyler).

Some physiological change evidently followed a widespread and pervasive environmental change around 1945-47. Increasing radioactive contamination fails to account for geographical variations in eggshell change, whereas these match the developing regional

Table 1. Measurements of eggshells of three British Raptors, 1900-1967.

Species	District 1 1900-46	District 2 1947-67	No. of eggs 3 1900-46	No. of eggs 4 1947-67	Mean eggshell weight (g) 5 1900-46	Mean eggshell weight (g) 6 1947-67	*Mean index of eggshell size, length x breadth (mm) 7 1900-46	*Mean index of eggshell size, length x breadth (mm) 8 1947-67	†Mean index of eggshell weight (mg) L x B 9 1900-46	†Mean index of eggshell weight (mg) L x B 10 1947-67	Probability of significant difference between data in columns 9 and 10
Peregrine	S. England N. England Wales Scotland Ireland	S. England N. England S. Scotland	371	158	3.81	3.09	2,072	2,102	1.84	1.47	<0.001
	As above	C. and E. Scottish Highlands	371	7	3.81	3.59	2,072	2,096	1.84	1.71	—
Sparrowhawk	S. England Midlands N. England Wales Scotland Sussex Surrey Kent	S. England Midlands N. England Wales Scotland Surrey	229	188	1.83	1.54	1,293	1,293	1.42	1.19	<0.001
		Surrey	25	51 Included in above totals	1.81	1.38	1,273	1,292	1.42	1.07	<0.001
Golden eagle	Western Central and Eastern Highlands	Galloway and Western Highlands	107	26	14.37	13.19	4,553	4,563	3.16	2.89	<0.001
	As above	C. and E. Highlands	107	14	14.37	14.45	4,553	4,630	3.16	3.12	—

* These measurements show a sufficiently close relationship to surface areas of the eggshells to justify using the more simply derived length x breadth (L x B) as an index of size.

† This is presumed to indicate thickness, but it could also indicate density of eggshell.

Fig. 50-1. Change in the ratio of weight to size (index of thickness) in eggshells of the peregrine falcon in Britain. Circles represent eggshells from the central and eastern Scottish Highlands, and dots represent eggshells from other districts (see Table 1).

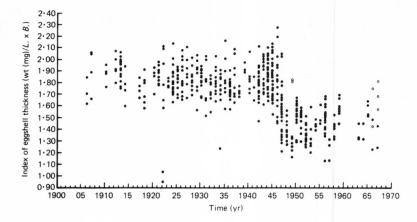

Fig. 50-2. Change in the ratio of weight to size (index of thickness) in eggshells of the sparrowhawk in Britain. Circles represent eggshells from south-eastern England, and dots represent eggshells from other districts (see Table 1).

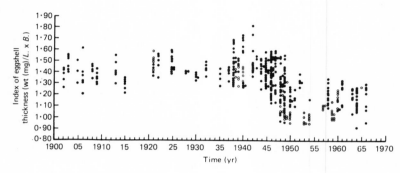

pattern of contamination by chemical pollutants during this period. Among urban-industrial pollutants, one waste product in smoke, the persistent polychlorinated biphenyl (PCB), has been found in tissues of fish, eagles and humans in Sweden, and was first detected in 1944 in an eagle (5). There was a notable boom in organic insecticides, fungicides and herbicides containing chlorine, mercury, phosphorus and sulphur after 1945, and environmental contamination by persistent residues has been widespread (6). British peregrines, sparrowhawks and golden eagles have shown widespread contamination by pp' DDT, pp' DDE, γ-BHC, dieldrin and heptachlor epoxide (7-9). The introduction of DDT into general use (about 1945-46) coincided closely with onset of the eggshell change. Dieldrin, aldrin and heptachlor appeared 10 yr later and, like DDT and γ-BHC, have been used extensively ever since. Contamination of birds by persistent organo-mercury compounds has received little attention in Britain, but in Sweden the introduction of these as seed dressings paralleled the

substantial increase in mercury content of raptor tissues during the 1940s (ref. 10).

Calcium metabolism in birds is controlled by oestrogen and parathyroid hormone (3), and is thus potentially sensitive to any chemical disturbing hormone regulation. Jefferies (11) has demonstrated a significant correlation between intake of pp' DDT by the Bengalese finch *Lonchura striata* and delay in ovulation, and interprets this as a hormonal effect. One dithio-carbamate fungicide affects eggshell thickness in poultry (12), but is non-persistent and of unknown relevance to raptors.

The time correlation between decrease in eggshell weight and increase in egg-breakage suggests a causal connexion. In the peregrine and golden eagle there is also geographical correlation, for in the East Highlands decrease in eggshell weight is slight or unknown and egg breakage unusual. Eating eggs is probably an instinctive adaptive response to unfavourable circumstances arising after laying, and seldom invoked before 1946. Other bird species normally eat or destroy their damaged eggs (13), and lighter raptor eggs are probably more prone to accidental damage than "normal" eggs. Yet, often, raptors have evidently destroyed undamaged eggs, perhaps in response to a calcium "hunger". Domestic fowl which have broken and eaten an egg often develop an incurable appetite for their eggs. While calcium is obviously implicated, in several raptor instances the egg contents had been eaten and most of the shell left.

Other bird species in which egg-breaking is unusual (hobby *Falco subbuteo*, merlin *F. columbarius*, buzzard *Buteo buteo*, carrion crow *Corvus corone*, golden plover *Charadrius apricarius*, greenshank *Tringa nebularia*, guillemot *Uria aalge*, and razorbill *Alca torda*) show no change in eggshell weight. In kestrel *F. tinnunculus* and raven *Corvus corax*, the eggs of some individuals show a slight decrease, but not the whole population samples.

For the species examined, frequency of egg-breakage, scale of decrease in eggshell weight, subsequent status of breeding population, and exposure to persistent organic pesticides are correlated. The possibility that these phenomena are links in a causal chain is being investigated. Recovery of locally depleted populations of peregrine began in 1946 and continued for several years after eggshells became lighter and egg eating frequent, even in districts, such as Dorset, where both changes were obvious. Population "crashes" in peregrine

and sparrowhawk after 1955 probably involved greatly increased adult mortality, but later factors contributing to low breeding success would tend to prevent recovery.

I thank D. Nethersole-Thompson, N. W. Moore, I. Prestt, E. Blezard, C. J. O. Harrison, I. Lyster, C. W. Benson, R. Stokoe, C. Best, R. Wagstaffe, A. Tynan, A. D. and M. Horrill, J. P. Dempster and Miss S. Batchelor for their help.

References

1. Ratcliffe, D. A., *Brit. Birds*, **51**, 23 (1958).
2. Tyler, C., and Geake, F. H., *J. Sci. Food Agric.*, **4**, 261 (1953).
3. Sturkie, P. D., *Avian Physiology* (Cornell Univ. Press, New York, 1954).
4. Tyler, C., *Brit. J. Nutrit.*, **4**, 112 (1950).
5. Jensen, S., *New Sci.*, **32**, 612 (1966).
6. Moore, N. W., *Brit. Ecol. Soc. Symp.*, Oxford (1965).
7. Ratcliffe, D. A., *Bird Study*, **12**, 66 (1965).
8. Prestt, I., *Univ. Wisconsin Publications* (in the press).
9. Lockie, J. D., and Ratcliffe, D. A., *Brit. Birds*, **57**, 89 (1964).
10. Berg, W., Johnels, A., Sjöstrand, B., and Westermark, T., *Oikos*, **17**, 71 (1966).
11. Jefferies, D. J. *Ibis*, **109**, 266 (1967).
12. Picco, D., *Notiz. Mal. Piante*, **59/60**, 281 (1962).
13. Nethersole-Thompson, C., and Nethersole-Thompson, D., *Brit. Birds*, **35**, 162, 190, 214, 241 (1942).

51

DDT RESIDUES IN PACIFIC SEA BIRDS: A PERSISTENT INSECTICIDE IN MARINE FOOD CHAINS

Robert W. Risebrough, Daniel B. Menzel,
D. James Martin, Jr., and Harold S. Olcott

The accumulation and biological concentration of DDT and its metabolites* within food chains of terrestrial (1), freshwater (2), and estuarine (3) ecosystems have been well documented. Significant residue concentrations have occasionally been reported in marine organisms, but these have usually been attributed to local sources of contamination (4). The present study, which is based on analyses of collections of birds, fish and invertebrates from Pacific Ocean localities, indicates that DDT is also a component of marine ecosystems and that pelagic species may accumulate high concentrations of DDT residues. The results of the work with fish will be published elsewhere (5).

Specimens collected for analysis were frozen and stored at −15°C. Some conversion of p,p'-DDT to p,p'-DDD may occur in these conditions (6), and so the reported values of these two compounds may be somewhat lower and higher, respectively, than those occurring in nature. Tissues, eggs and whole birds were digested with a mixture of acetic and perchloric acids, and the lipid fraction containing the pesticide was extracted from the diluted di-

* DDT residues include the two isomers of DDT, p,p'-DDT and o,p'-DDT and the metabolic derivatives of p,p'-DDT: p,p'-DDE, p,p'-DDD, and p,p'-DDMU: p,p'-DDT, 1,1,1-trichloro-2,2-bis(p-chlorophenyl)ethane; o,p'-DDT, 1,1,1-trichloro-2(o-chlorophenyl)-2-(p-chlorophenyl)ethane, p,p'-DDE, 1,1'-dichloro-2,2-bis(p-chlorophenyl)ethylene p,p'-DDD, also known as TDE, 1,1'-dichloro-2,2-bis(p-chlorophenyl)ethane p,p'-DDMU-1-chloro-2,2-bis(p-chlorophenyl)ethylene.

Reprinted from *Nature* 216: 489-90, 1967, with the permission of the publishers.

gestion mixture with petroleum ether or N-hexane (7). Recovery of DDT from fortified tissue samples averaged 96 per cent. Lipids were removed by passage of the extract through a modified Davidow column (7). Because aldrin, dieldrin and similar compounds are destroyed by this treatment, some extracts were prepared by the method of Bligh and Dyer (8), and were cleaned on 'Florisil' columns (9). Analyses of the purified extracts were performed on a Microtek 220 gas chromatograph, equipped with an all-glass system and an electron capture detector. The chromatograms were performed isothermally (190°C) on 3 per cent *QF*-1 or 5 per cent *SE*-30 on 'Chromosorb *W*,' 80-100 mesh treated with hexamethyldisilazane or on 10 per cent *DC*-200 on 'Gas Chrom *Q*' (ref. 5). The carrier gas was nitrogen. Identification of the chlorinated hydrocarbons recorded in the western gull and brown pelican was confirmed by thin-layer chromatography (10).

Residue levels in the resident California species (Table 1) were considerably higher than those in the northern migrants (Table 2) which spend the winter months off the California coast. It is not possible to estimate how much of the residue carried by the northern birds originated in California waters. The shearwaters (Table 2), which are strictly pelagic migrants from the southern hemisphere, contained as much as, or more pesticide than, the local birds. The sooty shearwater and the slender-billed shearwater are known as the mutton birds of New Zealand and of Bass Strait, Australia, respectively, and are a traditional source of food for the local human populations. After the nesting season both species migrate northwards across the Equator. During the summer months many thousands of sooty shearwaters are present in Monterey Bay. DDT has been extensively used for mosquito control in many countries and may therefore be relatively more prevalent in some areas of tropical seas.

A significant fraction of the pesticides present in breeding females may be passed on to the eggs. Three female Cassin's auklets, which lay a single egg each season, were collected with their eggs from burrows on the Farallon Islands. The total concentrations of residue in the eggs ranged from 9.4 per cent to

32 per cent of the total present in the adult female.

A mean value of 3.1 μg of dieldrin was found in three eggs of the western gull, but dieldrin was not present in the breast muscle of the brown pelican, or in fat samples of the Cassin's auklet. DDMU was detected in almost all avian tissues. It is part of the pathway by which p,p'-DDT is degraded to the water-soluble compounds DDA and dichlorobenzo-phenone in the chick embryo (11), and so we assume that its presence indicates some amount of DDT metabolism.

We have reported the pesticide content and the individual variation of pesticide content and concentration in collections of eight species of

Table 1. DDT residues (p,p'-DDT, o,p'-DDT, p,p'-DDE, p,p'-DDD, p,p'-DDMU in sea birds resident in California.

Sample	Total DDT residues (p.p.m.)	Percentages of residue as		
		p,p'-DDT	DDE	DDD
Ptychoramphus aleuticus (Cassin's auklet), nine adults*	5.1	0.4	95	1.1
Ptychoramphus aleuticus, one adult found dead*	15.4	0.1	96	1.0
Ptychoramphus aleuticus, two adults†	1.0	3.8	87	4.0
Ptychoramphus aleuticus, three adults*				
Breast muscle	2.0	11	81	1.0
Brain	0.7	32	54	5.9
Liver	1.0	9.7	79	3.9
Subcutaneous fat	56	1.5	92	1.5
Ptychoramphus aleuticus, fourteen eggs*	10.8	0.3	96	1.0
Larus occidentalis (Western gull), two adults*				
Breast muscle	9.2	0.1	89	6.9
Brain	1.8	2.2	83	4.4
Subcutaneous fat	211	0.4	94	3.1
Larus occidentalis, nine eggs, one-egg clutches*	6.5	2.9	82	7.3
Phalacrocorax pelagicus (pelagic cormorant), one adult‡				
Breast muscle	0.8	1.3	83	11.9
Liver	0.7	0.0	84	10.9
Phalacrocorax penicillatus (Brant's cormorant), five adults§				
Breast muscle	4.4	0.0	91	6.2
Liver	3.3	0.0	85	9.2
Brain (three birds)	1.2	0.0	92	5.2
Pelecanus occidentalis (Brown pelican)†				
Breast muscle	84.4	1.4	91	4.8
Uria aalge (common murre)†	7.3	0.3	93	4.0

* Farallon Islands, April and May 1966; † Monterey Bay, November and December 1966. Although these species breed in California, the individual birds may have come from elsewhere; ‡ Tomales Bay Marin Co., March 4, 1966; § Tomales Bay, December 31, 1965.

Concentrations are expressed in parts per million wet weight. Unless otherwise indicated the whole bird was analysed. Concentrations in eggs are based on the entire contents of the egg. The proportions of DDT (p,p'-DDT), DDE (p,p'-DDE) and DDD (p,p'-DDD) are expressed as a percentage of the total. o,p'-DDT and p,p'-DDMU constitute the balance.

Table 2. DDT residues in non-resident sea birds.

Sample	Total DDT residues (p.p.m.)	Percentages of residue as		
		p,p'-DDT	DDE	DDD
Synthliboramphus antiquus (ancient murrelet)*	0.75	0.2	90	4.5
Phalaropus fulicarius (red phalarope), two birds*	1.0	7.2	82	5.7
Cerorhinca monocerata (rhinoceros auklet), two birds*	2.7	0.6	92	3.2
Fulmarus glacialis (fulmar), three birds*	1.9	7.5	85	5.1
Rissa tridactyla (kittiwake)†	1.3	3.7	76	13.5
Puffinus griseus (sooty shearwater), three birds*	8.4	5.6	88	3.8
Puffinus tenuirostris (slender-billed shearwater)†	32	4.4	92	2.7

* Monterey Bay, November 1, 1966; † Monterey Bay, December, 18, 1966.
Notation as in Table 1.

Pacific marine fish (5). Total levels of DDT residue in tissues of the blue fin tuna *(Thunnus thynnus)* and the yellowfin tuna *(Thunnus albacares)* from Baja California, Central America, and the Galapagos Islands ranged from 0.1 to 0.6 p.p.m. Skipjack tuna *(Euthynnus pelamis)* from waters off Hawaii, the Galapagos Islands, and mainland Ecuador contained somewhat lower concentrations of DDT residue, which ranged from 10 to 100 parts per billion. Fish from California coastal waters contained more residue, but in general total concentrations were 10-20 per cent of those in the birds. Collections of the northern anchovy *(Engraulis mordax)*, English sole *(Parophrys vetulus)*, Pacific jack mackerel *(Trachurus symmetricus)* and of hake *(Merluccius productus)* from offshore waters between San Francisco and the Channel Islands north of Los Angeles averaged between 0.2 and 2.8 p.p.m. of total residue: 12.7 p.p.m. were present, however, in anchovies taken off Terminal Island, Los Angeles. Significantly lower concentrations of residue were found in anchovies and English sole from San Francisco Bay. San Francisco Bay receives drainage water from the Sacramento and San Joaquin Valleys, and so it seems unlikely that agricultural run-off can account for the observed distribution of DDT residues in the sea (5).

Residue levels in several marine invertebrates from coastal localities between Monterey and Point Arena were ten to fifty times lower than those in the fish analysed (Table 3). Most values ranged between 20 and 100 parts per billion. The snail *(Thais emarginata)* and the common starfish *(Pisaster ochraceus)* both feed on the mussel *Mytilus californianus*. No biological accumulation could be demonstrated in the starfish, but the snail contained two to five times the concentrations of residue present in its principal food source collected at the same localities. All the DDT recorded in the purple urchins was present in the gonads at a concentration of 5 parts per billion. No residue, or less than the detectable limit of 1 part per billion, was present in the other tissues of the urchins.

Unfortunately, our present knowledge permits only an imperfect estimate of the present and future effects of DDT accumulation in any species. Within the past few years the numbers of the peregrine falcon and the bald eagle have declined and both species have essentially disappeared as breeding birds on the Channel Islands of California (personal observation and records of Mr. W. G. Abbott). There is no evidence that the fanatical efforts of egg collectors in the early years of the century or recent pressure from hunters and falconers have been a significant factor. The comparatively

Table 3. DDT residues in marine invertebrates.

Samples	Total DDT residues (parts per billion)	Percentage of residue as		
		p,p'-DDT	DDE	DDD
Mytilus californianus (common mussel)*	19	26	26	26
Thais emarginata (short-spired purple snail)†	94	33	29	26
Pisaster ochraceus (common starfish), eight animals	20	15	24	32
Mitella polymerus (Pacific goose barnacle), forty animals	27	7	56	22
Crassostrea gigas (giant Pacific oyster), five animals	29	42	24	17
Strongylocentrotus purpuratus (purple urchin)‖	5	100	0	0
Patiria miniata (sea bat starfish), ten animals	78	19	55	14
Loligo opalescens (squid), thirteen animals**	28	36	32	14
Stichopus californicus (sea cucumber), three animals††	93	43	25	25
Pugettia producta (kelp crab), six animals‡‡	42	16	62	10
Thais emarginata (short-spired purple snail), Monterey §§	163	28	45	15
Mytilus californianus (common mussel), Monterey‖‖	84	32	38	18
Mytilus californianus Ensenada, Baja California¶¶	34	21	53	9
Mytilus californianus, Farallon Islands***	34	0	84	0

* Point San Pedro, San Mateo Co., May 26, 1966, pooled sample of twenty animals, shells removed before analysis; † Point San Pedro, San Mateo Co., May 26, 1966, pooled sample of eighty animals, shells removed before analysis; ‡ Point San Pedro, May 26, 1966; § Tomales Bay, Marin Co., September 15, 1965; ‖ Point Arena, Mendocino Co., September 16, 1966, gonads of eight animals; ¶ Monterey, March 6, 1966; ** Monterey, June 16, 1965; †† Monterey, March 12, 1966; ‡‡ Monterey, March 6, 1966; §§ April 11, 1966, pooled sample of thirty-six animals, shells removed; ‖‖ Monterey, April 11, 1966, pooled sample of 108 animals; ¶¶ July 17, 1965, pooled sample of fifteen animals; *** April 6, 1966, pooled sample of eleven animals.
Notation as in Table 1.

high amounts of DDT and its metabolites in fish from the vicinity of the Channel Islands suggest that food chain concentration would result in high levels of residue in fish-eating birds or in species such as the peregrine falcon which feed on other birds. Whether the high pesticide content of the single Cassin's auklet found dead on the Farallon Islands contributed to its death is a matter for speculation.

Reports on levels of residue in tropical areas where DDT is used for mosquito control are as yet lacking. The total DDT residues in the eggs of British sea birds (12) and in the tissues of birds from the coastal regions of Holland (13) suggest that DDT contamination is less in European seas, although more dieldrin and endrin are present. The recently published values of DDT concentrations in organisms of a Long Island, New York, estuary (3) suggest that contamination in the offshore waters of New England may be as high as in California.

Although chlorinated hydrocarbons in

solution or adsorbed to particulate matter are brought by rivers to the sea (14), transport by water circulation can scarcely account for the observed distribution of DDT in the sea and its occurrence in very remote areas (15). Chlorinated hydrocarbons readily evaporate with water from the surfaces of marshes and soil (16), are found associated with particulate matter in the air (17), and are present in the atmosphere as a result of air-spraying operations. Wind transport and subsequent fallout in rain (18) might therefore account for the apparent universal occurrence of DDT and its metabolites in the ocean.

This work was supported in part by the U.S. Public Health Service, Department of Health, Education and Welfare, the U.S. National Science Foundation, and the Bureau of Commercial Fisheries, U.S. Department of the Interior.

References

1. Cramp, S., *Brit. Birds,* **56,** 124 (1963); Davis, B. N. K., *J. App. Ecol.,* **3,** (suppl.) 133 (1966); Wurster, jun., C. F. Wurster, D. H., and Strickland, W. N., *Science,* **148** 90 (1965); Wurster, D. H.; Wurster, jun., C. F., and Strickland, W. N., *Ecology,* **46,** 488 (1965).

2. Cope, O. B., *J. App. Ecol.,* **3,** (suppl.), 33 (1966); Hickey, J. J., Keith, J. A., and Coon, F. B., ibid., 141 Keith, J. O., ibid., 71; Hunt, E. G., and Bischoff, A. I., *Calif. Fish and Game.* **46,** 91 (1960).

3. Woodwell, C. M., Wurster, jun., C. F., and Isaccson, P. A., *Science,* **156** 821 (1967).

4. Moore, N. W., *Ecology and the Industrial Society,* 219-237 (Blackwell, Oxford, 1965); *Report on Investigations of Fish Kills in Lower Mississippi River, Atchafalaya River and Gulf of Mexico* (U.S. Department of Health, Education and Welfare, Public Health Service).

5. Risebrough, R. W., Menzel, D. B., Martin, jun. D. J., and Olcott, H. S., Report to U.S. Department of the Interior, Fish and Wildlife Service, Bureau of Commercial Fisheries (in preparation).

6. Walker, C. H., *J. App. Ecol.,* **3,** (suppl.), 213 (1966).

7. Stanley, R. L., and LeFavoure, H. T., *J. Assoc. Off. Agric. Chem.,* **48,** 666 (1965).

8. Bligh, E. G., and Dyer, W. J., *Canad. J. Biochem. Physiol.,* **37,** 911 (1959).

9. *Pesticide Analytical Manual* (U.S. Department of Health, Education and Welfare, Food and Drug Administration).

10. Kovacs, M. F., *J. Assoc. Off. Agric. Chem.,* **46,** 884 (1963); Walker, K. C., and Beroza, M., ibid., 250.

11. Abou-Donia, M. B., thesis, Univ. California, Berkeley (1967).

12. DeWitt, J. B., and Buckley, J. L., *Audubon Field Notes,* **16,** 541 (1962) Moore, N. W., and Ratcliffe D. A., *Bird Study,* **9,** 242 (1962); Prestt, I., *J. App. Ecol.,* **3,** (suppl.), 107 (1966).

13. Keoman, J. M., and van Genderen, H., *J. App. Ecol.,* **3** (suppl.), 99 (1966).

14. Breidenbach, A. W., Gunnerson, C. G., Kawahara, F. K., Lichtenberg, J. J., and Green, R. S., *Public Health Rep.,* **82,** 139 (1967).

15. George, J. L., and Frear, D. E. H., *J. App. Ecol.,* **3** (suppl.), 155 (1966); Sladen, W. J. L., Menzie, C. M., and Reichel, W. L., *Nature,* **210,** 670 (1966); Tatton, J. O'g., and Ruzicka, J. H. A., *Nature,* **215,** 346 (1967).

16. Acree, F., Beroza, M., and Bowman, M. C., *Agric. Food Chem.,* **11,** 278 (1963); Bowman, M. C., Acree, jun., F., Lofgren, C. S., and Beroza, M., *Science,* **146,** 1480 (1964).

17. Antommaria, P., Corn, M., and De Maio, L., *Science,* **150,** 1476 (1965).

18. Cohen, J. M., and Pinkerton, C., *Organic Pesticides in the Environment,* 163-176 (American Chemical Society, 1966); Wheatley, G. A., and Hardman, J. A., *Nature,* **207,** 486 (1965).

52

ORGANOCHLORINE PESTICIDES IN ANTARCTICA

J. O'G. Tatton and J. H. A. Ruzicka

Considerable interest was aroused in 1965 by news from the United States that DDT had been discovered in Antarctic wildlife. Details of this finding were given later in two papers. The first of these by Sladen *et al.* (1) described the detection of DDT and two of its toxic metabolites, DDE and TDE, in six Adèlie penguins *(Pygoscelis adeliae)* and one crab-eater seal *(Lobodon carcinophagus).* All these specimens were taken at Cape Crozier on Ross Island (Fig. 52-1). The second paper by George and Frear (2) described a more ambitious study of samples taken on Ross Island and in the nearby McMurdo area. DDT only was detected in four out of sixteen Weddell seals *(Leptonychotes weddelli)* and four out of sixteen Adèlie penguins. Of sixteen skuas *(Catharacta skua maccormicki)* examined, nearly all contained DDT and DDE. No pesticides were detected in water and snow samples, nor in samples of four phyla of marine invertebrates and an Emperor penguin *(Aptenodytes forsteri).* Of three species of fish taken in the Ross Sea, only one specimen of *Rhigophila dearborni* contained DDT but no DDE.

These discoveries suggested that the contamination of the environment by the new persistent organochlorine pesticides had spread to what is usually regarded as the most remote and isolated part of the Earth. The nearest land mass to Antarctica is Cape Horn in South America (Fig. 52-1), about 1,000 km distant, and most other land masses are at least 2,000 km away. The character of Antarctica is such that the only human residents on the continent

Reprinted from *Nature* 215: 246-48, 1967, with the permission of the publishers, and by permission of the Government Chemist, Laboratory of the Government Chemist, London.

are explorers and research teams, but the traffic of men and supplies brings visiting airmen and sailors to the region. Although the number of men on the continent has grown in recent years (3) and at times there may be as many as 4,000 the population is still minute relative to the land mass of about 13 million sq. km. There are no insect pests in the Antarctic and therefore no need for insecticides. Moreover, there is a general international agreement, under the Antarctic Treaty of 1959, that Antarctica shall remain a faunal and floral preserve and that the existing ecosystems shall not be disturbed by, for example, the introduction of alien species or such powerful influences as pesticides. The detection of DDT in Antarctic wildlife therefore raised immediately the problem of its origin.

Both of the above reports referred to samples taken in the area served by the large United States base at McMurdo and it is perhaps significant that only DDT, and its first two metabolites DDE and TDE, were detected. It is now well known that the air and coastal waters of, for example, the United States and the British Isles contain traces of organochlorine pesticides (4-9) so that pesticides could have reached Antarctica by way of these two media. Air, rain and coastal waters, however, usually show traces not only of DDT and its metabolites but also of other organochlorine pesticides in common use, such as BHC and dieldrin. None of these other pesticides was detected in the samples from the McMurdo area. Therefore, there was always the possibility that no matter how vigilant the authorities concerned may have been, DDT had reached McMurdo simply because man himself had transported it there in his ships, food, clothing or stores.

If this latter supposition were correct, then other areas of Antarctica outside the environment of McMurdo might still be free from contamination. It was considered that this could be investigated by sampling in the area of the British Antarctic Survey Base at Signy Island in the South Orkney Islands (Fig. 52-1) some 4,500 km from the American base at McMurdo. If no DDT were detected there, then it would suggest that the contamination in the

Fig. 52-1. Antarctica.

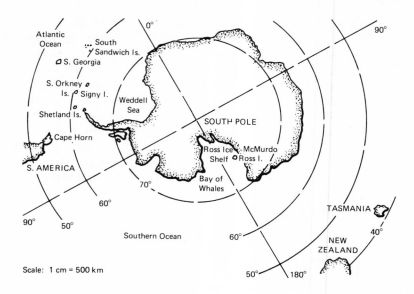

Scale: 1 cm = 500 km

McMurdo area was directly due to local human activities. If DDT were found at Signy Island then again it might be attributed to human activities but it would also reinforce the argument that there was general contamination of all Antarctica whether sea-borne or air-borne or both. The British Antarctic Survey generously agreed to co-operate in obtaining suitable samples from the Signy Island area and to transport them to England in a permanently frozen condition.

The samples included the livers, blubbers, abdominal fat and stomach contents of a number of chinstrap penguins *(Pygoscelis antarctica)*. Most of these were adult birds, 3-8 years old, at the end of the breeding season when they were moulting and very fat; three of the birds were described as immature but at least 1 year old. The samples also included three penguin eggs, probably chinstrap, the fat and livers of two brown skua and two blue-eyed shags *(Phalacrocorax atriceps),* and the livers of four fish *(Notothenia neglecta)* about 3 years old. All these specimens, except for the fish, were taken on Signy Island as far removed as possible from the Survey's base. The fish are the most abundant species in local waters and were taken in Borge Bay on the east side of the island. They are bottom feeders and are preyed on by shags and seals. The birds were killed by pithing or with a blunt instrument, except for

the shags which were shot with a rifle. Dissecting instruments were washed in acetone which was also sampled as a precaution and later found to be completely free from pesticide residues. The items for analysis were placed in glass containers with caps lined with metal foil. These containers had been specially cleaned and prepared in this Laboratory. The samples were then maintained in a continuously frozen state during the journey to London where they were stored at $-25°C$ pending analysis.

The samples were all in an excellent state of preservation when examined and showed no signs of decomposition. They were extracted with hexane or an acetone-hexane mixture, and these extracts cleaned up by the method of de Faubert Maunder *et al.* (10) which includes a dimethylformamide-hexane partition followed by passage through a column of prepared alumina. The solutions which resulted were then examined by gas-liquid chromatography using silicone, Apiezon and cyanosilicone columns, with electron-capture detection (11, 12). The solutions were further examined by a thin-layer chromatographic method (13, 14), by which the solutions were spotted on to silica gel plates and developed with a 1 per cent solution of acetone in hexane. These extracts were examined by gas-liquid chromatography and the identity and proportions of each of the compounds detected by the initial examination confirmed. The presence of *pp'*-DDT in the samples was further confirmed qualitatively and quantitatively by warming the appropriate thin-layer extract with ethanolic sodium hydroxide. The *pp'*-DDE formed by hydrolysis of the *pp'*-TDE was confirmed in a similar manner by hydrolysis to *pp'*-DEM (1-chloro-2,2-di-4-chlorophenylethylene).

The results of the analyses are set out in Table 1. They give clear indication that all the penguins examined contained small amounts of BHC isomers, dieldrin, *pp'*-DDT and *pp'*-DDE in their liver, blubber and fat. Most of these samples also contained small amounts of heptachlor epoxide and *pp'*-TDE. Not shown in the table, but also detected in some of the samples, were small amounts, generally less than 0.005 p.p.m. of *pp'*-DME, a further breakdown product of DDT and generally regarded as non-toxic. Most of the pesticide residues detected were of the order of 0.001-0.010 p.p.m. but some of the samples contained nearly 0.050 p.p.m. of *pp'*-DDE in the blubber and fat. There was no apparent relation between the age of the birds and the distribution of results. The three penguin eggs, each weighing about 100 g, also contained BHC isomers, dieldrin, *pp'*-DDT and *pp'*-DDE in similar proportions to those found in the birds.

The stomach contents of the birds consisted almost wholly of krill *(Euphausia sp.)*. The Antarctic seas are very rich in krill which form the main food of these penguins. Analysis of these krill samples indicated that here at least was one source of the pesticides found in the birds. Precisely the same compounds, but in lower proportions, were detected in the krill as in the birds, except that heptachlor epoxide was not detected in the krill, probably because the concentrations were less than those capable of being detected, allowing for the size of the samples and the methods used.

All the fish livers showed BHC isomers, heptachlor epoxide, dieldrin, DDT and its metabolites, in small amounts similar to those found in the penguin livers.

The skua is known to nest in Antarctica and the specimens taken for this study came from nests on Signy Island. Outside the breeding season, the birds range widely and often appear in the tropics. They are scavengers and predators and such birds have often been shown to contain large amounts of pesticide residues (17, 18). Nevertheless, 0.73 p.p.m. of heptachlor epoxide, 26 p.p.m. of *pp'*-DDE and 2.5 p.p.m. of *pp'*DDT are, by any standard, very high concentrations to find in the fat of a wild bird.

Blue-eyed shags nest in rookeries and are not wanderers. The specimens examined here were from a shag rookery on Signy Island and had probably never left the local waters. As might be expected, therefore, both the identity and proportion of the pesticides found in these birds are the same as those found in the penguins except that the *pp'*-DDE and *pp'*-DDT contents appear to be a little higher.

Shortly after receiving and analysing the samples described above, we also received the livers of three sheathbills *(Chionis alba)*. These had been taken on a separate occasion by the British Antarctic Survey on Signy Island following the sudden deaths of a number of these birds from unknown causes. All these livers contained *pp'*-DDE (0.030, 0.100 and 0.014 p.p.m) and two of them contained dieldrin (0.015 and 0.012 p.p.m.) but no other pesticide residues.

The picture revealed by this present investigation shows that all the wildlife sampled on Signy Island and in its surrounding waters was contaminated by the persistent organochlorine pesticides. The great majority of the samples contained small amounts of four of the most commonly used of these compounds or their toxic metabolites—BHC isomers, heptachlor epoxide (a very toxic metabolite of heptachlor), dieldrin, *pp'*-DDT, and two of its toxic metabolites, *pp'*-DDE and *pp'*-TDE. The pesticides themselves have now been in large scale agricultural and veterinary use for about 15-20 years. In this time, substantial amounts would have found their way down rivers to the oceans and have been carried away by deep sea currents. Large amounts would also have been lost to the atmosphere by volatilization and some of this would have returned to some other part of the land or sea by precipitation (8). It is clear from the analysis of the krill in the stomachs of the penguins and of the fish livers

Table 1. Organochlorine pesticide residues in Antarctic wildlife (p.p.m.).

	No. of samples	Alpha-BHC	Beta-BHC	Gamma-BHC	Heptachlor epoxide	Dieldrin	pp'-DDE	pp'-TDE	pp'-DDT
Penguin liver	11	0.000-0.002 Mean 0.001	0.002-0.008 Mean 0.005	0.000-0.003 Mean 0.002	0.00-0.006 Mean 0.002	0.001-0.006 Mean 0.002	0.001-0.018 Mean 0.006	ND –	0.001-0.010 Mean 0.005
Penguin blubber	10	0.001-0.002 Mean 0.002	0.000-0.006 Mean 0.003	0.001-0.002 Mean 0.001	0.001-0.003 Mean 0.002	0.004-0.010 Mean 0.007	0.013-0.048 Mean 0.032	0.000 0.006 Mean 0.003	0.005-0.012 Mean 0.008
Penguin abdominal fat	5	0.001-0.002 Mean 0.001	0.000-0.004 Mean 0.001	0.000-0.002 Mean 0.001	0.001-0.002 Mean 0.002	0.006-0.100 Mean 0.008	0.029-0.048 Mean 0.039	0.000 0.004 Mean 0.001	0.006-0.011 Mean 0.003
Penguin stomach contents	2	0.001, 0.001	0.005, ND	0.001, 0.001	ND, ND	0.001, 0.001	0.001, 0.001	ND, ND	0.001, 0.001
Penguin eggs	3	0.003-0.005 Mean 0.004	ND –	0.003-0.005 Mean 0.004	ND –	0.003-0.008 Mean 0.005	0.014-0.032 Mean 0.021	0.003-0.005 Mean 0.004	0.005-0.012 Mean 0.008
Notothenia (fish)	4	0.001-0.007 Mean 0.003	0.002-0.008 Mean 0.005	0.001-0.004 Mean 0.003	0.002-0.004 Mean 0.003	0.001-0.009 Mean 0.003	0.002-0.013 Mean 0.007	0.000-0.018 Mean 0.007	0.006-0.020 Mean 0.011
Brown skua liver	2	ND	ND	ND	0.100, 0.035	ND	4.00, 0.890	ND	0.33, 0.23
Brown skua fat	2	0.004, ND	0.040, ND	0.006, ND	0.120, 0.0730	ND	5.80 26.0	ND	0.890, 2.50
Blue-eyed shag liver	2	0.001, 0.002	0.006, 0.003	0.001, 0.003	0.002 ND	0.002 0.001	0.011, 0.015	ND	0.003, 0.009
Blue-eyed shag fat	2	ND	0.009, 0.010	ND, 0.002	ND	0.004, 0.006	0.051, 0.140	0.009, 0.018	0.012, 0.023

ND, Not detected.

that the Antarctic waters contain not only DDT but also traces of other organochlorine pesticides. The analysis of the penguins and their eggs and of the blue-eyed shags shows that this contamination is also present in the avian wildlife of the region. It thus seems possible that the DDT found in the early studies may, in fact, have been the first signs that contamination had reached Antarctica through the media of the seas and air.

The penguins of Antarctica have the auk family *(Alcidae)* as their ecological equivalent in the northern hemisphere. Some measure of the degree of contamination of Antarctic waters might be gained from a comparison of the results from the present study and those from studies already made of the auk family. Around the shores of the United Kingdom this family is represented chiefly by razorbills *(Alca torda)*, puffins *(Fratercula arctica)*, guillemots *(Uria aalge)* and black guillemots *(Cepphus grylle)*. The pesticide residues occurring in the eggs of the first three of these species have been studied closely for the past 4 years so that the general concentrations of these compounds in their eggs are well established (5, 15, 16). The concentrations are of the order of fifty times higher than were contained in the penguin eggs studied here which would suggest that the waters of Antarctica are still far less contaminated than those around the British Isles.

We thank the British Antarctic Survey for their co-operation in this enterprise and, in particular, Dr. J. R. Brotherhood, of the Survey, who took all the samples and arranged their dispatch to England.

References

1. Sladen, W. J. L., Menzie, C. M., and Reichel, W. L., *Nature* 210, 670 (1966).
2. George, J. L., and Frear, D. E. H., *J. Appl. Ecol,* 3 (suppl.), 155 (1966).
3. Stonehouse, B., *New Sci.,* 27, 273 (1965).
4. *Use of Pesticides, Rep. President's Sci. Adv. Comm.* (U.S. Government Printing Office, Washington, 1963).
5. Moore, N. W., and Tatton J. O'G., *Nature,* 207, 42 (1965).
6. Abbott, D. C., Harrison, R. B., Tatton J. O'G., and Thomson, J., *Nature,* 208, 1317 (1965).
7. Abbott, D. C., Harrison, R. B., Tatton, J. O'G., and Thomson, J., *Nature,* 211, 259 (1966).
8. West, I., *Arch. Environ. Health* 9, 626 (1964).
9. Ruzicka, J. H. A., Simmons, J. H., and Tatton, J. O'G., *J. Sci. Fd. Agric.* (in the press).
10. De Faubert Maunder, M. J. Egan, H., Godly, E. W., Hammond, J. W., Roburn, H., and Thomson, J., *Analyst (Lond.),* 89, 168 (1964).
11. De Faubert Maunder, M. J., Egan, H., and Roburn, J., *Analyst (Lond.),* 89, 157 (1964).
12. Simmons, J. H., and Tatton, J. O'G., *J. Chromatog.,* 27, 253 (1967).
13. Abbott, D. C., Egan, H., and Thomson, J., *J. Chromatog.* 16, 481 (1964).
14. Harrison, R. B., *J. Sci. Fd. Agric.,* 17, 10 (1966).
15. *Report of the Government Chemist, 1965,* 75 (HMSO, London, 1965).
16. *Report of the Government Chemist, 1966* (HMSO, London, in the press).

53

PESTICIDES: TRANSATLANTIC MOVEMENTS IN THE NORTHEAST TRADES

R. W. Risebrough, R. J. Huggett,
J. J. Griffin, and E. D. Goldberg

The transport and distribution of pesticides through the world ecosystem have been attributed to a combination of atmospheric and hydrospheric (oceanic and fluvial) currents (1), yet their relative contributions remain unclear. The high concentrations of residues of pesticides found in shearwaters *Puffinus tenuirostris* and *P. griseus* from the Pacific Ocean and skuas *Catharacta skua* from Antarctica suggest that coastal areas are not the sites of ingestion (1).

Various lines of evidence indicate air transport: (i) the codistillation of chlorinated hydrocarbons with water (2), and (ii) their detection in air and rainwater (3) and in atmospheric dust originating in Texas and subsequently deposited in Ohio (4). These observations, however, are not sufficient to support the hypothesis that much of the pesticides present in marine organisms was atmospherically transported to the oceans from the continents.

Complementing such work is the observation that the mineral talc that is used as a carrier and diluent for pesticides occurs in the solid-mineral phases of rains, glaciers, and rivers and in dusts recovered from the atmosphere in concentrations much higher than expected from natural occurrences (5); its existence in airborne particulate matter over the sea (6) suggests a link with the global dispersion of pesticides.

Although talc is perhaps diagnostic of the presence of insecticides, its use as a quantitative tracer is not fully warranted; it is gradually being displaced in pesticides by water or light

petroleum bases. Furthermore some insecticides are dispersed in Fuller's earth, a mixture of minerals not readily analyzed by x-ray diffraction.

Large-scale tropospheric transport from continents to oceans can best be approached by investigation of the three main zones of movement of air masses: the equatorial easterlies, the temperate westerlies, and the polar easterlies. Gram quantities of airborne particulate matter carried by the equatorial easterlies, the trade winds, over 6000 km from Europe and Africa across the Atlantic to Barbados were collected (7). Pronounced seasonal variations in the magnetic and biological fractions correlated with wind patterns off the African coast. Mineralogical and biological observations pointed to a continental origin of the solids, with Europe and Africa as the most likely sources. Each sample comprised a large fraction of the particulate material in several million cubic meters of air. An input rate of solid phases to the tropical Atlantic sediments of 0.6 x 10^{-4} cm/year was suggested (6). Knowledge of the pesticide levels in such materials would permit similar calculations of their inputs, for which purpose the Barbados samples have been analyzed.

The collecting screens (6), facing the wind, were made of 0.5-mm-diameter monofilament nylon woven to give about 50 percent voids; they were coated with a 50-percent water solution of glycerin for our work; collection efficiency was about 50 percent for particles larger than 1 μ. Rigorous standards of cleanliness minimized contamination by local dusts, which has always proved to be trivial. For blank runs for the pesticide analyses, acetone-washed dust was applied to screens with subsequent treatment as for the real samples. Less than 100 pg of any of the DDT compounds (8) or other pesticides per gram of sample was found.

The dust samples were Soxhlet-extracted for 6 hours with a 2:1 mixture of hexane and acetone. Blank runs, using the same solvent volumes, extraction times, and glassware, were made before and several times during the course of the analyses; less than 250 pg of any pesticide per gram of sample was present in the controls.

The extracts were concentrated and analyzed with a Micro Tek-220 gas chromatograph equipped with Ni-63 and H-3 electron-capture detectors. Two columns, a 5-percent QF-1 and a 10-percent DC-200, both on hexamethyl disilazane-treated Chromosorb W, 80- to 110-mesh, were used simultaneously. Differences in retention time between the polar and nonpolar columns, combined with occasional spiking of extracts with standards, initially confirmed the identities of several of the peaks observed. Peaks of unknown compounds fluctuating in intensity over the year were present in all Barbados extracts and occasionally interfered with determination of pp'-DDE and o,p'-DDT.

Extracts of samples between January and September were pooled and placed on a thin-layer plate covered with silica gel G that had been washed until chromatographically clean. A small fraction of the sample extract, mixed with standards, was applied to another area of the plate. After development with 10 percent ethyl ether in hexane, the plate was divided into two sets of 13 1-cm strips which were scraped off and washed with petroleum ether. A concentrate of the petroleum ether was then injected into both columns of the gas chromatograph.

Dieldrin, p,p'-DDT, and p,p'-DDD were quantitatively recovered from the corresponding areas of the plate occupied by the standards. In several extracts the interfering peaks made measurements of p,p'-DDE and of o,p'-DDT impossible; the thin-layer recoveries of these compounds were 150 percent. A trace amount of a compound having the retention times of o,p'-DDE was also recovered but a small peak provisionally attributed to heptachlor epoxide in one extract was not confirmed by thin-layer techniques. None of the unidentified peaks had retention times equivalent to those of the polychlorinated biphenyls (PCB), industrial pollutants widely dispersed in marine ecosystems (9). No attempt was made to isolate chemically pure pesticides from the thin-layer extracts in order to obtain infrared spectra; instead, several of the thin-layer extracts were treated with alcoholic KOH under conditions such that p,p'-DDT, o,p'-DDT, and p,p'-DDD

are converted to their dehydrochlorinated derivatives, which have characteristic retention times on QF-1 and DC-200 columns.

The thin-layer extracts containing most of the p,p'-DDT, p,p'-DDD, o,p'-DDT, and dieldrin peaks were evaporated almost to dryness in a graduated test tube to which 1 ml of 10 percent KOH in ethyl alcohol was added. After heating for 5 minutes in a steam bath, water and hexane were added and the solution was swirled. Analysis of the hexane layer showed that the p,p'-DDt, p,p'-DDD, and o,p'-DDT peaks had disappeared, but peaks having the retention times of p,p'-DDE, p,p'-DDMU, and o,p'-DDE had appeared in the respective extracts. The recoveries of these dehydrochlorinated derivatives were equivalent to those obtained in the saponification of chromatographically pure standards. No other breakdown products producing peaks in the electron-capture detector were identified. The dieldrin peak was not affected by the alkaline-alcohol treatment but could not be found after concentrated sulfuric acid was added to the evaporated extract.

All extracts were analyzed with both DC-200 and QF-1 columns, and each value presented (Table 1) is the average from two or more injections of a sample. The total concentrations of the chlorinated hydrocarbons in the dust were higher during the winter months, but the total pesticide content of the air displayed no evident seasonal changes during 1 year. A relatively high content of magnetic dust had been reported (6) for September, October, and April when the wind-circulations suggest that the dust originates in Morocco; on the other hand, the content was less between October and March, when the dust probably comes from tropical Africa south of the Sahara. Most of the biological material was present in the winter samples; fungal hyphae abounded, and bacteria, fragments of vascular plants, and marine and freshwater diatoms were observed. Among the last were *Melosira granulata,* which is worldwide in distribution, and *Denticula elegans,* which is found in the running waters of cold mountainous regions. There was no correlation between the pesticide content of the air and either the magnetic content or the number of fungal hyphae reported (6).

Table 1. Pesticides in airborne particles over Barbados. Concentrations in air are based on 50-percent efficiency of the collecting net; ND, not detected.

Date (1965-66)	Air volume ($\times 10^3/m^3$)	Material dry wt (g)		Pesticide concentrations						Total in air ($g \times 10^{-15}/m^3$)
		Total	Analyzed	In samples (ppb)						
				p,p'-DDT	p,p'-DDE	p,p'-DDT	DDD	Dieldrin	Total	
4-6 Oct.	2.3		0.82	52	12	13	7	3.1	87	150-380*
26-28 Oct.	3.3	17.8	7.70	<1.2	ND	ND	ND	ND	<1.2	<13†
7-21 Nov.	16.3	8.9	2.67	71	19	ND	ND	ND	90	99
1-15 Dec.	16.1	5.2	2.62	10	ND	ND	ND	ND	10	6.5
23-25 Dec.	2.3	1.7	1.33	88	49	13	8	6	164	242
26-28 Jan.	2.3	1.0	0.97	30	ND	ND	10.7	8.1	49	42
15-17 Feb.	3.2	3.3	3.32	18	13	6	ND	ND	37	77
17-19 Feb.	2.9	1.4	1.42	67	ND	17	ND	4.8	96	93‡
25-27 Mar.	2.4	1.3	1.04	14	2.1	ND	6.3	2.1	25	27
12-14 Apr.	2.8	4.7	3.10	11	ND	ND	ND	ND	11	37
14-16 May	1.5	9.0	5.43	2.7	ND	ND	ND	1.3	4.0	48
11-13 June	2.1	2.6	2.69	7.6	ND	ND	ND	3.1	10.7	28
21-23 July	1.5	6.8	2.29	5.4	3.4	0.9	1.1	1.3	12.1	110
10-12 Aug.	1.9	8.6	4.59	4.3	3.1	.4	1.4	1.2	10.4	90
13-15 Sept.	1.7	7.8	4.15	8.3	1.5	1.1	1.0	1.5	13.4	120

*Total dry weight not measured.
†Zero dust collected on 12 previous days.
‡Peak, with retention time of heptachlor epoxide also present, 7.2 ppb.

The pesticide concentration in air averages 7.8×10^{-14} g/m^3, or 41 ppb (parts per billion) by weight in the dust. Utilizing the sedimentation calculations on this dust (6), we can calculate the introduction of pesticides to the equatorial Atlantic by atmospheric transport in the following way. We assume that the area involved in dissemination by the trade winds lies between the equator and 30°N latitude, covering 1.94×10^{17} cm^2. The reported (6) rate of sedimentation for this area is 0.06 cm/1000 years, equivalent to an annual input of dust solids of 9.70×10^{12} g (density of dust, 2.5 g/cm^3 water content of the sediments, 50 percent). The value of 41 ppb of insecticides in the dust yields 600 kg/year.

The input of pesticides into San Francisco Bay, measured by the average total concentration in the San Joaquin River at Antioch (10) (0.1 μg/liter) and the mean outflow of 18.9×10^{12} liter/year, amounts to 1900 kg/year. A similar calculation for the Mississippi yields an input into the Gulf of Mexico of 10^4 kg/year (11).

These rates of input indicate the relative significance of wind and river transport to the marine environment. The atmospheric rate is clearly an underestimate inasmuch as the method of collection of the dusts fractionates against materials carried on particles of less than several microns or as vapors. We must conclude that the atmosphere can transport significant quantities of pesticides to the open-ocean ecosystem; where ocean currents and river drainages cannot explain the presence of residues, wind systems may provide conveyance from continents.

Similarly we have examined samples of airborne particulate matter from the central Pacific collected on glycerin-coated nylon nets mounted on the mast of R.V. *Argo* (12) at 12 stations between 17°N and 18°S near 180° longitude during the summer of 1967. No sample carried a detectable pesticide residue, but the weight of each sample did not exceeed 1 or 2 mg, and less than 1 part per million or 1 ng of a pesticide would have been undetectable. However, the presence of talc, the most important diffracting mineral, suggested the presence of pesticides (Fig. 53-1).

Dust collected from an ocean pier at La Jolla, California, between June and October 1967 yielded total pesticide contents in air ranging from 6 to 270×10^{-12} g/m^3 and averaging 7.0×10^{-11} g/m^3; the prevailing winds are landward, with an unknown admixture of air from neighboring agricultural areas. This average value is 1000 times greater than its Barbadian counterpart. Such is the difference in pesticide load between marine air adjacent to agricultural areas in which pesticides are used intensively and marine air remote from sites of application.

Extracts of the La Jolla dust samples were pooled, concentrated to a volume of about 1 ml, and refluxed for 10 minutes in 100 ml of 5 percent KOH in ethyl alcohol before 100 ml of hexane and 300 ml of concentrated aqueous solution of NaCl were added. The hexane layer, after concentration to a small volume,

Fig. 53-1. X-ray diffractogram (CuKα radiation) of atmospheric dust collected over the Coral Sea, with talc predominating.

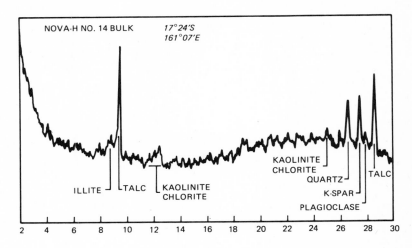

was then analyzed for PCB. Such treatment of extracts of marine fish from coastal waters in California reveals the characteristic profile, on gas chromatograms, of the PCB peaks (9); PCB are present in higher concentrations in marine birds, and the profile of the various peaks is usually evident in unsaponified extracts. No PCB, however, was detectable in the La Jolla dust samples; if PCB was present its maximum concentration in the airborne particulates was 5 ppb—10,000 times lower than that of total pesticides. The PCB are toxic compounds widely used in industry in the manufacture of plastics, paints, and many other products, and are components of industrial air. Unlike the chlorinated hydrocarbon pesticides, which they resemble somewhat in chemical structure, they apparently persist to a greater extent in the vapor phase. The concentration ratios of total PCB to total DDT in many seabirds, including two species of Pacific shearwaters that nest in Alaska, and in petrels and resident peregrine falcons from remote areas of Baja California are of the same order of magnitude (9); this fact suggests that PCB and pesticides are similarly dispersed. With other pollutants, including products of atomic explosions (13), they are probably universally present in air; thus their distribution in marine and terrestrial ecosystems remote from sites of application can be expected to depend on the prevailing patterns of wind circulation and the rates of fallout.

References and Notes

1. J. O'G. Tatton and J. H. A. Ruzicka, *Nature* **215**, 346 (1967); R. W. Risebrough, D. B. Menzel, D. J. Martin, Jr., H. S. Olcott, *ibid.* **216**, 589 (1967); W. J. L. Sladen, C. M. Menzie, W. L. Reichel, *ibid.* **210**, 570 (1966); J. L. George and D. E. H. Frear, *J. Appl. Ecol. Suppl.* **3**, 15 (1966).

2. M. C. Bowman, F. Acree, Jr., C. S. Lofgren, M. Beroza, *Science* **146**, 1480 (1964); F. Acree, Jr. M. Beroza, M. C. Bowman, *J. Agr. Food Chem.* **11**, 278 (1959); M. C. Bowman, F. Acree, Jr., C. H. Schmidt, M. Beroza, *J. Econ. Entomol.* **52**, 1038 (1959); C. R. Harris and E. P. Lichtenstein, *ibid.* **54**, 1038 (1961).

3. P. Antommaria, M. Corn, L. DeMaio, *Science* **150**, 1476 (1965), D. C. Abbott, R. B. Harrison, J. O'G. Tatton, J. Thomson, *Nature* **208**, 1317 (1965); *ibid.* **211**, 259 (1966); G. A. Wheatley and J. A. Hardman, *ibid.* **207**, 486 (1965).

4. J. M. Cohen and C. Pinkerton, in *Organic Pesticides in the Environment* (American Chemical Society, 1966), p. 163.

5. H. Windom, J. J. Griffin, E. D. Goldberg, *Environ. Sci. Technol.* **1**, 923 (1967).

6. A. C. Delany *et al. Geochim. Cosmochim. Acta* **31**, 885 (1967).

7. By a station of the Science Research Council, U.K. We thank A. C. Delany for them.

8. Residues of DDT include its two isomers p,p'-DDT and o,p'-DDT and the metabolic derivatives of p,p'-DDT p,p'-DDE, p,p'DDD, and p,p'-DDMU. p,p'-DDT, 1,1,1-trichloro-2,2-bis (p-chlorophenyl)ethane; o,p'-DDT. 1,1,1,-trichloro-2-(o-chlorophenyl)-2-(p-chlorophenyl) ethane; p,p'-DDE, 1,1-dichloro-2,2-bis (p-chlorophenyl) ethylene; p,p'-DDD (also known at TDE), 1,1-dichloro-2,2 bis (p-chlorophenyl) ethane p,p'-DDMU, 1-chloro-2,2-bis (p-chlorophenyl) ethylene.

9. D. C. Holmes, J. H. Simmons, J. O'G. Tatton, *Nature* **216**, 227 (1967); G. Widmark, *J. Nature Offic. Agr. Chem,* **50**, 1069 (1967); A. V. Holden and K. Marsden, *Nature,* **216**, 1274, (1967); R. W. Risebrough, M. N. Kirven, S. G. Herman, P. L. Ames, in preparation; R. W. Risebrough, in preparation.

10. T. E. Bailey and J. R. Hannum, *J. Sanit. Eng. Div. Amer. Soc. Civil Engrs.* **93**, 27 (1967).

11. A. W. Breidenbach, C. G. Gunnerson, F. K. Kawahara, J. J. Lichtenberg, R. S. Green, *Public Health Rept.* **82**, 139 (1967); H. P. Nicholson, *Science* **158**, 871 (1967).

12. Scripps, Institution of Oceanography.

13. G. M. Woodwell, *Sci. Amer.* **216**, 24 (1967).

14. Supported by NSF (grant GP 6362) and ONR.

54

LEVELS OF CHLORINATED HYDROCARBON PESTICIDES IN HUMAN TISSUES

Vera Fiserova-Bergerova, Jack L. Radomski, John E. Davies, and Joseph H. Davis

The storage and accumulation of chlorinated hydrocarbon pesticides in the tissue of humans has been studied both in the U.S.A. (1-6) and abroad (4, 7, 8). For the most part these studies were limited to the analysis of adipose tissue, since available colorimetric procedures were not sufficiently sensitive to detect pesticides in the other tissues of the body. The application of gas chromatography to pesticide analysis and the development of the electron capture detector have made possible the analysis of pesticide levels in these other tissues. In this investigation the fat, liver, kidney, brain and gonads of 71 people were analyzed as part of a total community study on pesticides in Dade County, Florida. The pesticides analyzed were lindane, p,p'-DDT, p,p'-DDE, p,p'-DDD, and dieldrin.

Methods

Determination of Pesticide Content

Chlorinated pesticides and their metabolites (lindane, dieldrin, DDT, DDE and DDD) were determined in adipose tissue (panniculus adiposes), liver, kidney, brain and gonads. The method used for these analyses was a simplified gas chromatographic procedure which was developed in this laboratory (9, 10), utilizing the electron capture detector. The use of clean-up procedures prior to the gas chromatographic analysis was found to be unnecessary.

Reprinted from *Industrial Medicine and Surgery* 36(1): 65-70, 1967, with the permission of the publishers.

A 250 mg sample of tissue (200 mg of adipose tissue) was ground in an all-glass Duval (size C) homogenizer in 5 ml (10 ml in the case of adipose tissue) of petroleum ether (30°-60°). With kidney and liver, approximately 2 gm of anhydrous sodium sulfate were added before grinding. Brain and gonads were desiccated before grinding, but the other tissues were ground fresh. When the tissue was dispersed the mixture was transferred to a graduated centrifuge tube. The homogenizer was rinsed with small quantities of additional petroleum ether and then the volume was adjusted to 5 ml (10 ml in the case of adipose tissue). This use of more solvent was possible because of the loss of solvent during grinding. The extract is centrifuged if turbidity exists. Five microliters (or less) were injected onto the gas chromatographic column. Two gas chromatographic columns were routinely used, 5% QF-1 on 60-80 mesh Chromport XXX in 6 ft. glass tubing and 5% SE-30 on 60-80 mesh Chromport XXX in 3 ft. stainless steel tubing. The gas chromatograph used was a Micro Tek 2000 MF. Typical examples of gas chromatograms obtained are shown in Fig. 54-1. QF-1 columns do not resolve DDD from DDT, although the DDD may be seen as a shoulder in the side of the DDT peak. SE-30 columns, on the other hand, do not distinguish between DDE and dieldrin but give good resolution between DDT and DDD.

In each instance, the level presented represents the mean of two analyses on an aliquot taken from the approximate center of the tissue sample, so as to minimize contamination.

The unfixed tissues were kept in a freezer in a polyethylene plastic bag and were defrosted immediately before the sample was taken for analysis. The differences between duplicate determinations never exceeded 10% of the mean. The concentrations giving peaks from 2 mm to 10 mm are reported as traces and correspond approximately to the following concentrations of pesticides in fat: 0.004-0.2 ppm of lindane; 0.01-0.5 ppm of DDT. For other tissues, the concentrations reported as traces are 0.0006-0.003 ppm of lindane; 0.0016-0.008 ppm of DDE and dieldrin and 0.016-0.08 ppm of DDT.

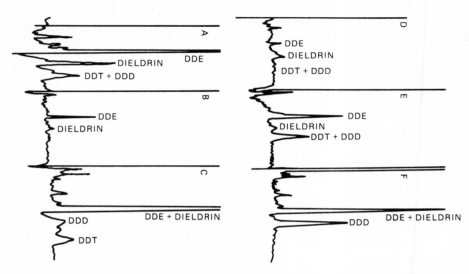

Fig. 54-1. A typical example of analysis of adipose tissue (ABC), Brain (D) and Liver (EF) in 5% QF-1 column (ABDE) and 5% SE-30 column (CF). Injected 5 μl of liver extract, 2 μl of fat or brain extract; (B) fat diluted with petroleum ether 1:10. Temperature: inlet 210°C, column 185°C, detector 195°C. Nitrogen flow rate: 140 cc/min and 75 cc/min. Sensitivity: 10 × 16.

Selection of Cases

With the exception of stillbirths and one pregnant woman (A.D.), the tissue samples were obtained from 64 persons accidentally killed in Dade County and autopsied by the Dade County Medical Examiner. Examination of the case histories of ten of these individuals revealed that they worked on farms where they were occupationally exposed to pesticides. These cases were segregated in a special group referred to as farm workers. To the best of our knowledge the others were normal and healthy prior to their accidental demise and therefore believed to be representative of the general population of the county. They were subdivided into five age groups (Table 1). In each group there were six males and six females with the exception of the 6-10 age group, where only three males and three females were available. Four stillbirths were analyzed and two fetuses from mothers accidentally killed were also tested.

Results

The results of our analysis are shown in Table 1. The levels of pesticides in each group are given as medians and ranges rather than averages and standard deviations, because the distribution curve was not symmetrical (Fig. 54-2), and because in a small group of six cases one high value would greatly influence the average. The levels of lindane obtained are omitted from Table 1. Lindane was found in fat in only six cases, ranging from 0.04 to 0.28 ppm.

The concentrations of pesticides in males and females were compared in all age groups using the Rank Test. No significant difference was found.

Since no significant difference in pesticides concentration was found between males and females, comparison of pesticide levels in different age groups was done without regard to sex. No dependence on age of the level of DDT, DDD and DDE was observed using the Rank Test (P > 0.05) with the exception of children 0-5 years, where the level of DDT and DDE in fat and kidney seems to be significantly lower than in the older population (P < 0.01). The level of dieldrin in tissues, except kidney, appears to increase with age (Fig. 54-3) when the regression coefficients of the medians are examined (fat: r = 0.89; liver: r = 0.82; brain: r = 0.77; gonad: r = 0.77). When these results

Fig. 54-2. Distribution curve of pesticides levels in adipose tissues and livers of the general population. Shaded area represents number of cases with the concentration of pesticides under the sensitivity of the method used.

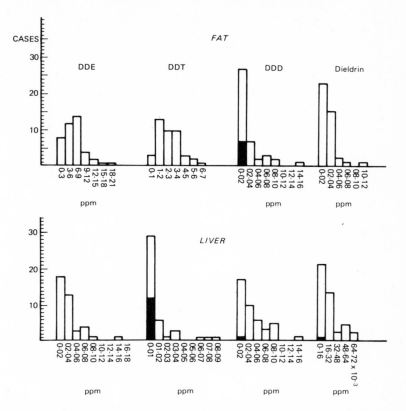

were examined by Rank Test, however, no significant differences were found between the age groups with any tissue, due possibly to the wide range in dieldrin concentrations.

Pesticide levels in the individuals above 5 years of age (42 cases) were compared with regard to race and whether they lived in a rural or urban area, using the Rank Test. Thirty-one per cent of the individuals comprising the total sample were Negro, (roughly evenly distributed among the various age groups). No significant

difference in pesticide level between the two races was observed (P > 0.1). Twenty-two per cent of the individuals were from rural areas. The place of residence was defined as rural if there was no more than one residence per acre of land. No difference in pesticide levels was found between rural and urban dwellers (P > 0.05). These rural dwellers were not occupationally exposed to pesticides as were the group designated as farm workers.

The difference of pesticide levels in the

Fig. 54-3. The dependence of the medians of the dieldrin concentration in tissues on age.

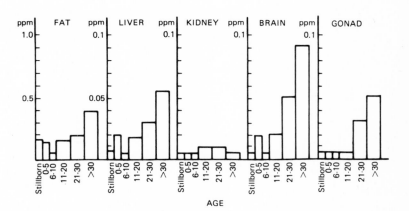

Table 1. Medians and ranges of pesticides in human tissues (ppm) according to sex and age.

Age	Sex	Adipose tissue				Liver			
		DDT	DDE	DDD	Dieldrin	DDT	DDE	DDD	Dieldrin
Stillborns and fetus 22-40 weeks	MF	1.35 0.38-2.70	4.30 0.94-5.03	0.03	0.17 tr.-0.38	0.05 0.00-0.22	0.055 tr.-0.08	0.005 tr.-0.18	0.007 0.00-0.06
0-5	M	0.79 tr.-2.70	1.32 0.91-1.96	0.03 tr.-0.50	0.145 0.11-0.34	0.02 0.00-0.08	0.075 0.04-0.09	0.23 0.11-0.16	0.02 tr.-0.01
	F	1.45 0.80-6.00	1.45 0.87-7.35	0.03 tr.-0.50	0.14 tr.-0.23	0.065 0.00-0.28	0.10 0.03-0.28	0.25 tr.-1.06	0.025 tr.-0.06
6-10	M	3.74 3.03-4.40	8.10 6.60-11.30	0.44 tr.-0.60	0.11 0.00-0.26	0.05	0.31 0.08-0.35	0.27 tr.-0.53	0.018 tr.-0.038
	F	3.90 3.50-6.50	8.80 5.30-13.40	0.65 0.00-0.92	0.03 tr.-0.18	0.18 tr.-0.36	0.40 0.17-0.54	0.11 tr.-0.89	0.005 0.00- tr.
11-20	M	2.10 1.20-4.40	3.90 3.20-9.80	0.25 tr.-0.40	0.165 0.11-0.32	0.02 0.00- tr.	0.20 0.10-0.84	0.23 tr.-0.46	0.01 tr.-0.03
	F	2.10 1.30-4.00	6.30 4.80-11.00	0.03 0.00- tr.	0.16 0.10-0.22	0.00 0.00-0.20	0.21 0.18-0.40	0.10 0.00-0.37	0.025 0.00-0.03
21-30	M	1.78 1.03-4.00	4.50 1.47-14.60	0.15 tr.-0.70	0.18 0.05-0.36	0.05 0.00-0.84	0.57 0.05-1.70	0.39 0.12-1.60	0.035 tr.-0.11
	F	2.40 tr.-5.00	3.65 2.00-7.00	0.03 tr.-1.00	0.20 0.16-0.30	0.05 0.00-0.96	0.13 0.06-0.22	0.53 tr.-0.92	0.017 tr.-0.05
31-83	M	3.90 0.52-5.75	8.30 1.90-19.00	0.19 0.00-1.52	0.29 tr.-0.54	0.175 tr.-0.38	0.70 0.30-1.10	0.52 0.28-0.81	0.015 tr.-0.10
	F	2.00 1.23-3.60	5.50 2.00-9.00	0.03 0.00-2.50	0.39 0.10-0.70	0.02 0.00-0.35	0.25 0.07-0.60	0.29 tr.-0.62	0.065 tr.-0.22
Farm workers 18-57	M	7.22 2.00-15.6	12.70 9.50-27.20	0.20 tr.-3.00	0.25 0.00-0.99	0.11 0.00-0.70	0.73 0.29-2.00	0.50 0.00-1.08	0.005 tr.-0.04

442

Table 1. (continued)

Kidney DDT	Kidney DDE	Kidney DDD	Kidney Dieldrin	Kidney DDT*	Brain DDE	Brain Dieldrin	Brain DDT*	Gonads DDE	Gonads Dieldrin
0.05 0.00-tr.	0.03 tr.-0.04	0.005 0.00-tr.	0.005	0.000 0.00-tr.	0.005 0.00-0.04	0.005 0.00-0.06	0.000 0.00-tr.	0.005 0.00-tr.	0.005 tr.-0.04
0.00 0.00-tr.	0.005 tr.-0.06	0.00 0.00-tr.	0.005 0.00-tr.	0.00 0.00	0.002 0.00-0.014	0.007 0.00-0.06	0.00 0.00-tr.	0.005 0.00-0.02	0.005 0.00-0.04
0.05 0.00-0.06	0.017 tr.-0.04	0.005 0.00-tr.	0.006 tr.-0.013	0.05 0.00-0.08	0.005 0.00-0.08	0.025 tr.-0.06	0.02 0.00-tr.	0.005 0.00-0.02	0.018 tr. 0.06
0.05	0.07 0.05-0.16	0.005 0.00-tr.	0.005	0.000 0.00-tr.	0.14 0.06-0.15	0.005 tr.-0.08	0.000 0.00-tr.	0.01 tr.-0.11	0.005 tr.-0.06
0.05 tr.-0.07	0.15 0.006-0.31	0.005 tr.-0.23	0.005 0.00-tr.	0.05 tr.-0.08	0.15 0.09-0.25	0.005 tr.-0.10	0.000 0.00-0.14	0.03 tr.-0.31	0.005 0.00-tr.
0.02 0.00-tr.	0.035 0.015-0.06	0.005 0.00-tr.	0.008 tr.-0.015	0.005 0.00-tr.	0.008 0.03-0.14	0.001 tr.-0.07	0.05 0.00-tr.	0.045 0.010-0.09	0.005 0.00-tr.
0.05 0.00-tr.	0.045 0.03-0.10	0.005 0.00-tr.	0.01 0.00-0.011	0.05 0.00-tr.	0.08 tr.-0.13	0.035 tr. 0.07	0.05 0.00-tr.	0.012 tr.-0.035	0.025 tr.-0.007
0.05 0.00-tr.	0.045 0.01-0.16	0.005	0.01 tr.-0.04	0.05 0.00-0.11	0.07 tr.-0.35	0.05 tr.-0.08	0.05 0.00-tr.	0.035 0.00-0.13	0.045 0.03-0.09
0.05 0.00-tr.	0.05 tr.-0.09	0.005	0.008 tr.-0.01	0.05 0.00-tr.	0.055 0.00-0.08	0.025 0.00-0.05	0.05 0.00-tr.	0.017 0.00-0.04	0.017 tr. 0.14
0.05 0.00-tr.	0.09 0.00-0.25	0.005 tr.-0.08	0.005 tr.-0.04	0.11 0.00-0.21	0.30 0.14-0.57	0.05 tr.-0.10	0.05 0.00-0.11	0.12 0.03-0.25	0.05 0.02-0.10
0.00 0.00-tr.	0.05 0.02-0.20	0.005 0.00-0.20	0.01 tr.-0.06	0.05 0.00-0.44	0.09 0.03-0.24	0.05 0.00-0.10	0.05 0.00-0.16	0.03 0.015-0.14	0.05 0.01-0.20
0.05 tr.-0.34	0.11 0.06-0.60	0.005 0.00-0.10	0.005 0.00-0.06	0.02 0.00-0.18	0.20 0.02-0.38	0.005 tr.-0.06	0.05 tr.-0.19	0.15 0.04-0.30	0.005 tr.-0.07

tr. = traces.
* Including eventually present DDD.

Table 2. The averages and standard errors of pesticides levels in tissues of general population (ppm) − 42 people.

Tissue	DDT	DDE	DDD	Total*	Dieldrin
Adipose	2.81	6.67	0.28	10.56	0.215
	±0.23	±0.63	±0.07	±0.88	±0.023
Liver	0.12	0.35	0.34	0.889	0.035
	±0.03	±0.05	±0.05	±0.106	±0.007
Kidney	0.036	0.077	0.017	0.141	0.013
	±0.004	±0.012	±0.008	±0.024	±0.002
Brain	traces	0.123	−	−	0.035
		±0.017			±0.005
Gonads	traces	0.059	−	−	0.035
		±0.011			±0.007

*Sum of DDT, DDD and DDE, calculated as DDT.

groups of people over 5 years of age was found not to depend on sex, race or residence. The averages and standard errors of the averages of the concentrations of pesticides in the five tissues were computed (Table 2). The averages and standard errors of DDT levels in brain and gonads were not calculated as mostly zero values or traces were found (Table 1).

As is evident from Table 1 the pesticide levels were about twice as high in farm workers' tissues as in the general population. These farm workers had significantly higher levels of DDT and its metabolites in all tissues (tested by the t-test) except for DDD in liver. Dieldrin levels, however, were the same in both groups (t-test).

The concentrations of DDT and its metabolites and dieldrin observed in the fetus and stillbirth group resembled those concentrations noted in the older age groups more than the 0-5 age group (tested by Rank test). In three cases of death of pregnant women it was possible to compare the concentrations of pesticides in the fetal tissues with those in maternal tissues. One case was omitted from Fig. 54-4 because fetal fat was not available.

Discussion

The tissues of an age and sex stratified sample of 71 persons from Dade County in apparent previous good health have been analyzed for their pesticide content by gas chromatography. The levels of DDT, DDE and dieldrin found in the fat agree well with the levels reported in the literature for the American population from other areas of the country (1-6). In agreement with the published results (4, 7, 8) no significant difference in tissue pesticide content between the sexes, races or place of residence was observed. In this study a significantly lower level of DDT and DDE was observed in children under 5 years of age. In other age groups, however, no correlation of the level of these pesticides with the age of the subject was noted. This observation is not in conflict with the studies performed by other authors mentioned above, for, to our knowledge, information on pesticide concentrations in children in these younger age groups has not been published heretofore. Obviously, one should not generalize dogmatically on the effects of age on pesticide concentrations, with a sample size as small as six in each age group. However, it is of interest to note that the prenatal fetal concentrations of pesticides more closely resemble the adult population than the 0-5 age group, suggesting that the fetal concentration more closely reflects the maternal concentration, and that the fetus in this instance behaves more like the maternal tissue with regard to pesticide storage. The data presented, however, does demonstrate that there is a passage of pesticides across the placental membrane and that this is demonstrable at least as early as the 22nd week of gestation. Of course, there is no reason to presume that the occurrence of these levels of pesticides in the fetus

Fig. 54-4. The concentrations of pesticides in fat, liver, and kidney of mother and fetus. Case A. D.: mother 28 years old, Negro, suffering from lymphosarcoma. Died from her lymphosarcoma three months after the pregnancy was terminated. Fetus: 32-week-old male. Case O. V.: mother 39 years old, Negro. Cause of death was pulmonary edema due to eclampsia. Stillborn: 9-month-old male.

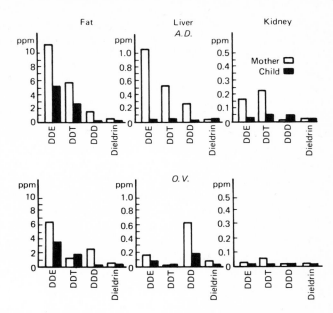

was in any way responsible for the fetal death.

With regard to the difference in pesticide levels found in the five tissues, fat liver, brain, kidney and gonads, the data indicates that the fat concentration is approximately ten times greater than the liver (with the exception of DDD) and 100 times greater than the concentration observed in the kidney, brain and gonads. Unquestionably the very much lower levels present in the kidney, brain and gonads is a reflection of the low fat content of these organs. The tendency of these non-polar pesticides to be deposited in fat has been reported many times. The fact that the concentrations in liver are approximately ten times those found in kidney, brain and gonads is probably a reflection of the function of the liver as an organ of metabolism and excretion.

Ten individuals dying accidentally who were occupationally exposed to pesticides in the course of their work as migrant laborers on local farms were also studied. The levels of DDT and its metabolite were approximately twice as high in all tested tissues as the general population. These results are in agreement with those of Hayes, et al. (2) who reported increased DDT levels in the fat of the occupationally exposed. The concentrations of dieldrin, however, were found to be essentially the same as the general population.

It has been reported by Peterson and Robinson (11) that DDT is metabolized in the livers of rats to DDD. This observation was confirmed by Klein, et al. (12-14). In addition, DDD has been found in fish liver (16). There has been no previous report, however, that DDT is converted to DDD in the human liver. In our experiments we found an average of 42.6% of the DDT derived substances as DDD in the livers of the general population (Table 3). In contrast, only 3% DDD was present in the fat and 13.5% in the kidney tissue (Table 3). It would seem that this reflects a metabolic change of DDT to DDD in human liver and perhaps also to a lesser extent in the kidney. It is also possible, however, that this represents a postmortem microbiological or enzymological change (15). Experiments in mice have been performed (17) which indicated that this conversion to DDD occurs after death, for if the mice administered DDT were sacrificed and

Table 3. The relation between DDT, DDE and DDD in human tissues. Percentage of the total concentration corrected for differences in molecular weight.

Tissue	*DDE*	*DDD*	*DDT*
Adipose	70.4	3.0	26.6
Liver	43.8	42.6	13.5
Kidney	61.0	13.5	25.5
Brain	73.3	—	26.7
Gonads	56.7	—	43.3

analyzed immediately, no DDD was found. The possibility, therefore, cannot be excluded that DDD originates after death. Experiments are planned to determine whether or not this is true.

During these studies, only casual attention was paid to the possible occurrence of the o,p'-isomer of DDT and its metabolites. The occurrence of o,p'-DDT, o,p'-DDE, α-hexachlorocyclohexane, β-hexachlorocyclohexane, and heptachlor epoxide is currently being studied and will be subsequently reported (10). It has been reported (3), using a gas chromatographic method, that o,p'-DDT occurs in 60% of the population but DDD was not found. In this study DDD was found in 95% of the population and o,p'-DDT in only 30% of the population. Our method clearly distinguished between these two substances in the QF-1 column.

Summary

DDT, DDE, DDD, dieldrin and lindane were determined in adipose tissue, liver, kidney, brain and gonads of 71 persons who died accidentally in Dade County. The gas chromatographic method developed in this laboratory for the determination of chlorinated hydrocarbon pesticides using the electron capture detector without prior clean-up was used. Essentially the same levels of DDT, DDE and dieldrin were found in the fat as was reported previously by others for the population of the United States. Pesticides concentrations were found to be 10 times less in liver and 100 times less in other tissues than in adipose tissue. No differences were observed because of sex and race, or between urban dwellers and rural dwellers. No correlation of the concentration of DDT or its metabolites with age was observed, with the exception of the 0-5 year age group. This youngest age group was found to have a significantly lower DDT and DDE burden than the four older age groups. A possible correlation of dieldrin level with age was observed in all five tissues.

In contrast to the low pesticide levels found in the 0-5 age group, the concentrations observed in six fetuses more closely resembled the concentration of the adult general population. In three cases, where it was possible to compare the levels of pesticide in the fetus with the mother, although slightly lower fetal levels than maternal levels were observed, there was evidence of the passage of pesticide across the placental membrane at least as early as the 22nd week of gestation.

Occupationally exposed farm laborers were found to have significantly higher levels (approximately double) of DDT and its metabolites.

Relatively high concentrations of DDD were found in livers of virtually all cases. The possibility is discussed that this conversion to DDD occurs postmortem.

References

1. Laug, E. P., Kunze, F. M. and Prickett, C. S. Occurrence of DDT in Human Fat and Milk. Arch. Industr. Hyg. 3:245, 1951.

2. Hayes, J. W., Quinby, G. E., Walker, K. C., Elliott, J. W. and Upholt, W. M. Storage of DDT and DDE in People with Different Degrees of Exposure to DDT. Arch. Industr. Health 18:398, 1958.

3. Dale, W. E. and Quinby, G. E. Chlorinated Insecticides in the Body Fat of People in the United States. Science 142:593, 1963.

4. Quinby, G. E., Hayes, J. W., Armstrong, J. F. and Durham W. F. DDT Storage in the US Population, J.A.M.A. 191:175, 1965.

5. Durham, W. F., Armstrong, J. F., Upholt, W. M. and Heller, C. Insecticide Content of Diet and Body Fat of Alaskan Natives. Science 134:1880, 1961.

6. Hoffman, W. S., Fishbein, W. J. and Andelman, M. B. The Pesticide Content of Human Fat Tissue. Arch. Environ. Health 9:387, 1964.

7. Robinson, J., Richardson, A., Hunter, C. G., Crabtree, A. N. and Rees, H. J. Organo-Chlorine Insecticide Content of Human Adipose Tissue in South-Eastern England. Brit. J. Industr. Med. 22:220, 1965.

8. Wasserman, M., Gon, M., Wasserman, D. and Zellermayer, L. DDT and DDE in the Body Fat of People in Israel. Arch. Environ. Health 11:375, 1965.

9. Radomski, J. L. and Fiserova-Bergerova, V. The Analyses of Pesticides in Human Tissue with the Electron Capture Detector without Prior Clean-up. Industr. Med. & Surg. 32:934, 1965.

10. Radomski, J. L. and Fiserova-Bergerova, V. The Determination of Chlorinated Hydrocarbon Pesti-

cides in Human and Animal Tissues. Industr. Med. & Surg. (in press).

11. Peterson, J. E. and Robinson, Wm. H. Metabolic Products of p,p'-DDT in Rat. Toxicol. Appl. Pharmacol. 6:321, 1964.

12. Datta, P. R., Laug, E. P. and Klein, A. K. Conversion of p,p'-DDT to p,p'-DDD in the Liver of the Rat. Science 145:1052, 1964.

13. Klein, A. K., Laug, E. P., Datta, P. R., Watts, J. O. and Chen, J. T. Metabolites Reductive Dechlorination of DDT to DDD and Isomeric Transformation of o,p'-DDT to p,p'-DDT in Vivo. J. of Assoc. Official Agriculture Chem. 47:1129, 1964.

14. Klein, A. K., Laug, E. P., Datta, P. R. and Mendel, J. L. Evidence for the Conversion of

o,p'-DDT (1>1>1-Trichloro-2-o-chlorophenyl-2-p-chlorophenylethane) to p,p'-DDT (1>1>1-Trichloro- 2>2 bis (p-chlorophenyl) ethane in Rats. J. Am. Chem. Soc. 87:2520, 1965.

15. Kallman, B. J. and Andrews, A. K. Reductive Dechlorination of DDT to DDD by Yeast. Science 141:1059, 1963.

16. Allison, D., Kallman, B. J., Cope, O. B. and Van Valin, C. C. Insecticides Effect on Cutthroat Trout of Repeated Exposure to DDT. Science 142:958, 1963.

17. Barker, P. S. and Morrison, F. O. Breakdown of DDT to DDD in Mouse Tissue, Can. J. of Zool. 42:324, 1964.

55

CHLORINATED HYDROCARBON INSECTICIDES IN PLASMA AND MILK OF PREGNANT AND LACTATING WOMEN

August Curley and Renate Kimbrough

Five pregnant women were studied for chlorinated hydrocarbon insecticide residues in their blood and milk. Blood samples were obtained from each between 30 days of pregnancy and 115 days postpartum. Three milk samples were collected from each between three and 96 days postpartum. Sample extracts of plasma and milk were analyzed by electron-capture gas-liquid chromatography for chlorinated hydrocarbon insecticides. Eight chlorinated insecticides were detected. The concentrations of these compounds in plasma were within the lower part of the range previously reported for nonpregnant women. A small but statistically significant decrease in the plasma concentration of p,p'-DDT, p,p'-DDE, o,p'-DDE, p,p'-DDD, and total BHC was observed one to six days postpartum. The concentration of the detected compounds in milk varied greatly among the individual women but was within the range reported by others.

Reprinted from the *Archives of Environmental Health* 18: 156-64, 1969, with the permission of the publishers.

In 1951, Laug et al. (1) found DDT (1,1,1-trichloro-2,2-bis [p-chlorophenyl]-ethane) in 30 of 32 human milk samples collected in the Washington D.C. area. Other reports from California (2), Hungary (3), and Russia (4) followed. Quinby et al. (5) reported DDT in individual and pooled samples of milk from women in Chicago, Wenatchee, Wash, and Phoenix, Ariz. The presence of DDT, its metabolites, and other chlorinated hydrocarbon insecticides—aldrin (1,2,3,4,10,10-hexachloro-1,4,4a,5,8,8a-hexahydro-1,4, *endo, exo*-5,8-dimethanonaphthalene), dieldrin (1,2,3,4,10, 10-hexachloro-6,7-epoxy-1,4,4a,5,6,7,8,8a-octa-hydro-1,4 *endo, exo*-5,8-dimethanonaphthalene), and benzene hexachloride (BHC) (1,2,3,4,5,6-hexachlorocyclohexane)—in human milk was also reported from England (6), Hungary (7), and Italy (8). Except for Damaskin (4) who found 1.22 ppm to 4.88 ppm DDT in 16 milk samples, all investigations reported comparable levels of DDT in milk ranging from about 0.05 to 0.26 ppm.

Dale et al. (9) from this laboratory reported the levels of several chlorinated hydrocarbons in plasma of men and women of the general population. No data on the blood levels of chlorinated hydrocarbon insecticides in women during the gestation and lactation period were available, nor was it known whether concentrations of these compounds in human milk vary during the early and late lactation period. Two studies were undertaken to gain information on the levels of insecticides in women during pregnancy and lactation. One investigation established the levels of chlorinated hydrocarbon insecticides in the plasma of women during early and late pregnancy, and in the plasma and milk for three months postpartum. In this study, a change in the concentration of these compounds in plasma was observed within the period of 30 days before to 55 days after delivery. In a second study, plasma from two additional subjects was examined during the period six days before to 30 days after delivery in order to determine the concentrations of these compounds prior to and immediately after delivery at closer intervals. This paper reports the results of these two studies.

Materials and Methods

Both groups (study 1 and 2) consisted of healthy women of the same socioeconomic group and metropolitan area, who had no known special exposure to pesticides. Table 1 presents their age, obstetrical history, and profession.

Study 1

Five women participated in this study. Individual blood samples were drawn from 240 to 120 and 30 to 7 days before delivery and between one to six, 36 to 55, and 90 to 115 days postpartum. The first milk samples were collected three to six days postpartum. Subsequent milk samples were collected simultan-

Table 1. Obstetrical history and drug therapy of the pregnant woman.

Patient	Age	Occupation	No. of pregnancies	Delivery	Medication in hospital	
					Prior to delivery	After delivery
Study 1						
1	30	Housewife	4	Caesarean	Spinal anesthesia	Meperidine Propoxyphene hydrochloride Secobarbital
2	21	Laboratory technician	1	Normal	Meperidine Scopolamine Promethazine Pentobarbital	Propoxyphene hydrochloride Secobarbital Ergonovine maleate
3	33	Physician	3	Normal	Propiomazine hydrochloride Chlorpromazine	Ergonovine maleate
4	20	Laboratory technician	1	Normal	Meperidine Scopolamine Levallorphan	Ergonovine maleate Secobarbital
5	22	Laboratory technician	2	Normal	Meperidine Scopolamine Propiomazine hydrochloride Levallorphan	Ergonovine maleate Secobarbital
Study 2						
6	25	Housewife	2	Normal	None	Propoxyphene hydrochloride Ergonovine maleate
7	26	Statistical assistant	2	Normal	Meperidine Promethazine Scopolamine	Propoxyphene hydrochloride Ergonovine maleate

eously with the other two postpartum blood samples. All blood samples were obtained before lunch except the samples of patient 1 which were obtained in the evening. The first blood sample and the last milk sample were not collected from one participant (patient 2) (Tables 2 and 3).

Study 2

Two women were subjects in this study in which only blood samples were obtained. These samples were drawn at six and seven days before delivery, at delivery, and at 6, 13 to 15, and 27 to 30 days postpartum. Cord blood was used as the sample at delivery. Milk samples were not collected for this study.

The blood samples from all subjects studied were collected in 10-ml tubes which contained potassium oxalate as an anticoagulant. The plasma was separated and refrigerated prior to analysis. These samples were analyzed by the method of Dale et al. (10) with the exception of the change in the column loading, column size, and nitrogen flow rates. The column consisted of an aluminum tube, 6 feet x ¼ inch, packed with 3% diethylene glycol succinate. The carrier gas flow was 40 cc/min, and no scavenger gas was used.

Controls

Blood was collected from ten nonpregnant women of comparable socioeconomic status and of the same city. The plasma of this group was analyzed for chlorinated hydrocarbon insecticides by the same method and the results compared with those obtained for the pregnant women in study 1.

The milk samples were collected by manually pumping the breast and were frozen for storage prior to analysis. Whole milk (0.2 ml) was pipetted into a ground-glass stoppered centrifuge tube. The sample was then partitioned with 2 ml of methanol and 3 ml of 1% potassium carbonate. The sample was extracted three times with 3 ml of *n*-hexane. The combined *n*-hexane extracts were concentrated to a volume of 50 μl or 100 μl. An appropriate aliquot from the 50 μl or 100 μl *n*-hexane concentrate was analyzed by electron-capture gas-liquid chromatography.

Results

Study 1

Table 2 presents the analytical results for *p,p'*-DDT, *o,p'*-DDT, *p,p'*-DDE, *o,p'*-DDE, *p,p'*-DDD, total DDT (all isomers, metabolites, and analogues) total BHC, heptachlor epoxide, and dieldrin in plasma at various intervals during pregnancy and after delivery. Table 3 gives concentrations of these same chlorinated insecticides found in the milk samples at various intervals after delivery. Figure 55-1 illustrates the mean concentrations in parts per

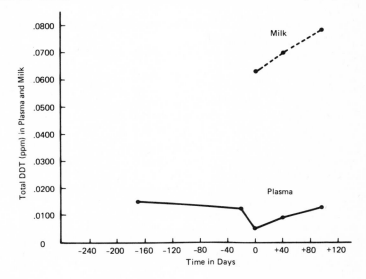

Fig. 55-1. Mean concentration of total DDT (ppm) in plasma of five women at different intervals during pregnancy and in plasma and milk after delivery.

Table 2. Concentration* of chlorinated insecticides and related compounds in plasma of five women in study 1 at various intervals before and after delivery.

Days†		p,p'-DDT	o,p'-DDT	p,p'-DDE	o,p'-DDE
−240 to	Range	0.0009-0.0046	<0.0001-0.0019	0.0027-0,0132	<0.0001-0.0014
−120 Days	Mean	0.0032	0.0007	0.0084	0.0004
N=4	SE±	0.0009	0.0004	0.0022	0.0003
−30 to	Range	0.0013-0.0068	<0.0001-0.0074	0.0027-0.0092	<0.0001-0.0002
−7 Days	Mean	0.0031	0.0029	0.0052	0.0001
N=5	SE±	0.0011	0.0013	0.0012	0.00005
+1 to	Range	0.0007-0.0032	<0.0001-0.0006	0.0012-0.0051	<0.0001-0.0002
+6 Days	Mean	0.0019	0.0002	0.0024	0.0001
N=5	SE±	0.0005	0.0001	0.0007	0.0004
+35 to	Range	0.0010-0.0044	<0.0001-0.0008	0.0022-0.0068	<0.0001-0.0007
+5 Days	Mean	0.0025	0.0002	0.0048	0.0003
N=5	SE±	0.0006	0.0001	0.0010	0.0001
+90 to	Range	0.0006-0.0063	<0.0001-0.0003	0.0014-0.0090	<0.0001-0.0020
+115 Days	Mean	0.0033	0.0001	0.0045	0.0005
N=5	SE±	0.0010	0.00006	0.0013	0.0004
Females of	Range	0.0026-0.0095	<0.0001-0.0011	0.0050-0.0203	<0.0001
general population	Mean	0.0053	0.0007	0.0130	—
N=10	SE±	0.0007	0.0001	0.0015	—

* Parts per million.
† The delivery day was designated as day 0. Counting backwards from day 0, the days of pregnancy were designated as (−) days. The days postpartum were designated as (+) days counting from the day of delivery.

Table 3. Concentration* of chlorinated insecticides and related compounds in milk of five women in study 1 at various intervals after delivery.

Days†		p,p'-DDT	o,p'-DDT	p,p'-DDE	o,p'-DDE
+3 to	Range	0.0146-0.0890	<0.0001-0.0072	0.0052-0.0268	<0.0001-0.0027
+6 Days	Mean	0.0341	0.0027	0.0177	0.0007
N=5	SE±	0.0138	0.0012	0.0038	0.0005
+37 to	Range	0.0078-0.0586	<0.0001-0.0036	0.0187-0.0435	<0.0001-0.0022
+60 Days	Mean	0.0328	0.0012	0.0274	0.0010
N=5	SE±	0.0107	0.0007	0.0049	0.0004
+90 to	Range	0.0137-0.0306	<0.0001-0.0108	0.0193-0.0981	<0.0001-0.0028
+96 Days	Mean	0.0223	0.0037	0.0411	0.0010
N=4	SE±	0.0040	0.0025	0.0190	0.0007

* Parts per million.
† The delivery day was designated as day 0. Counting backwards from day 0, the days of pregnancy were designated as (−) days. The days postpartum were designated as (+) days counting from the day of delivery.

p,p'-DDD	*Total as DDT*	*Total BHC*	*Heptachlor epoxide*	*Dieldrin*
< 0.0001-0.0027	0.0081-0.0197	0.0015-0.0097	< 0.0001-0.0019	0.0004-0.0020
0.0011	0.0149	0.0045	0.0005	0.0010
0.0006	0.0024	0.0019	0.0004	0.0003
< 0.0001-0.0010	0.0047-0.0170	0.0008-0.0034	0.0002-0.0015	0.0008-0.0030
0.0003	0.0122	0.0023	0.0007	0.0014
0.0002	0.0024	0.0005	0.0003	0.0004
< 0.0001-0.0005	0.0025-0.0095	< 0.0001-0.0044	< 0.0001-0.0033	< 0.0001-0.0024
0.0001	0.0050	0.0012	0.0008	0.0009
0.0001	0.0012	0.0008	0.0006	0.0004
< 0.0001-0.0011	0.0040-0.0130	< 0.0001-0.0023	0.0001-0.0006	0.0003-0.0061
0.0004	0.0088	0.0011	0.0003	0.0018
0.0002	0.0019	0.0004	0.0001	0.0010
< 0.0001-0.0003	0.0044-0.0152	0.0006-0.0028	< 0.0001-0.0005	0.0003-0.0010
0.0001	0.0091	0.0016	0.0002	0.0007
0.00006	0.0023	0.0004	0.00009	0.0001
< 0.0001	0.0088-0.0295	0.0014-0.0096	0.0003-0.0010	0.0001-0.0012
—	0.0205	0.0034	0.0006	0.0003
—	0.0022	0.0008	0.0001	0.0001

p,p'-DDD	*Total as DDT*	*Total BHC*	*Heptachlor epoxide*	*Dieldrin*
< 0.0001-0.0140	0.0500-0.0990	0.0006-0.0157	< 0.0001-0.0024	0.0030-0.0137
0.0053	0.0632	0.0075	0.0010	0.0069
0.0024	0.0090	0.0029	0.0004	0.0020
< 0.0001-0.0104	0.0422-0.1127	< 0.0001-0.0202	< 0.0001-0.0032	0.0034-0.0074
0.0039	0.0699	0.0098	0.0014	0.0045
0.0018	0.0127	0.0032	0.0005	0.0007
< 0.0001-0.0080	0.0404-0.1563	< 0.0001-0.0047	< 0.0001-0.0044	0.0029-0.0146
0.0049	0.0784	0.0024	0.0027	0.0073
0.0018	0.0263	0.0010	0.0009	0.0025

Fig. 55-2. Individual concentration of total DDT (ppm) in plasma of five women at different intervals during pregnancy and after delivery. Open circle indicates Patient 1; solid circle, Patient 2; open square, Patient 3; solid square, Patient 4; and x, Patient 5.

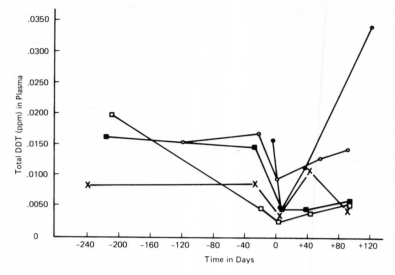

Fig. 55-3. Individual concentration of p,p'-DDT (ppm) in plasma of five women at different intervals during pregnancy and after delivery. Open circle indicates Patient 1; solid circle, Patient 2; open square, Patient 3; solid square, Patient 4; and x, Patient 5.

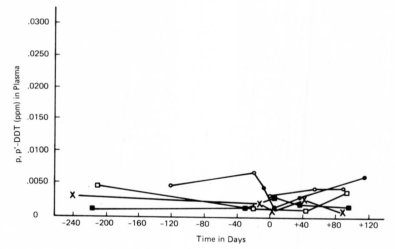

Fig. 55-4. Individual concentration of p,p'-DDE (ppm) in plasma of five women at different intervals during pregnancy and after delivery. Open circle indicates Patient 1; solid circle, Patient 2; open square, Patient 3; solid square, Patient 4; and x, Patient 5.

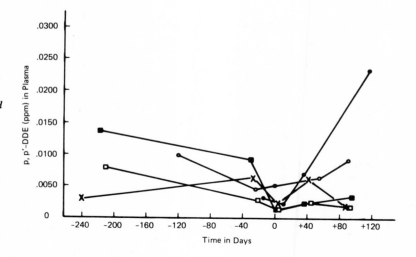

million of total DDT in the plasma and milk at various intervals during pregnancy and after delivery.

The concentrations of the detected chlorinated hydrocarbon insecticides in the plasma of the pregnant women were within the range previously reported (9) for healthy non-pregnant women in childbearing age of the same socioeconomic group and metropolitan area. The values for ten nonpregnant women were included in Table 2 for comparison. These volunteers also had no known special exposure to pesticides.

The plasma concentration of p,p'-DDT and its metabolites showed a small decrease at or soon after delivery. A decrease in the concentration of total BHC in plasma was also observed during this period. The observed decrease of the plasma level of the various chlorinated hydrocarbon insecticides was only significant for the p,p'-DDE fraction ($P < 0.05$) and for the sum of the DDT fractions ($P < 0.01$). Subsequently, the concentration of these compounds increased to approximately the levels found during pregnancy. The concentration of o,p'-DDT did not show this trend.

Figures 55-2 to 55-4 illustrate the small decrease in total DDT, p,p'-DDT, and p,p'-DDE in the plasma of five individuals at one to six days postpartum. The curves indicate corresponding plasma levels for these compounds in the five subjects. The individual curves (Fig.

55-5) for the plasma levels of dieldrin did not correspond as well to each other.

The mean total DDT concentrations in milk increased during the lactation period (Fig. 55-1). The individual levels of the total DDT, p,p'-DDT, and p,p'-DDE (Figs. 55-6 to 55-8) concentration show pronounced variation at the different intervals tested. The range of the total DDT levels falls within the limits reported by others (5). The mean concentration for p,p'-DDT decreases somewhat during lactation while that of p,p'-DDE increases. However, this was not statistically significant since the individual variation was very pronounced. Traces of α-, γ-, and β-BHC, heptachlor epoxide and dieldrin were also observed in the milk samples. Individual variation was found for these chlorinated hydrocarbon insecticides too. The values obtained for dieldrin and total BHC are comparable to those reported in England (6).

Study 2

Table 4 presents the concentrations of DDT, DDT and related materials, total BHC, heptachlor epoxide, and dieldrin in the plasma of the two women. The concentrations of all the chlorinated compounds detected were similar to those found in study 2. A statistical comparison of the mean values for the total DDT concentration in plasma obtained before delivery with the first plasma sample of study 1 is

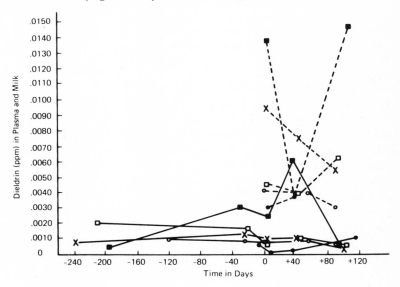

Fig. 55-5. Individual concentration of dieldrin (ppm) in plasma of five women at different intervals during pregnancy and in plasma (solid line) and milk (broken line) after delivery. Open circle indicates Patient 1; solid circle, Patient 2; open square, Patient 3; solid square, Patient 4; and x, Patient 5.

Table 4. Concentrations* of chlorinated insecticides and related compounds in the plasma of two women in study 2 before and after delivery.

Days before or after delivery†	p,p'-DDT	o,p'-DDT	p,p'-DDE	o,p'-DDE
−6 to −7 days	0.0010-0.0068	<0.0001	0.0012-0.0021	0.0008-0.0015
Delivery day	< 0.0001-0.0006	< 0.0001	0.0010-0.0047	< 0.0001-0.0001
+6 days	0.0012-0.0222	< 0.0001-0.0126	0.0013-0.0043	< 0.0001
+13 to +15 days	0.0005-0.0015	< 0.0001	0.0004-0.0036	< 0.0001
+27 to +30 days	0.0008-0.0016	< 0.0001	0.0016-0.0026	< 0.0001

* Parts per million.

† The delivery day was designated as day 0. Counting backwards from day 0, the days of pregnancy were designated as (−) days. The days postpartum were designated as (+) days counting from the day of delivery. The values were the same for both women.

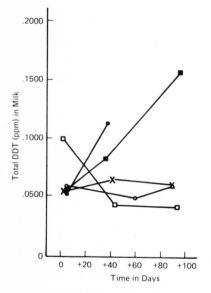

Fig. 55-6. Individual total DDT in milk after delivery. Open circle indicates Patient 1; solid circle, Patient 2; open square, Patient 3, solid square, Patient 4; and x, Patient 5.

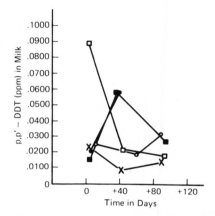

Fig. 55-7. Individual concentration of p,p'-DDT (ppm) in milk after delivery. Open circle indicates Patient 1; solid circle, Patient 2; open square, Patient 3; solid square, Patient 4; and x, Patient 5.

not significantly different. However, the sample taken at delivery ($P < 0.025$) and at 14 ($P < 0.05$) and 30 ($P < 0.05$) days after delivery showed a slight but significantly lower total DDT concentration than the first sample of study 1. At six days after delivery, a significant difference in the total DDT concentration of plasma could not be demonstrated when comparing the results of study 2 with the results of the first samples of study 1. A significant difference between the concentration of the other measured compounds was also not observed when the results of study 2 were compared with the results of the first sample of study 1.

Comment

The results in the present study show that the concentration of chlorinated hydrocarbon insecticides in plasma of pregnant and lactating women falls within the same range as that of nonpregnant women.

The mean plasma concentrations of p,p'-DDT and all DDT derived compounds, and total BHC showed a small but significant decrease at or soon after delivery and subsequently increased to the levels observed during early pregnancy. Dieldrin followed a similar trend. Despite the individual variation, the

p,p'-DDD	*Total as DDT*	*Total HBC*	*Heptachlor epoxide*	*Dieldrin*
< 0.0001	0.0042-0.0098	0.0008-0.0010	< 0.0001	< 0.0001-0.0002
< 0.0001	0.0017‡	< 0.0001-0.0015	< 0.0001	< 0.0001-0.0003
< 0.0001	0.0026-0.0395	0.0019-0.0029	< 0.0001-0.0002	< 0.0001
< 0.0001	0.0009-0.0055	0.0011-0.0025	< 0.0001	< 0.0001-0.0008
< 0.0001	0.0034-0.0037	0.0007-0.0016	< 0.0001	< 0.0001

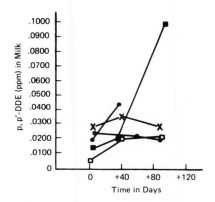

Fig. 55-8. Individual concentration of p.p'-DDT (ppm) in milk after delivery. Open circle indicates Patient 1; solid circle, Patient 2; open square, Patient 3; solid square, Patient 4; and x, Patient 5.

mean concentration of p,p'-DDT, its isomers and metabolites reported as total DDT, increased in plasma during the lactation period studied. These findings suggest but do not prove that delivery leads to lower plasma levels of these compounds.

A variety of physiological changes that occur in pregnancy could affect the plasma level of the chlorinated hydrocarbon insecticides. During this period serum albumin values decrease (25%), the total serum lipid values increase (46%), progesterone and estrogen production is increased, water is retained to a total volume of about 7 liters in normal pregnancy, and the blood volume increases in late pregnancy (11). Any one or a combination of these factors may influence the level of chlorinated hydrocarbon insecticides in plasma. Furthermore, the subjects received a variety of drugs

(Table 1) during and after delivery which might have stimulated the activity of oxidative enzymes in the liver microsomes (12, 13).

The levels of the studied insecticides in milk showed a great deal of individual variation and were within the range of those reported by others (1-3, 5, 6, 8). Conversely Damaskin (4) reported much higher values.

The number of subjects was small, and the apparent increase of p,p'-DDE in the milk in the later part of the lactation period must be considered with great reservation since it was not statistically significant. A correlation between the milk and plasma levels of the studied compounds could not be established.

Mrs. Estelle Gray assisted with the statistical analysis, and Mrs. Catherine L. Thrasher and Miss Helen Mann assisted with the insecticide determinations.

Generic and Trade Names of Drugs
Meperidine—*Demerol.*
Propoxyphene hydrochloride—*Darvon.*
Secobarbital—*Seconal.*
Promethazine—*Phenergan.*
Pentobarbital—*Nembutal.*
Propiomazine hydrochloride—*Largon Hydrochloride.*
Chlorpromazine—*Thorazine.*
Levallorphan—*Lorfan.*

References

1. Laug, E. P.; Kunse, F. M.; and Prickett, C. S.: Occurrence of DDT in Human Fat and Milk, *Arch. Industr. Hyg.* 3:245-246 (March) 1951.

2. West, I.: Pesticides as Contaminants, *Arch. Environ. Health* 9:626-631 (Nov.) 1964.

3. Dénes, A.: Investigation of Chlorinated Hydrocarbon Residues in Animal and Vegetable Fats, *Year-Book of the Institute of Nutrition*, 1963 (Budapest), pp 46-47, 1964.

4. Damaskin, V. I.: The Extent of Accumulation of DDT in the Human Body Due to Its Presence in Food and Its Toxic Effect, *Gig. Sanit.* 30:109, 1965.

5. Quinby, G. E., Armstrong, F. J.; and Durham, W. F.: DDT in Human Milk, *Nature* 207:726-728 (Aug. 14) 1965.

6. Egan, H., et al.: Organochlorine Pesticide Residues in Human Fat and Human Milk, *Brit. Med. J.* 2:66-69 (July 10) 1965.

7. Dénes, A.: Dieldrin Residues in Foodstuffs and Biological Material, *Year Book of the Institute of Nutrition*, 1965 (Budapest) pp 47-49, 1966.

8. Kanitz, S., and Castello, G.: Sulla presenza di residui di alcuni disinfestanti nel tessuto adiposo umano ed in alcuni alimenti, *G. Ig. Med. Prev.* 7:1-19, 1966.

9. Dale, W. E.; Curley, A.; and Hayes, W. J., Jr.: Determination of Chlorinated Insecticides in Human Blood, *Industr. Med. Surg.* 36:275-280 (April) 1967.

10. Dale, W. E.; Curley, A.; and Cueto, C., Jr.: Hexane Extractable Chlorinated Insecticides in Human Blood, *Life Sci.* 5:47-54 (Jan.) 1966.

11. Williams, J. W.: *Obstetrics*, **ed 13,** by N. J. Eastman, and L. M. Hellman (eds.), New York: Appleton-Century-Crofts, 1966.

12. Conney, A. H., et al.: Adaptive Increases in Drug-Metabolizing Enzymes Induced by Phenobarbital and Other Drugs, *J. Pharmacol. Exp. Ther.* 130:1-8, 1960.

13. Conney, A. H., et al.: Effects of Pesticides on Drug and Steroid Metabolism, *Clin. Pharmacol. Ther.* 8:2-10, 1967.

56

INSECTICIDE RESISTANCE COMES OF AGE

A. W. A. Brown

It is now 21 years since DDT-resistant house flies were first discovered in northern Sweden, and since the report of Wilson and Gahan that a DDT-resistant strain could be produced by laboratory selection at Orlando. Although the resistance of the San Jose scale to lime-sulfur was detected by Melander in Washington state nearly 60 years ago, the resistance problem as we know it came on the scene with the organic residual insecticides in 1946. Now that this year it has come of age, we might well examine how the economic entomologist has fared with this cuckoo in the nest; is it a clear case of defeat, or is it peaceful coexistence?

At least we know the nature of the enemy. It is produced by selection, not habituation.

Reprinted from the *Bulletin of the Entomological Society of America* 14: 3-9, 1968.

You can expose flies to non-killing doses of DDT for 150 generations, as Lüers has done with *Drosophila*, and you don't get resistance. But as soon as the dose begins to kill a segment of the population, as Gaines Eddy and co-workers have shown with body lice, the resistance to DDT develops. As the susceptible individuals are selected out, the more resistant genotypes are left to produce the succeeding generations. The insecticide cannot produce postadaptations; it can only favour the proportion of the preadaptations for resistance already just barely present in the population.

Moreover resistance is specific. DDT selection produces resistance to DDT and its relatives such as methoxychlor and TDE, and not to the cyclodiene derivatives. On the other hand, selection with aldrin or dieldrin induces resistance to the cyclodiene derivatives but not DDT-resistance. Thus there are 2 types of resistance within the organochlorine insecticides, gamma-BHC belonging with the cyclodienes, as Busvine pointed out in 1953. Neither of them carry any cross-resistance to the organophosphorus compounds, at least in insects, although selection with OP compounds usually induces or preserves the organochlorine resistances. Our troubles of today, therefore, involve DDT-resistance, cyclodiene-resistance and OP-resistance, with carbamate-resistance a possible fourth.

Before 1946, our experience with the problem was limited to 10 species (Table 1), with resistance to hydrogen cyanide in 3 scale insects, to arsenicals in 2 cattle ticks, the codling moth and peach twig borer, and to tartar emetic in 2 species of thrips.

Table 1. Resistance to inorganic and botanical insecticides, 1945.

Lime-sulphur	1	*Aspidiotus*
Hydrogen cyanide	3	*Saissetia, Aonidiella, Coccus*
Lead arsenate	2	*Carpocapsa, Anarsia*
Sodium arsenite	2	*B. microplus, B. decoloratus*
Tartar emetic	2	*Scirtothrips, Taeniothrips*
	10	

Now in 1967 we know resistance to have developed in 224 species of insects and acarines (Table 2). Of these 97 are of public-health or veterinary importance, and 127 attack field or forest crops or stored products. The most widespread type is cyclodiene-resistance, often

Table 2. Numbers of species with resistances of various types, 1967.

	DDT	Dld	OP	Other	Total
Diptera	44	68	14	3	88
Lepidoptera	14	14	6	5	34
Hemiptera	10	15	14	4	36
Acarina	3	7	16	4	25
Coleoptera	5	19	1	1	22
Other orders	15	12	3	2	19
Total	91	135	54	20	224

called dieldrin-resistance, involving 135 species, as compared to 91 with DDT-resistance. The total of OP-resistant species now reaches 54 insects, mites and ticks. Additional to this tabulation is carbamate-resistance—now developed in the light-brown apple moth in Tasmania, the tobacco budworm in Texas, and the cotton leafworm in Egypt—and 2 other resistance types. Pyrethrin-resistance has developed in the tobacco moth in Georgia, the house fly in Sweden, the mushroom phorid in England, and certain populations of the bed bug and body louse. Rotenone-resistance devel-

oped in the Mexican bean beetle in the northeast USA as long ago as 1949, but nicotine-resistance has never made an appearance.

That makes a total of 9 resistance types developed by insects; the tetranychids or red mites have developed 9 more, to 9 different groups of acaricides (Table 3). The two-spotted mite and the European red mite have become resistant in succession to 5 groups of chlorinated acaricides. *Tetranychus urticae* (formerly *T. bimaculatus* or *telarius*) has gone on to develop resistance to the sulfur-containing

Table 3. Resistance of greenhouse and orchard mites to acaricides.

	T. urticae	*P. ulmi*
Ovex (Ovotran®)	E. USA 53	Calif. 54
Genite® and fenson	Calif. 54	Calif. 54
Chlorobenzilate and chloro-benside	Calif. 55	Calif. 54
Dicofol (Kelthane®)	Connecticut 55	W. Va., Penn. 61
Tetradifon (Tedion®)	USA and Europe 64	Penn. 61
Aramite®	Ohio 55	None
Azobenzene	England 65	—
Selenium	E. USA 43	—
Binapacryl (*T. mcdanieli*)	—	Washington 66

Aramite ® as well as the nitrogenous azobenzene, having developed resistance to compounds of selenium long ago; the McDaniel mite last year developed resistance to the dinitro compound binapacryl in Washington state. At least 13 species of mites, to be listed later, have developed resistance to OP compounds; moreover in mites, in contrast to insects, selection with chlorinated acaricides produces OP-resistance, and not vice versa.

Among insects of agricultural importance, DDT-resistance made its appearance in 1951 (Table 4), developing in the codling moth and oriental peach moth, the cabbage worm and cabbage looper, the potato beetle and potato tuber-worm, the cotton bollworm and pink bollworm, and the tobacco budworm and northern tobacco hornworm. On grape and apple,

Table 4. Plant-feeding insects resistant to DDT and TDE.

	Apple and Peach		Cabbage		Tobacco
Lep.	*Carpocapsa pomonella*	Lep.	*Pieris rapae*	Lep.	*Heliothis virescens*[3]
	Grapholitha molesta		*Trichoplusia ni*[1]		*Protoparce quinquemaculata*
	Argyrotaenia velutinana				
	Epiphyas postvittana		Potato		Grape
Hem.	*Erythroneura lawsoniana*[2]	Lep.	*Phthorimaea operculella*	Hem.	*Erythroneura variabilis*
	Typhlocyba pomaria	Col.	*Leptinotarsa decemlineata*[1]		*E. elegantula*
	Myzus persicae		*Epitrix cucumeris*		
			Cotton		
		Lep.	*Heliothis zea*		
			Pectinophora gossypiella		

[1] Also Dld-resistant.
[2] Also OP-resistant.
[3] Also carbamate-resistant.

Table 5. Plant-feeding insects resistant to cyclodienes and BHC.

	Cotton		Sugar Cane		Rice
Lep.	*Alabama argillacea*	Lep.	*Diatraea saccharalis*	Lep.	*Chilo suppressalis*
	Spodoptera littoralis		*Aeneolamia varia*	Col.	*Lema oryzae*
	Estigmene acraea				*Lissorhoptrus oryzophilus*
	Earias insulana		Tobacco	Hem.	*Delphacodes striatella*
	Bucculatrix thurberiella	Lep.	*Protoparce sexta*		*Leptocoris varicornis*
Col.	*Anthonomus grandis*		*Heliothis virescens*		*Scotinophora lurida*
Hem.	*Dysdercus peruvianus*		*Euxoa messoria*		
	Psallus serialus		*Euxoa detersa*		
	Aphis gossypii		*Phthorimaea operculella*		

4 species of leafhoppers have become DDT-resistant. On apple the red-banded leaf roller has developed resistance to TDE. The spruce budworm and others not listed here raise the total of DDT-resistant plant-feeding insects to 29.

No less than 53 species of phytophagous insects have developed resistance to the cyclodiene insecticides and gamma-BHC (Table 5). Treatment of cotton with toxaphene and endrin led to resistance in the boll weevil, leafworm, fleahopper and aphid in the southeastern states, and the leaf-perforator and salt-marsh caterpillar in the southwest, besides the leafworm *Spodoptera* in Egypt, the spiny bollworm *Earias* in Israel, and the cottonstainer *Dysdercus* in Peru. On tobacco, 5 lepidopterous species have developed cyclodiene-resistance, namely the budworm and northern hornworm in the southeast, 2 kinds of *Euxoa* cutworms in Ontario and the splitworm *Phtorimaea* in Queensland. On rice, resistance to BHC has been developed by the stem-borer *Chilo* and the leaf beetle *Lema* in Japan, and by 3 species of leafhoppers in East Asia, while in the Mississippi Valley the rice water weevil has developed resistance to aldrin. On sugar-cane, BHC-resistance in the froghopper *Aeneolamia* in Trinidad was followed by endrin-resistance in the borer *Diatraea* in Louisiana. Other cyclodiene-resistant insects not listed here include 3 species of thrips, and endosulfan-resistant strawberry aphids in Washington state.

It is with soil insects that this type of resistance has become so striking in the past decade (Table 6), involving 2 species of wireworms in the Carolinas and 1 in Washington state, the white-fringed beetle *Graphognathus* in Alabama, and 4 species of *Diabrotica* rootworms, mainly in corn fields, in the states east of the Rockies. The alfalfa weevil now shows this resistance in areas stretching from California to New York. Among the root maggots, cyclodiene-resistance has developed in 3 species

Table 6. Soil insects resistant to dieldrin and heptachlor.

Coleoptera	Diptera
Conoderus fallii	*Hylemya liturata*
C. vespertinus	*H. platura*
Limonius californicus	*Euxesta notata*
Diabrotica virgifera	*Hylemya brassicae*
D. balteata	*H. floralis*
D. longicornis	*H. antiqua*
D. undecimpunctata	*H. arambourgi*
Graphognathus leucoloma	*Merodon equestris*
Hypera postica	*Psila rosae*

on tobacco, and in the cabbage maggot, turnip maggot, onion maggot and carrot rust fly, and overseas in the barley fly and large bulb fly.

Resistance to organophosphorus compounds is now present in 32 species of plant-feeding arthropods (Table 7). Of these, 10 are tetranychids and 3 others are also mites. Of the 12 hemipterous species, 9 are aphids and 2 are leafhoppers. Caterpillars now OP-resistant include the rice borer in Japan, the apple moth in Tasmania, and the cotton leafworm in Egypt, as

well as 2 stored-products insects to be discussed later. Two fruit maggots complete the list.

Too often now has insecticide-resistance endangered the principal crop of an entire country (Table 8). In Ghana the staple export crop is cocoa and its principal pest is the cocoa capsid, combatted almost exclusively with lindane until BHC-resistance spelled its failure in 1961. The same thing happened to toxaphene applied against the leafworm on the cotton crop of Egypt, to parathion and BHC applied against the stem borer of the rice crop in Japan, and to BHC and dioxathion which were already the last resort in cattle dips against ticks in Queensland. The boll weevil, codling moth, sugarcane froghopper and spruce budworm are other examples of similar importance.

Stored-products insects have not yet challenged fumigants with control failures, but significant resistance to BHC has developed in local populations of the rice weevil, granary weevil, maize weevil and red flour beetle (Table 9). Resistance to malathion has developed in the red flour beetle, the tobacco moth and the

Table 7. Resistance of plant-feeding pests to Op compounds.

Acarina	Hemiptera	Lepidoptera
Tetranychus urticae	*Myzus persicae*	*Chilo suppressalis*
T. cinnabarinus	*M. cerasi*	*Epiphyas postvittana*
T. mecdanieli	*Sapaphis pyri*	*Spodoptera littoralis*
T. medanieli	*S. plantaginis*	*Ephestia cautella*
T. schoenei	*Therioaphis maculata*	*Plodia interpunctella*
T. canadensis	*Chromaphis juglandicola*	
T. atlanticus	*Aphis pomi*	Diptera
T. pacificus	*Phorodon humuli*	*Dasyneura pyri*
Panonychus ulmi	*Toxoptera graminum*	*Tryporyza incertula*
P. citri	*Erythroneura elegantula*	
Vasates schlechtendali	*Nephotettix cincticeps*	
Aculus cornutus	*Blissus leucopterus*	
Bryobia practiosa		

Table 8. Resistant insects of principal crops of countries.

Ghana	Cocoa	*Distantiella theobroma*	γ-BHC
U.A.R.	Cotton	*Spodoptera littoralis*	Toxaphene
S-E. U.S.A.	Cotton	*Anthonomus grandis*	Endrin
Trinidad	Sugar-cane	*Aeneolamia varia*	γ-BHC
Japan	Rice	*Chilo suppressalis*	BHC, OP
Wash. and B.C.	Apple	*Carpocapsa pomonella*	DDT
New Brunswick	Spruce	*Choristoneura fumiferana*	DDT
Queensland	Cattle	*Boophilus microplus*	Dld, OP

Table 9. Resistance developed by stored-products insects.

Field			
Field	Gamma-BHC	*Sitophilus oryzae*	Queensland and England
		S. granarius	South Africa
		S. zea-mays	Kenya
		Tribolium castaneum	Kenya
	DDT	*Sitophilus oryzae*	Queensland
	Malathion	*Tribolium castaneum*	Nigeria, England, U.S.A.
		Ephestia cautella	Georgia, Florida
		Plodia interpunctella	Georgia
Laboratory	DDT	*Tribolium castaneum*	PIL, Slough
	Pyrethrins	*Sitophilus granarius*	Parkin and Lloyd
	Arprocarb	*Sitophilus granarius*	Kumar and Morrison

Table 10. Beneficial invertebrates resistant to insecticides.

Honey bee	*Apis mellifera*	DDT	California
Parasitic wasp	*Macrocentrus ancylivorus*	DDT	Ontario
Mayfly nymphs	*Heptagenia hebe* and		
	Stenonema fuscum	DDT	New Brunswick
Predacious mite	*Typhlodromus occidentalis*	Parathion	Brit. Columbia

Indian meal moth. Laboratory selection of the granary weevil has induced resistance to pyrethrins and very recently to the carbamate Baygon or arprocarb.

Several beneficial species have been found to have developed resistance to insecticides (Table 10), and there may well be more. The predacious mite *Typhlodromus* became as parathion-resistant as its spider mite prey in B.C. orchards. Two species of mayflies have developed more DDT-resistance than the budworm in northeastern spruce forests. The braconid *Macrocentrus* parasitic on the oriental peach moth can develop DDT-resistance, and the boll weevil parasite *Bracon mellitor* has recently been proved to be equally adaptable. Colonies of honey bees at Riverside and Baton Rouge have been found to be more DDT-tolerant than they used to be. Among the vertebrates (Table 11) inhabiting the cotton-growing areas of Mississippi, strong resistance to cyclodiene insecticides has now been developed by 3 species of fish and 2 cricket frogs. Even the pine mouse in Virginia has developed resistance to the endrin used to control it, and considerable DDT-tolerance has been induced by laboratory selection of white mice.

Resistance in insects of medical and veterin-

ary importance has so often been described that we'll simply say that one or both types of organochlorine-resistance is known in 5 species of fleas, 5 ticks, 2 cockroaches, 2 bed bugs, the body louse and 4 lice on livestock (Table 12). The German cockroach, bed bug and Australian cattle tick have gone on to develop OP-resistance. Among the flies (Table 13), some type of organochlorine-resistance has been developed by 20 species, indeed in all genera except *Glossina* tsetse flies and *Phlebotomus* sand flies, and OP-resistance by the house fly, horn fly, Australian sheep blow fly, African faeces fly and a pest midge in Florida.

Among the culicine mosquitoes, 11 species of *Aedes* have developed resistance, 4 of them

Table 11. Vertebrates resistant to chlorohydrocarbon insecticides.

Fish	Mosquito-fish, *Gambusia affinis*
	Golden shiner, *Notemigonus crysoleucas*
	Green sunfish, *Lepomis cyanellus*
	Bluegill sunfish, *Lepomis macrochirus*
Amphibians	Northern cricket-frog, *Acris crepitans*
	Southern cricket-frog, *Acris gryllus*
Mammals	Laboratory mouse, *Mus musculus*
	Pine mouse, *Pitymys pinetorum*

Table 12. Resistance to arthropods of medical and veterinary importance.

Lice				Fleas			
Pediculus corporis	DDT,	DL		*Zenopsylla cheopis*	DDT,	DL	
Linognathus vituli	DDT			*Z. astia*	DDT,	DL	
Haematopinus eurysternus	DDT			*Pulex irritans*	DDT,	DL	
Bovicola limbata		DL		*Ctenocephalides canis*	DDT,	DL	
B. caprae		DL		*C. felis*	DDT,	DL	
Cockroaches				Ticks			
Blattella germanica	DDT,	DL,	OP	*Boophilus microplus*	DDT,	DL,	OP
Blatta orientalis		DL		*B. decoloratus*	DDT,	DL	
Bed bugs				*Amblyomma americana*		DL	
Cimex lectularius	DDT,	DL,	OP	*Rhipicephalus sanguineus*		DL	
C. hemipterus	DDT,	DL		*R. evertsi*		DL	
				R. appendiculatus		DL	
				Dermacentor variabilis	DDT,	DL	

Table 13. Resistance of the 3 types developed in flies.

Musca domestica	DDT,	Dl,	OP	*Culicoides furens*			DL
Chrysomyia putoria	DDT,	DL,	OP	*Hippelates collusor*			DL
Glyptotendipes paripes		DL,	OP	*Fannia canicularis*	DDT		
Chironomus zealandicus		DL		*Phormia terrgaenovae*	DDT		
Haematobia irritans		DL,	OP	*Simulium aokii*	DDT		
Phaenicia cuprina		DL,	OP	*S. venustum*	DDT		
P. sericata		DL		*Drosophila melanogaster*	DDT		
Stomoxys calcitrans	DDT,	DL		*D. virilis*	DDT		
Psychoda alternata	DDT,	DL		*Leptoconops kerteszii*	DDT		
Leptocera hirtula	DDT,	DL		*Chaoborus astictopus*	DDT		

Table 14. Resistance in aedes mosquitoes.

DDT		*Dieldrin*	*Org. Phos.*
aegypti	cantator	aegypti	taeniorhynchus
sollicitans	detritus	sollicitans	nigromaculis
taeniorhynchus	cantans	taeniorhynchus	melanimon
nigromaculis	albopictus	nigromaculis	dorsalis
melanimon	vittatus	melanimon	
atropalpus	vexans	cantator	

to OP compounds (Table 14). DDT-resistance has been a problem in the eradication of *A. aegypti* in the Caribbean area. The 2 salt-marsh mosquitoes of Florida were developing DDT-resistance by 1946, and now OP-resistance is becoming significant in *A. taeniorhynchus*. The 2 irrigation-water mosquitoes of California were strongly organochlorine-resistant by 1951, and *A. nigromaculis* has gone on to develop resistance in succession to parathion, methyl parathion and fenthion. Among the 9 species of *Culex* and 2 of *Psorophora* that have developed

resistance (Table 15), *C. quinquefasciatus* is especially important since it transmits filariasis; but although it rapidly develops resistance to DDT or to BHC-dieldrin, it is slow to develop OP-resistance and this readily reverts.

During the global campaign to eradicate the transmission of malaria, no less than 35 species of anopheline mosquitoes have developed resistance, 34 of them to dieldrin and 12 to DDT (Table 16). The situation is worst where the same population has developed both resistances, as with *A. sacharovi* in Greece, *A.*

Table 15. Resistance in culex and psorophora mosquitoes.

DDT	Dieldrin	Org. Phos
quinquefasciatus	quinquefasciatus	quinquefasciatus
pipiens	pipiens	tarsalis
tarsalis	tarsalis	
coronator	tritaeniorhynchus	
tritaeniorhynchus	restuans	
peus	Ps. confinnis	
salinarius	Ps. discolor	
erythrothorax		

Table 16. Resistant anophelines, in order of first appearance.

DDT	Dieldrin	
sacharovi	sacharovi	m. flavirostris
sundaicus	quadrimaculatus	pharoensis
stephensi	gambiae	albitarsis
subpictus	subpictus	labranchiae
albimanus	coustani	strodei
pharoensis	pulcherrimus	triannulatus
quadrimaculatus	albimanus	sundaicus
annularis	pseudopunctipennis	aconitus
culicifacies	aquasalis	neomaculipalpus
albitarsis	culicifacies	crucians
nunez-tovari	vagus	filipinae
aconitus	barbirostris	maculipennis
	annularis	l.atroparvus
	sergenti	m. messeae
	fluviatilis	rangeli
	splendidus	philippinensis
	stephensi	funestus

pharoensis in Egypt, *A. stephensi* around the Persian Gulf, *A. sundaicus* in Java and *A. albimanus* in Central America; this last species has now shown increased tolerance to malathion. Two species in Mexico have shown behavioristic resistance deriving from an increase in irritability to DDT. That such changes in response can be brought about by selection and may be based on a decrease in detoxication has been proved in the laboratory.

The mechanism of physiological resistance— what makes a fly now resist DDT—has been found to be mainly the detoxication of DDT to DDE. Although oxidation to dicofol is possible, the principal process is dehydrochlorination. The DDT-dehydrochlorinase enzyme requires glutathione for its activity, and has been found in DDT-resistant strains of house flies and mosquitoes, and in normally-tolerant species like the Mexican bean beetle and southern tobacco hornworm. DDT-resistant strains of the pink bollworm also detoxify it to DDE, while some resistant strains of the cotton bollworm have increased detoxication, others decreased absorption. Attempts to counteract DDT-resistance by adding DMC or WARF-antiresistant as DDT synergists to inhibit the detoxifying enzyme, or by substitution Dilan ® which lacks the aliphatic chlorine to be dehydrochlorinated, were ultimately rendered unsuccessful by the house flies developing resistance to them too. And so DDT-resistance has been met simply by substituting a cyclodiene insecticide, or more recently some OP compound.

The mechanism of cyclodiene-resistance remains unknown, detoxication being negligible or lacking. Some resistant strains and individuals have more body fat than normal, but this is not consistent and cannot account for the characteristic intensity of cyclodiene-resistance. House flies resistant to gamma-BHC absorb less and detoxify more of this compound, to PCCH and thiophenols, but this strong resistance seems to lie in the ganglion itself. Some dieldrin-resistant populations have been successfully combatted by switching back to DDT, as in *Anopheles sundaicus* on the south coast of Java; but usually the next step is to OP compounds with the consequent avoidance of the persistent cyclodiene residues.

The mechanism of OP-resistance is mainly detoxication, by esterase enzymes hydrolysing the insecticide (e.g. parathion) and the real toxicant produced by oxidation in the insect (e.g. paraoxon). Most OP-resistant strains of house flies have a lower aliesterase activity to match the increase in the phosphatase-like detoxication enzyme. Malathion-resistant strains of insects and mites are however characterized by increased carboxyesterase, to attack the unique weak-point of this OP molecule. A mechanism derived from a less-sensitive cholinesterase target enzyme has been found in cattle ticks and one strain of the two-spotted mite, but in other strains and in all insects studied the mechanism is detoxication. Only malathion seems to be set apart from the other OP compounds in the cross-resistance picture. Although inhibitors for the enzymic detoxication are known, notably EPN for carboxyesterase, they have not seen use as OP synergists. Instead an empirical search is continued for OP compounds to which minimal cross-resistance is shown and minimal resistance is developed, such as dimethoate in house flies, and bidrin and certain phosphoroamidothioates in red mites.

Carbamate-resistance also derives from esterase detoxication, and varying cross-resistance is shown between OP compounds and carbamates. Oxidative enzymes in the microsome cellular fraction are also involved in the detoxication of carbamates and also OP compounds.

Genetical studies of the different resistance types have shown that most of them are mainly caused by a single gene (Table 17); this was found for DDT-resistance in 13 species, for dieldrin-resistance in 19 species and for OP-resistance in 6 species. Multiple-factor inheritance was found only in arsenic-resistance and low-order tolerances to carbamates, malathion and DDT in 4 species. The OP-resistance gene has always proved to be dominant, and so has that for carbamate-resistance. DDT has usually been found to be recessive, except in the house fly. Dieldrin-resistance is nearly always intermediate, the dosage-mortality lines of the heterozygotes lying midway between those of either parental strain and sharply distinct from both.

Many resistance genes have now been precisely located on certain chromosomes by linkage studies with marker strains. In *Droso-*

Table 17. Instances of monofactorial inheritance of insecticide-resistances.

	Dld-Res.		*DDT-Res.*		*OP-Res.*		*Carbamate-R.*		*HCN-Res.*
I	*Musca*	D	*Musca*[3]	D	*Musca*	D	*Musca*	I	*Aonidiella*
I	*Anopheles*, 7 spp.[1]	R	*Anopheles*, 5 spp.	D	*Chrysomya*	D	*Drosophila*		
I	*C. fatigans*	D	*C. fatigans*	D	*C. tarsalis*				
I	*A. aegypti*	I	*A. aegypti*	D	*Tetranychus*, 2 spp.				
I	*Phaenicia*	I	*Euxesta*	D	*Boophilus*				
I	*Chrysomyia*	D	*Drosophila*						
I	*Hylemya*, 2 spp.	R	*Blattella*						
I	*Euxesta*	R	*Boophilus*						
I	*Blattella*	I	*Pediculus*						
I	*Cimex*					R	recessive		
I	*Pediculus*					I	intermediate		
D	*Boophilus*[2]					D	dominant		

[1] D in Ivory-coast *A. Gambiae.*
[2] Some overdominance.
[3] Secondary *kdr* gene is R.

phila melanogaster, the principal resistance gene is located near the middle of chromosome 2, with a second gene in the middle of chromosome 3. In the house fly, the dominant gene that causes strong DDT-resistance, called *Deh* because it determined the dehydrochlorinase enzyme, is located on chromosome 5, while a second gene *kdr* causing knockdown-resistance and determining nerve sensitivity to DDT is on chromosome 2. The main OP-resistance gene, called *a* from its association with reduced aliesterase activity, is located on chromosome 5, as also the gene for carbamate-resistance. The genes for resistance to dieldrin in BHC have been found in different linkage groups in different strains. In culicine mosquitoes, the genes for DDT-resistance and for dieldrin-resistance in *Aedes aegypti* lie very close together on chromosome 2, whereas in *Culex quinquefasciatus* the dieldrin-resistance gene is on chromosome 3. In the malaria mosquito *Anopheles quadrimaculatus* the dieldrin-resistance gene is on its chromosome 3, and in *A. pharoensis* the DDT-resistance is linked with dieldrin-resistance on the same chromosome.

These genetical studies shed light on the observation that *Aedes aegypti* and *A. taeniorhynchus* develop both organochlorine resistances when treated either with DDT or with dieldrin, whereas *C. quinquefasciatus* develops them separately; and on the common experience that OP selection induces or maintains DDT-resistance in the house fly. They suggest that the reason the European corn borer in North America has not developed DDT-resistance is a lack of the gene for it. The stable fly has also failed to develop DDT-resistance in North America, although it has done so in Europe. Dieldrin-resistance in *Anopheles gambiae,* due to a single powerful gene, has developed in West Africa but not in continental East Africa. One species or subspecies may readily develop a resistance, while another close relative may not; examples with respect to dieldrin-resistance are *Musca domestica* versus *nebulo* in India, *Hylemya liturata* versus *platura* in North America, and the cocoa capsid versus the brown capsid in Ghana; as a result the first to develop resistance became the dominant species.

DDT-resistance usually develops after an initial latent period of several generations before it steeply increases. Evidently the genome as a whole must be remodelled so that insects with the DDT-resistance gene are no longer handicapped. They must have been at first, for otherwise they would have been DDT-resistant from the first. Cyclodiene-resistance on the other hand develops without delay, not needing new supporting alleles. Indeed, dieldrin-resistant strains of the cabbage maggot in eastern Canada live twice as long and produce twice as many eggs, due to an associated multifactorial system. OP-resistance in insects develops very slowly, even the house fly requiring more than 100 generations of laboratory selection. It usually first develops as a weak polyfactorial system before the strong monofactorial resistance eventually declares itself. Even then it is liable to revert, since the OP-resistant individuals are usually handicapped by low fertility. Carbamate-resistance also develops very slowly. This slowness cuts both ways, for when the apple maggot fails to drift to parathion, the body louse to carbaryl, and the boll weevil to methylparathion, we cannot know whether they won't get there eventually. By contrast, DDT-resistance may reach an upper plateau of intensity, as it has in some anopheline mosquitoes, where an increase in dosage or frequency of applications is sufficient to regain practical effectiveness.

Resistance may arise simultaneously at many points which then coalesce, as in house flies, mosquitoes and body lice; but in some plant-feeding insects it appears in certain fields or orchards and then spreads from them. Aldrin-resistance in the western corn rootworm diffused from a single spot in Nebraska into 7 states in 5 years. Resistance develops and spreads faster not only the higher the selection pressure but also the wider the area covered by the insecticide, since fewer susceptible individuals are left to dilute the resistant survivors of the applications. Residual insecticides are more liable to induce resistance, because they continue to select long after they have been applied. Resistance also develops faster in subtropical climates than temperate, because there are more generations per year. The boll weevil in the southern USA, the cotton leafworm in the Nile Delta, and mosquitoes in interior California and coastal Florida are perfect examples of such consequences.

The substitution of measures which achieve 100% control over circumscribed areas and leave no penumbra of partial kill may be expected to avoid or delay resistance; such would be the use of pyrethrins or nicotine instead of organochlorine insecticides, or root maggot control by side dressings instead of broadcast treatments, or mosquito control at isolated bases in Canada surrounded by large untouched populations. Mixtures of 2 different insecticides have been advocated, but laboratory model experiments on the house fly, bed bug and the German cockroach have found that resistance to both is developed as fast as to one or the other used separately. Alternations or rotations of sulfur-containing, chlorinated and OP acaricides have delayed resistance to any one of them by the European red mite in eastern orchards. Selection of the boll weevil with toxaphene mixed with DDT has not led to resistance to the mixture, but has induced a high tolerance to OP compounds and carbamates. Pairs of negatively-correlated insecticides, where resistance to the one is accompanied by an increase in susceptibility to the other, have been discovered in *Drosophila* between DDT and phenylthiourea, the DDT-resistance gene allele giving the increased PTU-susceptibility. Examples of negative correlation have turned up in the house fly, body louse and boll weevil, but they have not held good for all populations, being fortuitous rather than tied to the same gene allele.

As insecticide-resistance comes of age, we find that there are now certain species that have run the whole gamut of resistance to DDT, cyclodienes, OP compounds and sometimes carbamates; examples are the house fly, the cattle tick and the sheep blow fly in Australia, the cotton leafworm in Egypt, and the two-spotted mite. Although there are few populations even of these species that cannot be controlled by some compound or other, there is a real need for insecticides of entirely new chemical configuration and toxic action. Such are the new acaricides Morestan (a dithiol quinoxaline) and Phenoflurazole (a fluorinated benzimidazole), and the substituted ureas and salicylanilides appearing as candidate insecticides. They may not be resistance-proof, for even *Bacillus thuringiensis* toxin has induced resistance in house flies (Table 18). The new chemosterilants in laboratory selection experiments have had successively diminishing sterilizing effect, although the situation often reverses due to the inheritance of deleterious mutations. We would therefore not assume that any chemical would never induce resistance, even if it were an insect hormone.

At present our real need is a means of knowing where each pest population stands with respect to resistance, since the practical danger is not the lack of some insecticide to do the job, but of incurring a control failure due to unsuspected resistance to the compound being used. Standard test methods for resistance, judiciously applied, will tell us the answer by asking the insects themselves, as they have done over the past decade for malaria mosquitoes and other insects of concern to WHO. It is a pleasure to report that the first test methods for insects of agricultural importance were drawn up by an E.S.A. special conference last month; consisting of a standard method for the boll weevil and a tentative method for red mites, they constitute a start which will be pursued by FAO itself as well as E.S.A. These 21 years have taught us that there is no single

Table 18. Laboratory induction of resistance to "non-insecticides."

Chemosterilant		
Apholate	*Aedes aegypti*	Hazard et al. 1964
Metepa	*Aedes aegypti*	Klassen and Matsumura 1966
Metepa	*Musca domestica*	Sacca and Scirocchi 1966
Hempa	*Aedes aegypti*	George and Brown 1967
Bacterial toxin		
Thuricide	*Musca domestica*	Harvey and Howell 1965

doctrinaire answer to the resistance problem; we can only deal with it in detail, by having a good intelligence system, and by understanding the biochemical and genetical principles underlying it. Insecticide-resistance has been a challenge that has involved us in every facet of modern biology, and thereby has enriched our professional life immeasurably. With the chemical synthetic activities of industry, the strategic

recommendations of government, and the basic investigations of universities, we shall continue to meet that challenge.

Note

Full citations for the instances of resistance described above may be found in: Brown, A. W. A. (1968) *In* Pesticides, ed. R. H. White-Stevens, Vol II, Chapt. 12. Marcel Dekker, New York.

57

ANTIBIOTICS ON THE FARM— MAJOR THREAT TO HUMAN HEALTH

Bernard Dixon

So nothing is yet to be done to curb the reckless and dangerous exploitation of antibiotics in farming. There is now a mass of evidence showing that the misuse of antibiotics as growth-promoting food supplements and as mass prophylactic agents has caused a serious increase in bacterial drug resistance in recent years. The threat to human and animal health has been made abundantly clear, and warnings from experts in the field have mounted over the past year.

A committee, under the chairmanship of Lord Netherthorpe, has been considering the matter. First convened by the Medical Research Council and the Agricultural Research Council in 1960, the committee has, since 1965, been considering the particularly disquieting rise in *infective* resistance (by which drug resistant bacteria render previously sensitive organisms resistant). Last year the committee presented a report to the MRC and the ARC and made recommendations. Earlier this year the report went to the Ministry of Health and the Ministry

Reprinted from the *New Scientist* 36: 33-35, 1967, with the permission of the publishers.

of Agriculture, Fisheries and Food. Action seemed to be imminent.

Mr. Robinson and Mr. Peart have now announced that "an appropriate body with sufficiently wide terms of reference should consider the evidence about the use of antibiotics in both animal husbandry and veterinary medicine and its implications in the field of public health and make recommendations", and that they have "accepted in principle" that "the Veterinary Investigation Service, in conjunction with the Public Health Laboratory Service, should be asked to seek further information regarding enteric infections in calves and on the therapeutic and prophylactic use of antibiotics to control such infections."

The Netherthorpe committee consists of scientific "elder statesmen", rather than active research workers, but over the past few years microbiologists have published a stream of facts and figures illustrating the growing seriousness of the situation. Those experts I have spoken to in the past fortnight are now staggered that further inquiry should be thought necessary. Once again we see the success of the irritating British habit of seeking expert guidance on a technical matter and then pigeon-holing the advice when it comes.

The recent statement by the two Ministries excited almost no press comment—not surprisingly, as it was an entirely negative document. The story is in the weight of evidence that has apparently been ignored.

What are the facts? More than two years ago, Dr. E. S. Anderson and Dr. M. J. Lewis, working at the Enteric Reference Laboratory, Colindale, drew attention to the prevalence in calves of a particular drug-resistant strain of the food-poisoning organism, *Salmonella typhimurium.* They showed that human infection with this particular strain (phage type 29) was also common, and that most of the organisms isolated from human infections were also drug resistant. An even more disturbing discovery was that healthy calves from an infected herd carried strains of the normal gut inhabitant, *Escherichia coli*, which was resistant to the same drugs as the salmonella. Moreover they had infective resistance. In other words, here was a dangerous reservoir of resistant organisms, not themselves harmful or even noticeable to anyone but a bacteriologist, but which could affect animal and human pathogens and render then invulnerable to antibiotics.

But how did the resistance originate? Investigations revealed that in an area in which ampicillin resistance appeared in type 29 *S. typhimurium*, the drug was being used to treat salmonellosis in calves. It seemed likely that this was the determining factor in the emergence of resistant strains. Dr. Anderson and Dr. Lewis later actually monitored the rapid rise in incidence of ampicillin resistant organisms in a herd of calves given the drug, and they suggested that the emergence of resistant organisms was bound up with the unhygienic conditions on intensive rearing units, and with the marketing and distribution of very young calves. They warned about the possible spread of infective resistance from organisms communicated between animals and man to those specifically pathogenic for man, and called for "a re-examination of the whole question of the use of antibiotics and other drugs in the rearing of livestock."

These warnings were amply substantiated even in 1965, and their wisdom has been vindicated since by other research workers in Britain and abroad. The staggering rise in infectively-resistant strains of *S. typhimurium* in recent years—and a similar increase in salmonellosis in calves—has been paralleled by the growth of intensive farming. Of 450 cultures of *S. typhimurium* examined at Colindale between December 1964 and February 1965, 61 per cent were resistant to one or more drugs, compared with 21 per cent for the corresponding period of 1963-64. Most of the resistance was of the infective type, and almost all cultures of the predominant strain—type 29—had infective drug resistance, usually multiple. For the whole of 1965, 73 per cent of the 1756 bovine cultures of *S. typhimurium* examined, belonged to type 29 and 99.7 per cent of them were drug resistant. There were 26 different combinations of resistance to ampicillin, streptomycin, sulphonamides, chloramphenicol, tetracycline, neomycin, kanamycin and furazolidine, and one strain was resistant to every one of these drugs.

A Universal Panacea

The "barley beef" system of husbandry is particularly blameworthy. Surplus bull calves from dairy herds in the West Country are collected together and trundled cross country to the grain-producing areas of the north and east. The animals are weaned a few days after birth and fed on barley and protein supplement until they are sent to the abattoir at 12 months of age. Whereas salmonellosis was formerly a sporadic disease, occurring in scattered farms, it now spreads across country as calves are herded together during transport, being sold and re-sold. Antibiotics are used liberally in an attempt to minimize the losses. They are even used as a universal panacea, in an attempt to combat the "dysadaptation syndrome" (not an infection) that results when calves are so badly treated. Yet in some units as many as 10 to 15 per cent of calves affected die of the dysadaptation syndrome. And the number of calves dying of *Salmonella* infection has increased about 10 times during the last eight years.

Even in 1965, there were at least 590 human infections with type 29 *S. typhimurium*, including six deaths. The vast majority of the human cases were directly connected with bovine infection, and even when such a connection could not be demonstrated, it could usually be inferred from the fact that human cultures were resistant to furazolidine, a drug that is widely used in calves but not for enteritis in man. Though human enteritis is acquired relatively rarely from animals the potential danger from infectively resistant *E. Coli* is probably much greater. Such strains of *E. Coli* must be transmitted to man on a grand scale and their drug resistance may therefore find its way into human pathogens, either directly or by way of the non-pathogenic organisms normally found in the human intestine. The most important human pathogen here is *S. typhi,* the agent of typhoid fever, and the resistance most to be feared is that to chloramphenicol, which is still the only drug that is effective against this disease.

Indiscriminate use of antibiotics in human medicine was recognized many years ago—and led, for example, to the withdrawal from general sale of penicillin throat lozenges. It is to be condemned in veterinary medicine for the same reasons: blanket use of anti-microbial drugs provides an environment that both favours the appearance of resistant organisms, and allows the organisms to operate freely.

Diarrhoea in Babies

The evidence incriminating antibiotic feed supplements goes back even further. Ten years ago Dr. H. Williams Smith and Mr. W. E. Crabb, working at the Animal Health Trust at Stock in Essex, first found that many strains of *E. Coli* isolated from the faeces of pigs and fowls fed diets containing tetracycline, even in extremely low concentrations, were resistant to the drug. (They had great difficulty in finding "control farms" where tetracycline feeding had never been practised; many farmers simply did not know whether they used, or had used, such supplements.) Since then Dr. Smith and his colleagues have endorsed the importance of this observation and have found that the resistance of such organisms is often infectious. They have also shown that multiple infective resistance is prevalent in animal strains of *E. Coli,* and that people in contact with such animals may be infected with these potentially dangerous strains. Other strains of *E. Coli* that cause neonatal diarrhoea in babies, and similar conditions in calves, pigs and fowls, have infective resistance; the incidence of resistance in "pig strains" was twice as great in 1965 as in

1960-1962, and resistance against neomycin had appeared for the first time.

Dr. Smith, a veterinary surgeon, is alarmed about the consequences for veterinary medicine, let alone human medicine, of using a great quantity and variety of drugs for "nutritional" purposes. The longer a drug is used as a food additive, the less its clinical value. Drug-resistant pathogens are now causing a considerable proportion of the disease hitherto caused by sensitive ones. There is, in fact, little difference between the two misuses of drugs, as feed supplements or for prophylaxis. Both provide selective pressures that favour the removal of sensitive strains from an environment and their replacement by resistant strains. In the first case the pressure is low and of long duration; in the second case, it is a strong pressure acting for a shorter time.

Are the administrators unaware of these facts? Either that or they believe that a leisurely approach is needed to deal with the situation. The dangers have been clearly demonstrated, and there is already sufficient information to enable a competent committee to begin to revise our policy regarding the agricultural use of antibiotics. What should be done? Improving the hygienic conditions on intensive units, and making salmonellosis a notifiable disease would help. And Dr. Smith suggests that calves should stay with their mothers until at least six weeks, and be moved only after being vaccinated against salmonellosis.

But many of the experts in this field also believe that the time has come to impose a strict demarcation between human and veterinary medicine. Certain antibiotics should be reserved entirely for treating human infections, and others used solely in veterinary medicine. Other antibiotics, which are of little therapeutic value, could be used as food supplements to promote growth. Unfortunately, the one recent step that has been taken in this direction was a misguided one. After applications by the respective manufacturers, bacitracin was turned down as a food supplement, while another antibiotic, tylosin, was accepted as a supplement. Bacitracin is used to treat human infections, though only rarely. Tylosin is not used in human medicine, and to that extent its use in animals could be reasonable. But what was apparently forgotten is that tylosin is a member of the extremely useful macrolide group of antibiotics, which includes erythromycin and oleandomycin, and many organisms that are resistant to one of these drugs are resistant to others. Thus bacteria that acquire resistance to tylosin in the animal gut could later render a serious human infection untreatable.

Euphemisms and Officialese

One particularly ironic feature of this present situation is that much of the pioneer research on infective drug resistance has been carried out in this country. Two groups of bacteriologists in Tokyo were the first to observe the phenomenon about seven years ago. Shortly afterwards Dr. Naomi Datta reported its occurrence in Britain, and it was then that Dr. Anderson's group began their researches. He has both pioneered studies into the mechanism of infective drug resistance, particularly the genetic aspects, and has repeatedly drawn attention to the Public Health hazards. Only in the past year, however, have the dangers

dawned on authorities throughout the world. Yet in America, for example, there is very much more official concern. The Food and Drugs Administration held a special conference to discuss the subject in June, and action seems likely. There has been nothing comparable in this country. In fact, discussion of any sort of official action has been shrouded in mystery. A fortnight before the recent statement, I rang each of the two Ministries concerned, but was told no more than that a statement *might* be made *at some time.*

The official press release is couched in a regrettable mixture of euphemism and reassuring officialese: "In 1965 the attention of the Councils was drawn to . . . work that showed that a pattern of multiple resistance to antibiotics *appeared to be occurring* among members of the *Salmonella* and *E. Coli* groups, the former *being regarded as* of animal origin". (My italics.) The facts are that multiple infective resistance was unambiguously described in 1965, that it has increased at an alarming rate in recent years, that the evidence for its association with the misuse of antibiotics in husbandry is compelling, that research workers in this field have issued repeated warnings. And that no action is to be taken.

58

DIFFERENTIAL EFFECT OF NOISE ON TASKS OF VARYING COMPLEXITY

David H. Boggs and J. Richard Simon

The method of simultaneous tasks was used to test the hypothesis that the deleterious effect of noise on performance varies as a function of task complexity. 48 Ss performed on 1 of 2 complexity levels of a 4-choice RT task and, at the same time, performed a secondary auditory monitoring task. All Ss performed in both quiet and in noise. Performance indexes were RT and secondary-task errors. Noise produced a significantly greater increase in secondary-task errors when the secondary task was paired with the complex primary task than when it was paired with the simple primary task. Secondary-task performance provided a more sensitive measure of both task complexity and the effect of noise than did the RT measure.

Reprinted from the *Journal of Applied Psychology* 52: 148-53, 1968. Copyright 1968 by the American Psychological Association, and reproduced by permission.

The purpose of this experiment was to test the hypothesis that the deleterious effect of noise on performance increases as a function of increasing task complexity. There have been numerous studies conducted to investigate the effect of environmental noise on performance. Some have indicated a decremental effect of noise (e.g., Broadbent, 1953, 1954, 1958a; Jerison, 1959; Jerison & Wing, 1957; Sanders,

1961; Woodhead, 1964), while others have indicated an incremental effect (e.g., Kirk & Hecht, 1963; Wilbanks, Webb, & Tolhurst, 1956). A substantial number of studies, however, have revealed no significant effect whatsoever (e.g., Broadbent, 1957; Hyman, 1950; Jerison, 1957; Kryter, 1950; Kurz, 1964; Wilbanks, Webb & Tolhurst, 1956). If research which has remained unpublished as a consequence of achieving negative results were to be made available (e.g., Chisman, 1963), the weight of evidence indicating that noise does not significantly affect performance would be considerably increased.

One explanation for the prevalence of negative results in laboratory studies involving noise might be that *S* were able to draw upon unused perceptual capacity and thereby maintain their performance despite the distracting noise. In order to detect changes in unused capacity associated with performance in noise, the present study utilized a procedure called the "method of simultaneous tasks." The procedure involved having *S* perform, simultaneously with the primary experimental task, a secondary task which effectively occupied that portion of *S*'s perceptual capacity which was not occupied by the requirements of the primary task. Thus, performance on the secondary task provided a measure of unused capacity, and any effect of noise sufficient to require the use of this excess capacity to maintain primary-task performance was evidenced as a decrement in secondary-task performance. According to Poulton (1965), this method was first employed by Bornemann (1942a, 1942b) although it was apparently also developed independently by Bahrick, Noble, and Fitts (1954).

Of special relevance to the present research are two studies which utilized the method of simultaneous tasks. Poulton (1958) used secondary-task performance as a measure of the amount of attention required by a perceptual-motor task and was able to demonstrate a difference in difficulty between two versions of the task which was not apparent by comparing performance on the two tasks when performed alone. Broadbent (1964) employed the method to investigate the relationship between at-tention required to a reaction-time (RT) task and degree of stimulus-response (S-R) compatibility. Using a secondary, mental-arithmetic task he compared the performance of *S*s working on compatible and incompatible versions of an RT task. The incompatible task caused more interference with the secondary task than did the compatible task demonstrating that a perceptual-motor task may be made more difficult by making the S-R code less compatible, and that this difference in difficulty may be measured indirectly by observing performance on a simultaneous, secondary task.

There are probably many reasons for the apparent conflicting results concerning the effects of noise on performance. One important factor seems to be that some tasks are more vulnerable to noise than others. According to Broadbent (1958b), noise produces brief failures of perception which, in turn, result in the marked decrements observed on vigilance tasks and tasks which require continuous handling of information. Jerison (1957) suggests that the primary factor determining the effect of noise on performance may be the "flexibility of attention" required by the task. Noise seems to have a decremental effect on vigilance tasks which involve several sources of information whereas tasks which require attention to only one information source are not affected.

Task difficulty may also be important in determining whether noise has a decremental effect on performance. Broadbent (1954) found a noise-induced decrement on a "difficult" watch-keeping task (Twenty Dials Test) but not on an "easy" task (Twenty Lights Test). Park and Payne (1963), however, found no evidence of an interaction between noise conditions and the level of difficulty of division problems.

The present experiment was concerned with the variable of difficulty or, more properly, task complexity. In this study, *S*s performed two tasks simultaneously. The overall complexity or perceptual load imposed by these simultaneous tasks was manipulated by altering the S-R compatibility of the primary task, a four-choice RT task. Performance on a secondary, auditory-monitoring task was used to measure Ss' available excess perceptual capacity. It was hypothesized that the introduction of noise would increase the total perceptual load, reduce Ss' reserve capacity, and thereby result in a performance decrement on the secondary task. It was further hypothesized that this noise-induced performance decrement on the secondary task would be more marked under the condition of high task complexity.

Method

All Ss performed two tasks simultaneously under quiet conditions and also while exposed to an intermittent, annoying noise. The primary task was of the perceptual-motor type and was presented in either of two levels of complexity. The secondary auditory-monitoring task was held constant under these two complexity levels and was used to detect changes in overall perceptual load.

Primary Task

The primary task was a four-choice reaction-time (RT) task in which Ss, after being alerted by a green warning light, responded as rapidly as possible to the onset of one of four red stimulus lights by pressing the appropriate one of four switches which were located directly below each of the lights. In the simple condition, the correct switch corresponded to the light directly above it. In the complex condition, there was no spatial correspondence between light and switch. In this latter condition, Ss were instructed to respond: (1) to the left light by pressing the second switch from the left; (2) to the second light by pressing the switch at the extreme left; (3) to the second light from the right by pressing the extreme right switch; and (4) to the right light by pressing the second switch from the right. The four stimulus lights were arranged 3½ in. apart in a horizontal row, located at a distance of approximately 24 in. from S's eyes, slightly below shoulder level.

Presentation of warning and stimulus lights

in the RT task was controlled automatically by three Hunter interval timers. The first timer activated the warning light for a duration of 0.5 sec. The second timer provided a 1.0-sec. interval between warning light and stimulus light and also activated the stimulus light. The third timer provided a 5.0-sec. delay following the onset of the stimulus light, and then automatically initiated a recycling of the three timers. A Hunter Klockounter began at the onset of the stimulus light and stopped when S pressed one of the switches, thus providing a measure of RT. Pressing the switch also extinguished the stimulus light. The order of presentation of stimulus lights was controlled manually by E according to a predetermined sequence. The lights were presented in this same sequence on every block of trials, each of the four stimulus lights appearing 23 times. Signal lights on E's side of the apparatus permitted detection of errors in S's choice of switch. Since pressing any of the four switches caused the stimulus light to be extinguished, S received no information concerning the correctness of his responses.

The S pressed the switches with the index finger of his preferred hand. To control hand-travel time, S began each trial from a rest position which was marked on the table 7 in. in front of the RT apparatus, on an imaginary line bisecting, and perpendicular to, a line passing through the four switch knobs.

Secondary Task

The secondary task was similar to one used by Brown (1965). A continuous sequence of digits was presented to S through a headphone placed over his left ear. He was instructed to listen for odd-even-odd sequences of digits, and to respond immediately by saying "yes" whenever such a sequence was detected. The digits were recorded on one channel of a stereophonic magnetic tape at regular intervals of 1.5 sec. One odd-even-odd sequence was located randomly within every 15-sec. period of the 10-min. tape, so that the tape contained a total of 40 odd-even-odd sequences. The second channel contained signals, audible only to E, indicating the location of each odd-even-odd sequence. The tape was played on a Sony Model 464 stereophonic recorder. The *S* listened to the digits channel through a Grason-Stadler Model TDH-39 earphone (equipped with MX 41-AR rubber cushion) connected directly to the output of the appropriate internal playback amplifier of the recorder, while *E* listened to the marker signals through headphones connected through a Sony external power amplifier to the playback-preamplifier output of the second channel. The playback-preamplifier gain of the channel containing the signals was reduced to a minimum to prevent leakage into the digits channel. This arrangement permitted constant synchronization of the digits with the signals to *E*, and provided complete consistency throughout the experiment in the scoring of errors on the secondary task.

Noise

The noise consisted of recorded 0.5-sec. bursts of the sound produced by a bandsaw cutting aluminum. Acoustical frequency analysis revealed strong peaks at approximately 1800 and 1900 cps. A total of 90 bursts (ps db. SPL) were presented in the course of each 10-min. experimental run. These bursts were recorded on the tape containing the digits. The bursts were located randomly, but with the restriction that they never overlap any of the secondary-task digits. The masking effect of noise, therefore, was not a factor in this experiment. The digits on the "noise" tape were copied directly from the "quiet" tape, using a second recorder, so that the only difference between the two tapes was, in fact, the presence of noise on the "noise" tape.

Subjects

The *S* were 24 males and 24 females from the elementary psychology courses at the University of Iowa. All *S*s reported having normal hearing.

Experimental Design

A mixed design involving one within- and three between-*S* dimensions was employed

(Lindquist, 1953). Twelve men and 12 women performed on the simple RT task, and 12 men and 12 women performed on the complex RT task. Within each complexity condition, 12 *S*s (6 men and 6 women) performed first in quiet and then in noise, while the remaining 12 *S*s (6 men and 6 women) performed first in noise and then in quiet. Complexity level and sequence were assigned randomly to *S*s within each sex group.

Procedure

Each *S* served in one experimental session consisting of one run in quiet and one in noise. Each run was 10 min. in duration. The *S* listened first to a 1-min. tape demonstrating the correct method of responding to the digits task. He was then given two consecutive 1-min. practice sessions on the digits task alone. If he failed to respond without error during the first min. of practice, the tape was stopped and the instructions repeated. All *S*s succeeded in performing without error during the second min. of practice. Next, the RT-task instructions were read, followed by the appropriate instructions for the first experimental condition, that is, quiet or noise. In order to establish the relative primacy of the RT task, *S* was instructed repeatedly that he should do as well as he could on the digits task, but that he should not let the digits task interfere with the RT task. After completing the first run, the instructions for the second condition were read, and *S* was again cautioned not to let the digits task interfere with the RT task. The entire session lasted approximately 45 min.

Scoring

Records were kept of RT, errors on the RT task, and errors on the digits task. Omissive errors (failure to report the occurrence of an odd-even-odd sequence in the 1.5-sec. interval after the completion of the sequence) and commissive errors (inappropriate "yes" responses) on the digits task were recorded separately. The first 12 RT trials of both experimental runs were considered practice trials and were not included in the calculation of RT medians and error totals.

Table 1. Total errors on secondary task as a function of sequence, noise, task complexity, and sex.

Task	Sequence	Males Condition			Females Condition			Overall M
		Quiet	Noise	M	Quiet	Noise	M	
Simple	Quiet-Noise	7.67	11.83	9.75	10.33	13.67	12.00	10.88
	Noise-Quiet	8.67	11.17	9.92	7.33	10.33	8.83	9.38
	M	8.17	11.50	9.83	8.83	12.00	10.42	10.13
Complex	Quiet-Noise	14.17	21.00	17.58	11.67	18.33	15.00	16.29
	Noise-Quiet	8.83	17.83	13.33	10.33	17.00	13.67	13.50
	M	11.50	19.42	15.46	11.00	17.67	14.33	14.90
Combined mean for both complexity levels		9.83	15.46	12.65	9.92	14.83	12.38	

Results

Performance data from both primary and secondary tasks were analyzed to determine the effects of noise on performance.

Primary Task

An analysis of variance[1] indicated no significant effect of noise on RT (787 vs. 784 msec.). There was a tendency for males to respond faster than females (776 vs. 806 msec.), and for RT on the complex task to be slower than on the simple task (808 vs. 763 msec.). but neither of these effects was significant.[2] The only significant factor affecting RT was order; $F(1/40) = 11.76$, $p < .01$, with the first run being slower than the second (805 vs. 766 msec.). No errors were made on the primary task during the experimental runs.

[1] Summaries of analyses of variance and other summary tables have been deposited with the American Documentation Institute. Order Document No. 9747 from ADI Auxiliary Publications Project, Photoduplication Service, Library of Congress, Washington, D. C. 20540. Remit in advance $1.25 for microfilm or $1.25 for photocopies and make checks payable to: Chief, Photoduplication Service, Library of Congress.

[2] In a separate experiment, 20 Ss performed the RT task alone, that is, without the simultaneous secondary task. Half of the Ss performed the simple version of the task while the other half performed the complex version. Performance on the complex task was significantly slower than on the simple task (708 vs. 587 msec.; $t = 2.45$, $p < .05$).

Secondary Task

Table 1 shows the effects of sequence, noise, task complexity, and sex on the total number of secondary-task errors, that is, omissive plus commissive errors. It may be seen that mean error totals for all sex-sequence groups were higher in noise than in quiet, and that, in general, a greater number of errors was made under the complex task condition than under the simple condition. An analysis of variance revealed that the main effect of noise was significant; $F(1/40) = 562.52$, $p < .001$. The analysis also indicated a significant main effect of complexity; $F(1/40) = 8.31$, $p < .01$. Of major interest, however, was a significant Noise × Complexity interaction; $F(1/40) = 9.19$, $p < 0.01$. Table 2 summarizes this effect. It will be noted that the introduction of noise produced a greater increase in errors under the complex task condition than under the simple task condition. There was no sequence effect to complicate the interpretation.

Table 2. Effect of noise on secondary-task performance under simple and complex task conditions.

Task	Mean errors			Difference (noise minus quiet)
	Quiet	Noise	Overall M	
Simple	8.50	11.75	10.13	3.25
Complex	11.25	18.54	14.90	7.29

Separate analyses of variance were performed for omissive and for commissive errors on the secondary task. Results of the analysis of omissive errors were identical to those of the total errors; that is, the effects of both noise and task complexity were significant, and there was a significant Noise x Complexity interaction. In the analysis of commissive errors, noise was the only significant factor.

Discussion

Results of this study demonstrate that noise produces a significant decrement in performance and that the magnitude of this decrement varies as a function of task complexity. Results also suggest that noise effects may have gone undetected in much previous research for lack of a sensitive criterion measure.

Many tasks demand less than the total perceptual capacity which an individual has available. In these situations, the person possesses what may be termed a reserve capacity, which is free from the demands of the task. Should the perceptual demands of the task or of the situation increase, he may draw upon this reserve capacity and, by so doing, may be able to maintain task performance at a constant high level. In the present study, the fact that increased task complexity, and the introduction of noise, did not affect RT performance is attributed to this compensatory mechanism.

The method of simultaneous tasks provides a means of detecting changes in reserve capacity associated with changes in the task and/or environment. Secondary-task performance was used in this study as a measure of reserve perceptual capacity. In this experiment, the complex primary task made greater perceptual demands than the simple primary task. Therefore, less reserve capacity was available for the secondary task when it was paired with the simple task. This resulted in the greater number of errors on the secondary task when it was paired with the complex primary task. The introduction of noise "used up" some of S's reserve capacity, that is, S had to draw from his reserve so that primary-task performance would not suffer as a consequence of the noise. There was, therefore, less perceptual capacity available for secondary-task performance, and, consequently, errors increased. The fact that the noise produced a greater increase in secondary-task errors when the secondary task was paired with the complex primary task than when it was paired with the simple primary task may be attributed to the fact that the noise occupied proportionally more of the reserve capacity in the former case than in the latter.

References

Bahrick, H. P., Noble, M., & Fitts, P. M. Extra-task performance as a measure of learning a primary task. *Journal of Experimental Psychology*, 1954, 48, 298-302.

Bornemann, E. Untersuchungen über den Grad der geistigen Beanspruchung: Ausarbeitung der Methode. *Arbeitsphysiologie*, 1942, 12, 142-172. (a)

Bornemann, E. Untersuchungen über den Grad der geistigen Beanspruchung: praktische Ergebnisse. *Arbeitsphysiologie*, 1942, 12, 173-191. (b)

Broadbent, D. E. Noise, paced performance and vigilance tasks. *British Journal of Psychology*, 1953, 44, 295-303.

Broadbent, D. E. Some effect of noise on visual performance. *Quarterly Journal of Experimental Psychology*, 1954, 6, 1-5.

Broadbent, D. E. Effects of noise on behavior. In C. M. Harris (Ed.), *Handbook of noise control*. New York: McGraw-Hill, 1957. Ch. 10.

Broadbent, D. E. Effect of noise on an "intellectual" task. *Journal of the Acoustical Society of America*, 1958, 30, 824-827 (a).

Broadbent, D. E. *Perception and communication*. New York: Pergamon Press, 1958. (b)

Broadbent, D. E. S-R compatibility and the processing of information. *Acta Psychologica*, 1964, 23, 325-327.

Brown, I. D. A comparison of two subsidiary tasks used to measure fatigue in car drivers. *Ergonomics*, 1965, 8, 467-473.

Chisman, J. A. The effects of continuous noise on the performance time and forces exerted in performing a subminiature assembly task. Unpublished doctoral dissertation, University of Iowa, Iowa City, 1963.

Hyman, D. E. An investigation of the effect of various noise levels on performance on three mental tasks. Unpublished master's thesis, Purdue University, Lafayette, Indiana, 1950. Cited by E. J. McCormick, *Human factors engineering*. New York: McGraw-Hill, 1964. P. 475.

Jerison, H. J. Performance on a simple vigilance task in noise and quiet. *Journal of the Acoustical Society of America*, 1957, 29, 1163-1165.

Jerison, H. J. Effects of noise on human performance. *Journal of Applied Psychology*, 1959, 43, 96-101.

Jerison, H. J., and Wing, S. Effects of noise on a complex vigilance task. USAF WADC Tech. Rep. TR 57-14, AD 110700, 1957.

Kirk, R. E., and Hecht, E. Maintenance of vigilance by programmed noise. *Perceptual and Motor Skills,* 1963, 16, 553-560.

Kryter, K. D. The effects of noise on man. *Journal of Speech and Hearing Disorders Monograph Suppl. 1*, 1950, 1-95.

Kurz, R. B. Effects of three kinds of stressors on human learning and performance. *Psychological Reports*, 1964, 14, 161-162.

Lindquist, E. F. *Design and analysis of experiments in psychology and education.* Boston: Houghton Mifflin, 1953.

Park J. F., and Payne, M. C., Jr. Effects of noise level and difficulty of task in performing division. *Journal of Applied Psychology*, 1963, 47, 367-368.

Poulton, E. C. Measuring the order of difficulty of visual-motor tasks. *Ergonomics*, 1958, 1, 234-239.

Poulton, E. C. On increasing the sensitivity of measures of performance. *Ergonomics*, 1965, 8, 69-76.

Sanders, A. F. The influence of noise on two discrimination tasks. *Ergonomics*, 1961, 4, 253-258.

Wilbanks, W. A., Webb, W. B., and Tolhurst, G. C. A study of intellectual activity in a noise environment. United States Naval School of Aviation Medicine, Research Project NM 001 104 100, Report 1, October 31, 1956.

Woodhead, M. M. The effect of bursts of noise on an arithmetic task. *American Journal of Psychology*, 1964, 77, 627-633.

59

ASSESSING DAMAGE FROM SONIC BOOMS

Ron Brown

Sonic bangs and the damage they may cause have been subjects for speculation and argument for over a decade, but until now there has been little hard technical information on which to base predictions of these effects. Today the situation is changing rapidly. At a conference on sonically induced vibration, held at the University of Liverpool last week, engineers discussed new experimental methods of investigating sonic bang damage and some promising ways of relating such damage to that caused by more normal vibrations. Assessing the effect of regular supersonic flight over property is still recognized as a very complex problem, but the general feeling at the conference seemed to be that reasonably accurate judgment will be possible in the near future.

This is just as well, at the dawn of the supersonic transport era. The routes over which

Reprinted from the *New Scientist* 41: 116-17, 1969, with the permission of the publishers.

the Concorde will be able to fly at supersonic speeds could depend to a large extent on a firm knowledge of the effects of sonic bangs on property, from cathedrals to greenhouses. It will also be important to have methods of distinguishing geniune claims of sonic damage from spurious ones. Just how difficult this problem might become was made clear by last year's notorious experiments in which planes were flown supersonically over a number of British cities. In this country one complaint for every 200,000 or so people affected by each sonic bang was received, yet in a similar experiment in the United States the figure was only one per million people. Obviously the British figures are greatly exaggerated. They must include a number of incidents of damage caused by other events occurring at the same time as the sonic boom, and of damage caused before the boom and noticed only after the boom had caused people to inspect their property.

How, then, can we learn to predict the effects of sonic boom? According to Mr. D. R. B. Webb of the Royal Aircraft Establishment, Farnborough, there are two possible approaches. The first is to analyse the response of a room or building to a sound wave with the same characteristics as a sonic boom. Unfortunately, it is extremely difficult to analyse the response of buildings even to much simpler waves. Moreover, sonic boom can cause damage even in circumstances when conventional theory and measurement suggest that things such as the stress velocities produced are too low to have this effect. For one thing, the "modal density" of even a small room is extremely high when it is subjected to a sonic boom. This means that the room will vibrate in a number of different ways at the same time, which makes analysis a complex, if not impossible, procedure. Mr. Webb said that tests had shown that a 16 ft by 14 ft room, for example, will vibrate in 24 different modes in the frequency range below 100 Hz.

Despite this finding, several investigators are attacking the problem from this angle and it was clear from some of the papers given at the conference that the work is throwing fresh light on the problem of how buildings respond to complex waveforms. But this approach is unlikely to be of practical value in assessing the effects of sonic booms for some considerable time to come.

For the moment, says Mr. Webb, the better approach is to use the language of statistics—apparently a somewhat heretical suggestion in this field. At the RAE they have set out to quote the response of a building to a sonic bang in terms of its response to existing environmental forces such as wind and traffic. Statistics can then be used to relate the damage that will be caused, and the extra maintenance costs that will be incurred directly to existing damage and the maintenance costs resulting from normal everyday events. The investigators chose a group of cathedrals for examination, because details of the environmental effects and the maintenance work had been kept for long periods and were relatively well documented. Apart from natural effects such as wind, thunder and earthquakes (important even in the UK), these buildings are also subjected to the effects of wanted and unwanted Man-made noise from such things as tolling of the bells, the striking of the clock, and the thundering of the organ—as well as the traffic noise which so often gets the blame.

Luckily, the very complexity of the way in which buildings respond to sound waves is a great help in relating the effects of sonic bangs

to the effects of these more everyday assaults. It seems that a building which oscillates in many modes when vibrated suffers damage that is directly related to the root mean square value of the acceleration it experiences. What is more, the damage caused by vibrations from one of the well documented effects such as wind or traffic vibrations will be the same as that produced by another type of vibration such as a sonic boom—if they have the same root mean square acceleration.

This is the crux of the method. Whether it proves valid in the long run is not altogether clear, but the first results are encouraging, and have already helped the RAE team to make a useful start on the sonic boom problem. What the team has set out to do is to see if there is any difference between the maintenance costs of cathedrals in noisy situations and those in quiet situations—those subject to different root mean square accelerations. If there is, then the investigators will work out, from the increased root mean square accelerations due to sonic bangs and the frequency with which such bangs occur, the extra damage and the extra maintenance costs for which they will account. The results should be reliable in the case of cathedrals because of their large mass, which makes them respond in a fairly consistent manner.

There are two separate problems to be investigated: the effects of single large sonic bangs and the fatigue effects of bangs that occur regularly. Here Mr. Webb was very encouraging. He said that investigations of damage caused by a sonic bang often revealed that the building was already in a dreadful condition and the damage was about to occur anyway. Also, though fears expressed have been about the possibility of priceless church windows being blown out, tests at RAE seem to have shown that they are particularly well suited to withstand sonic bangs. The fact that a hard material (glass) is used in a soft support (lead) means that such windows are well capable of withstanding severe shocks. Normally, church windows are replaced about every 200 years because they "creep" very slowly. Repeated sonic bangs might increase the rate of creep, but there does not seem to have been any increase in the creep rate of test windows at RAE which have been subjected to 150 bangs.

Producing sonic bangs to order for this sort of test is very expensive if a supersonic jet has to be sent up each time. The resulting bang is of course, also heard over a far wider area than the test site, with consequent annoyance and damage. Investigators can use scale models in laboratory size sonic bang simulators, but this is also far from satisfactory. A much more useful and more economic approach is to use explosive charges to simulate the sonic bang. Work that has resulted in the development of suitable charges for this technique was described at the meeting by Mr. M. J. Harper, of the Explosives Research and Development Establishment, at Waltham Abbey, Essex.

The chief problem here is how to produce a sound wave that lasts as long as the normal sonic bang. As Mr. Harper pointed out, all properties of the sound wave are a function of the total energy released. A one kilogramme charge will produce a wave with a "positive duration" of five milliseconds. However, a sonic bang has a positive duration 10 times as long as this, and since the length of the sound wave from an explosion is proportional to the cube root of the energy, a charge of 1000 kilogrammes would be necessary. This is clearly out

of the question and what Mr. Harper did at first was to use a series of small spaced charges laid in a line pointing towards the building or structure to be tested. The charges were exploded at the same time. In each case the sound from the near end charge reached the building first, and that from the other charges arrived slightly later, so that a long sound wave impinged on the building.

Strips of guncotton of different lengths placed side by side give a much closer approximation to the true shape of the sonic wave. The cost of this method is very low compared with that of flying a supersonic aircraft. A sonic bang with a positive duration of 100 milliseconds can be simulated with a charge costing only £4. The resulting waveform is not a true replica of the sonic bang waveform; but it seems to be close enough to make possible accurate assessments of the effects of a sonic bang on buildings up to the size of a house, provided the test is limited to frequencies up to 100 Hz. Coupled with Mr. Webb's "language of statistics" approach, these cheap sonic bang simulators should help solve many of the outstanding questions about the effects we may expect to suffer in the future from Concorde and other supersonic commercial jet aircraft.

60

DIGGING OUT FROM UNDER

Edward Gross

Like the Four Horsemen of the Apocalypse, three modern horsemen ravage the land today. Two of the riders are well known. They are pollutants of air and water. The third, solid waste, largely pollutes the land.

Federal statutes were enacted 13 years ago to fight air pollution and 21 years ago to fight water pollution. But it wasn't until 1965 that Congress passed the Solid Waste Disposal Act, giving the Department of Health, Education and Welfare and the Department of the Interior $4.3 million for a national research and development program to solve the problem.

But not much has happened yet.

"We're very early in the development of technology that would improve the state of the art," says Director Richard D. Vaughan of HEW'S Bureau of Solid Waste Management. "The real black eye is how well we're doing— the state of practice. We're doing a poor job in this country."

Although still not as popular an issue as air

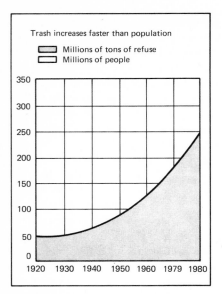

Trash increases faster than population

▢ Millions of tons of refuse
▢ Millions of people

Fig. 60-1. The trash explosion exceeds the population explosion in the United States. (Courtesy of American Chemical Society.)

and water pollution, which they also produce, solid wastes have generated a mountain of statistics almost as voluminous as the problem itself (see Fig. 60-1).

Any expert in the field can rattle off the facts:

1. The total amount of all types of solid waste generated in the United States yearly is 3.5 billion tons.
2. The amount of refuse collected per person per day is about 5 pounds, or a total of 190 million tons a year.
3. By 1975 the amount collected annually will be 225 million tons, and by 1980 it will reach 340 million tons.
4. Each year about 55 billion cans, 23 billion bottles, 60 billion metal and plastic bottle caps and 7 million junked autos are discarded.
5. The country's total annual trash bill: $4.5 billion.

The most apparent aspect of the problem is the refuse and garbage generated by households, businesses, industry and municipalities.

But these wastes, created by an affluent society that casually discards whatever it no longer needs, have produced a domino effect.

Communities are running out of places to dump their refuse, and are destroying irreplaceable resources in the frantic effort to stay ahead of the flood. A prime example is San Fransisco Bay, a dumping site for years, which is now filling up to the point where conservationists fear it may one day disappear (SN: 8/2, p. 102).

San Francisco, forced to recognize the problem by pressure to save the bay, was considering a plan to haul refuse by train to a desert area. But that plan collapsed in August when contract negotiations failed. Other cities, Philadelphia for one, are considering railhaul as an answer to the trash problem, but costs and local residents' objections stand in the way.

Since European and Asiatic countries must be frugal with their resources, it is not surprising to find these countries ahead of the United States in the art of waste utilization. Some European countries, for example, use the heat from incinerator plants to produce steam for electricity. The outstanding example is the Issy-les Moulineaux project near Paris, where the electricity produced is fed into a national grid.

Montreal also plans constructing such a plant.

The United States is further behind. New York City may some day have a $110 million plant, and the Combustion Power Company of Palo Alto, Calif., is designing a fluidized bed incinerator that burns solid wastes at high pressure to produce hot gases to power a turbine.

A recent development by the Japanese combines trash disposal and the development of building material. They compress trash into rock-hard blocks, which are coated with asphalt or cement (SN: 5/19, p. 49).

But in the United States the primary method of getting rid of refuse is open dumping; it is also the most condemned method. The reasons are legion: odors, rats, flies, roaches and runoff that pollutes ground and surface water, and air pollution when the refuse is burned.

A recent HEW report states that 94 percent of the 12,000 disposal sites are unacceptable and threaten diseases, pollution and blight.

But, says BSWM Director Vaughan, "now

the country is starting to wake up to the problem. Several states have passed laws that prohibit open burning dumps and approve new facilities. New technology is starting to come off the shelf. We've still got a long way to go, though."

Logically, one solution would be to bury the trash in a sanitary landfill, rather than dump. Vaughan calls the landfill "the most important disposal method, and consequently a great deal of effort is being made to improve this technique."

But it too has drawbacks, stemming largely from packaging materials of paper and plastics that do not readily compact, thereby shortening the life span of a landfill and reducing its effectiveness. Rapidly biodegradable materials would be a blessing here, but the current trend in packaging is away from them.

The landfill also does not eliminate the problems of ground water and surface water pollution and adds the problem of hazardous methane buildup and dust. And as population increases, space for landfills will be harder to get and more expensive.

A cousin to the sanitary landfill is composting, in which waste organic material is used as a solid conditioner. Unfortunately, no great agricultural market has opened for the method, mainly because of the economic difficulty of separating metal, plastic and glass from organic matter, and competition from commercial fertilizers.

"Compost is not really fertilizer," explains Clyde J. Dial, staff engineer at BSWM. "It's a soil conditioner, and so it can't compete with chemical fertilizers because it doesn't have the nutrients they do. We are finding composting depends on local conditions. You can't make a blanket statement on composting. Houston has a composting plant, which the city pays for handling its waste, and it's a successful operation." Dial points out that compost can be modified to provide needed nutrients, and so might be made practical.

As a garbage disposal method, dumping at sea has been largely discontinued because much of the material is washed ashore. Nevertheless, ocean dumping of refuse such as chemicals and oil refinery wastes is on the upswing, though

pressure is building against it, too (SN: 9/13, p. 213).

Though it draws the sharpest opposition from clean-air advocates, incineration is the best weight and volume reducer of the lot.

The Bureau of Mines is testing a junk car incinerator in Salt Lake City that burns off all combustible materials, such as upholstery and plastics, leaving only steel hulk. Metals with melting points lower than that of steel will, it is hoped, melt off and be collected. Until recently, incineration techniques were inadequate to deal with these contaminant metals.

In July, the American Gas Association announced plans for a $1.5 million natural gas pilot plant to be built in New York State. It will convert every item of household refuse, from the kitchen sink to the television set, into a clear, gravel-like residue.

But residues must still be disposed of and so remain an incinerator problem. The Bureau of Mines has a continuous processing plant in the pilot stage on the University of Maryland campus. The plant could make salvage a reality by removing metals and glass that account for 75 percent of residue weight.

In addition, since municipal incinerators in the United States don't have sophisticated air pollution control devices, such as electrostatic precipitators and scrubbers, they contribute to air pollution. Plastics in incinerators create a special problem because they often give off chlorides and fluorides, which eat away the incinerator lining and in large amounts could be harmful to people.

"There is no problem in getting them out of the stack effluent," points out Edward Higgins, special adviser at BSWM's Cincinnati branch. "A caustic solution can do that. The problem is in the incinerator itself. There is no real solution available at present to solve that problem."

In addition to refuse and garbage, the U.S. economy produces more than one billion tons of mineral wastes from mines, mills, smelters, refineries and foundries and two billion tons of agricultural (animal and crop) waste.

The solution to the entire solid wastes problem calls for a combined, full-scale attack by chemistry, engineering (mechanical, civil, chemical and sanitary) plus social and political action.

The outlook isn't promising. "We need support," cries one Administration official. "It's been pretty short because of the Vietnam War. Funds have leveled off and this year they are decreasing."

"We're losing," simply states Charles B. Kenahan, staff metallurgist at the Bureau of Mines. "We're literally being buried by our solid wastes. But there is a way out from beneath the pile through research and proper solid waste management."

61

OIL IN THE ECOSYSTEM

Robert W. Holcomb

Oil pollution has been a human problem for most of this century, but it took the grounding of the tanker *Torrey Canyon* and the blowout of the well off the coast of Santa Barbara to draw public attention to the major problems that can arise in the production and shipping of petroleum. A five-fold increase in oil production is expected by 1980, and the potential for large-scale pollution can increase even faster because of changes in drilling location and shipping practice. Knowledge of how oil affects the environment is fragmentary and gives only dim clues about what to expect in the future.

The problems involved in oil studies are complex. Crude oil is not a single chemical but a collection of hundreds of substances of widely different properties and toxicities. Paul Galtsoff of the Bureau of Commercial Fisheries at Woods Hole, Massachusetts, stated recently that "oil in sea water should be regarded not as an ordinary pollutant but as a dynamic system actively reacting with the environment."

Viewing the problem of oil this way, one finds that biologists present an essentially unified account of how oil came to be an important part of the environment and that they can give a rough outline of the way oil

interacts with the rest of the ecological system. However, it is still impossible to predict the behavior of specific oil spills, and little is known about the long-term effects of oil in the marine environment.

Most current research is directed toward the immediate problem of handling oil spills. There is little prospect that detailed ecological studies will increase dramatically in the near future but plans are being considered for the establishment of broad-based environmental-monitoring programs.

Oil at Sea

In 1966, 700 million tons of oil—about half the world's total ocean tonnage—were shipped in 3281 tankers. In the best of worlds, this oil would remain in that part of the "ecological" system of interest only to humans—wells, tankers, refineries, and, finally, furnaces and machines. It is difficult to estimate just how far short we are of living in the best of worlds, but Max Blumer of Woods Hole Oceanographic Institution estimates that somewhere between 1 million and 100 million tons of oil are added to our oceans each year.

The major sources of this oil are handling errors, leaks from natural deposits, tanker and barge accidents, and illegal tanker bilge washings. Normal techniques of transferring oil to small coastal tankers, barges, and shore facilities result in a chronic source of coastal oil. The total amount of oil from this source is unknown, but the Massachusetts Division of Natural Resources says that, in Boston Harbor alone, a spill involving several tons of oil can be expected every third week. Less frequent, but more spectacular, are leaks from offshore deposits. These can occur naturally, but they have been associated with drilling operations since the 1930's, when fields in the Gulf of Mexico were opened. The biggest loss associated with the more than 9000 off-shore wells was the million-gallon blowout early this year off the California coast near Santa Barbara. Tanker accidents are similar to well blowouts in that an occasional major catastrophe highlights a constant source of contamination. The grounding of the *Torrey Canyon* off the southwest coast of England in March 1967 was simply the most dramatic example of a type of accident that, on a worldwide basis, occurs more than once a week. Finally, deliberate dumping of bilge washings adds a considerable, but unknown, amount of oil to the oceanic environment. In 1962 Shell Oil Company developed a method to separate oil from such washings, and there is a tacit international agreement to use the method; however, shipmasters find the procedure inconvenient, and the dumping practice continues.

Although our oil resources are not unlimited, a quick look to the future indicates that pumping and shipping operations will continue to expand for the next few decades. The continental shelves of North and South America, Africa, and Australia all have oil. Seismic profiling has indicated the probable presence of oil in the North Sea, Persian Gulf, and Indonesia, and large deposits have been discovered in Alaska and Canada.

Oil from these new sources will be transported through pipelines and by gigantic tankers. Construction has already begun on a road that will be used to build the 800-mile, 48-inch, 900-million-dollar pipeline from Alaska's North Slope to Valdez Bay, an ice-free port on the Gulf of Alaska. The large United States merchant vessel S.S. *Manhattan* was specially strengthened for travel in ice and fought her way through the Canadian Arctic in September. If such trial runs are judged successful, a fleet of six, quarter-million-ton vessels will be built for year-round service. (The *Torrey Canyon*, considered a large ship at the time of her grounding, had a displacement of 127,000 tons.)

The proposed drilling activities will involve greater risks of major losses because work must be done at sea or in inhospitable northern latitudes. The use of large tankers will reduce the probability of collisions and groundings, but there are few port facilities for these giants, so the possibility of spills during transfers to smaller tankers or barges will be increased. Major accidents, of course, will be of colossal proportions.

Behavior in Water

After coming in contact with water, crude oil rapidly spreads into a thin layer and the lighter fractions evaporate. In protected areas the oil often becomes adsorbed on particulate matter and sinks, but in open seas it tends to remain on the surface where wind and wave action aid in further evaporation. Some oil dissolves in seawater and some is oxidized but the hundreds of species of bacteria, yeasts, and molds that attack different fractions of hydrocarbons under a variety of physical conditions are primarily responsible for oil degradation.

Bacteria found in open seas tend to degrade only straight-chain hydrocarbons of moderate molecular weight, so branched-chain hydrocarbons of high molecular weight in the form of tarry chunks may persist for a long time. In still waters, a series of complex events results in almost complete degradation. In 1950, Soviet microbiologists showed that, after the lighter fractions of oil spilled on the Moskva River evaporated, the remaining oil was adsorbed by particles and sank. Bottom-dwelling microorganisms produced a new mixture of organic substances that were carried to the surface with bubbles of methane and other light gases. The new compounds again were adsorbed, sank, and the cycle was repeated. A number of cycles, repeated over several months, were necessary to degrade most of the oil.

Studies on the thoroughness of degradation have produced conflicting results. Research at Terrebonne Bay, Louisiana, in 1966 showed that essentially complete degradation occurs within a period of several months. Oil has been a consistent pollutant in the Bay since the

1930's, but analysis of bottom mud showed that significant concentrations of petrochemicals could be found only in areas that had received oil relatively recently. However, studies in the French Mediterranean, which will be discussed later, indicate that important chemicals are persistent in bottom sediments.

There is now a considerable body of literature on the interactions of microorganisms and petroleum products, most of it based on laboratory studies and much of it dating back to Soviet work in the 1930's and American work in the 1940's. However, these studies are scarcely past the descriptive stage, and, even when combined with field studies, they are not adequate for predicting the course of degradation of an oil spill.

Oil and Marine Life

The most visible victims of ocean oil are sea birds. It is impossible to even guess how many are killed each year, and about the only thing known for sure is that, once oiled, very few birds survive. After the *Torrey Canyon* disaster, 5711 oiled birds were cleaned off; apparently 150 of them returned to health and were released, but banding counts of these indicate that at least 37 died within the first month after release. Similar figures were obtained from French efforts at bird rehabilitation after the same disaster, and few of the 1500 diving birds cleaned after the Santa Barbara blowout survived.

It is believed that most deaths are the result of diseases, such as pneumonia, which attack the birds after they are weakened by the physical effects of the oil (feather matting, loss of buoyancy, flying difficulty, and others). However, the high death rate of cleaned birds is unexplained, so long-term toxicity of the oil cannot be ruled out.

The major studies of the effects of oil spills on species other than birds have produced a wide variety of results. Dr. Robert Holmes, the first director of a major study after the Santa Barbara blowout, has stated that plankton populations were unaffected, and, although his remark was challenged at the Massachusetts

Institute of Technology symposium where it was made, it is generally agreed that visible damage to organisms other than birds has been relatively light.

On the other hand, in what is probably the best "before and after" study of a major spill, it was conclusively shown that almost the entire population of a small cove was killed by dark diesel oil from the tanker *Tampico Mara*. In March 1957, the tanker grounded at the mouth of a small, previously unpolluted cove on the Pacific coast of Baja California, Mexico, and, until destroyed by the sea, it blocked most of the cove's entrance. All signs of oil disappeared sometime between November 1957 and May 1958, but the ecology of the cove was radically changed. A few species returned within 2 months, but 2 years had elapsed before significant improvements were noted. Four years after the accident, sea urchin and abalone populations were still greatly reduced; and, at the last observations in 1967, several species present 10 years earlier had not returned.

Although toxicity studies in the ocean have been limited to a few large spills, considerable laboratory work has been done to determine the lethal concentrations of a number of chemicals on various species. Most toxic are the aromatic hydrocarbons (for example, benzene, toluene, and the xylenes), and investigators have recently shown that the low-boiling, saturated hydrocarbons are more toxic than formerly believed. The destructiveness of the *Tampico Mara* grounding was probably due to the saturated hydrocarbons, and it has been shown that aromatic hydrocarbons used to dissolve detergents in the effort to disperse oil from *Torrey Canyon* caused much of the damage. When a spill occurs at sea, a large portion of both these classes of compounds evaporates before reaching shore. This is probably the main reason that the Santa Barbara blowout was not more disastrous to shore life other than birds.

Biochemical Studies

Just enough is known about the higher-boiling, saturated hydrocarbons and the high-boiling, aromatic hydrocarbons to indicate that more study is needed. Saturated, higher-boiling compounds occur naturally in both crude oil and marine organisms, so they are probably not toxic; but work reported this year indicates that these compounds may affect the behavior of sea animals.

Blumer points out that very small amounts of certain chemicals are used by many species of sea animals as behavior signals in the vital activities of food finding, escaping from predators, homing, and reproduction. He has shown, for example, that starfish are attracted to their oyster prey by chemicals in concentrations of a few parts per billion. The responsible chemicals have not been identified, but Blumer believes that in many cases they may resemble the high-boiling, saturated hydrocarbons found in petroleum products. Because of the extreme sensitivity of the response and the similarity of the animal and petroleum chemicals, he thinks it is possible that pollution interferes with chemically stimulated behavior "by blocking the taste receptors and by mimicking natural stimuli."

Studies on chemically stimulated behavior of marine animals are in such an early stage that ideas about the role of sea oil in the process can only be considered speculative. However, the speculation indicates that the consequences— altered behavior of entire populations of commercially valuable species—are so serious that the matter deserves early attention.

Another matter still in the speculative stage, but with potentially hazardous consequences, is the significance of high-boiling, aromatic hydrocarbons. Crude oil and crude oil residues contain alkylated 4- and 5-ring aromatic hydrocarbons similar to those found in tobacco tars, but little is known about their role in the marine environment.

In 1964 Lucien Mallet, a French marine chemist, reported the presence of 3,4-benzopyrene, a known carcinogen, in sediments of the French Mediterranean. Concentrations ranged from 5.0 parts per million at a depth of 8 to 13 cm to 0.016 part per million at 200 cm. Similar concentrations have been found in other waters that had been polluted for a long time. Near the port of Villefranche, 3,4-benzo-

pyrene in concentrations from 0.025 to 0.04 part per million have been found in plankton.

Benzopyrenes can be formed by algae, and they occur naturally in many soils in concentrations ranging from parts per million to parts per billion; thus their presence in marine sediments may not be cause for concern. However, the detection in sea cucumbers of concentrations that were slightly greater than those in the bottom sediments where these animals feed indicates that benzopyrenes in the marine environment may find their way into the food chain.

Pollutants tend to enter the food chain more easily and to pass through it with fewer changes in aquatic environments than they do in terrestrial environments. They can be introduced in solution through bottom sediments and even in dispersed droplets that are ingested by the numerous filter feeders that constitute an important part of aquatic food.

The presence of DDT in Lake Michigan's coho salmon drew public attention to the fact that some hydrocarbons pass through the aquatic food chain relatively unchanged. Work at Woods Hole has demonstrated that the ratios of olefinic hydrocarbons in zooplankton to those in livers of basking sharks and herring that feed on the plankton are so constant that they can be used to determine the feeding grounds of these species.

Obviously, studies should be conducted to see what concentrations of 3,4-benzopyrene and other potentially dangerous hydrocarbons must be in seawater or sediments before they are introduced into the food chain and whether the chemicals persist as they pass through the chain.

Priorities

Although the possible ill effects of long-term oil pollution point to the need for more studies on the complex chemical-biological relationships of oil and the environment, there is still work to be done on the immediate effects of oil spills. Dale Straugh, who now directs the large Santa Barbara study, said in a telephone interview that oil spills will undoubtedly continue and that much of the research effort should concentrate on methods of handling them.

Present alternatives are (i) to "corral" the oil and hold it at sea, (ii) to pick it up mechanically, or (iii) to treat it chemically so it will emulsify, dissolve, or sink. None of these methods is particularly successful, and research on all of them is continuing. The major requirement for further development is engineering and chemical knowledge, but biological expertise is necessary in some areas.

It is primarily biological studies, especially those after the *Torrey Canyon* incident, that precipitated the government decision not to use chemical treatment when the shore area is used as a source of fresh water or as a beach, or when it is necessary for commercially valuable species. Toxicity tests of chemicals developed to treat oil are now routinely conducted, and the Federal Water Pollution Control Administration is developing a standard procedure for such tests. This action was prompted in part by reports that a dispersal agent, Corexit, used at Santa Barbara was more toxic than earlier tests indicated.

The step beyond toxicity tests is a giant one of determining subtle and long-term effects of sunken, dissolved, or dispersed oil. Biological knowledge has advanced far enough to cast doubt on any sinking or dispersal scheme, but not far enough to rule them out or to provide unquestionably safe alternatives. This task would require difficult, long-term studies on the complex interactions of oil, seawater, and marine life, and there is nothing on the horizon to indicate that these studies will progress rapidly enough to play a large role in decisions about methods of handling oil spills.

Another area in which biological knowledge could be helpful is in simply monitoring the oil that enters the oceans and determining, at least by sampling, its effects. On this horizon there seems to be some light. Several studies designed to determine the feasibility of establishing broad-based centers for environmental study are now in progress.

Early in September, after the announcement by the National Science Foundation of the availability of funds, the Ecological Society of America and the Washington, D.C., firm of Peat, Marwick, Mitchell, and Company, signed a contract for the first part of a feasibility study on the formation of a National Institute of Ecology. The study will consider information-collecting, environmental-monitoring, and possibly graduate-education functions. An international organization with similar functions is being considered by the International Biological Program under the auspices of the International Scientific Union. The next step for this effort was to be determined this week after Frank Blair of the United States, Bengt Lundholm of Sweden, and N. N. Smirnov of the Soviet Union had met in London to discuss the results of their consultations with various individuals and groups involved with worldwide ecological problems. Finally, as a result of a conference in Paris last September, the United Nations charged UNESCO with the formation of a "Man and the Biosphere" program. National governments were to submit statements discussing their part in the program by 30 August, and in October or November technical groups will meet to discuss specific actions. The director general will then have the duty of developing a plan on the basis of their reports and submitting it to the UNESCO Executive Board next year.

It is too early to know how these programs will fit together, or even if all of them will be pursued, but Blair thinks it is reasonable that the International Biological Program might form the backbone of overall scientific capability; the National Institute of Ecology, in addition to its own special capabilities, would form the United States arm of the international program; and UNESCO would function in tactical matters (for example, obtaining agreements among governments) and, hopefully, would provide financial support.

Whatever final form these organizations take, it is not likely that they will have specific research programs for oil studies. However, the systematic monitoring of the oceans, including their oil content, is a necessary step toward development of the capability of determining the worldwide consequences of effects that at present can be measured only in the laboratory or in relatively small field studies.

62

WARM-WATER IRRIGATION: AN ANSWER TO THERMAL POLLUTION?

Luther J. Carter

Eugene, Oregon. Electric utilities in the Northwest, as well as elsewhere, have been finding it difficult to announce plans to build a nuclear plant without stirring criticism that the proposed plant might cause major environmental problems. Fear of thermal pollution has often been enough to bring out opposition. Now, however, some Oregon utilities are thinking positively about the heated effluents that their power plants will discharge. They hope to show that these effluents can benefit farmers. It is even being suggested that eventually systems may be developed whereby heated effluents will serve agriculture as they are being cooled for recycling through the power plant.

Two utility-financed projects to test or "demonstrate" the beneficial uses of heated water on croplands are actually under way in Oregon, although some people opposing the siting of nuclear power plants in Willamette Valley suspect that the sponsors' interest in the projects springs largely from public relations motives. The Eugene Water and Electric Board (EWEB), with the cooperation of seven local farmers, this past spring began a warm-water irrigation project near here on a 170-acre tract lying within a bend of the McKenzie River. The goal is to demonstrate that warm water (being obtained in this case from a Weyerhaeuser paper mill) can be used to stimulate and enhance plant growth and to protect fruit trees from killing frosts. Water not used on crops is discharged from a blow-valve, its temperature thus being reduced by evaporation to that of the ambient air before it hits the ground and trickles off back into the McKenzie.

Reprinted from *Science* 165: 478-80, 1969, with the permission of the publishers. Copyright 1969 by the American Association for the Advancement of Science.

The utility has invested $475,000 in the project, which it says will continue even if an application now pending before the Federal Water Pollution Control Administration for a $1.1 million, 3-year grant should be rejected. According to W. A. Cawley, FWPCA's acting director of water quality research, his agency is interested in the utility's proposal and is likely to support it if an acceptable project budget can be worked out. The agency has received no other proposals on the use of warm water in agriculture, and EWEB believes its project is unique.

The Pacific Power and Light Company (PPL) is supporting a small project at Oregon State University (OSU) to see if growing seasons cannot be lengthened and crop yields increased by warming the soil with buried electric cables. The cables simulate what could be a network of pipes carrying heated water from power plants. Larry L. Boersma, an OSU soils scientist who designed the project last year with PPL's encouragement, believes that some day there may be agricultural enterprises relying on the availability of heated water from such plants.

"Such a development could occur on several scales," Boersma says. "It might consist of only one farm, the operator of which could call for warm water when needed. The power plant still would have an independent cooling system. The farmer would be a customer purchasing heat for his land as he would purchase fertilizer. It might also consist of several large food factory type operations, including greenhouses, using all available heat, thus eliminating the need for an alternate cooling system."

The Atomic Energy Commission, which has been under attack by conservationists and some members of Congress for failing to take thermal pollution problems into account in the licensing of nuclear power plants, is eager to see beneficial uses found for thermal discharges. Glenn T. Seaborg, chairman of the AEC, has praised the EWEB venture, appearing in a film about the project which was produced recently under the sponsorship of Oregon's State Department of Economic Development. Ernest B. Tremmel, director of AEC's division of industrial participation, also is enthusiastic. "I consider the project one of the most pioneering and forward-looking ever undertaken in this country," he told *Science.*

Hanford Project at Standstill

Last year the AEC itself had a part in trying to get an ambitious warm-water irrigation project under way. Its Richland (Washington) Operations Office, together with the State of Washington and two AEC contractors, Battelle Northwest and Douglas United Nuclear, drafted a proposal for a $2.6-million project that would use the effluent from the Hanford works' nuclear-fired steam-electric plant. Funding from power companies or other sources has not yet been found, however, and the project is at a standstill.

Promoters of warm-water irrigation think it fitting that experiments and demonstration projects be done in the Northwest. This region has millions of acres of potentially irrigable land and a rising demand for electric power which will have to be met by construction of steam plants now that few hydropower sites remain undeveloped. Furthermore, many of the region's rivers have valuable fishery resources, and state and federal pollution-control agencies will not allow EWEB or other utilities to draw cold water from a salmon stream such as Willamette River and then dump it back as a heated effluent.

Cooling lakes or large evaporative cooling towers can provide means of dissipating heat from plant effluents. But cooling towers and lakes have their drawbacks. A tower may cost $10 million or more. A cooling lake costs less but may be controversial if the utility must condemn farmland for the site. And, under certain atmospheric conditions, either a cooling lake or tower may cause fogging or icing.

Thus, if it should prove possible to develop a closed system in which heated plant effluents are cooled through useful farm applications and then recycled, the power industry's problem of heat disposal would have been turned to good account. Development of a "once-through" system, in which plant effluents were cooled through farm use and then discharged back into a stream, would be less of a breakthrough but would still represent a major gain. Even if heated water were no better for crops than unheated water, either the closed-loop or once-through systems would allow utilities to dissipate their effluent heat without large cooling lakes or towers.

Thus far, findings from the EWEB and Boersma projects are limited and inconclusive, but they are regarded by the project leaders as encouraging. The Vitro Corporation of America is managing the EWEB project, and Herman Miller, of Vitro's Portland office, has been one of the project's prime movers and principal spokesmen. According to Miller, fruit trees on the demonstration area were protected from killing frosts on seven occasions this spring by the sprinkling of warm water.

Researchers at agricultural colleges in the United States and Europe have shown that frost damage can be prevented by sprinkling water at ambient temperatures, for as the water freezes on the buds and tree limbs there is a release of latent heat. Miller acknowledges this, but says that when unheated water is used, heavy icing on the fruit trees can occur, with the result that losses from limb breakage may exceed losses that would have occurred from the frost. When, on the other hand, warm water was used this spring, no icing occurred on the upper three-fourths of the trees, and there was only light icing on the lower parts, where limbs were sturdiest and least susceptible to breakage.

In June, strawberries grown as part of the project and irrigated with warm-water sprinklers ripened 11 days earlier than other strawberries in the Willamette Valley, according to Miller. During one period when the ambient temperature was about 28°F, water was released from the sprinkler at 105°, 34 inches above the strawberry plants. The droplets hit the ground at 67°F. "It was like forming a hothouse around the plants," Miller says. A full report on the first year's experience with warm-water sprinkling will not be available until November, following summer and fall harvests. Apples, cherries, pears, peaches, filberts, and walnuts are being grown in the project area, as are a variety of row crops, such as beans, corns, tomatoes, and cauliflower. It will not be known before the end of the 3-year project, if then, whether warm-water irrigation will extend the growing season enough to allow some "double cropping."

Corn Grows Taller

A few weeks ago, when a reporter visited Boersma's 2-acre experimental plot, where electric cables have been buried to simulate warm-water pipes, corn that had been planted in the heated soil was about a foot higher than corn grown in unheated soil. String beans grown in heated soil had germinated faster, and the plants were fuller than other beans. However, no difference could be observed between the alfalfa, soybeans, and lima beans grown in heated soil and those grown as controls. Boersma's project is to continue for two more years.

Though the Boersma and EWEB projects are not being coordinated, next year EWEB will actually do what Boersma is now simulating. Warm water running through buried pipes will raise the soil temperature in a 3-acre plot, and, if the results are as expected, a bumper crop of sweet corn and beans will be produced. Thrusting upward at intervals from the buried pipe will be "risers" to which sprinklers can be attached. Warming of the soil and irrigation can go on simultaneously if desired. It was discovered recently that corn plants growing above one of the EWEB project's warm-water trunk lines is taller and has tasseled out earlier than other corn in the same field.

The EWEB project is now being criticized and derided by some people in the Eugene area. Chiefly, this seems to be because the project is linked with the utility's plans to build a 1000-megawatt nuclear plant somewhere in the upper Willamette Valley. The Oregon Environmental Council, a body on which a number of conservation groups are represented, believes that EWEB and other Oregon utilities, encouraged by state and federal authorities, are moving into the field of nuclear power generation precipitously. The council is concerned about possible hazards, such as it fears will arise from persistent low-level emission of radioactive substances or from a catastrophic reactor accident.

Opposition to the proposed plant also has developed among some farmers who are afraid they will lose land to the plant and its 2500-acre cooling lake. The lake is an essential part of the project, for, with the plant scheduled to go on the line in 1976, EWEB cannot gamble on using still hazily formulated and unproved concepts for a closed-loop system to cool plant effluents and serve agriculture simultaneously. Warm water from the lake would be made available for irrigation, but the water used by the farmers would be in addition to the amount the power plant would require for its closed-cycle cooling system.

Opponents of the nuclear plant tend to regard EWEB's warm-water irrigation project as a public relations gimmick. The project, they note, was well publicized during EWEB's highly successful campaign last fall to win the approval of Eugene voters for a $225-million bond issue. Yet the idea for the warm-water irrigation project clearly did not originate within EWEB as a public relations ploy. Miller, of the Vitro Corporation, believes in warm-water irrigation with evangelistic fervor, and he came to the utility with the idea. Promoting it, too, was William Puustinen, a commercial salmon fisherman and a long-time crusader against water pollution. Puustinen is a farmer as well as a fisherman and is one of the seven orchardists taking part in the EWEB project.

The project is encountering some criticism on its own merits as well as on the grounds that EWEB is using it as a public relations device. Some of its critics are University of Oregon professors who believe that the project promises much more than it is likely to deliver—and, further, that it could lead ultimately to health hazards. For example, Howard T. Bonnett, a botanist and associate professor of biology, indicates that the project's claims for providing frost protection are inflated. "This spring was an excellent spring for flower and fruit development," he says. "All orchardists in the Eugene vicinity had excellent crops, whether they were parties to the warm-water experiment or not." Bonnett also questions whether the enormous quantities of warm water—up to 500,000 gallons a minute or more—that a 1000-megawatt plant would be continuously discharging could be used by farmers in the area surrounding it. In the Willamette Valley, he observes, "irrigation is only needed a few months during the year.

Frost control [is needed] only a few days a year."

Bonnett's major concern, however, is that an irrigation system using effluents from a nuclear plant would lead to the contamination of plants and livestock. "Numerous radioactive isotopes, such as tritium, are released in the cooling water during normal function of nuclear plants," he says. "The possible dangers of directly providing for the accumulation and concentration of radioisotopes during plant and animal growth, followed by human consumption of such crops, should be carefully studied. This issue is exceedingly complex and may be of overriding importance."

Furthermore, Bonnett, as well as some scientists in the School of Agriculture at Oregon State University, feel that a utility has no business conducting what is essentially an agricultural experiment. While EWEB speaks of its project as a "demonstration," not much is known scientifically about how crops respond to warm water under actual field conditions, nor can one predict yet how warm water will affect insects and plant disease organisms. In the critics' view, research problems of the complexity of those presented by the EWEB project could best be dealt with by a university, which could bring a greater wealth of scientific resources to bear than any utility could, and which might be less likely to have axes to grind.

In sum, by searching for a beneficial use for the heat that is a troublesome by-product of electric power generation, EWEB has taken a forward-looking step; but, if the fears expressed by Bonnett and others have merit, the utility has ventured upon a course beset with more problems and uncertainties than it has imagined.

PART SIX

Conservation and the Future

The amount of affluence we achieve, the extent of the leisure we enjoy, our
longevity, our relative happiness or misery, the potential for our survival either
as individuals or as a species, are all intimately influenced by the decisions we make
regarding the *level* at which we are to maintain our regional population densities and the
use to which we are to put the resources of our ecosystems.

The word *compromise* was introduced in the last part in regard to the economics of
pollution. We must return to it again when we examine the question of the "carrying
capacity" of the various ecosystems that comprise our global ecosphere and the
"optimum human populations" for its component habitats. Our species cannot even
exist in an ecosystem without reaching some kind of compromise between what it was
like without us and what it becomes when we invade it.

The opening paper (63) by J. H. Fremlin discusses the problem of carrying capacity
and optimum population in terms of one small, and somewhat isolated, country. The
crucial feature of any decision on such issues is that it must be based on quantified
value judgments. The second paper (64), by Nathan Keyfitz, examines the impact that
population density has on living standards, which can readily be quantified. The size
of the optimum population in each instance will have to be determined by the
summation of individual and national decisions. The nature of the data on which such
decisions will have to be based is indicated by two successive papers (65, 66). In the
former, Charles C. Bradley examines what is possible in terms of optimum populations
when due regard is given to the limiting factor of water, and in the latter, Preston E.
Cloud, Jr., examines what is possible with minerals as the limiting factor. Other limits
may intervene, especially those imposed by restricted or prohibited energy sources, which
may be partly overcome by tapping some as yet unexploited natural supply, such as the
earth's heat, according to Lawrence Lessing (67).

We are still uncertain of the extent to which we need to have access to such features
as wilderness areas and to participate in such atavistic, predatory activities as
hunting and fishing. Moreover, we suspect that the maintenance of biotic diversity
in areas reserved for such purposes imposes an inherent stability on their ecosystems.
The preservation of this biotic diversity in national parks is implicit or explicit in

two presentations, one by A. S. Leopold et al. (68) and the other by Edward C. Stone (69). A more artificial kind of preservation of animal diversity in zoo banks is described by William G. Conway (70).

The other side of the coin, how we conserve the human population, is the subject of the last three papers. Joseph J. Spengler addresses the problem of increasing economic growth on a worldwide basis (71). The technological progress that is possible with this continuing economic growth is described by the late David Sarnoff (72). As the founder of a now far-flung electronics empire General Sarnoff saw some of his visionary dreams come true. Many readers of his article may well live to experience the realization of at least some of these further prophecies. While such industrial growth and development is the major proximate criterion for measuring progress, it may not be the ultimate one. This possibility is stressed in the final paper (73) by Archibald MacLeish, who points out that even the full realization of our technological potential may still leave us unhappy and dissatisfied.

Many of the selections in this part and some of the papers listed in the Additional Readings section emphasize that for the majority of our present global population of between three and four billion, life can at best be expressed by the single word *dismal.* Hardship and suffering we may have been selected to endure, but not *monotony,* for we are also adapted to be a curious and an opportunistic species. Whatever the level of security and affluence we attain, we must still have the opportunity to explore and inquire. The failure to produce a satisfactory philosophical goal for our technological society is leading to an increasing sense of frustration. Many of us, especially the underprivileged, can still be lured by the materialistic siren call of competitive free enterprise. In biological rather than philosophical terms, the issue may resolve itself into a matter of the balance between altruistic and egocentric behavior. Our Western societies have lost their social guidelines during the twentieth century through a tacit rejection of the Judeo-Christian principles that steered the Western world through the more immediate ethical perils of the Industrial Revolution. We have not yet determined the extent to which we must all be drafted into making some altruistic contribution to society. There is still no clear definition of this social trade-off that balances indulgence in the egocentric biological pursuits that provide each of us with the motivation necessary for survival.

Additional Readings

Ackerman, E. A. "Population, natural resources, and technology," *Ann. Amer. Acad. Pol. Soc. Sci.* 369: 84-97, 1967.

Anon. "Blasphemy with a trowel," *New Scientist* 42: 676-77, 1969.

Bajema, C. J., ed. *Natural Selection in Human Populations*, New York: Wiley, 1971.

Bascom, W. "Mining the ocean depths," *Geoscience News* 1: 10-11, 26-28, 1967.

Beller, W. S. "Gearing up for coastal zone management," *Environ. Sci. Technol.* 4(6): 482-86, 1970.

Bogdanov, B. "Conservation and economics," English translation from "Agricultural Economics" No. 2, pp. 7-11, in *Current Digest of the Soviet Press* 23(19): 7-9, 1970.

Boughey, A. S. "Man and the African environment," *Proc. Trans. Rhodesia Sci. Assn.* 48: 8-18, 1960.

Brooks, H., and Bowers, R. "The assessment of technology," *Scientific American* 222(2): 13-22, 1970.

Brown, H. S. "Population resources and technology," *Bioscience* 18: 31-33, 1968.

Brues, A. M. "Genetic load and its varieties," *Science* 164: 1130-36, 1969.

Burton, L. "Quality of the environment: a review," *Geog. Rev.* 58(3): 472-81, 1968.

Carpenter, R. A. "Information for decisions in environmental policy," *Science* 168: 1316-22, 1970.

Carter, L. J. "Development in the poor nations: How to avoid fouling the nest," *Science* 163: 1046-1048, 1969.

Center Report. "Crisis of affluence," *Center Mag.* 3(1): 72-83, 1970.

Cerowsky, J. "Conservation in East Europe," *New Scientist* 46(697): 122-26, 1970.

Ciriacy-Wantrup, S. V., and Parsons, J. J., eds. *Natural Resources—Quality and Quantity*, Berkeley: University of California Press, 1967.

Clark, C. *Population Growth and Land Use*, New York: St. Martin's Press, 1967.

Clark, W. "How to harness sunpower and avoid pollution," *Smithsonian* 2(8): 14-21, 1971.

Clarkson, F. E., Vogel, S. R., Broverman, I. K., Boverman, D. M., and Rosenkranz, P. S. "Family size and sex-role stereotypes," *Science* 167: 390-92, 1970.

Coale, A. J. "Man and his environment," *Science* 170: 132-36, 1970.

Cole, LaMont C. "Can the world be saved?" *Bioscience* 18: 679-84, 1968.

Commoner, B. *Science and Survival*, New York: Ballantine, 1970.

Conservation Foundation. *National Parks for the Future*, Washington: Conservation Foundation, 1972.

Crowe, B. L. "The tragedy of the commons revisited," *Science* 166: 1103-04, 1969.

Dansereau, P., ed. *Challenge for Survival: Land, Air, and Water for Man in Megalopolis*, New York and London: Columbia University Press, 1970.

Darling, F. Fraser. "Conservation and ecological theory," *J. Ecol.* 52(suppl.): 39-45, 1964.

——, and Milton, J. P., eds. *Future Environments of North America*, New York: Natural History Press, 1966.

De Bell, G., ed. *The Voter's Guide to Environmental Politics*, New York: Ballantine, 1970.

Detwyler, T. R., ed. *Man's Impact on Environment*, New York: McGraw-Hill, 1971.

Dorst, J. *Before nature dies*, translated by C. D. Sherman, Boston: Houghton Mifflin, 1970.

Drew, E. B. "Dam outrage: The story of the Army engineers," *Atlantic* 225 (April), 51-62, 1970.

Dubos R. "A social design for science," editorial in *Science* 166(3907), November 14, 1969.

Egler, F. E. "Wildlife habitat measurement for the citizen," *Atlantic Naturalist* 22: 166-69, 1967.

Ehrenfeld, D. W. *Biological Conservation*, New York: Holt, Rinehart and Winston, 1970.

Ehrlee, E. B. "California's anti-evolution ruling," *Bioscience* 20: 291, 1970.

Ehrlich, P. R., and Ehrlich, A. H. *Population Resources, Environment—Issues in Human Ecology*, San Francisco: Freeman, 1970.

——, and Holdren, J. P. "Impact of population growth," *Science* 171: 1212-17, 1971.

Eichenwald, H. F., and Fry, P. C. "Nutrition and learning," *Science* 164: 644-48, 1969.

Enke, S., and Zind, R. G. "Effects of fewer births on average income," *J. Biol. Sci.* 1: 41-55, 1969.

Environment Staff Report. "Diminishing returns," *Environment* 11: 6-40, 1969.

Eysenck, H. "The technology of consent," *New Scientist* 42: 688-99, 1969.

Fertig, D. S., and Edmonds, V. W. "The physiology of the house mouse," *Scientific American* 221(4): 103-10, 1969.

Flack, J. E., and Shipley, M. C., eds. *Man and the Quality of His Environment*, Boulder: University of Colorado Press, 1968.

Flawn, P. T. *Environmental Geology: Conservation, Land-Use, and Resource Management*, New York: Harper & Row, 1970.

Ford, A. B. "Casualties of our time," *Science* 167: 256-63, 1970.

Glaser, P. E. "Beyond nuclear power—the large-scale use of solar energy," *Trans. N.Y. Acad. Sci. Suppl.* 31(8): 951-67, 1969.

Glass, H. Bentley, "Science: Endless horizons or golden age," *Science* 171: 23-29, 1971.

Gough, W. C., and Eastlund, B. J. "The prospects of fusion power," *Scientific American* 224(2): 50-64, 1971.

Gulick, A. "A biological prologue for human values," *Bioscience* 18: 1109-12, 1968.

Hardin, G. "Computers and the slave society," *Information Display* 6: 215-17, 1969.

———. "Not peace, but ecology," in "Diversity and stability in ecological systems," *Brookhaven Symp. Biol. No. 22*, 1969, pp. 151-61.

Hare, F. K. "How should we treat environment?" *Science* 167: 352-55, 1970.

Helfrich, H. W., ed. *The Environmental Crisis*, New Haven: Yale University Press, 1970.

Hoffman, L. "Saving Europe's wetlands," *New Scientist* 46(697): 120-22, 1970.

Idyll, C. P. "The Everglades: A threatened ecology," *Science J.* 5A(2): 66-71, 1969.

Iltis, H. H., Loucks, O. L., and Andrews, P. "Criteria for an optimum human environment," *Bull. Atomic Scientists* 26 (January): 2-6, 1970.

Jacoby, N. H. "The progress of peoples," *Center Occasional Papers*, 2(4), 1969.

Johnson, H. D., ed. *No Deposit—No Return: Man and His Environment: A View Towards Survival*, Reading, Mass.: Addison-Wesley, 1970.

Jordan, P. A. "Ecology, conservation, and human behaviour," *Bioscience* 18: 1023-29, 1968.

Katz, M. "Decision-making in the production of power," *Scientific American* 224(3): 191, 1971.

Kesteven, G. L. "A policy for conservationists," *Science* 160: 857-60, 1968.

Kneese, A. "The problem shed as a unit of environmental control," *Arch. Environ. Health* 16(1): 124-27, 1968.

Krantz, G. S. "Human activities and megafauna extinctions," *Amer. Scientist* 58(2): 164-70, 1970.

Kyllonen, R. L. "Crime rate vs. population density in United States cities: A model," *Yearbook of the Society for General Systems Research* 12: 137-45, 1967.

Lacey, M. J. "Man, nature, and the ecological perspective," *Amer. Studies* 8(103): 13-27, 1970.

Landsberg, H. H. "The U.S. resource outlook: Quantity and quality," *Daedalus* 96: 1034-57, 1967.

Lear, J., ed. "Science, technology and the law," *Saturday Review*, August 3, 1968, 39-52.

Leopold, A. *A Sand County Almanac*, New York: Ballantine, 1970.

Leopold, L. B. "Hydrology for urban land planning—A guidebook on the hydrologic effects of urban land use," *U.S. Geol. Survey Circ. 554*, 1968

———. "Landscape esthetics: How to quantify the scenics of a river valley," *Natural History*, October 1969, pp. 37-44.

Linton, R. M. *Terracide: America's Destruction of Her Living Environment*, Boston: Little, Brown, 1970.

Love, R. M. "The rangelands of the Western U.S.," *Scientific American* 222(2):89-96, 1970.

McElroy, W. D. "A crisis of crises," *Science* 167: 9, 1970.

McHarg, I. L. "An ecological method for landscape architecture," *Landscape Architecture*, January 1967, pp. 105-07.

McVay, S. "The last of the great whales," *Scientific American* 215(2): 13-21, 1966.

Marx, L. "American institutions and ecological ideals," *Science* 170: 945-52, 1970.

Matley, I. A. "The Marxist approach to the geographical environment," *Annals. Assn. Amer. Geograph.* 56: 97-111, 1966.

Means, R. L., "The new conservation," *Natural History* 78: 16-25, 1969.

Mellanby, K. "Can Britain afford to be clean?" *New Scientist* 42: 648-50, 1969.

Mesthene, E. G. *Technological Change: Its Impact on Man and Society*, Cambridge, Mass.: Harvard University Press, 1970.

Moncrief, L. V. "The cultural basis for our environmental crisis," *Science* 170: 508-12, 1970.

Murdoch, W. W., and Connell, J. H. "All about ecology," *Center Mag.* 3(1): 56-63, 1970.

Murphey, R. "Man and nature in China," *Modern Asian Studies* 1(4): 313-33, 1967.

Nash, R. *Wilderness and the American Mind*, New Haven: Yale University Press, 1967.

Nussenveig, H. M. "Migration of scientists from Latin America," *Science* 165: 1328-32, 1969.

Oberle, M. W. "Endangered species: Congress curbs international trade in rare animals," *Science* 167: 152-54, 1970.

Panero, R. G. "Adam across the Amazon," *Science J.* 5A(3): 56-60, 1969.

Pecora, W. T. "Searching our resource limits," *Texas Quart.* 11(2): 148-54, 1968.

Peterson, M. "The space available," *Environment* 12(2): 1-9, 1970.

Platt, J. B. "What we must do," *Science* 166: 1115-21, 1969.

Rantz, S. E. "Urban sprawl and flooding in Southern California," *U.S. Geol. Survey Circ.* 601-B, 1970.

Riney, T. "Criteria for land-use planning," *Symp. Wildlife Management and Land Use, Proc. E. Africa Agric. For. J.* 33: 34-37, 1968.

Sax, K. "Ethical aspects of the population crisis," *Bioscience* 19: 303, 1969.

Schneider, W. J., and Spicker, A. M. "Water for the cities—the outlook," *U.S. Geol. Survey Circ.* 601-A, 1969.

Seaborg, G. T., and Bloom, J. L. "Fast breeder reactors," *Scientific American* 223(5): 13-21, 1970.

Sewell, W. R. D. "NAWAPA: A continental water system; pipedream of practical possibility," *Bull. Atomic Scientists* 23(7): 8-13, 1967.

Shepard, P. "Introduction: Ecology and man—a viewpoint," in *The Subversive Science*, P. Shepard and D. McKinley, eds., Boston: Houghton Mifflin, 1969, pp. 1-10.

Singer, S. F. "The energy revolution: Population growth and environmental change," *Bioscience* 21: 163, 1971.

Smith, F. E. "Today the environment, tomorrow the world," *Bioscience* 19: 317-20, 1969.

Spicker, A. M. "Water in urban planning, Salt Creek Basin, Illinois," *U.S. Geol. Survey Water-Supply Paper* 2002, 1970.

Starr, C. "Energy and power," *Scientific American* 224(3): 36-49, 1971.

Stone, E. C., and Vasey, R. B. "Preservation of coast redwood on alluvial flats," *Science* 159: 157-61, 1968.

Talbot, L. M. "Endangered species," *Bioscience* 20: 331, 1970.

Thomas, H. E., and Schneider, W. J. "Water as an urban resource and nuisance," *U.S. Geol. Survey Circ.* 601-D, 1970.

Tinker, J. "One flower in 10 faces extinction," *New Scientist and Science J.* 50: 408-13, 1971.

Tuan, Y. "Our treatment of the environmental ideal and actuality," *American Scientist* 58(3): 244-49, 1970.

Wagar, J. A. "Growth versus the quality of life," *Science* 168: 1179-84, 1970.

Waller, R. "Modern husbandry and soil deterioration," *New Scientist* 45: 262-64, 1970.

Watt, K. E. F. *Ecology and Resource Management*, New York: McGraw-Hill, 1968.

Weinberg, A. M., and Hammond, R. P. "Limits to the use of energy," *Amer. Scientist* 58: 412-18, 1970.

Weiss, R. F., Buchanan, W., Alstatt, L., and Lombardo, J. P. "Altruism is rewarding," *Science* 171: 1262-63, 1971.

Westhoff, V. "New criteria for nature reserves," *New Scientist* 46(497): 108-13, 1970.

White, L. "The historic roots of our ecologic crisis," *Science* 155: 1203-07, 1967.

Williams, R. E., Allred, B. W., Denio, R. M., and Paulson, H. A. "Conservation, development and use of the world's range lands," *J. Range Management* 21: 355-60, 1968.

Woodwell, G. M. "Science and the gross national pollution," *Ramparts* 8: 51-52, 1970.

——, and Smith, H. H., eds. "Diversity and stability in ecological systems," *Brookhaven Symp. Biol. No. 22*, 1969.

63

AN OPTIMUM POPULATION FOR BRITAIN

J. H. Fremlin

For the first time in history we can choose the size of population that we would like to have. I am not writing this article with any expectation that anyone will actually do anything about it now. Nevertheless, when you have power to choose what you should do, to decide to do nothing is itself a choice. Recognizing that this is the choice which most of us are going to make, it is still worth considering some of the other choices which we could make.

First of all, there is a big difference between the choices which are open in the long run and those which are open in the short run. Over, say, 1000 generations we have an enormous choice as to how many people we have; in round figures Britain could be inhabited by fifty million times fewer, leaving it with but a single person, or could have about a million times more, giving 150 per square yard, in multistorey buildings, before we reached the heat limit (at which the heat generated by the population and its machines can no longer be radiated into space—see my "How many people can the world support?" *New Scientist*, Vol. 24, p. 285). Over such a period we have, however, almost no choice at all about our average rate of multiplication. If our total population changed continuously in either direction by as much as one tenth of one per cent per year we should, in 1000 generations, exceed the above wide limits and exterminate ourselves. (We neglect emigration and immigration, as we must if we suppose that the rest of the world may make choices comparable with ours.)

On the other hand, in a short run of say two generations, nothing that we can do, short of

Reprinted from the *New Scientist* 36: 717-19, 1967, with the permission of the publishers.

wholesale massacre or artificial reproduction on an enormous scale, will change the population by more than a factor of five or ten at the outside in either direction, but we could choose a net reproductive index anywhere between a highly improbable 3 and even less likely 0.

I shall limit myself to the choices available in a short run of say 100 years and a total population between a million and 1000 million.

Perhaps belatedly, I will begin the discussion by saying that I do not believe that, in any absolute sense, there is an optimum population for Britain. Any such optimum is relative to the chosen way of life. If your ideal is that of the Canadian trapper who finds his area to be abominably over-crowded and moves on when he finds two different people in the same 20 mile round, the optimum population for Britain is under 50,000. If everybody's ideal is that attributed by some country people to Londoners, of living between a pub and a Bingo Hall over a fish and chip shop and opposite to a department store, then 1000 million is probably too small and would leave a lot of people out in the suburbs or even in the cold and muddy countryside.

These preferences seem at present to be rather rare extremes. Let us look at the advantages and disadvantages of something not quite so unlikely.

First, let us see what ways of life would profit by an increase to 1000 million, nearly 20 times our present population. (Note that, in the terms of the study cited above, this situation corresponds to only the first and least populous of five imaginable stages of expansion.)

There are some very big advantages in having a large density of population if this is adequately organized. The cost per head, in human effort, of electric power, with short transmission lines and/or larger stations, would be far less than now.

The mass production of food by direct chemical synthesis or by micro-organisms under factory conditions would be on a scale appropriate to nearly complete automation and would again be far cheaper in human effort than its production in small units such as farms. The latter would of course be impossible for 40 times our present intake and it would be prudent to assume that little natural food (or any other bulk raw material) would be available for import. While independent motor transport would clearly be impossible in the main inhabited areas and would have to be strictly rationed outside, full protection from the weather could be obtained by roofing in all large cities. Multispeed moving ways could move far more people over a few miles far more quickly than can present services on the main internal routes. Cities built to a fairly uniform height could have such moving ways on several levels with moving ramps or stairs between them. Little power would be needed for heating in winter, although more than at present would be needed for ventilation and for cooling in summer; it might well be economic to plan for a population density which would roughly equalize the winter heating power and the summer cooling power so as to use the power stations more efficiently than now. Paradoxically, therefore, it might be technically advantageous to concentrate the British population even more than at present into the midlands and the south east.

London Life for All

The efficiency of large-scale automated production of the main needs of life could leave much more leisure than now to individuals and more (indoor) choices as to what to do with it. People could engage in a wide range of the more compact sports, including sex. Music and painting and other arts would profit from the fact that innovators would have a much greater chance than now to find an adequate audience or understanding collaborators within 20 minutes "walk" on the moving ways. Internal decoration, fancy cooking, and various constructional hobbies could develop into major popular arts. Serious drinking would not need to be controlled by breathalysers and of course there could be hundreds of television channels.

Since a rapidly expanding population would be young and much concerned with children, a large part of the business of life would consist in bringing them up (which in comfortable circumstances most parents enjoy), and one could expect adequate provision for play space and activity to be built into all town plans. The basic housing unit could well consist of several families, each with its own sleeping and perhaps eating rooms but with a common room, nearly unfurnished apart from sand and water big enough for runabout games for the two to five-year-olds, together with a couple of big play-rooms equipped for the older children. Most people would be in towns big enough to support five or 10 theatres. Nearly all could have the choice of outside lectures that London alone can now provide.

Intellectual life would be exciting. One could expect several Newtons and Shakespeares, Jane Austens and Constables to be alive at the same time. There could be more kinds of jobs and professions to choose between than there are now names in the London telephone directory.

Of course there would be difficulties. The technical ones such as food distribution, sewage disposal and continuous artificial lighting are trivial, given the will, but the human ones might not be. There would be plenty of open space outside the cities so long as not more than one in a thousand wanted to spend more than a few hours in it per year. Nearly everyone would have to want to stay under cover nearly all the time. Remembering how my sister and I as children had to be hounded out of the house to enjoy the lovely sunshine when we wanted to go on reading or playing patience indoors, I doubt very much whether this would be a difficult state to achieve in a generation or two. Many animals become dangerously disturbed when heavily overcrowded, but we can learn to accept enormous numbers of human contacts if we don't have to take any notice of most of them and if we each have our own in-group with whom we feel secure.

Going Down

Now let us come down to a level lower than the present; say 30 million in the UK against the present level of 53 million. This also has several advantages, though not appealing to the same people. If the reduction took place in the midlands and south east, which have been expanding in numbers for decades, the housing problem would disappear, becoming merely those of maintenance and replacement of less popular by more popular types. A percentage of empty houses everywhere might seem wasteful, but would increase mobility and hence freedom. Since a smaller part than now of the population would be children, proportionally far more families could have houses with their own gardens or play spaces. School classes could be much smaller with the same proportion of adults teaching. With a very few decades of further development of farm efficiency, it would be perfectly practicable to grow all of our food naturally on our own farms, without battery hens or calves if we preferred and without taking over any further land for cultivation. The proportion of people who enjoy coastal or country recreations could increase, though not indefinitely, as the number over 18 would not be much less than now. Although the road network would still need a good deal of improvement, an individual motor vehicle for every adult would be perfectly practicable outside the central areas of the larger towns.

While the overall variety of jobs available might be a good deal less than in a country of 1000 million, the proportion which could be independently individual in the sense that a farmer's or forester's is individual would be much greater. Such a population might be the best for freedom to travel; many more will get in each other's way and many fewer could not afford extensive roads.

The costs of this system too are considerable. First, the economic problems would be formidable. We have for two centuries or more been geared to an increasing population. A rather rigid economic control might initially be essential for stability with a decreasing one. We could produce little for export that could compete with production from larger and more densely populated countries, and, in general, would have to work a great deal harder than they would for a similar material standard of living, with a much higher proportion of old people only partly balanced by a smaller number of children to support. So long as we are willing to accept this however (and nobody

knows the amount of real leisure that we can stand) the problems do not seem insurmountable. Foreign tourists from high-density civilization might pay for most of our imports. We could afford to take a high proportion of foreign students and to give them a better education than could be provided by rapidly expanding populations elsewhere. So long as we charged enough for it, the brain drain could even become our major export.

Many people fear that in a static or declining population the steady increase in the burden of old people could not be supported by the dwindling young. It is worth pointing out that, in an only slowly varying population, even if nobody ever died again the number over 65 can increase only by around 1½ per cent of the number under 65 each year. This is much less than the increase of productivity of which we are technically entirely capable.

In a population of only a million the advantages would be far more specialized and the disadvantages more numerous. While there would be room for every adult to have his or her own helicopter, making minor road maintenance largely unnecessary, we could hardly support the industrial base to build them for ourselves. The number of occupations available would be few and it is difficult to think even of any invisible export except for catering for tourists. A nation of rich hoteliers and tourist guides, buying all their manufactured needs abroad, could be extremely free and comfortable, but would be unlikely to have any very rich and distinctive cultural life. This would be regarded as an optimum state by very few of us.

I like to travel around and I like a choice between many ways of life. My personal preference, therefore, would be for the 30 million people, But I would be very hesitant about calling it the only optimum, although to many who do not share my interest in the countryside and its wild life it might still have an appeal simply because conditions of life could remain more stable (or stagnant according to another view) than with a higher population. It would be socially much easier to achieve than the others, as a far smaller change would be needed in our present family size. Many people who are concerned with the difficult problems of today have failed to realize that most of Britain's population increase over the last few decades has been due to the increase of expectation of life rather than, except briefly during the "bulge", to a large birth rate. We have at the moment a birth rate very little above the replacement rate, and if we could but ensure that no unwanted children were born we might well find ourselves below it without any positive action at all. If we did decide to take positive action to reduce our numbers faster, little might be needed beyond, for example, subsidizing comfortable small flats for childless couples.

Finally, what do I think we *will* do? I don't

know. One of the biggest difficulties facing a scientist interested in human problems is that, after addressing himself at pressing public request and with fair success to the problem of how everyone can have more cake, he discovers that what the public really want is to eat it. We can have the advantages of any one of the ways of living I have discussed, but we can't simultaneously have the advantages of all of them. It would be nice to think of several quite different densities coexisting with free transfer between them, but I think that Britain is too small for this to be stable. I hope the world is not too small, so that whatever most of us choose the rest have a way out.

64

POPULATION DENSITY AND THE STYLE OF SOCIAL LIFE

Nathan Keyfitz

To see how population density can occur at a rudimentary level of culture and what its effects may be, think of hunting groups with given apparatus, say spears or bows and arrows. Following Clifford Geertz (1963) and Julian Steward (1955) we observe that if the animals which they hunt move in herds, as do caribou, then large groups of hunters can pursue them. When they find a herd and attack successfully, there will be food for all. This herding of the animal prey is reflected in the gathering together of men, and communities can be large. If on the other hand the prey consists of small animals spread through a forest and caught one at a time, then men will have to spread out correspondingly; the large community cannot

Reprinted from *Bioscience* 16: 868-73, 1966, with the permission of the publishers.

come into existence; human life will be lived out in isolated families. This latter condition, says Steward, applies to the Bushman and Eskimo, who have little in common but the dispersion of their game. Larger groups appeared among the Athabaskans and Algonkians of Canada and probably the prehorse plains' bison hunters.

This primary fact of dispersion or concentration will determine other circumstances. Isolated families cannot evolve the division of labor that is possible in bigger communities. In larger groups, specialization is likely to arise as some individuals become more adept at making spears, others at sighting herds, others at the tasks of surrounding the prey. Specialization will mean a variety of occupations, and, insofar as men are made by their work, a variety of men. Some of the occupations will have more prestige than others, perhaps because they require rarer skills. Even at this primitive level, where money may not exist in any form, the notion of a market for talent and a corresponding prestige hierarchy has a possible bearing.

Prestige is a source of power. Ambitious individuals can use occupational prestige to gain further power, especially if they have organizational ability. This suggests an interaction of economic and political phases, never entirely separated in real life. My only point here is that both the economy and the polity are more elaborated in large communities than in small, and hence more to be looked for in tribes living off herds of big game than in those living on dispersed small animals. The sociability of the animal, so to speak, permits a higher degree of sociability in the men; density causes density. To go one step more, and exaggerate somewhat, the animals have created the economic and political structures in the human group.

Human history and ecology did not stop at the hunting culture. The great change in society was the invention of agriculture, which even in the form of neolithic shifting cultivation permits much higher density than does hunting. Is the discovery of planting and tilling the cause of greater human density? Or was the causation the other way, the density coming first and forcing men to utilize their environment more intensively? Fortunately we do not need to stop here to investigate this question of metahistory. The important fact is that agriculturalists can produce a surplus, which hunters can rarely manage. Robert M. Adams (1965) has described the agricultural base of the early cities. The farmer can grow enough for himself and his family and have, let us say, 5% left over. Once this technological achievement occurs, then 5% of the population can live in cities. It becomes worthwhile for a ruler to dominate the farmer, to collect the food as booty or taxes, and use it to support an army and a court. The patriarch becomes a prince.

Some of the troubles, as well as the glories, of civilization are implicit in the first cities, however small they may have been by modern standards. The total number of people which could congregate was limited, because strong political organization was needed to dominate a countryside, and an organization that tried to spread too far would be diluted and lose its control; the ancient empires often did outreach themselves in this way and fell apart. Physically, the area of control could not be too extended, since the transport of grain by ox-cart, the means used in the land empires of Asia, has natural limits set by the fact that the ox has to be fueled from the cargo. Among premachine cities, Rome did attain a population of nearly a million, but this was by virtue of extraordinarily competent, and harsh, organization of the lands around the Mediterranean, and by the use of sea transport for the movement of North African and Balkan grain.

Long before ecology or sociology became formal studies, a North African writer and politician called Ibn Khaldhun described with the utmost clarity how the population that could be concentrated in the capital city of an empire increased when the skill of the ruler and the discipline of his army and tax collectors enabled him to dominate a larger area of countryside, and how the population of the same city diminished when the rule was weaker so that the outlying provinces could successfully revolt from the exactions of the capital.

I have referred, then, to several levels of density—the dispersed hunters, the larger hunting group, the agriculturists, the preindustrial city of landlords and princes organizing the countryside and living off the proceeds.

The city which constituted the capital of a despotic empire or of one of its provinces is not the only historical type. In Europe cities grew up specifically released from feudal ties, exempted from the domination of princes or land-holders, their sustenance obtained by trade, religious, or entertainment functions, their independence assured by a sworn brotherhood of armed merchants. Not having to oppress a peasantry in order to secure their food, they could be loose in their internal arrangements; a medieval proverb says that "City air makes men free." The typical modern western city lives by a great extension of these same nonpolitical functions, and especially by manufacturing with mechanical power. Far from having to squeeze its food from the countryside, the city has become an autonomous economic force. Today, the countryside wants city goods more than the city wants food. The concentrated population of cities, which in the preindustrial empires was parasitic, has now become incredibly productive. Exploitation, if that is the right word, goes the other way from that of Ibn Khaldhun's account; rural legislators tax the cities to maintain support prices for grains, butter and other foods. Today's pattern, at least in the United States, England, and other western countries, is that men are more productive in dense settlements than in sparse ones.

The increase of cities, especially the increase of very large cities, is to be seen on all continents. Not only in the rich countries as foci of industry and trade, but in the poorest, to which industry has hardly come, the cities are expanding. In fact, during the 1950's the urban populations of developed countries increased by 25%, while those of underdeveloped countries increased by 55%. The increase of poor, dense populations was twice as rapid as that of rich ones, Bourgeois-Pichat (1966) tells us.

How could that 55% increase occur, if what I have said about the preindustrial city being dependent on the limited surplus of a countryside is true? The surplus food of the Asian peasantry did not increase by 55% in the 1950's; it hardly increased at all. How can Djakarta be five times as populous as it was before World War II, and three times as populous as ancient Rome at the highest point of its imperial power? Djakarta has not much more industry than Rome had. Its weak civil or military domination of an island territory, in some degree democratic, cannot compare in extractive power with the iron rule of Rome. The answer, of course, is that it draws food from foreign territories, including the United States; some of it paid for with the export of raw materials; some of it borrowed; some as gifts.

Unable or unwilling to exploit its own peasantry, the large contemporary nonindustrial city more and more bases itself ecologically on the fields of the American west, together with the ships and harbors which link those fields with its massive populations. Population in the Asian countryside itself is growing beyond food supplies; far from having a surplus to ship to the city, the peasant is himself hungry.

Once the local countryside can no longer produce enough food for its own inhabitants so that these must be supported by foreign food, they tend naturally to gather into such seaport cities as Djakarta, Calcutta, and Rio de Janeiro, as close as possible to the spot where the boats will discharge their cargoes of American, or

occasionally Burmese or Cambodian, grain. If people are to be fed from abroad it is cheaper to have them at the seaports than dispersed through the countryside. At the present time the United States is shipping about 800,000 tons of grain per month to India alone. At the Asian standard of about one pound per person per day, this is enough for 40,000,000 people to live on; that number happens to be about equal to all the citizens of India living in the seacoast cities. If population continues to increase in the countryside and food does not, one can expect further flight to those cities.

One could say much about what density and size will do to the condition of dependence of those cities. We know that their inhabitants tend to perform services rather than make goods. The services have the function of distributing the claim to the food shipments, the dominant ideal being to give employment rather than to get work done. Some studies have indicated that the new migrants to the cities retain links with the countryside. Others show that the simple and traditional patterns of association in the countryside are transferred to the city, which thereby seems like a number of contiguous villages, lacking only their fields and their crops. These dense cities of rural culture are a new phenomenon in the world.

For some quite different concomitants of density, shown in their most accentuated form, we must go to those world cities of the 19th century which were ecological consequences of the railroad and steamship—New York, London, Paris, Berlin. In the 20th-century West a process of dispersal has occurred; cities produced by the automobile are less dense than those produced by the railroad and street car. We are getting strip cities, of which the best known is Megalopolis, the name Jean Gottman (1961) gave to Boston—New York—Washington.

The industrial city of the 19th century as well as the strip city of the late 20th century intensifies competition on many levels. We must not only find a livelihood, we must find a life, each of us for himself, in the crowded city. This search for a tolerable physical and moral existence preoccupies every city dweller, and it has drastic consequences for urban society as a whole. Just as Darwin saw the animal or plant adapting to a niche in which it is partly sheltered from competition, so the sociologist Durkheim (1960) sees the city man restlessly searching for, and adapting to, a niche constituted by a specialized occupation and specialized personality. During the strike of airplane mechanics I was part of an undifferentiated mass seeking tickets at an airline counter. If one had to face daily the direct competition of millions of people, the struggle would so weigh on each of us that existence would be impossible for our spirits as well as our bodies. One's niche may be teacher, stock broker, or truck driver; it requires skills that others lack, or involves work that others do not want to do. It gives each a place with a certain minimum of predictable security. We are under constant inducement to better our position, and we seek to do so by further specialization.

Now the electronics engineer in Chicago, say, has to concern himself, at most, with the competition of other electronics engineers. But he does not even have to cope with them, at least in the short run. There are a hundred specialties within the field of electronics, and within each of these recognized specialties an individual practitioner, through his own tastes and capacities, can make himself unique. People in a particular plant come to depend on him. If the city is, on the one side, a jungle of potentially infinite and destroying competition, on the other, it shows a nearly infinite capacity of its members to differentiate themselves, to become useful to one another, to become needed.

The differentiated citizen can afford to be tolerant of those he meets, even to like them. This could not be true if competition were more direct, with individuals as personally ambitious as we know them to be in western countries. The struggle for upward mobility, characterizing all developed societies, can only through the process of specialization avoid the harshness of personal character that the blast of full competition would create.

The differentiation is only possible within an economic space that is honeycombed with organizations that are themselves competing, at a supra-individual level, and have their own lives, usually longer than those of individual men. The plants and firms live among a host of other organizations which serve varied interests—trade unions, professional societies, sporting clubs.

Corresponding to the infinite shades and gradations of personalities and types of work, spread through a complex social space, an unprecedented sensitivity to symbol systems comes into existence in the city. The contemporary mathematician, or biologist, or sociologist, along with such other products of city culture as the banker, the store manager, or the traffic analyst, each has his own characteristic set of symbols and has to cope with unprecedented variety, subtlety, and sheer mass of material. Typically 8 or 10 years of intense training, for most of us only possible between the ages of about 15 and 25, are the necessary means to develop the sensitivity, the awareness of issues, the minimum basic storehouse of facts in a given field. You only put up with me, if you do, because you suppose that I have an extensive and powerful storehouse of facts in my own field, which is the mathematics of population. This reciprocal imputation of subtle, mysterious, and extensive knowledge is what permits mutual respect in the more specialized residents of the city. We do not know just what it is that the other man knows, but we assume he knows something and is capable of doing his own job with reasonable competence, whether it is embryology or pants cutting.

Such a basis of respect is characteristically metropolitan. In a society of smaller volume such as a village, each gets to know all about the few score or the few hundred people with whom he will have contact in the course of a lifetime. He knows them as whole people, is concerned with literally everything about them.

Each of us as city people has contact in a day with as many individuals as the villager meets in the course of a lifetime; this includes store clerks, bus conductors, taxi drivers, students, colleagues, theatre ushers, not to mention those we pass as we walk or drive along the street. It would destroy us if we had to react to every one of them as people. We want to know about each of them only enough to cover his particular relationship with us. We care only that the bus conductor is an authorized employee of the company and will take our fare and drop us at the corner of Madison and 42nd Street. Whether he is happily married with four children or a debauched bachelor, whether he is Presbyterian or Catholic, we never inquire. His uniform tells us everything about him that we need to know. It is mere personal whim on our part if we even look at his face.

The well adapted citizen of the high income metropolis has learned to protect himself against its potentially infinitely varied stimulation. In some measure he becomes blasé; whatever happens he has seen something more exciting. He becomes absent-minded and dulls his recollection of gross stimuli and even his perception of them in order to accentuate his capacity to react to the subtler issues and symbols of his own business, professional, technical, or scholarly life. He goes out of his way to cultivate ignorance of fields outside his own. Whereas constant full exposure to what the city offers and demands would weary and frustrate him, by protecting himself sufficiently against stimuli he need show only a slight antipathy or even be perfectly good-natured. This is the nature of urban contacts, suggestively portrayed by Georg Simmel (1964). Note that this characterization applies only to those members of the city who have adapted to city life over two or three generations, and as a result are suitably educated, and are productive enough to command the facilities of the city. They do not apply to the recent migrant to Chicago from the rural south, or to Calcutta from inland Bengal.

The ultimate refuge against the pressures of the metropolis is flight. A quiet place in the country becomes the ideal of all and, in one form or another, the seasonal recuperation of most. But with the acceleration of the population growth, and especially with the improvement of transport through the private automobile, that quiet place in the country, the most precious of resources, is bound to become scarcer. We not only are a larger population, and able to get out of the city more easily, but a larger fraction of us has the means to travel. We are 197 million people in the 3.6 million square miles of the United States. Deducting

the areas of the cities, superhighways, lakes, deserts (both natural and those made by man, for instance by mining operations), we could still each have 4 acres of countryside—which means just enough to get out of the sight of one another. But not very long ago the United States was growing at 1.5% per year, a pace which would double our numbers each 45 years. It would halve the 4 acres in 45 years, quarter it in 90 years. I mention these figures only to show that within the lifetime of children now born, at an increase of 1.5% per year, dispersion would become impossible; no amount of redeployment would enable us to get out of sight of one another.

Simultaneous with the increase in numbers, the advance of technology makes each of us more mobile, and requires more space—especially highways—to be set aside merely for facilitating our movement. Aside from this, if effective density is counted in units of potential contact rather than in people per square mile, we increase our effective density merely in improving transportation. Man is unlike other creatures in drastically remaking his means of locomotion. United States' automobile and truck registrations were 86 million in 1964, and will pass the 100 million mark by the end of the 1960's. Nearly 10 million new vehicles are being put on the road each year, offset by only two-thirds that number of scrappings; this fact alone would tend to crowd us even if we were the same number of people. Year by year we are both more in numbers *and* are moving faster, always within a fixed people-container, the terrestrial area of the United States. The result is rising pressure and temperature, apparently under the operation of laws analogous to those governing the behavior of gases.

I do not know how we shall respond. Will we build up higher capacity for discretion and reserve? Will we develop the sort of etiquette of noninterference with our neighbors—silence, dignity, and good humor—that helps make life tolerable on a long submarine voyage? I knew a charming family in Paris during the housing shortage who had two and a half rooms, counting the bathroom, for five people. They managed the situation well, and despite proximity each was able to have his private thoughts without interference. The life required a degree of self-discipline that not all of us could furnish. Events on the city streets this hot summer do not suggest that our civilization is moving toward those standards of reserve, discretion and respect for the rights of others that would make greater density acceptable.

In fact, the response of society to higher density is usually the very opposite of reserve and respect for the privacy of individuals; it is rather interference and planning. The frontier had no traffic lights or parking regulations. People did not have to regulate their activities by the activities of others. If the clocks and watches of frontier families were randomly in error, little inconvenience would have resulted; but if those of a modern city were wrong, say by 2 hours, all its activities would be brought to a halt. Everything we do interlocks with what others do. The frontier needed no zoning bylaws or building standards. The necessity for all these forms of planning has come with density. Richard Meier (1962) describes an arrangement of the city of Madras in South India, one of the growing harbor cities I have spoken of, such that 100 million people could live in it, but life would have to be planned in the most excruciating detail. People would not even be allowed to own bicycles, simply because parking individually owned bicycles would tie up the streets. Movement would be restricted, and all that was necessary would be provided by mass transportation.

The density continuum from the frontier to Meier's imaginary Madras is also a planning continuum; density and planning seem to be positively correlated.

Less clear is the degree in which freedom in the West has declined with planning, and hence with density. George Orwell's *1984* is inconceivable without high population density, supplemented by closed circuit television and other devices to eliminate privacy. It exhibits in extreme form an historical process by which the State has been extending its power at the expense of the Church, the Family, and the Local Community, a process extending over 150 years.

Though the trend to State power has accompanied the increase of density, I do not know whether, up to now, density, even com-bined with the march of technology, and combined with State control, has diminished the individual's effective freedom on balance. After all, the individual benefits from the State and from the increasing wealth that has gone along with density and with planning, including clocks and traffic lights. In the United States the gain to freedom through rising average wealth may offset the attack on freedom through State measures. In the USSR increasing wealth seems to be bringing about a loosening of totalitarian structures.

A convincing account of the relation between sparseness and abundance on the one side and national character on the other is presented by David Potter (1954). The wealth of the economy, first on the frontier and then in the cities, encouraged mobility and individual success as an ideal. The real wealth of the country—and this arose from spaciousness in the largely agricultural epoch when national character was being formed—was great enough that a mobile, optimistic, ambitious, and generous attitude would have scope for success and would often succeed. One man who succeeded with these traits encouraged the growth of similar qualities in others. In the United States, sparsely settled during most of its history, when men were scarce and resources plentiful, labor was sought after by employers rather than the other way round. This gave the common man confidence in himself; self-confidence made him open-handed and he taught his children open-handedness.

Plenty also encouraged freedom—if there are enough goods for everyone, let each one take the part of the patrimony he wants or can earn. If there are enough seats on the train each passenger can choose the one he wants without supervision; a shortage of seats compels a system of reservations, which is to say planning. Abundance brings men to potential economic equality—at least in the sense that each can hope to find the resources that will make his labor fruitful. By virtue of the same fact, it inclines them to political equality. Density and poverty make for the opposite of democracy—as Wittfogel (1957) argues in his study of hydraulic civilization.

If density tends to shackle us, and wealth to free us, then the question of what will happen in the United States in the 21st century that is only 34 years away is still an open question. I do not know enough of the conditions of the present race between exhaustion of raw materials on the one hand and technology on the other to make a firm statement, but suppose technology wins and we become much denser but also much richer. For us the wealth worked counter to the density. But what about those dense societies which have little prospect of attaining the wealth of the United States and whose density, combined with their traditional agricultural techniques, already places them near the point of starvation?

I started this discussion with the pre-industrial environment, and went on to those contemporary preindustrial cities clustered around the coasts of the underdeveloped world in which ports, built for the export of now obsolete colonial tropical products, are operating at capacity to unload cargoes of food. Here are larger cities than Ibn Khaldhun contemplated. If those city dwellers oppress any peasantry it is that of the United States. But it is not that of the United States either, since American productivity has increased faster in agriculture than in industry these last years. The labor cost of that food to the American farmer is at an all-time low, and in any case, the city dweller is paying for PL480 shipments, for which the Prairie farmer gets spendable cash. I said that if poor peasant populations are to be fed by imported grain rather than by grain from their own countryside, then it is convenient for them to bring their mouths to the harbors where the grain is unloaded, rather than having the grain carried to them dispersed over the countryside, and that this is the basis for much contemporary urban growth.

How different the case would be if the United States had given fertilizer factories rather than wheat. Then more grain could sprout throughout the South Asian mainland, and there would be no reason for the peasants to accumulate in the city in numbers beyond the industrial jobs available.

I have spoken of the problem of privacy in the dense industrial city. The problem is accentuated in the cities of Asia, where millions of similar beings exist in close contact, without the shelter provided to each through special-ization and the division of labor. In the West we each come to have a special claim on the production of others through our own special-ized production, especially through the volum-inous contribution which each of us can make in our highly capitalized society. We have some degree of uniqueness of personality through all those devices by which we differentiate our-selves, some of them arising out of our work, but others quite separate; sports and hobbies for instance, which the affluent society lavishly supports and equips. Education, also a result of our wealth, inducts us into elaborate, differ-entiated symbol systems and into that etiquette of restraint and reserve which mitigates the closeness of city living.

The citizen of the poor crowded city is in all these respects disadvantaged. He has neither specialized work, nor capital to make his work productive, nor hobbies to reinforce a personal identity, nor education to make him sensitive to complex symbol systems. Here is the hurt of density without its benefits.

The only defense for the poverty-stricken urbanite in the tropics is through the retention of some of his rural habits; he may manage a kind of village existence, with village ecological relations complete in all respects except that the village fields are absent. The village within the city of Calcutta or Madras may well have its own temple and traditional service occupations: sweepers, watchmen, priests, headmen. Some physical production by village methods goes on, and there are tanners, potters, and makers of bullock-carts—but very few farmers. Each com-pressed village in the city may have some residue of the administrative structure of the village its inhabitants have left, and village factionalism need not be forgotten on the move to the city. The village in the city may have a rate of growth more rapid than the old village, because its death rate may be low, its birth rate remains almost up to rural levels, and the city is swelled by new entrants from the countryside. It is hungry, as the rural village often was, but now its hunger is a matter of high political importance, affecting both national and inter-national politics.

Our picture now is of two dense agglomer-ations of mankind facing one another, both urban, one rich and one poor. America takes its cities into the countryside—it becomes an urban society through and through. Asia remains rural, even to parts of the dense agglomerations at the seaports—it brings its rural culture into the cities. In a sense, the rich city has called the poor one into existence, first by DDT and medicine which lower the death rate of India from perhaps 35 per thousand to 20 per thousand, and then by the provision of food.

In a quite different sense, Europe had earlier contributed to Asian population. The industrial revolution of Europe and America demanded raw materials, and this demand was translated into a demand for people who would produce its goods. The needs of Europe for sugar, spices, and rubber brought into existence large populations, for 'example in Indonesia; Java grew from under 5 million in 1815 to 40 million by World War II. And when our technical advance, especially western synthetics, enabled us to make the things that formerly could only be produced by tropical sunshine and tropical labor, those populations were left high and dry. They are functionless in relation to the Western industrial machine which brought them into existence, but they keep growing nonetheless.

Western governments and electorates sense the tragic state of affairs, and, at least vaguely, feel responsible for this aftermath of colonialism; therefore we provide food and other kinds of aid. But such are the dilemmas of doing good in this difficult world that each shipment of food draws more people to the seaports, and we arrive at nothing more constructive than a larger population than before dependent on shipments of food. If the need for food is a temporary emergency, philanthropy is highly recommended, but the condition of tropical agriculture and population seems to be chronic rather than acute.

And yet the aid cannot be stopped. As the populations of these port cities grow so does the problem of producing and shipping food to them. But so also do the economic, political, and moral problems of cutting off the aid. When famine was the work of God, whose acts man lacked the technical capacity to offset, such issues did not arise.

The only escape is through the economic development of the countries of Asia, Africa, and Latin America. With increase of income

arises the sort of communication system through which people can receive and act on signals in regard to the size of their families. Americans since 1957 have come to understand that their families had been too large—signals reached them to this effect through the price system and through the difficulties of placing children in college and in a job. For underdeveloped people such a signalling system of prices and costs is not in existence, and messages that create a desirable feedback and permit automatic control do not carry.

On the other hand, the growth of population for many reasons itself inhibits the development process which could solve the population problem. That is why some students of the matter think that the control of population should be tackled directly. Each point by which the birth rate falls makes the process of saving and investment and hence development that much easier.

I have spoken of two sorts of dense agglomerations of people looking at one another across the oceans. The one is wealthy, modern, productive, highly differentiated by occupation, handling complex symbol systems, dominating the environment. The other is poor, traditional, nonproductive except for services that are not badly wanted, less differentiated by occupation, illiterate or barely literate, highly dependent on the environment. Our rich American cities contain a minority which is taking refuge from rural poverty. Some Asian cities consist of a majority of such refugees.

I have refrained from reference to the individual human tragedy of the multiplying homeless sidewalk-dwellers of Calcutta and other cities of the tropics. No one can say that their plight is irremediable; evidently a number of countries are achieving development today, including Hong Kong, Taiwan, Mexico, Turkey. On the other hand, I see no grounds for the facile optimism that declares that development is inevitable for all. To turn the despairing kind of density into the affluent kind requires that three issues be squarely met: food supplies must be assured, industry established, population controlled. Only in some of the underdeveloped countries are these seen as key issues and seriously tackled.

Is the hardship of life in the crowded and

poor city itself a stimulus to effective action? Do density and poverty make for greater sensitivity to the real problems and greater judiciousness in their treatment? Not necessarily; especially not for the miserable newcomers, the first ill-adapted migrant generation to the city. In the slums of first settlement, whether in 19th century London and Paris or 20th century Chicago and Calcutta, city mobs can be readily aroused by their troubles to action and to violence, but they do not necessarily see the root of their frustrations and the way to overcome them. Penetrating analysis does not guide mob action. The crowd, mobilized by some incident, acts with a violence out of all proportion to the event that excited its anger. It streams through a city street, stops to throw bottles at the police who reply with tear gas, overturns automobiles, is finally dispersed by a National Guard armed with bayonets. Far from being a disappearing relic of the past, it is with us both in the temperate zone and in the tropics, in wealthy countries and in poor ones. Food riots occur in Bombay and civil riots in Chicago, New York and Cleveland. This ultimate manifestation of population density, which colors the social history of all continents, is a challenge to learn more about the causes of tension and frustration in city life.

References

Adams, R. M. 1965. *Land Behind Baghdad.* University of Chicago Press, Chicago, Ill.

Bourgeois-Pichat, Jean. 1966. *Population Growth and Development.* International Conciliation, No. 556, January. Carnegie Endowment for International Peace.

Durkheim, Emile. 1960. *De la division du travail social.* 7th ed. Chap. III, La solidarité due à la division du travail ou organique, Presses Universitaires de France, Paris. pp. 79-102.

Geertz, Clifford. 1963. *Agricultural Involution: The Process of Ecological Change in Indonesia.* University of California Press, Berkeley, Calif.

Gottman, Jean. 1961. *Megalopolis: The Urbanized Northeastern Seaboard of the United States.* Twentieth Century Fund, New York.

Hawley, Amos H. 1950. *Human Ecology: A theory of Community Structure.* Ronald Press, New York.

Meier, R. L. 1962. Relations of technology to the design of very large cities. In *India's Urban Future* (Roy Turner Ed.). University of California Press, Berkeley, Calif. pp. 299-323.

Potter, David M. 1954. *People of Plenty: Economic Abundance and the American Character.* University of Chicago Press, Chicago, Ill.

Riesman, David. 1950. *The Lonely Crowd: A Study of the Changing American Character.* University of Chicago Press, Chicago, Ill.

Simmel, Georg. 1964. The Metropolis and Mental Life. In *The Sociology of Georg Simmel* (edited and translated by Kurt H. Wolff). Free Press of Glencoe, Collier-Macmillan, London. pp. 409-424.

Steward, J. 1955. *Theory of Culture Change.* University of Illinois Press, Urbana, Ill.

Wirth, Louis, 1964. Urbanism as a Way of Life. In *On Cities and Social Life,* University of Chicago Press, Chicago, Ill. pp. 60-83.

Wittfogel, Karl A. 1957. *Oriental Despotism: A Comparative Study of Total Power.* Yale University Press, New Haven, Conn.

Wolff, Kurt H. (Ed.) 1964. *The Sociology of Georg Simmel.* Collier-Macmillan, London.

65

HUMAN WATER NEEDS AND WATER USE IN AMERICA

Charles C. Bradley

The current rapid rise in population poses many problems, among them the question, Where are the limits, if any? More carefully stated for America, the question seems to be, how many people can we sustain at what standard of living?

My purpose in this article is to examine one vital resource, water—(i) to show the minimum amount necessary to sustain human life, (ii) to show the amount we are now using in the United States to maintain our standard of living, and (iii) to indicate from these figures when we may expect to find certain ceilings imposed on the crop of human beings in this country.

While water economics is admittedly important in the complex problem of water supply, no discussion of this aspect of the problem is attempted in this article.

Water Needs of Man

The 2 quarts or so of water which a man needs daily for drinking is a requirement obvious to anyone. Less obvious is the equally vital but much larger volume of water needed to sustain a man's food chain from soil to stomach. This is the water necessary to raise the wheat for his daily bread and the vegetables that fill his salad bowl. This is also the still larger volume required to raise alfalfa to feed a steer from which a man may get his daily slice of meat. All this water represents a rather rigid requirement for human life, and it is water which is consumed, in the sense that it is

removed from the hydrosphere and returned to the atmosphere.

An adult human has a daily food requirement of about 2½ pounds, dry weight. If he is strictly a vegetarian, an illustrative approximation of the water requirements for his food chain can be made by assuming man *can* "live by bread alone."

Wheat has a transpiration ratio of 500 (1); that is, ideally it takes 500 pounds of water circulating through the wheat plant from the soil to the air to bring 1 pound (dry weight) of wheat plant to maturity. If grain to be milled represents half the weight of the wheat plant, we can say that it takes 1000 pounds of water to make 1 pound of bread. Therefore, it takes 2500 pounds of water, or approximately 300 gallons, to make 2½ pounds of bread. Three hundred gallons per day per person is, therefore, probably not far from the theoretical minimum water requirement to sustain human life.

The introduction of animal protein to a man's diet lengthens the food chain, thereby greatly increasing water requirement. To illustrate, let us assume what might be called a simplified but generous American diet of 1 pound of animal fat and protein (beef) and 2 pounds of vegetable foods (bread) per day. It takes about 2 years to raise a steer. If butchered when it is 2 years old, the animal may yield 700 pounds of meat. Distributed over the 2 years, this is about 1 pound of meat per day. It may be seen, therefore, that this diet requires a steady-state situation of about one steer per person.

A mature steer consumes between 25 and 35 pounds of alfalfa a day and drinks about 12 gallons of water (2). Alfalfa has a transpiration ratio of 800 (1) hence 20,000 pounds of water are required to bring 25 pounds of alfalfa to maturity. In other words, a little over 2300 gallons per day per man are required to introduce 1 pound of beef protein and fat into a person's diet. Add to this the 200 gallons necessary to round out his diet with 2 pounds of vegetable matter and we have a total water requirement of about 2500 gallons per day per person for a substantial American diet.

It should be remembered that these are

conservative figures, because transpiration ratios are derived from carefully controlled laboratory experiments and not from data collected in the field, where perhaps half the total rainfall is lost directly by evaporation and does not pass through the plant body. It should be noted, too, that the water cost of a pound of meat is about 25 times that of a pound of vegetable. We should anticipate a similar ratio for the water cost of wool to that of cotton or for the water cost of butter to that of margarine. In any case, somewhere between 300 and 2500 gallons per day is the bare subsistence water cost for one naked human being.

Water Use in the United States

When we talk about "use" we have to add to the foregoing figures the water requirements for all our fibers, lumber, and newsprint, as well as the water needed to process steel, to run the washing machine, to flush the toilet, and to operate our air conditioning and our local laundries, and especially that required to sweep our sewage to the sea. It is therefore pertinent, at this point, to digress slightly in order to clarify our concept of the American standard of living, or at least that portion sustained by water use. The American standard of living is not a wholly unmixed blessing. In achieving such luxuries as the flush toilet, synthetic detergents, cheap newspapers, and atomic power we find ourselves also achieving polluted streams, sudsy well-water, radioactive milk, and poisoned oysters.

Underlying and supporting our standard of living are powerful industrial centers and a mass production scheme which creates inexpensive commodities. This scheme rests firmly upon certain prodigal wastes, polluted streams being a prime example. To clean up the streams would take a tremendous amount of money which might otherwise be spent on cheap commodities. On the basis of some standard of values, this could be construed as a lowering of the standard of living.

To illustrate the magnitude of the practical problems we have created for ourselves, we note that if river-disposal of waste were suddenly denied the city of St. Louis, the city fathers would have to decide what else to do with the daily discharge of 200,000 gallons of urine and 400 tons of solid body-wastes, to say nothing of all the industrial wastes. River disposal of human waste, though cheap, involves a double loss of resources. On the one hand there is the polluted river; on the other, the depleted soil. So long as these losses are deemed less important than the production of inexpensive commodities which they support, we will have to accept our befouled streams and depleted soil as part of the cost of our standard of living. In addition to waste disposal we can see that water power, river transportation, fisheries, and water recreation are all well-established items in our standard of living. Therefore, as we move into a discussion of water use, especially future use of surface waters, we must remember that most of our runoff is already committed to our living standard and is working hard to support it.

A figure for water use in the United States can be obtained by subtracting that water which we are *not* using from the total water available.

Thirty inches of annual rainfall on the surface area of the United States (exclusive of Alaska and Hawaii) gives us theoretically nearly 5000 billion gallons per day, a figure which represents the total water available for our use (3). Of this 5000 billion gallons, about 1300 billion gallons a day, or about one-fourth of the rainfall, is discharged by our rivers (4). It may also be said that this discharge figure contains the groundwater increment, since stream flow is largely maintained by effluent seepage from the ground.

It can be seen that 75 percent of our rainfall is returned to the atmosphere through evaporation and transpiration. It is difficult to assess the relative contributions of these two factors. A ratio of 50:50 is probably not far from the truth. From a utilitarian standpoint, evaporation constitutes pure waste, and it may be that here some significant gains in water conservation can be made. But until this is done, we have to reckon this loss, too, as part of the price being paid for our standard of living.

Very little of the area of the United States which could produce crops for man is not actually doing so. The largest nonproducing area is, of course, our desert, and even here we are irrigating, using stream water exported from regions of water surplus. Additionally, we are forcing the desert to raise crops through the use of ground water. But in many such areas we have considerable evidence that the annual draft from the ground-water reservoir exceeds the annual recharge. Consequently, some of these operations will be short-lived and perhaps socially and economically catastrophic for the people involved.

About 2 percent or more of the surface of the United States is "paved" with cities and roads and will probably remain agriculturally unproductive until some far-sighted city planners provide for extensive roof gardens. Another 2 or 3 percent of the land in this country is devoted to wilderness and national parks. While these do not directly produce crops for man, we do include them and their waters in our standard of living. Finally, we can say that bad agricultural management had reduced the productivity of a fraction of our arable land, and that this percentage must be added to our total for unproductive lands. Let us make a quasi-educated guess and say that as much as 10 percent of our land in areas of abundant rainfall is, at the moment, non-productive.

Three-fourths of the nation's rain (3700 billion gallons per day) falls on about half the nation's area, and it is this three-fourths, largely unmetered, that does the big job of raising crops for America. As concluded previously, perhaps one-tenth of this rain falls on unproductive areas. Hence we may say that 3300 billion gallons per day are productive of crops or surplus water. Of this, about one-fourth is unconsumed runoff, giving a remainder of about 2500 billion gallons per day which we are *consuming*, though perhaps wastefully, to raise our crops. In a population of 180 million people, this amounts to approximately 13,800 gallons per day per person. In addition, 240 billion gallons per day are metered out of our streams, lakes, and ground-water reservoirs to serve industry, municipalities, and rural areas

(4); over half of it is consumed in irrigation and other processes. This 240 billion gallons per day is almost 1400 gallons per day per person, a figure which now must be added to the 13,800 gallons for a grand total of 15,200 gallons per day per person, Thus we find that the per capita daily use of water in the United States is in excess of 15,000 gallons, 95 percent of which is consumed.

Some Population Limits in the United States

How many people could we feed if all the rainfall in the United States were completely utilized? Since 300 gallons per person per day is needed for a vegetarian diet, we could, in theory, sustain about 17 billion people, or approximately 8 times the present world population. If, on the other hand, we decided to feed people on the "generous American" diet, we discover, by the same sort of calculation, that we could feed about 2 billion people, or somewhat less than the present world population. If we admit that loss of water through evaporation is unavoidable, as discussed earlier in this article, we must cut these figures to 8 billion and 1 billion, respectively.

Assuming a population of 180 million and a rainfall of 5000 billion gallons per day, we discover that each person today theoretically has about 28,000 gallons per day for his use. We are now using 15,000 gallons per day per person, 95 percent of it consumptively. We might, therefore, conclude that if we could use every drop of rain that falls we could almost double our population with no decrease in the standard of living. But this is far from possible because there would then be no surface water to generate power, float ships, raise fish, and carry away the national sewage and waste.

The extent to which we can consume our runoff before our standard of living suffers is difficult to foresee. Involved are not only the waste-disposal and commercial uses of rivers but the fact that river water is generally most abundant and most available where it is least needed for agriculture.

Let us guess that we might safely and profitably use one-third of our remaining river water, or 400 billion gallons per day, for future development without expecting a resultant drop in our standard of living. Add to this figure the amount of water that falls on unproductive areas which might rather easily be made productive. We now have a total of about 750 billion gallons per day for future development. At 15,000 gallons per day per person we seemingly can accommodate 50 million more people, or a total population of 230 million, before our standard of living starts to suffer. There is little doubt that America will have reached that population figure well before the year 2000. The evidence of the moment suggests, then, that young Americans alive today will see a significant deterioration in their standard of living before they are much past middle age. Improved cropping, mulching, and other conservation practices could, of course, extend the grace period by a few years.

How far deterioration in the American standard of living will progress depends, of course, upon what action Americans choose to take on their own numbers problem—upon *what* action, and especially upon *when* they take it. Fortunately we have at our disposal human intelligence and considerable time in which intelligence can function. At present rates of rainfall and of population growth we should have almost 200 years before the American standard of living drops to subsistence level and Malthusian controls eliminate the necessity for intelligent action.

References and Notes

1. N. A. Maximov, *The Plant in Relation to Water* (Macmillan, New York, 1929).
2. F. W. Woll, *Productive Feeding of Farm Animals* (Lippincott, New York, 1921).
3. It is doubtful whether artificial conversion of salt water will ever make a significant difference in this total, although it may be of great significance to certain communities.
4. L. B. Leopold and W. B. Langbein, *A Primer on Water* (U.S. Government Printing Office, Washington, D.C., 1960).

66

REALITIES OF MINERAL DISTRIBUTION

Preston E. Cloud, Jr.

"*Is there intelligent life on earth?*"—Anonymous astronomer (Annual Report, Travelers Research Centre, Inc., Hartford, Conn., 1966, p. 4).

Introduction

No one could be more surprised than I at my being here on such an occasion, to talk on the realities of mineral distribution. In considering what qualifications your last two morning

Reprinted from the *Texas Quarterly* 11:103-26, 1968, with the permission of the author.

speakers have in common, however, I can see how it happened. What my good friend Alvin Weinberg and I share in confronting the problem of Mineral Resource Limits is innocence. We could, therefore, in the eyes of your symposium organizers, approach the subject without prejudice; although, as you are already aware or will soon find out, this is a deficiency easily overcome.

Optimism and imagination are happy human traits. They often make bad situations appear tolerable or even good. Man's ability to imagine solutions, however, commonly outruns his ability to find them. What does he do when it becomes clear that he is plundering, overpopulating, and despoiling his planet at such a horrendous rate that it is going to take some kind of a big leap, and soon, to avert irreversible degradation?

Dr. Weinberg, with his marvelous conception of a world set free by nuclear energy sees man at this juncture in history as comparable to the frog who was trying, unsuccessfully, to jump out of a deep rut. A second frog came along, and, seeing his friend in distress, told him to rest awhile while he fetched some sticks to build a platform from which it would be but a short leap to the top of the rut. When frog number two returned, however, his friend was nowhere to be seen. A glance around soon revealed him sitting at the top of the rut. "How did you get up there?" the second frog exclaimed. "Well," said the first frog, "I had to—a hell of a big truck came down the road." In this story we are the first frog, the truck is overpopulation, pollution, and dwindling mineral resources, and the extra oomph that gets us out of the rut is nuclear power—specifically the breeder reactor, and eventually contained fusion.

The inventive genius of man has got him out of trouble in the past. Why not now? Why be a spoil-sport when brilliant, articulate, and well-intentioned men assure us that all we need is more technology? Why? Because the present crisis is exacerbated by four conditions that reinforce each other in a very undesirable manner: (1) the achievements of medical technology which have brought on the run-away imbalance between birth and death rates, to which Dr. Ehrlich addresses himself; (2) the hypnotic but unsustainable national dream of an ever-increasing real Gross National Product based on obsolescence and waste; (3) the finite nature of the earth and particularly its accessible mineralized crust; and (4) the increased risk of irreversible spoilation of the environment which accompanies overpopulation, overproduction, waste, and the movement of ever-larger quantities of source rock for ever-smaller proportions of useful minerals.

Granted the advantages of big technological leaps, therefore, provided they are in the right direction, I see real hope for permanent long-range solutions to our problems as beginning with the taking of long-range views of them. Put in another way, we should not tackle vast problems with half-vast concepts. We must build a platform of scientific and social comprehension, while concurrently endeavoring to fill the rut of ignorance, selfishness, and complacency with knowledge, restraint, and demanding awareness on the part of an enlightened electorate. And we must not be

satisfied merely with getting the United States or North America through the immediate future, critical though that will be. We must consider what effects current and proposed trends and actions will have on the world as a whole for several generations hence, and how we can best influence those trends favorably the world over. Above all, we must consider how to preserve for the yet unborn the maximum flexibility of choices consistent with meeting current and future crises.

Rhetoric, however, either cornucopian or Malthusian, is no substitute for informed foresight and rational action or purposeful inaction.

What are the problems and misconceptions that impede the desired progress? And what must we invest in research and action—scientific, technological, *and* social—to assure a flexibility of resource options for the long range as well as for the immediate future? Not only until 1985, not only until the year 2000, not only even until the year 2050, but for a future as long as or longer than our past. In the nearly five billion years of earth history is man's brief stay of now barely a million years to be only a meteoric flash, and his industrial society less than that? Or will he last with reasonable amenities for as long as the dinosaurs?

Nature and Geography of Resources

Man's concept of resources, to be sure, depends on his needs and wants, and thus to a great degree on his locale and place in history, on what others have, and on what he knows about what they have and what might be possible for him to obtain. Food and fiber from the land, and food and drink from the waters of the earth have always been indispensable resources. So have the human beings who have utilized these resources and created demands for others—from birch bark to beryllium, from buffalo hides to steel and plastic. It is these other resources, the ones from which our industrial society has been created, about which I speak today. I refer, in particular, to the nonrenewable or wasting resources—mineral fuels which are converted into energy plus carbon, nuclear fuels, and the metals, chemicals, and industrial materials of geological origin which to some extent can be and even are recycled but which tend to become dispersed and wasted.

All such resources, except those that are common rocks whose availability and value depend almost entirely on economic factors plus fabrication, share certain peculiarities that transcend economics and limit technology and even diplomacy. They occur in local concentrations that may exceed their crustal abundances by thousands of times, and particular resources tend to be clustered within geochemical or metallogenic provinces from which others are excluded. Some parts of the earth are rich in mineral raw materials and others are poor.

No part of the earth, not even on a continent-wide basis, is self-sufficient in all critical metals. North America is relatively rich in molybdenum and poor in tin, tungsten, and manganese and, apparently, less well supplied with molybdenum. The great bulk of the world's gold appears to be in South Africa, which has relatively little silver but a good supply of platinum. Cuba and New Caledonia have well over half the world's total known reserves of nickel. The main known reserves of cobalt are in the Congo Republic, Cuba, New Caledonia, and parts of Asia. Most of the world's mercury is in Spain, Italy, and parts of the Sino-Soviet bloc. Industrial diamonds are still supplied mainly by the Congo.

Consider tin. Over half the world's currently recoverable reserves are in Indonesia, Malaya, and Thailand, and much of the rest is in Bolivia and the Congo. Known North American reserves are negligible. For the United States loss of access to extra-continental sources of tin is not likely to be offset by economic factors or technological changes that would permit an increase in potential North American production, even if present production could be increased by an order of magnitude. It is equally obvious that other peculiarities in the geographical distribution of the world's geological resources will continue to encourage interest both in trading with some ideologically remote nations and in seeking alternative sources of supply.

Economic geology, which in its best sense brings all other fields of geology to bear on resource problems, is concerned particularly with questions of how certain elements locally attain geochemical concentrations that greatly exceed their crustal abundance and with how this knowledge can be applied to the discovery of new deposits and the delineation of reserves. Economics and technology play equally important parts with geology itself in determining what deposits and grades it is practicable to exploit. Neither economics, nor technology, nor geology can *make* an ore deposit where the desired substance is absent or exists in insufficient quantity.

Estimated Recoverable Reserves of Selected Mineral Resources

Consider now some aspects of the apparent lifetimes of estimated recoverable reserves of a selection of critical mineral resources and the position of the United States with regard to some of these. The selected resources are those for which suitable data are available.

Figure 66-1 shows such lifetimes for different groups of metals and mineral fuels at *current* minable grades and rates of consumption. No allowance is made for increase of populations, or for increased rates of consumption which, in the United States, tend to increase at twice the rate of population growth. Nor is allowance made for additions to reserves that will result from discovery of submarine deposits, use of submarginal grades, or imports—which may reduce but will not eliminate the impact of growth factors. Data are from U.S. Bureau of Mines compendia *Mineral Facts and Problems* and its *Minerals Yearbooks*, as summarized by Flawn (*Mineral Resources*, Rand McNally, 1966). The thin lines represent lifetimes of world reserves for a stable population of roughly 3.3×10^9 at current rates of use. The heavy lines represent similar data for a United States population of about 200 million. Actual availability of some such commodities

Fig. 66-1. Lifetimes of estimated recoverable reserves of mineral resources at current mineable grades and rates of consumption (no allowance made for increasing populations and rates of consumption, or for submerged or otherwise concealed deposits, use of now submarginal grades, or imports). (Data from Flawn, 1966.)

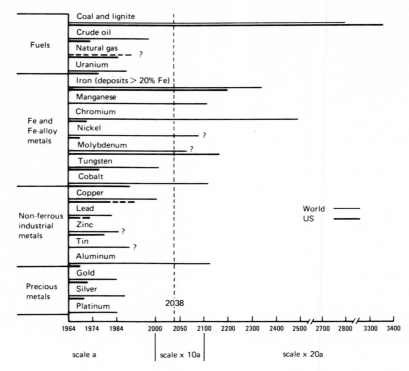

to the United States will, of course, be extended by imports from abroad, just as that of others will be reduced by population growth, increased per capita demands, and perhaps by political changes. The dashed vertical line represents the year 2038. I have chosen this as a reference line because it marks that point in the future which is just as distant from the present as the invention of the airplane and the discovery of radioactivity are in the past. I might have used 2089, which is only as far from the present as the admission of Texas to the Union in 1845.

The prospect is hardly conducive to unrestrained optimism. Of the nineteen commodities considered, only fourteen for the world and four or five for the United States have assured lifetimes beyond 1984; only ten for the world and three for the United States persist beyond the turn of the century; and only eight for the world and three for the United States extend beyond 2038. I do not suggest that we equate these lines with revealed truth. Time will prove some too short and others perhaps too long. New reserves will be found, lower-grade reserves will become minable for economic or technological reasons, substitutes will be discovered or synthesized, and some critical materials can be conserved by waste control and recycling. The crucial questions are: (1) how do we reduce these generalities to specifics; (2) can we do so fast enough to sustain current rates of consumption; (3) can we increase and sustain production of industrial materials at a rate sufficient to meet the rising expectations of a world population of nearly three and one-half billion, now growing with a doubling time of about thirty to thirty-five years, and for how long, and (4) if the answer to the last question is no, what then?

A more local way of viewing the situation is to compare the position of the United States or North America with other parts of the world. Figures 66-2 to 66-4 show such a comparison for sixteen commodities with our favorite measuring stick, the Sino-Soviet bloc. Figure 66-2 shows the more cheerful side of the coin. The United States is a bit ahead in petroleum, lignite, and phosphate, and neither we nor Asia

Fig. 66-2. Estimated recoverable reserves of minerals (above sea level) for which U.S. reserve estimates exceed, equal, or fall only slightly below those of the U.S.S.R. plus Mainland China. (Data from Flawn, 1966.)

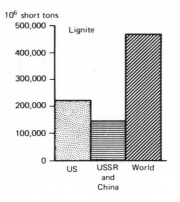

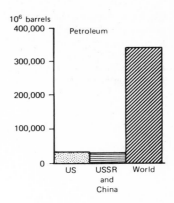

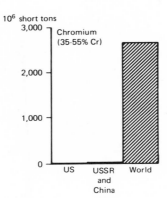

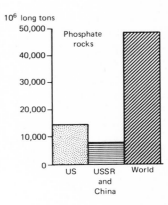

Fig. 66-3. Estimated recoverable reserves of minerals (above sea level) for which U.S. reserve estimates are less than those of the U.S.S.R. plus Mainland China. (Data from Flawn, 1966.)

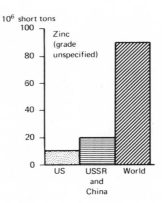

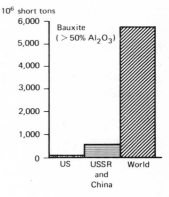

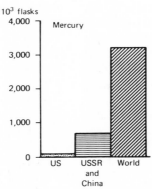

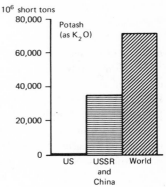

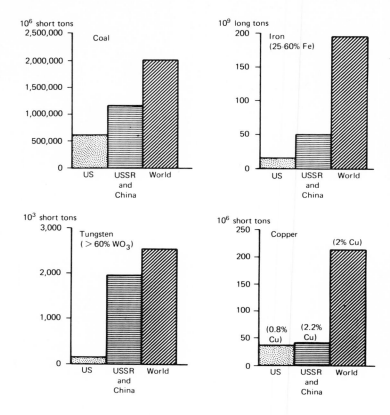

Fig. 66-4. Estimated recoverable reserves of minerals (above sea level) for which U.S. reserve estimates are less than those of the U.S.S.R. plus Mainland China. (Data from Flawn, 1966.)

have much chromium—known reserves are practically all in South Africa and Rhodesia. Figures 66-3, however, shows the Sino-Soviet bloc to have a big lead in zinc, mercury, potash, and bauxite. And Fig. 66-4 shows similar leads in tungsten, copper, iron, and coal.

Again there are brighter aspects to the generally unfavorable picture. Ample local low grade sources of alumina other than bauxite are available with metallurgical advances and at a price. The United States coal supply is not in danger of immediate shortage. Potassium can be extracted from sea water. And much of the world's iron is in friendly hands, including those of our good neighbor Canada and our more distant friend Australia.

No completely safe source is visible, however, for mercury, tungsten, and chromium. Lead, tin, zinc, and the precious metals appear to be in short supply throughout the world. And petroleum and natural gas will be exhausted or nearly so within the lifetimes of many of those here today unless we decide to

conserve them for petrochemicals and plastics. Even the extraction of liquid fuels from oil shales and "tar sands," or by hydrogenation of coal, will not meet energy requirements over the long term. If they were called upon to supply all the liquid fuels and other products now produced by the fractionation of petroleum, for instance, the suggested lifetime for coal the reserves of which are probably the most accurately known of all mineral products, would be drastically reduced below that indicated in Fig. 66-1—and such a shift will be needed to a yet unknown degree before the end of the century.

The Cornucopian Premises

In view of these alarming prospects, why do intelligent men of good faith seem to assure us that there is nothing to be alarmed about? It can only be because they visualize a completely nongeological solution to the problem, or because they take a very short-range view of it, or because they are compulsive optimists or are misinformed, or some combination of these things.

Let me first consider some of the basic concepts that might give rise to a cornucopian view of the earth's mineral resources and the difficulties that impede their unreserved acceptance. Then I will suggest some steps that might be taken to minimize the risks or slow the rates of mineral-resources depletion.

The central dilemma of all cornucopian premises is, of course, how to sustain an exponential increase of anything—people, mineral products, industrialization, or solid currency—on a finite resource base. This is, as everyone must realize, obviously impossible in the long run and will become increasingly difficult in the short run. For great though the mass of the earth is, well under 0.1 percent of that mass is accessible to us by any imaginable means (the entire crust is only about 0.4 percent of the total mass of the earth) and this relatively minute accessible fraction, as we have seen and shall see, is very unequally mineralized.

But the cornucopians are not naive or mischievous people. On what grounds do they deny the restraints and belittle the difficulties?

The five main premises from which their conclusions follow are:

Premise I. The promise of essentially inexhaustible cheap useful energy from nuclear resources.

Premise II. The thesis that economics is the sole factor governing availability of useful minerals and metals.

Premise III. The fallacy of essentially uninterrupted variation from ore of a metal to its average crustal abundance, which is inherent in Premise II; and from which emanates the strange and misleading notion that quantity of a resource available is essentially an inverse exponential function of its concentration.

Premise IV. The crucial assumption of population control, without which there can be no future worth living for most of the world (or, worse, the belief that quantity of people is of itself the ultimate good, which,

astounding as it may seem, is still held by a few people who ought to know better—see, for instance, Colin Clark, *Population Growth and Land Use*, Macmillan, 1967).

Premise V. The concept of the "technological fix."

Now these are appealing premises, several of which contain large elements of both truth and hope. Why do I protest their unreserved acceptance? I protest because, in addition to elements of truth, they also contain assumptions that either are gross over-simplifications, outright errors, or are not demonstrated. I warn because their uncritical acceptance contributes to a dangerous complacency toward problems that will not be solved by a few brilliant technological "breakthroughs," a wider acceptance of deficit economy, or fall-out of genius from unlimited expansion of population. They will be solved only by intensive, wide-ranging, and persistent scientific and engineering investigation, supported by new social patterns and wise legislation.

I will discuss these premises in the order cited.

Premise I

The concept of essentially inexhaustible cheap useful energy from nuclear sources offers by all odds the most promising prospect of sweeping changes in the mineral resource picture, as Dr. Weinberg so brilliantly argued. We may be on the verge of developing a workable breeder reactor just in time to sustain an energy-hungry world facing the imminent exhaustion of traditional energy sources. Such a development, it has been persuasively stated, will also banish many problems of environmental pollution and open up unlimited reserves of metals in common crustal rocks. There are, unhappily, some flaws in this delightful picture, of which it is important to be aware.

As Dr. Weinberg has told you, uranium 235 is the only naturally occurring spontaneously fissionable source of nuclear power. When a critical mass of uranium is brought together, the interchange of neutrons back and forth generates heat and continues to do so as long as the U^{235} lasts. In the breeder reactors some of the free neutrons kick common U^{238} over to plutonium 239, which is fissionable and produces more neutrons, yielding heat and accelerating the breeder reaction. Even in existing reactors some breeding takes place, and, if a complete breeding system could be produced, the amount of energy available from uranium alone would be increased about 140 fold. If thorium also can be made to breed, energy generated could be increased about 400 fold over that now attainable. This would extend the lifetime of visible energy resources at demands anticipated by 1980 by perhaps 1000 to 3000 years and gain time to work on contained nuclear fusion.

The problem is that it will require about 275,000 short tons of $6.00 to $10.00 per pound U_3O_8 (not ore, not uranium) to fuel reactors now on order to 1980, plus another 400,000 tons to sustain them until the turn of the century, burning only U^{235} with currently available enrichments from slow breeding (Charles T. Baroch, U.S. Bureau of Mines, oral comment). Only about 195,000 of the 675,000 tons of uranium needed is known to be available at this price, although known geologic conditions indicate the possibility of another 325,000 tons. Thus we now appear to be about 155,000 tons short of the U_3O_8 needed to produce the hoped-for 150,000 megawatts of nuclear energy on a sustained basis from 1985 until the end of the century without a functioning breeder reactor. Unless we find a lot more uranium, or pay a lot more money for it, or get a functioning complete breeder reactor or contained nuclear fusion within ten or fifteen years, the energy picture will be far from bright. There is good reason to hope that the breeder will come, and after it contained fusion, *if* the U^{235} and helium hold out—but there is no room for complacency.

If and when the breeder reactor or contained fusion does become available as a practicable energy source, however, how will this help with mineral resources? It is clear immediately that it will take pressure off the fossil "fuels" so that it will become feasible, and should become the law, to reserve them for petrochemicals,

polymers, essential liquid propellants, and other special purposes not served by nuclear fuels. It is also clear that cheap massive transportation, or direct transmittal of large quantities of cheap electric power to, or its generation at, distant sources will bring the mineral resources of remote sites to the market place—either as bulk ore for processing or as the refined or partially refined product.

What is not clear is how this very cheap energy will bring about the extraction of thinly dispersed metals in large quantity from common rock. This task is very different from the recovery of liquid fuels or natural gas by nuclear fracturing. The procedure usually suggested is the break-up of rock in place at depth with a nuclear blast, followed by hydrometallurgical or chemical mining. The problems, however, are great. Complexing solutions, in large quantity also from natural resources, must be brought into contact with the particles desired. This means that the enclosing rock must be fractured to that particle size. Then other substances, unsought, may use up and dissipate valuable reagents. Or the solvent reagents may escape to ground waters and become contaminants. Underground electrolysis is no more promising in dealing with very low concentrations. And the bacteria that catalyze reactions of metallurgical interest are all aerobic, so that, in addition to having access to the particles of interest, they must also be provided with a source of oxygen underground if they are to work there.

Indeed the energy used in breaking rock for the removal of metals is not now a large fraction of mining cost in comparison with that of labor and capital. The big expense is in equipping and utilizing manpower, and, although cheap energy will certainly reduce manpower requirements, it will probably never adequately substitute for the intelligent man with the pick at the mining face in dealing with vein and many replacement deposits, where the sought-after materials are irregularly concentrated in limited spaces. There are also limits to the feasible depths of open pit mining, which would be by all odds the best way to mine common rock. Few open pit mines now reach much below about 1,500 feet. It is unlikely that such depths can be increased by as much as an order of magnitude. The quantity of rock removable decreases exponentially with depth because pit circumference must decrease downward to maintain stable walls.

It may also not be widely realized by non-geologists that many types of ore bodies have definite floors or pinch-out downward, so that extending exploitative operations to depth gains no increase in ore produced. Even where mineralization does extend to depth, of course, exploitability is ultimately limited by temperature and rock failure.

Then there is the problem of reducing radioactivity so that ores can be handled and the refined product utilized without harm—not to mention heat dispersal (which in some but not all situations could itself be a resource) and the disposal of waste rock and spent reagents.

Altogether the problems are sufficiently formidable that it would be foolhardy to accept them as resolved in advance of a working efficient breeder reactor plus a demonstration that either cheap electricity or nuclear explosions will significantly facilitate the removal of metals from any common rock.

A pithy comment from Peter Flawn's recent book on *Mineral Resources* (Rand McNally, 1966, p. 14) is appropriate here. It is to the effect that "average rock will never be mined." It is the uncommon features of a rock that make it a candidate for mining! Even with a complete nuclear technology, sensible people will seek, by geological criteria, to choose and work first those rocks or ores that show the highest relative recoverable enrichments in the desired minerals.

The reality is that even the achievement of a breeder reactor offers no guarantee of unlimited mineral resources in the face of geologic limitations and expanding populations with increased per capita demands, even over the middle term. To assume such for the long term would be sheer folly.

Premise II

The thesis that economics is the sole, or at least the dominant, factor governing availability of useful minerals and metals is one of those vexing part-truths which has led to much seemingly fruitless discussion between economists and geologists. This proposition bears examination.

It seems to have its roots in that interesting economic index known as the Gross National Product, or GNP. No one seems to have worked out exactly what proportion of the GNP is in some way attributable to the mineral resource base. It does, however, appear that the dollar value of the raw materials themselves is small compared to the total GNP, and that it has decreased proportionately over time to something like 2 per cent of the present GNP, as I recall. From this it is logically deduced that the GNP could, if necessary, absorb a several-fold increase in cost of raw materials. The gap in logic comes when this is confused with the notion that all that is necessary to obtain inexhaustible quantities of any substance is either to raise the price or to increase the volume of rock mined. In support of such a notion, of course, one *can* point to diamond, which in the richest deposit ever known occurred in a concentration of only one to twenty-five million, but which, nevertheless, has continued to be available. The flaw is not only that we cannot afford to pay the price of diamond for many substances, but also that no matter how much rock we mine we can't get diamonds out of it if there were none there in the first place.

Daniel Bell (1967, Notes on the Post-industrialist Society II: *in the Public Interest,* no. 7, p. 102-118) comments on the distorted sense of relations that emerges from the cumulative nature of GNP accounting. Thus, when a mine is developed, the costs of the new facilities and payroll become additions to the GNP, whether the ore is sold at a profit or not. Should the mine wastes at the same time pollute a stream, the costs of cleaning up the stream or diverting the wastes also become additions to the GNP. Similarly if you hire someone to wash the dishes this adds to GNP, but if your wife does them it does not count.

From this it results that mineral raw materials and housework are not very impressive fractions of the GNP. What seems to get lost sight of is what a mess we would be in without either!

Assuming an indefinite extension of their

curves and continuance of access to foreign markets, economists appear to be on reasonably sound grounds postulating the relatively long-term availability of certain sedimentary, residual, and disseminated ores, such as those of iron, aluminum, and perhaps copper. What many of them do not appreciate is what I expect Dr. Lovering will amplify in his discussion—namely, that the type of curve that can with some reason be applied to such deposits and metals is by no means universally applicable. This difficulty is aggravated by the fact that conventional economic indexes minimize the vitamin-like quality for the economy as a whole of the raw materials whose enhancement in value through benefication, fabrication, and exchange accounts for such a large part of the material assets of society.

In a world that wants to hear only good news some economists are perhaps working too hard to emancipate their calling from the epithet of "dismal science," but not all of them. One voice from the wilderness of hyper-optimism and overconsumption is that of Kenneth Boulding, who observes that, *"The essential measure of the success of the economy is not production and consumption at all, but the nature, extent, quality, and complexity of the total capital stock, including in this the state of the human bodies and minds included in the system"* (p. 9 *in* K. E. Boulding, 1966, "The economics of the coming spaceship Earth," pp. 3-14 *in Environmental Quality in a Growing Economy,* Resources of the Future, Inc., The Johns Hopkins Press). Until this concept penetrates widely into the councils of government and the conscience of society, there will continue to be a wide gap between the economic aspects of national and industrial policy and the common good and the intrinsic significance of raw materials will remain inadequately appreciated.

The reality is that economics per se, powerful though it can be when it has material resources to work with, is not all powerful. Indeed, without material resources to start with, no matter how small a fraction of the GNP they may represent, economics is of no consequence at all. The current orthodoxy of economic well-being through obsolescence, over-consumption, and waste will prove, in the long term, to be a cruel and a preposterous illusion.

Premise III

Premise III, the postulate of essentially uninterrupted variation from ore to average crustal abundance is seldom if ever stated in that way, but it is inherent in Premise II. It could almost as well have been treated under Premise II; but it is such an important and interesting idea, whether true or false, that separate consideration is warranted.

If the postulated continuous variation were true for mineral resources in general, volume of "ore" (not metal) produced would be an exponential reverse function of grade mined, the handling of lower grades would be compensated for by the availability of larger quantities of elements sought, and reserve estimates would depend only on the accuracy with which average crustal abundances were known. Problems in extractive metallurgy, of course, are not considered in such an outlook.

This delightfully simple picture would supplant all other theories of ore deposits, invalidate the foundations of geochemistry, divest geology of much of its social relevance, and place the fate of the mineral industry squarely in the hands of economists and nuclear engineers.

Unfortunately this postulate is simply untrue in a practical sense for many critical minerals and is only crudely true, leaving out metallurgical problems, or particular metals, like iron and aluminum, whose patterns approach the predicted form. Sharp discontinuities exist in the abundances of mercury, iron, nickel, and even such staples as lead and zinc, for example. But how many prophets of the future are concerned about where all the lead or cadmium will come from for all those electric automobiles that are supposed to solve the smog problem?

Helium is a good example of a critical substance in short supply. Although a gas which has surely at some places diffused in a continuous spectrum of concentrations, particular concentrations of interest as a source of supply appear from published information to vary in a stepwise manner. Here I draw on data summarized by H. W. Lipper in the 1965 edition of the U.S. Bureau of Mines publication *Mineral Facts and Problems*. Although an uncommon substance, helium serves a variety of seemingly indispensable uses. A bit less than half of the helium now consumed in the U.S. is used in pressurizing liquid fueled missiles and space ships. Shielded-arc welding is the next largest use, followed closely by its use in producing controlled atmospheres for growing crystals for transistors, processing fuels for nuclear energy, and cooling vacuum pumps. Only about 5.5 per cent of the helium consumed in the United States is now used as a lifting gas. It plays an increasingly important role, however, as a coolant for nuclear reactors and a seemingly indispensable one in cryogenics and superconductivity. In the latter role, it could control the feasibility of massive long-distance transport of nuclear-generated electricity. High-helium low-oxygen breathing mixtures may well be critical to man's long-range success in attempting to operate at great depths in the exploration and exploitation of the sea. Other uses are in research, purging, leak detection, chromatography, etc.

Helium thus appears to be a very critical element, as the Department of the Interior has recognized in establishing its helium-conservation program. What are the prospects that there will be enough helium in 2038?

The only presently utilized source of helium is in natural gas, where it occurs at a range of concentrations from as high as 8.2 per cent by volume to zero. The range, however, in particular gas fields of significant volume, is apparently not continuous. Dropping below the one field (Pinta Dome) that shows an 8.2 per cent concentration, we find a few small isolated fields (Mesa and Hogback, New Mexico) that contain about 5.5 per cent helium, and then several large fields (e.g., Hugoton and Texas Panhandle) with a range of 0.3 to 1.0 per cent helium. Other large natural gas fields contain either no helium or show it only in quantities of less than 5 parts per 10,000. From the latter there is a long jump down to the atmosphere

with a concentration of only 1 part per 200,000.

Present annual demand for helium is about 700 million cubic feet, with a projected increase in demand to about 2 billion cubic feet annually by about 1985. It will be possible to meet such an accelerated demand for a limited time only as a result of Interior's current purchase and storage program, which will augment recovery from natural gas then being produced. As now foreseen, if increases in use do not outrun estimates, conservation and continued recovery of helium from natural gas reserves will meet needs to slightly beyond the turn of the century. When known and expected discoveries of reserves of natural gas are exhausted shortly thereafter, the only potential sources of new supply will be from the atmosphere, as small quantities of He^3 from nuclear reactor technology, or by synthesis from hydrogen—a process whose practical feasibility and adequacy remain to be established.

Spending even a lot more money to produce more helium from such sources under existing technology just may not be the best or even a very feasible way to deal with the problem. Interior's conservation program must be enlarged and extended, under compulsory legislation if necessary. New sources must be sought. Research into possible substitutions, recovery and re-use synthesis, and extraction from the atmosphere must be accelerated—*now* while there is still time. And we must be prepared to curtail, if necessary, activities which waste the limited helium reserves. Natural resources are the priceless heritage of all the people; their waste cannot be tolerated.

Problems of the adequacy of reserves obtain for many other substances, especially under the escalating demands of rising populations and expectations, and it is becoming obvious to many geologists that time is running out. Dispersal of metals which could be recycled should be controlled. Unless industry and the public undertake to do this voluntarily, legislation should be generated to define permissible mixes of material and disposal of "junk" metal. Above all the wastefulness of war and preparation for it must be terminated if reasonable options for posterity are to be preserved.

The reality is that a healthy mineral resource industry, and therefore a healthy industrial economy, can be maintained only on a firm base of geologic knowledge, and geochemical and metallurgical understanding of the distribution and limits of metals, mineral fuels, and chemicals in the earth's crust and hydrosphere.

Premise IV

The assumption that world populations will soon attain and remain in a state of balance is central to all other premises. Without this the rising expectations of the poor are doomed to failure, and the affluent can remain affluent only by maintaining existing shameful discrepancies. Taking present age structures and life expectancies of world populations into account, it seems certain that, barring other forms of catastrophe, world population will reach six or seven billion by about the turn of the century, regardless of how rapidly family planning is accepted and practiced.

On the most optimistic assumptions, this is probably close to the maximum number of people the world can support on a reasonably sustained basis, even under strictly regularized conditions, at a general level of living roughly comparable to that now enjoyed in Western Europe. It would, of course, be far better to stabilize at a much smaller world population. In any case, much greater progress than is as yet visible must take place over much larger parts of the world before optimism on the prospects of voluntary global population control at any level can be justified. And even if world population did level off and remain balanced at about seven billion, it would probably take close to one hundred years of intensive, enlightened, peaceful effort to lift all mankind to anywhere near the current level of Western Europe or even much above the level of chronic malnutrition and deprivation.

This is not to say that we must therefore be discouraged and withdraw to ineffectual diversions. Rather it is a challenge to focus with energy and realism on seeking a truly better life for all men living and yet unborn and on keeping the latter to the minimum. On the other hand, an uncritical optimism, just for the sake of that good feeling it creates, is a luxury the world cannot, at this juncture, afford.

A variation of outlook on the population problem which, surprisingly enough, exists among a few nonbiological scholars is that quantity of people is of itself a good thing. The misconception here seems to be that frequency of effective genius will increase, even exponentially, with increasing numbers of people and that there is some risk of breeding out to the merely high level of mediocrity in a stabilized population. The extremes of genius and idiocy, however, appear in about the same frequency at birth from truly heterogeneous gene pools regardless of size (the data from Montgomery County, Maryland, are really no exception to this). What is unfortunate, among other things, about overly dense concentrations of people is that this leads not only to reduced likelihood of the identification of mature genius, but to drastic reductions in the development of potential genius, owing to malnutrition in the weaning years and early youth, accompanied by retardation of both physical and mental growth. If we are determined to turn our problems over to an elite corps of mental prodigies a more sure-fire method is at hand. Nuclear transplant from various adult tissue cells into fertilized ova whose own nuclei have been removed has already produced identical copies of amphibian nucleus-donors and can probably do the same in man (Joshua Lederberg, 1966, *Bull. Atomic Scientists*, v. 22, no. 8, p. 9). Thus we appear to be on the verge of being able to make as many "xerox" copies as we want or need of any particular genius as long as we can get a piece of his or her nucleated tissue and find eggs and incubators for the genome aliquots to develop in. Female geniuses would be the best because (with a little help) they could copy themselves.

The reality is that without real population control and limitation of demand all else is drastically curtailed, not to say lost. And there is as yet not the faintest glimmer of hope that such limitation may take place voluntarily. Even were all unwanted births to be eliminated, populations would still be increasing at runaway rates in the absence of legal limitation of family size, as Dr. Ehrlich has so passionately argued. The most fundamental freedom should be the right not be be born into a world of want and smothering restriction. I am convinced that we must give up (or have taken away from us) the right to have as many children as we want or see all other freedoms lost for them. Nature, to be sure, will restore a dynamic balance between our species and the world ecosystem if we fail to do so ourselves—by famine, pestilence, plague, or war. It seems, but is not, unthinkable that this should happen. If it does, of course, mineral resources may then be or appear to be relatively unlimited in relation to demand for them.

Premise V

The notion of the "technological fix" expresses a view that is at once full of hope and full of risk. It is a gripping thought to contemplate a world set free by nuclear energy. Imagine soaring cities of aluminum, plastic, and thermopane where all live in peace and plenty at unvarying temperature and without effort, drink distilled water, feed on produce grown from more distilled water in coastal deserts, and flit from heliport to heliport in capsules of uncontaminated air. Imagine having as many children as you want, who, of course, will grow up seven stories above the ground and under such germ-free conditions that they will need to wear breathing masks if they ever do set foot in a park or a forest. Imagine a world in which there is no balance of payments problem, no banks, or money, and such mundane affairs as acquiring a shirt or a wife are handled for us by central computer systems. Imagine, if you like, a world in which the only problem is boredom, all others being solved by the state-maintained system of genius-technologists produced by transfer of nuclei from the skin cells of certified gene donors to the previously fertilized ova of final contestants in the annual ideal-pelvis contest. Imagine the problem of getting out of this disease-free world gracefully at the age of 110 when you just can't stand it any longer!

Of course this extreme view may not appeal to people not conditioned to think in those terms, and my guess is that it doesn't appeal to Dr. Weinberg either. But the risk of slipping bit by bit into such a smothering condition as one of the better possible outcomes is inherent in any proposition that encourages or permits people or industries to believe that they can leave their problems to the invention of technological fixes by someone else.

Although the world ecosystem has been in a constant state of flux throughout geologic time, in the short and middle term it is essentially homeostatic. That is to say, it tends to obey Le Chatelier's general principle—when a stress is applied to a system such as to perturb a state of near equilibrium, the system tends to react in such a way as to restore the equilibrium. But large parts of the world ecosystem have probably already undergone or are in danger of undergoing irreversible changes. We cannot continue to plunder and pollute it without serious or even deadly consequences.

Consider what would be needed in terms of conventional mineral raw materials merely to raise the level of all 3.3 billion people now living in the world to the average of the 200 million now living in the United States. In terms of present staple commodities, it can be estimated (revised from Harrison Brown, James Bonner, and John Weir, 1947, *The Next Hundred Years*, Viking Press, p. 33) that this would require a "standing crop" of about 30 billion tons of iron, 500 million tons of lead, 330 million tons of zinc, and 50 billion tons of tin. This is about 100 to 200 times the present annual production of these commodities. Annual power demands would be the equivalent of about 3 billion tons of coal and lignite, or about ten times present production. To support the doubled populations expected by the year 2000 at the same level would require, of course, a doubling of all the above numbers of substitute measures. The iron needed could probably be produced over a long period of time, perhaps even by the year 2000, given a sufficiently large effort. But, once in circulation, merely to replace losses due to oxidation, friction, and dispersal, not counting production of new iron for larger populations, would take around 200,000 tons of new iron every year (somewhat more than the current annual production of the United States), or a drastic curtailment of losses below the present rate of 1 per cent every two or three years. And the molybdenum needed to convert the iron to steel could become a serious limiting factor. The quantities of lead, zinc, and tin also called for far exceed all measured, indicated, and inferred world reserves of these metals.

This exercise gives a crude measure of the pressures that mineral resources will be under. It seems likely, to be sure, that substitutions, metallurgical research, and other technological advances will come to our aid, and that not all peoples of the world will find a superfluity of obsolescing gadgets necessary for the good life. But this is balanced by the equal likelihood that world population will not really level off at 6.6 or 7 billion and that there will be growing unrest to share the material resources that might lead at least to an improved standard of living. The situation is also aggravated by the attendant problems of disposal of mine wastes and chemically and thermally polluted waters on a vast scale.

The "technological fix," as Dr. Weinberg well understands, is not a panacea but an anesthetic. It may keep the patient quiet long enough to decide what the best long-range course of treatment may be, or even solve *some* of his problems permanently, but it would be tragic to forget that a broader program of treatment and recuperation is necessary. The flow of science and technology has always been fitful, and population control is a central limiting factor in what can be achieved. It will require much creative insight, hard work, public enlightenment, and good fortune to bring about the advances in discovery and analysis, recovery and fabrication, wise use and conservation of materials, management and recovery of wastes, and substitution and synthesis that will be needed to keep the affluent comfortable and bring the deprived to tolerable levels. It will probably also take some revision of criteria for self-esteem, achievement, and pleasure if the gap between affluent and deprived is to be narrowed and demand for raw materials kept within bounds that will permit man to enjoy a future as long as his past, and under conditions that would be widely accepted as agreeable.

The reality is that the promise of the "technological fix" is a meretricious premise, full of glittering appeal but devoid of heart and comprehension of the environmental and social problems. Technology and "hard" science we must have, in sustained and increasing quality, and in quantities relevant to the needs of man—material, intellectual, and spiritual. But in dealing with the problems of resources in relation to man, let us not lose sight of the fact that this is the province of the environmental and social sciences. A vigorous and perceptive technology will be an essential handmaiden in the process, but it is a risky business to put the potential despoilers of the environment in charge of it.

The Nub of the Matter

The realities of mineral distribution, in a nutshell, are that it is neither inconsiderable nor limitless, and that we just don't know yet in the detail required for considered weighting of comprehensive and national long-range alternatives where or how the critical lithophilic elements are concentrated. Stratigraphically controlled substances such as the fossil fuels, and, to a degree, iron and alumina, we can comprehend and estimate within reasonable limits. Reserves, grades, locations, and recoverability of many critical metals, on the other hand, are affected by a much larger number of variables. We in North America began to develop our rich natural endowment of mineral resources at an accelerated pace before the rest of the world. Thus it stands to reason that, to the extent we are unable to meet needs by imports, we will feel the pinch sooner than countries like the U.S.S.R. with a larger component of virgin mineral lands.

In some instances nuclear energy or other technological fixes may buy time to seek better solutions or will even solve a problem permanently. But sooner or later man must come to terms with his environment and its limitations. The sooner the better. The year 2038, by which time even current rates of consumption will have exhausted presently known recoverable reserves of perhaps half the world's now useful metals (more will be found but consumption will increase also), is only as far from the present as the invention of the airplane and the discovery of radioactivity. In the absence of real population control or catastrophe there could be fifteen billion people on earth by then! Much that is difficult to anticipate can happen in the meanwhile, to be sure, and to place faith in a profit-motivated technology and refuse to look beyond a brief "foreseeable future" is a choice widely made. Against this we must weigh the consequences of error or thoughtless inaction and the prospects of identifying constructive alternatives for deliberate courses of long-term action, or inaction, that will affect favorably the long-range future. It is well to remember that to do nothing is equally to make a choice.

Geologists and other environmental scientists now living, therefore, face a great and growing challenge to intensify the research needed to ascertain and evaluate the facts governing availability of raw material resources, to integrate their results, to formulate better predictive models, and to inform the public. For only a cognizant public can generate the actions and exercise the restraints that will assure a tolerable life and a flexibility of options for posterity. The situation calls neither for gloomy foreboding nor facile optimism, but for positive and imaginative realism. That involves informed foresight, comprehensive and long-range outlooks, unremitting effort, inspired research, and a political and social climate conducive to such things.

Conclusions and Proposed Actions

Every promising avenue must be explored. The most imperative objective, after peace and population control, is certainly a workable breeder reactor—with all it promises in reduced energy costs, outlook for desalting saline waters and recovering mineral products from the effluent wastes, availability of now uselessly remote mineral deposits, decrease of cutoff grades, conservation of the so-called fossil "fuels" for more important uses, and the reduction of contaminants resulting from the burning of fossil fuels in urban regions.

But, against the chance that this may not come through on schedule, we should be vigorously seeking additional geological sources of U^{235} and continuing research on controlled nuclear fusion.

A really comprehensive geochemical census of the earth's crustal materials should be accelerated and carried on concurrently, and as far into the future as may be necessary to delineate within reasonable limits the metallogenic provinces of our planet's surface, including those yet poorly-known portions beneath the sea. Such a census will be necessary not only in seeking to discover the causes and locations of new metalliferous deposits, but also in allowing resource data to be considered at the design stage, and in deciding which "common rocks" to mine first, should we ever be reduced to that extreme. Of course, this can be done meaningfully only in context with a good comprehension of sequence and environment based on careful geologic mapping, valid geochronology, perceptive biogeology, and other facets of interpretive earth science.

Programs of geophysical, geochemical, and geological prospecting should meanwhile be expanded to seek more intensively for subglacial, subsoil, submarine, and other concealed mineral resources in already defined favorable target areas—coupled with engineering, metallurgical, and economic innovation and evaluations of deposits found.

Only as we come to know better what we have, where it is, and what the problems of bringing it to the market place are likely to be will it be feasible to formulate the best and most comprehensive long range plans for resource use and conservation. Meanwhile, however, a permanent, high-level, and adequately funded monitoring system should be established under federal auspices to identify stress points in the mineral economy, or likely future demands, well in advance of rupture. Thus the essential lead time could be allowed in initiating search for new sources or substitutes, or in defining necessary conservation programs.

Practices in mixing materials during fabrication and in disposal of scrap metal should be examined with a view to formulating workable legislation that will extend resource lifetimes through more effective re-use.

Management of the nation's resources and of

wastes from their extraction, beneficiation, and use should be regarded in the true democratic tradition as national problems and not left entirely to the conscience and discretion of the individual or private firm. Where practices followed are not conducive to the national, regional, or local welfare, informed legal inducement should make them so.

Research into all phases of resource problems and related subjects should be maintained at some effective level not dependent on political whimsey. It would be a far-sighted and eminently fair and logical procedure to set apart some specific fraction of taxes derived from various natural resources to be ploughed back into research designed to assure the integrity of the environment and the sufficiency of resources over the long term.

Much of the work suggested would naturally be centered in the U.S. Department of the Interior and in various state agencies, whose traditionally effective cooperative arrangements with the nation's universities should be enlarged.

Institutions like the one whose dedication we celebrate today are central to the problem of sustaining a healthy industrial society. For they are the source of that most indispensable of all resources—the trained minds that will discern the facts and evolve the principles via which such a society comes to understand its resources and to use them wisely. The essential supplements are adequate support and a vision of the problem that sweeps and probes all aspects of the environmental sciences the world over. The times cry for the establishment of schools and institutes of environmental science in which geologists, ecologists, meteorologists, oceanographers, geophysicists, geographers, and others will interact and work closely together.

I can think of no more fitting way to close these reflections than to quote the recent words of Sir Macfarlane Burnet (p. 29, *in* "Biology and the appreciation of life," The Boyer Lectures, 1966, ABC, 45p)—*"There are three imperatives: to reduce war to a minimum; to stabilize human populations; and to prevent the progressive destruction of the earth's irreplaceable resources."* If the primary sciences and technology are to be our salvation it will necessarily be in an economic framework that evaluates success by some measure other than rate of turnover, and in the closest possible working liaison with the environmental and social sciences.

Acknowledgments

I am obligated to literally scores of people whose brains I have picked and whose ideas, data, and words have influenced me or have even been appropriated in formulating the above statement. Among these I acknowledge a special debt to T. S. Lovering, M. K. Hubbert, Peter Flawn, H. L. James, A. L. Weinberg, Frank Forward, and Walter Hibbard, Jr.

I also had the advantage in preparing this paper of having been the Chairman of a Committee on Resources and Man of the National Academy of Sciences, whose final report was being prepared for publication as I was working on this. The views expressed above, of course, are not the official views of that Committee. They are also cast in a more hortative vein than would be appropriate in a report by such a Committee.

67

POWER FROM THE EARTH'S OWN HEAT

Lawrence Lessing

Men have long dug in the earth for materials that produce power, but only recently have they begun on any significant scale to tap the immense energy source lying all the while beneath their feet—the great heat stored in the depths of the earth. Emanating from the earth's crust in the form of natural steam, this geothermal energy can be utilized to generate electricity by a direct and simple method that requires no fuel, no heavy boilers, and no high dams. Only in the last few years has the economics of this form of power, in competition with other energy sources, been clearly proved.

All together, geothermal plants around the world are currently generating only about one million kilowatts of electricity, and until early in the decade practically all the activity was abroad—in Italy, New Zealand, Japan, Mexico, and the Soviet Union. In 1960, Pacific Gas & Electric became the first U.S. utility to generate geothermal power. Since then it has tripled its original pilot-plant capacity in the Big Geysers area of northern California to 82,000 kilowatts, and recently it announced that it would more than double capacity again by 1972. The significance of the P.G. & E. development goes far beyond its size. For while all the foreign projects are government-owned, obscuring their true costs, the expanding California plant is entirely built by private capital and initiative, which means that it must be economically viable to survive.

Though P.G. & E. is still the lone U.S. utility in the field, others are sure to follow. For the swirl of interest, activity, and speculation that has sprung up around geothermal power is reminiscent of the early days of oil. Indeed, in

Reprinted from *Fortune* 79 (2): 138-41, 1969, with the permission of the publishers.

the U.S. the oil industry, preceded by enterprising wildcatters, has taken a major role in the primary development of geothermal sources, which calls for similar capability in geologic exploration and well drilling, and also fits into the industry's current strategy of building a more diversified energy base. Half a dozen large companies, including Union Oil, Sun Oil, and Signal, are now at work in geothermal prospecting.

Many problems, risks, and uncertainties remain in the path of development, not the least of them in the area of government policy. But under the vigorous stirring of venturesome promoters, geothermal power may come to rival hydroelectric power, and perhaps even in the long run nuclear energy.

The World's Biggest Nuclear Plant

This great potential is based on the fantastic, practically inexhaustible heat still being generated deep in the earth. Geologists have measured the heat in deep mines and deeper boreholes, and taken the temperature of active volcanoes, and they calculate that the temperature increases on the average about ten degrees Fahrenheit every 1,000 feet. Twenty to thirty miles down, where the earth's mantle lies under continents, it reaches about 2,000° Fahrenheit. In the earth's core, beginning some 1,800 miles down, temperatures are estimated to range from 2,500° to 3,500°. This tremendous heat is not left over, as was once thought, from the early, fiery birth of the planet. More recent evidence indicates that it is constantly being produced by the measurable decay of radioactive elements found in small traces in all rock. Slowly over the eons these elements have heated the earth's interior and they continue to keep it red-hot.

Geothermal power, therefore, is ultimately derived from the world's biggest nuclear plant, the earth itself. It has been calculated that if the earth's center could be cooled by only one degree Fahrenheit, it would release enough heat energy to run all existent power plants for 20 million years. Just under the surface of the U.S. the heat stored to a depth of six miles is equivalent to the energy obtained from the burning of 900 trillion tons of coal. Such calculations are not realistic, of course, for the heat stored immediately beneath the surface is generally too diffuse to be gathered for power generation. And it is beyond present technology to drill down to the earth's mantle to tap more intense heat. But in many places where enormous forces from down deep meet weaknesses in the earth's crust, molten rock or magma from the mantle is extruded up into the crust. Here it lies close to, or sometimes breaks through, the surface in such displays of power as volcanoes, whose lava flows run 1,600° Fahrenheit and up, or in more benign hot springs, geysers, and fumaroles (natural steam vents).

These "hot spots" are the areas that can most immediately be exploited for geothermal energy. Far from being rare, they are now seen to be features of the great worldwide system of oceanic ridges and continental rifts, discovered only a decade or so ago, in which molten magma is constantly welling up through great interconnected cracks in the earth's crust. Associated with this system are wide zones marked by intense earthquakes, volcanic eruptions, and other geothermal activity. One geothermal belt extends all the way from Alaska down the West Coast, through Mexico, Central and South America, as well as east through the Aleutians, the Kamchatka Peninsula, Japan, Taiwan, and the Philippines, thus embracing the whole fiery rim of the Pacific. Another pushes up the mid-Atlantic from the south through the Canary Islands to Iceland, while a big spur goes off in the northern Mediterranean through Italy, Greece, Turkey, the Middle East, and out into the Indian Ocean.

The Pacific belt runs down through the whole western U.S., and all recent activity indicates that there is more potential geothermal energy here than meets the eye. California's Big Geysers area alone is now estimated to have a producing capacity of as much as one million kilowatts, and its boundaries and total reserve are by no means yet fully known. Elsewhere in California and twelve other western states—excluding Yellowstone National Park, which cannot be commercially ex-

ploited—there are roughly 86 million acres that may have geothermal resources. And this estimate is based on only the most cursory survey of surface indications of hot springs, steam leaks, or geysers.

The Underground Hot-Water System

Until recently, geothermal resources were discovered much as oil was found in the early days, by observing surface seepages. Even now so few geothermal wells have been drilled, and those to such relatively shallow depths, that there remains a vast underground area of the unknown. But with the new prospecting tools and deep-drilling techniques that are being rapidly developed, geologists and engineers are beginning to get a firmer grip on the underground workings of geothermal systems.

Geothermal sources are found generally where a large intrusion of magma, slightly cooled from past volcanic action, lies relatively near the surface, heating a deep underground reservoir of water trapped in permeable rock. The water is critical for power, for it is the medium that carried the heat to the surface; in the process, the water turns to steam, which drives the turbines.

There are two broad classes of geothermal fields. One is the fumarole, in which heat, pressure, and reservoir flow are so balanced that the vents or wells at the surface produce mainly "dry," slightly superheated steam. The Big Geysers area (misnamed, since it contains no true geysers) is a rare example of a fumarole field, ideal for power production. The second class, much more common, is the hot-spring or geyser system, in which a super-abundant reservoir of high-pressure hot water produces mainly boiling water at the surface, only a portion of which flashes into steam. A geyser is simply a hot spring that throws up an intermittent spout of hot water and steam.

Within these broad classes lie many local variations in conditions and composition, including hot-water fields in which the mineral content is so high that it may become the major product for exploitation, with energy the by-product. The precise geologic underpinnings

Fig. 67-1. Some of the raw power contained deep in the earth surfaces is this runaway steam well in the Big Geysers area north of San Francisco, where the first geothermal electric power in the U.S. is being generated. When the well was drilled in 1957, the pressure blew the nose off a hill; it has been blowing huge volumes of steam uncontrollably ever since. Eighteen other wells, successfully controlled, are supplying steam to generate almost 100,000 killowatts of power for Pacific Gas & Electric.

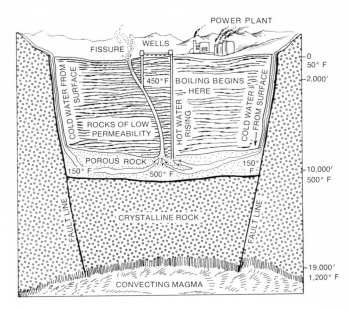

of geothermal areas are not yet understood very well. One of the few geologic models based on extensive field research is the typical hot-spring system (see Fig. 67-1) devised by Donald E. White, who began studying hot springs and geysers for the U.S. Geological Survey nearly thirty years ago, long before there was any practical interest.

Geologists are involved in a major controversy about the source of water in these deep reservoirs. White's finding from his hot-spring studies, based on isotropic analysis of water from great depths, is that over 95 percent of the water comes from surface rain and snow seeping down through fissures over long periods into deep, permeable zones of rock. Other geologists and field workers maintain that since these reservoirs are found at depths where water is not normally encountered in well drilling, most of this hot water must be magmatic—i.e., it was trapped in the magma early in the formation of the earth. Despite these and other geologic uncertainties, however, men have not been deterred from developing some amazingly consistent geothermal power sources.

Drilling into Dante's Hell

In 1904 Italian engineers hitched a small turbine to a shallow well drilled in a long-known fumarole field in northern Italy, called Larderello, which is said to have inspired Dante's lurid visions of inferno. This was the world's first geothermal power plant. Under government auspices, the engineers went on to develop all the basic techniques for drilling, casing, capping, and controlling steam wells to generate power. By World War II they had built Larderello's capacity up to some 135,000 kilowatts. The plant was destroyed by bombing in the war, but was quickly rebuilt on more modern lines to a capacity of over 300,000 kilowatts.

For half a century the Larderello plant remained the only one of its kind in the world. In the more richly endowed industrial nations, particularly the U.S., power development concentrated on the more flexible, more easily exploitable, or more visible resources of coal, oil, gas, and rushing water. The Big Geysers area was drilled in the Twenties, but rigs collapsed and the promoters were quickly discouraged by the lack of interest in what steam they found and by the then primitive state of geothermal engineering. Modern steels and techniques were not available to cope with the pressures and temperatures of drilling and the often corrosive impurities found in geothermal steam. Larderello's steam, for instance, contained boric acid, borax, and other chemicals, which the Italians thriftily removed and sold. But power experts generally regarded Larderello as a freak, practical only in an economy deficient in other native power sources.

After World War II, however, it became apparent that geothermal energy required a second look. Power demand in developed countries continued to rise at a rate that called for a doubling of capacity about every ten years and threatened to exhaust the ever diminishing reserves of fossil fuels and suitable hydroelectric sites. Pressures rose even higher in lands less well endowed. Even with the promise of nuclear energy, every feasible power source would be needed by the end of the century.

Early in the Fifties, New Zealand, faced by a shortage of power from meager conventional sources, began developing its great geyser area at Wairakei, and by the late Fifties it was producing nearly 200,000 kilowatts of geothermal power. This opened a new era in geothermal development, for Wairakei was a hot-water field of a type that had never been shown to produce power before. Later Japan, Mexico, and the Soviet Union came in with small plants drawing on similar sources.

Salesmen for Steam

In the U.S., as was the case with oil, risk-taking wildcatters or independents were in the vanguard of geothermal development. In 1955, Barkman C. McCabe, a man with a background in oil and lumber, organized a small exploratory company called Magma Power, in Los Angeles. A year later it teamed up with a San Francisco company called Thermal Power, newly organized by Dan A. McMillan Jr., whose experience was in mining, to prospect and drill jointly on some leases they had acquired in the Big Geysers area.

Drilling for steam is a chancy and sometimes spectacular business. As in the early oil days, the procedure is to put down drills some short and likely distance away from a natural surface vent. As soon as a steam fault is hit, the well hole must be quickly capped. Otherwise it may blow wildly and scaldingly out of control. One such well, early in the Magma-Thermal venture, blew out with the earth-shaking roar of a rocket, and shot steam and some 3,000 tons of debris high into the air. It resisted all attempts to cool or plug it, and over a decade later it is still blowing free in a mighty exhibition of raw power.

By 1957, however, with steadily improving techniques, Magma-Thermal had brought in three controlled wells producing over 200,000 pounds of steam per hour, at a temperature of 375° Fahrenheit and a pressure of about 100 pounds per square inch. The companies approached Pacific Gas & Electric with a proposal to sell it steam for power production. After a year of study, P.G. & E. agreed to build two small, essentially experimental plants in tandem on the site. Up to World War II, the utility had been a wholly hydroelectric system, but with waterpower sites running out, it had turned to conventional steam and prospectively to nuclear energy, and it was ready to consider any new source that promised low-cost power. Geothermal energy had to be approached cautiously, however, for in order to cover any substantial plant investment in the future the utility had to be reasonably sure of at least a twenty-year supply of steam.

The first plant was built around a second-hand, 12,500-kilowatt turbine generator, salvaged from an older conventional steam plant, and the first power went out over a ten-mile transmission line into P.G. & E.'s system in 1960. A second plant went into operation three years later, bringing total capacity to 26,000 kilowatts, at a cost of $3,800,000. P.G. & E. quickly solved the problems of dealing with the small amount of impurities found in the steam and designing anticorrosive equipment for critical areas. It was found that the plants could be run around the clock at high load, unattended except for a small daytime maintenance crew, making them very economical for their size. Gaining confidence, P.G. & E. soon proposed two larger units, adding 56,000 kilowatts at a cost of almost $7 million, to start up in 1967-68.

This expansion put something of a strain on Magma-Thermal. They had drilled fifteen producing wells to supply steam to the first two units, and the second pair required ten more, drilled deeper to get bigger output. With drilling costs running between $50,000 and $250,000 per well, depending on depth, these were pretty big stakes for small companies. Meanwhile, P.G. & E. was talking of five still larger units, each of 50,000 kilowatts, for the 1971-75 period. The utility does not commit itself to ordering turbines until it has proved steam wells to feed them, and delivery time on turbines is now four to five years. This means that wells must be drilled far in advance and do not begin earning their money back—currently at a contracted rate of about 2 mills per kilowatt-hour generated—for a long time.

Seeking more working capital, Magma-Thermal concluded an agreement in 1967 with Union Oil, which put up $3,500,000 and became a party to the venture. Union took over the operation of existing wells, and made a commitment to drill new ones. The company already had some interests of its own in geothermal energy. Shortly before making the Magma-Thermal deal it had acquired Pure Oil Co., which had a wholly owned subsidiary called Earth Energy, Inc. In 1964, Earth Energy had joined with Magma to drill the world's deepest geothermal well (8,100 feet) in the Salton Sea area south of Los Angeles, and it later acquired on its own nearly 10,000 acres of geothermal leases in the more immediately productive Geysers area. When these were pooled with Magma-Thermal's leases, the combine had over 15,000 acres in the heart of the Geysers. Alltogether, it now has fifty-one productive wells (half currently on standby) out of a total of fifty-five drilled, a record unheard of in the oil business.

Union as field operator has good reason to press drilling and development vigorously. Under the agreement, income from the first 200,000 kilowatts generated goes wholly to Magma-Thermal, and income from the second 200,000 kilowatts is to be equally divided between Magma-Thermal and Union, but the oil company will take all the proceeds from the third 200,000 kilowatts. Consequently, Union

is now urging P.G. & E. to hurry its 50,000-kilowatt plants and go on beyond.

Costing out the Geothermal Current

Patently, geothermal power is paying off, even on a small scale as generating facilities go. P.G. & E.'s conservative judgment is that geothermal is competitive with other ways of producing power (and it has had experience with all of them, including nuclear reactors). More specifically, the utility has compared the unit cost of power in its newest 28,000-kilowatt geothermal unit with that in its latest 750,000-kilowatt conventional steam plant; the result is practically a standoff at about 5 mills per kilowatt-hour. While the conventional plant operates with great efficiency on very high-pressure, high-temperature steam, to get the utmost energy out of every pound of fuel, the geothermal plant runs less efficiently because the steam that comes out of the ground is at much lower temperatures and pressures than manufactured steam. Hence huge volumes of steam and cooling water must be put through the plant for each kilowatt-hour of energy produced. But since steam costs are low, and no expensive high-pressure boilers are needed to generate the steam, geothermal power costs come out about even with, or a fraction under, those of the newest, most efficient conventional steam plants.

Geothermal enthusiasts maintain that costs are actually even more favorable than they appear in these analyses. To compare small, not-yet-refined plants, feeding on relatively shallow wells, with the huge, highly developed conventional steam or nuclear giants is not realistic. Plant size has a dramatic impact on power costs. Between P.G. & E.'s first pair of geothermal units and the second pair, total power costs dropped from 5.7 to 4.7 mills per kilowatt-hour, and costs in two scheduled 55,000-kilowatt units will drop further to about 4 mills.

Moreover, say the enthusiasts, cost accounting on geothermal power is still highly conservative. Because of lingering uncertainty about how long the steam will hold out, costs are weighted with relatively short amortization periods for wells, and with relatively high values placed on land. As more lengthy experience is gained in well production and plants move up in size, this source of energy should prove to be the cheapest of all.

The Scramble in the Steam Fields

The steam suppliers have already made money. In 1967, Magma-Thermal turned their first profit, on gross sales of $716,000. Last year the gross climbed close to $1 million, and this year it is running up at a rate that will reach $1,500,000. Once a well is drilled and tied into a generating plant, there is little more to do than collect the ever accumulating revenues on the steam. At an average of 2 mills per kilowatt-hour, a well producing 10,000 kilowatts of power can earn some $150,000 a year and pay off its drilling costs in short order. Since the joint venture has a contract to supply P.G. & E. exclusively with steam from its Geysers properties for fifty years, during which generating capacity will undoubtedly continue to build up, the profits could be quite handsome.

The lure of such a strike has drawn a number of adventurers, wildcatters, and even big corporations into the steam fields. They have found the prospecting every bit as risky as in oil and have much fewer geological guidelines to work with. In 1965, Sierra Pacific Power Co. financed the drilling of two promising wells in Beowawe, Nevada, by Magma and Vulcan Thermal Power Co., but within two years the steam petered out and a projected geothermal plant was cancelled. Other promising wells were drilled in California's Casa Diablo Hot Springs area, with California Electric Power prepared to buy the steam, but disposal of their waste water proved to be a problem. Even in the general Geysers area, Signal Oil & Gas got three dry wells in a row before striking steam, and pulled back for a more intensive study of the geology.

So far nothing has turned up that is as good as the Geysers, where large stores of high-quality steam are available wholly on privately owned land, close to population centers. Most of the speculative activity therefore still centers there. One of the most energetic promoters is Ronald C. Dick, thirty-four, who came to the area about 1960 to establish the R. C. Dick Mercury Mines Corp. When he saw what Magma-Thermal was up to, he jumped in to acquire leases on some 1,000 adjacent acres. To get drilling under way, he subleased his acres to Geothermal Resources International Inc., a substantial exploration company organized by former Occidental Petroleum executives; it now has over 13,000 acres of its own under lease in the area, as well as other geothermal, gas and oil holdings elsewhere.

Geothermal Resources struck the first commercial-volume steam well on Dick's property in 1967, quickly followed by a second, larger one. Dick thereupon organized Geothermal Electric Corp. to raise capital and acquire more acreage. Last year this corporation bought a half interest in a 30,000-acre leasehold in the Geysers-Clear Lake-Wilbur Hot Springs area owned by D. D. Feldman, a Dallas oilman. Dick then negotiated a joint venture between Feldman and Sun Oil Co., which has brought Sun's subsidiary, Cordero Mining Co., into the area on a major drilling program.

The big problem in this intricate game is to find customers for the steam. Geothermal Resources has raised capital to drill twenty-five additional wells to supply a 300,000-kilowatt generating plant to be financed by eleven municipalities seeking lower-cost power under a new Northern California Power Agency. But this is contingent on getting approval from the U.S. Department of the Interior, and its help in persuading P.G. & E. to allow the municipal plant to transmit power over its lines. So far, though drilling continues, no firm commitment has been made for a plant, no steam has been sold, and the prospects for the project remain cloudy.

The next most active geothermal area in the U.S. is the Salton Sea area in southern California. This great depression below sea level in the Imperial Valley, south of Los Angeles, is an entirely different kettle of steam from the Geysers. Underlying it is an enormous hot-water field; there temperatures at the bottom of drill holes have registered as high as 600° to

700° Fahrenheit at tremendous pressures, and mineral content reaches up to 33 percent by volume, the highest ever recorded. The minerals are mainly sodium and potassium chloride, but include a wide variety of elements from arsenic to gold, silver, and platinum. First to drill in the Salton Sea area was O'Neill Geothermal Inc., a company formed by a group of Texas oilmen. It was followed by, among others, the Union-Magma joint venture, and recently Morton International came in with a $30-million project aimed primarily at exploiting the salt and minerals. Byproduct electricity would be sold to the valley's irrigation district.

But drilling in this area has been plagued with problems. The mixture of steam, chemicals, and solids is highly corrosive and clogs the pipes. It is hard to separate out the usable elements and to dispose of the great volumes of brackish water and polluting wastes. Nearly all the prospectors have drawn back to search for better processes and economic methods to get out products. But, so great is the potential store of energy and minerals, particularly in metals that are in short supply, that no one has yet quit the area or has doubts that it will be ultimately developed.

Is It Mineral, Gas, or Water?

Elsewhere in the U.S., geothermal prospecting, after reaching a peak about 1965, has slowly dropped off, discouraged by high development costs and great uncertainties over federal land and tax policies. About half of all the territory west of the Mississippi is federal land or land on which the government reserves underground mineral rights under the Homestead Act of 1918. Specific legislation has regulated the granting of mineral, oil, and other leases on this land for private development, but since geothermal development was unforeseen, there has been no leasing policy to guide it. In 1966, Congress passed a geothermal-leasing bill designed to fill the breach, but President Johnson vetoed it, mainly because it contained a "grandfather clause" allowing owners of old mining leases to convert them into geothermal leases without new competitive bidding. Since

then revised bills have been repeatedly blocked, stalling geothermal developers who have been seeking federal leases or holding mineral leases in anticipation of converting them.

More paralyzing still is the uncertainty about federal tax policy. The big tax question is whether geothermal resources are depletable, like gas, oil, and mineral deposits, or whether, as Internal Revenue insists, they are to be classed with ordinary replenishable water wells or river systems and do not qualify for depletion allowances. People in the budding industry argue that steam wells are no ordinary water wells, but more nearly resemble oil wells in that they require high initial risk capital and long development time, and encounter large local variables and uncertainties in getting sustained production. Not enough experience has yet accumulated to determine whether geothermal reservoirs are replenishable or will ultimately be depleted.

The lack of a depletion allowance has caused developers to hold off further work in such areas as Nevada and in Calfornia's Casa Diablo Hot Springs, where initial strikes showed great promise but further development would run up expenses that would take a long time to recoup. Magma-Thermal are now challenging the Internal Revenue ruling in a federal court at Los Angeles. They are asking for the full 27½ percent oil-depletion allowance on steam, and the industry is watchfully awaiting the court's judgment.

Up to now the entire development of U.S. geothermal energy has been borne by private risk capital, with little or no government assistance—and indeed some discouragement. Ruefully, one of the developers says that perhaps they should have gone after a big federal subsidy from the start; if they had got a fraction of what has been poured into the development of atomic energy, they would be sitting pretty now.

Measuring the Underground Reservoirs

Geothermal development, nevertheless, continues to make strides. Though no instrument

as resourceful as the seismograph in oil exploration has yet turned up for detecting underground geothermal reservoirs, engineers are
working with a wide range of new techniques.
These include infrared surveying, geochemical
analysis, measuring the earth's electric conductivity, which rises where hot water is
present underground, and plotting the locations
of micro-earthquakes, which seem to correlate
with areas of geothermal activity. Using some
of these new methods, the Italians have recently opened up three new steam fields where
there had been little or no surface indication.
Ultimately, geothermal exploration may follow
oil in the ability to sniff out large and as yet
hidden reservoirs.

Engineers are also beginning to assay the
reserve capacity and probable productivity of
geothermal reservoirs with some of the assurance they have in appraising oil fields. The
first such reservoir study was made for New
Zealand's Wairakei field by two American
consultants, Robert L. Whiting, head of Texas
A & M University's department of petroleum
engineering, and Henry J. Ramey, now at
Stanford University and a consultant to Union
Oil. After reviewing the geology and past-
performance records of Wairakei wells, drilling
test boreholes on the presumed perimeters of
the field, and simulating the field's present and
future performance in a computer, they estimated that the reservoir contains a potential
10,000 trillion pounds of high-pressure steam,
enough at present production rates to last a
thousand years. The ability to estimate geo-
thermal-steam reserves is a big advance, for it
permits future investments to be planned with
much greater confidence.

Down to the Earth's Mantle

The next big step is toward deeper wells,
which have an electrifying effect on production. The first round of wells drilled in the
Big Geysers were shallow ones, between 500
and 2,000 feet deep; the second round went
down to about 5,000 feet or nearly a mile. This
added depth increased the average power output per well from 3,000 to 10,000 kilowatts.

One of the latest and deepest wells in the area
has now reached a steam potential of nearly
15,000 kilowatts, while the record-breaking
Salton Sea well shows a steam output equivalent to about 25,000 kilowatts. Mexico is
reported to have drilled two 25,000-kilowatt
wells in Cerro Prieto, just south of the border in
an extension of the Salton Sea formation, in
preparation for a 75,000-kilowatt power plant
to go into operation by 1971. The U.S. could in
the near future carry this further, on present
technology, to wells of 50,000-kilowatt
capacity.

As wells go deeper, of course, drilling costs
rise almost geometrically, but at the same time
the unit cost of the steam energy declines. No
one yet knows at what depth an economic dead
end might be reached. Some engineers believe
that the future lies in drilling right down to or
close to the earth's mantle to tap the immense
heat and untold mineral resources at these
tremendous depths. The U.S. might have had a
big lead in deep-drilling technology by now if
the Mohole Project, mounted early in the
decade as part of an international scientific
effort to drill down to the mantle, had not
become tangled in Johnsonian politics and been
scuttled by Congress. The lead has now slipped
to the Soviet Union, which went on with its
part of the program, and is reported to be well
on its way to drilling holes nine miles deep in
the Kola Peninsula and Baku area.

The Russians are alive to the geothermal
prospects. Their geologists have discovered a
great underground hot-water basin, bigger than
the Mediterranean, underlying a great part of
Siberia east of the Urals, with water temperatures between 140° and 320° Fahrenheit in its
upper and lower reaches. Most of the initial
development is going into health spas, mineral
recovery, and space heating for Siberian towns.
But an experimental geothermal plant is in
operation using Freon gas to convert rather low
heat of these underground waters to higher
pressures for power production. Deep-drilling
techniques may uncover much hotter sources.
Eventually the U.S. will probably find it necessary to revive·the Mohole Project.

Deep-drilling to the mantle would make it
possible to tap great energy sources almost

anywhere on earth where power is needed. Engineers envision using deep underground nuclear explosions to create huge reservoirs at these depths. Water would then be injected and recirculated in these hot cavities, producing high-pressure steam and a slurry of metals and minerals. (Recirculation techniques are already being experimented with in geothermal fields.) Such subterranean architecture could move geothermal energy into a scale with nuclear power, and make cheap energy available all over the world.

68

WILDLIFE MANAGEMENT IN THE NATIONAL PARKS

A. S. Leopold, S. A. Cain, C. Cottam, I. N. Gabrielson, and T. L. Kimball

Historical

In the Congressional Act of 1916 which created the National Park Service, preservation of native animal life was clearly specified as one of the purposes of the parks. A frequently quoted passage of the act states, ". . . which purpose is to conserve the scenery and the natural and historic objects and the wild life therein and to provide for the enjoyment of the same in such manner and by such means as will leave them unimpaired for the enjoyment of future generations."

In implementing this act, the newly formed Park Service developed a philosophy of wildlife *protection*, which in that era was indeed the most obvious and immediate need in wildlife conservation. Thus the parks were established as refuges, the animal populations were protected from hunting and their habitats were protected from wildfire. For a time predators were controlled to protect the "good" animals from the "bad" ones, but this endeavor mercifully ceased in the 1930's. On the whole, there was little major change in the Park Service practice of wildlife management during the first 40 years of its existence.

During the same era, the concept of wildlife management evolved rapidly among other agencies and groups concerned with the production of wildlife for recreation hunting. It is now an accepted truism that maintenance of suitable habitat is the key to sustaining animal populations, and that protection though it is important, is not of itself a substitute for habitat. Moreover, habitat is not a fixed or stable entity that can be set aside and preserved behind a fence, like a cliff dwelling or a petrified tree. Biotic communities change through natural stages of succession. They can be changed deliberately through manipulation of plant and animal populations. In recent years the National Park Service has broadened its concept of wildlife conservation to provide for purposeful management of plant and animal communities as an essential step in preserving wildlife resources ". . . unimpaired for the enjoyment of future generations." In a few parks active manipulation of habitat is being tested, as, for example, in the Everglades where controlled burning is now used experimentally to maintain the open glades and piney woods with their interesting animal and plant life. Excess populations of grazing ungulates are being controlled in a number of parks to preserve the forage plants on which the animals depend. The question already has been posed—how far should the National Park Service go in utilizing the tools of management to maintain wildlife populations?

Reprinted from *American Forests* 69: 32-35, 61-63, 1963, with the permission of the publishers.

The Concept of Park Management

The present report proposes to discuss wild-life management in the national parks in terms of three questions which shift emphasis progressively from the general to the specific:

1. What should be the *goals* of wildlife management in the national parks?
2. What general *policies* of management are best adapted to achieve the pre-determined goals?
3. What are some of the *methods* suitable for on-the-ground implementation of policies?

It is acknowledged that this advisory board was requested by the Secretary of the Interior to consider particularly one of the methods of management, namely, the procedure of removing excess ungulates from some of the parks. We feel that this specific question can only be viewed objectively in the light of goals and operational policies, and our report is framed accordingly. In speaking of national parks we refer to the whole system of parks and monuments; national recreation areas are discussed briefly near the end of the report.

As a prelude to presenting our thoughts on the goals, policies, and methods of managing wildlife in the parks of the United States, we wish to quote in full a brief report on "Management of National Parks and Equivalent Areas" which was formulated by a committee of the First World Conference on National Parks that convened in Seattle in July, 1962. The committee consisted of 15 members of the conference, representing eight nations; the chairman was François Bourliere of France. In our judgment this report suggests a firm basis for park management. The statement of the committee follows:

1. Management is defined as any activity directed toward achieving or maintaining a given condition in plant and/or animal population and/or habitats in accordance with the conservation plan for the area. A prior definition of the purposes and objectives of each park is assumed.

Management may involve active manipulation of the plant and animal communities, or protection from modification or external influences.

2. Few of the world's parks are large enough to be in fact self-regulatory ecological units; rather, most are ecological islands subject to a direct or indirect modification by activities and conditions in the surrounding areas. These influences may involve such factors as immigration and/or emigration of animal and plant life, changes in the fire regime, and alterations in the surface or subsurface water.

3. There is no need for active modification to maintain large examples of the relatively stable 'climax' communities which under protection perpetuate themselves indefinitely. Examples of such communities include large tracts of undisturbed rain forest, tropical mountain paramos, and arctic tundra.

4. However, most biotic communities are in a constant state of change due to natural or man-caused processes of ecological succession. In these 'successional' communities it is necessary to manage the habitat to achieve or stabilize it at a desired state. For example, fire is an essential management tool to maintain East African open savanna or American prairie.

5. Where animal populations get out of balance with their habitat and threaten the continued existence of a desired environment, population control becomes essential. This principle applies, for example, in situations where ungulate populations have exceeded the carrying capacity of their habitat through loss of predators, immigration from surrounding areas, or compression of normal migratory patterns. Specific examples include excess populations of elephants in some African parks and of ungulates in some mountain parks.

6. The need for management, the feasibility of management methods, and evaluation of results must be based upon current and continuing scientific research. Both the research and management itself should be undertaken only by qualified personnel. Research, management planning, and execution must take into account, and if necessary regulate, the human uses for which the park is intended.

7. Management based on scientific research is, therefore, not only desirable but often essential to maintain some biotic communities in accordance with the conservation plan of a national park or equivalent area.

The Goal of Park Management

Item 1 in the report just quoted specifies that "a prior definition of the purposes and objectives of each park is assumed." In other words, the goal must first be defined.

As a primary goal, we would recommend that the biotic associations within each park be maintained, or where necessary recreated, as nearly as possible in the condition that prevailed when the area was first visited by the white man. A national park should represent a vignette of primitive America.

The implications of this seemingly simple aspiration are stupendous. Many of our national parks—in fact most of them—went through periods of indiscriminate logging, burning, livestock grazing, hunting and predator control. Then they entered the park system and shifted abruptly to a regime of equally unnatural protection from lightning fires, from insect outbreaks, absence of natural controls of ungulates, and in some areas elimination of normal fluctuations in water levels. Exotic vertebrates, insects, plants, and plant diseases have inadvertently been introduced. And of course lastly there is the factor of human use—of roads and trampling and campgrounds and pack stock. The resultant biotic associations in many of our parks are artifacts, pure and simple. They represent a complex ecologic history but they do not necessarily represent primitive America.

Restoring the primitive scene is not done easily nor can it be done completely. Some species are extinct. Given time, an eastern hardwood forest can be regrown to maturity but the chestnut will be missing and so will the roar of pigeon wings. The colorful drapanid finches are not to be heard again in the lowland forests of Hawaii, nor will the jack-hammer of the ivory-bill ring in southern swamps. The wolf and grizzly bear cannot readily be reintroduced into ranching communities, and the factor of human use of the parks is subject only to regulation, not elimination. Exotic plants, animals, and diseases are here to stay. All these limitations we fully realize. Yet, if the goal cannot be fully achieved it can be approached. A reasonable illusion of primitive America could be recreated, using the utmost in skill, judgment, and ecologic sensitivity. This, in our opinion, should be the objective of every national park and monument.

To illustrate the goal more specifically, let us cite some cases. A visitor entering Grand Teton National Park from the south drives across Antelope Flats. But there are no antelope. No one seems to be asking the question—why aren't there? If the mountain men who gathered here in rendezvous fed their squaws on antelope, a 20th century tourist at least should be able to see a band of these animals. Finding out what aspect of the range needs rectifying, and doing so, would appear to be a primary function of park management.

When the forty-niners poured over the Sierra Nevada into California, those that kept diaries spoke almost to a man of the wide-spaced columns of mature trees that grew on the lower western slope in gigantic magnificence. The ground was a grass parkland, in springtime carpeted with wildflowers. Deer and bears were abundant. Today much of the west slope is a dog-hair thicket of young pines, white fir, incense cedar, and mature brush—a direct function of overprotection from natural ground fires. Within the four national parks—Lassen, Yosemite, Sequoia, and Kings Canyon—the thickets are even more impenetrable than elsewhere. Not only is this accumulation of fuel dangerous to the giant sequoias and other mature trees but the animal life is meager, wildflowers are sparse, and to some at least the vegetative tangle is depressing, not uplifting. Is it possible that the primitive open forest could be restored, at least on a local scale? And if so, how? We cannot offer an answer. But we are posing a question to which there should be an answer of immense concern to the National Park Service.

The scarcity of bighorn sheep in the Sierra Nevada represents another type of management problem. Though they have been effectively protected for nearly half a century, there are fewer than 400 bighorns in the Sierra. Two-thirds of them are found in summer along the crest which lies within the eastern border of Sequoia and Kings Canyon National Parks. Obviously, there is some shortcoming of habitat that precludes further increase in the population. The high country is still recovering slowly from the devastation of early domestic sheep grazing so graphically described by John Muir. But the present limitation may not be in the high summer range at all but rather along the eastern slope of the Sierra where the bighorns winter on lands in the jurisdiction of the Forest Service. These areas are grazed in summer by domestic livestock and large numbers of mule deer, and it is possible that such competitive use is adversely affecting the bighorns. It would seem to us that the National Park Service might well take the lead in studying this problem and in formulating co-operative management plans with other agencies even though the management problem lies outside the park boundary. The goal, after all, is to restore the Sierra bighorn. If restoration is achieved in the Sequoia-Kings Canyon region, there might follow a program of reintroduction and restoration of bighorns in Yosemite and Lassen National Parks, and Lava Beds National Monument, within which areas this magnificent native animal is presently extinct.

We hope that these examples clarify what we mean by the goal of park management.

Policies of Park Management

The major policy change which we would recommend to the National Park Service is that it recognize the enormous complexity of ecologic communities and the diversity of management procedures required to preserve them. The traditional, simple formula of protection may be exactly what is needed to maintain such climax associations as arctic-alpine heath, the rain forests of Olympic Peninsula, or the Joshua trees and saguaros of southwestern deserts. On the other hand, grasslands, savannas, aspen, and other successional shrub and tree associations may call for very different treatment. Reluctance to undertake biotic management can never lead to a realistic presentation of primitive America, much of which supported successional communities that were maintained by fires, floods, hurricanes, and other natural forces.

A second statement of policy that we would reiterate—and this one conforms with present Park Service standards—is that management be limited to native plants and animals. Exotics have intruded into nearly all of the parks but they need not be encouraged, even those that have interest or ecologic values of their own. Restoration of antelope in Jackson Hole, for example, should be done by managing native forage plants, not by planting crested wheat grass or plots of irrigated alfalfa. Gambel quail in a desert wash should be observed in the shade of a mesquite, not a tamarisk. A visitor who climbs a volcano in Hawaii ought to see mamane trees and silver-swords, not goats.

Carrying this point further, observable artificiality in any form must be minimized and obscured in every possible way. Wildlife should not be displayed in fenced enclosures; this is the function of a zoo, not a national park. In the same category is artificial feeding of wildlife. Fed bears become bums, and dangerous. Fed elk deplete natural ranges. Forage relationships in wild animals should be natural. Management may at times call for the use of the tractor, chainsaw, rifle, or flame-thrower but the signs and sounds of such activity should be hidden from visitors insofar as possible. In this regard, perhaps the most dangerous tool of all is the road-grader. Although the American public demands automotive access to the parks, road systems must be rigidly prescribed as to extent and design. Roadless wilderness areas should be permanently zoned. The goal, we repeat, is to maintain or create the mood of wild America. We are speaking here of restoring wildlife to enhance this mood, but the whole effect can be lost if the parks are overdeveloped for motorized travel. If too many tourists crowd the roadways, then we should ration the tourists rather than expand the roadways.

Additionally, in this connection, it seems incongruous that there should exist in the national parks mass recreation facilities such as golf courses, ski lifts, motorboat marinas, and other extraneous developments which completely contradict the management goal. We urge the National Park Service to reverse its policy of permitting these non-conforming uses, and to liquidate them as expeditiously as possible (painful as this will be to concessionaires). Above all other policies, the maintenance of naturalness should prevail.

Another major policy matter concerns the research which must form the basis for all management programs. The agency best fitted to study park management problems is the National Park Services itself. Much help and guidance can be obtained from ecologic research conducted by other agencies, but the objectives of park management are so different from those of state fish and game departments, the Forest Service, etc., as to demand highly skilled studies of a very specialized nature. Management without knowledge would be a dangerous policy indeed. Most of the research now conducted by the National Park Service is oriented largely to interpretive functions rather than to management. We urge the expansion of the research activity in the service to prepare for future management and restoration programs. As models of the type of investigation that should be greatly accelerated we cite some of the recent studies of elk in Yellowstone and of bighorn sheep in Death Valley. Additionally, however, there are needed equally critical appraisals of ecologic relationships in various plant associations and of many lesser organisms such as azaleas, lupines, chipmunks, towhees, and other non-economic species.

In consonance with the above policy statements, it follows logically that every phase of management itself be under the full jurisdiction of biologically trained personnel of the Park Service. This applies not only to habitat manipulation but to all facets of regulating animal populations. Reducing the numbers of elk in Yellowstone or of goats on Haleakala Crater is part of an over-all scheme to preserve or restore a natural biotic scene. The purpose is single-minded. We cannot endorse the view that responsibility for removing excess game animals be shared with state fish and game departments whose primary interest would be to capitalize on the recreational value of the public hunting that could thus be supplied. Such a proposal imputes a multiple use concept of park management which was never intended, which is not legally permitted, nor for which can we find any impelling justification today.

Purely from the standpoint of how best to achieve the goal of park management, as here defined, unilateral administration directed to a single objective is obviously superior to divided responsibility in which secondary goals, such as recreational hunting, are introduced. Additionally, uncontrolled public hunting might well operate in opposition to the goal, by removing roadside animals and frightening the survivors, to the end that public viewing of wildlife would

be materially impaired. In one national park, namely Grand Teton, public hunting was specified by Congress as a method to be used in controlling elk. Extended trial suggests this to be an awkward administrative tool at best.

Since this whole matter is of particular current interest it will be elaborated in a subsequent section on methods.

Method of Habitat Management

It is obviously impossible to mention in this brief report all the possible techniques that might be used by the National Park Service in manipulating plant and animal populations. We can, however, single out a few examples. In so doing, it should be kept in mind that the total area of any one park, or of the parks collectively, that may be managed intensively is a very modest part indeed. This is so for two reasons. First, critical areas which may determine animal abundance are often a small fraction of total range. One deer study on the west slope of the Sierra Nevada, for example, showed that important winter range, which could be manipulated to support the deer, constituted less than two per cent of the year-long herd range. Roadside areas that might be managed to display a more varied and natural flora and fauna can be rather narrow strips. Intensive management, in short, need not be extensive to be effective. Secondly, manipulation of vegetation is often exorbitantly expensive. Especially will this be true when the objective is to manage "invisibly"—that is, to conceal the signs of management. Controlled burning is the only method that may have extensive application.

The first step in park management is historical research, to ascertain as accurately as possible what plants and animals and biotic associations existed originally in each locality. Much of this has been done already.

A second step should be ecologic research on plant-animal relationships leading to formulation of a management hypothesis.

Next should come small scale experimentation to test the hypothesis in practice. Experimental plots can be situated out of sight of roads and visitor centers.

Lastly, application of tested management methods can be undertaken on critical areas.

By this process of study and pre-testing, mistakes can be minimized. Likewise, public groups vitally interested in park management can be shown the results of research and testing before general application, thereby eliminating possible misunderstanding and friction.

Some management methods now in use by the National Park Service seem to us potentially dangerous. For example, we wish to raise a serious question about the mass application of insecticides in the control of forest insects. Such application may (or may not) be justified in commercial timber stands, but in a national park the ecologic impact can have unanticipated effects on biotic community that might defeat the over-all management objective. It would seem wise to curtail this activity, at least until research and small scale testing have been conducted.

Of the various methods of manipulating vegetation, the controlled use of fire is the most "natural" and much the cheapest and easiest to apply. Unfortunately, however, forest and chaparral areas that have been completely protected from fire for long periods may require careful advance treatment before even the first experimental blaze is set. Trees and mature brush may have to be cut, piled, and burned before a creeping ground fire can be risked. Once fuel is reduced, periodic burning can be conducted safely and at low expense. On the other hand, some situations may call for a hot burn. On Isle Royale, moose range is created by periodic holocausts that open the forest canopy. Maintenance of the moose population is surely one goal of management on Isle Royale.

Other situations may call for the use of the bulldozer, the disc harrow, or the spring-tooth harrow to initiate desirable changes in plant succession. Buffalo wallows on the American prairie were the propagation sites of a host of native flowers and forbs that fed the antelope and the prairie chicken. In the absence of the great herds, wallows can be simulated.

Artificial reintroduction of rare native plants is often feasible. Overgrazing in years past led to local extermination of many delicate peren-

nials such as some of the orchids. Where these are not reappearing naturally they can be transplanted or cultured in a nursery. A native plant, however small and inconspicuous, is as much a part of the biota as a redwood tree or a forage species of elk.

In essence, we are calling for a set of ecologic skills unknown in this country today. Americans have shown a great capacity for degrading and fragmenting native biotas. So far we have not exercised much imagination or ingenuity in rebuilding damaged biotas. It will not be done by passive protection alone.

Control of Animal Populations

Good park management requires that ungulate populations be reduced to the level that the range will carry in good health and without impairment to the soil, the vegetation, or to habitats of other animals. This problem is worldwide in scope, and includes non-park as well as park lands. Balance may be achieved in several ways.

Natural Predation

Insofar as possible, control through natural predation should be encouraged. Predators are now protected in the parks of the United States, although unfortunately they were not in the early years and the wolf, grizzly bear, and mountain lion became extinct in many of the national parks. Even today populations of large predators, where they still occur in the parks, are kept below optimal level by programs of predator control applied outside the park boundaries. Although the National Park Service has attempted to negotiate with control agencies of federal and local governments for the maintenance of buffer zones around the parks where predators are not subject to systematic control, these negotiations have been only partially successful. The effort to protect large predators in and around the parks should be greatly intensified. At the same time, it must be recognized that predation alone can seldom be relied upon to control ungulate numbers, particularly the larger species such as bison, moose, elk, and deer; additional artificial controls frequently are called for.

Trapping and Transplanting

Traditionally in the past the National Park Service has attempted to dispose of excess ungulates by trapping and transplanting. Since 1892, for example, Yellowstone National Park alone has supplied 10,478 elk for restocking purposes. Many of the elk ranges in the western United States have been restocked from this source. Thousands of deer and lesser numbers of antelope, bighorns, mountain goats, and bison also have been moved from the parks. This program is fully justified so long as breeding stocks are needed. However, most big game ranges of the United States are essentially filled to carrying capacity, and the cost of a continuing program of trapping and transplanting cannot be sustained solely on the basis of controlling populations within the parks. Trapping and handling of a big game animal usually costs from $50 to $150 and in some situations much more. Since annual surpluses will be produced indefinitely into the future, it is patently impossible to look upon trapping as a practical plan of disposal.

Shooting Excess Animals That Migrate Outside the Parks

Many park herds are migratory and can be controlled by public hunting outside the park boundaries. Especially is this true in mountain parks which usually consist largely of summer game range with relatively little winter range. Effective application of this form of control frequently calls for special regulations, since migration usually occurs after normal hunting dates. Most of the western states have co-operated with the National Park Service in scheduling late hunts for the specific purpose of reducing park game herds, and in fact most excess game produced in the parks is so utilized. This is by far the best and the most widely applied method of controlling park populations of ungulates. The only danger is that migratory habits may be eliminated from a herd by differential removal, which would favor

survival of non-migratory individuals. With care to preserve, not eliminate, migratory traditions, this plan of control will continue to be the major form of herd regulation in national parks.

Control by Shooting, Within the Parks

Where other methods of control are inapplicable or impractical, excess park ungulates must be removed by killing. As stated above in the discussion of park policy, it is the unanimous recommendation of this board that such shooting be conducted by competent personnel, under the sole jurisdiction of the National Park Service, and for the sole purpose of animal removal, not recreational hunting. If the magnitude of a given removal program requires the services of additional shooters beyond regular Park Service personnel, the selection, employment, training, deputization and supervision of such additional personnel should be entirely the responsibility of the National Park Service. Only in this manner can the primary goal of wildlife management in the parks be realized. A limited number of expert riflemen, properly equipped and working under centralized direction, can selectively cull a herd with a minimum of disturbance to the surviving animals or to the environment. General public hunting by comparison is often non-selective and grossly disturbing.

Moreover, the numbers of game animals that must be removed annually from the parks by shooting is so small in relation to normally hunted populations outside the parks as to constitute a minor contribution to the public bag, even if it were so utilized. All of these points can be illustrated in the example of the north Yellowstone elk population which has been a focal point of argument about possible public hunting in national parks.

The Case of Yellowstone

Elk summer in all parts of Yellowstone Park and migrate out in nearly all directions, where they are subject to hunting on adjoining public and private lands. One herd, the so-called Northern Elk Herd, moves only to the vicinity of the park border where it may winter largely inside or outside the park, depending on the severity of the winter. This herd was estimated to number 35,000 animals in 1914 which was far in excess of the carrying capacity of the range. Following a massive die-off in 1919-20 the herd has steadily decreased. Over a period of 27 years, the National Park Service removed 8,825 animals by shooting and 5,765 by live-trapping; concurrently, hunters took 40,745 elk from this herd outside the park. Yet the range continued to deteriorate. In the winter of 1961-62 there were approximately 10,000 elk in the herd and carrying capacity of the winter range was estimated at 5,000. So the National Park Service at last undertook a definitive reduction program, killing 4,283 elk by shooting, which along with 850 animals removed in other ways (hunting outside the park, trapping, winter kill) brought the herd down to 5,725 as censused from helicopter. The carcasses of the elk were carefully processed and distributed to Indian communities throughout Montana and Wyoming; so they were well used. The point at issue is whether this same reduction could or should have been accomplished by public hunting.

In autumn during normal hunting season the elk are widely scattered through rough inaccessible mountains in the park. Comparable areas, well stocked with elk, are heavily hunted in adjoining national forests. Applying the kill statistics from the forests to the park, a kill of 200-400 elk might be achieved if most of the available pack stock in the area were used to transport hunters within the park. Autumn hunting could not have accomplished the necessary reduction.

In mid-winter when deep snow and bitter cold forced the elk into lower country along the north border of the park, the National Park Service undertook its reduction program. With snow vehicles, trucks, and helicopters they accomplished the unpleasant job in temperatures that went as low as -40°F. Public hunting was out of the question. Thus, in the case most bitterly argued in the press and in legislative bills, reduction of the herd by recreational hunting would have been a practical impossibility, even if it had been in full conformance with park management objectives.

From now on, the annual removal from this herd may be in the neighborhood of 1,000 to 1,800 head. By January 31, 1963, removals had totalled 1,300 (300 shot outside the park by hunters, 600 trapped and shipped, and 406 killed by park rangers). Continued special hunts in Montana and other forms of removal will yield the desired reduction by spring. The required yearly maintenance kill is not a large operation when one considers that approximately 100,000 head of big game are taken annually by hunters in Wyoming and Montana.

Game Control in Other Parks

In 1961-62, excluding Yellowstone elk, there were approximately 870 native animals transplanted and 827 killed on 18 national parks and monuments. Additionally, about 2,500 feral goats, pigs and burros were removed from three areas. Animal control in the park system as a whole is still a small operation. It should be emphasized, however, that removal programs have not in the past been adequate to control ungulates in many of the parks. Future removals will have to be larger and in many cases repeated annually. Better management of wildlife habitat will naturally produce larger annual surpluses. But the scope of this phase of park operation will never be such as to constitute a large facet of management. On the whole, reductions will be small in relation to game harvests outside the parks. For example, from 50 to 200 deer a year are removed from a problem area in Sequoia National Park; the deer kill in California is 75,000 and should be much larger. In Rocky Mountain National Park 59 elk were removed in 1961-62 and the trim should perhaps be 100 per year in the future; Colorado kills over 10,000 elk per year on open hunting ranges. In part, this relates to the small area of the national park system, which constitutes only 3.9 per cent of the public domain; hunting ranges under the jurisdiction of the Forest Service and Bureau of Land Management make up approximately 70 per cent.

In summary, control of animal populations in the national parks would appear to us to be an integral part of park management, best handled by the National Park Service itself. In this manner excess ungulates have been controlled in the national parks of Canada since 1943, and the same principle is being applied in the parks of many African countries. Selection of personnel to do the shooting likewise is a function of the Park Service. In most small operations this would logically mean skilled rangers. In larger removal programs, there might be included additional personnel, selected from the general public, hired and deputized by the service or otherwise engaged, but with a view to accomplishing a task, under strict supervision and solely for the protection of park values. Examples of some potentially large removal programs where expanded crews may be needed are mule deer populations on plateaus fringing Dinosaur National Monument and Zion National Park (west side), and white-tailed deer in Acadia National Park.

Wildlife Management on National Recreation Areas

By precedent and logic, the management of wildlife resources on the national recreation areas can be viewed in a very different light than in the park system proper. National recreation areas are by definition multiple use in character as regards allowable types of recreation. Wildlife management can be incorporated into the operational plans of these areas with public hunting as one objective. Obviously, hunting must be regulated in time and place to minimize conflict with other uses, but it would be a mistake for the National Park Service to be unduly restrictive of legitimate hunting in these areas. Most of the existing national recreation areas are federal holdings surrounding large water impoundments; there is little potentiality for hunting. Three national seashore recreational areas on the East Coast (Hatteras, Cape Cod, and Padre Island) offer limited waterfowl shooting. But some of the new areas being acquired or proposed for acquisition will offer substantial hunting opportunity for a variety of game species. This opportunity should be developed with skill, imagination, and (we would hopefully suggest) with enthusiasm.

On these areas as elsewhere, the key to wildlife abundance is a favorable habitat. The skills and techniques of habitat manipulation applicable to parks are equally applicable on the recreation areas. The regulation of hunting, on such areas as are deemed appropriate to open for such use, should be in accord with prevailing state regulations.

New National Parks

A number of new national parks are under consideration. One of the critical issues in the establishment of new parks will be the manner in which the wildlife resources are to be handled. It is our recommendation that the basic objectives and operating procedures of new parks be identical with those of established parks. It would seem awkward indeed to operate a national park system under two sets of ground rules. On the other hand, portions of several proposed parks are so firmly established as traditional hunting grounds that impending closure of hunting may preclude public acceptance of park status. In such cases it may be necessary to designate core areas as national parks in every sense of the word, establishing protective buffer zones in the form of national recreation areas where hunting is permitted. Perhaps only through compromises of this sort will the park system be rounded out.

Summary

The goal of managing the national parks and monuments should be to preserve, or where necessary to recreate, the ecologic scene as viewed by the first European visitors. As part of this scene, native species of wild animals should be present in maximum variety and reasonable abundance. Protection alone, which has been the core of Park Service wildlife policy, is not adequate to achieve this goal. Habitat manipulation is helpful and often essential to restore or maintain animal numbers. Likewise, populations of the animals themselves must sometimes be regulated to prevent habitat damage; this is especially true of ungulates.

Active management aimed at restoration of natural communities of plants and animals demand skills and knowledge not now in existence. A greatly expanded research program, oriented to management needs, must be developed within the National Park Service itself. Both research and the application of management methods should be in the hands of skilled park personnel.

Insofar as possible, animal populations should be regulated by predation and other natural means. However, predation cannot be relied upon to control the populations of larger ungulates, which sometimes must be reduced artificially.

Most ungulate populations within the parks migrate seasonally outside the park boundaries where excess numbers can be removed by public hunting. In such circumstances the National Park Service should work closely with state fish and game departments and other interested agencies in conducting the research required for management and in devising cooperative management programs.

Excess game that does not leave a park must be removed. Trapping and transplanting has not proven to be a practical method of control, though it is an appropriate source of breeding stock as needed elsewhere.

Direct removal by killing is the most economical and effective way of regulating ungulates within a park. Game removal by shooting should be conducted under the complete jurisdiction of qualified park personnel and solely for the purpose of reducing animals to preserve park values. Recreational hunting is an inappropriate and non-conforming use of the national parks and monuments.

Most game reduction programs can best be accomplished by regular park employees. But as removal programs increase in size and scope, as well may happen under better wildlife management, the National Park Service may find it advantageous to employ or otherwise engage additional shooters from the general public. No objection to this procedure is foreseen so long as the selection, training, and supervision of shooting crews is under rigid control of the service and the culling operation is made to conform to primary park goals.

Recreational hunting is a valid and potentially important use of national recreation areas, which are also under jurisdiction of the National Park Service. Full development of hunting opportunities on these areas should be provided by the service.

69

PRESERVING VEGETATION IN PARKS AND WILDERNESS

Edward C. Stone

Federal efforts to preserve natural vegetation go back to 1872, when Yellowstone National Park was carved out of the public domain; state efforts go back to 1885, when the New York

Adirondack Forest Preserve was established (1). All efforts, however, have been largely unsuccessful because of a failure to appreciate fully that vegetation is a living, dynamic complex and cannot be preserved in the sense in which a building or an archeological site can be preserved. Even the most uniform vegetation is a mosaic created by local variations in the environment and by prior events such as fire, drought, and insect infestation. When a mature plant dies, hundreds of seedlings spring up to take its place, some or all of which may be of different species. Which seedlings survive, and for how long, depends upon their relative growth potential, what effect the dead plant had on its environment before it died, and what kind of environment resulted when it died. Vegetation can only be preserved by controlling the complicated successional forces that have created it and that, if unchecked, will in turn destroy it.

The very efforts made to preserve a natural system of vegetation may bring on unplanned and undesired changes in it. That steps taken to preserve animal wildlife may have this effect is well known to the general public. By 1930 there were overpopulations of elk and bison in Yellowstone National Park, of mule deer in Zion National Park, and of deer and elk in Rocky Mountain National Park, all brought about by control of predators in and around the parks (2). Recognition of the problem led to a reconsideration of these practices, and today, although hampered by lack of basic data and a restrictive budget, specialists in wildlife preservation are employed in the national parks to plan and apply sounder regulatory methods. While not so dramatic and not so widely publicized as imbalances in wildlife populations, drastic changes in the composition of many of the plant communities in the national parks have occurred during the last 50 years under fire-protection policies and heavy concentrations of use. In a number of cases these changes have progressed so far that even the once dominant plants in a wide variety of plant communities have been replaced, and now trees and shrubs occupy slopes and meadows once clothed in grass and sedge (3).

There are two federal agencies largely responsible for the management of national wildlands, each by charter concerned with conservation of this resource but each with different primary objectives. The Forest Service was organized in 1905 within the Department of Agriculture to manage the forest reserves—later renamed national forests—to secure favorable watershed conditions and to furnish a continuous supply of timber. Shortly thereafter, however, the Forest Service recognized that recreation was an important use of these areas compatible with its other uses, and began developing the recreational facilities that now serve 125 million visitors a year. Some 15 years later it recognized the need for wilderness reserves, and by appropriate administrative action over the next several years set aside almost 12 million acres for this purpose. Subsequently both of these administrative decisions

have been sanctioned by congressional action (4).

The Park Service was organized in 1916 within the Department of the Interior to bring together under one administrative head a number of independent national parks formerly administered by several federal departments. It was specifically charged with preserving on these lands plant and animal life, and geological and archeological features of national value, for the enjoyment of the public. Vegetation preservation thus constitutes a minor part of the Forest Service's responsibilities but a major part of the Park Service's responsibilities.

The Forest Service has moved ahead rapidly in meeting its responsibilities as watershed and timber manager and purveyor of recreation facilities. It has been able to do so for a number of reasons. From its inception it was able to staff its key administrative posts with men trained for the job of managing forests for watershed and timber; it could draw upon a wealth of European experience, and it had an excellent research staff engaged in developing workable silvicultural techniques, based upon sound understanding of ecology, for use by its foresters operating in the field. In its minor role as vegetation-preservation manager of 12 million acres of wilderness, the Forest Service has yet to do much of anything.

The Park Service has moved slowly in its major role, that of preservation manager, although it has successfully operated the land under its control for the enjoyment of the public. When established, the Park Service, unlike the Forest Service, had no ready source of professional help to which it could turn. There was no such thing as a vegetation specialist versed in preservation management— that is, a vegetation-preservation manager. Furthermore, administrators could not rely upon European experience for guidance, because there was none. Nor could they turn to a research staff for developing the necessary management techniques, because again there was none. To make matters even more difficult, they were forced almost from the beginning to fight a rear-guard action with private companies and government agencies that wanted to open park lands for mining, hunting, water impoundment behind massive dams, logging, and other commercial activities. Thus administrative energies and funds were all but exhausted in maintaining existing park boundaries; and the problem of preserving a variety of undescribed ecosystems, in which changes at the time were not well advanced or readily apparent to the untrained eye, was largely solved as far as the administrator was concerned once an efficient fire-control system had been established, livestock excluded, and insect epidemics brought under control. This does not imply that the Park Service has failed to attract competent biologists to its professional staff and that there has been no effort to stem the successional tide; this is not true. Characteristically, however, individuals in the Park Service who have been trained as biologists have been called upon more for protective and interpretive service than for specialized management of the vegetation complex, because overall park policies have not until recently included the concept of

vegetation management except in the narrow aspects of fire, insect, and disease control. (See Fig. 69-1.)

In 1963, public attention was drawn to this state of affairs in the national parks by a report of a committee appointed by the National Academy of Sciences at the request of Secretary of the Interior Udall to aid in "the planning and organizing of an expanded research program of natural history research by the National Park Service." The committee presented "the pressing need for research in the national parks by citing specific examples in which degradation or deterioration has occurred because research on which proper management operations should have been based was not carried out in time; because the results of research known to operational management were not implemented; or because the research staff was not consulted before action was taken" (5). The report stresses the need to

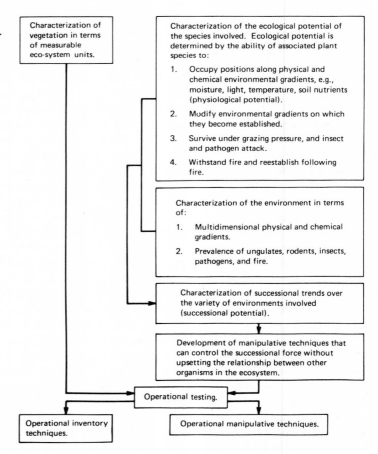

Fig. 69-1. Information required to develop manipulative techniques for vegetation preservation.

develop, by means of extensive research, the ecological basis for managing the preservation of both plant and animal life in the ecosystems involved. "It is inconceivable," the authors remark, "that property so unique and valuable as the national parks, used by such a large number of people, and regarded internationally as one of the finest examples of our national spirit should not be provided adequately with competent research scientists in natural history as elementary insurance for the preservation and best use of the parks." This is an excellent, long overdue report, exhaustive in its treatment of research needs, but it did not in my opinion focus strongly enough on the need for professional vegetation specialists at the operational level, specialists who will be responsible for carrying out the manipulative steps recommended by the research staff, much as the Forest Service's professional foresters carry out the cutting practices recommended by its research staff.

The various state agencies that administer park and forest preserves with preservation as the stated objective have come into existence at different times in response to different pressures and differ widely in the composition of their administrative staffs. All engage in protection of some kind, but none, as far as I can ascertain, is involved in manipulative procedures to preserve the integrity of specific types of vegetation. Some ecological research is under way, but again there are no professional vegetation specialists available to carry out the manipulative program that will come out of this research.

The Objectives of Preservation

Since vegetation is never static, preservation must consist, in effect, of managing change. Consequently, it is necessary to determine exactly what the objective is, and thereby to determine how much change, and what kind, can be tolerated.

One of the most common objectives is to keep park lands green or, in the arid West, green and golden. Fire protection is considered the principal means to this end. The fact that vegetation protected from fire may change completely in a relatively short period has rarely been considered, because administrators and the public have not appreciated that this can happen.

Probably the next most common objective is the preservation of certain favored dominant species within the vegetative complex. When this is the objective, the fact that certain successional stages may be fast disappearing and that the overall vegetative structure may be changing within rather broad limits is usually ignored, as long as the dominants remain dominant and the general appearance of the landscape is not altered. Change that does not interfere with the effective display of the dominant species has, in general, been acceptable. Preservation of the redwood tree, for example, has been the sole objective in the world-famous string of redwood parks that extends from south of San Francisco to the Oregon border. Consequently, change among associated species has been ignored. (See Fig. 69-2.)

A less common but still popular objective is the preservation of particular successional stages. Most often this objective has reflected a desire to preserve a piece of virgin forest or native grassland and generally has involved a *climax* phase of vegetation, that is, a condition of dynamic equilibrium in which species composition remains more or less constant. On occasion, however, there has been a strong desire to preserve a particular *subclimax* phase, such as Douglas fir on the Olympic Peninsula, red pine in the Lake States, and Caribbean pine in the Everglades, where successional change may be proceeding rapidly. (See Fig. 69-3.) In support of this type of preservation, a committee appointed by Secretary Udall to review wildlife-management practices in the national parks has recently recommended that certain successional stages be re-created and maintained in order to present "vignettes" of early America to the park visitor (6). The ease with which various successional sequences can be maintained varies with the area and the type of vegetation involved. Consequently, preservation may not be as cheaply achieved in one area as in another. Provided he is aware of this, the

Fig. 69-2. Coast redwood is physiologically attuned to periodic inundation and is provoked by the accompanying deposition of silt to regenerate a new, possibly more active, feeder-root system. Large amounts of organic matter incorporated in the silt can be fatal, however, and the vegetation-preservation manager must be ready to test for this condition and remove these silt deposits quickly if necessary. What steps he will need to take once upstream flood-control measures have altered this peculiar environment are not yet clear.

Fig. 69-3. Fire and browsing by deer (see trees in left foreground) have been important in the creation and maintenance of grass prairies in the redwood-Douglas fir forest along the north coast of California. The vegetation-preservation manager can use fire but is not dependent upon it to maintain this open, parklike intermingling of grassy glades and trees. A variety of selective herbicides — none of which enter the biotic food chain — is available and can be used effectively in conjunction with either spot burning or mowing.

park manager can select appropriate areas and achieve his objectives with a minimum of effort.

A closely associated objective is that of slowing succession. Supporters of this objective argue that it is futile to try to stop succession, that if it can be slowed sufficiently a vegetation mosaic containing most of the successional stages could be maintained, and that such a mosaic is what we should strive for in the national parks. Certainly the degree of preservation desired is always an important consideration. Succession can often be slowed for only a few cents per acre, while costs of stopping succession can run to several hundred dollars per acre.

Today, many wilderness supporters argue that we should leave large areas of vegetation alone to change as they may; that man should keep his hands off and let nature run its course, unimpeded by controls against fire, insect, and disease. (See Fig. 69-4.) When pressed on the point of fire control, however, proponents of this policy have usually agreed that some fire control is reasonable, provided it does not interfere with the occurrence of natural fire. Accordingly, lighning fires would be allowed to run unchecked, and if the aboriginal arsonist were alive today he would not be discouraged because he would be a part of the natural environment. Paradoxically, fire started by a careless camper would be dealt with vigorously.

On most of the areas that might be affected by such a program, succession is extremely slow and, because of extensive areas of exposed rock, wildfires soon burn themselves out. With sufficient control of human use these areas will change little in the next 100 or even 200 years, and this is probably what most proponents of a hands-off policy visualize. There are other areas, however, where the understory is now very dense and highly inflammable throughout much of the year and not in the condition that prevailed when the areas were set aside. Uncontrolled wildfire would be catastrophic. Thus, in the absence of fire control, vegetation in one area would be maintained more or less as it is today for many years to come, while in another area it might be violently changed within the next few years.

Fig. 69-4. Big cone spruce, shown against the sky line, is not a fire-resistant species but has survived in the chaparral of Southern California because of natural firebreaks created by shallow soils and the regular occurrence of widespread fires in the past. Today these natural firebreaks are overgrown and no longer offer protection. The vegetation-preservation manager must reestablish these firebreaks if stands of big cone spruces are to be preserved.

Compatibility of Objectives

Many preservationists consider management per se to be an unwarranted interference with nature by man. This need not be true. Management consists merely of those actions that are necessary to achieve one or more objectives, whatever they may be, even if the objective is "no management." Management dealing with vegetation may be intensive or extensive, depending upon the objectives, but unless the objectives are thoroughly outlined effective management is impossible. Because vegetation preservation may be only one of several objectives, all must be carefully considered together to determine whether they are compatible with a specific policy of preserving dominant species or particular stages in a successional sequence. Probably incompatible objectives are much more widespread in current efforts to preserve vegetation than is generally recognized, because change in vegetation can proceed for many years without detection by the public or even by the park administrator responsible for its preservation.

Research on Vegetation Preservation

The National Academy of Sciences Advisory Committee, in reviewing the research program of the National Park Service, "was shocked to learn that for the year 1962 the research staff (including the chief naturalist and fieldmen in natural history) was limited to ten people and that the Service budget for national history research was $28,000—about the cost of one campground comfort station" (5). If we consider only the magnitude of the research job required to support a realistic vegetation-preservation program, it is easy to understand why the committee was shocked. A million-dollar annual budget and a staff of several hundred scientists, with several times as many supporting personnel, are needed. The Yellowstone National Park staff, for example, has indicated (5) that the research required to support its vegetation-preservation program would entail an analysis of the current climatic trends; a detailed soil survey; and analyses of the vegetative mosaic and the factors creating it; successional patterns in the various biotic communities; the interrelationships of plants and animals, particularly dominant species like ungulates; variations of current ecological conditions from the original; the factors that have caused these deviations; the practicability of re-creating original ecological conditions where ecological damage or deterioration, for instance, soil loss, has occurred; and the direct effect of visitors on important natural features. Thus, dealing effectively with the problem of vegetation preservation in this one park, only one of 31 national parks, will require a dozen or more scientists—climatologists, pedologists, and ecologists of various specializations—with a supporting staff of perhaps a hundred or more.

The Forest Service has not as yet committed its research staff to studying the overall problems of vegetation preservation, but much of what its silviculture and range-management researchers have discovered over the last 35 years is directly applicable. (See Fig. 69-5.) Both the silviculturist and the range manager, like the vegetation-preservation manager, are interested in successional processes and their control. The distinction lies in the end products desired and the tools that can be used to obtain them. The silviculturist is interested in the amount and quality of timber produced. He selects trees to this end and in the process completely alters the structure of the vegetation units involved. His imprint in the form of skid trails, neatly sawn stumps, and extraction roads is everywhere apparent. The range manager is interested in the weight and quality of beef or mutton that vegetation produces. He uses his animals, through rotational grazing schemes of various kinds, to control plant succession. Except for the presence of domestic animals, fences, and occasional scars of a disc harrow on a reseeded, overgrazed range, his mark is not apparent and the structure of the vegetation units involved may not be greatly altered.

What is most needed to get a full-scale vegetation-preservation research program underway by the Forest Service is an administrative decision to do so. Only a few shifts in research emphasis at key points within the present research program, along with a relatively

Fig. 69-5. Top aerial photograph was taken shortly before the grass-covered slopes in the right foreground were purchased by a local park district and cattle were excluded. Bottom aerial photograph was taken early in 1965 — 35 years later — and shows the extent to which brush has replaced grass within the park boundaries. If the grass cover is to be preserved, the vegetation-preservation manager must remove the brush and take steps to keep it out. Fire as a tool has been ruled out by local smog-control officials. Introducing cattle is difficult because of the number of youth groups using the area. Bulldozers, herbicides, and mowing machines appear to be the alternative tools available.

modest augmentation of the basic research staff, are needed. Once embarked upon such a program, the Forest Service soon would be able to develop suitable operational techniques for preserving vegetation on the 12 million acres of wilderness that are its responsibility. (See Fig. 69-5.)

All the state parks involved in vegetation preservation need research support, but few are receiving it. The State Division of Beaches and Parks in California, for example, has an annual support budget of $10,000,000 and is re-

sponsible for vegetation preservation on more than 600,000 acres. The size of the individual parks varies from a few hundred to several thousand acres, and the type of vegetation to be preserved varies through cactus and scrub on the Mohave Desert, oak woodland in the Central Valley, mixed conifers in the Sierra, and redwoods along the North Coast. Its annual research budget amounts to only $28,000. A third of this is being spent on a crash program to develop recommendations for preserving redwood groves along the Eel River which are subjected to periodic flooding and to more than 500,000 visitors annually. The rest is being spent by the interpretive-services section. Nothing is being spent on research to determine how the variety of vegetation types that occur in the other parks in the state should be maintained.

The type of information required to develop manipulative techniques for the preservation of vegetation is summarized in Fig. 69-1. Some of this information, obtained through the efforts of university-based scientists, their graduate students, and Forest Service researchers, is already available for certain types of vegetation. Rarely, however, will this information be complete from a vegetation-preservation viewpoint, partly because preservation has not generally been the objective of the studies, but mostly because studies of plant succession in this country have closely followed an approach developed by the well-known ecologist F. E. Clements (7). Clements was convinced that successional sequences, which involve changes with time, can be determined by observing changes in vegetative patterns in space, and through his persuasive pen he was able to convince others that this was feasible. The major difficulty encountered in this approach has been that the only method of evaluating the accuracy of a researcher's estimate of successional trends, that is, his first approximation, has been to wait and see.

Where short-lived grasses and herbs have been involved and reestablishment of a dynamic equilibrium following disturbance has been rapid, the Clementsian approach has been reasonably effective. Researchers have been able to modify their first approximation through several subsequent approximations, improving the accuracy of their estimate each time. This is the approach that largely has been used by range-management researchers. Recently, however, they also have experienced its limitations and have begun to turn to detailed environmental analyses and growth-performance studies under controlled environments.

Where long-lived plants have been involved and reestablishment of a dynamic equilibrium following disturbance has been slow and will not be reached for another hundred years or so,

first approximations based on Clements' approach are often little better than educated guesses. In dealing with vegetation of this type a more sophisticated analysis of the ecological potential and the relative magnitude of the environmental factors involved will be required (see Fig. 69-1). Studies of comparative growth performance of associated species in controlled environments along the lines suggested by Hellmers (8), and environmental-gradient analyses along the lines suggested by Whittaker (9), Bakuzis (10), and Waring and Major (11), are essential.

Specialists in Vegetation-Preservation Management

The National Academy of Sciences Advisory Committee (5) points out briefly that the Park Service has applied research in a piecemeal fashion and has "failed to insure the implementation of the results of research in operational management." The committee concludes with the comment that "Reports and recommendations on the subject will remain futile unless and until the National Park Service itself becomes research-minded and is prepared to support research and to apply its findings." That the "implementation of the results of research" calls for experts on the management of vegetation has as yet not been recognized. Even preservation-oriented conservationists, who are the backbone of the leading conservation groups in this country, have been slow to perceive this. Many of them still regard vegetation much as they do their own gardens and are quick to suggest how a particular vegetative cover can best be preserved, whether it be in the local nature reserve, in a state park dominated by 1000-year-old redwood trees, or in an untrammeled wilderness.

Obviously the decision as to what should be preserved cannot be left entirely to the specialist. The concerned public, although amateurs in vegetation preservation, must be heard and heeded. But at the same time a realistic assessment must be made of what can be achieved at costs commensurate with public interest, and this depends upon a knowledge of various alternatives and the relative cost and feasibility of achieving each one. Only the vegetation specialist can furnish this kind of information.

The vegetation-preservation specialist must be trained in management, must possess a thorough knowledge of ecology, must be experienced in assessing the relative growth potential of each species in the vegetative mosaic, must be experienced in the use of various manipulative techniques, and must understand research methods. Today there are few men so qualified. There is an impressive number of competent plant ecologists scattered throughout related professions who are oriented toward management, but there are relatively few who have had experience in a detailed assessment of the environmental complex, and even fewer who have had experience in manipulative techniques.

The vegetation-preservation specialist will not replace the research ecologist and to a large extent will be dependent upon him. He must be competent to understand research, to evaluate research findings in terms of his management function, and to translate research into manipulative techniques particularly suited to the specific vegetation he must manage. These manipulative techniques must be based on an understanding of the ecology of the vegetation in question; if such information is not available and ecologists are not employed to develop it, the preservation specialist will be forced to forego his primary responsibility and to spend his time collecting basic ecological data.

Because success in the field of vegetation preservation requires several—usually many—years to evalute, the vegetation-preservation specialist often will operate in an atmosphere in which unsubstantiated opinions are forcefully urged. Many fire enthusiasts, for example, are convinced that fire protection should be curtailed, and do not recognize that merely because fire control has led to some undesired effects it does not necessarily follow that fire control should be abandoned or prescribed burning introduced. Involved is the whole process of recognizing the management objective, evaluating the ecological forces in play, identifying the conditions which must be achieved to develop the desired vegetation

response, and, finally, evaluating all the possible ways of moving toward those conditions economically and with a minimum of unwanted side effects. In all of this the vegetation-preservation specialist will need a fine sense of perspective.

Little can be accomplished in the field of vegetation-preservation management until a source of competently trained specialists has been developed—and perhaps not until considerable numbers of these specialists have infiltrated the various responsible adminstrative bodies. How can we develop such a source? At the moment I can see only one solution: Ask those universities that have strong programs both in ecology and in land management, for example, those with forestry and range-management curricula, to take on the job. It should be possible to train these specialists by means of a 2-year graduate program, provided it is preceded by an undergraduate degree with a proper emphasis on basic biology and is followed by an appropriate period of apprenticeship. Several universities could readily meet this challenge, provided financial support were assured. The question that remains to be answered is: How soon will the universities that have staffs capable of carrying out this graduate program be asked to join in creating this new profession?

References

1. Yellowstone National Park Establishment Act, **17,** *Stat.* 32 (1872); S. W. Allen, *An Introduction to American Forestry* (McGraw-Hill, New York, ed. 2, 1938).
2. J. Ise, *Our National Park Policy* (Johns Hopkins Univ. Press, Baltimore, 1961).
3. R. P. Gibbens and H. F. Heady, "The influence of modern man on the vegetation of Yosemite Valley," *Calif. Agr. Exp. Sta. Manual No. 36* (1964); Univ. of Calif. Wildland Research Center, *Outdoor Recreation Resources Rev. Comm. Study Rept. No. 3* (Government Printing Office, Washington, D.C., 1962).
4. Multiple Use Sustained Yield Act, **86** *Stat.* 517 (1960); The National Wilderness Preservation System Act, **78** *Stat.* 890 (1964).
5. National Academy of Sciences–National Research Council, *A Report by the Advisory Committee to the National Park Service on Research* (Washington, D.C., 1963).

6. A. S. Leopold, S. A. Cain, I. N. Gabrielson, C. M. Cottam, T. L. Kimball, *Living Wilderness* **83**, 11 (1963).
7. F. E. Clements, "Plant succession," *Carnegie Inst. Wash. Publ. No. 242* (1916).
8. H. Hellmers and W. P. Sundahl, *Nature* **184**, 1247 (1959).
9. R. H. Whittaker, "Vegetation of the Great Smoky Mountains," *Ecol. Monographs* **26**, 1 (1956).
10. E. V. Bakuzis, thesis, Univ. of Minnesota (1959).
11. R. Waring and J. Major, "Some vegetation of the California coastal redwood region in relation to gradients of moisture, nutrients, light, and temperature," *Ecol. Monographs* **34**, 167 (1964).

70

ZOOS: THEIR CHANGING ROLES

William G. Conway

The expansion of urban populations now makes it necessary for zoos to educate the generations growing up without any natural contact with wild creatures. Except at the zoo, the opportunities to know or even to become interested in wild creatures are largely vicarious for most city dwellers. Yet, the opinions of these urbanites may ultimately shape the future policies of conservation in this country. Seen in this light, the educational challenges to the zoo naturalist and the conservationist are identical.

The educational functions and methods of zoos (as of museums) are not those of the classroom, although zoos do collaborate with schools to supplement classroom education. Departments of education at several zoos, such as those in London, San Diego, and New York, supply programs, lectures, and tours for the local schools. The education departments of the San Diego and Bronx zoos now send lecturers with living animals to nearby elementary and secondary schools, operate an inservice teachers' course on the use of the zoo, conduct special summer courses, give tours, and manage an educational film program. In Philadelphia and Chicago, "zoo mobiles," each containing animal exhibits and a lecturer, visit schools and

Reprinted from *Science* 163:48-52, 1969, with the permission of the publishers. Copyright 1969 by the American Association for the Advancement of Science.

playgrounds. Zoos and universities located close to each other often establish joint programs.

Subjects that might be taught in zoos include geography, evolution, and an appreciation of the term "renewable resources." At the 1967 annual conference of the American Association of Zoological Parks and Aquariums, in a symposium entitled "The use of zoos and aquaria in teaching animal behavior," A. W. Stokes remarked that

Over 100 colleges now offer graduate training in this [animal behavior] field. The increase in courses in animal behavior is meteoric. For these courses to be really effective they should expose students to actual observation of animal behavior. . . . Such places [zoos and aquaria] offer a variety of animals exhibited in far more spacious quarters that one could never attain in a laboratory, thus allowing opportunity to observe behavior patterns not possible indoors.

Education at the zoo has always seemed like recreation. Adults and children come to the zoo without urging, and many educators are convinced that this fact points the way to use of the zoo as a motivational stimulus for inner-city children, although there are as yet no conclusive programs to explore this possibility. Since the zoo presents unusual variety amid the homogeneous municipal habitat, its excitement and mystery would seem to be an effective way of interesting children in reading and thus in education—a way of arousing curiosity.

Satisfying curiosity about kinds of animals and what they look like has always been an important function at the zoo; through new techniques, exhibits at the zoo are broadening the visitors' basic scientific knowledge. Habitat exhibits, as opposed to cages in which pairs of animals are confined, are being constructed as fast as funds permit. New group displays of social animals and increasing birth rates at zoos enable city dwellers to begin to understand animal behavior.

The promise of more leisure time in the future will help to change the zoo's role. As a recreational resource for the family, zoos seem beyond compare. More than 85 million visits were recorded by American zoological collections last year, more than the combined attendance of all botanical gardens and natural history museums, and also more than the combined attendance of all national football and baseball games. In short, the zoo can successfully compete in the amusement field while educating the public.

Exhibits

It was not until recently that any major zoo had a department of exhibition comparable to those of most museums. In 1964, the New York Zoological Society established a department of exhibition and graphic arts patterned, in some ways, after that of the American Museum of Natural History. Prior to this time, the Arizona-Sonora Desert Museum, which in many aspects is like a zoo, had established a curator of exhibits, and, since 1964, exhibition departments have been initiated in Chicago's Brookfield Zoo and the Philadelphia Zoo. This development reflects not only an increasing concern with the problem of presenting animals in exhibits that appear more natural and introducing more information about them but also the availability of new exhibit materials and techniques from other fields. In natural history museums habitat groups and interpretive graphics do not have to be designed for animals' eating, digging, climbing, chewing, and so forth. With new synthetic materials such as fiber glass and polyethylene, the appearance of animal environments, even under conditions of close confinement, can be simulated. A better understanding of animals' needs and behavior enables the visitor to the zoo to have a less obstructed view of the animals. Open-fronted exhibits, the use of moats rather than bars, and habitat settings are being used widely (Fig. 70-1).

The desire to keep wild animals, which may harbor persistent parasites, in areas that can be quickly and efficiently cleaned, is usually in conflict with the need to exhibit them in a display simulating some part of their natural habitat. For this reason, a tile wall or "lavatory" type of display has its supporters, particularly for the exhibition of primates. However, as the new techniques become less expensive, the need for this type of housing will disappear. The addition of exhibition departments to zoos will also release the curatorial staffs from many specialized aspects of exhibit preparation, and the zoo should be able to proceed more rapidly toward the goal of displaying all of its animals within the ecological and evolutionary context implied by a "natural" background rather than as disenfranchised creatures in steel, tile, or concrete confinement (see Fig. 70-1).

The basic concepts of exhibition are changing too. Exhibits based on taxonomic affinities—the big cats, the bears, the ungulates—are being supplemented by thematic presentations founded on zoogeography, ecology, and behavior. The Munich Zoo was arranging its exhibits by continent as early as 1932, and the same concept was important in the development of the Detroit Zoo. The new Milwaukee Zoo has combined predator-prey presentations, first developed by Hagenbeck at Stellingen in Hamburg, with zoogeography to show lions in juxtaposition with zebras, jaguars with tapirs, and tigers with deer. Exhibits of nocturnal animals are the first substantial behavioral displays, but sophisticated smaller exhibits developed at Chicago's Brookfield Zoo by Rabb to demonstrate dominance hierarchies and territorial marking are additional examples. The Aquatic Birds Building at the Bronx Zoo houses a contrasting series of exaggerated views of wetland habitats subtly emphasizing the waterbirds' dependence on the preservation of swamps, marshes, and beaches.

However, European zoos have enjoyed one unsought advantage over their sister institutions in the United States. They were bombed. Many are no longer plagued with unsuitable buildings constructed before the recent renaissance in thought and design of zoological parks. Furthermore, buildings for zoos are extraordinarily

Fig. 70-1. *A modern moated exhibit of African antelopes and lions in adjacent enclosures at the New York Zoological Park. New York Zoological Society Photo.*

expensive to construct because they are specialized in almost every detail. Structures designed to exhibit elephants, hummingbirds, gorillas, cobras, storks, crocodiles, pack-rats, and flamingos have to incorporate innumerable requirements. The need for new physical facilities is urgent in American zoos, all the more because their facilities are so sorely tried by reason of their very popularity.

Zoos and Conservation

One of the reasons for the exhibition of live animals is to encourage those visitors who can to become more deeply concerned with their surroundings and to take advantage of local wildlife and the out-of-doors. It is customary for biologists to urge those who can to seek animals in the wild, to hike, and to visit

national parks, but it is now evident that such visits in great quantity will finally destroy these wild areas. The fragility of many animal and plant communities subjected to human pressures in some of our national parks has become all too evident (1), and the real value of the zoo's role in this context is to act as a partial substitute for visits to natural areas and to fulfill certain functions of parks in the field of environmental education and conservation.

Conservation of wild animals would seem to find a natural base in zoological parks. Where better can the plight of a vanished species arouse widespread public sentiment and support than in presentations of the animal itself located in human population centers? It seems strange that more conservationists have not sought to make zoos headquarters for efforts in conservation education. The wildlife protection work of Hornaday (2), who was the first director of the New York Zoological Park, stands almost alone in the early days of this century. He was a moving force in the development of the Migratory Bird Act, which stopped the potentially disastrous trade in bird plumage, and in the establishment of the American Bison Society, which eventually won protection for the bison and led to stocked bison refuges. But recently, and especially within the last decade, conservationists associated with zoos and captive collections have included some of the most prominent wildlife protectionists—men like Osborn of the New York Zoological Society, Grzimek of the Frankfurt Zoo, and the well-known aviculturists and ornithologists Delacour, Scott, and Ripley.

Nevertheless, zoos are frequently and inaccurately accused of depleting wildlife populations. Until the zoos' boycotts of orangutans *(Pongo pygmaeus)*, first initiated in the United States in 1962, zoos did contribute to the precarious status of this species, but evidence is lacking to show that collecting by zoos has been of major importance to any other animal population, although zoos have also restricted their importations of giant tortoises and monkey-eating eagles. The problem lies elsewhere. The U.S. Department of the Interior reported importations for 1967 totaling 74,304 mammals (62,526 of which were primates largely for laboratory study), 203,189 birds, 405,134 reptiles, 137,697 amphibians, and 27,759,332 fish (3). Zoos required not more than a fraction of 1 percent of this number, and, most alarmingly, the total number of live mammals and reptiles imported for the laboratory, pet, and zoo trade are but a fraction of the number represented by the trade in hides and animal products (4).

However, some critics feel that to cage any animal is immoral, and this strong antagonism against captivity, from well-intentioned persons who may give little thought to hunting or destruction of habitats, probably delayed the union of zoo-naturalists and the conservationists. The bond was inevitable, not only because of the zoos' obligatory interest in conservation, but also because several species have become so rare that they would not exist were it not for zoos. The zoos and other captive

collections can act as reservoirs for the preservation of certain species which may even be reintroduced in newly protected parks in their native lands at some time in the future. The Pere David deer *(Elaphurus davidianus)*, the Przewalski horse *(Equus przewalski)*, the wisent *(Bison bonasus)*, the Hawaiian goose *(Branta candicensis)*, the Laysan teal *(Anas platyrhynchos laysanensis)*, and the Swinhoe pheasant *(Lophura swinhoei)* are prominent among endangered species which have benefited from captive management.

The Pere David deer is thought to have been a resident of the plains of northeastern China; however, the last of the species in China died in 1921 leaving its fate with a single captive herd which the Duke of Bedford had gathered from European zoos and placed on his estate, Woburn Abbey, in 1898. Bedford obtained only 18 of these great ungainly deer but, by World War I, his herd had increased to 88. Only 50 survived the privations of the war (5) but by 1948 the herd numbered 300 (6). The 1967 census of the *International Zoo Yearbook* (7) lists 452 animals in 46 collections. Two hundred sixty-five of this number were still at Woburn Abbey, and four represent animals returned to China as a gift from the London Zoological Society to the Peking Zoo.

The last of the true wild horses, the Przewalski horse, once ranged through southwestern Mongolia and northeastern Sinkiang. In 1966 a sighting raised hopes for the survival of a few of these extremely rare and believed possibly extinct animals in the wild. Captive stocks in 33 zoos totaled 149 (8), and 14 colts were bred in that year. In this case, the surviving captive herd owes its existence to Carl Hagenbeck and the zoological gardens in Prague and Munich. Hagenbeck sent an expedition to Mongolia that returned in 1901, after surmounting almost incredible difficulties, with 28 Przewalski horses. About 24 of the progeny of these animals survived World War II in the Prague and Munich zoos. From these two herds the present stock was established, and it is heartening to reflect that the number of horses has more than doubled during the past 7 years.

Still another dramatic instance of the successful captive breeding of an endangered species is the story of the wisent or European bison. Once widespread in European forests and perhaps in Siberia, this tall, rangy relative of the American bison was gradually diminished by destruction of forests and by hunting, until by 1900 it was largely confined to the Bialowieza Forest in eastern Poland and to the foothills of the Caucasus. World War I and its aftermath put an end to the wild populations which finally disappeared in the early 1920's. Fortunately, enough animals had been sent to zoos and bred so that the Bialowieza Forest could be re-stocked in 1929, and remnants of this reintro-duced herd and scattered groups in zoos were still extant after World War II. Today the world stock numbers more than 300 in 64 zoos and in the forest reserve.

No significant captive stocks of endangered fish or amphibians are being bred in zoological parks, but the San Diego zoo has been notably successful with one famous reptile, the Gala-pagos tortoise *(Testudo elephantopus)*, and successfully hatched 17 young tortoises from 1961 through 1965 (9). Birds have received less care than mammals, but important captive stocks of a surprising number of rare waterfowl and pheasants are being maintained in zoos and private collections. The Hawaiian goose has been bred in sufficient numbers to permit birds bred in captivity to be reintroduced with the wild population, and the Laysan teal, so rare 30 years ago that it was doubted whether more than 24 birds survived, has become common in collections. During 1967 and 1968, the Bureau of Sports Fisheries and Wildlife successfully reared whooping cranes from eggs taken in the wild and thereby raised new hopes for the captive propagation of this bird.

Current successes arouse curiosity about lost opportunities, and a review of the responsi-bilities that the last four centuries of extinction would have posed to modern collections of birds is instructive (10). I examined (11) the 162 extinct birds with captive propagation potentials in mind. Fifty-eight forms had characteristics or living relatives with charac-teristics which suggest that the possibility of breeding them in captivity, with modern methods, would be a good one. Species in-cluded in this list are among the most spectac-ular of vanished birds, for example, the ele-phant bird *(Aepyornis maximus)*, the lesser moa *(Megalapteryx didinus)*, and the dodo *(Raphus cucullatus)*. Thirteen species, including the Carolina parakeet *(Conuropsis carolinensis)* and the passenger pigeon, both of which were bred in captivity, could readily be propagated at the present stage of avicultural technology. Twenty-seven forms had characteristics of groups which have not yielded to aviculture, and 64 species belonged to groups for which information is so scanty as to make any evaluation impractical. Of the 307 existing birds listed as rare by the International Union for the Conservation of Nature and Natural Resources in 1965, useful information was available for 241. Of these, 101 are unsuited for captive management at this stage of propa-gation science. In this group, I include such species as the ivory-billed woodpecker *(Campephilus principalis)*, the Atitlan grebe *(Podilymbus gigas)*, the monkey-eating eagle *(Pithecophaga jefferyi)*, and the pygmy swift *(Micropanyptila furcata)*. A further 84 species show characteristics suggesting that they may have propagation potential, and 47 more are already being propagated or most certainly could be.

In the United States, accelerated interest in breeding of endangered forms in zoos resulted in the incorporation of the Wild Animal Propa-gation Trust under the aegis of the American Association of Zoological Parks and Aquariums in 1963. Formed to coordinate and promote the breeding of endangered animals in captivity, the Wild Animal Propagation Trust is develop-ing national breeding programs with especially important species and is receiving such remark-able cooperation in the case of the orangutan that it virtually controls all movement and pairing of these animals in zoos in the United States. However, obtaining animals—even those scheduled for propagation—sometimes poses technical problems.

The zoo is often dealing with creatures subject to stringent regulations by the United States Public Health Service and the Depart-ment of Agriculture. In order to import an ungulate, such as an antelope or a giraffe, it is necessary for the zoo to obtain special permits and to reserve quarantine space, usually at the Quarantine Station of the Department of Agriculture in Clifton, New Jersey, and at certain approved quarantine stations abroad. The prospective exhibit must be confined 60 days in a foreign quarantine station and then must spend 30 days in Clifton as a precaution against introducing such diseases as rinderpest and foot-and-mouth disease. Gallinaceous birds, waterfowl, doves, pigeons, and parrots are also subject to various quarantine regulations, but, in the case of the hoofed animal, the specimen must remain in a state of "permanent post-entry quarantine" throughout its life, and upon death the body must be disposed of in an approved manner. Fewer than 50 American zoos have been approved for the importation of ungulates. Because the United States Department of Agriculture adheres to a policy of eradicating disease by slaughtering animals, in American zoos there is a constant fear of an outbreak of foot-and-mouth disease that might mean the destruction of major herds of vanishing animals.

Potential for Research

To zoologists unfamiliar with animal keeping and heavily attended zoos, the zoological park may seem a natural research facility; however, there are serious problems to be overcome. Recent developments suggest that obstacles to research at zoos are now being solved.

Although many European zoological parks have conducted regular, if modest, scientific programs since their inception, in the United States only the New York and Philadelphia zoological societies have a long history of scientific inquiry. Jarvis (12) once suggested that it was "... quite extraordinary that, whereas collections of dead animals should be generally accepted as scientifically valuable, so few people have ever realized the high scientific potential of a collection of living animals." One obstacle to research in zoos has been inadequate scientific staffs.

Usually, American zoos cannot afford to hire scientific curators without primary duties in the maintenance and exhibition of the collection. Modern labor practices have further complicated the curator's job. The 5-day week combined with ever more generous leave policies makes it difficult to provide 7-day-a-week care for animals, and zoos are situated in a city environment where it is especially difficult to find potential keepers with experience in caring for animals. There is little likelihood that machines will replace human caretakers in zoos, because the care of complex living exhibits requires responsive unprogrammed maintenance from intelligent people. Because the management of wild animals is often poorly understood, the zoo curator finds himself committed professionally and morally to applying his skills to the development programs for the care of animals. Indeed, the successful acclimatization and breeding of a difficult species comprise a major professional goal. The need to improve the exhibition and health of the living collections, combined with substantial administrative and public educational responsibilities, leaves the curator with little time for basic research.

A more direct obstacle to research is that zoos rarely have sufficient numbers of any one species to constitute a scientific sample. Because animals may require years to become acclimatized, and because of possible public indignation, programs involving surgical manipulation of captive animals have been eschewed at zoos. Only certain kinds of behavior are available to the scientist working at a zoo, even in the best planned captive exhibits. Nevertheless, captive animals have too much to tell about man's evolution, behavior, and disease for large living collections in the heart of our urban educational and research centers to be ignored. Conditions at the zoo lend an intimacy and consistency to animal observation usually unparalleled in the field. While not all of a species normal behavior can be observed in captivity (or is likely to be observed in the wild), the captive's reduction of flight distance (13), and inurement to observers outside his enclosure are partial compensations. Subjects from a zoo can be of known age, weight, sex, and parentage yet available within a far less restricting confinement than is usually practical in the laboratory. At the zoo an animal may be studied conveniently and can be tested in ways and with equipment impossible to use in the wild; even the animal's parasites and food intake may be measured without endangering other observations. Although surgical manipulation of wild animals has not yet won wide acceptability, advances in techniques for restraining wild animals and in anesthesiology promise to open unique opportunities for experimentation that will be less traumatic.

Naturally, a major attraction of the zoo for scientists is the availability of unusual subjects. Elephants, hummingbirds, hellbenders, and monitors may each offer an as yet unrealized opportunity for species-specific research. The zoo staff's experience with little-known creatures and their care is an especial lure for the scientist who knows little of animal care, but the good health and adjustment of the acclimated zoo animal in its captive environment are even more important.

Today, there are promising scientific developments at several large zoos in the form of more or less independent research institutes. The biologists in an institute connected with a zoo may have few, if any, responsibilities for exhibits, yet they can benefit from the stimulus of the living collection and from association with experienced curators. The curators and, ultimately, the collection can be benefited as well, for the investigator who concentrates on one or two species, or on a particular aspect of the biology of several species, is likely to develop information on management of captives that the diffuse curatorial efforts might never reveal. There are several pace-setting examples of such semiautonomous institutes in the United States and in Great Britain.

The Penrose Institute, in the Philadelphia Zoo, was established in 1901. Directed by H. L. Ratcliffe, the institute is generally concerned with studies in pathology and has been especially concerned with tuberculosis and nutrition. While the zoo has provided much material for the institute's work, the institute has aided the zoo's programs in animal care and nutrition. Two comparable efforts at the London Zoo are the Nuffield Institute of Comparative Medicine, started in 1962, and the Wellcome Institute of Comparative Physiology, which began in 1965.

At these organizations, housed in impressively modern zoo laboratories, but including associates at various universities, infectious diseases, pharmacology, radiology, biochemistry, surgery, and reproductive physiology are being studied. In California, the Zoological Society of San Diego recently established an Institute for Comparative Biology under the direction of C. York, and work is proceeding in several fields including comparative primate behavior, general physiology and pathology, comparative neuro-physiology, toxicology, biochemistry, and hematology (14). The New York Zoological Society is developing a still different kind of research institute. The society and the Rockefeller University joined forces to create an institute for Research in Animal Behavior under the direction of D. R. Griffin. This cooperative effort, which may well be a model for future relations between zoos and universities includes facilities at both zoo and university and includes the New York Zoological Society William Beebe Tropical Research Station in Trinidad. Staff appointments carry appropriate titles within society and university and there is a cost-sharing plan. The work and goals of the institute were described by Penney (15). Additional cooperative programs exist in several cities including Oklahoma City, St. Louis, Chicago, and Portland, Oregon, and a promising program in behavioral biology has been started by J. Eisenberg at the National Zoo in Washington.

The zoo, perhaps, is most easily utilized for comparative studies on a broad spectrum of species; its special facilities can provide an important supplement for intensive field investigations of a particular species and can suggest new approaches to old problems. The biologist familiar with marsupial reproduction finds mammals available for observation at an extraordinarily early stage. The giraffe watcher may wonder how this walking scaffold avoids a stroke when he lowers his head 18 feet in one swift movement. The viewer of the vulture may be moved to determine why his subjects do not die of food poisoning, while the geneticist may learn of the opportunities presented by the armadillo's polyembryony or the parthenogenetic success of certain *Lacerta* and *Cnemidophorus* lizards. Navigation may be studied in experiments with birds which migrate over trackless oceans at night, echolocation with bats, and learning and transmission of song patterns in birds can compete for the investigators' attention with the problem of animal play and the evolution of facial expression. Unfortunately, it seems probable that investigation of a number of species will only be possible in the zoo for they will exist nowhere else.

Summary

The zoo's urban location, recent changes in concepts, and improvements in technology have come at a time when environmental education requires much attention. As an urban institution and a resource of diminishing wild creatures, the zoo seems destined to fulfill an increasingly important role in education, conservation, and research.

References and Notes

1. S. A. Cain, in *Future Environments of North America*, F. F. Darling and J. P. Milton, Eds. (Natural History Press, Garden City, N.Y., 1966), pp. 53-54.
2. W. T. Hornaday, *Thirty Years War for Wild Life* (Scribners, Stamford, Conn., 1931).
3. U.S. Department of the Interior, news summary 19 February 1968 (U.S. Government Printing Office, Washington, D.C., 1968).
4. W. G. Conway, *Animal Kingdom* 3, 21 (1968).
5. R. Fitter, *Oryx* 9, 89 (1967).
6. L. S. Crandall, *The Management of Wild Mammals in Captivity* (Univ. of Chicago Press, Chicago, 1964), p. 584.
7. C. Jarvis, *International Zoo Yearbook* (Zoological Society of London, London, 1968), vol. 8, pp. 350-381.
8. ———, *ibid.* (Zoological Society of London, London, 1967), vol. 7, p. 370.
9. C. E. Shaw, *Oryx* 9, 122 (1967).
10. J. Vincent, "List of birds either known or thought to have become extinct since 1600," *Inst. Union Conserv. Nature Natur. Resour. Bull.* (Spec. Suppl.) 16, 1 (1965).
11. W. G. Conway, *Oryx* 9, 156 (1967).
12. V. Jarvis, *ibid.*, p. 130.
13. H. Hediger, *Wild Animals in Captivity* (Dover, New York, 1964), p. 33.
14. C. R. Schroeder, in *International Zoo Yearbook*, C. Jarvis, Ed. (Zoological Society of London, London, 1962), vol. 4, p. 145.
15. R. Penney, *Science* 158, 144 (1967).
16. For discussions, I thank L. S. Crandall, C. F. Freiheit, J. Perry, H. Reed, and C. S. Schroeder.

71

POPULATION AND WORLD ECONOMIC DEVELOPMENT

Joseph J. Spengler

"In the long run, the lack of adequate space and resources is logically certain—unless fertility is reduced—to impose a ceiling on rising consumption, then to lower the availability of food per consumer, and ultimately to cause a rise in death rates. These conclusions all follow from the mathematics of geo-

Reprinted from *Science* 131: 1497-1502, 1960, with the permission of the publishers. Copyright 1960 by the American Association for the Advancement of Science.

metric increase. . . . At current growth rates, the population of the United States would outweigh the earth in 2500 years" (1, pp. 330-31).

The economic development of any particular society is envisaged as entailing changes both in its aggregative economic magnitudes and in its economic composition. Of these changes there are various indicators, not all of which move in wholly parallel paths. For the sake of convenience in exposition, however, use may be made primarily of a single indicator, per capita real income, since the movement of this indicator is highly correlated with the movement of other welfare-oriented indicators, and since changes in it provide a great deal of information respecting the extent to which a community of people has become better or worse off. It is assumed, therefore, that economic development is reflected in the movement of per capita income, and that the role played by population growth in economic development is ultimately expressible in terms of its incidence upon the movement of per capita income.

This article is composed of two main parts: in the first the underlying theory is set down and in the second the prospective incidence of population growth upon the movement of per capita income is examined for each of the main demographic regions of the world. Analysis is restricted to quantitative aspects of the subject under discussion; genetical and most euthenic issues are disregarded. In a final section some implications of the population question are touched upon.

Economic-Demographic Theory

A complete economico-demographic theory would have to account adequately both for the response of aggregate income to population growth for the response of population to income growth. In this article, however, major attention is devoted to the former response. The latter response is examined only in so far as it bears on one question: Does population growth respond to slight output changes in the same manner as it responds to large output changes? Relevant theory may therefore be expressed in terms of four principles: (i) changing age composition; (ii) changing factor complementarity; (iii) changing economic homosphere; and (iv) critical minimum economico-demographic stimulus. These principles are described below.

The per capita income in terms of which the course of economic development is plotted is a collection of goods and services, the enjoyment of many of which is contingent upon the availability of sufficient leisure. Increases in the size of this collection tend to be accompanied by increases in its variety and its quality, presumably because the eudemonic property of income depends upon variety as well as upon quantity. This fact is overlooked in much of the popular literature relating to population, in which it is suggested that so long as the food supply, irrespective of its composition, can be

made to keep pace with numbers, there is no population problem. Unfortunately, man has taste buds and hence is not disposed to live on algae, or on a 21-cent daily mess of lard, beef liver, orange juice, and soybean meal, or on similar unpalatable minimum-cost diets (2). Nor is he content to live on minimum-cost, nonfood allowances. It is not very relevant, therefore, to ask how many people a given country can support. It is more relevant to ask why population continues to increase in a country after population growth has ceased to confer a *net* advantage upon the country's inhabitants.

Changing Age Composition

Potential productivity per capita depends, *ceteris paribus*, upon the size of the fraction of a country's population that is in the labor force. The size of this fraction, though subject to the influence of socioeconomic conditions, depends upon the age composition of a country's population. Furthermore, though this fraction may be only some 5 to 10 percent higher in developed than in underdeveloped countries, the margin of productivity enjoyed by developed countries will be greater; for around 10 or more percent of the labor force of underdeveloped countries is made up of children under 15, whereas the labor force of advanced countries includes almost no children (3).

When a population is growing, its age composition is less favorable than when it is stationary, and when a population's natural rate of growth increases (or decreases), its age composition becomes less (or more) favorable, within limits. More generally, under *ceteris paribus* conditions, the proportion of the population of working age (say 15 to 59 or 20 to 64 years) increases greatly as the gross reproduction rate falls and declines somewhat as life expectancy at birth increases. Model stable populations serve to illustrate this tendency (see Table 1). Suppose we postulate a set of age-specific fertility rates which give us a gross reproduction rate of 3, or a crude birth rate of 43 to 46; then the percentage of the population falling within the age group 15 to 59 will range, in the associated stable populations, between

Table 1. Gross reproduction and percentage of population aged 15 to 59 in model stable populations (23).

Gross reproduction rate (%)	Life expectancy at birth (yr)					
	40		60.4		70.2	
	Percent aged 15-59	*Birth rate (No./1000)*	*Percent aged 15-59*	*Birth rate (No./1000)*	*Percent aged 15-59*	*Birth rate (No./1000)*
3.0	52.5	46.0	49.6	43.8	48.4	42.9
2.0	58.8	31.7	55.8	30.6	54.7	30.1
1.5	61.6	23.1	58.7	22.5	57.7	22.3
1.0	62.6	13.6	59.4	13.3	58.6	13.3

48.4, if life expectancy at birth is 70.2 years, and 52.5 if life expectancy is only 40 years. Should this set of age-specific fertility rates be replaced by another set yielding a gross reproduction rate of 1.5 and a crude birth rate of 22 to 23, the percentage of persons aged 15 to 59 would rise one-sixth or more, to between 58 and 62. In short, if fertility declines from levels such as are found in much of Asia, Africa, and Latin America to those found in Europe, the fraction of the population of working age would be something like one-sixth higher under stable-population conditions. This amounts to an increase of one-sixth or more in potential productivity per capita. This theoretical finding is borne out, of course, in the real world; for example, 66.28 percent of the Swedish population but only 56.69 percent of the Brazilian population is aged 15 to 64 years.

High-fertility, underdeveloped countries would derive two advantages from the improvement in age composition that would result if fertility should decline until their populations had become approximately stationary. First, their potential per capita productivity would rise 10 to 15 or more percent; some of this potential productivity would assume the form of income and some the form of leisure. Second, the disposition of parents to put children to work and deny them education would be greatly reduced, and the capacity of the population to educate the children and so make them much more productive would be greatly augmented. Of this we have some evidence in the fact that in the slowly growing populations of developed European countries the ratio of children under, say, 15 to persons of an age (say 15 to 64) to be teachers is only about half as high as in the rapidly growing populations of underdeveloped countries.

Changing Factor Complementarity

Population growth would not affect productivity per capita adversely if output were entirely the product of labor and hence imputable solely to labor. Productivity partly depends, however, upon the number of complementary agents or factors of production (4) at the disposal of a population. This number governs the amount of equipment the average worker has to assist him in his occupational assignments. It also governs the rapidity with which technological advances can be given concrete form and the degree to which individuals can be trained and enabled to carry on that basic and applied research which underlies technological progress. Such progress is very important; it seems to have been responsible for some four-fifths of the increase in output per man-hour recently experienced in the United States (5). It is because population growth reduces when it does not altogether prevent increase in the number of productive factors available per capita that it tends to depress the rate at which output per capita increases. Population growth has this effect because it entails transformation of a given population, together with its replaceable and irreplaceable environment, into a successor population and environment, with the double result that increases in numbers are achieved at the expense of physical environment and that a portion of this physical environment is permanently dissipated (6).

These factors or agents of production are of two sorts: (i) those which are reproducible and augmentable and (ii) those which are nonaugmentable because their aggregate stock is either roughly fixed (for example, potential supply of water power) or depletable (for example, proved and potential oil reserves) and hence subject to the relentless march of economic entropy consequent upon their use (7). While the rate at which the stock of agents (i) is increased depends immediately upon the level of income and the average propensity of the community to save, it is affected, as may be the marginal productivity of this stock of capital, by the scarcity of agents (ii). For in so far as agents (ii) are in short supply, this shortage must be made up by agents (i), with the result that average income is somewhat lower than it otherwise would be.

Population growth slows down the rate at which the number of agents (i) available per capita can be increased. Inasmuch as a nation's stock of utilized wealth usually amounts to something like five times its national income (8), saving rates of 5 and 10 percent, respectively, are required to keep the wealth-population ratio constant when the population is growing 1 or 2 percent per year. Close association of this ratio and per capita income is prevented by various circumstances, however, among them variation in the composition of wealth, in the wealth-income ratio, in the extent to which increase in wealth is accompanied by technical progress, and in the manner in which wealth and income are measured (9). The wealth-income ratio does, however, provide a rough, internationally comparable index of the extent to which population growth absorbs output which might otherwise have been consumed or utilized to increase wealth or capital per head. It may be inferred that, even though the capital output ratio in industry or agriculture is sometimes as low as 3:1 or lower, savings of 8 to 10 or more percent are required in the longer run to offset the population growth rates of 2 or more percent found in many underdeveloped countries. For assets are normally accumulated not only to equip and house people but also for various other reasons which in the longer run bring the ratio of total physical assets to income up to 4 or 5 to 1.

Up to now the nonaugmentable factors have not seriously retarded the growth of output per head, because unused reserves remained, because substitutes were available, because technical progress has reduced the input of these factors per unit of output, and because the use of materials other than minerals and water has grown little more rapidly than population. Furthermore, technical improvements have increased the output of minerals per composite unit input of labor and capital. It is shortage of water and space that bids to restrict expansion here and there. In time, however, population growth, together with rising per capita consumption, will greatly increase the overall use of minerals and water and may even increase the marginal cost of produce, particularly if considerable amounts of cultivable land are diverted to nonagricultural purposes. Consumption of materials originating in non-augmentable sources has been increasing markedly only since the late 19th century; this increase may not make itself felt in terms of rising costs for some decades, however, and even then the initial impact of such cost increases will be minor. Dearth of suitably situated space is likely to make itself felt, however (10).

Changing Homosphere

Man's earthly habitat, or homosphere, is a component of the comparatively, invariant biosphere in which living matter flourishes (11). The capacity of this homosphere to sustain human life at a given level is conditioned in some measure by the growth process as such, independently of the operation of the principle of changing complementarity touched upon in the preceding section. The effects of growth may be adverse or favorable. They are adverse when growth permanently dissipates a portion of the environment capable of subserving human life without at the same time replacing it with a suitable substitute.

Illustrative perhaps is erosion consequent upon population pressure, or the dissipation of potential utility associated with increase in economic entropy, noted above. Illustrative also would be the covering of much land by water should continuing population growth so step up man's production of carbon dioxide that the oceans failed to absorb all of it, with the result that the carbon-dioxide content, and hence the temperature, of the atmosphere rose sufficiently to melt the polar icecaps.

Illustrative of the favorable effects are reductions in composite inputs per unit of output made possible, within limits, by economies consequent upon increase in the size of a population and in the apparatus of production. Of minor importance is the resulting fuller use of such indivisible agents as a railroad bed. Of major importance is the increase in organizational, and other, specialization made possible by population growth, together with the tendency of large economies to be more competitive and hence more inclined to make optimum use of factors than are small economies. Much of the restraint to which specialization and competition are subject is attributable, of course, not to smallness of population but to smallness of country or economy. This condition, usually inherited from the 18th century or from earlier centuries, when the optimum-size state was smaller than today, is now being partially rectified through the creation of metastates (12).

Population growth, when accompanied by corresponding growth in employment and income, may stimulate both the growth of firms which have not yet expanded to the greatest extent that seems economically desirable and the introduction of equipment and methods superior to those in use. For, so long as an economy is growing and expected to grow, stimulus is given to the disposition to plan and invest for the morrow and to suppose that enhanced output will find market outlets as satisfactory as those currently relied upon. Under these cirumstances, also, it is relatively easy for labor and other factors, whether newly employed or situated in nonexpanding industries, to move into expanding industrial sectors. These various potential advantages of population growth, though realizable in a developed country, are not likely to be realized in a heavily populated, underdeveloped country where divers other preconditions for development are lacking. Their role in a developed country may be exaggerated, since in such a country, even if the population is stationary,

death and retirement alone permit considerable and rapid readjustment of the labor force, while depreciation and obsolescence permit rapid modification of the composition of capital. Such flexibility is particularly marked when, as in advanced societies, governments are economically powerful enough to support aggregate demand at a level favorable to needed readjustment.

Critical Minimum Economico-Demographic Stimulus

Much of Asia, Africa, and Latin America—perhaps two-thirds of the world's population—is caught in a Malthusian trap, in "a quasi-stable equilibrium system" in which forces making for increase in income evoke counterbalancing income-depressing forces, among them a high rate of population growth.

Escape from this trap or system presupposes a stimulus, or set of continuing stimuli, sufficient to make the income-increasing and the population-growth-retarding effects dominant. This stimulus must operate both to increase income faster than population and to reduce the rate of population growth so that per capita income and expectations respecting the future course of per capita income rise sufficiently. What is called for is heavy investment over a sustained period of time—investment that is oriented not so much toward providing traditional support for a growing population as toward augmenting the stock of income-producing equipment, toward educating and urbanizing the population and rendering it productive and forward-looking, and toward replacing wants that foster population growth by different aspirations (13).

What alone is in dispute is the extent to which a people, even when its government is strong and well entrenched, can be induced to extend its time horizon, sacrifice today's simple material pleasures for tomorrow's uncertain returns, and substitute ideals of the sort found among advanced European peoples for those regnant in tradition-bound societies. Puerto Rico's experience demonstrates how very difficult it is to introduce effective family planning.

The significance of the above argument,

subscribed to in part already by J. S. Mill, derives from the fact that population growth has been revolutionized in underdeveloped countries by the introduction of modern health measures that increase life expectancy. As a result, numbers increase, or soon will increase, two or three or more times as fast in these countries as they increased in Western Europe when that part of the world was undergoing modernization. The low rate of population growth characteristic of Western Europe (it was generally near or below 1 percent per year) permitted initially low rates of saving to set self-sustaining economic development in motion. Similarly, in Japan, the only non-European country to undergo substantial modernization in the late 19th century, the rate of natural increase long remained close to 1 percent, and savings were relatively high and were put to good use. Even so the agricultural population has remained at the Meiji-era level; moreover, despite considerable modernization and the early adoption of family-limitation practices, Japan's birth rate did not fall sharply until after legal barriers to such limitation were relaxed, in and after 1949 (14). The demographic history of Japan suggests that, without strong governmental efforts to augment the rate of capital formation markedly and to stimulate effective control of fertility, underdeveloped countries, especially those which are already heavily populated and less productive of income than was early 19th-century England, are unlikely to escape their Malthusian trap, low incomes and excessive fertility.

Empirical Findings

Having noted ways in which population growth may affect the movement of per capita income and (if we may ignore Pope's dictum: "Fixed to no spot is happiness sincere") "welfare," we may turn to the current demographic situation, a conspectus of which is presented in Table 2. Prospective rates of growth for Asia (exclusive of Japan), Africa, Middle America, and South America (exclusive of its temperate-zone countries) are much higher than for other areas. In these four areas fertility is uncon-

trolled, natality is high, and the diffusion of effective family limitation practices is retarded by a predominance of rural conditions, often accompanied by a high degree of illiteracy, elimination of which is difficult. While age composition is unfavorable to productivity in all these rapidly growing regions and per capita incomes are generally much lower than in the remainder of the world (that is, in Europe, northern North America, the Soviet Union, Japan, and most of Oceania), where fertility is subject to quite effective control (though this is not always exercised), population density appears to be a powerful depressant of income only in the Far East (where about half the world's population lives) and in Middle America. The low level of income in most of Africa and much of South America is primarily attributable, as are low income levels to some extent in the Far East, to conditions associated with economic underdevelopment as such rather than with population density, a considerable amount of which is compatible with relatively high per capita incomes (for example, population density is approximately 200 individuals per square mile in the northeastern United States and exceeds 300 in much of Europe and 500 in Japan).

Lowness of income is almost invariably associated with a heavy concentration of the labor force in agriculture, a condition found in Asia and Africa and in much of Middle and South America. There results a heavy pressure of agricultural population on the land under cultivation, especially when arable land per head of agricultural population amounts to less than 1 acre, as in Asia, or to about 2, as in Middle America, instead of more than 3, as in Europe and much of Africa and Latin America, or about 20, as in North America (15, pp. 474-477). Hence, agricultural income is very low in Asia and is augmentable principally through the reduction of the agricultural population by half or more and the augmentation of the frequently low yields per acre and per man; for, as the data in Table 3 indicate, pasture land is scarce and there is little utilizable forest or potentially productive land to bring into use. In the Near East, to some degree in Middle America, and in South America and much of

Table 2. Demographic and economic characteristics, by region, about 1950-55 (see 24). The density and population estimates for A.D. 2000 are based on United Nations "medium" forecasts.

Demographic and economic characteristics

Region	Population (in millions)		Persons per km²		Birth rate (No./1000) in 1950	Per capita income (dollars) about 1955	Labor force (%)		Population (%)	
	In 1955	*In 2000*	*In 1955*	*In 2000*			*In agri- culture*	*In in- dustry*	*Aged 15-19*	*In cities over 100,000*
World	2690	6267	20	46	39	50-1864	59	18	56	13
Asia	1490	3870	55	143	46	50-487	73	10	55	8
Africa	216	517	7	17	47	50-284	75	11	54	5
South America	125	394	7	22	25-45	107-391	55	18	54	18
Central America and Caribbean	58	198	21	72	35-50	80-126	62	16	53	12
Rest of world	801	1288	14	23	20-26	150-1864	13-45	30-37	59-62	18-41

Table 3. Amount of land, per capita and by use, 1955 (25).

Region	Agricultural area				Forest land (millions of hectares)	Unused but potentially productive land (millions of hectares)
	Arable land and land under tree crops		Permanent meadows and pastures			
	Total (millions of hectares)	Per capita (hectares)	Total (millions of hectares)	Per capita (hectares)		
U.S.S.R.	220	1.10	267	1.33	743	161
Europe	150	0.37	85	0.21	136	8
Northern North America*	228	1.26	278	1.54	668	79
Rest of North America†	27	0.47	78	1.34	71	17
South America	69	0.56	313	2.52	887	53
Oceania	24	1.71	376	24.00	87	6
Far East	355	0.25	271	0.19	475	60
Near East	78	0.56	295	2.11	145	116
Africa	219	1.29	502	2.95	652	76

* "Northern North America" includes Alaska, Canada, and the U.S.

† "Rest of North America" includes the balance of North and Central America.

Africa, the amount of land under cultivation apparently is still significantly augmentable. In all these areas, moreover, as in much of the Far East, output per acre could be greatly increased, given scientific methods of cultivation and a sufficiency of plant nutrients and moisture (15, p. 531; 16). There is little prospect, however, with current population trends, that the peoples of Asia, the Middle East, or Middle America can greatly reduce their excessive dependence on cereals and tubers (15, chap. 9).

While the easing of population pressure in agriculture depends in part upon greatly increased investment in agriculture, together with modernization of techniques, it depends largely upon the provision of relatively productive non-agricultural employment for both the excess agricultural population and additions to the labor force resulting from natural increase. Such provision requires not only considerable investment in suitable forms of education but also the formation of capital and the availability of the requisite mineral and other natural resources. Let us consider investment in education and capital formation first. In most underdeveloped countries investment in suitable facilities for education at the secondary and advanced levels is too low, and in many not even a full primary education is provided. In

many, savings are barely adequate (if that) to offset population growth, probably averaging less than 10 percent of the national income in the whole of the semi- and nonindustrialized world (17). In Asia, with the exception of China, Israel, Japan, and possibly one or two small communities, the rate of capital formation is around 10 percent or less of income, and even in thrifty Japan gross fixed capital formation per capita is only one-ninth of that in the United States and one-third of that in Western Europe (18). In Latin America gross investment in fixed capital (some of foreign origin) has been in the neighborhood of 17 percent of the gross national product, and net investment, around 11 percent of the net national product (19). In Africa capital formation has varied greatly, ranging from levels of below 10 percent of national income, through perhaps close to 10 percent in Egypt, to much higher rates in Rhodesia, the Union of South Africa, and other countries (20). Much higher rates of savings are required in most of the underdeveloped world, given current population growth, than are presently manifest.

While a number of underdeveloped countries are equipped with the natural resources requisite for economic development, in others the amounts of such resources are small or are offset by heavy population. China's iron-ore reserves (6.7 tons per capita), comparable to Mexico's, are greatly inferior to India's (54.2 tons per capita), which are superior to those of the United States; but India's coal reserves, roughly comparable in per capita terms to those of France, are greatly inferior to China's. Japan, with some coal, lacks iron ore as well as many other minerals. With the exception of these three countries and the partial exception of Korea, no Asian country is able to develop a considerable iron and steel industry and related industries; nor is a comparable industrial base now being provided by other minerals, or, in the long run, by petroleum (most heavily produced in the Near East). In South and Middle America, Brazil, Venezuela, and Cuba are well equipped with iron ore but are short of coal. Most of the coal and iron ore in Africa is in Southern Rhodesia and the Union of South Africa. In sum, a shortage of minerals in relation to population is likely to limit industrial development and the increase of per capita income in Asia, even in the absence of further population growth, and analogous limitation is likely eventually to become operative in much of Latin America and in parts of subsaharan Africa. Only a detailed inventory and study of available resources could disclose when and to what degree such limitation would become evident. Were such a study undertaken now and something like an optimum population determined for subsaharan Africa and South America, policy might be oriented toward reducing the actual and the potential rate of growth (21).

Implications

It was suggested above that if a population were stationary instead of growing 2 or 3 percent per year it would have at its disposal, for improving the state of the existing population, current productive power and income amounting, in per capita income terms, to something like 20 to 25 percent of national income under *ceteris paribus* conditions. The precise magnitude of this figure depends upon the economic significance of differences in age composition and upon the relevant wealth-population ratio. It affords a rough measure of the current cost of a 2 to 3 percent yearly rate of population growth. The magnitude of this cost, together with the disadvantages, from the standpoint of education, of an unfavorable age composition, suggests that countries like Brazil which require larger populations for the optimum exploitation of their resources can progress more rapidly if they reduce their annual rates of population growth from the present 2 or 3 percent to, say, 1 percent.

The adverse effects of population growth in heavily populated underdeveloped countries have been well summarized by Coale and Hoover in their study of India. Assuming two postulates, that expectation of life at birth would rise from 32 years in 1951 to 52 years in 1986 and that fertility might either remain unchanged or decline 50 percent by 1986, the decline beginning in 1956 or not until 1966, they examined the economic implications of the population changes that would take place. They found that, if fertility began to decline at once, to be halved by 1986, income per consumer by the 1980's would be rising nearly four times as fast as would have been the case had fertility not declined at all. Moreover, the population, though still increasing 0.9 percent per year, would be approaching a stationary state, whereas, if fertility had not declined, the population would be increasing 2.6 percent per year and escape from the Malthusian trap would be even more difficult than it had been 30 years earlier (1, pp. 38, 273, 280). Analogous results were yielded by a similar inquiry in Mexico, where population has been growing faster than in India and where per capita income is two or three times that in India. Given a 50-percent decline in fertility, income per consumer would, as in India, be about 41 percent higher at the end of 30 years than it would have been in the absence of any decline in fertility (1, pp. 280, 305-306). Reduction in fertility, in short, makes possible higher and much more rapidly growing average incomes.

Because of the geometrical character of population growth and the fact that numbers rarely decline, the problem now confronting India or Mexico may eventually confront

Europe or the United States or any other region where population is not yet so dense as it is in Europe, or where it is growing less rapidly than in, say, Latin America. It is sometimes supposed that maintenance (as in the United States) of two- to four-child families—that is, of a three-child-family average—would constitute a sufficient degree of control. Yet, under the conditions that exist in the United States, maintenance of a level of three children per family would result in an increase of population of about 1.3 percent per year, and this rate could easily be raised to 1.5 percent, approximately the rate at which the American population has been growing since 1950 (22). With an annual rate of increase of 1.5 percent, a population doubles every 47 years. In a mere 200 years, therefore, at this rate of increase the population of the United States would rise from a current 179 million to about 3.5 billion, or nearly 1200 persons per square mile, a density roughly double that presently found in Massachusetts and New Jersey.

In most of the world, persisting population growth constitutes the most serious of the long-run threats to the continuing improvement of man's material lot. Because of the existence of limitational factors, if only that of suitably situated space, there is a limit to the extent to which populations can grow, in any country or in the world as a whole. It is sometimes argued that fertility will never endanger man's standard of life, since men, having acquired a standard, are unwilling to surrender it, whether to population growth or to other income depressants. This argument overlooks a more fundamental ethical and eudemonic issue posed by population growth, however. It ignores the fact that resources currently used to support the costs of population growth might otherwise serve to augment welfare per capita. It fails to ask to what degree maximum welfare per capita would be more nearly realized if those preferring population growth, whether in the United States or elsewhere, were required to support more of its costs than at present. It neglects the fact that in much of the world living standards already are desperately low and will prove hard to raise even if the stork's wings are clipped.

References and Notes

1. A. J. Coale and E. M. Hoover, *Population Growth and Economic Development in Low-Income Countries* (Princeton Univ. Press, Princeton, N.J., 1958).
2. See *Time* 74, 84 (7 Dec. 1959). The mess described, reportedly the cheapest capable of supplying man with his minimum daily requirement of nutrients, was rejected even by the laboratory dog. Linear programming and related methods have indicated, however, ways in which the housewife can provide an adequate and reasonably palatable diet at minimum cost. See R. Dorfman, P. A. Samuelson, R. M. Solow, *Linear Programming and Economic Analysis* (McGraw-Hill, New York, 1958), p. 9 ff.
3. *The World's Working Population* (International Labour Office, Geneva, Switzerland, 1956); J. D. Durand, "Population Structure as a Factor in Manpower and Dependency Problems of Under-Developed Countries," *Population Bull. of the United Nations No. 3* (Oct. 1953), pp. 1-16.
4. P. A. Samuelson has urged that the expression "factor of production" be avoided entirely. I have, however, retained it, in part because the discussion does not call for a precise, empirical, quantitative definition of the term. See *Foundations of Economic Analysis* (Harvard Univ. Press, Cambridge, Mass., 1947), pp. 84-85.
5. For example, see R. M. Solow, *Rev. Economics and Statistics* 39, 320 (1957), where seven-eighths of the increase in gross output per man-hour in 1909-49 is attributed to "technical change."
6. I have ignored the waste in resources resulting from high child mortality, since it does not, at worst, much exceed 2 percent of national income. See T. K. Ruprecht, "The cost of child mortality in developed and underdeveloped countries," *Proc. Conf. Western Economic Assoc. 33rd Conf.* (1958), pp. 21-25.
7. See J. J. Spengler, *Southern Econ. J.* 14, 238 (1948); *Kyklos* 7, 227 (1954).
8. See S. Kuznets, *Econ. Develop. and Cultural Change* 7, No. 3, pt. 2, app. B (1959).
9. See ——, *ibid.* 7, No. 3, pt. 2, 63, 65, 68, (1959).
10. For data on resources, see President's Materials Policy Commission, *Resources for Freedom* (Government Printing Office, Washington, D.C., 1952); *Univ. Maryland Studies in Business and Economics 12, No. 1* (June 1958); E. A. Ackerman, *Water Resources in the United States* (Resources for the Future, Washington, D.C., 1958).
11. See W. I. Vernadsky, *Am. Scientist* 33, 1 (1945). Living matter, some complementary and some antagonistic to man, constitutes an insignificant (about 0.0025 percent) and essentially unchanging fraction of the biosphere.

12. For example, see S. Kuznets, "Economic growth of small nations," in A. Bonne, Ed., *The Challenge of Development* (Hebrew Univ., Jerusalem, 1958); F. Gehrels and B. F. Johnston, *J. Polit. Econ.* 63, 275 (1955).

13. The argument set forth in this paragraph has been admirably developed by H. Leibenstein in *Economic Backwardness and Economic Growth* (Wiley, New York, 1957). See also R. R. Nelson, *Am. Econ. Rev.* 46, 894 (1956) and J. J. Spengler, *Econ. Develop. and Cultural Change* 4, 321 (1956). For a critique of the above argument, see H. S. Ellis, *Quart, J. Econ.* 72, 485 (1958).

14. See I. B. Taeuber, *The Population of Japan* (Princeton Univ. Press, Princeton, N.J., 1958). Compare R. Hill *et al.*, *The Family and Population Control: A Puerto Rican Experiment in Social Change* (Univ. of North Carolina Press, Chapel Hill, 1959).

15. See W. S. Woytinsky and E. S. Woytinsky, *World Population and Production* (Twentieth Century Fund, New York, 1953).

16. In Europe and America, yields per acre are more than double those reported for Africa and are higher by a fifth or more than those reported for Asia; see W. S. Woytinsky and E. S. Woytinsky, *World Population and Production*, p. 531, and also yield figures for most crops reported periodically in *U.S. Dept. Agr. Foreign Crops and Markets*. Output per capita of agricultural population is only about one-fourth as high in Asia as in Europe; it is only about half as high in Africa as in Asia.

17. The Netherlands Economic Institute estimates at about 5 and 7 percent, respectively, the over-all domestic rates of saving in non-industrialized and semi-industrialized countries [cited in *Bull. from the European Community No. 37* (August.-Sept. 1959), p. 2]. These rates seem to be too low.

18. *Economic Survey of Asia and the Far East*, 1958 (United Nations, Bangkok, Thailand, 1959), pp. 91-93, and *Econ. Bull. for Asia and the Far East* 9, No. 3, 19, 25 (1958). That gross investment has formed 22 to 23 percent of the gross national product in mainland China and only 13 to 14 percent in India is indicated by W. Malenbaum's estimates in *Am. Econ. Rev.* 49, 285 (1959). Investment in China is more efficient also *[ibid.* 49, 299 (1959)]. In 1955, 986 million of Asia's population of 1490 million were in China and India.

19. For example, see *Economic Survey of Latin America*, 1956 (United Nations, New York, 1957), pp. 6-7, and *Analyses and Projections of Economic Development* (United Nations, New York, 1955), p. 11. In 1956 about 9 percent of gross investment in Latin America was of foreign origin.

20. See F. Harbison and I. A. Ibrahim, *Human Resources for Egyptian Enterprise* (McGraw-Hill, New York, 1958), p. 33; *Structure and Growth of Selected African Economies* (United Nations, New York, 1958), pp. 32-34, 121-122, 149.

21. On resources in Asia see *Econ. Bull. for Asia and the Far East* 9, 38 (1958); also the following UN surveys. *World Iron Ore Resources and Their Utilization* (1950); *Survey of World Iron Ore Resources* (1955); *Nonferrous Metals in Underdeveloped Countries* (1955); *New Sources of Energy and Economic Development* (1957); *La Energia En America Latina* (1957). See also W. S. Woytinsky and E. S. Woytinsky, *World Population and Production*, chaps. 21-25, and E. A. Ackerman, *Japan's Natural Resources and Their Relations to Japan' s Economic Future* (Univ. of Chicago Press, Chicago, 1953).

22. See R. Freedman, P. K. Whelpton, A. A. Campbell, *Family Planning, Sterility and Population Growth* (McGraw-Hill, New York, 1959), pp. 372, 376-385.

23. Data given in Table 1 are based on *The Aging of Populations and its Economic and Social Implications* (United Nations, New York, 1956), Table 16, p. 27.

24. This conspectus is based upon the following publications: *The Future Growth of World Population* (United Nations, New York, 1958); *The World's Working Population* (International Labour Office, Geneva, Switzerland), p. 503; K. Davis and H. Hertz, "The world distribution of urbanization," reprinted in J. J. Spengler and O. D. Duncan, *Demographic Analysis: Selected Readings* (Free Press, Glencoe, Ill., 1956), pp. 325-326; *Demographic Yearbook, 1956* (United Nations, New York, 1956), chap. 1; P. Studenski, *The Income of Nations* (New York Univ. Press, New York, 1958), pp. 228-233.

25. Data given in Table 3 are from *Food and Agr. Organization UN Yearbook of Food and Agr. Statistics* (1957), vol. 10, pt. 1, pp. 3-9, 15. Estimates of the amount of cultivable land in the world range from 2.6 to around 5 billion acres. The FAO reported, for 1956, 1.37 billion hectares in land and tree crops; 2,466 billion in permanent meadow and pasture; 3.864 billion in forest; and about 0.6 billion unused but potentially productive. According to R. M. Salter, of the 1.3 billion acres that might still be developed, only 100 million in islands south of Asia lie near areas of population concentration on that continent; 300 million are in northern North America and Eurasia; and 900 million are in Africa and South America. The yield of these acres, Salter estimates might double pre-1939 world food production.

72

BY THE END OF THE TWENTIETH CENTURY

David Sarnoff

Science and technology will advance more in the next thirty-six years than in all the millennia since man's creation. By the century's end, man will have achieved a growing ascendancy over his physical being, his earth, and his planetary environs.

The primary reason is man's increasing mastery of the electron and the atom from which it springs. Through this knowledge he is capable of transforming everything within his reach, from the infinitesimally small to the infinitely large. He is removing the fetters that for more than a million years have chained him to the earth, limited his hegemony over nature, and left him prey to biological infirmities.

By the year 2000 A.D. I believe our descendants will have the technological capacity to make obsolete starvation, to lengthen appreciably the Biblical life-span, and to change hereditary traits. They will have a limitless abundance of energy sources and raw materials. They will bring the moon and other parts of the solar system within the human domain. They will endow machines with the capacity to multiply thought and logic a millionfold.

Food

The Western nations by the turn of the century will be able to produce twice as much food as they consume, and—if political conditions permit—advanced food production and conservation techniques could be extended to the overpopulated and undernourished areas. New approaches—the protein enrichment of foods, genetic alteration of plant and animals,

Reprinted from *Fortune* 69(5): 116-19, 1964, with the permission of the publishers.

accelerated germination and growth by electronic means—will be widely used. The desalinization of ocean waters and tapping of vast underground fresh-water lakes, such as the one some believe to underlie the Sahara, can turn millions of desert acres to bloom. The ocean itself, covering seven-tenths of the earth's surface, will systematically be cultivated for all kinds of plant crops and fish—floating sea farms. Man's essential nutrients are reducible to chemical formula, and ultimately the laboratory will create highly nutritive synthetic foods, equaling in palatability and price the products of the land. As that happens, his total dependence upon the products of the soil will terminate.

Raw Materials

Technology will find ways of replenishing or replacing the world's industrial materials. The ocean depths will be mined for nickel, cobalt, copper, manganese, and other vital ores. Chemistry will create further substitutes for existing materials, transmute others into new forms and substances, and find hitherto unsuspected uses for the nearly 2,000 recognized minerals that lie within the earth's surface. Oil and coal will be used increasingly as the basis for synthetics. Long before we have exhausted the existing mineral resources, the world will have developed extraction and processing techniques to keep its industries going largely on raw materials provided by the ocean waters and floor, the surface rocks, and the surrounding air. The rocks that crust the earth contain potentially extractable quantities of such basic metals as iron, copper, aluminum, and lead. The ocean abounds in a variety of chemicals.

Energy

The energy at man's disposal is potentially without limit. One pound of fissionable uranium the size of a golf ball has the potential energy of nearly 1,500 tons of coal, and the supply of nuclear resources is greater than all the reserves of coal, oil, and gas. Increasingly, electric-power plants will be nuclear, and atomic energy will be a major power source particularly in the underdeveloped areas. Small atomic generators will operate remote installations for years without refueling. Electronic generators, converting energy directly to electricity, will light, heat, and cool homes, as will solar energy. Many areas of the world also may draw power from thermal gases and fluids within the earth's crust. Ultimately, even more powerful energy sources will be developed—thermonuclear fusion, the tapping of heat from deep rock layers, the mutual annihilation of matter and anti-matter.

Health

Science will find increasingly effective ways of deferring death. In this country, technology will advance average life expectancy from the Biblical three score and ten toward the five-score mark, and it will be a healthier, more vigorous, and more useful existence. The electron has become the wonder weapon of the assault on disease and disability. Ultraminiature electronic devices implanted in the body will regulate human organs whose functions have become impaired—the lungs, kidney, heart—or replace them entirely. Electronics will replace defective nerve circuits, and substitute for sight, speech, and touch. Chemistry will help to regenerate muscles and tissues. Laser beams—highly concentrated light pulses—operating inside the body within needle-thin tubes will perform swift, bloodless surgery. By the end of the century, medical diagnosis and treatment will be indicated by computers, assembling and analyzing the latest medical information for use by doctors anywhere in the world.

Genetics

Before the century ends, it will be possible to introduce or eliminate, enhance or diminish, specific hereditary qualities in the living cell—whether viral, microbic, plant, animal, or human. Science will unravel the genetic code which determines the characteristics that pass from parent to child. Science will also take an inanimate grouping of simple chemicals and breathe into it the spark of elementary life, growth, and reproduction. When this occurs, man will have extended his authority over nature to include the creative processes of life. New and healthier strains of plants and animals will be developed. Transmitted defects of the mind or body will be corrected in the gene before life is conceived. If cancer proves to be genetic or viral, it may be destroyed at the source. There appear, in fact, to be few ultimate limits to man's capacity to modify many forms of living species.

Communications

Through communication satellites, laser beams, and ultraminiaturization, it will be possible by the end of the century to communicate with anyone, anywhere, at any time, by voice, sight, or written message. Satellites weighing several hundred tons will route telephone, radio, and television, and other communication from country to country, continent to continent, and between earth and space vehicles and the planets beyond. Participants will be in full sight and hearing of one another through small desk instruments and three-dimensional color-TV screens on the wall. Ultimately, individuals equipped with miniature TV transmitter-receivers will communicate with one another via radio, switchboard, and satellite, using personal channels similar to today's telephone number. Overseas mail will be transmitted via satellite by means of facsimile reproduction. Satellite television will transmit on a worldwide basis directly to the home, and a billion people may be watching the same program with automatic language translation for instant comprehension. Newspaper copy, originating on one continent, will be transmitted and set in type instantly on another. Indeed, by the year 2000 key newspapers will appear in simultaneous editions around the world.

Travel

From techniques developed for lunar travel and other purposes, new forms of terrestrial transport will emerge. Earth vehicles riding on air cushions and powered by nuclear energy or fuel cells will traverse any terrain and skim across water. Forms of personal transportation will include such devices as a rocket belt to carry individuals through the air for short distances. Cities at opposite points of the globe will be no more than three to four hours apart in travel time, and individuals will breakfast in New York, lunch in Buenos Aires, and be back in New York for dinner. Indeed, the greatest problem will be the adjustment of time and habit to the tremendous acceleration in the speed of travel. As rocket systems are perfected and costs reduced, it is possible to foresee the transport of cargo across continents and oceans in tens of minutes. Within and among cities and countries, the foundation will be laid for the movement of freight through underground tubes, automatically routed to its destination by computers.

Defense

In tomorrow's national command post, the country's civilian and military leaders will see displayed on a cycloramic color-television screen a continuously changing, instantly updated computer synthesis of pertinent events around the world. One section of the cyclorama might be a status map showing the global situation. Another would show an area in detail. A third would present live TV coverage of a critical event, transmitted via satellite from TV cameras on the spot, operating from remote-controlled planes, or from inspection satellites. The computer will report, in written form, what and where the problems are. Another section will delineate the alternatives, and suggest appropriate actions, and still another will assess the probable and actual results. But in all cases, final decisions will be matters for human judgment.

Air and Space

Around the earth, a network of weather satellites will predict with increasing accuracy next season's floods and droughts, extremes of heat and cold. It will note the beginnings of typhoons, tornadoes, and hurricanes in time for the disturbances to be diverted or dissipated before they reach dangerous intensity. Ultimately, the development of worldwide, long-range meteorological theory may lead to the control of weather and climate. Space will become hospitable to sustained human habitation. Manned laboratories will operate for extended periods in space, expanding our basic and practical knowledge about the nature of the universe, the planets, and earth. Permanent bases will be established on the more habitable planetary neighbors, and from these a stream of televised reports and radioed data, inanimate and conceivably also living matter, will flow to earth.

Despite these enormous changes, the machine in the year 2000 will still be the servant of man. The real promise of technology is that it will release man from routine drudgeries of mind and body and will remove the final imprint of the cave. In doing so science will give new validity to Alfred North Whitehead's profound observation that civilization advances "by extending the number of important operations we can perform without thinking about them." Man's mind will then be free for the creative thinking that must be done if the impact of science is to be harmonized with man's enduring spiritual, social, and political needs.

73

THE GREAT AMERICAN FRUSTRATION

Archibald MacLeish

That Americans have changed their nature since Andrew Jackson's day or Theodore Roosevelt's or even Harry Truman's is now taken as self-evident—at least among the Americans. No visiting European from Crèvecoeur to Somerset Maugham would have reported us to the world in the terms in which we now report ourselves, nor would Charles Dickens, who liked us least and used almost every other derogatory term to describe us, have used the word we repeat most frequently today. Arrogant, perhaps. Self-confident and bumptious, certainly. But frustrated? If there was one people on earth incapable of frustration it was people who inhabited the United States . . . a hundred years ago.

But not now. Not to us. Not in the newspapers or the television programs or the lecture circuits or anywhere else our national mania for prodding and poking at our national psyche indulges itself. For a time last winter the word frustration was almost as frequently seen and heard in those quarters as the word America itself, and when Robert Kennedy was shot in Los Angeles, though the talk was all of the "sickness of American society," it was still the American sense of frustration and helplessness which spoke. We have not only accepted our frustration, we have embraced it. To the young it seems somehow to explain what is otherwise inexplicable in the numb uneasiness with which they approach their lives. To the old it provides an alternative to the exhausting labor of struggling to comprehend an increasingly incomprehensible epoch.

But what the great frustration actually means is not so obvious. Most of us, questioned

Reprinted from the *Saturday Review*, July 13, 1968, pp. 13-16, with the permission of the publishers. ©1968 Saturday Review Inc.

about it, would reply Vietnam, meaning one of two quite different things; either that the stupidity of our involvement in the war in Vietnam has shaken our confidence in our ability to manage our own affairs, or that our astonishing failure to win the war once we had involved ourselves has undermined our belief in our greatness as a world power. But is either reply correct? Would we believe in our greatness as a world power today if we had used our incontestable superiority in weapons to blast what Governor Reagan refers to as "a water buffalo economy" off the earth? Or would we now regain our political self-confidence if we were to repudiate the President, whosoever he was, who involved us in Vietnam in the first place? I doubt it. I think any such washing of the hands would end where, indeed, it has already ended; in the realization that no one, whether Eisenhower or Kennedy or Johnson, can usefully be blamed for the events which led to our involvement in Vietnam because no one of them was really in control of those events. And that realization, far from curing our sense of frustration, would only deepen it.

Or more precisely, it would show us what this frustration which we confess so readily really is. It is not, as we like to think, Vietnam. Not the sense of individual helplessness which plagues the citizens of a large country when they become aware of the blindness and ineptitude of their rulers, the stupidity of those in power. Not the impotent rage which follows the failure of events to conform to expectations, the failure of history to keep to the plot as written—the refusal of the water buffalo economy to collapse before the electronic power. Not the first mistake which committed us to the Asian war, or the last mistake which has left us in it, or anything else which has to do with Vietnam alone—which began in Vietnam and will end there. It is none of these things but something larger and more troubling: a numb, unformed, persistent sense, like the hinting pinch of a pain which is not yet brutal hurt but will be, that we, as Americans, we perhaps as members of our generation on this earth, have somehow lost control of the management of our human affairs, of the direction of our lives, of what our ancestors would have called our destiny.

It is a sense we have had in one form or another for a long time now, but not as an explicit, a formulated fear until we found ourselves deep in the present century with its faceless slaughters, its mindless violence, its fabulous triumphs over space and time and matter ending in terrors space and time and matter never held. Before that there were only hints and intimations, but they were felt, they were recorded where all the hints and intimations are recorded—in poems, fictions, works of art. From the beginning of what we used to call the industrial revolution—what we see today more clearly as a sort of technological coup d'etat—men and women, particularly men and women of imaginative sensibility, have seen that something was happening to the human role in the shaping of civilization.

A curious automatism, human in origin but not human in action, seemed to be taking over. Cities were being built and rebuilt not with human purposes in mind but with technological means at hand. It was no longer the neighborhood which fixed the shape and limits of the town but the communications system, the power grid. Technology, our grandfathers said, "advanced" and it was literally true: it was technology which was beating the tambours, leading the march. Buildings crowded into the air not because their occupants had any particular desire to lift them there, but because the invention of electric elevators and new methods of steel and glass construction made these ziggurats possible and the possibility presented itself as economic compulsion.

Wildness and silence disappeared from the countryside, sweetness fell from the air, not because anyone wished them to vanish or fall but because throughways had to floor the meadows with cement to carry the automobiles which advancing technology produced first by the thousands and then by the thousand thousands. Tropical beaches turned into high-priced slums where thousand-room hotels elbowed each other for glimpses of once-famous surf not because those who loved the beaches wanted them there but because enormous jets could bring a million tourists every year—and therefore did.

The result, seen in a glimpse here, a perception there, was a gradual change in our attitude toward ourselves as men, toward the part we play as men in the direction of our lives. It was a confused change. We were proud—in England, and even more in America, raucously proud—of our technological achievements, but we were aware also, even from the beginning, that these achievements were not altogether ours or, more precisely, not altogether ours to direct, to control—that the *process* had somehow taken over leaving the purpose to shift for itself so that we, the ostensible managers of the process, were merely its beneficiaries.

Not, of course, that we complained of that, at least in the beginning. A hundred years ago, with the rare exception of a Dickens or a Zola, we were amenable enough—amenable as children at a Christmas party. Inventions showered on our heads: steam engines and electric lights and telegraph messages and all the rest. We were up to our knees, to our necks, in Progress. And technology had made it all possible. Science was the giver of every good and perfect gift. If there were aspects of the new world which were not perfect—child labor for example—progress would take care of them. If the ugliness and filth and smoke of industrial cities offended us, we put up with them for the sake of the gas lights and the central heating. We were rich and growing richer.

But nevertheless the uneasiness remained and became more and more evident in our books, our paintings, our music—even the new directions of our medical sciences. Who were *we* in this strange new world? What part did *we* play in it? Someone had written a new equation somewhere, pushed the doors of ignorance back a little, entered the darkened room of knowledge by one more step. Someone else had found a way to make use of that new knowledge, put it to work. Our lives had changed but without *our* changing them, without our intending them to change. Improvements had appeared and we had accepted them. We had bought Mr. Ford's machines by the hundreds of thousands. We had ordered radios by the millions and then installed TVs. And now we took to the air, flew from city to city, from continent to continent, from climate to climate, following summer up and down the earth like birds. We were new men in a new life in a new world . . . but a world *we* had not made—had not, at least, intended to make.

And a new world, moreover, that we were increasingly unsure, as time went by, we would have wanted to make. We wanted its conveniences, yes. Its comforts, certainly. But the world as a world to live in? As a human world? It was already obvious by the beginning of this century that many of our artists and writers—those not so silent observers of the human world who sit in its windows and lurk in its doorways watching—were not precisely in love with the modern world, were, indeed, so little in love with it that they had turned against life itself, accepting absurdity and terror in its place and making of human hopelessness the only human hope. And there were other nearer, stranger witnesses. Before the century was two-thirds over numbers of our children—extraordinary numbers if you stop to think about it—were to reject, singly and secretly, or publicly in curious refugee encampments, the whole community of our modern lives, and most particularly those aspects of our lives which were most modern: their conveniences, their comforts . . . their affluence.

It was inevitable under these circumstances that some sort of confrontation should occur between the old idea of man as the liver of his own life, the shaper of his own existence, and the new idea of world, the newly autonomous world—world autonomous in its economic laws, as the Marxists hoped, or autonomous in its scientific surge, its technological compulsions, as some in the West began to fear. And, of course, the confrontation did occur: first in rather fatuous academic ructions in which science and the humanities were made to quarrel with each other in the universities, and then, in 1945, at Hiroshima. What happened at Hiroshima was not only that a scientific break-through—"breakthrough" in the almost literal sense—had occurred and that a great part of the population of a city had been burned to death, but that the problem of the relation of the triumphs of modern science to the human purposes of man had been explicitly defined and the whole question of the role of humanity in the modern scientific age had been exposed

in terms not even the most unthinking could evade.

Prior to Hiroshima it had still been possible—increasingly difficult but still possible—to believe that science was by nature a human tool obedient to human wishes and that the world science and its technology could create would therefore be a human world reflecting our human needs, our human purposes. After Hiroshima it was obvious that the loyalty of science was not to humanity but to truth—its own truth—and that the law of science was not the law of the good—what humanity thinks as good, meaning moral, decent, humane—but the law of the possible. What it is *possible* for science to know science must know. What it is possible for technology to do technology will have done. If it is possible to split the atom, then the atom must be split. Regardless. Regardless of . . . anything.

There was a time, just after Hiroshima, when we tried—we in the United States, at least—to escape from that haunting problem by blaming the scientists as individuals; the scientists, in particular, who had made the bomb—the mysterious workers in the cellars at Stagg Field and the laboratories of the Manhattan Project. And the scientists themselves, curious as it now may seem, cooperated; many of them, many of the best, assuming, or attempting to assume, burdens of personal guilt or struggling, somehow, anyhow, to undo what had been done.

I remember—more vividly perhaps than anything else which happened to me in those years—a late winter evening after Hiroshima in a study at the Institute at Princeton—Einstein's study, I think—when Niels Bohr, who was as great a man as he was a physicist, walked up and down for hours besides the rattling radiators urging me to go to President Truman, whom I did not know, to remind him that there had been an understanding between Mr. Roosevelt and the scientists about the future neutralization of the bomb. I guessed that Bohr, even as he talked that evening, realized there was nothing Mr. Truman or anyone on earth could do to unknow what was known. And yet he walked up and down the freezing study talking. Things, of course, *were* "done"—attempted anyway. In the brief time when we alone possessed what was called "the secret," the American Government offered to share it with the world (the Baruch Plan) for peaceful exploitation. What we proposed, though we did not put it in these words, was that humanity as a whole should assert its control of science, or at least of this particular branch of science, nuclear physics, limiting its pursuit of possibility to possibilities which served mankind. But the Russians, with their faith in the dialectics of matter, demurred. They preferred to put their trust in *things*, and within a few short months their trust was justified; they had the bomb themselves.

The immediate effect in the United States was, of course, the soaring fear of Russia which fed the Cold War abroad and made the black plague of McCarthyism possible at home. But there was also a deeper and more enduring consequence. Our original American belief in our human capability, our human capacity to manage our affairs ourselves, "govern ourselves," faltered with our failure to control the greatest and most immediate of human dangers. We began to see science as a kind of absolute beyond our reach, beyond our understanding even, known, if it was known at all, through proxies who, like priests in other centuries, could not tell us what they knew.

In short, our belief in ourselves declined at the very moment when the Russian belief in the mechanics of the universe confirmed itself. No one talked any longer of a Baruch Plan, or even remembered that there had been one. The freedom of science to follow the laws of absolute possibility to whatever conclusions they might lead had been established, or so we thought, as the unchallengeable fixed assumption of our age, and the freedom of technology to invent whatever world it happened to invent was taken as the underlying law of modern life. It was enough for a manufacturer of automobiles to announce on TV that he had a better idea—any better idea: pop-open gas-tank covers or headlights that hide by day. No one thought any longer of asking whether his new idea matched a human purpose.

What was happening in those years, as the bitterly satirical fictions of the period never tired of pointing out, was that we were ceasing to think of ourselves as men, as self-governing

men, as proudly self-governing makers of a new nation, and were becoming instead a society of consumers: recipients—grateful recipients—of the blessings of a technological civilization. We no longer talked in the old way of logical civilization. We no longer talked in the old way of The American Proposition, either at home or abroad—particularly abroad. We talked instead of The American Way of Life. It never crossed our minds apparently—or if it did we turned our minds away—that a population of consumers, though it may constitute an affluent society, can never compose a nation in the great, the human, sense.

But the satirical novels, revealing as they were, missed the essential fact that we were becoming a population of consumers, an affluent society, not because we preferred to think of ourselves in this somewhat less than noble role but because we were no longer able to think of ourselves in that other role—the role our grandfathers had conceived for us two hundred years ago. We were not, and knew we were not, Whitman's Pioneers O Pioneers.

It is here, rather than in the floundering failures and futile disappointments of Vietnam, that this famous frustration of ours is rooted. Vietnam alone, disastrous as the whole experience has been, could never have produced, in a confident and self-reliant people such as the Americans once were, a mood like the American mood of these past months. Not even the riots of last summer and this spring could have afflicted us as we are now afflicted if we had still believed that our principal business was the making of a nation, the government of ourselves. Indeed the riots are, if anything, the consequence, not the cause, of our self-doubt— or, more precisely, the consequence of the *actual* causes of that doubt. It is not without significance that the targets of the mobs in the burning streets are supermarkets and television outlets rather than the courthouses and city halls which would have drawn the mobs of earlier times. Courthouses and city halls stand— or stood once—for The American Proposition. Supermarkets and television outlets are the symbols of The American Way of Life. Mobs strike for the Bastille in any rising and the Bastille in the United States today is whatever stands for the American Way of Life: the goods and services, the material wealth, which the majority claim as the mark of their Americanism and which the minority are denied.

It is because we are unwilling to recognize this fact and unable to face the crisis as a crisis in the long struggle for the creation of a true Republic—because, indeed, we are no longer primarily concerned with the creation of a true Republic—that the majority respond to these riots with nothing but a demand for more police and more repression, while the Congress sits impotent and paralyzed in Washington.

Which means, of course, however we put it, that we no longer believe in man. And it is that fact which raises, in its turn, the most disturbing of all the swarming questions which surround us: how did we come to this defeated helplessness? How were we persuaded of our impotence as men? What convinced us that the fundamental law of a scientific age must be the scientific law of possibility and that our human part must be a passive part, a subservient part, the part of the recipient, the beneficiary . . . the victim? Have the scientists taught us this? A few months ago one of the greatest of living scientists told an international gathering composed of other scientists: "We must not ask where science and technology are taking us, but rather how we can manage science and technology so that they can help us get where we want to go." It is not reported that Dr. René Dubos was shouted down by his audience, and yet what he was asserting was precisely what we as a people seem to have dismissed as unthinkable: that "we," which apparently means mankind, must abandon our modern practice of asking where science and technology are "taking *us*," and must ask instead how *we* can "manage" science and technology so that they will help us to achieve *our* purposes—our purposes, that is to say, as men.

Dr. Dubos, it appears, scientist though he is and great scientist, believes rather more in man than we do. Why, then, do we believe so little? Perhaps we can answer that question best by asking another: how was our original, American belief in man achieved? Where did it come from? Thomas Jefferson, who had as much to do with the definition of our American belief as

anyone, reflected on that subject towards his life's end. It was that famous trio at William and Mary, he decided, who "fixed" his "destinies." It was his education in his college, the teaching of Small and Wythe and the rest, which shaped his mind, gave it its direction. John Adams would have said the same and doubtless did: it was in Harvard College that he found those Greeks and Romans who taught him what a man could be and therefore *should*.

Is it *our* education, then, which has shaped the very different estimate of man we live by? In part, I think; in considerable part. Education, particularly higher education, has altered its relation to the idea of man in fundamental ways since Adams's day and Jefferson's. From the time when Harvard President Charles Eliot introduced the elective system there—from the time, that is to say, of the renunciation by the university of an intention to produce a certain *kind* of man, a man shaped by certain models, certain texts— the university's concern with "man" as such has grown less and less and its concern with what it calls "subjects" has become greater and greater. The important thing has become the academic "offering" (revealing word): the range of subjects from which the student, with his eye on his career, may choose. And the ultimate consequence, only too evident in the time we live in, has been the vocationalization of the higher schools. The college no longer exists to produce men *qua* men, men prepared for life in a society of men, but men as specialized experts, men prepared for employment in an industry or a profession.

"Getting ahead in the world," says Professor Allen Tate of the University of Minnesota, "is now the purpose of education and the University must therefore provide education for our time, not for all time: it must discover and then give to society what society thinks it wants. . . ." Some of us, looking at the present state of American society—the decay of its cities, the bewilderment of its citizens—may wonder whether the university has really provided "education for our time," but no one, I think, will deny that Professor Tate's emphatic irony has its bite. The vocationalism which a technological society demands of the graduate schools has produced a secondary vocationalism which the graduate schools impose on the colleges, and the result is that undergraduate education—far more important to the preparation for citizenship than graduate education—is increasingly affected by the vocational taint.

What is happening, and in the greatest universities as well as in the less great, is that the entire educational process is becoming fixed—hung-up as the phrase goes now—on its vocational end result. The job out there in the profession or the industry dictates the "training" (their word, not mine) in the graduate schools, and the graduate schools dictate the preparation in the colleges, and the whole system congeals from the top down like a pond freezing. The danger is that, the society may congeal with it, for nothing is more certain in the history of our kind than the fact that frozen societies perish.

As specialized, professional training, higher education in the United States today is often magnificent. Young doctors are better and better as their specialties become more specialized: so much better that it is now a recommendation in almost any field to say of a young doctor that he is young. Student physicists in the great graduate schools are so notoriously productive at twenty-two that a professional physicist of thirty regards himself, or is regarded by his juniors, as middle-aged. But the educated *man*, the man capable not of providing specialized answers, but of asking the great and liberating questions by which humanity makes its way through time, is not more frequently encountered than he was two hundred years ago. On the contrary, he is rarely discovered in public life at all.

I am not arguing—though I deeply believe—

that the future of the Republic and the hope for a recovery of its old vitality and confidence depend on the university. I am confining myself to Dr. Dubos's admonition that we must give up the childishness of our present attitude toward science and technology, our constant question where *they* are taking *us*, and begin instead to ask how *we* can manage *them* "so that they can help us get where we want to go." "Where we want to go" depends, of course, on ourselves and, more particularly, on our conception of ourselves. If our conception of ourselves as the university teaches it or fails to teach it is the conception of the applicant preparing for his job, the professional preparing for his profession, then the question will not be answered because it will not be asked. But if our conception of ourselves as the university teaches it is that of men preparing to be men, to achieve themselves as men, then the question will be asked *and* answered because it cannot be avoided. Where do we want to go? Where men can be most themselves. How should science and technology be managed? To help us to become what we can be.

There is no quarrel between the humanities and the sciences. There is only a need, common to them both, to put the idea of man back where it once stood, at the focus of our lives; to make the end of education the preparation of men to be men, and so to restore to mankind—and above all to this nation of mankind—a conception of humanity with which humanity can live.

The frustration—and it is a real and debasing frustration—in which we are mired today will not leave us until we believe in ourselves again, assume again the mastery of our lives, the management of our means.

Glossary

Acheulian—A Lower Stone Age culture characterized by bifacial stone artifacts; named after an archeological site (Saint-Acheul, France) with such remains.

Adiabatic lapse rate—The rate of change in temperature correlated with change in altitude of an air mass, and resulting from the expansion of the air as it rises or its compression as it falls.

Aerobic—Refers to living systems which function only in the presence of free oxygen.

Agglutination—The clumping together of cells that are normally individually dispersed.

Albedo—The proportion of light falling upon a surface that is reflected from that surface.

Aldehydes—Colorless volatile organic fluids with choking odors, having a terminal carbonal group ($C = O$) on the carbon chain.

Aldrin—A chlorinated hydrocarbon type of pesticide derived from napthaline.

Allele—A particular form of a gene that has arisen by mutation and that is expressed as a given character state.

Allometry—The study of relative growth.

Allopatric—Refers to populations that are dispersed over different geographic areas.

Amino acid—An organic compound with both *amine* (NH_2) and *carboxyl* (COOH) groups, bonding with other amino acids to form proteins.

Anaerobic—Refers to living systems that function in the absence of free oxygen.

Aneuploid—A karyotype variant in which a limited number of chromosomes are either added or missing.

Anodromous—Describes species of fish that migrate from salt water to fresh water for breeding purposes.

Anthropocentric—Regarding man and his activities as the central function of the universe.

Anthropoid—A member of a suborder of Primates, including monkeys, apes, and man.

Antibody—A protein forming in mammalian blood and neutralizing particular antigens.

Antigen—Foreign and usually toxic organic substance introduced into an animal body.

Aquifer—A comparatively porous section of a geological formation along which ground water can pass relatively freely.

Arboreal—Occupying a tree habitat.

Arthropods—An invertebrate animal phylum in which mature individuals have jointed

limbs and bodies enclosed in a chitinous exoskeleton; familiar examples are
crustaceans, insects, and spiders.

Artifacts—Material relics of human cultural activity.

Atavistic—The occurrence in a contemporary organism of form or behavior characterizing
ancestral groups.

Autosome—A chromosome not directly involved in sex determination.

Autotoxic—Refers to a substance that is toxic to the living system that produced it.

Autotroph—An organism that synthesizes its food from inorganic substances, using an
external source of energy.

Auxin—A general group of growth-promoting plant hormones.

BP—Before present; converted to other dating forms by calculating from the year
A.D. 1950 as the base starting point.

Benthic—Refers to bottom-living populations in aquatic ecosystems.

Bioassay—Quantitative assessment of a physico-chemical parameter by the use of living
organisms.

Biocide—A chemical substance that is toxic to living systems.

BOD—Biological oxygen deficiency; commonly indicated in polluted water where aerobic
metabolic activity has temporarily lowered the amount of dissolved oxygen.

Biomass—The total weight of living matter in a given ecosystem.

Biome—A regional group of interrelated ecosystems, such as tundra, taiga, and tropical
rain forest.

Biosphere—The totality of populations and environmental factors in that portion of this
planet in which life exists.

Biota—The totality of organisms in one place or time.

Bipedal—Locomotion by means of the two hind limbs only.

Brachiation—Arboreal locomotion by means of the upper limbs only, as in gibbons.

Carcinogen—A chemical substance inducing cancer.

Cenozoic—The present geological era, beginning 70,000 years BP and including the
Tertiary and Quaternary periods.

Cerebellum—The portion of the brain controlling muscular coordination.

Cerebrum—The portion of the brain where ideas are formulated.

Chaparral—A vegetation type dominated by evergreen, deep-rooted, and usually small-leafed
shrubs; characteristic of Mediterranean-type climates, and indicating this
type in the American Pacific Southwest.

Chlorinated hydrocarbon—A synthetic pesticide containing chlorine, hydrogen, and
carbon. Effective over a broad spectrum of insects; persistent and fat soluble.

Chromatography—The use of the different migration rates of molecules through a
solvent to separate them chemically.

Curie—The amount of radionuclide that undergoes 3.7×10^{10} disintegrations per
second; the unit of radioactivity.

Cusp—A projection on the upper surface of molar or premolar teeth in primates.

Deciduous—Shed seasonally as with leaves in winter or with deer antlers before the
rutting season, or shed at some time, as with the deciduous or milk teeth.

Deme—A local segment of a species, forming a freely interbreeding population.

Diatom—A major component of phytoplankton, belonging to a group of unicellular or
colonial algae whose cell walls are heavily impregnated with silica, and
which therefore persist long after the death of the organism.

Dieldrin—A chlorinated hydrocarbon with the empirical formula $C_{12}Cl_6H_8O$
produced by the oxidation of aldrin.

Diurnal—Occurring daily, or active during the daytime.

Dominance (social)—The enforcement of a subordinate social role in a social animal population by a dominant individual or clique.

Dominant—In bioenergetics, the particular populations in an ecosystem through which the major portion of energy transfer occurs at each trophic level.

Ecological niche—The totality of environmental factors that a given species may tolerate when exposed.

Edaphic—Referring to the influence of soil as an ecological factor.

Electrophoresis—A chemical technique separating compounds according to their different rates of migration in an electric field.

Endemic—Native to a given dispersal area.

Endothermic—Applied to a chemical reaction that absorbs heat; also used for warm-blooded animals.

Endrin—A broad spectrum pesticide of the chlorinated hydrocarbon group with the empirical formula $C_{12}Cl_6H_8O$.

Epidemiology—The study of the incidence and spread of a given disease through a population.

Epilimnion—The water depths above a thermocline.

Epoch—A major division of geological time, less than a *period* and greater than an *age*.

Era—The primary division of geological time, greater than a *period*.

Ethology—The study of animal behavior.

Ethylene—A colorless, highly flammable gas that is toxic to plants and to some other forms of life at very low concentrations.

Euryhaline—A population whose members are able to tolerate a wide range of salinity.

Eustatic—Refers to changes of sea level that take place simultaneously over the whole world.

Eutrophic—Refers to waters which are rich in dissolved nutrients; frequently now applied to those that have been enriched by organic pollutants, consequentially usually having an oxygen deficiency.

Exogamy—Outbreeding in animals, involving no inter-sibling or parent-offspring crosses.

Exothermic—Refers to cold-blooded, or poikilothermous, animals.

Extractive efficiency—A measurement used in anthropology to quantify the ability of a human group to obtain food from a given ecosystem.

Feral—Population segments of a domestic animal species that have escaped and established themselves in a wild condition.

Gene—A portion of a DNA molecule in a chromosome that determines the expression of one or more characters.

Gene frequency—The proportionate ratio of representation of two or more alleles of a given gene in the genotypes of a particular population.

Gene pool—The sum total of genic alleles included in the genotypes of a given population.

Genetic drift—A phenomenon of small populations in which there is a random but directional fluctuation in gene frequencies.

Genome—A karyotype set having a particular genotype.

Genotype—The totality of genes represented in the genetic information possessed by a particular individual member of a population.

Geomorphology—The study of the topographical form of the earth and its development into landscapes.

Geophyte—Plant type perennating by underground food storage organs such as tubers, bulbs, rhizomes, and corms.

Geosphere—Also sometimes known as the lithosphere, the solid portion of the abiotic segment of the ecosphere; contrasts with the *atmosphere* and the *hydrosphere*.

Geothermal—Refers to the heat contained in the interior of the earth.

Groin (also groyne)—An obstruction built out into tidal waters to reduce erosion by trapping wave-transported sand.

Ground water—Water in any saturated zone below ground that is subject to gravity flow.

Habitat—That portion of the environment occupied or occupiable by one or more populations.

Hectare—10,000 square meters; 2.47 acres.

Heptachlor—A chlorinated type of pesticide with the empirical formula $C_{10}H_5Cl_7$.

Herbicide—A substance used to kill plants.

Herbivore—An animal that eats plants.

Heterotroph—An organism requiring food in organic form from other organisms.

Heterozygote (adj., *heterozygous*)—A plant or an animal with different alleles of particular genes on two homologous chromosomes.

Homeostasis—An equilibrium in a living system achieved by coordinated compensations in response to any disturbance.

Homeotherm (adj., *homeothermous*)—An endothermic animal, regulating its body temperature principally by physiological mechanisms.

Hominid—A humanlike ape, including all the forms included in the genera *Ramapithecus, Paranthropus, Homo,* and synonymous taxa.

Homozygote (adj., *homozygous*)—A plant or an animal with identical alleles of particular genes on the two homologous chromosomes.

Hydrograph—A graph showing the level or the rate of flow of water at a particular time.

Hydrologic cycle—The movement of water through an ecosystem as it condenses and falls from the atmosphere on to the land or water, and returns following evaporation.

Hydrosphere—The aqueous portion of the ecosphere, including the water vapor in the atmosphere.

Hypolimnion—The water depths lying below a thermocline.

Indigenous—Native.

Inversion—An atmospheric state resulting from a meteorological condition where temperature rises with increasing altitude instead of falling; this holds the surface layers of air below the inversion and prevents atmospheric circulation beyond it.

Isohalines—Lines entered on a chart indicating points of equal salinity.

Isohyets—Lines on a map indicating points that receive equal amounts of rainfall over a particular time.

Isopleths—Lines on a map connecting similar numerical values of any environmental parameter.

Karyotype—A chromosome set characterizing the nuclei of a particular species.

Keratin—Fibrous protein commonly incorporated in animal epidermal tissues.

Laterite—A tropical soil containing large amounts of iron and aluminum oxides as the result of leaching through exposure to alternating dry and wet seasons; sets very hard when exposed to the air.

Lindane—A chlorinated hydrocarbon pesticide having the empirical formula $C_6H_6Cl_6$.

Lipid—Any form of fat or wax compound.

Littoral—Refers to the area adjoining the shoreline.

Locus—The particular position in a chromosome occupied by a given gene.

Melanin—A dark pigment present in the epidermal tissues of many animals.

Mentifact—A cultural concept, idea, or belief.

Mercaptans—Sulfur compounds representing an odoriferous gaseous pollutant; a biproduct of paper pulp manufacture.

Meristic—Segmented into portions.

Moa—An extinct, large, flightless bird of New Zealand belonging to the genus *Dinormis*.

Mutualism—An association between populations that is mutually advantageous.

Niche—*see* Ecological niche.

Oligotrophic—Refers to bodies of water having a low dissolved nutrient content.

Organochlorine insecticide—A chlorinated hydrocarbon.

Organophosphates—A group of nonpersistent synthetic pesticides operating especially by causing the breakdown of muscle and nerve response.

Orogeny—Mountain chain formation and uplift.

Ozone—A molecule of oxygen composed of three atoms, produced by photochemical reaction with various air pollutants, such as hydrocarbons and nitrogen oxides, and also produced from oxygen by electric discharge and some other methods.

Palynology—The stratigraphical study of micro-fossils such as pollen and spores, more particularly those in organic deposits such as peat, and sedimentary ones such as alluvium.

Passerine—The largest order of birds, actually including more than half the total of species, and chiefly songbirds.

Peptide—An organic compound formed from two or more amino acids.

Periglacial—Relates to the area bordering an icecap, particularly the polar icecaps.

Period—A major division of geological time, less than an *era*, greater than an *epoch*.

Permafrost—An edaphic condition where the ground remains permanently frozen.

Peroxyacyl (PAN)—A secondary pollutant in photochemical smog that is responsible for plant damage and causes eye irritation and other damage to humans.

Phenotype—The total expression in an organism of the reaction during development between its genotype and its environment.

Photochemical—Refers to a chemical reaction that is promoted by the light component of radiant energy.

Photolysis—A chemical reaction promoted by light.

Plankton—Free-floating, microscopic, aquatic plants and animals.

Pleistocene—The geological epoch that began the Quaternary Period some four million years ago and ended about 15,000 years ago to be succeeded by a second and present epoch, the Holocene.

Poikilotherm (adj., *poikilothermous*)—An exothermic or cold-blooded animal, regulating body temperature primarily by behavioral mechanisms.

Polygenic—Where several genes act complementarily on the same character.

Polymorphic—With two or more forms of expression of the same character.

Polypoid—An organism with more than two sets of chromosomes in each nucleus.

Pongid—A fossil or living ape; a tailless anthropoid with canines projecting beyond the general surface of the teeth.

Potable—Refers to water suitable for drinking purposes.

Quaternary—The present geological period that began about four million years ago; includes the Pleistocene and Holocene epochs.

Radionuclide—A radioactive isotope of a chemical element.

Recessive—Refers to an allele that is only expressed as a character state in the phenotype when in homozygotes.

Relative humidity—The ratio of the actual amount of water present in a given volume of air to that which it would contain if it were saturated.

Riparian—Located on the bank of a water course.

Sociofact—A cultural behavioral pattern.

Sonic boom—The loud explosive sound like that of a heavy gun, produced by the shock wave of an aircraft traveling beyond the speed of sound.

Stenohaline—Refers to an aquatic population whose members are intolerant of substantial changes in the salinity.

Steroid—A chemical compound with a basic structure of four rings of carbon atoms, for example, Vitamin D.

Stratosphere—The upper region of the atmosphere above the troposphere, but below the mesosphere and ionosphere.

Sympatric—Refers to populations with overlapping dispersal areas.

Synonymy—Refers to the existence of two or more valid names for the same population.

Taiga—Refers to the Northern Coniferous Forest or Boreal Forest biome of the North Temperate zone.

Thermocline—A layer in a water body separating an upper and warmer circulation zone from a distinct and lower, colder one.

Tropopause—The boundary between the troposphere and the stratosphere; usually about 10 kilometers above sea level.

Troposphere—That portion of the atmosphere immediately above the ground and below the stratosphere; height varies with season and latitudes, but usually lies somewhere around 10 kilometers above sea level.

Tundra—The arctic biome dominated by low shrubby plants or herbs.

Volcanism—Volcanic eruptions and other volcanic activity.

Author Index

Subject Index